Calculus

Concepts and Contexts | 4e

Calculus and the Architecture of Curves

The cover photograph shows the DZ Bank in Berlin, designed and built 1995–2001 by Frank Gehry and Associates. The interior atrium is dominated by a curvaceous four-story stainless steel sculptural shell that suggests a prehistoric creature and houses a central conference space.

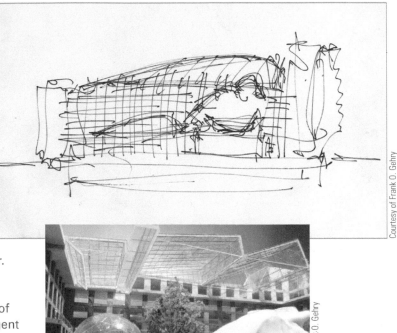

Courtesy of Frank O. Gehry

The highly complex structures that Frank Gehry designs would be impossible to build without the computer. The CATIA software that his architects and engineers use to produce the computer models is based on principles of calculus—fitting curves by matching tangent lines, making sure the curvature isn't too large, and controlling parametric surfaces. "Consequently," says Gehry, "we have a lot of freedom. I can play with shapes."

Courtesy of Frank O. Gehry

The process starts with Gehry's initial sketches, which are translated into a succession of physical models. (Hundreds of different physical models were constructed during the design of the building, first with basic wooden blocks and then evolving into more sculptural forms.) Then an engineer uses a digitizer to record the coordinates of a series of points on a physical model. The digitized points are fed into a computer and the CATIA software is used to link these points with smooth curves. (It joins curves so that their tangent lines coincide; you can use the same idea to design the shapes of letters in the Laboratory Project on page 208 of this book.) The architect has considerable freedom in creating these curves, guided by displays of the curve, its derivative, and its curvature. Then the curves are

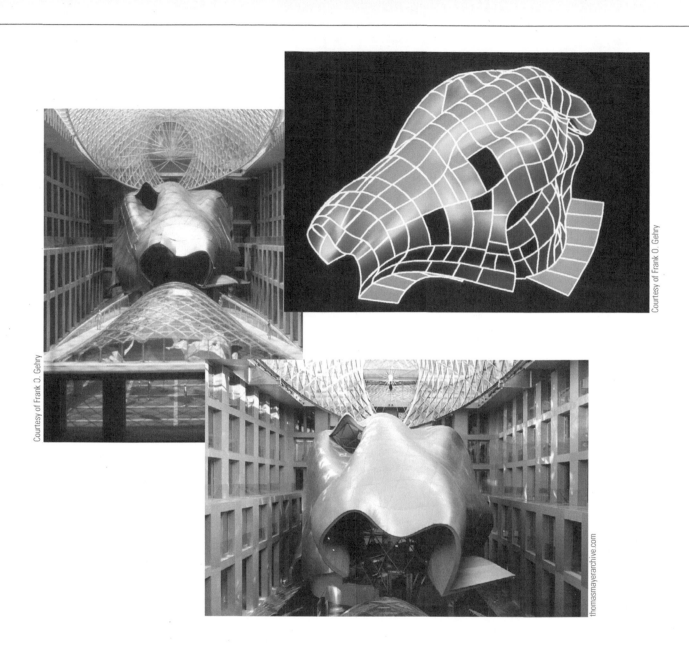

connected to each other by a parametric surface, and again the architect can do so in many possible ways with the guidance of displays of the geometric characteristics of the surface.

The CATIA model is then used to produce another physical model, which, in turn, suggests modifications and leads to additional computer and physical models.

The CATIA program was developed in France by Dassault Systèmes, originally for designing airplanes, and was subsequently employed in the automotive industry. Frank Gehry, because of his complex sculptural shapes, is the first to use it in architecture. It helps him answer his question, "How wiggly can you get and still make a building?"

Calculus

Volume 1 - Math 251 and 252

Custom Edition for Portland Community College

James Stewart

CENGAGE
Learning·

Australia · Brazil · Japan · Korea · Mexico · Singapore · Spain · United Kingdom · United States

CENGAGE
Learning·

Calculus
Volume 1 - Math 251 and 252
Custom Edition for Portland Community
College

Calculus: Concepts and Contexts, Fourth Edition
James Stewart

© 2010, 2005 Cengage Learning. All rights reserved.

Library of Congress Control Number: 2008941257

Senior Project Development Manager:
 Linda deStefano

Market Development Manager:
 Heather Kramer

Senior Production/Manufacturing Manager:
 Donna M. Brown

Production Editorial Manager:
 Kim Fry

Sr. Rights Acquisition Account Manager:
 Todd Osborne

For product information and technology assistance, contact us at
Cengage Learning Customer & Sales Support, 1-800-354-9706

For permission to use material from this text or product,
submit all requests online at **cengage.com/permissions**
Further permissions questions can be emailed to
permissionrequest@cengage.com

This book contains select works from existing Cengage Learning resources and was produced by Cengage Learning Custom Solutions for collegiate use. As such, those adopting and/or contributing to this work are responsible for editorial content accuracy, continuity and completeness.

Compilation © 2013 Cengage Learning
ISBN-13: 978-1-285-88841-5

ISBN-10: 1-285-88841-3

Cengage Learning
5191 Natorp Boulevard
Mason, Ohio 45040
USA
Cengage Learning is a leading provider of customized learning solutions with office locations around the globe, including Singapore, the United Kingdom, Australia, Mexico, Brazil, and Japan. Locate your local office at:
international.cengage.com/region.

Cengage Learning products are represented in Canada by Nelson Education, Ltd.
For your lifelong learning solutions, visit **www.cengage.com/custom.**
Visit our corporate website at **www.cengage.com.**

Printed in the United States of America

Contents

Student Solutions Manual

DOCUMENTATION STANDARDS FOR MATHEMATICS

All work in this course will be evaluated for your ability to meet the following writing objectives as well as for "mathematical content."

1. Every solution must be written in such a way that the question that was asked is clear.

2. Any table or graph that appears in the original problem must also appear somewhere in your solution.

3. All graphs that appear in your solution must have a figure number, a caption, and contain axis names and scales. When the graph is referenced in your written work, the reference must be by figure number. For applied problems, variables on each axis must be well defined and include units.

4. All tables that appear in your solution must have well-defined column headings, an assigned table number, and a brief caption (description). When the table is referenced in your written work, the reference must be by table number.

5. A brief introduction to the problem is almost always appropriate.

6. In applied problems, all variables and constants must be defined.

7. If you used the graph or table feature of your calculator in the problem solving process, you must include the graph or table in your written solution.

8. If you used some other non-trivial feature of your calculator (e.g., SOLVER), you must state this in your solution.

9. All (relevant) information given in the problem must be stated somewhere in your solution.

10. A sentence that orients the reader to the purpose of the mathematics should precede symbolic mathematical work.

11. Your conclusion shall not be encased in a box, but rather stated at the end of your solution in complete sentence form.

12. Remember to line up your equal signs.

13. If work is word-processed, all mathematical symbols must be generated with a math equation editor.

MATH 251 LAB 1 WRITE-UP EXAMPLE

The following lab write-up example is based upon problems similar to problems found in Lab 1. The questions have not been explicitly restated on this write-up. One of your writing objectives is to write your *solutions* in such a way that the question that was asked is clearly *implied*. Since the Lab 1 homework is purely algebraic/graphical, there is limited need for words.

Activity 1.x We are given $g(x) = x^2 - 2x + 5$. For this function the difference quotient is:

$$\frac{g(x+h) - g(x)}{h} = \frac{(x+h)^2 - 2(x+h) + 5 - (x^2 - 2x + 5)}{h}$$

$$= \frac{x^2 + 2xh + h^2 - 2x - 2h + 5 - x^2 + 2x - 5}{h}$$

$$= \frac{2xh + h^2 - 2h}{h}$$

$$= \frac{h(2x + h - 2)}{h}$$

$$= 2x + h - 2, \text{ for all } h \neq 0$$

Activity 1.y All function values stated in this activity are based upon the curves $y = f(x)$ and $y = g(x)$ shown in Figure 1.

$$(g \circ f)(3) = g(f(3))$$
$$= g(0)$$
$$= 3$$

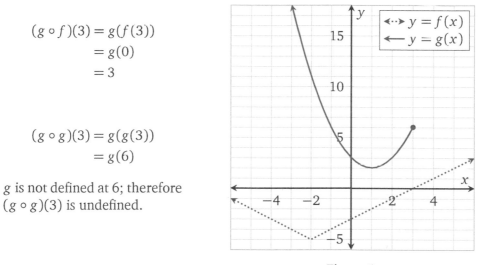

$$(g \circ g)(3) = g(g(3))$$
$$= g(6)$$

g is not defined at 6; therefore $(g \circ g)(3)$ is undefined.

Figure 1

Calculus

Concepts and Contexts | 4e

A Preview of Calculus

Calculus is fundamentally different from the mathematics that you have studied previously: calculus is less static and more dynamic. It is concerned with change and motion; it deals with quantities that approach other quantities. For that reason it may be useful to have an overview of the subject before beginning its intensive study. Here we give a glimpse of some of the main ideas of calculus by showing how the concept of a limit arises when we attempt to solve a variety of problems.

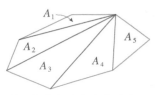

$$A = A_1 + A_2 + A_3 + A_4 + A_5$$

FIGURE 1

The Area Problem

The origins of calculus go back at least 2500 years to the ancient Greeks, who found areas using the "method of exhaustion." They knew how to find the area A of any polygon by dividing it into triangles as in Figure 1 and adding the areas of these triangles.

It is a much more difficult problem to find the area of a curved figure. The Greek method of exhaustion was to inscribe polygons in the figure and circumscribe polygons about the figure and then let the number of sides of the polygons increase. Figure 2 illustrates this process for the special case of a circle with inscribed regular polygons.

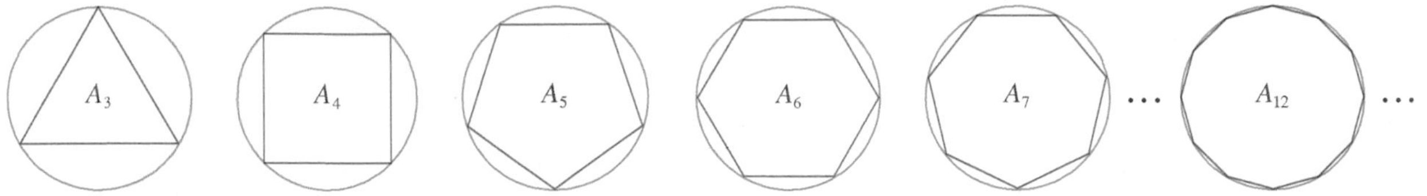

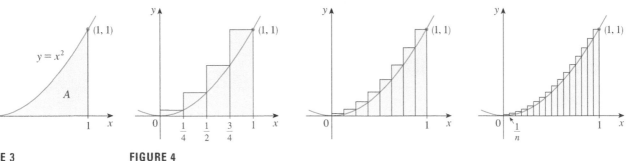

FIGURE 2

Let A_n be the area of the inscribed polygon with n sides. As n increases, it appears that A_n becomes closer and closer to the area of the circle. We say that the area of the circle is the *limit* of the areas of the inscribed polygons, and we write

TEC In the Preview Visual, you can see how inscribed and circumscribed polygons approximate the area of a circle.

$$A = \lim_{n \to \infty} A_n$$

The Greeks themselves did not use limits explicitly. However, by indirect reasoning, Eudoxus (fifth century BC) used exhaustion to prove the familiar formula for the area of a circle: $A = \pi r^2$.

We will use a similar idea in Chapter 5 to find areas of regions of the type shown in Figure 3. We will approximate the desired area A by areas of rectangles (as in Figure 4), let the width of the rectangles decrease, and then calculate A as the limit of these sums of areas of rectangles.

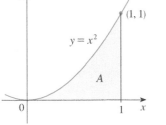

FIGURE 3   **FIGURE 4**

The area problem is the central problem in the branch of calculus called *integral calculus*. The techniques that we will develop in Chapter 5 for finding areas will also enable us to compute the volume of a solid, the length of a curve, the force of water against a dam, the mass and center of gravity of a rod, and the work done in pumping water out of a tank.

The Tangent Problem

Consider the problem of trying to find an equation of the tangent line t to a curve with equation $y = f(x)$ at a given point P. (We will give a precise definition of a tangent line in

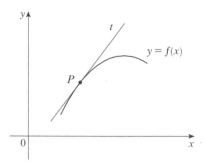

FIGURE 5

The tangent line at P

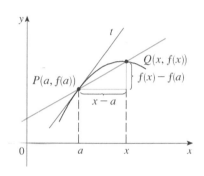

FIGURE 6

The secant line PQ

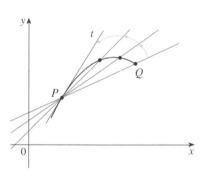

FIGURE 7

Secant lines approaching the
tangent line

Chapter 2. For now you can think of it as a line that touches the curve at P as in Figure 5.)
Since we know that the point P lies on the tangent line, we can find the equation of t if we
know its slope m. The problem is that we need two points to compute the slope and we
know only one point, P, on t. To get around the problem we first find an approximation to
m by taking a nearby point Q on the curve and computing the slope m_{PQ} of the secant line
PQ. From Figure 6 we see that

$$\boxed{1} \qquad m_{PQ} = \frac{f(x) - f(a)}{x - a}$$

Now imagine that Q moves along the curve toward P as in Figure 7. You can see that
the secant line rotates and approaches the tangent line as its limiting position. This means
that the slope m_{PQ} of the secant line becomes closer and closer to the slope m of the tangent line. We write

$$m = \lim_{Q \to P} m_{PQ}$$

and we say that m is the limit of m_{PQ} as Q approaches P along the curve. Since x approaches
a as Q approaches P, we could also use Equation 1 to write

$$\boxed{2} \qquad m = \lim_{x \to a} \frac{f(x) - f(a)}{x - a}$$

Specific examples of this procedure will be given in Chapter 2.

The tangent problem has given rise to the branch of calculus called *differential calculus,*
which was not invented until more than 2000 years after integral calculus. The main ideas
behind differential calculus are due to the French mathematician Pierre Fermat
(1601–1665) and were developed by the English mathematicians John Wallis
(1616–1703), Isaac Barrow (1630–1677), and Isaac Newton (1642–1727) and the German
mathematician Gottfried Leibniz (1646–1716).

The two branches of calculus and their chief problems, the area problem and the tangent problem, appear to be very different, but it turns out that there is a very close connection between them. The tangent problem and the area problem are inverse problems in a
sense that will be described in Chapter 5.

Velocity

When we look at the speedometer of a car and read that the car is traveling at 48 mi/h,
what does that information indicate to us? We know that if the velocity remains constant,
then after an hour we will have traveled 48 mi. But if the velocity of the car varies, what
does it mean to say that the velocity at a given instant is 48 mi/h?

In order to analyze this question, let's examine the motion of a car that travels along a
straight road and assume that we can measure the distance traveled by the car (in feet) at
1-second intervals as in the following chart:

t = Time elapsed (s)	0	1	2	3	4	5
d = Distance (ft)	0	2	9	24	42	71

As a first step toward finding the velocity after 2 seconds have elapsed, we find the average velocity during the time interval $2 \leqslant t \leqslant 4$:

$$\text{average velocity} = \frac{\text{change in position}}{\text{time elapsed}}$$

$$= \frac{42 - 9}{4 - 2}$$

$$= 16.5 \text{ ft/s}$$

Similarly, the average velocity in the time interval $2 \leqslant t \leqslant 3$ is

$$\text{average velocity} = \frac{24 - 9}{3 - 2} = 15 \text{ ft/s}$$

We have the feeling that the velocity at the instant $t = 2$ can't be much different from the average velocity during a short time interval starting at $t = 2$. So let's imagine that the distance traveled has been measured at 0.1-second time intervals as in the following chart:

t	2.0	2.1	2.2	2.3	2.4	2.5
d	9.00	10.02	11.16	12.45	13.96	15.80

Then we can compute, for instance, the average velocity over the time interval $[2, 2.5]$:

$$\text{average velocity} = \frac{15.80 - 9.00}{2.5 - 2} = 13.6 \text{ ft/s}$$

The results of such calculations are shown in the following chart:

Time interval	[2, 3]	[2, 2.5]	[2, 2.4]	[2, 2.3]	[2, 2.2]	[2, 2.1]
Average velocity (ft/s)	15.0	13.6	12.4	11.5	10.8	10.2

The average velocities over successively smaller intervals appear to be getting closer to a number near 10, and so we expect that the velocity at exactly $t = 2$ is about 10 ft/s. In Chapter 2 we will define the instantaneous velocity of a moving object as the limiting value of the average velocities over smaller and smaller time intervals.

In Figure 8 we show a graphical representation of the motion of the car by plotting the distance traveled as a function of time. If we write $d = f(t)$, then $f(t)$ is the number of feet traveled after t seconds. The average velocity in the time interval $[2, t]$ is

$$\text{average velocity} = \frac{\text{change in position}}{\text{time elapsed}} = \frac{f(t) - f(2)}{t - 2}$$

which is the same as the slope of the secant line PQ in Figure 8. The velocity v when $t = 2$ is the limiting value of this average velocity as t approaches 2; that is,

$$v = \lim_{t \to 2} \frac{f(t) - f(2)}{t - 2}$$

and we recognize from Equation 2 that this is the same as the slope of the tangent line to the curve at P.

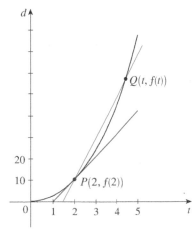

FIGURE 8

Thus, when we solve the tangent problem in differential calculus, we are also solving problems concerning velocities. The same techniques also enable us to solve problems involving rates of change in all of the natural and social sciences.

The Limit of a Sequence

In the fifth century BC the Greek philosopher Zeno of Elea posed four problems, now known as *Zeno's paradoxes,* that were intended to challenge some of the ideas concerning space and time that were held in his day. Zeno's second paradox concerns a race between the Greek hero Achilles and a tortoise that has been given a head start. Zeno argued, as follows, that Achilles could never pass the tortoise: Suppose that Achilles starts at position a_1 and the tortoise starts at position t_1. (See Figure 9.) When Achilles reaches the point $a_2 = t_1$, the tortoise is farther ahead at position t_2. When Achilles reaches $a_3 = t_2$, the tortoise is at t_3. This process continues indefinitely and so it appears that the tortoise will always be ahead! But this defies common sense.

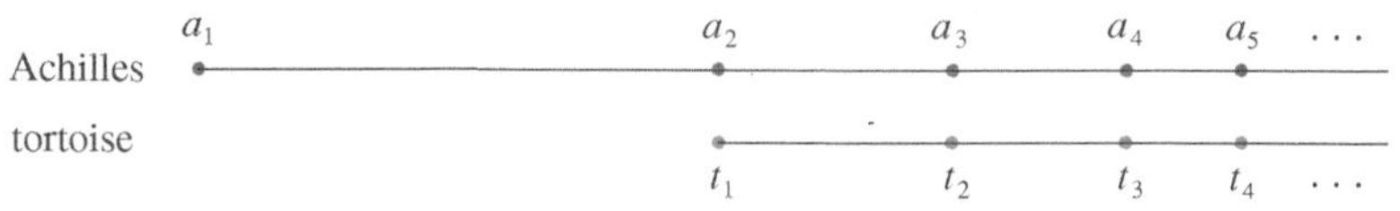

FIGURE 9

One way of explaining this paradox is with the idea of a *sequence.* The successive positions of Achilles $(a_1, a_2, a_3, \ldots)$ or the successive positions of the tortoise $(t_1, t_2, t_3, \ldots)$ form what is known as a sequence.

In general, a sequence $\{a_n\}$ is a set of numbers written in a definite order. For instance, the sequence

$$\left\{1, \tfrac{1}{2}, \tfrac{1}{3}, \tfrac{1}{4}, \tfrac{1}{5}, \ldots\right\}$$

can be described by giving the following formula for the nth term:

$$a_n = \frac{1}{n}$$

FIGURE 10

We can visualize this sequence by plotting its terms on a number line as in Figure 10(a) or by drawing its graph as in Figure 10(b). Observe from either picture that the terms of the sequence $a_n = 1/n$ are becoming closer and closer to 0 as n increases. In fact, we can find terms as small as we please by making n large enough. We say that the limit of the sequence is 0, and we indicate this by writing

$$\lim_{n \to \infty} \frac{1}{n} = 0$$

In general, the notation

$$\lim_{n \to \infty} a_n = L$$

is used if the terms a_n approach the number L as n becomes large. This means that the numbers a_n can be made as close as we like to the number L by taking n sufficiently large.

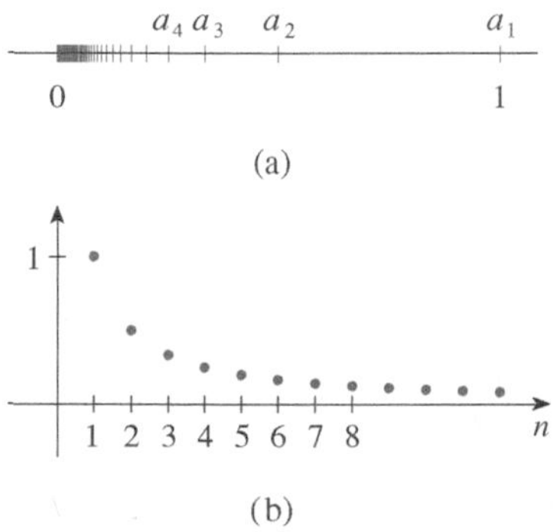

The concept of the limit of a sequence occurs whenever we use the decimal representation of a real number. For instance, if

$$a_1 = 3.1$$

$$a_2 = 3.14$$

$$a_3 = 3.141$$

$$a_4 = 3.1415$$

$$a_5 = 3.14159$$

$$a_6 = 3.141592$$

$$a_7 = 3.1415926$$

$$\vdots$$

then
$$\lim_{n \to \infty} a_n = \pi$$

The terms in this sequence are rational approximations to π.

Let's return to Zeno's paradox. The successive positions of Achilles and the tortoise form sequences $\{a_n\}$ and $\{t_n\}$, where $a_n < t_n$ for all n. It can be shown that both sequences have the same limit:

$$\lim_{n \to \infty} a_n = p = \lim_{n \to \infty} t_n$$

It is precisely at this point p that Achilles overtakes the tortoise.

The Sum of a Series

Another of Zeno's paradoxes, as passed on to us by Aristotle, is the following: "A man standing in a room cannot walk to the wall. In order to do so, he would first have to go half the distance, then half the remaining distance, and then again half of what still remains. This process can always be continued and can never be ended." (See Figure 11.)

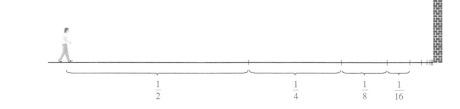

FIGURE 11

Of course, we know that the man can actually reach the wall, so this suggests that perhaps the total distance can be expressed as the sum of infinitely many smaller distances as follows:

3

$$1 = \frac{1}{2} + \frac{1}{4} + \frac{1}{8} + \frac{1}{16} + \cdots + \frac{1}{2^n} + \cdots$$

Zeno was arguing that it doesn't make sense to add infinitely many numbers together. But there are other situations in which we implicitly use infinite sums. For instance, in decimal notation, the symbol $0.\overline{3} = 0.3333\ldots$ means

$$\frac{3}{10} + \frac{3}{100} + \frac{3}{1000} + \frac{3}{10,000} + \cdots$$

and so, in some sense, it must be true that

$$\frac{3}{10} + \frac{3}{100} + \frac{3}{1000} + \frac{3}{10,000} + \cdots = \frac{1}{3}$$

More generally, if d_n denotes the nth digit in the decimal representation of a number, then

$$0.d_1 d_2 d_3 d_4 \ldots = \frac{d_1}{10} + \frac{d_2}{10^2} + \frac{d_3}{10^3} + \cdots + \frac{d_n}{10^n} + \cdots$$

Therefore some infinite sums, or infinite series as they are called, have a meaning. But we must define carefully what the sum of an infinite series is.

Returning to the series in Equation 3, we denote by s_n the sum of the first n terms of the series. Thus

$$s_1 = \tfrac{1}{2} = 0.5$$
$$s_2 = \tfrac{1}{2} + \tfrac{1}{4} = 0.75$$
$$s_3 = \tfrac{1}{2} + \tfrac{1}{4} + \tfrac{1}{8} = 0.875$$
$$s_4 = \tfrac{1}{2} + \tfrac{1}{4} + \tfrac{1}{8} + \tfrac{1}{16} = 0.9375$$
$$s_5 = \tfrac{1}{2} + \tfrac{1}{4} + \tfrac{1}{8} + \tfrac{1}{16} + \tfrac{1}{32} = 0.96875$$
$$s_6 = \tfrac{1}{2} + \tfrac{1}{4} + \tfrac{1}{8} + \tfrac{1}{16} + \tfrac{1}{32} + \tfrac{1}{64} = 0.984375$$
$$s_7 = \tfrac{1}{2} + \tfrac{1}{4} + \tfrac{1}{8} + \tfrac{1}{16} + \tfrac{1}{32} + \tfrac{1}{64} + \tfrac{1}{128} = 0.9921875$$
$$\vdots$$
$$s_{10} = \tfrac{1}{2} + \tfrac{1}{4} + \cdots + \tfrac{1}{1024} \approx 0.99902344$$
$$\vdots$$
$$s_{16} = \frac{1}{2} + \frac{1}{4} + \cdots + \frac{1}{2^{16}} \approx 0.99998474$$

Observe that as we add more and more terms, the partial sums become closer and closer to 1. In fact, it can be shown that by taking n large enough (that is, by adding sufficiently many terms of the series), we can make the partial sum s_n as close as we please to the number 1. It therefore seems reasonable to say that the sum of the infinite series is 1 and to write

$$\frac{1}{2} + \frac{1}{4} + \frac{1}{8} + \cdots + \frac{1}{2^n} + \cdots = 1$$

In other words, the reason the sum of the series is 1 is that

$$\lim_{n \to \infty} s_n = 1$$

In Chapter 8 we will discuss these ideas further. We will then use Newton's idea of combining infinite series with differential and integral calculus.

Summary

We have seen that the concept of a limit arises in trying to find the area of a region, the slope of a tangent to a curve, the velocity of a car, or the sum of an infinite series. In each case the common theme is the calculation of a quantity as the limit of other, easily calculated quantities. It is this basic idea of a limit that sets calculus apart from other areas of mathematics. In fact, we could define calculus as the part of mathematics that deals with limits.

After Sir Isaac Newton invented his version of calculus, he used it to explain the motion of the planets around the sun. Today calculus is used in calculating the orbits of satellites and spacecraft, in predicting population sizes, in estimating how fast oil prices rise or fall, in forecasting weather, in measuring the cardiac output of the heart, in calculating life insurance premiums, and in a great variety of other areas. We will explore some of these uses of calculus in this book.

In order to convey a sense of the power of the subject, we end this preview with a list of some of the questions that you will be able to answer using calculus:

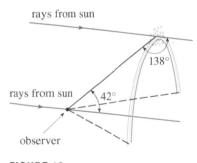

rays from sun

138°

rays from sun   42°

observer

FIGURE 12

1. How can we explain the fact, illustrated in Figure 12, that the angle of elevation from an observer up to the highest point in a rainbow is 42°? (See page 270.)

2. How can we explain the shapes of cans on supermarket shelves? (See page 311.)

3. Where is the best place to sit in a movie theater? (See page 464.)

4. How far away from an airport should a pilot start descent? (See page 209.)

5. How can we fit curves together to design shapes to represent letters on a laser printer? (See page 208.)

6. Where should an infielder position himself to catch a baseball thrown by an outfielder and relay it to home plate? (See page 530.)

7. Does a ball thrown upward take longer to reach its maximum height or to fall back to its original height? (See page 518.)

8. How can we explain the fact that planets and satellites move in elliptical orbits? (See page 726.)

9. How can we distribute water flow among turbines at a hydroelectric station so as to maximize the total energy production? (See page 821.)

10. If a marble, a squash ball, a steel bar, and a lead pipe roll down a slope, which of them reaches the bottom first? (See page 889.)

Functions and Models

1

The fundamental objects that we deal with in calculus are functions. This chapter prepares the way for calculus by discussing the basic ideas concerning functions, their graphs, and ways of transforming and combining them. We stress that a function can be represented in different ways: by an equation, in a table, by a graph, or in words. We look at the main types of functions that occur in calculus and describe the process of using these functions as mathematical models of real-world phenomena. We also discuss the use of graphing calculators and graphing software for computers and see that parametric equations provide the best method for graphing certain types of curves.

1.1 Four Ways to Represent a Function

Functions arise whenever one quantity depends on another. Consider the following four situations.

A. The area A of a circle depends on the radius r of the circle. The rule that connects r and A is given by the equation $A = \pi r^2$. With each positive number r there is associated one value of A, and we say that A is a *function* of r.

B. The human population of the world P depends on the time t. The table gives estimates of the world population $P(t)$ at time t, for certain years. For instance,

$$P(1950) \approx 2{,}560{,}000{,}000$$

But for each value of the time t there is a corresponding value of P, and we say that P is a function of t.

C. The cost C of mailing a large envelope depends on the weight w of the envelope. Although there is no simple formula that connects w and C, the post office has a rule for determining C when w is known.

D. The vertical acceleration a of the ground as measured by a seismograph during an earthquake is a function of the elapsed time t. Figure 1 shows a graph generated by seismic activity during the Northridge earthquake that shook Los Angeles in 1994. For a given value of t, the graph provides a corresponding value of a.

Year	Population (millions)
1900	1650
1910	1750
1920	1860
1930	2070
1940	2300
1950	2560
1960	3040
1970	3710
1980	4450
1990	5280
2000	6080

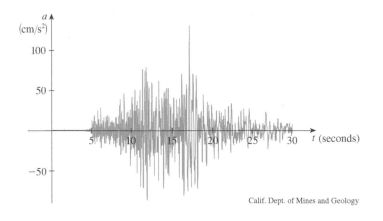

FIGURE 1

Vertical ground acceleration during the Northridge earthquake

Calif. Dept. of Mines and Geology

Each of these examples describes a rule whereby, given a number (r, t, w, or t), another number (A, P, C, or a) is assigned. In each case we say that the second number is a function of the first number.

> A **function** f is a rule that assigns to each element x in a set D exactly one element, called $f(x)$, in a set E.

We usually consider functions for which the sets D and E are sets of real numbers. The set D is called the **domain** of the function. The number $f(x)$ is the **value of f at x** and is read "f of x." The **range** of f is the set of all possible values of $f(x)$ as x varies throughout the domain. A symbol that represents an arbitrary number in the *domain* of a function f is called an **independent variable**. A symbol that represents a number in the *range* of f is called a **dependent variable**. In Example A, for instance, r is the independent variable and A is the dependent variable.

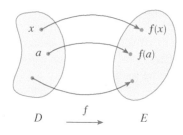

FIGURE 2

Machine diagram for a function f

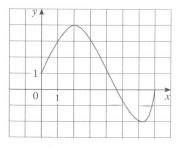

FIGURE 3

Arrow diagram for f

It's helpful to think of a function as a **machine** (see Figure 2). If x is in the domain of the function f, then when x enters the machine, it's accepted as an input and the machine produces an output $f(x)$ according to the rule of the function. Thus we can think of the domain as the set of all possible inputs and the range as the set of all possible outputs.

The preprogrammed functions in a calculator are good examples of a function as a machine. For example, the square root key on your calculator computes such a function. You press the key labeled $\sqrt{}$ (or $\sqrt{x}$) and enter the input x. If $x < 0$, then x is not in the domain of this function; that is, x is not an acceptable input, and the calculator will indicate an error. If $x \geq 0$, then an *approximation* to $\sqrt{x}$ will appear in the display. Thus the $\sqrt{x}$ key on your calculator is not quite the same as the exact mathematical function f defined by $f(x) = \sqrt{x}$.

Another way to picture a function is by an **arrow diagram** as in Figure 3. Each arrow connects an element of D to an element of E. The arrow indicates that $f(x)$ is associated with x, $f(a)$ is associated with a, and so on.

The most common method for visualizing a function is its graph. If f is a function with domain D, then its **graph** is the set of ordered pairs

$$\{(x, f(x)) \mid x \in D\}$$

(Notice that these are input-output pairs.) In other words, the graph of f consists of all points (x, y) in the coordinate plane such that $y = f(x)$ and x is in the domain of f.

The graph of a function f gives us a useful picture of the behavior or "life history" of a function. Since the y-coordinate of any point (x, y) on the graph is $y = f(x)$, we can read the value of $f(x)$ from the graph as being the height of the graph above the point x (see Figure 4). The graph of f also allows us to picture the domain of f on the x-axis and its range on the y-axis as in Figure 5.

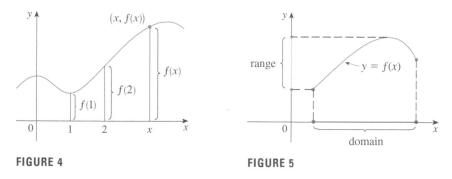

FIGURE 4   **FIGURE 5**

EXAMPLE 1 **Reading information from a graph** The graph of a function f is shown in Figure 6.

(a) Find the values of $f(1)$ and $f(5)$.

(b) What are the domain and range of f?

SOLUTION

(a) We see from Figure 6 that the point $(1, 3)$ lies on the graph of f, so the value of f at 1 is $f(1) = 3$. (In other words, the point on the graph that lies above $x = 1$ is 3 units above the x-axis.)

When $x = 5$, the graph lies about 0.7 unit below the x-axis, so we estimate that $f(5) \approx -0.7$.

(b) We see that $f(x)$ is defined when $0 \leq x \leq 7$, so the domain of f is the closed interval $[0, 7]$. Notice that f takes on all values from -2 to 4, so the range of f is

$$\{y \mid -2 \leq y \leq 4\} = [-2, 4]$$

FIGURE 6

The notation for intervals is given in Appendix A.

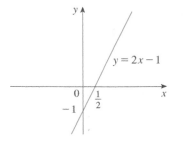

FIGURE 7

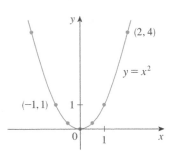

FIGURE 8

EXAMPLE 2 Sketch the graph and find the domain and range of each function.

(a) $f(x) = 2x - 1$ (b) $g(x) = x^2$

SOLUTION

(a) The equation of the graph is $y = 2x - 1$, and we recognize this as being the equation of a line with slope 2 and y-intercept -1. (Recall the slope-intercept form of the equation of a line: $y = mx + b$. See Appendix B.) This enables us to sketch a portion of the graph of f in Figure 7. The expression $2x - 1$ is defined for all real numbers, so the domain of f is the set of all real numbers, which we denote by $\mathbb{R}$. The graph shows that the range is also $\mathbb{R}$.

(b) Since $g(2) = 2^2 = 4$ and $g(-1) = (-1)^2 = 1$, we could plot the points $(2, 4)$ and $(-1, 1)$, together with a few other points on the graph, and join them to produce the graph (Figure 8). The equation of the graph is $y = x^2$, which represents a parabola (see Appendix B). The domain of g is $\mathbb{R}$. The range of g consists of all values of $g(x)$, that is, all numbers of the form x^2. But $x^2 \geq 0$ for all numbers x and any positive number y is a square. So the range of g is $\{y \mid y \geq 0\} = [0, \infty)$. This can also be seen from Figure 8.

EXAMPLE 3 Evaluating a difference quotient

If $f(x) = 2x^2 - 5x + 1$ and $h \neq 0$, evaluate $\dfrac{f(a + h) - f(a)}{h}$.

SOLUTION We first evaluate $f(a + h)$ by replacing x by $a + h$ in the expression for $f(x)$:

$$f(a + h) = 2(a + h)^2 - 5(a + h) + 1$$

$$= 2(a^2 + 2ah + h^2) - 5(a + h) + 1$$

$$= 2a^2 + 4ah + 2h^2 - 5a - 5h + 1$$

Then we substitute into the given expression and simplify:

$$\frac{f(a + h) - f(a)}{h} = \frac{(2a^2 + 4ah + 2h^2 - 5a - 5h + 1) - (2a^2 - 5a + 1)}{h}$$

$$= \frac{2a^2 + 4ah + 2h^2 - 5a - 5h + 1 - 2a^2 + 5a - 1}{h}$$

$$= \frac{4ah + 2h^2 - 5h}{h} = 4a + 2h - 5$$

The expression

$$\frac{f(a + h) - f(a)}{h}$$

in Example 3 is called a **difference quotient** and occurs frequently in calculus. As we will see in Chapter 2, it represents the average rate of change of $f(x)$ between $x = a$ and $x = a + h$.

Representations of Functions

There are four possible ways to represent a function:

- verbally   (by a description in words)
- numerically   (by a table of values)
- visually   (by a graph)
- algebraically   (by an explicit formula)

If a single function can be represented in all four ways, it's often useful to go from one representation to another to gain additional insight into the function. (In Example 2, for instance, we started with algebraic formulas and then obtained the graphs.) But certain functions are described more naturally by one method than by another. With this in mind, let's reexamine the four situations that we considered at the beginning of this section.

A. The most useful representation of the area of a circle as a function of its radius is probably the algebraic formula $A(r) = \pi r^2$, though it is possible to compile a table of values or to sketch a graph (half a parabola). Because a circle has to have a positive radius, the domain is $\{r \mid r > 0\} = (0, \infty)$, and the range is also $(0, \infty)$.

Year	Population (millions)
1900	1650
1910	1750
1920	1860
1930	2070
1940	2300
1950	2560
1960	3040
1970	3710
1980	4450
1990	5280
2000	6080

B. We are given a description of the function in words: $P(t)$ is the human population of the world at time t. The table of values of world population provides a convenient representation of this function. If we plot these values, we get the graph (called a *scatter plot*) in Figure 9. It too is a useful representation; the graph allows us to absorb all the data at once. What about a formula? Of course, it's impossible to devise an explicit formula that gives the exact human population $P(t)$ at any time t. But it is possible to find an expression for a function that *approximates* $P(t)$. In fact, using methods explained in Section 1.5, we obtain the approximation

$$P(t) \approx f(t) = (0.008079266) \cdot (1.013731)^t$$

and Figure 10 shows that it is a reasonably good "fit." The function f is called a *mathematical model* for population growth. In other words, it is a function with an explicit formula that approximates the behavior of our given function. We will see, however, that the ideas of calculus can be applied to a table of values; an explicit formula is not necessary.

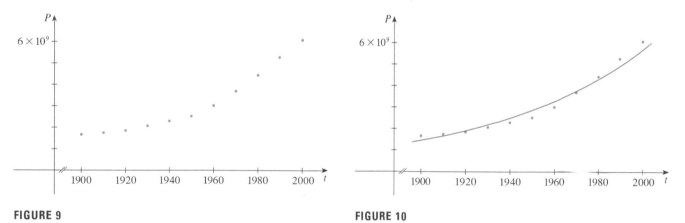

FIGURE 9   **FIGURE 10**

The function P is typical of the functions that arise whenever we attempt to apply calculus to the real world. We start with a verbal description of a function. Then we may be able to construct a table of values of the function, perhaps from instrument readings in a scientific experiment. Even though we don't have complete knowledge of the values of the function, we will see throughout the book that it is still possible to perform the operations of calculus on such a function.

A function defined by a table of values is called a *tabular* function.

w (ounces)	$C(w)$ (dollars)
$0 < w \leqslant 1$	0.83
$1 < w \leqslant 2$	1.00
$2 < w \leqslant 3$	1.17
$3 < w \leqslant 4$	1.34
$4 < w \leqslant 5$	1.51
.	.
.	.
.	.
$12 < w \leqslant 13$	2.87

C. Again the function is described in words: $C(w)$ is the cost of mailing a large envelope with weight w. The rule that the US Postal Service used as of 2008 is as follows: The cost is 83 cents for up to 1 oz, plus 17 cents for each additional ounce (or less) up to 13 oz. The table of values shown in the margin is the most convenient representation for this function, though it is possible to sketch a graph (see Example 10).

D. The graph shown in Figure 1 is the most natural representation of the vertical acceleration function $a(t)$. It's true that a table of values could be compiled, and it is even possible to devise an approximate formula. But everything a geologist needs to know—amplitudes and patterns—can be seen easily from the graph. (The same is true for the patterns seen in electrocardiograms of heart patients and polygraphs for lie-detection.)

T

0 ———————————————→ t

FIGURE 11

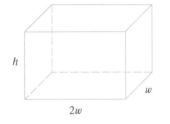

h

w

$2w$

FIGURE 12

PS In setting up applied functions as in Example 5, it may be useful to review the principles of problem solving as discussed on page 83, particularly *Step 1: Understand the Problem.*

Domain Convention

If a function is given by a formula and the domain is not stated explicitly, the convention is that the domain is the set of all numbers for which the formula makes sense and defines a real number.

EXAMPLE 4   Drawing a graph from a verbal description   When you turn on a hot-water faucet, the temperature T of the water depends on how long the water has been running. Draw a rough graph of T as a function of the time t that has elapsed since the faucet was turned on.

SOLUTION   The initial temperature of the running water is close to room temperature because the water has been sitting in the pipes. When the water from the hot-water tank starts flowing from the faucet, T increases quickly. In the next phase, T is constant at the temperature of the heated water in the tank. When the tank is drained, T decreases to the temperature of the water supply. This enables us to make the rough sketch of T as a function of t in Figure 11.

In the following example we start with a verbal description of a function in a physical situation and obtain an explicit algebraic formula. The ability to do this is a useful skill in solving calculus problems that ask for the maximum or minimum values of quantities.

V   EXAMPLE 5   Expressing a cost as a function   A rectangular storage container with an open top has a volume of 10 m³. The length of its base is twice its width. Material for the base costs $10 per square meter; material for the sides costs $6 per square meter. Express the cost of materials as a function of the width of the base.

SOLUTION   We draw a diagram as in Figure 12 and introduce notation by letting w and $2w$ be the width and length of the base, respectively, and h be the height.

The area of the base is $(2w)w = 2w^2$, so the cost, in dollars, of the material for the base is $10(2w^2)$. Two of the sides have area wh and the other two have area $2wh$, so the cost of the material for the sides is $6[2(wh) + 2(2wh)]$. The total cost is therefore

$$C = 10(2w^2) + 6[2(wh) + 2(2wh)] = 20w^2 + 36wh$$

To express C as a function of w alone, we need to eliminate h and we do so by using the fact that the volume is 10 m³. Thus

$$w(2w)h = 10$$

which gives

$$h = \frac{10}{2w^2} = \frac{5}{w^2}$$

Substituting this into the expression for C, we have

$$C = 20w^2 + 36w\left(\frac{5}{w^2}\right) = 20w^2 + \frac{180}{w}$$

Therefore the equation

$$C(w) = 20w^2 + \frac{180}{w} \qquad w > 0$$

expresses C as a function of w.

EXAMPLE 6   Find the domain of each function.

(a) $f(x) = \sqrt{x + 2}$ (b) $g(x) = \dfrac{1}{x^2 - x}$

SOLUTION

(a) Because the square root of a negative number is not defined (as a real number), the domain of f consists of all values of x such that $x + 2 \geqslant 0$. This is equivalent to $x \geqslant -2$, so the domain is the interval $[-2, \infty)$.

(b) Since

$$g(x) = \frac{1}{x^2 - x} = \frac{1}{x(x - 1)}$$

and division by 0 is not allowed, we see that $g(x)$ is not defined when $x = 0$ or $x = 1$. Thus the domain of g is

$$\{x \mid x \neq 0, x \neq 1\}$$

which could also be written in interval notation as

$$(-\infty, 0) \cup (0, 1) \cup (1, \infty)$$

The graph of a function is a curve in the xy-plane. But the question arises: Which curves in the xy-plane are graphs of functions? This is answered by the following test.

> **The Vertical Line Test** A curve in the xy-plane is the graph of a function of x if and only if no vertical line intersects the curve more than once.

The reason for the truth of the Vertical Line Test can be seen in Figure 13. If each vertical line $x = a$ intersects a curve only once, at (a, b), then exactly one functional value is defined by $f(a) = b$. But if a line $x = a$ intersects the curve twice, at (a, b) and (a, c), then the curve can't represent a function because a function can't assign two different values to a.

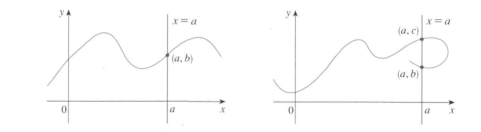

FIGURE 13

For example, the parabola $x = y^2 - 2$ shown in Figure 14(a) is not the graph of a function of x because, as you can see, there are vertical lines that intersect the parabola twice. The parabola, however, does contain the graphs of *two* functions of x. Notice that the equation $x = y^2 - 2$ implies $y^2 = x + 2$, so $y = \pm\sqrt{x + 2}$. Thus the upper and lower halves of the parabola are the graphs of the functions $f(x) = \sqrt{x + 2}$ [from Example 6(a)] and $g(x) = -\sqrt{x + 2}$. [See Figures 14(b) and (c).] We observe that if we reverse the roles of x and y, then the equation $x = h(y) = y^2 - 2$ *does* define x as a function of y (with y as the independent variable and x as the dependent variable) and the parabola now appears as the graph of the function h.

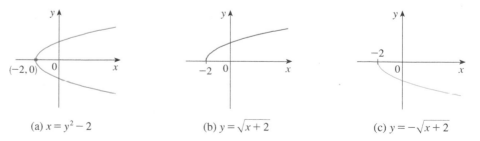

FIGURE 14   (a) $x = y^2 - 2$ (b) $y = \sqrt{x + 2}$ (c) $y = -\sqrt{x + 2}$

Piecewise Defined Functions

The functions in the following four examples are defined by different formulas in different parts of their domains.

V   EXAMPLE 7   Graphing a piecewise defined function   A function f is defined by

$$f(x) = \begin{cases} 1 - x & \text{if } x \le 1 \\ x^2 & \text{if } x > 1 \end{cases}$$

Evaluate $f(0)$, $f(1)$, and $f(2)$ and sketch the graph.

SOLUTION   Remember that a function is a rule. For this particular function the rule is the following: First look at the value of the input x. If it happens that $x \le 1$, then the value of $f(x)$ is $1 - x$. On the other hand, if $x > 1$, then the value of $f(x)$ is x^2.

$$\text{Since } 0 \le 1, \text{ we have } f(0) = 1 - 0 = 1.$$

$$\text{Since } 1 \le 1, \text{ we have } f(1) = 1 - 1 = 0.$$

$$\text{Since } 2 > 1, \text{ we have } f(2) = 2^2 = 4.$$

How do we draw the graph of f? We observe that if $x \le 1$, then $f(x) = 1 - x$, so the part of the graph of f that lies to the left of the vertical line $x = 1$ must coincide with the line $y = 1 - x$, which has slope -1 and y-intercept 1. If $x > 1$, then $f(x) = x^2$, so the part of the graph of f that lies to the right of the line $x = 1$ must coincide with the graph of $y = x^2$, which is a parabola. This enables us to sketch the graph in Figure 15. The solid dot indicates that the point $(1, 0)$ is included on the graph; the open dot indicates that the point $(1, 1)$ is excluded from the graph.

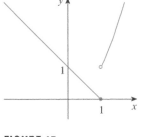

FIGURE 15

The next example of a piecewise defined function is the absolute value function. Recall that the **absolute value** of a number a, denoted by $|a|$, is the distance from a to 0 on the real number line. Distances are always positive or 0, so we have

For a more extensive review of absolute values, see Appendix A.

$$|a| \ge 0 \qquad \text{for every number } a$$

For example,

$$|3| = 3 \qquad |-3| = 3 \qquad |0| = 0 \qquad |\sqrt{2} - 1| = \sqrt{2} - 1 \qquad |3 - \pi| = \pi - 3$$

In general, we have

$$\begin{aligned} |a| &= a \qquad \text{if } a \ge 0 \\ |a| &= -a \quad \text{if } a < 0 \end{aligned}$$

(Remember that if a is negative, then $-a$ is positive.)

EXAMPLE 8   Sketch the graph of the absolute value function $f(x) = |x|$.

SOLUTION   From the preceding discussion we know that

$$|x| = \begin{cases} x & \text{if } x \ge 0 \\ -x & \text{if } x < 0 \end{cases}$$

Using the same method as in Example 7, we see that the graph of f coincides with the line $y = x$ to the right of the y-axis and coincides with the line $y = -x$ to the left of the y-axis (see Figure 16).

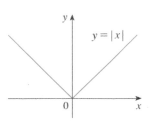

FIGURE 16

EXAMPLE 9 Find a formula for the function f graphed in Figure 17.

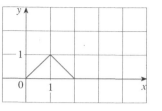

FIGURE 17

SOLUTION The line through $(0, 0)$ and $(1, 1)$ has slope $m = 1$ and y-intercept $b = 0$, so its equation is $y = x$. Thus, for the part of the graph of f that joins $(0, 0)$ to $(1, 1)$, we have

$$f(x) = x \qquad \text{if } 0 \leqslant x \leqslant 1$$

Point-slope form of the equation of a line:
$$y - y_1 = m(x - x_1)$$
See Appendix B.

The line through $(1, 1)$ and $(2, 0)$ has slope $m = -1$, so its point-slope form is

$$y - 0 = (-1)(x - 2) \qquad \text{or} \qquad y = 2 - x$$

So we have $\qquad f(x) = 2 - x \qquad \text{if } 1 < x \leqslant 2$

We also see that the graph of f coincides with the x-axis for $x > 2$. Putting this information together, we have the following three-piece formula for f:

$$f(x) = \begin{cases} x & \text{if } 0 \leqslant x \leqslant 1 \\ 2 - x & \text{if } 1 < x \leqslant 2 \\ 0 & \text{if } x > 2 \end{cases}$$

EXAMPLE 10 **Graph of a postage function**   In Example C at the beginning of this section we considered the cost $C(w)$ of mailing a large envelope with weight w. In effect, this is a piecewise defined function because, from the table of values on page 15, we have

$$C(w) = \begin{cases} 0.83 & \text{if } 0 < w \leqslant 1 \\ 1.00 & \text{if } 1 < w \leqslant 2 \\ 1.17 & \text{if } 2 < w \leqslant 3 \\ 1.34 & \text{if } 3 < w \leqslant 4 \\ \vdots \end{cases}$$

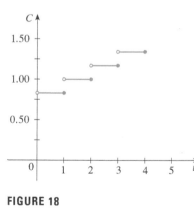

FIGURE 18

The graph is shown in Figure 18. You can see why functions similar to this one are called **step functions**—they jump from one value to the next. Such functions will be studied in Chapter 2.

Symmetry

If a function f satisfies $f(-x) = f(x)$ for every number x in its domain, then f is called an **even function**. For instance, the function $f(x) = x^2$ is even because

$$f(-x) = (-x)^2 = x^2 = f(x)$$

The geometric significance of an even function is that its graph is symmetric with respect to the y-axis (see Figure 19). This means that if we have plotted the graph of f for $x \geqslant 0$, we obtain the entire graph simply by reflecting this portion about the y-axis.

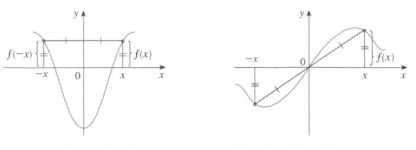

FIGURE 19 An even function   **FIGURE 20** An odd function

If f satisfies $f(-x) = -f(x)$ for every number x in its domain, then f is called an **odd function**. For example, the function $f(x) = x^3$ is odd because

$$f(-x) = (-x)^3 = -x^3 = -f(x)$$

The graph of an odd function is symmetric about the origin (see Figure 20). If we already have the graph of f for $x \geqslant 0$, we can obtain the entire graph by rotating this portion through $180°$ about the origin.

V EXAMPLE 11 Determine whether each of the following functions is even, odd, or neither even nor odd.
(a) $f(x) = x^5 + x$ (b) $g(x) = 1 - x^4$ (c) $h(x) = 2x - x^2$

SOLUTION
(a)
$$f(-x) = (-x)^5 + (-x) = (-1)^5 x^5 + (-x)$$
$$= -x^5 - x = -(x^5 + x)$$
$$= -f(x)$$

Therefore f is an odd function.

(b)
$$g(-x) = 1 - (-x)^4 = 1 - x^4 = g(x)$$

So g is even.

(c)
$$h(-x) = 2(-x) - (-x)^2 = -2x - x^2$$

Since $h(-x) \neq h(x)$ and $h(-x) \neq -h(x)$, we conclude that h is neither even nor odd.

The graphs of the functions in Example 11 are shown in Figure 21. Notice that the graph of h is symmetric neither about the y-axis nor about the origin.

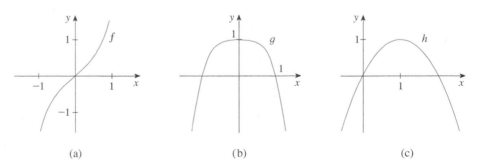

FIGURE 21   (a)   (b)   (c)

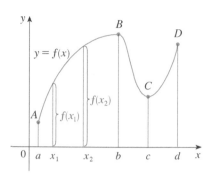

FIGURE 22

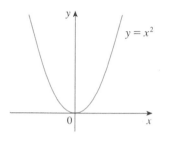

FIGURE 23

Increasing and Decreasing Functions

The graph shown in Figure 22 rises from A to B, falls from B to C, and rises again from C to D. The function f is said to be increasing on the interval $[a, b]$, decreasing on $[b, c]$, and increasing again on $[c, d]$. Notice that if x_1 and x_2 are any two numbers between a and b with $x_1 < x_2$, then $f(x_1) < f(x_2)$. We use this as the defining property of an increasing function.

A function f is called **increasing** on an interval I if

$$f(x_1) < f(x_2) \qquad \text{whenever } x_1 < x_2 \text{ in } I$$

It is called **decreasing** on I if

$$f(x_1) > f(x_2) \qquad \text{whenever } x_1 < x_2 \text{ in } I$$

In the definition of an increasing function it is important to realize that the inequality $f(x_1) < f(x_2)$ must be satisfied for *every* pair of numbers x_1 and x_2 in I with $x_1 < x_2$.

You can see from Figure 23 that the function $f(x) = x^2$ is decreasing on the interval $(-\infty, 0]$ and increasing on the interval $[0, \infty)$.

1.1 Exercises

1. The graph of a function f is given.
   (a) State the value of $f(1)$.
   (b) Estimate the value of $f(-1)$.
   (c) For what values of x is $f(x) = 1$?
   (d) Estimate the value of x such that $f(x) = 0$.
   (e) State the domain and range of f.
   (f) On what interval is f increasing?

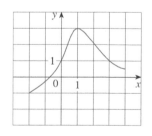

2. The graphs of f and g are given.
   (a) State the values of $f(-4)$ and $g(3)$.
   (b) For what values of x is $f(x) = g(x)$?
   (c) Estimate the solution of the equation $f(x) = -1$.
   (d) On what interval is f decreasing?

   (e) State the domain and range of f.
   (f) State the domain and range of g.

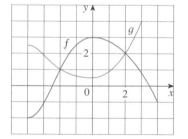

3. Figure 1 was recorded by an instrument operated by the California Department of Mines and Geology at the University Hospital of the University of Southern California in Los Angeles. Use it to estimate the range of the vertical ground acceleration function at USC during the Northridge earthquake.

4. In this section we discussed examples of ordinary, everyday functions: Population is a function of time, postage cost is a function of weight, water temperature is a function of time. Give three other examples of functions from everyday life that are described verbally. What can you say about the domain and range of each of your functions? If possible, sketch a rough graph of each function.

---

1. Homework Hints available in TEC

5–8 Determine whether the curve is the graph of a function of x. If it is, state the domain and range of the function.

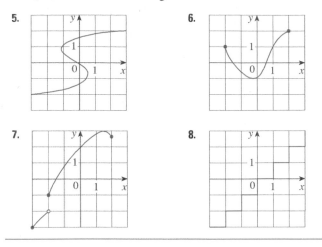

5.

6.

7.

8.

9. The graph shown gives the weight of a certain person as a function of age. Describe in words how this person's weight varies over time. What do you think happened when this person was 30 years old?

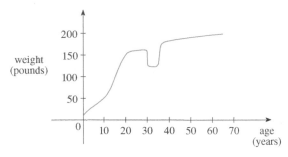

10. The graph shows the height of the water in a bathtub as a function of time. Give a verbal description of what you think happened.

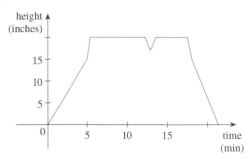

11. You put some ice cubes in a glass, fill the glass with cold water, and then let the glass sit on a table. Describe how the temperature of the water changes as time passes. Then sketch a rough graph of the temperature of the water as a function of the elapsed time.

12. Three runners compete in a 100-meter race. The graph depicts the distance run as a function of time for each runner. Describe

in words what the graph tells you about this race. Who won the race? Did each runner finish the race?

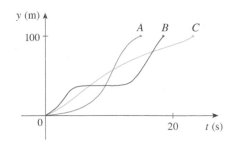

13. The graph shows the power consumption for a day in September in San Francisco. (P is measured in megawatts; t is measured in hours starting at midnight.)
(a) What was the power consumption at 6 AM? At 6 PM?
(b) When was the power consumption the lowest? When was it the highest? Do these times seem reasonable?

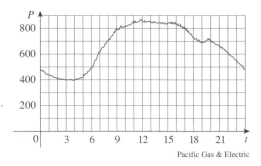

Pacific Gas & Electric

14. Sketch a rough graph of the number of hours of daylight as a function of the time of year.

15. Sketch a rough graph of the outdoor temperature as a function of time during a typical spring day.

16. Sketch a rough graph of the market value of a new car as a function of time for a period of 20 years. Assume the car is well maintained.

17. Sketch the graph of the amount of a particular brand of coffee sold by a store as a function of the price of the coffee.

18. You place a frozen pie in an oven and bake it for an hour. Then you take it out and let it cool before eating it. Describe how the temperature of the pie changes as time passes. Then sketch a rough graph of the temperature of the pie as a function of time.

19. A homeowner mows the lawn every Wednesday afternoon. Sketch a rough graph of the height of the grass as a function of time over the course of a four-week period.

20. An airplane takes off from an airport and lands an hour later at another airport, 400 miles away. If t represents the time in minutes since the plane has left the terminal building, let $x(t)$ be the horizontal distance traveled and $y(t)$ be the altitude of the plane.

(a) Sketch a possible graph of $x(t)$.

(b) Sketch a possible graph of $y(t)$.

(c) Sketch a possible graph of the ground speed.

(d) Sketch a possible graph of the vertical velocity.

21. The number N (in millions) of US cellular phone subscribers is shown in the table. (Midyear estimates are given.)

t	1996	1998	2000	2002	2004	2006
N	44	69	109	141	182	233

(a) Use the data to sketch a rough graph of N as a function of t.

(b) Use your graph to estimate the number of cell-phone subscribers at midyear in 2001 and 2005.

22. Temperature readings T (in °F) were recorded every two hours from midnight to 2:00 PM in Baltimore on September 26, 2007. The time t was measured in hours from midnight.

t	0	2	4	6	8	10	12	14
T	68	65	63	63	65	76	85	91

(a) Use the readings to sketch a rough graph of T as a function of t.

(b) Use your graph to estimate the temperature at 11:00 AM.

23. If $f(x) = 3x^2 - x + 2$, find $f(2)$, $f(-2)$, $f(a)$, $f(-a)$, $f(a + 1)$, $2f(a)$, $f(2a)$, $f(a^2)$, $[f(a)]^2$, and $f(a + h)$.

24. A spherical balloon with radius r inches has volume $V(r) = \frac{4}{3}\pi r^3$. Find a function that represents the amount of air required to inflate the balloon from a radius of r inches to a radius of $r + 1$ inches.

25–28 Evaluate the difference quotient for the given function. Simplify your answer.

25. $f(x) = 4 + 3x - x^2$, $\quad \dfrac{f(3 + h) - f(3)}{h}$

26. $f(x) = x^3$, $\quad \dfrac{f(a + h) - f(a)}{h}$

27. $f(x) = \dfrac{1}{x}$, $\quad \dfrac{f(x) - f(a)}{x - a}$

28. $f(x) = \dfrac{x + 3}{x + 1}$, $\quad \dfrac{f(x) - f(1)}{x - 1}$

29–33 Find the domain of the function.

29. $f(x) - \dfrac{x + 4}{x^2 - 9}$

30. $f(x) = \dfrac{2x^3 - 5}{x^2 + x - 6}$

31. $f(t) = \sqrt[3]{2t - 1}$

32. $g(t) = \sqrt{3 - t} - \sqrt{2 + t}$

33. $h(x) = \dfrac{1}{\sqrt[4]{x^2 - 5x}}$

34. Find the domain and range and sketch the graph of the function $h(x) = \sqrt{4 - x^2}$.

35–46 Find the domain and sketch the graph of the function.

35. $f(x) = 2 - 0.4x$

36. $F(x) = x^2 - 2x + 1$

37. $f(t) = 2t + t^2$

38. $H(t) = \dfrac{4 - t^2}{2 - t}$

39. $g(x) = \sqrt{x - 5}$

40. $F(x) = |2x + 1|$

41. $G(x) = \dfrac{3x + |x|}{x}$

42. $g(x) = |x| - x$

43. $f(x) = \begin{cases} x + 2 & \text{if } x < 0 \\ 1 - x & \text{if } x \geqslant 0 \end{cases}$

44. $f(x) = \begin{cases} 3 - \frac{1}{2}x & \text{if } x \leqslant 2 \\ 2x - 5 & \text{if } x > 2 \end{cases}$

45. $f(x) = \begin{cases} x + 2 & \text{if } x \leqslant -1 \\ x^2 & \text{if } x > -1 \end{cases}$

46. $f(x) = \begin{cases} x + 9 & \text{if } x < -3 \\ -2x & \text{if } |x| \leqslant 3 \\ -6 & \text{if } x > 3 \end{cases}$

47–52 Find an expression for the function whose graph is the given curve.

47. The line segment joining the points $(1, -3)$ and $(5, 7)$

48. The line segment joining the points $(-5, 10)$ and $(7, -10)$

49. The bottom half of the parabola $x + (y - 1)^2 = 0$

50. The top half of the circle $x^2 + (y - 2)^2 = 4$

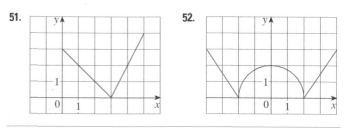

53–57 Find a formula for the described function and state its domain.

53. A rectangle has perimeter 20 m. Express the area of the rectangle as a function of the length of one of its sides.

54. A rectangle has area 16 m². Express the perimeter of the rectangle as a function of the length of one of its sides.

55. Express the area of an equilateral triangle as a function of the length of a side.

56. Express the surface area of a cube as a function of its volume.

57. An open rectangular box with volume 2 m³ has a square base. Express the surface area of the box as a function of the length of a side of the base.

58. A Norman window has the shape of a rectangle surmounted by a semicircle. If the perimeter of the window is 30 ft, express the area A of the window as a function of the width x of the window.

59. A box with an open top is to be constructed from a rectangular piece of cardboard with dimensions 12 in. by 20 in. by cutting out equal squares of side x at each corner and then folding up the sides as in the figure. Express the volume V of the box as a function of x.

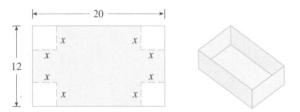

60. An electricity company charges its customers a base rate of $10 a month, plus 6 cents per kilowatt-hour (kWh) for the first 1200 kWh and 7 cents per kWh for all usage over 1200 kWh. Express the monthly cost E as a function of the amount x of electricity used. Then graph the function E for $0 \le x \le 2000$.

61. In a certain country, income tax is assessed as follows. There is no tax on income up to $10,000. Any income over $10,000 is taxed at a rate of 10%, up to an income of $20,000. Any income over $20,000 is taxed at 15%.
(a) Sketch the graph of the tax rate R as a function of the income I.
(b) How much tax is assessed on an income of $14,000? On $26,000?
(c) Sketch the graph of the total assessed tax T as a function of the income I.

62. The functions in Example 10 and Exercise 61(a) are called *step functions* because their graphs look like stairs. Give two other examples of step functions that arise in everyday life.

63–64 Graphs of f and g are shown. Decide whether each function is even, odd, or neither. Explain your reasoning.

63. **64.**

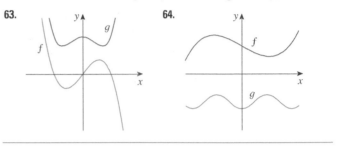

65. (a) If the point $(5, 3)$ is on the graph of an even function, what other point must also be on the graph?
(b) If the point $(5, 3)$ is on the graph of an odd function, what other point must also be on the graph?

66. A function f has domain $[-5, 5]$ and a portion of its graph is shown.
(a) Complete the graph of f if it is known that f is even.
(b) Complete the graph of f if it is known that f is odd.

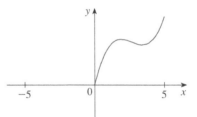

67–72 Determine whether f is even, odd, or neither. If you have a graphing calculator, use it to check your answer visually.

67. $f(x) = \dfrac{x}{x^2 + 1}$ **68.** $f(x) = \dfrac{x^2}{x^4 + 1}$

69. $f(x) = \dfrac{x}{x + 1}$ **70.** $f(x) = x|x|$

71. $f(x) = 1 + 3x^2 - x^4$ **72.** $f(x) = 1 + 3x^3 - x^5$

73. If f and g are both even functions, is $f + g$ even? If f and g are both odd functions, is $f + g$ odd? What if f is even and g is odd? Justify your answers.

74. If f and g are both even functions, is the product fg even? If f and g are both odd functions, is fg odd? What if f is even and g is odd? Justify your answers.

1.2 Mathematical Models: A Catalog of Essential Functions

A **mathematical model** is a mathematical description (often by means of a function or an equation) of a real-world phenomenon such as the size of a population, the demand for a product, the speed of a falling object, the concentration of a product in a chemical reaction, the life expectancy of a person at birth, or the cost of emission reductions. The purpose of the model is to understand the phenomenon and perhaps to make predictions about future behavior.

Figure 1 illustrates the process of mathematical modeling. Given a real-world problem, our first task is to formulate a mathematical model by identifying and naming the independent and dependent variables and making assumptions that simplify the phenomenon enough to make it mathematically tractable. We use our knowledge of the physical situation and our mathematical skills to obtain equations that relate the variables. In situations where there is no physical law to guide us, we may need to collect data (either from a library or the Internet or by conducting our own experiments) and examine the data in the form of a table in order to discern patterns. From this numerical representation of a function we may wish to obtain a graphical representation by plotting the data. The graph might even suggest a suitable algebraic formula in some cases.

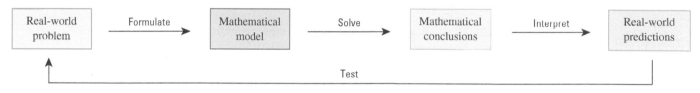

FIGURE 1 The modeling process

The second stage is to apply the mathematics that we know (such as the calculus that will be developed throughout this book) to the mathematical model that we have formulated in order to derive mathematical conclusions. Then, in the third stage, we take those mathematical conclusions and interpret them as information about the original real-world phenomenon by way of offering explanations or making predictions. The final step is to test our predictions by checking against new real data. If the predictions don't compare well with reality, we need to refine our model or to formulate a new model and start the cycle again.

A mathematical model is never a completely accurate representation of a physical situation—it is an *idealization*. A good model simplifies reality enough to permit mathematical calculations but is accurate enough to provide valuable conclusions. It is important to realize the limitations of the model. In the end, Mother Nature has the final say.

There are many different types of functions that can be used to model relationships observed in the real world. In what follows, we discuss the behavior and graphs of these functions and give examples of situations appropriately modeled by such functions.

Linear Models

The coordinate geometry of lines is reviewed in Appendix B.

When we say that y is a **linear function** of x, we mean that the graph of the function is a line, so we can use the slope-intercept form of the equation of a line to write a formula for the function as

$$y = f(x) = mx + b$$

where m is the slope of the line and b is the y-intercept.

A characteristic feature of linear functions is that they grow at a constant rate. For instance, Figure 2 shows a graph of the linear function $f(x) = 3x - 2$ and a table of sample values. Notice that whenever x increases by 0.1, the value of $f(x)$ increases by 0.3. So $f(x)$ increases three times as fast as x. Thus the slope of the graph $y = 3x - 2$, namely 3, can be interpreted as the rate of change of y with respect to x.

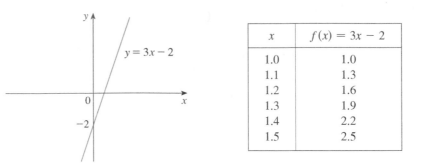

x	$f(x) = 3x - 2$
1.0	1.0
1.1	1.3
1.2	1.6
1.3	1.9
1.4	2.2
1.5	2.5

FIGURE 2

V   EXAMPLE 1   Interpreting the slope of a linear model

(a) As dry air moves upward, it expands and cools. If the ground temperature is 20°C and the temperature at a height of 1 km is 10°C, express the temperature T (in °C) as a function of the height h (in kilometers), assuming that a linear model is appropriate.

(b) Draw the graph of the function in part (a). What does the slope represent?

(c) What is the temperature at a height of 2.5 km?

SOLUTION

(a) Because we are assuming that T is a linear function of h, we can write

$$T = mh + b$$

We are given that $T = 20$ when $h = 0$, so

$$20 = m \cdot 0 + b = b$$

In other words, the y-intercept is $b = 20$.

We are also given that $T = 10$ when $h = 1$, so

$$10 = m \cdot 1 + 20$$

The slope of the line is therefore $m = 10 - 20 = -10$ and the required linear function is

$$T = -10h + 20$$

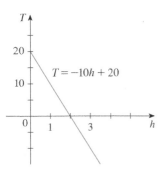

FIGURE 3

(b) The graph is sketched in Figure 3. The slope is $m = -10°C/km$, and this represents the rate of change of temperature with respect to height.

(c) At a height of $h = 2.5$ km, the temperature is

$$T = -10(2.5) + 20 = -5°C$$

If there is no physical law or principle to help us formulate a model, we construct an **empirical model**, which is based entirely on collected data. We seek a curve that "fits" the data in the sense that it captures the basic trend of the data points.

☑ **EXAMPLE 2** **A linear regression model** Table 1 lists the average carbon dioxide level in the atmosphere, measured in parts per million at Mauna Loa Observatory from 1980 to 2006. Use the data in Table 1 to find a model for the carbon dioxide level.

SOLUTION We use the data in Table 1 to make the scatter plot in Figure 4, where t represents time (in years) and C represents the CO_2 level (in parts per million, ppm).

TABLE 1

Year	CO_2 level (in ppm)	Year	CO_2 level (in ppm)
1980	338.7	1994	358.9
1982	341.1	1996	362.6
1984	344.4	1998	366.6
1986	347.2	2000	369.4
1988	351.5	2002	372.9
1990	354.2	2004	377.5
1992	356.4	2006	381.9

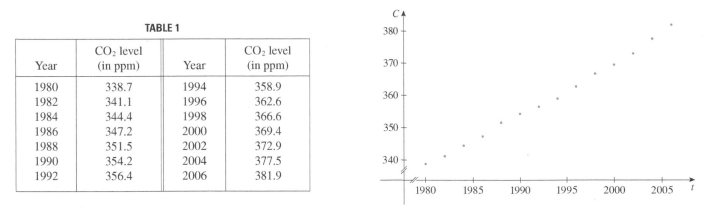

FIGURE 4 Scatter plot for the average CO_2 level

Notice that the data points appear to lie close to a straight line, so it's natural to choose a linear model in this case. But there are many possible lines that approximate these data points, so which one should we use? One possibility is the line that passes through the first and last data points. The slope of this line is

$$\frac{381.9 - 338.7}{2006 - 1980} = \frac{43.2}{26} \approx 1.6615$$

and its equation is

$$C - 338.7 = 1.6615(t - 1980)$$

or

1
$$C = 1.6615t - 2951.07$$

Equation 1 gives one possible linear model for the carbon dioxide level; it is graphed in Figure 5.

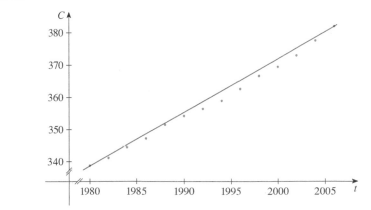

FIGURE 5
Linear model through
first and last data points

Notice that our model gives values higher than most of the actual CO_2 levels. A better linear model is obtained by a procedure from statistics called *linear regression*. If we use

A computer or graphing calculator finds the regression line by the method of **least squares**, which is to minimize the sum of the squares of the vertical distances between the data points and the line. The details are explained in Section 11.7.

a graphing calculator, we enter the data from Table 1 into the data editor and choose the linear regression command. (With Maple we use the fit[leastsquare] command in the stats package; with Mathematica we use the Fit command.) The machine gives the slope and y-intercept of the regression line as

$$m = 1.62319 \qquad b = -2876.20$$

So our least squares model for the CO_2 level is

$$\boxed{2} \qquad C = 1.62319t - 2876.20$$

In Figure 6 we graph the regression line as well as the data points. Comparing with Figure 5, we see that it gives a better fit than our previous linear model.

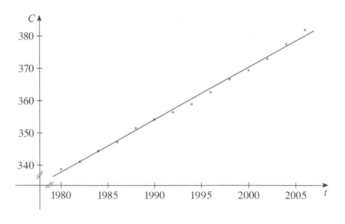

FIGURE 6
The regression line

V   EXAMPLE 3   Using a linear model for prediction   Use the linear model given by Equation 2 to estimate the average CO_2 level for 1987 and to predict the level for the year 2012. According to this model, when will the CO_2 level exceed 400 parts per million?

SOLUTION   Using Equation 2 with $t = 1987$, we estimate that the average CO_2 level in 1987 was

$$C(1987) = (1.62319)(1987) - 2876.20 \approx 349.08$$

This is an example of *interpolation* because we have estimated a value *between* observed values. (In fact, the Mauna Loa Observatory reported that the average CO_2 level in 1987 was 348.93 ppm, so our estimate is quite accurate.)

With $t = 2012$, we get

$$C(2012) = (1.62319)(2012) - 2876.20 \approx 389.66$$

So we predict that the average CO_2 level in the year 2012 will be 389.7 ppm. This is an example of *extrapolation* because we have predicted a value *outside* the region of observations. Consequently, we are far less certain about the accuracy of our prediction.

Using Equation 2, we see that the CO_2 level exceeds 400 ppm when

$$1.62319t - 2876.20 > 400$$

Solving this inequality, we get

$$t > \frac{3276.20}{1.62319} \approx 2018.37$$

We therefore predict that the CO_2 level will exceed 400 ppm by the year 2018. This prediction is risky because it involves a time quite remote from our observations. In fact, we see from Figure 6 that the trend has been for CO_2 levels to increase rather more rapidly in recent years, so the level might exceed 400 ppm well before 2018.

Polynomials

A function P is called a **polynomial** if

$$P(x) = a_n x^n + a_{n-1} x^{n-1} + \cdots + a_2 x^2 + a_1 x + a_0$$

where n is a nonnegative integer and the numbers $a_0, a_1, a_2, \ldots, a_n$ are constants called the **coefficients** of the polynomial. The domain of any polynomial is $\mathbb{R} = (-\infty, \infty)$. If the leading coefficient $a_n \neq 0$, then the **degree** of the polynomial is n. For example, the function

$$P(x) = 2x^6 - x^4 + \tfrac{2}{5}x^3 + \sqrt{2}$$

is a polynomial of degree 6.

A polynomial of degree 1 is of the form $P(x) = mx + b$ and so it is a linear function. A polynomial of degree 2 is of the form $P(x) = ax^2 + bx + c$ and is called a **quadratic function**. Its graph is always a parabola obtained by shifting the parabola $y = ax^2$, as we will see in the next section. The parabola opens upward if $a > 0$ and downward if $a < 0$. (See Figure 7.)

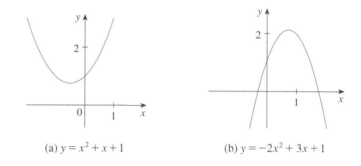

FIGURE 7
The graphs of quadratic functions are parabolas.

(a) $y = x^2 + x + 1$

(b) $y = -2x^2 + 3x + 1$

A polynomial of degree 3 is of the form

$$P(x) = ax^3 + bx^2 + cx + d \qquad a \neq 0$$

and is called a **cubic function**. Figure 8 shows the graph of a cubic function in part (a) and graphs of polynomials of degrees 4 and 5 in parts (b) and (c). We will see later why the graphs have these shapes.

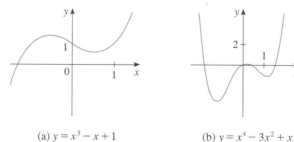
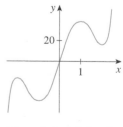

FIGURE 8

(a) $y = x^3 - x + 1$

(b) $y = x^4 - 3x^2 + x$

(c) $y = 3x^5 - 25x^3 + 60x$

Polynomials are commonly used to model various quantities that occur in the natural and social sciences. For instance, in Section 3.8 we will explain why economists often use a polynomial $P(x)$ to represent the cost of producing x units of a commodity. In the following example we use a quadratic function to model the fall of a ball.

TABLE 2

Time (seconds)	Height (meters)
0	450
1	445
2	431
3	408
4	375
5	332
6	279
7	216
8	143
9	61

EXAMPLE 4 A quadratic model   A ball is dropped from the upper observation deck of the CN Tower, 450 m above the ground, and its height h above the ground is recorded at 1-second intervals in Table 2. Find a model to fit the data and use the model to predict the time at which the ball hits the ground.

SOLUTION We draw a scatter plot of the data in Figure 9 and observe that a linear model is inappropriate. But it looks as if the data points might lie on a parabola, so we try a quadratic model instead. Using a graphing calculator or computer algebra system (which uses the least squares method), we obtain the following quadratic model:

$$\boxed{3} \qquad\qquad h = 449.36 + 0.96t - 4.90t^2$$

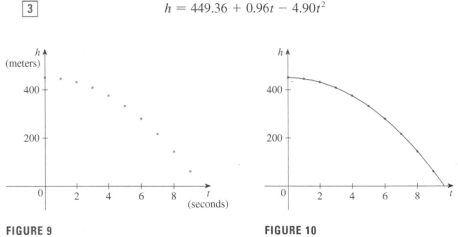

FIGURE 9
Scatter plot for a falling ball

FIGURE 10
Quadratic model for a falling ball

In Figure 10 we plot the graph of Equation 3 together with the data points and see that the quadratic model gives a very good fit.

The ball hits the ground when $h = 0$, so we solve the quadratic equation

$$-4.90t^2 + 0.96t + 449.36 = 0$$

The quadratic formula gives

$$t = \frac{-0.96 \pm \sqrt{(0.96)^2 - 4(-4.90)(449.36)}}{2(-4.90)}$$

The positive root is $t \approx 9.67$, so we predict that the ball will hit the ground after about 9.7 seconds.

Power Functions

A function of the form $f(x) = x^a$, where a is a constant, is called a **power function**. We consider several cases.

(i) $a = n$, where n is a positive integer

The graphs of $f(x) = x^n$ for $n = 1, 2, 3, 4$, and 5 are shown in Figure 11. (These are polynomials with only one term.) We already know the shape of the graphs of $y = x$ (a line through the origin with slope 1) and $y = x^2$ [a parabola, see Example 2(b) in Section 1.1].

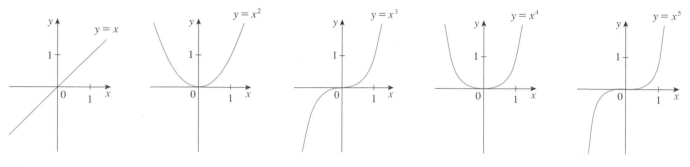

FIGURE 11   Graphs of $f(x) = x^n$ for $n = 1, 2, 3, 4, 5$

The general shape of the graph of $f(x) = x^n$ depends on whether n is even or odd. If n is even, then $f(x) = x^n$ is an even function and its graph is similar to the parabola $y = x^2$. If n is odd, then $f(x) = x^n$ is an odd function and its graph is similar to that of $y = x^3$. Notice from Figure 12, however, that as n increases, the graph of $y = x^n$ becomes flatter near 0 and steeper when $|x| \geqslant 1$. (If x is small, then x^2 is smaller, x^3 is even smaller, x^4 is smaller still, and so on.)

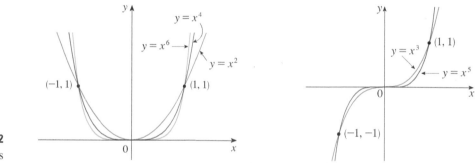

FIGURE 12
Families of power functions

(ii) $a = 1/n$, where n is a positive integer

The function $f(x) = x^{1/n} = \sqrt[n]{x}$ is a **root function**. For $n = 2$ it is the square root function $f(x) = \sqrt{x}$, whose domain is $[0, \infty)$ and whose graph is the upper half of the parabola $x = y^2$. [See Figure 13(a).] For other even values of n, the graph of $y = \sqrt[n]{x}$ is similar to that of $y = \sqrt{x}$. For $n = 3$ we have the cube root function $f(x) = \sqrt[3]{x}$ whose domain is $\mathbb{R}$ (recall that every real number has a cube root) and whose graph is shown in Figure 13(b). The graph of $y = \sqrt[n]{x}$ for n odd ($n > 3$) is similar to that of $y = \sqrt[3]{x}$.

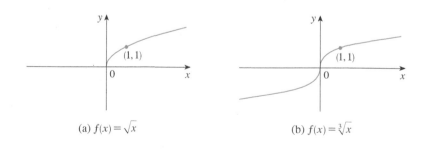

FIGURE 13
Graphs of root functions

(a) $f(x) = \sqrt{x}$ (b) $f(x) = \sqrt[3]{x}$

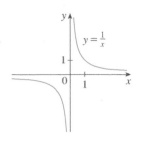

FIGURE 14
The reciprocal function

(iii) $a = -1$

The graph of the **reciprocal function** $f(x) = x^{-1} = 1/x$ is shown in Figure 14. Its graph has the equation $y = 1/x$, or $xy = 1$, and is a hyperbola with the coordinate axes as its asymptotes. This function arises in physics and chemistry in connection with Boyle's Law, which says that, when the temperature is constant, the volume V of a gas is inversely proportional to the pressure P:

$$V = \frac{C}{P}$$

where C is a constant. Thus the graph of V as a function of P (see Figure 15) has the same general shape as the right half of Figure 14.

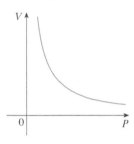

FIGURE 15
Volume as a function of pressure
at constant temperature

Another instance in which a power function is used to model a physical phenomenon is discussed in Exercise 26.

Rational Functions

A **rational function** f is a ratio of two polynomials:

$$f(x) = \frac{P(x)}{Q(x)}$$

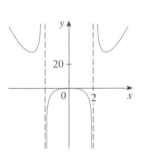

FIGURE 16

where P and Q are polynomials. The domain consists of all values of x such that $Q(x) \neq 0$. A simple example of a rational function is the function $f(x) = 1/x$, whose domain is $\{x \mid x \neq 0\}$; this is the reciprocal function graphed in Figure 14. The function

$$f(x) = \frac{2x^4 - x^2 + 1}{x^2 - 4}$$

is a rational function with domain $\{x \mid x \neq \pm 2\}$. Its graph is shown in Figure 16.

Algebraic Functions

A function f is called an **algebraic function** if it can be constructed using algebraic operations (such as addition, subtraction, multiplication, division, and taking roots) starting with polynomials. Any rational function is automatically an algebraic function. Here are two more examples:

$$f(x) = \sqrt{x^2 + 1} \qquad g(x) = \frac{x^4 - 16x^2}{x + \sqrt{x}} + (x - 2)\sqrt[3]{x + 1}$$

When we sketch algebraic functions in Chapter 4, we will see that their graphs can assume a variety of shapes. Figure 17 illustrates some of the possibilities.

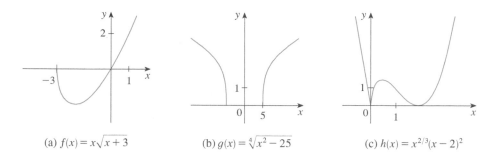

FIGURE 17   (a) $f(x) = x\sqrt{x+3}$ (b) $g(x) = \sqrt[4]{x^2 - 25}$ (c) $h(x) = x^{2/3}(x-2)^2$

An example of an algebraic function occurs in the theory of relativity. The mass of a particle with velocity v is

$$m = f(v) = \frac{m_0}{\sqrt{1 - v^2/c^2}}$$

where m_0 is the rest mass of the particle and $c = 3.0 \times 10^5$ km/s is the speed of light in a vacuum.

Trigonometric Functions

The Reference Pages are located at the front and back of the book.

Trigonometry and the trigonometric functions are reviewed on Reference Page 2 and also in Appendix C. In calculus the convention is that radian measure is always used (except when otherwise indicated). For example, when we use the function $f(x) = \sin x$, it is understood that $\sin x$ means the sine of the angle whose radian measure is x. Thus the graphs of the sine and cosine functions are as shown in Figure 18.

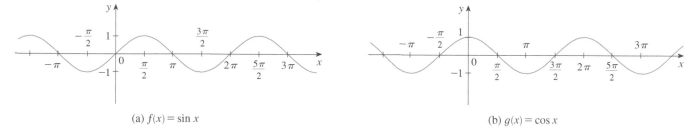

(a) $f(x) = \sin x$ (b) $g(x) = \cos x$

FIGURE 18

Notice that for both the sine and cosine functions the domain is $(-\infty, \infty)$ and the range is the closed interval $[-1, 1]$. Thus, for all values of x, we have

$$-1 \leqslant \sin x \leqslant 1 \qquad -1 \leqslant \cos x \leqslant 1$$

or, in terms of absolute values,

$$|\sin x| \leqslant 1 \qquad |\cos x| \leqslant 1$$

Also, the *zeros* of the sine function occur at the integer multiples of π; that is,

$$\sin x = 0 \qquad \text{when} \qquad x = n\pi \quad n \text{ an integer}$$

An important property of the sine and cosine functions is that they are periodic functions and have period 2π. This means that, for all values of x,

$$\sin(x + 2\pi) = \sin x \qquad \cos(x + 2\pi) = \cos x$$

The periodic nature of these functions makes them suitable for modeling repetitive phenomena such as tides, vibrating springs, and sound waves. For instance, in Example 4 in Section 1.3 we will see that a reasonable model for the number of hours of daylight in Philadelphia t days after January 1 is given by the function

$$L(t) = 12 + 2.8 \sin\left[\frac{2\pi}{365}(t - 80)\right]$$

The tangent function is related to the sine and cosine functions by the equation

$$\tan x = \frac{\sin x}{\cos x}$$

and its graph is shown in Figure 19. It is undefined whenever $\cos x = 0$, that is, when $x = \pm\pi/2, \pm3\pi/2, \ldots$. Its range is $(-\infty, \infty)$. Notice that the tangent function has period π:

$$\tan(x + \pi) = \tan x \qquad \text{for all } x$$

The remaining three trigonometric functions (cosecant, secant, and cotangent) are the reciprocals of the sine, cosine, and tangent functions. Their graphs are shown in Appendix C.

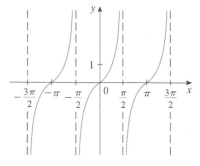

FIGURE 19
$y = \tan x$

Exponential Functions

The **exponential functions** are the functions of the form $f(x) = a^x$, where the base a is a positive constant. The graphs of $y = 2^x$ and $y = (0.5)^x$ are shown in Figure 20. In both cases the domain is $(-\infty, \infty)$ and the range is $(0, \infty)$.

Exponential functions will be studied in detail in Section 1.5, and we will see that they are useful for modeling many natural phenomena, such as population growth (if $a > 1$) and radioactive decay (if $a < 1$).

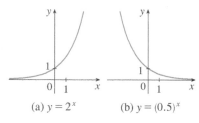

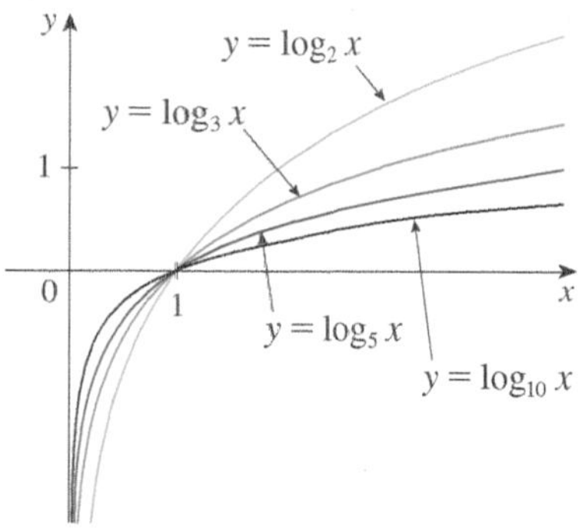

(a) $y = 2^x$ (b) $y = (0.5)^x$

FIGURE 20

Logarithmic Functions

The **logarithmic functions** $f(x) = \log_a x$, where the base a is a positive constant, are the inverse functions of the exponential functions. They will be studied in Section 1.6. Figure 21 shows the graphs of four logarithmic functions with various bases. In each case the domain is $(0, \infty)$, the range is $(-\infty, \infty)$, and the function increases slowly when $x > 1$.

EXAMPLE 5   Classify the following functions as one of the types of functions that we have discussed.

(a) $f(x) = 5^x$

(b) $g(x) = x^5$

(c) $h(x) = \dfrac{1 + x}{1 - \sqrt{x}}$

(d) $u(t) = 1 - t + 5t^4$

FIGURE 21

SOLUTION

(a) $f(x) = 5^x$ is an exponential function. (The x is the exponent.)

(b) $g(x) = x^5$ is a power function. (The x is the base.) We could also consider it to be a polynomial of degree 5.

(c) $h(x) = \dfrac{1 + x}{1 - \sqrt{x}}$ is an algebraic function.

(d) $u(t) = 1 - t + 5t^4$ is a polynomial of degree 4.

1.2 Exercises

1–2 Classify each function as a power function, root function, polynomial (state its degree), rational function, algebraic function, trigonometric function, exponential function, or logarithmic function.

1. (a) $f(x) = \log_2 x$

(b) $g(x) = \sqrt[4]{x}$

(c) $h(x) = \dfrac{2x^3}{1 - x^2}$

(d) $u(t) = 1 - 1.1t + 2.54t^2$

(e) $v(t) = 5^t$

(f) $w(\theta) = \sin \theta \cos^2\theta$

2. (a) $y = \pi^x$

(b) $y = x^\pi$

(c) $y = x^2(2 - x^3)$

(d) $y = \tan t - \cos t$

(e) $y = \dfrac{s}{1 + s}$

(f) $y = \dfrac{\sqrt{x^3 - 1}}{1 + \sqrt[3]{x}}$

3–4 Match each equation with its graph. Explain your choices. (Don't use a computer or graphing calculator.)

3. (a) $y = x^2$ (b) $y = x^5$ (c) $y = x^8$

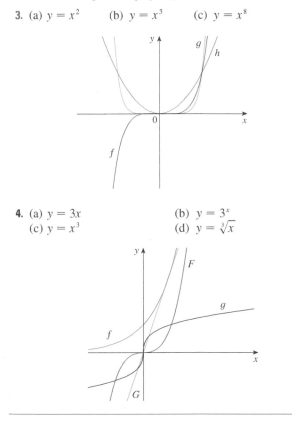

4. (a) $y = 3x$ (b) $y = 3^x$
(c) $y = x^3$ (d) $y = \sqrt[3]{x}$

5. (a) Find an equation for the family of linear functions with slope 2 and sketch several members of the family.
(b) Find an equation for the family of linear functions such that $f(2) = 1$ and sketch several members of the family.
(c) Which function belongs to both families?

6. What do all members of the family of linear functions $f(x) = 1 + m(x + 3)$ have in common? Sketch several members of the family.

7. What do all members of the family of linear functions $f(x) = c - x$ have in common? Sketch several members of the family.

8. Find expressions for the quadratic functions whose graphs are shown.

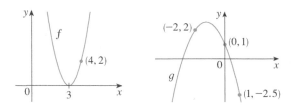

9. Find an expression for a cubic function f if $f(1) = 6$ and $f(-1) = f(0) = f(2) = 0$.

10. Recent studies indicate that the average surface temperature of the earth has been rising steadily. Some scientists have modeled the temperature by the linear function $T = 0.02t + 8.50$, where T is temperature in °C and t represents years since 1900.
(a) What do the slope and T-intercept represent?
(b) Use the equation to predict the average global surface temperature in 2100.

11. If the recommended adult dosage for a drug is D (in mg), then to determine the appropriate dosage c for a child of age a, pharmacists use the equation $c = 0.0417D(a + 1)$. Suppose the dosage for an adult is 200 mg.
(a) Find the slope of the graph of c. What does it represent?
(b) What is the dosage for a newborn?

12. The manager of a weekend flea market knows from past experience that if he charges x dollars for a rental space at the market, then the number y of spaces he can rent is given by the equation $y = 200 - 4x$.
(a) Sketch a graph of this linear function. (Remember that the rental charge per space and the number of spaces rented can't be negative quantities.)
(b) What do the slope, the y-intercept, and the x-intercept of the graph represent?

13. The relationship between the Fahrenheit (F) and Celsius (C) temperature scales is given by the linear function $F = \frac{9}{5}C + 32$.
(a) Sketch a graph of this function.
(b) What is the slope of the graph and what does it represent? What is the F-intercept and what does it represent?

14. Jason leaves Detroit at 2:00 PM and drives at a constant speed west along I-96. He passes Ann Arbor, 40 mi from Detroit, at 2:50 PM.
(a) Express the distance traveled in terms of the time elapsed.

(b) Draw the graph of the equation in part (a).
(c) What is the slope of this line? What does it represent?

15. Biologists have noticed that the chirping rate of crickets of a certain species is related to temperature, and the relationship appears to be very nearly linear. A cricket produces 113 chirps per minute at 70°F and 173 chirps per minute at 80°F.
   (a) Find a linear equation that models the temperature T as a function of the number of chirps per minute N.
   (b) What is the slope of the graph? What does it represent?
   (c) If the crickets are chirping at 150 chirps per minute, estimate the temperature.

16. The manager of a furniture factory finds that it costs $2200 to manufacture 100 chairs in one day and $4800 to produce 300 chairs in one day.
   (a) Express the cost as a function of the number of chairs produced, assuming that it is linear. Then sketch the graph.
   (b) What is the slope of the graph and what does it represent?
   (c) What is the y-intercept of the graph and what does it represent?

17. At the surface of the ocean, the water pressure is the same as the air pressure above the water, 15 lb/in². Below the surface, the water pressure increases by 4.34 lb/in² for every 10 ft of descent.
   (a) Express the water pressure as a function of the depth below the ocean surface.
   (b) At what depth is the pressure 100 lb/in²?

18. The monthly cost of driving a car depends on the number of miles driven. Lynn found that in May it cost her $380 to drive 480 mi and in June it cost her $460 to drive 800 mi.
   (a) Express the monthly cost C as a function of the distance driven d, assuming that a linear relationship gives a suitable model.
   (b) Use part (a) to predict the cost of driving 1500 miles per month.
   (c) Draw the graph of the linear function. What does the slope represent?
   (d) What does the C-intercept represent?
   (e) Why does a linear function give a suitable model in this situation?

19–20 For each scatter plot, decide what type of function you might choose as a model for the data. Explain your choices.

19. (a)   **(b)**

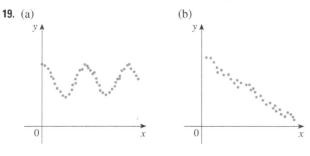

20. (a)   **(b)**

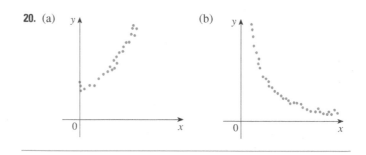

21. The table shows (lifetime) peptic ulcer rates (per 100 population) for various family incomes as reported by the National Health Interview Survey.

Income	Ulcer rate (per 100 population)
$4,000	14.1
$6,000	13.0
$8,000	13.4
$12,000	12.5
$16,000	12.0
$20,000	12.4
$30,000	10.5
$45,000	9.4
$60,000	8.2

   (a) Make a scatter plot of these data and decide whether a linear model is appropriate.
   (b) Find and graph a linear model using the first and last data points.
   (c) Find and graph the least squares regression line.
   (d) Use the linear model in part (c) to estimate the ulcer rate for an income of $25,000.
   (e) According to the model, how likely is someone with an income of $80,000 to suffer from peptic ulcers?
   (f) Do you think it would be reasonable to apply the model to someone with an income of $200,000?

22. Biologists have observed that the chirping rate of crickets of a certain species appears to be related to temperature. The table shows the chirping rates for various temperatures.

Temperature (°F)	Chirping rate (chirps/min)	Temperature (°F)	Chirping rate (chirps/min)
50	20	75	140
55	46	80	173
60	79	85	198
65	91	90	211
70	113		

   (a) Make a scatter plot of the data.
   (b) Find and graph the regression line.
   (c) Use the linear model in part (b) to estimate the chirping rate at 100°F.

23. The table gives the winning heights for the Olympic pole vault competitions up to the year 2000.

Year	Height (m)	Year	Height (m)
1896	3.30	1956	4.56
1900	3.30	1960	4.70
1904	3.50	1964	5.10
1908	3.71	1968	5.40
1912	3.95	1972	5.64
1920	4.09	1976	5.64
1924	3.95	1980	5.78
1928	4.20	1984	5.75
1932	4.31	1988	5.90
1936	4.35	1992	5.87
1948	4.30	1996	5.92
1952	4.55	2000	5.90

(a) Make a scatter plot and decide whether a linear model is appropriate.
(b) Find and graph the regression line.
(c) Use the linear model to predict the height of the winning pole vault at the 2004 Olympics and compare with the actual winning height of 5.95 meters.
(d) Is it reasonable to use the model to predict the winning height at the 2100 Olympics?

24. The table shows the percentage of the population of Argentina that has lived in rural areas from 1955 to 2000. Find a model for the data and use it to estimate the rural percentage in 1988 and 2002.

Year	Percentage rural	Year	Percentage rural
1955	30.4	1980	17.1
1960	26.4	1985	15.0
1965	23.6	1990	13.0
1970	21.1	1995	11.7
1975	19.0	2000	10.5

25. Use the data in the table to model the population of the world in the 20th century by a cubic function. Then use your model to estimate the population in the year 1925.

Year	Population (millions)	Year	Population (millions)
1900	1650	1960	3040
1910	1750	1970	3710
1920	1860	1980	4450
1930	2070	1990	5280
1940	2300	2000	6080
1950	2560		

26. The table shows the mean (average) distances d of the planets from the sun (taking the unit of measurement to be the distance from the earth to the sun) and their periods T (time of revolution in years).

Planet	d	T
Mercury	0.387	0.241
Venus	0.723	0.615
Earth	1.000	1.000
Mars	1.523	1.881
Jupiter	5.203	11.861
Saturn	9.541	29.457
Uranus	19.190	84.008
Neptune	30.086	164.784

(a) Fit a power model to the data.
(b) Kepler's Third Law of Planetary Motion states that

"The square of the period of revolution of a planet is proportional to the cube of its mean distance from the sun."

Does your model corroborate Kepler's Third Law?

1.3 New Functions from Old Functions

In this section we start with the basic functions we discussed in Section 1.2 and obtain new functions by shifting, stretching, and reflecting their graphs. We also show how to combine pairs of functions by the standard arithmetic operations and by composition.

Transformations of Functions

By applying certain transformations to the graph of a given function we can obtain the graphs of certain related functions. This will give us the ability to sketch the graphs of many functions quickly by hand. It will also enable us to write equations for given graphs. Let's first consider **translations**. If c is a positive number, then the graph of $y = f(x) + c$ is just the graph of $y = f(x)$ shifted upward a distance of c units (because each y-coordinate is increased by the same number c). Likewise, if $g(x) = f(x - c)$, where $c > 0$, then the value of g at x is the same as the value of f at $x - c$ (c units to the left of x). Therefore the graph of $y = f(x - c)$ is just the graph of $y = f(x)$ shifted c units to the right (see Figure 1).

Vertical and Horizontal Shifts Suppose $c > 0$. To obtain the graph of

$y = f(x) + c$, shift the graph of $y = f(x)$ a distance c units upward

$y = f(x) - c$, shift the graph of $y = f(x)$ a distance c units downward

$y = f(x - c)$, shift the graph of $y = f(x)$ a distance c units to the right

$y = f(x + c)$, shift the graph of $y = f(x)$ a distance c units to the left

---

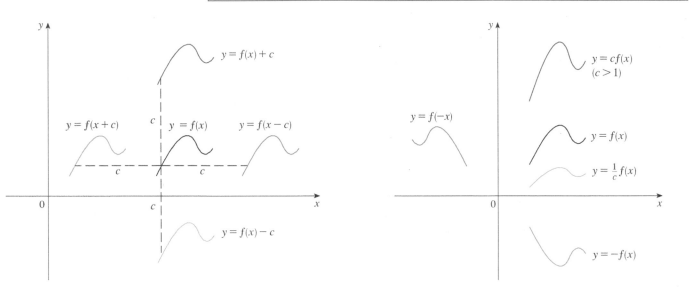

FIGURE 1
Translating the graph of f

FIGURE 2
Stretching and reflecting the graph of f

Now let's consider the **stretching** and **reflecting** transformations. If $c > 1$, then the graph of $y = cf(x)$ is the graph of $y = f(x)$ stretched by a factor of c in the vertical direction (because each y-coordinate is multiplied by the same number c). The graph of $y = -f(x)$ is the graph of $y = f(x)$ reflected about the x-axis because the point (x, y) is replaced by the point $(x, -y)$. (See Figure 2 and the following chart, where the results of other stretching, shrinking, and reflecting transformations are also given.)

Vertical and Horizontal Stretching and Reflecting Suppose $c > 1$. To obtain the graph of

$y = cf(x)$, stretch the graph of $y = f(x)$ vertically by a factor of c

$y = (1/c)f(x)$, shrink the graph of $y = f(x)$ vertically by a factor of c

$y = f(cx)$, shrink the graph of $y = f(x)$ horizontally by a factor of c

$y = f(x/c)$, stretch the graph of $y = f(x)$ horizontally by a factor of c

$y = -f(x)$, reflect the graph of $y = f(x)$ about the x-axis

$y = f(-x)$, reflect the graph of $y = f(x)$ about the y-axis

---

Figure 3 illustrates these stretching transformations when applied to the cosine function with $c = 2$. For instance, in order to get the graph of $y = 2 \cos x$ we multiply the y-coordinate of each point on the graph of $y = \cos x$ by 2. This means that the graph of $y = \cos x$ gets stretched vertically by a factor of 2.

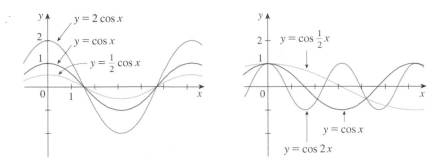

FIGURE 3

V EXAMPLE 1 Transforming the root function Given the graph of $y = \sqrt{x}$, use transformations to graph $y = \sqrt{x} - 2$, $y = \sqrt{x - 2}$, $y = -\sqrt{x}$, $y = 2\sqrt{x}$, and $y = \sqrt{-x}$.

SOLUTION The graph of the square root function $y = \sqrt{x}$, obtained from Figure 13(a) in Section 1.2, is shown in Figure 4(a). In the other parts of the figure we sketch $y = \sqrt{x} - 2$ by shifting 2 units downward, $y = \sqrt{x - 2}$ by shifting 2 units to the right, $y = -\sqrt{x}$ by reflecting about the x-axis, $y = 2\sqrt{x}$ by stretching vertically by a factor of 2, and $y = \sqrt{-x}$ by reflecting about the y-axis.

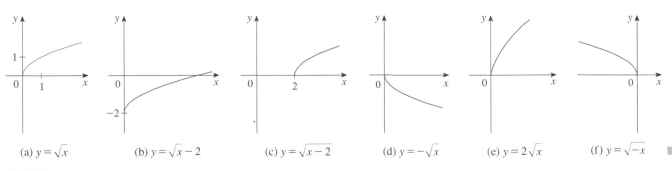

(a) $y = \sqrt{x}$ (b) $y = \sqrt{x} - 2$ (c) $y = \sqrt{x - 2}$ (d) $y = -\sqrt{x}$ (e) $y = 2\sqrt{x}$ (f) $y = \sqrt{-x}$

FIGURE 4

EXAMPLE 2 Sketch the graph of the function $f(x) = x^2 + 6x + 10$.

SOLUTION Completing the square, we write the equation of the graph as

$$y = x^2 + 6x + 10 = (x + 3)^2 + 1$$

This means we obtain the desired graph by starting with the parabola $y = x^2$ and shifting 3 units to the left and then 1 unit upward (see Figure 5).

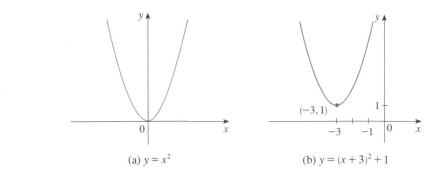

FIGURE 5

(a) $y = x^2$ (b) $y = (x + 3)^2 + 1$

EXAMPLE 3 Sketch the graphs of the following functions.

(a) $y = \sin 2x$ (b) $y = 1 - \sin x$

SOLUTION

(a) We obtain the graph of $y = \sin 2x$ from that of $y = \sin x$ by compressing horizontally by a factor of 2. (See Figures 6 and 7.) Thus, whereas the period of $y = \sin x$ is 2π, the period of $y = \sin 2x$ is $2\pi/2 = \pi$.

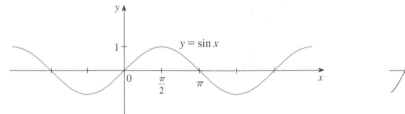

FIGURE 6

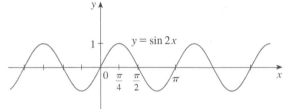

FIGURE 7

(b) To obtain the graph of $y = 1 - \sin x$, we again start with $y = \sin x$. We reflect about the x-axis to get the graph of $y = -\sin x$ and then we shift 1 unit upward to get $y = 1 - \sin x$. (See Figure 8.)

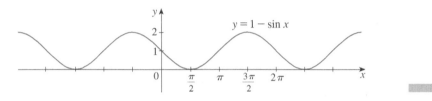

FIGURE 8

EXAMPLE 4 **Modeling amount of daylight as a function of time of year** Figure 9 shows graphs of the number of hours of daylight as functions of the time of the year at several latitudes. Given that Philadelphia is located at approximately 40°N latitude, find a function that models the length of daylight at Philadelphia.

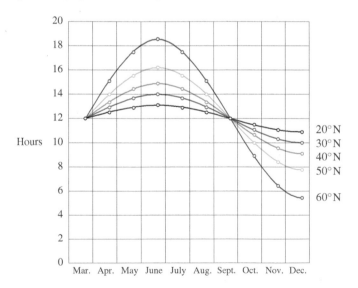

FIGURE 9

Graph of the length of daylight
from March 21 through December 21
at various latitudes

Lucia C. Harrison, *Daylight, Twilight, Darkness and Time*
(New York: Silver, Burdett, 1935) page 40.

SOLUTION Notice that each curve resembles a shifted and stretched sine function. By looking at the blue curve we see that, at the latitude of Philadelphia, daylight lasts about 14.8 hours on June 21 and 9.2 hours on December 21, so the amplitude of the curve (the factor by which we have to stretch the sine curve vertically) is $\frac{1}{2}(14.8 - 9.2) = 2.8$.

By what factor do we need to stretch the sine curve horizontally if we measure the time t in days? Because there are about 365 days in a year, the period of our model should be 365. But the period of $y = \sin t$ is 2π, so the horizontal stretching factor is $c = 2\pi/365$.

We also notice that the curve begins its cycle on March 21, the 80th day of the year, so we have to shift the curve 80 units to the right. In addition, we shift it 12 units upward. Therefore we model the length of daylight in Philadelphia on the tth day of the year by the function

$$L(t) = 12 + 2.8 \sin\left[\frac{2\pi}{365}(t - 80)\right]$$

Another transformation of some interest is taking the *absolute value* of a function. If $y = |f(x)|$, then according to the definition of absolute value, $y = f(x)$ when $f(x) \geqslant 0$ and $y = -f(x)$ when $f(x) < 0$. This tells us how to get the graph of $y = |f(x)|$ from the graph of $y = f(x)$: The part of the graph that lies above the x-axis remains the same; the part that lies below the x-axis is reflected about the x-axis.

☑ EXAMPLE 5 **The absolute value of a function**
Sketch the graph of the function $y = |x^2 - 1|$.

SOLUTION We first graph the parabola $y = x^2 - 1$ in Figure 10(a) by shifting the parabola $y = x^2$ downward 1 unit. We see that the graph lies below the x-axis when $-1 < x < 1$, so we reflect that part of the graph about the x-axis to obtain the graph of $y = |x^2 - 1|$ in Figure 10(b).

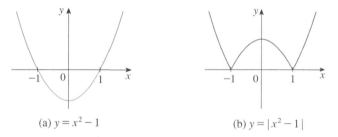

FIGURE 10   (a) $y = x^2 - 1$ (b) $y = |x^2 - 1|$

Combinations of Functions

Two functions f and g can be combined to form new functions $f + g$, $f - g$, fg, and f/g in a manner similar to the way we add, subtract, multiply, and divide real numbers. The sum and difference functions are defined by

$$(f + g)(x) = f(x) + g(x) \qquad (f - g)(x) = f(x) - g(x)$$

If the domain of f is A and the domain of g is B, then the domain of $f + g$ is the intersection $A \cap B$ because both $f(x)$ and $g(x)$ have to be defined. For example, the domain of $f(x) = \sqrt{x}$ is $A = [0, \infty)$ and the domain of $g(x) = \sqrt{2 - x}$ is $B = (-\infty, 2]$, so the domain of $(f + g)(x) = \sqrt{x} + \sqrt{2 - x}$ is $A \cap B = [0, 2]$.

Similarly, the product and quotient functions are defined by

$$(fg)(x) = f(x)g(x) \qquad \left(\frac{f}{g}\right)(x) = \frac{f(x)}{g(x)}$$

The domain of fg is $A \cap B$, but we can't divide by 0 and so the domain of f/g is $\{x \in A \cap B \mid g(x) \neq 0\}$. For instance, if $f(x) = x^2$ and $g(x) = x - 1$, then the domain of the rational function $(f/g)(x) = x^2/(x - 1)$ is $\{x \mid x \neq 1\}$, or $(-\infty, 1) \cup (1, \infty)$.

There is another way of combining two functions to obtain a new function. For example, suppose that $y = f(u) = \sqrt{u}$ and $u = g(x) = x^2 + 1$. Since y is a function of u

and u is, in turn, a function of x, it follows that y is ultimately a function of x. We compute this by substitution:

$$y = f(u) = f(g(x)) = f(x^2 + 1) = \sqrt{x^2 + 1}$$

The procedure is called *composition* because the new function is *composed* of the two given functions f and g.

In general, given any two functions f and g, we start with a number x in the domain of g and find its image $g(x)$. If this number $g(x)$ is in the domain of f, then we can calculate the value of $f(g(x))$. The result is a new function $h(x) = f(g(x))$ obtained by substituting g into f. It is called the *composition* (or *composite*) of f and g and is denoted by $f \circ g$ ("f circle g").

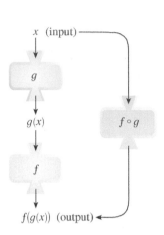

Definition Given two functions f and g, the **composite function** $f \circ g$ (also called the **composition** of f and g) is defined by

$$(f \circ g)(x) = f(g(x))$$

---

x (input)

$g(x)$

$f(g(x))$ (output)

FIGURE 11

The $f \circ g$ machine is composed of the g machine (first) and then the f machine.

The domain of $f \circ g$ is the set of all x in the domain of g such that $g(x)$ is in the domain of f. In other words, $(f \circ g)(x)$ is defined whenever both $g(x)$ and $f(g(x))$ are defined. Figure 11 shows how to picture $f \circ g$ in terms of machines.

EXAMPLE 6 **Composing functions** If $f(x) = x^2$ and $g(x) = x - 3$, find the composite functions $f \circ g$ and $g \circ f$.

SOLUTION We have

$$(f \circ g)(x) = f(g(x)) = f(x - 3) = (x - 3)^2$$

$$(g \circ f)(x) = g(f(x)) = g(x^2) = x^2 - 3$$

⊘   **Note:** You can see from Example 6 that, in general, $f \circ g \neq g \circ f$. Remember, the notation $f \circ g$ means that the function g is applied first and then f is applied second. In Example 6, $f \circ g$ is the function that *first* subtracts 3 and *then* squares; $g \circ f$ is the function that *first* squares and *then* subtracts 3. .

▶ **EXAMPLE 7** If $f(x) = \sqrt{x}$ and $g(x) = \sqrt{2 - x}$, find each function and its domain.
(a) $f \circ g$ (b) $g \circ f$ (c) $f \circ f$ (d) $g \circ g$

SOLUTION

(a) $(f \circ g)(x) = f(g(x)) = f(\sqrt{2 - x}) = \sqrt{\sqrt{2 - x}} = \sqrt[4]{2 - x}$

The domain of $f \circ g$ is $\{x \mid 2 - x \geq 0\} = \{x \mid x \leq 2\} = (-\infty, 2]$.

(b) $(g \circ f)(x) = g(f(x)) = g(\sqrt{x}) = \sqrt{2 - \sqrt{x}}$

If $0 \leq a \leq b$, then $a^2 \leq b^2$.

For $\sqrt{x}$ to be defined we must have $x \geq 0$. For $\sqrt{2 - \sqrt{x}}$ to be defined we must have $2 - \sqrt{x} \geq 0$, that is, $\sqrt{x} \leq 2$, or $x \leq 4$. Thus we have $0 \leq x \leq 4$, so the domain of $g \circ f$ is the closed interval $[0, 4]$.

(c) $(f \circ f)(x) = f(f(x)) = f(\sqrt{x}) = \sqrt{\sqrt{x}} = \sqrt[4]{x}$

The domain of $f \circ f$ is $[0, \infty)$.

(d) $$(g \circ g)(x) = g(g(x)) = g(\sqrt{2-x}) = \sqrt{2 - \sqrt{2-x}}$$

This expression is defined when both $2 - x \geqslant 0$ and $2 - \sqrt{2-x} \geqslant 0$. The first inequality means $x \leqslant 2$, and the second is equivalent to $\sqrt{2-x} \leqslant 2$, or $2 - x \leqslant 4$, or $x \geqslant -2$. Thus $-2 \leqslant x \leqslant 2$, so the domain of $g \circ g$ is the closed interval $[-2, 2]$. ▪

It is possible to take the composition of three or more functions. For instance, the composite function $f \circ g \circ h$ is found by first applying h, then g, and then f as follows:

$$(f \circ g \circ h)(x) = f(g(h(x)))$$

EXAMPLE 8 Find $f \circ g \circ h$ if $f(x) = x/(x+1)$, $g(x) = x^{10}$, and $h(x) = x + 3$.

SOLUTION
$$(f \circ g \circ h)(x) = f(g(h(x))) = f(g(x+3))$$
$$= f((x+3)^{10}) = \frac{(x+3)^{10}}{(x+3)^{10} + 1}$$ ▪

So far we have used composition to build complicated functions from simpler ones. But in calculus it is often useful to be able to *decompose* a complicated function into simpler ones, as in the following example.

EXAMPLE 9 **Decomposing a function**   Given $F(x) = \cos^2(x + 9)$, find functions f, g, and h such that $F = f \circ g \circ h$.

SOLUTION Since $F(x) = [\cos(x + 9)]^2$, the formula for F says: First add 9, then take the cosine of the result, and finally square. So we let

$$h(x) = x + 9 \qquad g(x) = \cos x \qquad f(x) = x^2$$

Then
$$(f \circ g \circ h)(x) = f(g(h(x))) = f(g(x+9)) = f(\cos(x+9))$$
$$= [\cos(x+9)]^2 = F(x)$$ ▪

1.3 Exercises

1. Suppose the graph of f is given. Write equations for the graphs that are obtained from the graph of f as follows.
   (a) Shift 3 units upward.
   (b) Shift 3 units downward.
   (c) Shift 3 units to the right.
   (d) Shift 3 units to the left.
   (e) Reflect about the x-axis.
   (f) Reflect about the y-axis.
   (g) Stretch vertically by a factor of 3.
   (h) Shrink vertically by a factor of 3.

2. Explain how each graph is obtained from the graph of $y = f(x)$.
   (a) $y = f(x) + 8$ (b) $y = f(x + 8)$
   (c) $y = 8f(x)$ (d) $y = f(8x)$
   (e) $y = -f(x) - 1$ (f) $y = 8f(\frac{1}{8}x)$

3. The graph of $y = f(x)$ is given. Match each equation with its graph and give reasons for your choices.
   (a) $y = f(x - 4)$ (b) $y = f(x) + 3$

   (c) $y = \frac{1}{3}f(x)$ (d) $y = -f(x + 4)$
   (e) $y = 2f(x + 6)$

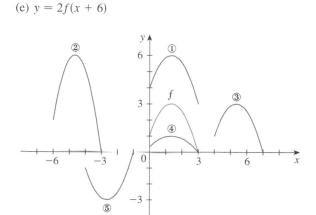

4. The graph of f is given. Draw the graphs of the following functions.

(a) $y = f(x) - 2$ (b) $y = f(x - 2)$

(c) $y = -2f(x)$ (d) $y = f\left(\frac{1}{3}x\right) + 1$

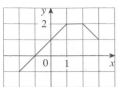

5. The graph of f is given. Use it to graph the following functions.

(a) $y = f(2x)$ (b) $y = f\left(\frac{1}{2}x\right)$

(c) $y = f(-x)$ (d) $y = -f(-x)$

6–7 The graph of $y = \sqrt{3x - x^2}$ is given. Use transformations to create a function whose graph is as shown.

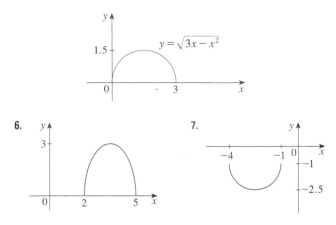

$y = \sqrt{3x - x^2}$

6.

7.

8. (a) How is the graph of $y = 2\sin x$ related to the graph of $y = \sin x$? Use your answer and Figure 6 to sketch the graph of $y = 2\sin x$.

(b) How is the graph of $y = 1 + \sqrt{x}$ related to the graph of $y = \sqrt{x}$? Use your answer and Figure 4(a) to sketch the graph of $y = 1 + \sqrt{x}$.

9–24 Graph the function by hand, not by plotting points, but by starting with the graph of one of the standard functions given in Section 1.2, and then applying the appropriate transformations.

9. $y = -x^3$

10. $y = 1 - x^2$

11. $y = (x + 1)^2$

12. $y = x^2 - 4x + 3$

13. $y = 1 + 2\cos x$

14. $y = 4\sin 3x$

15. $y = \sin(x/2)$

16. $y = \dfrac{1}{x - 4}$

17. $y = \sqrt{x + 3}$

18. $y = |x| - 2$

19. $y = \frac{1}{2}(x^2 + 8x)$

20. $y = 1 + \sqrt[3]{x - 1}$

21. $y = |x - 2|$

22. $y = \dfrac{1}{4}\tan\left(x - \dfrac{\pi}{4}\right)$

23. $y = |\sqrt{x} - 1|$

24. $y = |\cos \pi x|$

25. The city of New Orleans is located at latitude 30°N. Use Figure 9 to find a function that models the number of hours of daylight at New Orleans as a function of the time of year. To check the accuracy of your model, use the fact that on March 31 the sun rises at 5:51 AM and sets at 6:18 PM in New Orleans.

26. A variable star is one whose brightness alternately increases and decreases. For the most visible variable star, Delta Cephei, the time between periods of maximum brightness is 5.4 days, the average brightness (or magnitude) of the star is 4.0, and its brightness varies by ±0.35 magnitude. Find a function that models the brightness of Delta Cephei as a function of time.

27. (a) How is the graph of $y = f(|x|)$ related to the graph of f?

(b) Sketch the graph of $y = \sin|x|$.

(c) Sketch the graph of $y = \sqrt{|x|}$.

28. Use the given graph of f to sketch the graph of $y = 1/f(x)$. Which features of f are the most important in sketching $y = 1/f(x)$? Explain how they are used.

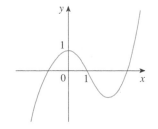

29–30 Find (a) $f + g$, (b) $f - g$, (c) fg, and (d) f/g and state their domains.

29. $f(x) = x^3 + 2x^2$, $g(x) = 3x^2 - 1$

30. $f(x) = \sqrt{3 - x}$, $g(x) = \sqrt{x^2 - 1}$

31–36 Find the functions (a) $f \circ g$, (b) $g \circ f$, (c) $f \circ f$, and (d) $g \circ g$ and their domains.

31. $f(x) = x^2 - 1$, $g(x) = 2x + 1$

32. $f(x) = x - 2$, $g(x) = x^2 + 3x + 4$

33. $f(x) = 1 - 3x$, $g(x) = \cos x$

34. $f(x) = \sqrt{x}$, $g(x) = \sqrt[3]{1 - x}$

35. $f(x) = x + \dfrac{1}{x}, \quad g(x) = \dfrac{x+1}{x+2}$

36. $f(x) = \dfrac{x}{1+x}, \quad g(x) = \sin 2x$

37–40 Find $f \circ g \circ h$.

37. $f(x) = x + 1, \quad g(x) = 2x, \quad h(x) = x - 1$

38. $f(x) = 2x - 1, \quad g(x) = x^2, \quad h(x) = 1 - x$

39. $f(x) = \sqrt{x-3}, \quad g(x) = x^2, \quad h(x) = x^3 + 2$

40. $f(x) = \tan x, \quad g(x) = \dfrac{x}{x-1}, \quad h(x) = \sqrt[3]{x}$

41–46 Express the function in the form $f \circ g$.

41. $F(x) = (2x + x^2)^4$

42. $F(x) = \cos^2 x$

43. $F(x) = \dfrac{\sqrt[3]{x}}{1 + \sqrt[3]{x}}$

44. $G(x) = \sqrt[3]{\dfrac{x}{1+x}}$

45. $u(t) = \sqrt{\cos t}$

46. $u(t) = \dfrac{\tan t}{1 + \tan t}$

47–49 Express the function in the form $f \circ g \circ h$.

47. $H(x) = 1 - 3^{x^2}$

48. $H(x) = \sqrt[8]{2 + |x|}$

49. $H(x) = \sec^4(\sqrt{x})$

---

50. Use the table to evaluate each expression.
  (a) $f(g(1))$ (b) $g(f(1))$ (c) $f(f(1))$
  (d) $g(g(1))$ (e) $(g \circ f)(3)$ (f) $(f \circ g)(6)$

x	1	2	3	4	5	6
$f(x)$	3	1	4	2	2	5
$g(x)$	6	3	2	1	2	3

51. Use the given graphs of f and g to evaluate each expression, or explain why it is undefined.
  (a) $f(g(2))$ (b) $g(f(0))$ (c) $(f \circ g)(0)$
  (d) $(g \circ f)(6)$ (e) $(g \circ g)(-2)$ (f) $(f \circ f)(4)$

52. Use the given graphs of f and g to estimate the value of $f(g(x))$ for $x = -5, -4, -3, \ldots, 5$. Use these estimates to sketch a rough graph of $f \circ g$.

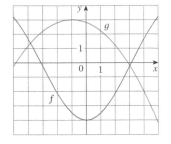

53. A stone is dropped into a lake, creating a circular ripple that travels outward at a speed of 60 cm/s.
  (a) Express the radius r of this circle as a function of the time t (in seconds).
  (b) If A is the area of this circle as a function of the radius, find $A \circ r$ and interpret it.

54. A spherical balloon is being inflated and the radius of the balloon is increasing at a rate of 2 cm/s.
  (a) Express the radius r of the balloon as a function of the time t (in seconds).
  (b) If V is the volume of the balloon as a function of the radius, find $V \circ r$ and interpret it.

55. A ship is moving at a speed of 30 km/h parallel to a straight shoreline. The ship is 6 km from shore and it passes a lighthouse at noon.
  (a) Express the distance s between the lighthouse and the ship as a function of d, the distance the ship has traveled since noon; that is, find f so that $s = f(d)$.
  (b) Express d as a function of t, the time elapsed since noon; that is, find g so that $d = g(t)$.
  (c) Find $f \circ g$. What does this function represent?

56. An airplane is flying at a speed of 350 mi/h at an altitude of one mile and passes directly over a radar station at time $t = 0$.
  (a) Express the horizontal distance d (in miles) that the plane has flown as a function of t.
  (b) Express the distance s between the plane and the radar station as a function of d.
  (c) Use composition to express s as a function of t.

57. The **Heaviside function** H is defined by

$$H(t) = \begin{cases} 0 & \text{if } t < 0 \\ 1 & \text{if } t \geq 0 \end{cases}$$

It is used in the study of electric circuits to represent the sudden surge of electric current, or voltage, when a switch is instantaneously turned on.
  (a) Sketch the graph of the Heaviside function.
  (b) Sketch the graph of the voltage $V(t)$ in a circuit if the switch is turned on at time $t = 0$ and 120 volts are applied instantaneously to the circuit. Write a formula for $V(t)$ in terms of $H(t)$.
  (c) Sketch the graph of the voltage $V(t)$ in a circuit if the switch is turned on at time $t = 5$ seconds and 240 volts are

applied instantaneously to the circuit. Write a formula for $V(t)$ in terms of $H(t)$. (Note that starting at $t = 5$ corresponds to a translation.)

58. The Heaviside function defined in Exercise 57 can also be used to define the **ramp function** $y = ctH(t)$, which represents a gradual increase in voltage or current in a circuit.
(a) Sketch the graph of the ramp function $y = tH(t)$.
(b) Sketch the graph of the voltage $V(t)$ in a circuit if the switch is turned on at time $t = 0$ and the voltage is gradually increased to 120 volts over a 60-second time interval. Write a formula for $V(t)$ in terms of $H(t)$ for $t \leqslant 60$.
(c) Sketch the graph of the voltage $V(t)$ in a circuit if the switch is turned on at time $t = 7$ seconds and the voltage is gradually increased to 100 volts over a period of 25 seconds. Write a formula for $V(t)$ in terms of $H(t)$ for $t \leqslant 32$.

59. Let f and g be linear functions with equations $f(x) = m_1x + b_1$ and $g(x) = m_2x + b_2$. Is $f \circ g$ also a linear function? If so, what is the slope of its graph?

60. If you invest x dollars at 4% interest compounded annually, then the amount $A(x)$ of the investment after one year is $A(x) = 1.04x$. Find $A \circ A$, $A \circ A \circ A$, and $A \circ A \circ A \circ A$. What do these compositions represent? Find a formula for the composition of n copies of A.

61. (a) If $g(x) = 2x + 1$ and $h(x) = 4x^2 + 4x + 7$, find a function f such that $f \circ g = h$. (Think about what operations you would have to perform on the formula for g to end up with the formula for h.)
(b) If $f(x) = 3x + 5$ and $h(x) = 3x^2 + 3x + 2$, find a function g such that $f \circ g = h$.

62. If $f(x) = x + 4$ and $h(x) = 4x - 1$, find a function g such that $g \circ f = h$.

63. Suppose g is an even function and let $h = f \circ g$. Is h always an even function?

64. Suppose g is an odd function and let $h = f \circ g$. Is h always an odd function? What if f is odd? What if f is even?

1.4 Graphing Calculators and Computers

In this section we assume that you have access to a graphing calculator or a computer with graphing software. We will see that the use of such a device enables us to graph more complicated functions and to solve more complex problems than would otherwise be possible. We also point out some of the pitfalls that can occur with these machines.

Graphing calculators and computers can give very accurate graphs of functions. But we will see in Chapter 4 that only through the use of calculus can we be sure that we have uncovered all the interesting aspects of a graph.

A graphing calculator or computer displays a rectangular portion of the graph of a function in a **display window** or **viewing screen**, which we refer to as a **viewing rectangle**. The default screen often gives an incomplete or misleading picture, so it is important to choose the viewing rectangle with care. If we choose the x-values to range from a minimum value of $Xmin = a$ to a maximum value of $Xmax = b$ and the y-values to range from a minimum of $Ymin = c$ to a maximum of $Ymax = d$, then the visible portion of the graph lies in the rectangle

$$[a, b] \times [c, d] = \{(x, y) \mid a \leqslant x \leqslant b, c \leqslant y \leqslant d\}$$

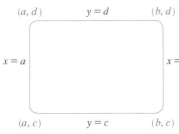

FIGURE 1
The viewing rectangle $[a, b]$ by $[c, d]$

shown in Figure 1. We refer to this rectangle as the $[a, b]$ *by* $[c, d]$ *viewing rectangle.*

The machine draws the graph of a function f much as you would. It plots points of the form $(x, f(x))$ for a certain number of equally spaced values of x between a and b. If an x-value is not in the domain of f, or if $f(x)$ lies outside the viewing rectangle, it moves on to the next x-value. The machine connects each point to the preceding plotted point to form a representation of the graph of f.

EXAMPLE 1 Choosing a good viewing rectangle Draw the graph of the function $f(x) = x^2 + 3$ in each of the following viewing rectangles.
(a) $[-2, 2]$ by $[-2, 2]$
(b) $[-4, 4]$ by $[-4, 4]$
(c) $[-10, 10]$ by $[-5, 30]$
(d) $[-50, 50]$ by $[-100, 1000]$

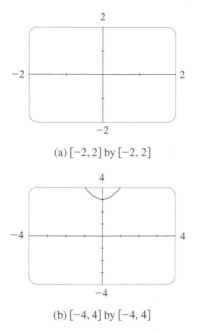

(a) $[-2, 2]$ by $[-2, 2]$

(b) $[-4, 4]$ by $[-4, 4]$

FIGURE 2 Graphs of $f(x) = x^2 + 3$

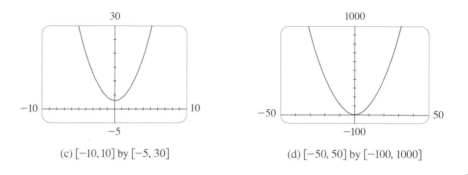

(c) $[-10, 10]$ by $[-5, 30]$

(d) $[-50, 50]$ by $[-100, 1000]$

SOLUTION For part (a) we select the range by setting $Xmin = -2$, $Xmax = 2$, $Ymin = -2$, and $Ymax = 2$. The resulting graph is shown in Figure 2(a). The display window is blank! A moment's thought provides the explanation: Notice that $x^2 \geqslant 0$ for all x, so $x^2 + 3 \geqslant 3$ for all x. Thus the range of the function $f(x) = x^2 + 3$ is $[3, \infty)$. This means that the graph of f lies entirely outside the viewing rectangle $[-2, 2]$ by $[-2, 2]$.

The graphs for the viewing rectangles in parts (b), (c), and (d) are also shown in Figure 2. Observe that we get a more complete picture in parts (c) and (d), but in part (d) it is not clear that the y-intercept is 3.

We see from Example 1 that the choice of a viewing rectangle can make a big difference in the appearance of a graph. Often it's necessary to change to a larger viewing rectangle to obtain a more complete picture, a more global view, of the graph. In the next example we see that knowledge of the domain and range of a function sometimes provides us with enough information to select a good viewing rectangle.

EXAMPLE 2 Determine an appropriate viewing rectangle for the function $f(x) = \sqrt{8 - 2x^2}$ and use it to graph f.

SOLUTION The expression for $f(x)$ is defined when

$$8 - 2x^2 \geqslant 0 \quad \Longleftrightarrow \quad 2x^2 \leqslant 8 \quad \Longleftrightarrow \quad x^2 \leqslant 4$$
$$\Longleftrightarrow \quad |x| \leqslant 2 \quad \Longleftrightarrow \quad -2 \leqslant x \leqslant 2$$

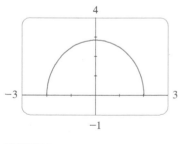

FIGURE 3
$y = \sqrt{8 - 2x^2}$

Therefore the domain of f is the interval $[-2, 2]$. Also,

$$0 \leqslant \sqrt{8 - 2x^2} \leqslant \sqrt{8} = 2\sqrt{2} \approx 2.83$$

so the range of f is the interval $\left[0, 2\sqrt{2}\right]$.

We choose the viewing rectangle so that the x-interval is somewhat larger than the domain and the y-interval is larger than the range. Taking the viewing rectangle to be $[-3, 3]$ by $[-1, 4]$, we get the graph shown in Figure 3.

EXAMPLE 3 Graph the function $y = x^3 - 150x$.

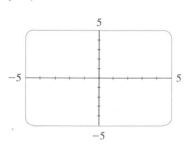

FIGURE 4

SOLUTION Here the domain is $\mathbb{R}$, the set of all real numbers. That doesn't help us choose a viewing rectangle. Let's experiment. If we start with the viewing rectangle $[-5, 5]$ by $[-5, 5]$, we get the graph in Figure 4. It appears blank, but actually the graph is so nearly vertical that it blends in with the y-axis.

If we change the viewing rectangle to $[-20, 20]$ by $[-20, 20]$, we get the picture shown in Figure 5(a). The graph appears to consist of vertical lines, but we know that can't be correct. If we look carefully while the graph is being drawn, we see that the graph leaves the screen and reappears during the graphing process. This indicates that we need to see more in the vertical direction, so we change the viewing rectangle to $[-20, 20]$ by $[-500, 500]$. The resulting graph is shown in Figure 5(b). It still doesn't quite reveal all the main features of the function, so we try $[-20, 20]$ by $[-1000, 1000]$ in Figure 5(c). Now we are more confident that we have arrived at an appropriate viewing rectangle. In Chapter 4 we will be able to see that the graph shown in Figure 5(c) does indeed reveal all the main features of the function.

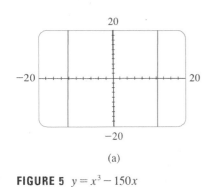

(a)

(b)

(c)

FIGURE 5 $y = x^3 - 150x$

V   EXAMPLE 4   Graph the function $f(x) = \sin 50x$ in an appropriate viewing rectangle.

SOLUTION Figure 6(a) shows the graph of f produced by a graphing calculator using the viewing rectangle $[-12, 12]$ by $[-1.5, 1.5]$. At first glance the graph appears to be reasonable. But if we change the viewing rectangle to the ones shown in the following parts of Figure 6, the graphs look very different. Something strange is happening.

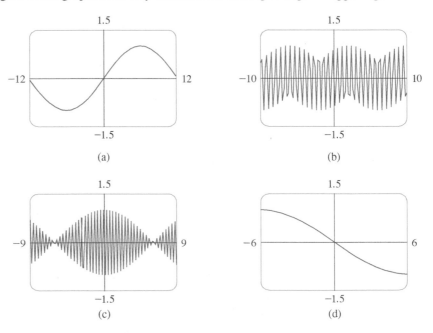

The appearance of the graphs in Figure 6 depends on the machine used. The graphs you get with your own graphing device might not look like these figures, but they will also be quite inaccurate.

(a)

(b)

(c)

(d)

FIGURE 6
Graphs of $f(x) = \sin 50x$
in four viewing rectangles

In order to explain the big differences in appearance of these graphs and to find an appropriate viewing rectangle, we need to find the period of the function $y = \sin 50x$. We know that the function $y = \sin x$ has period 2π and the graph of $y = \sin 50x$ is shrunk horizontally by a factor of 50, so the period of $y = \sin 50x$ is

$$\frac{2\pi}{50} = \frac{\pi}{25} \approx 0.126$$

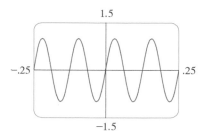

FIGURE 7

$f(x) = \sin 50x$

This suggests that we should deal only with small values of x in order to show just a few oscillations of the graph. If we choose the viewing rectangle $[-0.25, 0.25]$ by $[-1.5, 1.5]$, we get the graph shown in Figure 7.

Now we see what went wrong in Figure 6. The oscillations of $y = \sin 50x$ are so rapid that when the calculator plots points and joins them, it misses most of the maximum and minimum points and therefore gives a very misleading impression of the graph.

We have seen that the use of an inappropriate viewing rectangle can give a misleading impression of the graph of a function. In Examples 1 and 3 we solved the problem by changing to a larger viewing rectangle. In Example 4 we had to make the viewing rectangle smaller. In the next example we look at a function for which there is no single viewing rectangle that reveals the true shape of the graph.

V EXAMPLE 5 **Sometimes one graph is not enough**

Graph the function $f(x) = \sin x + \frac{1}{100} \cos 100x$.

SOLUTION Figure 8 shows the graph of f produced by a graphing calculator with viewing rectangle $[-6.5, 6.5]$ by $[-1.5, 1.5]$. It looks much like the graph of $y = \sin x$, but perhaps with some bumps attached. If we zoom in to the viewing rectangle $[-0.1, 0.1]$ by $[-0.1, 0.1]$, we can see much more clearly the shape of these bumps in Figure 9. The reason for this behavior is that the second term, $\frac{1}{100} \cos 100x$, is very small in comparison with the first term, $\sin x$. Thus we really need two graphs to see the true nature of this function.

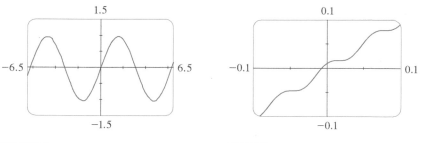

FIGURE 8   **FIGURE 9**

EXAMPLE 6 **Eliminating an extraneous line** Draw the graph of the function $y = \dfrac{1}{1 - x}$.

SOLUTION Figure 10(a) shows the graph produced by a graphing calculator with viewing rectangle $[-9, 9]$ by $[-9, 9]$. In connecting successive points on the graph, the calculator produced a steep line segment from the top to the bottom of the screen. That line segment is not truly part of the graph. Notice that the domain of the function $y = 1/(1 - x)$ is $\{x \mid x \neq 1\}$. We can eliminate the extraneous near-vertical line by experimenting with a change of scale. When we change to the smaller viewing rectangle $[-4.7, 4.7]$ by $[-4.7, 4.7]$ on this particular calculator, we obtain the much better graph in Figure 10(b).

Another way to avoid the extraneous line is to change the graphing mode on the calculator so that the dots are not connected.

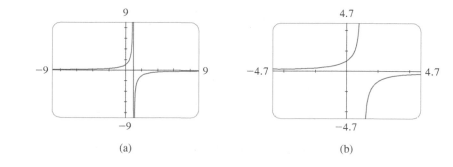

FIGURE 10   (a)   (b)

EXAMPLE 7 **How to get the complete graph of the cube root function**
Graph the function $y = \sqrt[3]{x}$.

SOLUTION Some graphing devices display the graph shown in Figure 11, whereas others produce a graph like that in Figure 12. We know from Section 1.2 (Figure 13) that the graph in Figure 12 is correct, so what happened in Figure 11? The explanation is that some machines compute the cube root of x using a logarithm, which is not defined if x is negative, so only the right half of the graph is produced.

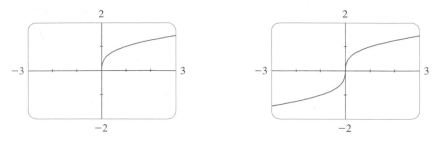

FIGURE 11   **FIGURE 12**

You can get the correct graph with Maple if you first type

You should experiment with your own machine to see which of these two graphs is produced. If you get the graph in Figure 11, you can obtain the correct picture by graphing the function

$$f(x) = \frac{x}{|x|} \cdot |x|^{1/3}$$

Notice that this function is equal to $\sqrt[3]{x}$ (except when $x = 0$).

To understand how the expression for a function relates to its graph, it's helpful to graph a **family of functions**, that is, a collection of functions whose equations are related. In the next example we graph members of a family of cubic polynomials.

☑ **EXAMPLE 8** **A family of cubic polynomials** Graph the function $y = x^3 + cx$ for various values of the number c. How does the graph change when c is changed?

SOLUTION Figure 13 shows the graphs of $y = x^3 + cx$ for $c = 2, 1, 0, -1$, and -2. We see that, for positive values of c, the graph increases from left to right with no maximum or minimum points (peaks or valleys). When $c = 0$, the curve is flat at the origin. When c is negative, the curve has a maximum point and a minimum point. As c decreases, the maximum point becomes higher and the minimum point lower.

TEC In Visual 1.4 you can see an animation of Figure 13.

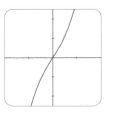

(a) $y = x^3 + 2x$ (b) $y = x^3 + x$ (c) $y = x^3$ (d) $y = x^3 - x$ (e) $y = x^3 - 2x$

FIGURE 13
Several members of the family of functions $y = x^3 + cx$, all graphed in the viewing rectangle $[-2, 2]$ by $[-2.5, 2.5]$

EXAMPLE 9 **Solving an equation graphically** Find the solution of the equation $\cos x = x$ correct to two decimal places.

SOLUTION The solutions of the equation $\cos x = x$ are the x-coordinates of the points of intersection of the curves $y = \cos x$ and $y = x$. From Figure 14(a) we see that there is only one solution and it lies between 0 and 1. Zooming in to the viewing rectangle [0, 1] by [0, 1], we see from Figure 14(b) that the root lies between 0.7 and 0.8. So we zoom in further to the viewing rectangle [0.7, 0.8] by [0.7, 0.8] in Figure 14(c). By moving the cursor to the intersection point of the two curves, or by inspection and the fact that the x-scale is 0.01, we see that the solution of the equation is about 0.74. (Many calculators have a built-in intersection feature.)

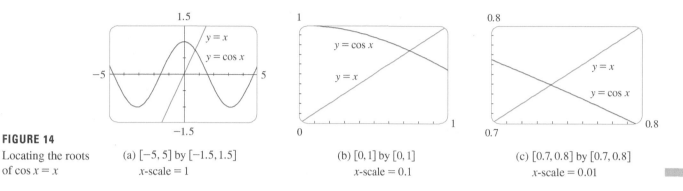

FIGURE 14
Locating the roots
of $\cos x = x$

(a) $[-5, 5]$ by $[-1.5, 1.5]$
x-scale $= 1$

(b) $[0, 1]$ by $[0, 1]$
x-scale $= 0.1$

(c) $[0.7, 0.8]$ by $[0.7, 0.8]$
x-scale $= 0.01$

1.4 Exercises

1. Use a graphing calculator or computer to determine which of the given viewing rectangles produces the most appropriate graph of the function $f(x) = \sqrt{x^3 - 5x^2}$.
 (a) $[-5, 5]$ by $[-5, 5]$ (b) $[0, 10]$ by $[0, 2]$
 (c) $[0, 10]$ by $[0, 10]$

2. Use a graphing calculator or computer to determine which of the given viewing rectangles produces the most appropriate graph of the function $f(x) = x^4 - 16x^2 + 20$.
 (a) $[-3, 3]$ by $[-3, 3]$ (b) $[-10, 10]$ by $[-10, 10]$
 (c) $[-50, 50]$ by $[-50, 50]$ (d) $[-5, 5]$ by $[-50, 50]$

3–14 Determine an appropriate viewing rectangle for the given function and use it to draw the graph.

3. $f(x) = x^2 - 36x + 32$ **4.** $f(x) = x^3 + 15x^2 + 65x$

5. $f(x) = \sqrt[4]{81 - x^4}$ **6.** $f(x) = \sqrt{0.1x + 20}$

7. $f(x) = x^3 - 225x$ **8.** $f(x) = \dfrac{x}{x^2 + 100}$

9. $f(x) = \sin^2(1000x)$ **10.** $f(x) = \cos(0.001x)$

11. $f(x) = \sin\sqrt{x}$ **12.** $f(x) = \sec(20\pi x)$

13. $y = 10\sin x + \sin 100x$ **14.** $y = x^2 + 0.02\sin 50x$

15. (a) Try to find an appropriate viewing rectangle for $f(x) = (x - 10)^3 2^{-x}$.
 (b) Do you need more than one window? Why?

16. Graph the function $f(x) = x^2\sqrt{30 - x}$ in an appropriate viewing rectangle. Why does part of the graph appear to be missing?

17. Graph the ellipse $4x^2 + 2y^2 = 1$ by graphing the functions whose graphs are the upper and lower halves of the ellipse.

18. Graph the hyperbola $y^2 - 9x^2 = 1$ by graphing the functions whose graphs are the upper and lower branches of the hyperbola.

19–20 Do the graphs intersect in the given viewing rectangle? If they do, how many points of intersection are there?

19. $y = 3x^2 - 6x + 1$, $y = 0.23x - 2.25$;
 $[-1, 3]$ by $[-2.5, 1.5]$

20. $y = 6 - 4x - x^2$, $y = 3x + 18$; $[-6, 2]$ by $[-5, 20]$

21–23 Find all solutions of the equation correct to two decimal places.

21. $x^4 - x = 1$ **22.** $\sqrt{x} = x^3 - 1$

23. $\tan x = \sqrt{1 - x^2}$

24. We saw in Example 9 that the equation $\cos x = x$ has exactly one solution.
 (a) Use a graph to show that the equation $\cos x = 0.3x$ has three solutions and find their values correct to two decimal places.
 (b) Find an approximate value of m such that the equation $\cos x = mx$ has exactly two solutions.

25. Use graphs to determine which of the functions $f(x) = 10x^2$ and $g(x) = x^3/10$ is eventually larger (that is, larger when x is very large).

26. Use graphs to determine which of the functions $f(x) = x^4 - 100x^3$ and $g(x) = x^3$ is eventually larger.

Graphing calculator or computer with graphing software required   **1.** Homework Hints available in TEC

27. For what values of x is it true that $|\sin x - x| < 0.1$?

28. Graph the polynomials $P(x) = 3x^5 - 5x^3 + 2x$ and $Q(x) = 3x^5$ on the same screen, first using the viewing rectangle $[-2, 2]$ by $[-2, 2]$ and then changing to $[-10, 10]$ by $[-10,000, 10,000]$. What do you observe from these graphs?

29. In this exercise we consider the family of root functions $f(x) = \sqrt[n]{x}$, where n is a positive integer.
   (a) Graph the functions $y = \sqrt{x}$, $y = \sqrt[4]{x}$, and $y = \sqrt[6]{x}$ on the same screen using the viewing rectangle $[-1, 4]$ by $[-1, 3]$.
   (b) Graph the functions $y = x$, $y = \sqrt[3]{x}$, and $y = \sqrt[5]{x}$ on the same screen using the viewing rectangle $[-3, 3]$ by $[-2, 2]$. (See Example 7.)
   (c) Graph the functions $y = \sqrt{x}$, $y = \sqrt[3]{x}$, $y = \sqrt[4]{x}$, and $y = \sqrt[5]{x}$ on the same screen using the viewing rectangle $[-1, 3]$ by $[-1, 2]$.
   (d) What conclusions can you make from these graphs?

30. In this exercise we consider the family of functions $f(x) = 1/x^n$, where n is a positive integer.
   (a) Graph the functions $y = 1/x$ and $y = 1/x^3$ on the same screen using the viewing rectangle $[-3, 3]$ by $[-3, 3]$.
   (b) Graph the functions $y = 1/x^2$ and $y = 1/x^4$ on the same screen using the same viewing rectangle as in part (a).
   (c) Graph all of the functions in parts (a) and (b) on the same screen using the viewing rectangle $[-1, 3]$ by $[-1, 3]$.
   (d) What conclusions can you make from these graphs?

31. Graph the function $f(x) = x^4 + cx^2 + x$ for several values of c. How does the graph change when c changes?

32. Graph the function $f(x) = \sqrt{1 + cx^2}$ for various values of c. Describe how changing the value of c affects the graph.

33. Graph the function $y = x^n 2^{-x}$, $x \geqslant 0$, for $n = 1, 2, 3, 4, 5$, and 6. How does the graph change as n increases?

34. The curves with equations

$$y = \frac{|x|}{\sqrt{c - x^2}}$$

are called **bullet-nose curves**. Graph some of these curves to see why. What happens as c increases?

35. What happens to the graph of the equation $y^2 = cx^3 + x^2$ as c varies?

36. This exercise explores the effect of the inner function g on a composite function $y = f(g(x))$.
   (a) Graph the function $y = \sin(\sqrt{x})$ using the viewing rectangle $[0, 400]$ by $[-1.5, 1.5]$. How does this graph differ from the graph of the sine function?
   (b) Graph the function $y = \sin(x^2)$ using the viewing rectangle $[-5, 5]$ by $[-1.5, 1.5]$. How does this graph differ from the graph of the sine function?

37. The figure shows the graphs of $y = \sin 96x$ and $y = \sin 2x$ as displayed by a TI-83 graphing calculator. The first graph is inaccurate. Explain why the two graphs appear identical. [*Hint:* The TI-83's graphing window is 95 pixels wide. What specific points does the calculator plot?]

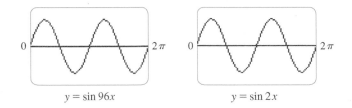

$y = \sin 96x$ $y = \sin 2x$

38. The first graph in the figure is that of $y = \sin 45x$ as displayed by a TI-83 graphing calculator. It is inaccurate and so, to help explain its appearance, we replot the curve in dot mode in the second graph. What two sine curves does the calculator appear to be plotting? Show that each point on the graph of $y = \sin 45x$ that the TI-83 chooses to plot is in fact on one of these two curves. (The TI-83's graphing window is 95 pixels wide.)

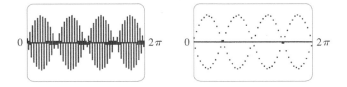

1.5 Exponential Functions

The function $f(x) = 2^x$ is called an *exponential function* because the variable, x, is the exponent. It should not be confused with the power function $g(x) = x^2$, in which the variable is the base.

In general, an **exponential function** is a function of the form

$$f(x) = a^x$$

where a is a positive constant. Let's recall what this means.

If $x = n$, a positive integer, then

$$a^n = \underbrace{a \cdot a \cdot \cdots \cdot a}_{n \text{ factors}}$$

If $x = 0$, then $a^0 = 1$, and if $x = -n$, where n is a positive integer, then

$$a^{-n} = \frac{1}{a^n}$$

If x is a rational number, $x = p/q$, where p and q are integers and $q > 0$, then

$$a^x = a^{p/q} = \sqrt[q]{a^p} = \left(\sqrt[q]{a}\right)^p$$

But what is the meaning of a^x if x is an irrational number? For instance, what is meant by $2^{\sqrt{3}}$ or 5^π?

To help us answer this question we first look at the graph of the function $y = 2^x$, where x is rational. A representation of this graph is shown in Figure 1. We want to enlarge the domain of $y = 2^x$ to include both rational and irrational numbers.

There are holes in the graph in Figure 1 corresponding to irrational values of x. We want to fill in the holes by defining $f(x) = 2^x$, where $x \in \mathbb{R}$, so that f is an increasing function. In particular, since the irrational number $\sqrt{3}$ satisfies

$$1.7 < \sqrt{3} < 1.8$$

we must have

$$2^{1.7} < 2^{\sqrt{3}} < 2^{1.8}$$

and we know what $2^{1.7}$ and $2^{1.8}$ mean because 1.7 and 1.8 are rational numbers. Similarly, if we use better approximations for $\sqrt{3}$, we obtain better approximations for $2^{\sqrt{3}}$:

$$1.73 < \sqrt{3} < 1.74 \quad \Rightarrow \quad 2^{1.73} < 2^{\sqrt{3}} < 2^{1.74}$$
$$1.732 < \sqrt{3} < 1.733 \quad \Rightarrow \quad 2^{1.732} < 2^{\sqrt{3}} < 2^{1.733}$$
$$1.7320 < \sqrt{3} < 1.7321 \quad \Rightarrow \quad 2^{1.7320} < 2^{\sqrt{3}} < 2^{1.7321}$$
$$1.73205 < \sqrt{3} < 1.73206 \quad \Rightarrow \quad 2^{1.73205} < 2^{\sqrt{3}} < 2^{1.73206}$$
$$\vdots \qquad \vdots \qquad\qquad \vdots \qquad \vdots$$

It can be shown that there is exactly one number that is greater than all of the numbers

$$2^{1.7}, \quad 2^{1.73}, \quad 2^{1.732}, \quad 2^{1.7320}, \quad 2^{1.73205}, \quad \ldots$$

and less than all of the numbers

$$2^{1.8}, \quad 2^{1.74}, \quad 2^{1.733}, \quad 2^{1.7321}, \quad 2^{1.73206}, \quad \ldots$$

We define $2^{\sqrt{3}}$ to be this number. Using the preceding approximation process we can compute it correct to six decimal places:

$$2^{\sqrt{3}} \approx 3.321997$$

Similarly, we can define 2^x (or a^x, if $a > 0$) where x is any irrational number. Figure 2 shows how all the holes in Figure 1 have been filled to complete the graph of the function $f(x) = 2^x$, $x \in \mathbb{R}$.

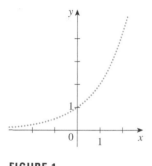

FIGURE 1

Representation of $y = 2^x$, x rational

A proof of this fact is given in J. Marsden and A. Weinstein, *Calculus Unlimited* (Menlo Park, CA: Benjamin/Cummings, 1981). For an online version, see

caltechbook.library.caltech.edu/197/

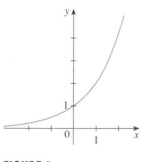

FIGURE 2

$y = 2^x$, x real

The graphs of members of the family of functions $y = a^x$ are shown in Figure 3 for various values of the base a. Notice that all of these graphs pass through the same point $(0, 1)$ because $a^0 = 1$ for $a \neq 0$. Notice also that as the base a gets larger, the exponential function grows more rapidly (for $x > 0$).

If $0 < a < 1$, then a^x approaches 0 as x becomes large. If $a > 1$, then a^x approaches 0 as x decreases through negative values. In both cases the x-axis is a horizontal asymptote. These matters are discussed in Section 2.5.

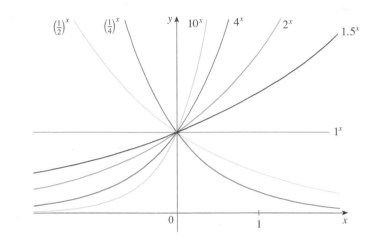

FIGURE 3

You can see from Figure 3 that there are basically three kinds of exponential functions $y = a^x$. If $0 < a < 1$, the exponential function decreases; if $a = 1$, it is a constant; and if $a > 1$, it increases. These three cases are illustrated in Figure 4. Observe that if $a \neq 1$, then the exponential function $y = a^x$ has domain $\mathbb{R}$ and range $(0, \infty)$. Notice also that, since $(1/a)^x = 1/a^x = a^{-x}$, the graph of $y = (1/a)^x$ is just the reflection of the graph of $y = a^x$ about the y-axis.

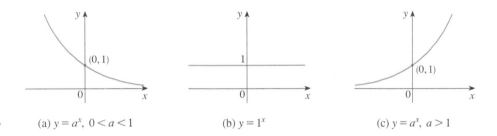

FIGURE 4   (a) $y = a^x$, $0 < a < 1$ (b) $y = 1^x$ (c) $y = a^x$, $a > 1$

One reason for the importance of the exponential function lies in the following properties. If x and y are rational numbers, then these laws are well known from elementary algebra. It can be proved that they remain true for arbitrary real numbers x and y.

www.stewartcalculus.com

For review and practice using the Laws of Exponents, click on *Review of Algebra*.

> **Laws of Exponents**   If a and b are positive numbers and x and y are any real numbers, then
>
> **1.** $a^{x+y} = a^x a^y$ **2.** $a^{x-y} = \dfrac{a^x}{a^y}$ **3.** $(a^x)^y = a^{xy}$ **4.** $(ab)^x = a^x b^x$

EXAMPLE 1   **Reflecting and shifting an exponential function**   Sketch the graph of the function $y = 3 - 2^x$ and determine its domain and range.

For a review of reflecting and shifting graphs, see Section 1.3.

SOLUTION   First we reflect the graph of $y = 2^x$ [shown in Figures 2 and 5(a)] about the x-axis to get the graph of $y = -2^x$ in Figure 5(b). Then we shift the graph of $y = -2^x$

upward 3 units to obtain the graph of $y = 3 - 2^x$ in Figure 5(c). The domain is $\mathbb{R}$ and the range is $(-\infty, 3)$.

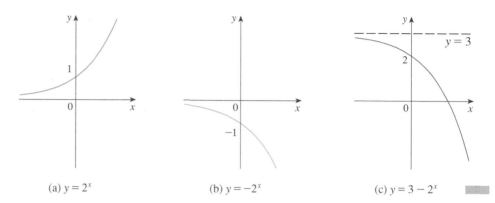

FIGURE 5   (a) $y = 2^x$ (b) $y = -2^x$ (c) $y = 3 - 2^x$

V EXAMPLE 2 An exponential function versus a power function   Use a graphing device to compare the exponential function $f(x) = 2^x$ and the power function $g(x) = x^2$. Which function grows more quickly when x is large?

SOLUTION   Figure 6 shows both functions graphed in the viewing rectangle $[-2, 6]$ by $[0, 40]$. We see that the graphs intersect three times, but for $x > 4$ the graph of $f(x) = 2^x$ stays above the graph of $g(x) = x^2$. Figure 7 gives a more global view and shows that for large values of x, the exponential function $y = 2^x$ grows far more rapidly than the power function $y = x^2$.

Example 2 shows that $y = 2^x$ increases more quickly than $y = x^2$. To demonstrate just how quickly $f(x) = 2^x$ increases, let's perform the following thought experiment. Suppose we start with a piece of paper a thousandth of an inch thick and we fold it in half 50 times. Each time we fold the paper in half, the thickness of the paper doubles, so the thickness of the resulting paper would be $2^{50}/1000$ inches. How thick do you think that is? It works out to be more than 17 million miles!

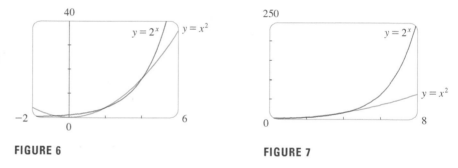

FIGURE 6   **FIGURE 7**

Applications of Exponential Functions

The exponential function occurs very frequently in mathematical models of nature and society. Here we indicate briefly how it arises in the description of population growth. In later chapters we will pursue these and other applications in greater detail.

First we consider a population of bacteria in a homogeneous nutrient medium. Suppose that by sampling the population at certain intervals it is determined that the population doubles every hour. If the number of bacteria at time t is $p(t)$, where t is measured in hours, and the initial population is $p(0) = 1000$, then we have

$$p(1) = 2p(0) = 2 \times 1000$$

$$p(2) = 2p(1) = 2^2 \times 1000$$

$$p(3) = 2p(2) = 2^3 \times 1000$$

It seems from this pattern that, in general,

$$p(t) = 2^t \times 1000 = (1000)2^t$$

This population function is a constant multiple of the exponential function $y = 2^t$, so it exhibits the rapid growth that we observed in Figures 2 and 7. Under ideal conditions (unlimited space and nutrition and freedom from disease) this exponential growth is typical of what actually occurs in nature.

What about the human population? Table 1 shows data for the population of the world in the 20th century and Figure 8 shows the corresponding scatter plot.

TABLE 1

Year	Population (millions)
1900	1650
1910	1750
1920	1860
1930	2070
1940	2300
1950	2560
1960	3040
1970	3710
1980	4450
1990	5280
2000	6080

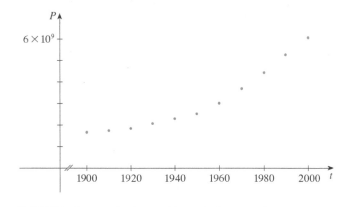

FIGURE 8 Scatter plot for world population growth

The pattern of the data points in Figure 8 suggests exponential growth, so we use a graphing calculator with exponential regression capability to apply the method of least squares and obtain the exponential model

$$P = (0.008079266) \cdot (1.013731)^t$$

Figure 9 shows the graph of this exponential function together with the original data points. We see that the exponential curve fits the data reasonably well. The period of relatively slow population growth is explained by the two world wars and the Great Depression of the 1930s.

FIGURE 9

Exponential model for population growth

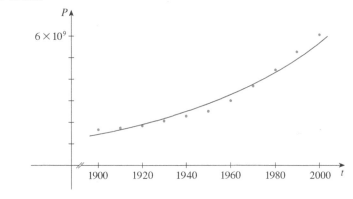

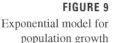 **EXAMPLE 3** The *half-life* of strontium-90, ^{90}Sr, is 25 years. This means that half of any given quantity of ^{90}Sr will disintegrate in 25 years.
(a) If a sample of ^{90}Sr has a mass of 24 mg, find an expression for the mass $m(t)$ that remains after t years.
(b) Find the mass remaining after 40 years, correct to the nearest milligram.
(c) Use a graphing device to graph $m(t)$ and use the graph to estimate the time required for the mass to be reduced to 5 mg.

SOLUTION

(a) The mass is initially 24 mg and is halved during each 25-year period, so

$$m(0) = 24$$

$$m(25) = \frac{1}{2}(24)$$

$$m(50) = \frac{1}{2} \cdot \frac{1}{2}(24) = \frac{1}{2^2}(24)$$

$$m(75) = \frac{1}{2} \cdot \frac{1}{2^2}(24) = \frac{1}{2^3}(24)$$

$$m(100) = \frac{1}{2} \cdot \frac{1}{2^3}(24) = \frac{1}{2^4}(24)$$

From this pattern, it appears that the mass remaining after t years is

$$m(t) = \frac{1}{2^{t/25}}(24) = 24 \cdot 2^{-t/25} = 24 \cdot (2^{-1/25})^t$$

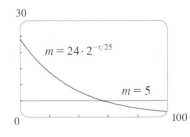

FIGURE 10

This is an exponential function with base $a = 2^{-1/25} = 1/2^{1/25}$.

(b) The mass that remains after 40 years is

$$m(40) = 24 \cdot 2^{-40/25} \approx 7.9 \text{ mg}$$

(c) We use a graphing calculator or computer to graph the function $m(t) = 24 \cdot 2^{-t/25}$ in Figure 10. We also graph the line $m = 5$ and use the cursor to estimate that $m(t) = 5$ when $t \approx 57$. So the mass of the sample will be reduced to 5 mg after about 57 years.

The Number e

Of all possible bases for an exponential function, there is one that is most convenient for the purposes of calculus. The choice of a base a is influenced by the way the graph of $y = a^x$ crosses the y-axis. Figures 11 and 12 show the tangent lines to the graphs of $y = 2^x$ and $y = 3^x$ at the point $(0, 1)$. (Tangent lines will be defined precisely in Section 2.6. For present purposes, you can think of the tangent line to an exponential graph at a point as the line that touches the graph only at that point.) If we measure the slopes of these tangent lines at $(0, 1)$, we find that $m \approx 0.7$ for $y = 2^x$ and $m \approx 1.1$ for $y = 3^x$.

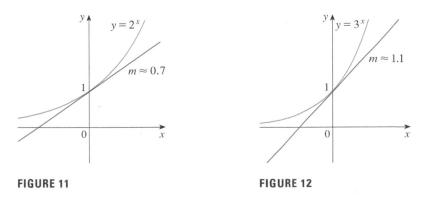

FIGURE 11   **FIGURE 12**

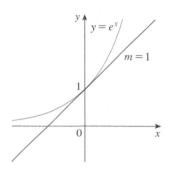

FIGURE 13

The natural exponential function crosses the y-axis with a slope of 1.

TEC Module 1.5 enables you to graph exponential functions with various bases and their tangent lines in order to estimate more closely the value of a for which the tangent has slope 1.

It turns out, as we will see in Chapter 3, that some of the formulas of calculus will be greatly simplified if we choose the base a so that the slope of the tangent line to $y = a^x$ at $(0, 1)$ is *exactly* 1. (See Figure 13.) In fact, there *is* such a number and it is denoted by the letter e. (This notation was chosen by the Swiss mathematician Leonhard Euler in 1727, probably because it is the first letter of the word *exponential*.) In view of Figures 11 and 12, it comes as no surprise that the number e lies between 2 and 3 and the graph of $y = e^x$ lies between the graphs of $y = 2^x$ and $y = 3^x$. (See Figure 14.) In Chapter 3 we will see that the value of e, correct to five decimal places, is

$$e \approx 2.71828$$

We call the function $f(x) = e^x$ the **natural exponential function**.

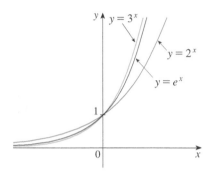

FIGURE 14

V EXAMPLE 4   Transforming the natural exponential function   Graph the function $y = \frac{1}{2}e^{-x} - 1$ and state the domain and range.

SOLUTION   We start with the graph of $y = e^x$ from Figures 13 and 15(a) and reflect about the y-axis to get the graph of $y = e^{-x}$ in Figure 15(b). (Notice that the graph crosses the y-axis with a slope of -1). Then we compress the graph vertically by a factor of 2 to obtain the graph of $y = \frac{1}{2}e^{-x}$ in Figure 15(c). Finally, we shift the graph downward one unit to get the desired graph in Figure 15(d). The domain is $\mathbb{R}$ and the range is $(-1, \infty)$.

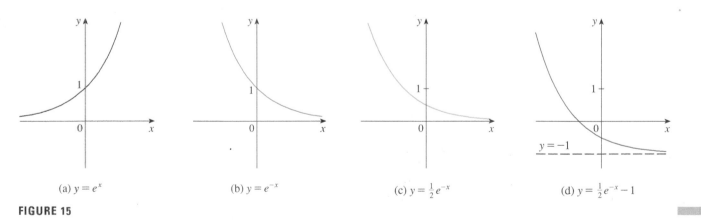

(a) $y = e^x$ (b) $y = e^{-x}$ (c) $y = \frac{1}{2}e^{-x}$ (d) $y = \frac{1}{2}e^{-x} - 1$

FIGURE 15

How far to the right do you think we would have to go for the height of the graph of $y = e^x$ to exceed a million? The next example demonstrates the rapid growth of this function by providing an answer that might surprise you.

EXAMPLE 5 **Exponential functions get big fast** Use a graphing device to find the values of x for which $e^x > 1,000,000$.

SOLUTION In Figure 16 we graph both the function $y = e^x$ and the horizontal line $y = 1,000,000$. We see that these curves intersect when $x \approx 13.8$. Thus $e^x > 10^6$ when $x > 13.8$. It is perhaps surprising that the values of the exponential function have already surpassed a million when x is only 14.

FIGURE 16

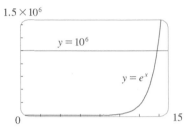

1.5 Exercises

1–4 Use the Law of Exponents to rewrite and simplify the expression.

1. (a) $\dfrac{4^{-3}}{2^{-8}}$ (b) $\dfrac{1}{\sqrt[3]{x^4}}$

2. (a) $8^{4/3}$ (b) $x(3x^2)^3$

3. (a) $b^8(2b)^4$ (b) $\dfrac{(6y^3)^4}{2y^5}$

4. (a) $\dfrac{x^{2n} \cdot x^{3n-1}}{x^{n+2}}$ (b) $\dfrac{\sqrt{a\sqrt{b}}}{\sqrt[3]{ab}}$

5. (a) Write an equation that defines the exponential function with base $a > 0$.
 (b) What is the domain of this function?
 (c) If $a \neq 1$, what is the range of this function?
 (d) Sketch the general shape of the graph of the exponential function for each of the following cases.
  (i) $a > 1$ (ii) $a = 1$ (iii) $0 < a < 1$

6. (a) How is the number e defined?
 (b) What is an approximate value for e?
 (c) What is the natural exponential function?

7–10 Graph the given functions on a common screen. How are these graphs related?

7. $y = 2^x$, $y = e^x$, $y = 5^x$, $y = 20^x$

8. $y = e^x$, $y = e^{-x}$, $y = 8^x$, $y = 8^{-x}$

9. $y = 3^x$, $y = 10^x$, $y = \left(\frac{1}{3}\right)^x$, $y = \left(\frac{1}{10}\right)^x$

10. $y = 0.9^x$, $y = 0.6^x$, $y = 0.3^x$, $y = 0.1^x$

11–16 Make a rough sketch of the graph of the function. Do not use a calculator. Just use the graphs given in Figures 3 and 13 and, if necessary, the transformations of Section 1.3.

11. $y = 10^{x+2}$ **12.** $y = (0.5)^x - 2$

13. $y = -2^{-x}$ **14.** $y = e^{|x|}$

15. $y = 1 - \frac{1}{2}e^{-x}$ **16.** $y = 2(1 - e^x)$

17. Starting with the graph of $y = e^x$, write the equation of the graph that results from
 (a) shifting 2 units downward
 (b) shifting 2 units to the right
 (c) reflecting about the x-axis
 (d) reflecting about the y-axis
 (e) reflecting about the x-axis and then about the y-axis

18. Starting with the graph of $y = e^x$, find the equation of the graph that results from
 (a) reflecting about the line $y = 4$
 (b) reflecting about the line $x = 2$

19–20 Find the domain of each function.

19. (a) $f(x) = \dfrac{1 - e^{x^2}}{1 - e^{1-x^2}}$ (b) $f(x) = \dfrac{1 + x}{e^{\cos x}}$

20. (a) $g(t) = \sin(e^{-t})$ (b) $g(t) = \sqrt{1 - 2^t}$

Graphing calculator or computer with graphing software required **1.** Homework Hints available in TEC

21–22 Find the exponential function $f(x) = Ca^x$ whose graph is given.

21.

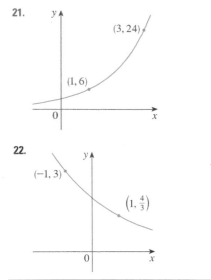

22.

23. If $f(x) = 5^x$, show that

$$\frac{f(x + h) - f(x)}{h} = 5^x \left(\frac{5^h - 1}{h} \right)$$

24. Suppose you are offered a job that lasts one month. Which of the following methods of payment do you prefer?
  I. One million dollars at the end of the month.
  II. One cent on the first day of the month, two cents on the second day, four cents on the third day, and, in general, 2^{n-1} cents on the nth day.

25. Suppose the graphs of $f(x) = x^2$ and $g(x) = 2^x$ are drawn on a coordinate grid where the unit of measurement is 1 inch. Show that, at a distance 2 ft to the right of the origin, the height of the graph of f is 48 ft but the height of the graph of g is about 265 mi.

26. Compare the functions $f(x) = x^5$ and $g(x) = 5^x$ by graphing both functions in several viewing rectangles. Find all points of intersection of the graphs correct to one decimal place. Which function grows more rapidly when x is large?

27. Compare the functions $f(x) = x^{10}$ and $g(x) = e^x$ by graphing both f and g in several viewing rectangles. When does the graph of g finally surpass the graph of f?

28. Use a graph to estimate the values of x such that $e^x > 1{,}000{,}000{,}000$.

29. Under ideal conditions a certain bacteria population is known to double every three hours. Suppose that there are initially 100 bacteria.
  (a) What is the size of the population after 15 hours?
  (b) What is the size of the population after t hours?
  (c) Estimate the size of the population after 20 hours.

  (d) Graph the population function and estimate the time for the population to reach 50,000.

30. A bacterial culture starts with 500 bacteria and doubles in size every half hour.
  (a) How many bacteria are there after 3 hours?
  (b) How many bacteria are there after t hours?
  (c) How many bacteria are there after 40 minutes?
  (d) Graph the population function and estimate the time for the population to reach 100,000.

31. The half-life of bismuth-210, ^{210}Bi, is 5 days.
  (a) If a sample has a mass of 200 mg, find the amount remaining after 15 days.
  (b) Find the amount remaining after t days.
  (c) Estimate the amount remaining after 3 weeks.
  (d) Use a graph to estimate the time required for the mass to be reduced to 1 mg.

32. An isotope of sodium, ^{24}Na, has a half-life of 15 hours. A sample of this isotope has mass 2 g.
  (a) Find the amount remaining after 60 hours.
  (b) Find the amount remaining after t hours.
  (c) Estimate the amount remaining after 4 days.
  (d) Use a graph to estimate the time required for the mass to be reduced to 0.01 g.

33. Use a graphing calculator with exponential regression capability to model the population of the world with the data from 1950 to 2000 in Table 1 on page 56. Use the model to estimate the population in 1993 and to predict the population in the year 2010.

34. The table gives the population of the United States, in millions, for the years 1900–2000. Use a graphing calculator with exponential regression capability to model the US population since 1900. Use the model to estimate the population in 1925 and to predict the population in the years 2010 and 2020.

Year	Population	Year	Population
1900	76	1960	179
1910	92	1970	203
1920	106	1980	227
1930	123	1990	250
1940	131	2000	281
1950	150		

35. If you graph the function

$$f(x) = \frac{1 - e^{1/x}}{1 + e^{1/x}}$$

you'll see that f appears to be an odd function. Prove it.

36. Graph several members of the family of functions

$$f(x) = \frac{1}{1 + ae^{bx}}$$

where $a > 0$. How does the graph change when b changes? How does it change when a changes?

1.6 Inverse Functions and Logarithms

Table 1 gives data from an experiment in which a bacteria culture started with 100 bacteria in a limited nutrient medium; the size of the bacteria population was recorded at hourly intervals. The number of bacteria N is a function of the time t: $N = f(t)$.

Suppose, however, that the biologist changes her point of view and becomes interested in the time required for the population to reach various levels. In other words, she is thinking of t as a function of N. This function is called the *inverse function* of f, denoted by f^{-1}, and read "f inverse." Thus $t = f^{-1}(N)$ is the time required for the population level to reach N. The values of f^{-1} can be found by reading Table 1 from right to left or by consulting Table 2. For instance, $f^{-1}(550) = 6$ because $f(6) = 550$.

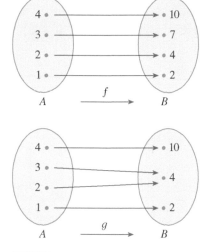

FIGURE 1

f is one-to-one; g is not

TABLE 1 N as a function of t

t (hours)	$N = f(t)$ = population at time t
0	100
1	168
2	259
3	358
4	445
5	509
6	550
7	573
8	586

TABLE 2 t as a function of N

N	$t = f^{-1}(N)$ = time to reach N bacteria
100	0
168	1
259	2
358	3
445	4
509	5
550	6
573	7
586	8

Not all functions possess inverses. Let's compare the functions f and g whose arrow diagrams are shown in Figure 1. Note that f never takes on the same value twice (any two inputs in A have different outputs), whereas g does take on the same value twice (both 2 and 3 have the same output, 4). In symbols,

$$g(2) = g(3)$$

but $$f(x_1) \neq f(x_2) \qquad \text{whenever } x_1 \neq x_2$$

Functions that share this property with f are called *one-to-one functions*.

In the language of inputs and outputs, this definition says that f is one-to-one if each output corresponds to only one input.

> **1** **Definition** A function f is called a **one-to-one function** if it never takes on the same value twice; that is,
>
> $$f(x_1) \neq f(x_2) \qquad \text{whenever } x_1 \neq x_2$$

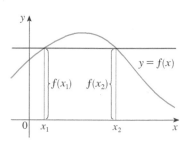

FIGURE 2

This function is not one-to-one because $f(x_1) = f(x_2)$.

If a horizontal line intersects the graph of f in more than one point, then we see from Figure 2 that there are numbers x_1 and x_2 such that $f(x_1) = f(x_2)$. This means that f is not one-to-one. Therefore we have the following geometric method for determining whether a function is one-to-one.

> **Horizontal Line Test** A function is one-to-one if and only if no horizontal line intersects its graph more than once.

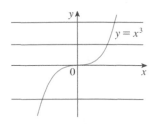

FIGURE 3

$f(x) = x^3$ is one-to-one.

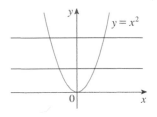

FIGURE 4

$g(x) = x^2$ is not one-to-one.

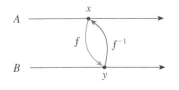

FIGURE 5

 **EXAMPLE 1** Is the function $f(x) = x^3$ one-to-one?

SOLUTION 1 If $x_1 \neq x_2$, then $x_1^3 \neq x_2^3$ (two different numbers can't have the same cube). Therefore, by Definition 1, $f(x) = x^3$ is one-to-one.

SOLUTION 2 From Figure 3 we see that no horizontal line intersects the graph of $f(x) = x^3$ more than once. Therefore, by the Horizontal Line Test, f is one-to-one. ∎

EXAMPLE 2 Is the function $g(x) = x^2$ one-to-one?

SOLUTION 1 This function is not one-to-one because, for instance,

$$g(1) = 1 = g(-1)$$

and so 1 and -1 have the same output.

SOLUTION 2 From Figure 4 we see that there are horizontal lines that intersect the graph of g more than once. Therefore, by the Horizontal Line Test, g is not one-to-one. ∎

One-to-one functions are important because they are precisely the functions that possess inverse functions according to the following definition.

> **2 Definition** Let f be a one-to-one function with domain A and range B. Then its **inverse function** f^{-1} has domain B and range A and is defined by
>
> $$f^{-1}(y) = x \iff f(x) = y$$
>
> for any y in B.

This definition says that if f maps x into y, then f^{-1} maps y back into x. (If f were not one-to-one, then f^{-1} would not be uniquely defined.) The arrow diagram in Figure 5 indicates that f^{-1} reverses the effect of f. Note that

> domain of f^{-1} = range of f
>
> range of f^{-1} = domain of f

For example, the inverse function of $f(x) = x^3$ is $f^{-1}(x) = x^{1/3}$ because if $y = x^3$, then

$$f^{-1}(y) = f^{-1}(x^3) = (x^3)^{1/3} = x$$

⊘ **CAUTION** Do not mistake the -1 in f^{-1} for an exponent. Thus

$$f^{-1}(x) \quad \text{does } not \text{ mean} \quad \frac{1}{f(x)}$$

The reciprocal $1/f(x)$ could, however, be written as $[f(x)]^{-1}$.

☑ **EXAMPLE 3** **Evaluating an inverse function** If $f(1) = 5$, $f(3) = 7$, and $f(8) = -10$, find $f^{-1}(7)$, $f^{-1}(5)$, and $f^{-1}(-10)$.

SOLUTION From the definition of f^{-1} we have

$$f^{-1}(7) = 3 \qquad \text{because} \qquad f(3) = 7$$

$$f^{-1}(5) = 1 \qquad \text{because} \qquad f(1) = 5$$

$$f^{-1}(-10) = 8 \qquad \text{because} \qquad f(8) = -10$$

The diagram in Figure 6 makes it clear how f^{-1} reverses the effect of f in this case.

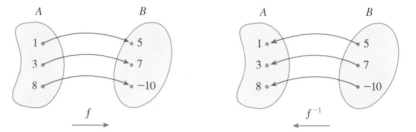

FIGURE 6
The inverse function reverses
inputs and outputs.

The letter x is traditionally used as the independent variable, so when we concentrate on f^{-1} rather than on f, we usually reverse the roles of x and y in Definition 2 and write

3
$$f^{-1}(x) = y \quad \Longleftrightarrow \quad f(y) = x$$

By substituting for y in Definition 2 and substituting for x in (3), we get the following **cancellation equations**:

4
$$f^{-1}(f(x)) = x \quad \text{for every } x \text{ in } A$$
$$f(f^{-1}(x)) = x \quad \text{for every } x \text{ in } B$$

The first cancellation equation says that if we start with x, apply f, and then apply f^{-1}, we arrive back at x, where we started (see the machine diagram in Figure 7). Thus f^{-1} undoes what f does. The second equation says that f undoes what f^{-1} does.

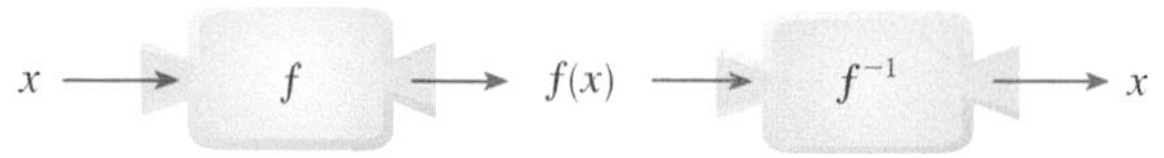

FIGURE 7

$$x \longrightarrow \boxed{f} \longrightarrow f(x) \longrightarrow \boxed{f^{-1}} \longrightarrow x$$

For example, if $f(x) = x^3$, then $f^{-1}(x) = x^{1/3}$ and so the cancellation equations become

$$f^{-1}(f(x)) = (x^3)^{1/3} = x$$
$$f(f^{-1}(x)) = (x^{1/3})^3 = x$$

These equations simply say that the cube function and the cube root function cancel each other when applied in succession.

Now let's see how to compute inverse functions. If we have a function $y = f(x)$ and are able to solve this equation for x in terms of y, then according to Definition 2 we must have

$x = f^{-1}(y)$. If we want to call the independent variable x, we then interchange x and y and arrive at the equation $y = f^{-1}(x)$.

---

5 **How to Find the Inverse Function of a One-to-One Function f**

Step 1 Write $y = f(x)$.

Step 2 Solve this equation for x in terms of y (if possible).

Step 3 To express f^{-1} as a function of x, interchange x and y. The resulting equation is $y = f^{-1}(x)$.

V **EXAMPLE 4** Find the inverse function of $f(x) = x^3 + 2$.

SOLUTION According to (5) we first write

$$y = x^3 + 2$$

Then we solve this equation for x:

$$x^3 = y - 2$$

$$x = \sqrt[3]{y - 2}$$

Finally, we interchange x and y:

$$y = \sqrt[3]{x - 2}$$

Therefore the inverse function is $f^{-1}(x) = \sqrt[3]{x - 2}$.

> In Example 4, notice how f^{-1} reverses the effect of f. The function f is the rule "Cube, then add 2"; f^{-1} is the rule "Subtract 2, then take the cube root."

The principle of interchanging x and y to find the inverse function also gives us the method for obtaining the graph of f^{-1} from the graph of f. Since $f(a) = b$ if and only if $f^{-1}(b) = a$, the point (a, b) is on the graph of f if and only if the point (b, a) is on the graph of f^{-1}. But we get the point (b, a) from (a, b) by reflecting about the line $y = x$. (See Figure 8.)

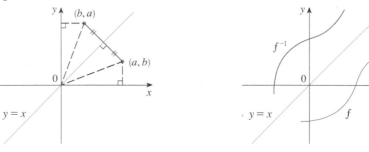

FIGURE 8   **FIGURE 9**

Therefore, as illustrated by Figure 9:

The graph of f^{-1} is obtained by reflecting the graph of f about the line $y = x$.

EXAMPLE 5 **Sketching a function and its inverse** Sketch the graphs of $f(x) = \sqrt{-1 - x}$ and its inverse function using the same coordinate axes.

SOLUTION First we sketch the curve $y = \sqrt{-1 - x}$ (the top half of the parabola $y^2 = -1 - x$, or $x = -y^2 - 1$) and then we reflect about the line $y = x$ to get the graph of f^{-1}. (See Figure 10.) As a check on our graph, notice that the expression for

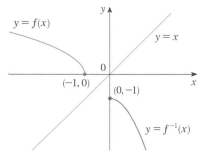

FIGURE 10

f^{-1} is $f^{-1}(x) = -x^2 - 1$, $x \geqslant 0$. So the graph of f^{-1} is the right half of the parabola $y = -x^2 - 1$ and this seems reasonable from Figure 10.

Logarithmic Functions

If $a > 0$ and $a \neq 1$, the exponential function $f(x) = a^x$ is either increasing or decreasing and so it is one-to-one by the Horizontal Line Test. It therefore has an inverse function f^{-1}, which is called the **logarithmic function with base a** and is denoted by $\log_a$. If we use the formulation of an inverse function given by (3),

$$f^{-1}(x) = y \iff f(y) = x$$

then we have

$$\log_a x = y \iff a^y = x$$

Thus, if $x > 0$, then $\log_a x$ is the exponent to which the base a must be raised to give x. For example, $\log_{10} 0.001 = -3$ because $10^{-3} = 0.001$.

The cancellation equations (4), when applied to the functions $f(x) = a^x$ and $f^{-1}(x) = \log_a x$, become

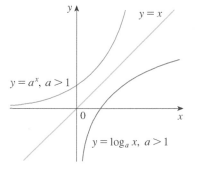

FIGURE 11

$$\log_a(a^x) = x \quad \text{for every } x \in \mathbb{R}$$
$$a^{\log_a x} = x \quad \text{for every } x > 0$$

The logarithmic function $\log_a$ has domain $(0, \infty)$ and range $\mathbb{R}$. Its graph is the reflection of the graph of $y = a^x$ about the line $y = x$.

Figure 11 shows the case where $a > 1$. (The most important logarithmic functions have base $a > 1$.) The fact that $y = a^x$ is a very rapidly increasing function for $x > 0$ is reflected in the fact that $y = \log_a x$ is a very slowly increasing function for $x > 1$.

Figure 12 shows the graphs of $y = \log_a x$ with various values of the base $a > 1$. Since $\log_a 1 = 0$, the graphs of all logarithmic functions pass through the point $(1, 0)$.

The following properties of logarithmic functions follow from the corresponding properties of exponential functions given in Section 1.5.

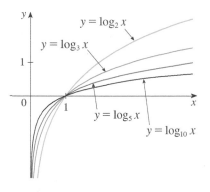

FIGURE 12

Laws of Logarithms If x and y are positive numbers, then

1. $\log_a(xy) = \log_a x + \log_a y$

2. $\log_a\left(\dfrac{x}{y}\right) = \log_a x - \log_a y$

3. $\log_a(x^r) = r \log_a x$ (where r is any real number)

EXAMPLE 6 Use the laws of logarithms to evaluate $\log_2 80 - \log_2 5$.

SOLUTION Using Law 2, we have

$$\log_2 80 - \log_2 5 = \log_2\left(\frac{80}{5}\right) = \log_2 16 = 4$$

because $2^4 = 16$.

Natural Logarithms

Of all possible bases a for logarithms, we will see in Chapter 3 that the most convenient choice of a base is the number e, which was defined in Section 1.5. The logarithm with base e is called the **natural logarithm** and has a special notation:

$$\log_e x = \ln x$$

If we put $a = e$ and replace $\log_e$ with "ln" in (6) and (7), then the defining properties of the natural logarithm function become

8

$$\ln x = y \iff e^y = x$$

9

$$\ln(e^x) = x \qquad x \in \mathbb{R}$$
$$e^{\ln x} = x \qquad x > 0$$

In particular, if we set $x = 1$, we get

$$\ln e = 1$$

EXAMPLE 7 Find x if $\ln x = 5$.

SOLUTION 1 From (8) we see that

$$\ln x = 5 \qquad \text{means} \qquad e^5 = x$$

Therefore $x = e^5$.

(If you have trouble working with the "ln" notation, just replace it by $\log_e$. Then the equation becomes $\log_e x = 5$; so, by the definition of logarithm, $e^5 = x$.)

SOLUTION 2 Start with the equation

$$\ln x = 5$$

and apply the exponential function to both sides of the equation:

$$e^{\ln x} = e^5$$

But the second cancellation equation in (9) says that $e^{\ln x} = x$. Therefore $x = e^5$.

EXAMPLE 8 Solve the equation $e^{5-3x} = 10$.

SOLUTION We take natural logarithms of both sides of the equation and use (9):

$$\ln(e^{5-3x}) = \ln 10$$
$$5 - 3x = \ln 10$$
$$3x = 5 - \ln 10$$
$$x = \tfrac{1}{3}(5 - \ln 10)$$

Since the natural logarithm is found on scientific calculators, we can approximate the solution: to four decimal places, $x \approx 0.8991$.

V **EXAMPLE 9** **Using the Laws of Logarithms** Express $\ln a + \frac{1}{2} \ln b$ as a single logarithm.

SOLUTION Using Laws 3 and 1 of logarithms, we have

$$\ln a + \tfrac{1}{2} \ln b = \ln a + \ln b^{1/2}$$
$$= \ln a + \ln \sqrt{b}$$
$$= \ln(a\sqrt{b})$$

The following formula shows that logarithms with any base can be expressed in terms of the natural logarithm.

---

10 **Change of Base Formula** For any positive number a $(a \neq 1)$, we have

$$\log_a x = \frac{\ln x}{\ln a}$$

PROOF Let $y = \log_a x$. Then, from (6), we have $a^y = x$. Taking natural logarithms of both sides of this equation, we get $y \ln a = \ln x$. Therefore

$$y = \frac{\ln x}{\ln a}$$

Scientific calculators have a key for natural logarithms, so Formula 10 enables us to use a calculator to compute a logarithm with any base (as shown in the following example). Similarly, Formula 10 allows us to graph any logarithmic function on a graphing calculator or computer (see Exercises 43 and 44).

EXAMPLE 10 Evaluate $\log_8 5$ correct to six decimal places.

SOLUTION Formula 10 gives

$$\log_8 5 = \frac{\ln 5}{\ln 8} \approx 0.773976$$

EXAMPLE 11 **Interpreting an inverse function** In Example 3 in Section 1.5 we showed that the mass of ^{90}Sr that remains from a 24-mg sample after t years is $m = f(t) = 24 \cdot 2^{-t/25}$. Find the inverse of this function and interpret it.

SOLUTION We need to solve the equation $m = 24 \cdot 2^{-t/25}$ for t. We start by isolating the exponential and taking natural logarithms of both sides:

$$2^{-t/25} = \frac{m}{24}$$

$$\ln(2^{-t/25}) = \ln\left(\frac{m}{24}\right)$$

$$-\frac{t}{25} \ln 2 = \ln m - \ln 24$$

$$t = -\frac{25}{\ln 2}(\ln m - \ln 24) = \frac{25}{\ln 2}(\ln 24 - \ln m)$$

So the inverse function is

$$f^{-1}(m) = \frac{25}{\ln 2}(\ln 24 - \ln m)$$

This function gives the time required for the mass to decay to m milligrams. In particular, the time required for the mass to be reduced to 5 mg is

$$t = f^{-1}(5) = \frac{25}{\ln 2}(\ln 24 - \ln 5) \approx 56.58 \text{ years}$$

This answer agrees with the graphical estimate that we made in Example 3(c) in Section 1.5.

Graph and Growth of the Natural Logarithm

The graphs of the exponential function $y = e^x$ and its inverse function, the natural logarithm function, are shown in Figure 13. Because the curve $y = e^x$ crosses the y-axis with a slope of 1, it follows that the reflected curve $y = \ln x$ crosses the x-axis with a slope of 1.

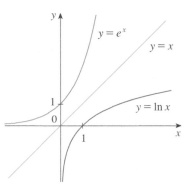

FIGURE 13
The graph of $y = \ln x$ is the reflection of the graph of $y = e^x$ about the line $y = x$

In common with all other logarithmic functions with base greater than 1, the natural logarithm is an increasing function defined on $(0, \infty)$ and the y-axis is a vertical asymptote. (This means that the values of $\ln x$ become very large negative as x approaches 0.)

EXAMPLE 12 Shifting the natural logarithm function
Sketch the graph of the function $y = \ln(x - 2) - 1$.

SOLUTION We start with the graph of $y = \ln x$ as given in Figure 13. Using the transformations of Section 1.3, we shift it 2 units to the right to get the graph of $y = \ln(x - 2)$ and then we shift it 1 unit downward to get the graph of $y = \ln(x - 2) - 1$. (See Figure 14.)

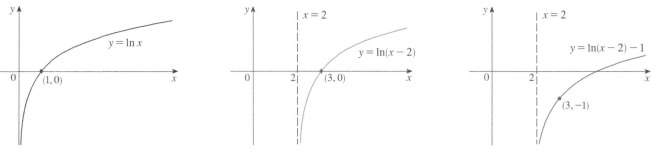

FIGURE 14

Although ln x is an increasing function, it grows *very* slowly when $x > 1$. In fact, ln x grows more slowly than any positive power of x. To illustrate this fact, we compare approximate values of the functions $y = \ln x$ and $y = x^{1/2} = \sqrt{x}$ in the following table and we graph them in Figures 15 and 16. You can see that initially the graphs of $y = \sqrt{x}$ and $y = \ln x$ grow at comparable rates, but eventually the root function far surpasses the logarithm.

x	1	2	5	10	50	100	500	1000	10,000	100,000
$\ln x$	0	0.69	1.61	2.30	3.91	4.6	6.2	6.9	9.2	11.5
$\sqrt{x}$	1	1.41	2.24	3.16	7.07	10.0	22.4	31.6	100	316
$\dfrac{\ln x}{\sqrt{x}}$	0	0.49	0.72	0.73	0.55	0.46	0.28	0.22	0.09	0.04

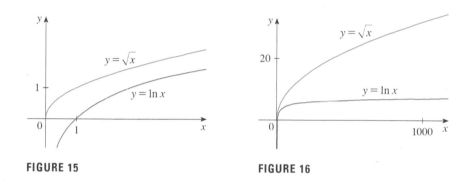

FIGURE 15   **FIGURE 16**

1.6 Exercises

1. (a) What is a one-to-one function?
(b) How can you tell from the graph of a function whether it is one-to-one?

2. (a) Suppose f is a one-to-one function with domain A and range B. How is the inverse function f^{-1} defined? What is the domain of f^{-1}? What is the range of f^{-1}?
(b) If you are given a formula for f, how do you find a formula for f^{-1}?
(c) If you are given the graph of f, how do you find the graph of f^{-1}?

3–14 A function is given by a table of values, a graph, a formula, or a verbal description. Determine whether it is one-to-one.

3.

x	1	2	3	4	5	6
$f(x)$	1.5	2.0	3.6	5.3	2.8	2.0

4.

x	1	2	3	4	5	6
$f(x)$	1.0	1.9	2.8	3.5	3.1	2.9

5.   **6.**

7.   **8.**

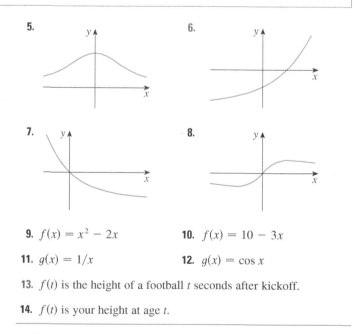

9. $f(x) = x^2 - 2x$ **10.** $f(x) = 10 - 3x$

11. $g(x) = 1/x$ **12.** $g(x) = \cos x$

13. $f(t)$ is the height of a football t seconds after kickoff.

14. $f(t)$ is your height at age t.

Graphing calculator or computer with graphing software required   CAS Computer algebra system required   **1.** Homework Hints available in TEC

15. If f is a one-to-one function such that $f(2) = 9$, what is $f^{-1}(9)$?

16. If $f(x) = x^5 + x^3 + x$, find $f^{-1}(3)$ and $f(f^{-1}(2))$.

17. If $g(x) = 3 + x + e^x$, find $g^{-1}(4)$.

18. The graph of f is given.
(a) Why is f one-to-one?
(b) What are the domain and range of f^{-1}?
(c) What is the value of $f^{-1}(2)$?
(d) Estimate the value of $f^{-1}(0)$.

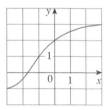

19. The formula $C = \frac{5}{9}(F - 32)$, where $F \geqslant -459.67$, expresses the Celsius temperature C as a function of the Fahrenheit temperature F. Find a formula for the inverse function and interpret it. What is the domain of the inverse function?

20. In the theory of relativity, the mass of a particle with speed v is

$$m = f(v) = \frac{m_0}{\sqrt{1 - v^2/c^2}}$$

where m_0 is the rest mass of the particle and c is the speed of light in a vacuum. Find the inverse function of f and explain its meaning.

21–26 Find a formula for the inverse of the function.

21. $f(x) = 1 + \sqrt{2 + 3x}$

22. $f(x) = \dfrac{4x - 1}{2x + 3}$

23. $f(x) = e^{2x-1}$

24. $y = x^2 - x, \quad x \geqslant \frac{1}{2}$

25. $y = \ln(x + 3)$

26. $y = \dfrac{e^x}{1 + 2e^x}$

27–28 Find an explicit formula for f^{-1} and use it to graph f^{-1}, f, and the line $y = x$ on the same screen. To check your work, see whether the graphs of f and f^{-1} are reflections about the line.

27. $f(x) = x^4 + 1, \quad x \geqslant 0$

28. $f(x) = 2 - e^x$

29–30 Use the given graph of f to sketch the graph of f^{-1}.

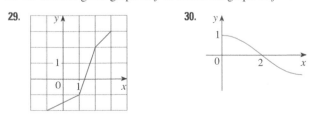

29.

30.

31. Let $f(x) = \sqrt{1 - x^2}, \ 0 \leqslant x \leqslant 1$.
(a) Find f^{-1}. How is it related to f?
(b) Identify the graph of f and explain your answer to part (a).

32. Let $g(x) = \sqrt[3]{1 - x^3}$.
(a) Find g^{-1}. How is it related to g?
(b) Graph g. How do you explain your answer to part (a)?

33. (a) How is the logarithmic function $y = \log_a x$ defined?
(b) What is the domain of this function?
(c) What is the range of this function?
(d) Sketch the general shape of the graph of the function $y = \log_a x$ if $a > 1$.

34. (a) What is the natural logarithm?
(b) What is the common logarithm?
(c) Sketch the graphs of the natural logarithm function and the natural exponential function with a common set of axes.

35–38 Find the exact value of each expression.

35. (a) $\log_5 125$ (b) $\log_3\left(\frac{1}{27}\right)$

36. (a) $\ln(1/e)$ (b) $\log_{10} \sqrt{10}$

37. (a) $\log_2 6 - \log_2 15 + \log_2 20$
(b) $\log_3 100 - \log_3 18 - \log_3 50$

38. (a) $e^{-2 \ln 5}$ (b) $\ln\left(\ln e^{e^{10}}\right)$

39–41 Express the given quantity as a single logarithm.

39. $\ln 5 + 5 \ln 3$

40. $\ln(a + b) + \ln(a - b) - 2 \ln c$

41. $\ln(1 + x^2) + \frac{1}{2} \ln x - \ln \sin x$

42. Use Formula 10 to evaluate each logarithm correct to six decimal places.
(a) $\log_{12} 10$ (b) $\log_2 8.4$

43–44 Use Formula 10 to graph the given functions on a common screen. How are these graphs related?

43. $y = \log_{1.5} x, \quad y = \ln x, \quad y = \log_{10} x, \quad y = \log_{50} x$

44. $y = \ln x, \quad y = \log_{10} x, \quad y = e^x, \quad y = 10^x$

45. Suppose that the graph of $y = \log_2 x$ is drawn on a coordinate grid where the unit of measurement is an inch. How many miles to the right of the origin do we have to move before the height of the curve reaches 3 ft?

46. Compare the functions $f(x) = x^{0.1}$ and $g(x) = \ln x$ by graphing both f and g in several viewing rectangles. When does the graph of f finally surpass the graph of g?

47–48 Make a rough sketch of the graph of each function. Do not use a calculator. Just use the graphs given in Figures 12 and 13 and, if necessary, the transformations of Section 1.3.

47. (a) $y = \log_{10}(x + 5)$ (b) $y = -\ln x$

48. (a) $y = \ln(-x)$ (b) $y = \ln|x|$

49–52 Solve each equation for x.

49. (a) $e^{7-4x} = 6$ (b) $\ln(3x - 10) = 2$

50. (a) $\ln(x^2 - 1) = 3$ (b) $e^{2x} - 3e^x + 2 = 0$

51. (a) $2^{x-5} = 3$ (b) $\ln x + \ln(x - 1) = 1$

52. (a) $\ln(\ln x) = 1$ (b) $e^{ax} = Ce^{bx}$, where $a \ne b$

53–54 Solve each inequality for x.

53. (a) $e^x < 10$ (b) $\ln x > -1$

54. (a) $2 < \ln x < 9$ (b) $e^{2-3x} > 4$

55–56 Find (a) the domain of f and (b) f^{-1} and its domain.

55. $f(x) = \sqrt{3 - e^{2x}}$ **56.** $f(x) = \ln(2 + \ln x)$

CAS **57.** Graph the function $f(x) = \sqrt{x^3 + x^2 + x + 1}$ and explain why it is one-to-one. Then use a computer algebra system to find an explicit expression for $f^{-1}(x)$. (Your CAS will produce three possible expressions. Explain why two of them are irrelevant in this context.)

CAS **58.** (a) If $g(x) = x^6 + x^4$, $x \ge 0$, use a computer algebra system to find an expression for $g^{-1}(x)$.
(b) Use the expression in part (a) to graph $y = g(x)$, $y = x$, and $y = g^{-1}(x)$ on the same screen.

59. If a bacteria population starts with 100 bacteria and doubles every three hours, then the number of bacteria after t hours is $n = f(t) = 100 \cdot 2^{t/3}$. (See Exercise 29 in Section 1.5.)
(a) Find the inverse of this function and explain its meaning.
(b) When will the population reach 50,000?

60. When a camera flash goes off, the batteries immediately begin to recharge the flash's capacitor, which stores electric charge given by

$$Q(t) = Q_0(1 - e^{-t/a})$$

(The maximum charge capacity is Q_0 and t is measured in seconds.)
(a) Find the inverse of this function and explain its meaning.
(b) How long does it take to recharge the capacitor to 90% of capacity if $a = 2$?

61. Starting with the graph of $y = \ln x$, find the equation of the graph that results from
(a) shifting 3 units upward
(b) shifting 3 units to the left
(c) reflecting about the x-axis
(d) reflecting about the y-axis
(e) reflecting about the line $y = x$
(f) reflecting about the x-axis and then about the line $y = x$
(g) reflecting about the y-axis and then about the line $y = x$
(h) shifting 3 units to the left and then reflecting about the line $y = x$

62. (a) If we shift a curve to the left, what happens to its reflection about the line $y = x$? In view of this geometric principle, find an expression for the inverse of $g(x) = f(x + c)$, where f is a one-to-one function.
(b) Find an expression for the inverse of $h(x) = f(cx)$, where $c \ne 0$.

1.7 Parametric Curves

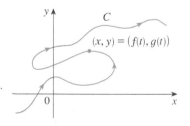

FIGURE 1

Imagine that a particle moves along the curve C shown in Figure 1. It is impossible to describe C by an equation of the form $y = f(x)$ because C fails the Vertical Line Test. But the x- and y-coordinates of the particle are functions of time and so we can write $x = f(t)$ and $y = g(t)$. Such a pair of equations is often a convenient way of describing a curve and gives rise to the following definition.

Suppose that x and y are both given as functions of a third variable t (called a **parameter**) by the equations

$$x = f(t) \qquad y = g(t)$$

(called **parametric equations**). Each value of t determines a point (x, y), which we can plot in a coordinate plane. As t varies, the point $(x, y) = (f(t), g(t))$ varies and traces out a curve C, which we call a **parametric curve**. The parameter t does not necessarily represent time and, in fact, we could use a letter other than t for the parameter. But in many applications of parametric curves, t does denote time and therefore we can interpret $(x, y) = (f(t), g(t))$ as the position of a particle at time t.

EXAMPLE 1 **Graphing a parametric curve** Sketch and identify the curve defined by the parametric equations

$$x = t^2 - 2t \qquad y = t + 1$$

SOLUTION Each value of t gives a point on the curve, as shown in the table. For instance, if $t = 0$, then $x = 0$, $y = 1$ and so the corresponding point is $(0, 1)$. In Figure 2 we plot the points (x, y) determined by several values of the parameter t and we join them to produce a curve.

t	x	y
-2	8	-1
-1	3	0
0	0	1
1	-1	2
2	0	3
3	3	4
4	8	5

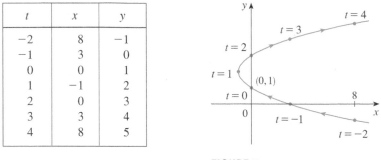

FIGURE 2

A particle whose position is given by the parametric equations moves along the curve in the direction of the arrows as t increases. Notice that the consecutive points marked on the curve appear at equal time intervals but not at equal distances. That is because the particle slows down and then speeds up as t increases.

It appears from Figure 2 that the curve traced out by the particle may be a parabola. This can be confirmed by eliminating the parameter t as follows. We obtain $t = y - 1$ from the second equation and substitute into the first equation. This gives

$$x = t^2 - 2t = (y - 1)^2 - 2(y - 1) = y^2 - 4y + 3$$

and so the curve represented by the given parametric equations is the parabola $x = y^2 - 4y + 3$.

This equation in x and y describes *where* the particle has been, but it doesn't tell us *when* the particle was at a particular point. The parametric equations have an advantage—they tell us *when* the particle was at a point. They also indicate the *direction* of the motion.

No restriction was placed on the parameter t in Example 1, so we assumed that t could be any real number. But sometimes we restrict t to lie in a finite interval. For instance, the parametric curve

$$x = t^2 - 2t \qquad y = t + 1 \qquad 0 \le t \le 4$$

shown in Figure 3 is the part of the parabola in Example 1 that starts at the point $(0, 1)$ and ends at the point $(8, 5)$. The arrowhead indicates the direction in which the curve is traced as t increases from 0 to 4.

In general, the curve with parametric equations

$$x = f(t) \qquad y = g(t) \qquad a \le t \le b$$

has **initial point** $(f(a), g(a))$ and **terminal point** $(f(b), g(b))$.

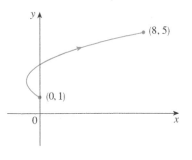

FIGURE 3

V EXAMPLE 2 **Identifying a parametric curve** What curve is represented by the following parametric equations?

$$x = \cos t \qquad y = \sin t \qquad 0 \le t \le 2\pi$$

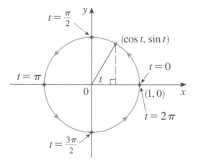

FIGURE 4

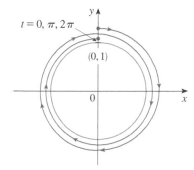

FIGURE 5

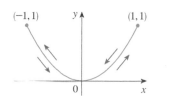

FIGURE 7

SOLUTION If we plot points, it appears that the curve is a circle. We can confirm this impression by eliminating t. Observe that

$$x^2 + y^2 = \cos^2 t + \sin^2 t = 1$$

Thus the point (x, y) moves on the unit circle $x^2 + y^2 = 1$. Notice that in this example the parameter t can be interpreted as the angle (in radians) shown in Figure 4. As t increases from 0 to 2π, the point $(x, y) = (\cos t, \sin t)$ moves once around the circle in the counterclockwise direction starting from the point $(1, 0)$.

EXAMPLE 3 What curve is represented by the given parametric equations?

$$x = \sin 2t \qquad y = \cos 2t \qquad 0 \leqslant t \leqslant 2\pi$$

SOLUTION Again we have

$$x^2 + y^2 = \sin^2 2t + \cos^2 2t = 1$$

so the parametric equations again represent the unit circle $x^2 + y^2 = 1$. But as t increases from 0 to 2π, the point $(x, y) = (\sin 2t, \cos 2t)$ starts at $(0, 1)$ and moves *twice* around the circle in the clockwise direction as indicated in Figure 5.

Examples 2 and 3 show that different sets of parametric equations can represent the same curve. Thus we distinguish between a *curve*, which is a set of points, and a *parametric curve*, in which the points are traced in a particular way.

EXAMPLE 4 Find parametric equations for the circle with center (h, k) and radius r.

SOLUTION If we take the equations of the unit circle in Example 2 and multiply the expressions for x and y by r, we get $x = r\cos t$, $y = r\sin t$. You can verify that these equations represent a circle with radius r and center the origin traced counterclockwise. We now shift h units in the x-direction and k units in the y-direction and obtain parametric equations of the circle (Figure 6) with center (h, k) and radius r:

$$x = h + r\cos t \qquad y = k + r\sin t \qquad 0 \leqslant t \leqslant 2\pi$$

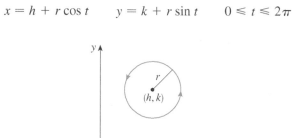

FIGURE 6
$x = h + r \cos t, \ y = k + r \sin t$

EXAMPLE 5 Sketch the curve with parametric equations $x = \sin t$, $y = \sin^2 t$.

SOLUTION Observe that $y = (\sin t)^2 = x^2$ and so the point (x, y) moves on the parabola $y = x^2$. But note also that, since $-1 \leqslant \sin t \leqslant 1$, we have $-1 \leqslant x \leqslant 1$, so the parametric equations represent only the part of the parabola for which $-1 \leqslant x \leqslant 1$. Since $\sin t$ is periodic, the point $(x, y) = (\sin t, \sin^2 t)$ moves back and forth infinitely often along the parabola from $(-1, 1)$ to $(1, 1)$. (See Figure 7.)

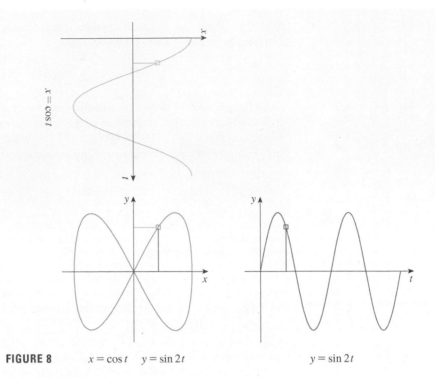

TEC Module 1.7A gives an animation of the relationship between motion along a parametric curve $x = f(t)$, $y = g(t)$ and motion along the graphs of f and g as functions of t. Clicking on TRIG gives you the family of parametric curves

$$x = a \cos bt \quad y = c \sin dt$$

If you choose $a = b = c = d = 1$ and click on **animate**, you will see how the graphs of $x = \cos t$ and $y = \sin t$ relate to the circle in Example 2. If you choose $a = b = c = 1$, $d = 2$, you will see graphs as in Figure 8. By clicking on **animate** or moving the t-slider to the right, you can see from the color coding how motion along the graphs of $x = \cos t$ and $y = \sin 2t$ corresponds to motion along the parametric curve, which is called a **Lissajous figure**.

FIGURE 8 $x = \cos t$ $y = \sin 2t$ $y = \sin 2t$

Graphing Devices

Most graphing calculators and computer graphing programs can be used to graph curves defined by parametric equations. In fact, it's instructive to watch a parametric curve being drawn by a graphing calculator because the points are plotted in order as the corresponding parameter values increase.

EXAMPLE 6   **Graphing x as a function of y**

Use a graphing device to graph the curve $x = y^4 - 3y^2$.

SOLUTION   If we let the parameter be $t = y$, then we have the equations

$$x = t^4 - 3t^2 \qquad y = t$$

Using these parametric equations to graph the curve, we obtain Figure 9. It would be possible to solve the given equation ($x = y^4 - 3y^2$) for y as four functions of x and graph them individually, but the parametric equations provide a much easier method.

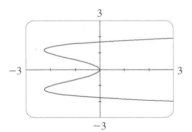

FIGURE 9

In general, if we need to graph an equation of the form $x = g(y)$, we can use the parametric equations

$$x = g(t) \qquad y = t$$

Notice also that curves with equations $y = f(x)$ (the ones we are most familiar with— graphs of functions) can also be regarded as curves with parametric equations

$$x = t \qquad y = f(t)$$

Graphing devices are particularly useful when sketching complicated curves. For instance, the curves shown in Figures 10, 11, and 12 would be virtually impossible to produce by hand.

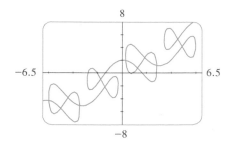

FIGURE 10
$x = t + 2 \sin 2t$
$y = t + 2 \cos 5t$

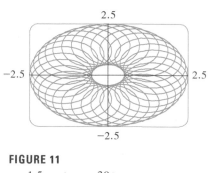

FIGURE 11
$x = 1.5 \cos t - \cos 30t$
$y = 1.5 \sin t - \sin 30t$

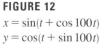

FIGURE 12
$x = \sin(t + \cos 100t)$
$y = \cos(t + \sin 100t)$

One of the most important uses of parametric curves is in computer-aided design (CAD). In the Laboratory Project after Section 3.4 we will investigate special parametric curves, called **Bézier curves**, that are used extensively in manufacturing, especially in the automotive industry. These curves are also employed in specifying the shapes of letters and other symbols in laser printers.

The Cycloid

TEC An animation in Module 1.7B shows how the cycloid is formed as the circle moves.

EXAMPLE 7   Deriving parametric equations for a cycloid   The curve traced out by a point P on the circumference of a circle as the circle rolls along a straight line is called a **cycloid** (see Figure 13). If the circle has radius r and rolls along the x-axis and if one position of P is the origin, find parametric equations for the cycloid.

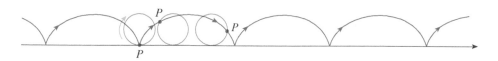

FIGURE 13

SOLUTION We choose as parameter the angle of rotation θ of the circle ($\theta = 0$ when P is at the origin). Suppose the circle has rotated through θ radians. Because the circle has been in contact with the line, we see from Figure 14 that the distance it has rolled from the origin is

$$|OT| = \text{arc } PT = r\theta$$

Therefore the center of the circle is $C(r\theta, r)$. Let the coordinates of P be (x, y). Then from Figure 14 we see that

$$x = |OT| - |PQ| = r\theta - r \sin\theta = r(\theta - \sin\theta)$$

$$y = |TC| - |QC| = r - r \cos\theta = r(1 - \cos\theta)$$

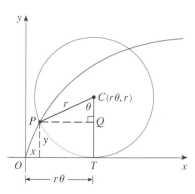

FIGURE 14

Therefore parametric equations of the cycloid are

$$\boxed{1} \qquad x = r(\theta - \sin\theta) \qquad y = r(1 - \cos\theta) \qquad \theta \in \mathbb{R}$$

One arch of the cycloid comes from one rotation of the circle and so is described by $0 \le \theta \le 2\pi$. Although Equations 1 were derived from Figure 14, which illustrates the case where $0 < \theta < \pi/2$, it can be seen that these equations are still valid for other values of θ (see Exercise 37).

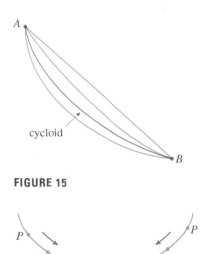

cycloid

FIGURE 15

FIGURE 16

Although it is possible to eliminate the parameter θ from Equations 1, the resulting Cartesian equation in x and y is very complicated and not as convenient to work with as the parametric equations.

One of the first people to study the cycloid was Galileo, who proposed that bridges be built in the shape of cycloids and who tried to find the area under one arch of a cycloid. Later this curve arose in connection with the **brachistochrone problem**: Find the curve along which a particle will slide in the shortest time (under the influence of gravity) from a point A to a lower point B not directly beneath A. The Swiss mathematician John Bernoulli, who posed this problem in 1696, showed that among all possible curves that join A to B, as in Figure 15, the particle will take the least time sliding from A to B if the curve is part of an inverted arch of a cycloid.

The Dutch physicist Huygens had already shown that the cycloid is also the solution to the **tautochrone problem**; that is, no matter where a particle P is placed on an inverted cycloid, it takes the same time to slide to the bottom (see Figure 16). Huygens proposed that pendulum clocks (which he invented) should swing in cycloidal arcs because then the pendulum would take the same time to make a complete oscillation whether it swings through a wide or a small arc.

1.7 Exercises

1–4 Sketch the curve by using the parametric equations to plot points. Indicate with an arrow the direction in which the curve is traced as t increases.

1. $x = t^2 + t, \quad y = t^2 - t, \quad -2 \le t \le 2$

2. $x = t^2, \quad y = t^3 - 4t, \quad -3 \le t \le 3$

3. $x = \cos^2 t, \quad y = 1 - \sin t, \quad 0 \le t \le \pi/2$

4. $x = e^{-t} + t, \quad y = e^t - t, \quad -2 \le t \le 2$

5–8

(a) Sketch the curve by using the parametric equations to plot points. Indicate with an arrow the direction in which the curve is traced as t increases.

(b) Eliminate the parameter to find a Cartesian equation of the curve.

5. $x = 3t - 5, \quad y = 2t + 1$

6. $x = 1 + 3t, \quad y = 2 - t^2$

7. $x = \sqrt{t}, \quad y = 1 - t$

8. $x = t^2, \quad y = t^3$

9–16

(a) Eliminate the parameter to find a Cartesian equation of the curve.

(b) Sketch the curve and indicate with an arrow the direction in which the curve is traced as the parameter increases.

9. $x = \sin \frac{1}{2}\theta, \quad y = \cos \frac{1}{2}\theta, \quad -\pi \le \theta \le \pi$

10. $x = \frac{1}{2}\cos\theta, \quad y = 2\sin\theta, \quad 0 \le \theta \le \pi$

11. $x = \sin t, \quad y = \csc t, \quad 0 < t < \pi/2$

12. $x = \tan^2\theta, \quad y = \sec\theta, \quad -\pi/2 < \theta < \pi/2$

13. $x = e^{2t}, \quad y = t + 1$

14. $x = e^t - 1, \quad y = e^{2t}$

15. $x = \sin\theta, \quad y = \cos 2\theta$

16. $x = \ln t, \quad y = \sqrt{t}, \quad t \ge 1$

17–20 Describe the motion of a particle with position (x, y) as t varies in the given interval.

17. $x = 3 + 2\cos t, \quad y = 1 + 2\sin t, \quad \pi/2 \le t \le 3\pi/2$

18. $x = 2\sin t, \quad y = 4 + \cos t, \quad 0 \le t \le 3\pi/2$

19. $x = 5\sin t, \quad y = 2\cos t, \quad -\pi \le t \le 5\pi$

20. $x = \sin t, \quad y = \cos^2 t, \quad -2\pi \le t \le 2\pi$

21. Suppose a curve is given by the parametric equations $x = f(t)$, $y = g(t)$, where the range of f is $[1, 4]$ and the range of g is $[2, 3]$. What can you say about the curve?

22. Match the graphs of the parametric equations $x = f(t)$ and $y = g(t)$ in (a)–(d) with the parametric curves labeled I–IV. Give reasons for your choices.

⊞ Graphing calculator or computer with graphing software required   **1.** Homework Hints available in TEC

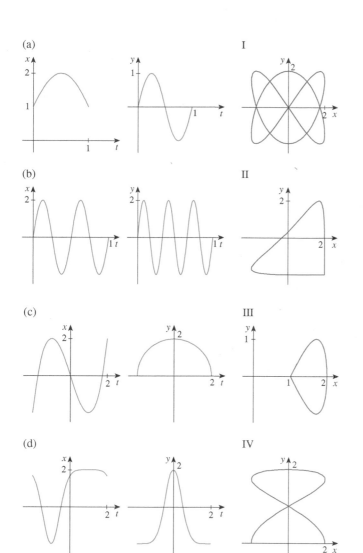

(a)   I

(b)   II

(c)   III

(d)   IV

23–25 Use the graphs of $x = f(t)$ and $y = g(t)$ to sketch the parametric curve $x = f(t)$, $y = g(t)$. Indicate with arrows the direction in which the curve is traced as t increases.

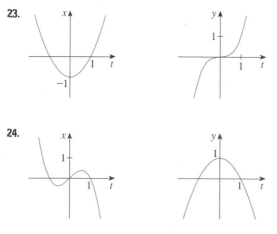

23.

24.

25.

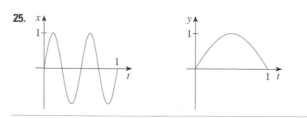

26. Match the parametric equations with the graphs labeled I-VI. Give reasons for your choices. (Do not use a graphing device.)
(a) $x = t^4 - t + 1$, $y = t^2$
(b) $x = t^2 - 2t$, $y = \sqrt{t}$
(c) $x = \sin 2t$, $y = \sin(t + \sin 2t)$
(d) $x = \cos 5t$, $y = \sin 2t$
(e) $x = t + \sin 4t$, $y = t^2 + \cos 3t$
(f) $x = \dfrac{\sin 2t}{4 + t^2}$, $y = \dfrac{\cos 2t}{4 + t^2}$

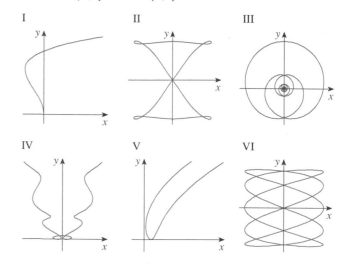

I   II   III

IV   V   VI

27. Graph the curve $x = y - 2 \sin \pi y$.

28. Graph the curves $y = x^3 - 4x$ and $x = y^3 - 4y$ and find their points of intersection correct to one decimal place.

29. (a) Show that the parametric equations
$$x = x_1 + (x_2 - x_1)t \qquad y = y_1 + (y_2 - y_1)t$$
where $0 \le t \le 1$, describe the line segment that joins the points $P_1(x_1, y_1)$ and $P_2(x_2, y_2)$.
(b) Find parametric equations to represent the line segment from $(-2, 7)$ to $(3, -1)$.

30. Use a graphing device and the result of Exercise 29(a) to draw the triangle with vertices $A(1, 1)$, $B(4, 2)$, and $C(1, 5)$.

31. Find parametric equations for the path of a particle that moves along the circle $x^2 + (y - 1)^2 = 4$ in the manner described.
(a) Once around clockwise, starting at $(2, 1)$
(b) Three times around counterclockwise, starting at $(2, 1)$
(c) Halfway around counterclockwise, starting at $(0, 3)$

32. (a) Find parametric equations for the ellipse
$x^2/a^2 + y^2/b^2 = 1$. [*Hint:* Modify the equations of
the circle in Example 2.]
(b) Use these parametric equations to graph the ellipse when
$a = 3$ and $b = 1, 2, 4$, and 8.
(c) How does the shape of the ellipse change as b varies?

33–34 Use a graphing calculator or computer to reproduce the
picture.

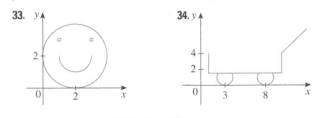

35–36 Compare the curves represented by the parametric equations. How do they differ?

35. (a) $x = t^3$, $y = t^2$ (b) $x = t^6$, $y = t^4$
(c) $x = e^{-3t}$, $y = e^{-2t}$

36. (a) $x = t$, $y = t^{-2}$ (b) $x = \cos t$, $y = \sec^2 t$
(c) $x = e^t$, $y = e^{-2t}$

37. Derive Equations 1 for the case $\pi/2 < \theta < \pi$.

38. Let P be a point at a distance d from the center of a circle of
radius r. The curve traced out by P as the circle rolls along a
straight line is called a **trochoid**. (Think of the motion of a
point on a spoke of a bicycle wheel.) The cycloid is the special case of a trochoid with $d = r$. Using the same parameter
θ as for the cycloid and, assuming the line is the x-axis and
$\theta = 0$ when P is at one of its lowest points, show that parametric equations of the trochoid are

$$x = r\theta - d \sin \theta \qquad y = r - d \cos \theta$$

Sketch the trochoid for the cases $d < r$ and $d > r$.

39. If a and b are fixed numbers, find parametric equations for
the curve that consists of all possible positions of the point P
in the figure, using the angle θ as the parameter. Then eliminate the parameter and identify the curve.

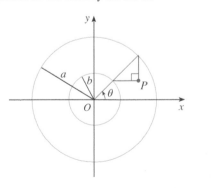

40. A curve, called a **witch of Maria Agnesi**, consists of all
possible positions of the point P in the figure. Show that
parametric equations for this curve can be written as

$$x = 2a \cot \theta \qquad y = 2a \sin^2\theta$$

Sketch the curve.

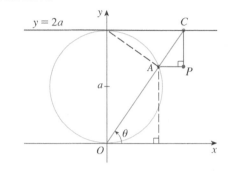

41. Suppose that the position of one particle at time t is given by

$$x_1 = 3 \sin t \qquad y_1 = 2 \cos t \qquad 0 \le t \le 2\pi$$

and the position of a second particle is given by

$$x_2 = -3 + \cos t \qquad y_2 = 1 + \sin t \qquad 0 \le t \le 2\pi$$

(a) Graph the paths of both particles. How many points of
intersection are there?
(b) Are any of these points of intersection *collision points*?
In other words, are the particles ever at the same place at
the same time? If so, find the collision points.
(c) Describe what happens if the path of the second particle
is given by

$$x_2 = 3 + \cos t \qquad y_2 = 1 + \sin t \qquad 0 \le t \le 2\pi$$

42. If a projectile is fired with an initial velocity of v_0 meters
per second at an angle α above the horizontal and air resistance is assumed to be negligible, then its position after t seconds is given by the parametric equations

$$x = (v_0 \cos \alpha)t \qquad y = (v_0 \sin \alpha)t - \tfrac{1}{2}gt^2$$

where g is the acceleration due to gravity (9.8 m/s²).
(a) If a gun is fired with $\alpha = 30°$ and $v_0 = 500$ m/s, when
will the bullet hit the ground? How far from the gun will
it hit the ground? What is the maximum height reached
by the bullet?
(b) Use a graphing device to check your answers to part (a).
Then graph the path of the projectile for several other
values of the angle α to see where it hits the ground.
Summarize your findings.
(c) Show that the path is parabolic by eliminating the
parameter.

43. Investigate the family of curves defined by the parametric
equations $x = t^2$, $y = t^3 - ct$. How does the shape change
as c increases? Illustrate by graphing several members of the
family.

44. The **swallowtail catastrophe curves** are defined by the
parametric equations $x = 2ct - 4t^3$, $y = -ct^2 + 3t^4$.

Graph several of these curves. What features do the curves have in common? How do they change when c increases?

45. The curves with equations $x = a \sin nt$, $y = b \cos t$ are called **Lissajous figures**. Investigate how these curves vary when a, b, and n vary. (Take n to be a positive integer.)

46. Investigate the family of curves defined by the parametric equations $x = \cos t$, $y = \sin t - \sin ct$, where $c > 0$. Start by letting c be a positive integer and see what happens to the shape as c increases. Then explore some of the possibilities that occur when c is a fraction.

LABORATORY PROJECT · Running Circles Around Circles

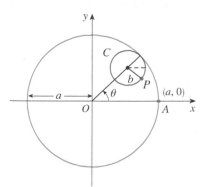

TEC Look at Module 1.7B to see how hypocycloids and epicycloids are formed by the motion of rolling circles.

In this project we investigate families of curves, called *hypocycloids* and *epicycloids*, that are generated by the motion of a point on a circle that rolls inside or outside another circle.

1. A **hypocycloid** is a curve traced out by a fixed point P on a circle C of radius b as C rolls on the inside of a circle with center O and radius a. Show that if the initial position of P is $(a, 0)$ and the parameter θ is chosen as in the figure, then parametric equations of the hypocycloid are

$$x = (a - b)\cos\theta + b\cos\left(\frac{a - b}{b}\theta\right) \qquad y = (a - b)\sin\theta - b\sin\left(\frac{a - b}{b}\theta\right)$$

2. Use a graphing device (or the interactive graphic in TEC Module 1.7B) to draw the graphs of hypocycloids with a a positive integer and $b = 1$. How does the value of a affect the graph? Show that if we take $a = 4$, then the parametric equations of the hypocycloid reduce to

$$x = 4\cos^3\theta \qquad y = 4\sin^3\theta$$

This curve is called a **hypocycloid of four cusps**, or an **astroid**.

3. Now try $b = 1$ and $a = n/d$, a fraction where n and d have no common factor. First let $n = 1$ and try to determine graphically the effect of the denominator d on the shape of the graph. Then let n vary while keeping d constant. What happens when $n = d + 1$?

4. What happens if $b = 1$ and a is irrational? Experiment with an irrational number like $\sqrt{2}$ or $e - 2$. Take larger and larger values for θ and speculate on what would happen if we were to graph the hypocycloid for all real values of θ.

5. If the circle C rolls on the *outside* of the fixed circle, the curve traced out by P is called an **epicycloid**. Find parametric equations for the epicycloid.

6. Investigate the possible shapes for epicycloids. Use methods similar to Problems 2–4.

⊞ Graphing calculator or computer with graphing software required

1 Review

Concept Check

1. (a) What is a function? What are its domain and range?
(b) What is the graph of a function?
(c) How can you tell whether a given curve is the graph of a function?

2. Discuss four ways of representing a function. Illustrate your discussion with examples.

3. (a) What is an even function? How can you tell if a function is even by looking at its graph?
(b) What is an odd function? How can you tell if a function is odd by looking at its graph?

4. What is an increasing function?

5. What is a mathematical model?

6. Give an example of each type of function.
(a) Linear function   (b) Power function
(c) Exponential function   (d) Quadratic function
(e) Polynomial of degree 5 (f) Rational function

7. Sketch by hand, on the same axes, the graphs of the following functions.
(a) $f(x) = x$ (b) $g(x) = x^2$
(c) $h(x) = x^3$ (d) $j(x) = x^4$

8. Draw, by hand, a rough sketch of the graph of each function.
(a) $y = \sin x$ (b) $y = \tan x$
(c) $y = e^x$ (d) $y = \ln x$
(e) $y = 1/x$ (f) $y = |x|$
(g) $y = \sqrt{x}$

9. Suppose that f has domain A and g has domain B.
(a) What is the domain of $f + g$?
(b) What is the domain of fg?
(c) What is the domain of f/g?

10. How is the composite function $f \circ g$ defined? What is its domain?

11. Suppose the graph of f is given. Write an equation for each of the graphs that are obtained from the graph of f as follows.
(a) Shift 2 units upward.
(b) Shift 2 units downward.
(c) Shift 2 units to the right.
(d) Shift 2 units to the left.
(e) Reflect about the x-axis.
(f) Reflect about the y-axis.
(g) Stretch vertically by a factor of 2.
(h) Shrink vertically by a factor of 2.
(i) Stretch horizontally by a factor of 2.
(j) Shrink horizontally by a factor of 2.

12. (a) What is a one-to-one function? How can you tell if a function is one-to-one by looking at its graph?
(b) If f is a one-to-one function, how is its inverse function f^{-1} defined? How do you obtain the graph of f^{-1} from the graph of f?

13. (a) What is a parametric curve?
(b) How do you sketch a parametric curve?
(c) Why might a parametric curve be more useful than a curve of the form $y = f(x)$?

True-False Quiz

Determine whether the statement is true or false. If it is true, explain why. If it is false, explain why or give an example that disproves the statement.

1. If f is a function, then $f(s + t) = f(s) + f(t)$.

2. If $f(s) = f(t)$, then $s = t$.

3. If f is a function, then $f(3x) = 3f(x)$.

4. If $x_1 < x_2$ and f is a decreasing function, then $f(x_1) > f(x_2)$.

5. A vertical line intersects the graph of a function at most once.

6. If f and g are functions, then $f \circ g = g \circ f$.

7. If f is one-to-one, then $f^{-1}(x) = \dfrac{1}{f(x)}$.

8. You can always divide by e^x.

9. If $0 < a < b$, then $\ln a < \ln b$.

10. If $x > 0$, then $(\ln x)^6 = 6 \ln x$.

11. If $x > 0$ and $a > 1$, then $\dfrac{\ln x}{\ln a} = \ln \dfrac{x}{a}$.

12. The parametric equations $x = t^2$, $y = t^4$ have the same graph as $x = t^3$, $y = t^6$.

Exercises

1. Let f be the function whose graph is given.
   (a) Estimate the value of $f(2)$.
   (b) Estimate the values of x such that $f(x) = 3$.
   (c) State the domain of f.
   (d) State the range of f.
   (e) On what interval is f increasing?
   (f) Is f one-to-one? Explain.
   (g) Is f even, odd, or neither even nor odd? Explain.

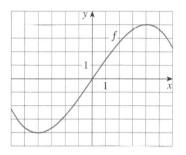

2. The graph of g is given.
   (a) State the value of $g(2)$.
   (b) Why is g one-to-one?
   (c) Estimate the value of $g^{-1}(2)$.
   (d) Estimate the domain of g^{-1}.
   (e) Sketch the graph of g^{-1}.

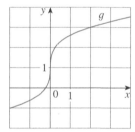

3. If $f(x) = x^2 - 2x + 3$, evaluate the difference quotient

$$\frac{f(a + h) - f(a)}{h}$$

4. Sketch a rough graph of the yield of a crop as a function of the amount of fertilizer used.

5–8 Find the domain and range of the function. Write your answer in interval notation.

5. $f(x) = 2/(3x - 1)$
6. $g(x) = \sqrt{16 - x^4}$
7. $h(x) = \ln(x + 6)$
8. $F(t) = 3 + \cos 2t$

9. Suppose that the graph of f is given. Describe how the graphs of the following functions can be obtained from the graph of f.
   (a) $y = f(x) + 8$ (b) $y = f(x + 8)$
   (c) $y = 1 + 2f(x)$ (d) $y = f(x - 2) - 2$
   (e) $y = -f(x)$ (f) $y = f^{-1}(x)$

10. The graph of f is given. Draw the graphs of the following functions.
   (a) $y = f(x - 8)$ (b) $y = -f(x)$
   (c) $y = 2 - f(x)$ (d) $y = \frac{1}{2}f(x) - 1$
   (e) $y = f^{-1}(x)$ (f) $y = f^{-1}(x + 3)$

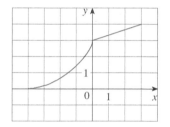

11–16 Use transformations to sketch the graph of the function.

11. $y = -\sin 2x$
12. $y = 3\ln(x - 2)$
13. $y = \frac{1}{2}(1 + e^x)$
14. $y = 2 - \sqrt{x}$
15. $f(x) = \dfrac{1}{x + 2}$
16. $f(x) = \begin{cases} -x & \text{if } x < 0 \\ e^x - 1 & \text{if } x \geq 0 \end{cases}$

17. Determine whether f is even, odd, or neither even nor odd.
   (a) $f(x) = 2x^5 - 3x^2 + 2$
   (b) $f(x) = x^3 - x^7$
   (c) $f(x) = e^{-x^2}$
   (d) $f(x) = 1 + \sin x$

18. Find an expression for the function whose graph consists of the line segment from the point $(-2, 2)$ to the point $(-1, 0)$ together with the top half of the circle with center the origin and radius 1.

19. If $f(x) = \ln x$ and $g(x) = x^2 - 9$, find the functions (a) $f \circ g$, (b) $g \circ f$, (c) $f \circ f$, (d) $g \circ g$, and their domains.

20. Express the function $F(x) = 1/\sqrt{x + \sqrt{x}}$ as a composition of three functions.

⌂ Graphing calculator or computer with graphing software required

21. Life expectancy improved dramatically in the 20th century. The table gives the life expectancy at birth (in years) of males born in the United States. Use a scatter plot to choose an appropriate type of model. Use your model to predict the life span of a male born in the year 2010.

Birth year	Life expectancy	Birth year	Life expectancy
1900	48.3	1960	66.6
1910	51.1	1970	67.1
1920	55.2	1980	70.0
1930	57.4	1990	71.8
1940	62.5	2000	73.0
1950	65.6		

22. A small-appliance manufacturer finds that it costs $9000 to produce 1000 toaster ovens a week and $12,000 to produce 1500 toaster ovens a week.
(a) Express the cost as a function of the number of toaster ovens produced, assuming that it is linear. Then sketch the graph.
(b) What is the slope of the graph and what does it represent?
(c) What is the y-intercept of the graph and what does it represent?

23. If $f(x) = 2x + \ln x$, find $f^{-1}(2)$.

24. Find the inverse function of $f(x) = \dfrac{x + 1}{2x + 1}$.

25. Find the exact value of each expression.
(a) $e^{2\ln 3}$
(b) $\log_{10} 25 + \log_{10} 4$

26. Solve each equation for x.
(a) $e^x = 5$
(b) $\ln x = 2$
(c) $e^{e^x} = 2$

27. The half-life of palladium-100, ^{100}Pd, is four days. (So half of any given quantity of ^{100}Pd will disintegrate in four days.) The initial mass of a sample is one gram.
(a) Find the mass that remains after 16 days.
(b) Find the mass $m(t)$ that remains after t days.
(c) Find the inverse of this function and explain its meaning.
(d) When will the mass be reduced to 0.01 g?

28. The population of a certain species in a limited environment with initial population 100 and carrying capacity 1000 is

$$P(t) = \frac{100{,}000}{100 + 900e^{-t}}$$

where t is measured in years.
(a) Graph this function and estimate how long it takes for the population to reach 900.

(b) Find the inverse of this function and explain its meaning.
(c) Use the inverse function to find the time required for the population to reach 900. Compare with the result of part (a).

29. Graph members of the family of functions $f(x) = \ln(x^2 - c)$ for several values of c. How does the graph change when c changes?

30. Graph the three functions $y = x^a$, $y = a^x$, and $y = \log_a x$ on the same screen for two or three values of $a > 1$. For large values of x, which of these functions has the largest values and which has the smallest values?

31. (a) Sketch the curve represented by the parametric equations $x = e^t$, $y = \sqrt{t}$, $0 \le t \le 1$, and indicate with an arrow the direction in which the curve is traced as t increases.
(b) Eliminate the parameter to find a Cartesian equation of the curve.

32. (a) Find parametric equations for the path of a particle that moves counterclockwise halfway around the circle $(x - 2)^2 + y^2 = 4$, from the top to the bottom.
(b) Use the equations from part (a) to graph the semicircular path.

33. Use parametric equations to graph the function

$$f(x) = 2x + \ln x$$

and its inverse function on the same screen.

34. (a) Find parametric equations for the set of all points P determined as shown in the figure such that $|OP| = |AB|$. (This curve is called the **cissoid of Diocles** after the Greek scholar Diocles, who introduced the cissoid as a graphical method for constructing the edge of a cube whose volume is twice that of a given cube.)
(b) Use the geometric description of the curve to draw a rough sketch of the curve by hand. Check your work by using the parametric equations to graph the curve.

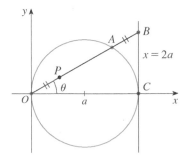

Principles of Problem Solving

There are no hard and fast rules that will ensure success in solving problems. However, it is possible to outline some general steps in the problem-solving process and to give some principles that may be useful in the solution of certain problems. These steps and principles are just common sense made explicit. They have been adapted from George Polya's book *How To Solve It*.

1 Understand the Problem

The first step is to read the problem and make sure that you understand it clearly. Ask yourself the following questions:

What is the unknown?

What are the given quantities?

What are the given conditions?

For many problems it is useful to

draw a diagram

and identify the given and required quantities on the diagram.

Usually it is necessary to

introduce suitable notation

In choosing symbols for the unknown quantities we often use letters such as a, b, c, m, n, x, and y, but in some cases it helps to use initials as suggestive symbols; for instance, V for volume or t for time.

2 Think of a Plan

Find a connection between the given information and the unknown that will enable you to calculate the unknown. It often helps to ask yourself explicitly: "How can I relate the given to the unknown?" If you don't see a connection immediately, the following ideas may be helpful in devising a plan.

Try to Recognize Something Familiar Relate the given situation to previous knowledge. Look at the unknown and try to recall a more familiar problem that has a similar unknown.

Try to Recognize Patterns Some problems are solved by recognizing that some kind of pattern is occurring. The pattern could be geometric, or numerical, or algebraic. If you can see regularity or repetition in a problem, you might be able to guess what the continuing pattern is and then prove it.

Use Analogy Try to think of an analogous problem, that is, a similar problem, a related problem, but one that is easier than the original problem. If you can solve the similar, simpler problem, then it might give you the clues you need to solve the original, more difficult problem. For instance, if a problem involves very large numbers, you could first try a similar problem with smaller numbers. Or if the problem involves three-dimensional geometry, you could look for a similar problem in two-dimensional geometry. Or if the problem you start with is a general one, you could first try a special case.

Introduce Something Extra It may sometimes be necessary to introduce something new, an auxiliary aid, to help make the connection between the given and the unknown. For instance, in a problem where a diagram is useful the auxiliary aid could be a new line drawn in a diagram. In a more algebraic problem it could be a new unknown that is related to the original unknown.

Take Cases   We may sometimes have to split a problem into several cases and give a different argument for each of the cases. For instance, we often have to use this strategy in dealing with absolute value.

Work Backward   Sometimes it is useful to imagine that your problem is solved and work backward, step by step, until you arrive at the given data. Then you may be able to reverse your steps and thereby construct a solution to the original problem. This procedure is commonly used in solving equations. For instance, in solving the equation $3x - 5 = 7$, we suppose that x is a number that satisfies $3x - 5 = 7$ and work backward. We add 5 to each side of the equation and then divide each side by 3 to get $x = 4$. Since each of these steps can be reversed, we have solved the problem.

Establish Subgoals   In a complex problem it is often useful to set subgoals (in which the desired situation is only partially fulfilled). If we can first reach these subgoals, then we may be able to build on them to reach our final goal.

Indirect Reasoning   Sometimes it is appropriate to attack a problem indirectly. In using proof by contradiction to prove that P implies Q, we assume that P is true and Q is false and try to see why this can't happen. Somehow we have to use this information and arrive at a contradiction to what we absolutely know is true.

Mathematical Induction   In proving statements that involve a positive integer n, it is frequently helpful to use the following principle.

Principle of Mathematical Induction   Let S_n be a statement about the positive integer n. Suppose that

1. S_1 is true.

2. S_{k+1} is true whenever S_k is true.

Then S_n is true for all positive integers n.

This is reasonable because, since S_1 is true, it follows from condition 2 (with $k = 1$) that S_2 is true. Then, using condition 2 with $k = 2$, we see that S_3 is true. Again using condition 2, this time with $k = 3$, we have that S_4 is true. This procedure can be followed indefinitely.

3 **Carry Out the Plan**

In Step 2 a plan was devised. In carrying out that plan we have to check each stage of the plan and write the details that prove that each stage is correct.

4 **Look Back**

Having completed our solution, it is wise to look back over it, partly to see if we have made errors in the solution and partly to see if we can think of an easier way to solve the problem. Another reason for looking back is that it will familiarize us with the method of solution and this may be useful for solving a future problem. Descartes said, "Every problem that I solved became a rule which served afterwards to solve other problems."

These principles of problem solving are illustrated in the following examples. Before you look at the solutions, try to solve these problems yourself, referring to these Principles of Problem Solving if you get stuck. You may find it useful to refer to this section from time to time as you solve the exercises in the remaining chapters of this book.

EXAMPLE 1 Express the hypotenuse h of a right triangle with area 25 m^2 as a function of its perimeter P.

PS Understand the problem

SOLUTION Let's first sort out the information by identifying the unknown quantity and the data:

$$\text{\textit{Unknown}: } \text{hypotenuse } h$$

$$\text{\textit{Given quantities}: } \text{perimeter } P, \text{ area 25 m}^2$$

PS Draw a diagram

It helps to draw a diagram and we do so in Figure 1.

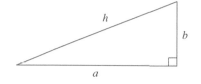

FIGURE 1

PS Connect the given with the unknown
PS Introduce something extra

In order to connect the given quantities to the unknown, we introduce two extra variables a and b, which are the lengths of the other two sides of the triangle. This enables us to express the given condition, which is that the triangle is right-angled, by the Pythagorean Theorem:

$$h^2 = a^2 + b^2$$

The other connections among the variables come by writing expressions for the area and perimeter:

$$25 = \tfrac{1}{2}ab \qquad P = a + b + h$$

Since P is given, notice that we now have three equations in the three unknowns a, b, and h:

$$\boxed{1} \qquad\qquad h^2 = a^2 + b^2$$

$$\boxed{2} \qquad\qquad 25 = \tfrac{1}{2}ab$$

$$\boxed{3} \qquad\qquad P = a + b + h$$

PS Relate to the familiar

Although we have the correct number of equations, they are not easy to solve in a straightforward fashion. But if we use the problem-solving strategy of trying to recognize something familiar, then we can solve these equations by an easier method. Look at the right sides of Equations 1, 2, and 3. Do these expressions remind you of anything familiar? Notice that they contain the ingredients of a familiar formula:

$$(a + b)^2 = a^2 + 2ab + b^2$$

Using this idea, we express $(a + b)^2$ in two ways. From Equations 1 and 2 we have

$$(a + b)^2 = (a^2 + b^2) + 2ab = h^2 + 4(25)$$

From Equation 3 we have

$$(a + b)^2 = (P - h)^2 = P^2 - 2Ph + h^2$$

Thus

$$h^2 + 100 = P^2 - 2Ph + h^2$$

$$2Ph = P^2 - 100$$

$$h = \frac{P^2 - 100}{2P}$$

This is the required expression for h as a function of P.

85

As the next example illustrates, it is often necessary to use the problem-solving principle of *taking cases* when dealing with absolute values.

EXAMPLE 2 Solve the inequality $|x - 3| + |x + 2| < 11$.

SOLUTION Recall the definition of absolute value:

$$|x| = \begin{cases} x & \text{if } x \geq 0 \\ -x & \text{if } x < 0 \end{cases}$$

It follows that

$$|x - 3| = \begin{cases} x - 3 & \text{if } x - 3 \geq 0 \\ -(x - 3) & \text{if } x - 3 < 0 \end{cases}$$

$$= \begin{cases} x - 3 & \text{if } x \geq 3 \\ -x + 3 & \text{if } x < 3 \end{cases}$$

Similarly

$$|x + 2| = \begin{cases} x + 2 & \text{if } x + 2 \geq 0 \\ -(x + 2) & \text{if } x + 2 < 0 \end{cases}$$

$$= \begin{cases} x + 2 & \text{if } x \geq -2 \\ -x - 2 & \text{if } x < -2 \end{cases}$$

PS Take cases

These expressions show that we must consider three cases:

$$x < -2 \qquad -2 \leq x < 3 \qquad x \geq 3$$

Case I If $x < -2$, we have

$$|x - 3| + |x + 2| < 11$$
$$-x + 3 - x - 2 < 11$$
$$-2x < 10$$
$$x > -5$$

Case II If $-2 \leq x < 3$, the given inequality becomes

$$-x + 3 + x + 2 < 11$$
$$5 < 11 \qquad \text{(always true)}$$

Case III If $x \geq 3$, the inequality becomes

$$x - 3 + x + 2 < 11$$
$$2x < 12$$
$$x < 6$$

Combining cases I, II, and III, we see that the inequality is satisfied when $-5 < x < 6$. So the solution is the interval $(-5, 6)$.

In the following example we first guess the answer by looking at special cases and recognizing a pattern. Then we prove our conjecture by mathematical induction.

In using the Principle of Mathematical Induction, we follow three steps:

Step 1 Prove that S_n is true when $n = 1$.

Step 2 Assume that S_n is true when $n = k$ and deduce that S_n is true when $n = k + 1$.

Step 3 Conclude that S_n is true for all n by the Principle of Mathematical Induction.

EXAMPLE 3 If $f_0(x) = x/(x + 1)$ and $f_{n+1} = f_0 \circ f_n$ for $n = 0, 1, 2, \ldots$, find a formula for $f_n(x)$.

PS Analogy: Try a similar, simpler problem

SOLUTION We start by finding formulas for $f_n(x)$ for the special cases $n = 1, 2,$ and 3.

$$f_1(x) = (f_0 \circ f_0)(x) = f_0(f_0(x)) = f_0\left(\frac{x}{x + 1}\right)$$

$$= \frac{\dfrac{x}{x + 1}}{\dfrac{x}{x + 1} + 1} = \frac{\dfrac{x}{x + 1}}{\dfrac{2x + 1}{x + 1}} = \frac{x}{2x + 1}$$

$$f_2(x) = (f_0 \circ f_1)(x) = f_0(f_1(x)) = f_0\left(\frac{x}{2x + 1}\right)$$

$$= \frac{\dfrac{x}{2x + 1}}{\dfrac{x}{2x + 1} + 1} = \frac{\dfrac{x}{2x + 1}}{\dfrac{3x + 1}{2x + 1}} = \frac{x}{3x + 1}$$

$$f_3(x) = (f_0 \circ f_2)(x) = f_0(f_2(x)) = f_0\left(\frac{x}{3x + 1}\right)$$

PS Look for a pattern

$$= \frac{\dfrac{x}{3x + 1}}{\dfrac{x}{3x + 1} + 1} = \frac{\dfrac{x}{3x + 1}}{\dfrac{4x + 1}{3x + 1}} = \frac{x}{4x + 1}$$

We notice a pattern: The coefficient of x in the denominator of $f_n(x)$ is $n + 1$ in the three cases we have computed. So we make the guess that, in general,

$$\boxed{4} \qquad\qquad f_n(x) = \frac{x}{(n + 1)x + 1}$$

To prove this, we use the Principle of Mathematical Induction. We have already verified that (4) is true for $n = 1$. Assume that it is true for $n = k$, that is,

$$f_k(x) = \frac{x}{(k + 1)x + 1}$$

Then
$$f_{k+1}(x) = (f_0 \circ f_k)(x) = f_0(f_k(x)) = f_0\left(\frac{x}{(k+1)x+1}\right)$$

$$= \frac{\dfrac{x}{(k+1)x+1}}{\dfrac{x}{(k+1)x+1}+1} = \frac{\dfrac{x}{(k+1)x+1}}{\dfrac{(k+2)x+1}{(k+1)x+1}} = \frac{x}{(k+2)x+1}$$

This expression shows that (4) is true for $n = k + 1$. Therefore, by mathematical induction, it is true for all positive integers n.

Problems

1. One of the legs of a right triangle has length 4 cm. Express the length of the altitude perpendicular to the hypotenuse as a function of the length of the hypotenuse.

2. The altitude perpendicular to the hypotenuse of a right triangle is 12 cm. Express the length of the hypotenuse as a function of the perimeter.

3. Solve the equation $|2x - 1| - |x + 5| = 3$.

4. Solve the inequality $|x - 1| - |x - 3| \geqslant 5$.

5. Sketch the graph of the function $f(x) = |x^2 - 4|x| + 3|$.

6. Sketch the graph of the function $g(x) = |x^2 - 1| - |x^2 - 4|$.

7. Draw the graph of the equation $x + |x| = y + |y|$.

8. Draw the graph of the equation $x^4 - 4x^2 - x^2y^2 + 4y^2 = 0$.

9. Sketch the region in the plane consisting of all points (x, y) such that $|x| + |y| \leqslant 1$.

10. Sketch the region in the plane consisting of all points (x, y) such that
$$|x - y| + |x| - |y| \leqslant 2$$

11. Evaluate $(\log_2 3)(\log_3 4)(\log_4 5) \cdots (\log_{31} 32)$.

12. (a) Show that the function $f(x) = \ln(x + \sqrt{x^2 + 1})$ is an odd function.
    (b) Find the inverse function of f.

13. Solve the inequality $\ln(x^2 - 2x - 2) \leqslant 0$.

14. Use indirect reasoning to prove that $\log_2 5$ is an irrational number.

15. A driver sets out on a journey. For the first half of the distance she drives at the leisurely pace of 30 mi/h; she drives the second half at 60 mi/h. What is her average speed on this trip?

16. Is it true that $f \circ (g + h) = f \circ g + f \circ h$?

17. Prove that if n is a positive integer, then $7^n - 1$ is divisible by 6.

18. Prove that $1 + 3 + 5 + \cdots + (2n - 1) = n^2$.

19. If $f_0(x) = x^2$ and $f_{n+1}(x) = f_0(f_n(x))$ for $n = 0, 1, 2, \ldots$, find a formula for $f_n(x)$.

20. (a) If $f_0(x) = \dfrac{1}{2 - x}$ and $f_{n+1} = f_0 \circ f_n$ for $n = 0, 1, 2, \ldots$, find an expression for $f_n(x)$ and use mathematical induction to prove it.

    (b) Graph f_0, f_1, f_2, f_3 on the same screen and describe the effects of repeated composition.

Graphing calculator or computer with graphing software required

2

Limits and Derivatives

In *A Preview of Calculus* (page 3) we saw how the idea of a limit underlies the various branches of calculus. Thus it is appropriate to begin our study of calculus by investigating limits and their properties. The special type of limit that is used to find tangents and velocities gives rise to the central idea in differential calculus, the derivative. We see how derivatives can be interpreted as rates of change in various situations and learn how the derivative of a function gives information about the original function.

2.1   The Tangent and Velocity Problems

In this section we see how limits arise when we attempt to find the tangent to a curve or the velocity of an object.

The Tangent Problem

The word *tangent* is derived from the Latin word *tangens*, which means "touching." Thus a tangent to a curve is a line that touches the curve. In other words, a tangent line should have the same direction as the curve at the point of contact. How can this idea be made precise?

For a circle we could simply follow Euclid and say that a tangent is a line that intersects the circle once and only once, as in Figure 1(a). For more complicated curves this definition is inadequate. Figure l(b) shows two lines l and t passing through a point P on a curve C. The line l intersects C only once, but it certainly does not look like what we think of as a tangent. The line t, on the other hand, looks like a tangent but it intersects C twice.

To be specific, let's look at the problem of trying to find a tangent line t to the parabola $y = x^2$ in the following example.

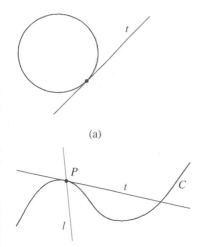

(a)

(b)

FIGURE 1

▼ **EXAMPLE 1**   Find an equation of the tangent line to the parabola $y = x^2$ at the point $P(1, 1)$.

SOLUTION   We will be able to find an equation of the tangent line t as soon as we know its slope m. The difficulty is that we know only one point, P, on t, whereas we need two points to compute the slope. But observe that we can compute an approximation to m by choosing a nearby point $Q(x, x^2)$ on the parabola (as in Figure 2) and computing the slope m_{PQ} of the secant line PQ. [A **secant line**, from the Latin word *secans*, meaning cutting, is a line that cuts (intersects) a curve more than once.]

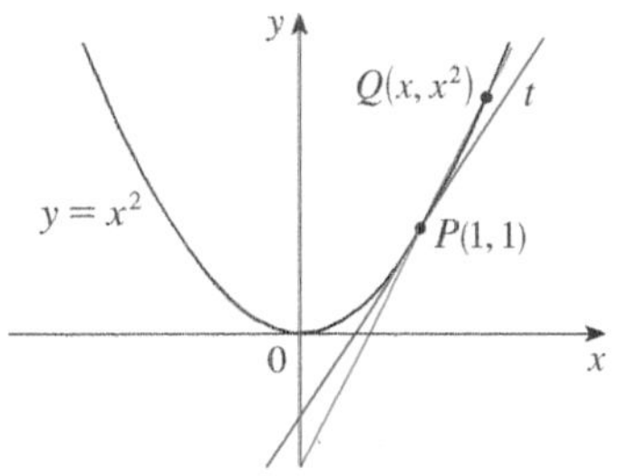

We choose $x \neq 1$ so that $Q \neq P$. Then

$$m_{PQ} = \frac{x^2 - 1}{x - 1}$$

For instance, for the point $Q(1.5, 2.25)$ we have

$$m_{PQ} = \frac{2.25 - 1}{1.5 - 1} = \frac{1.25}{0.5} = 2.5$$

FIGURE 2

x	m_{PQ}
2	3
1.5	2.5
1.1	2.1
1.01	2.01
1.001	2.001

x	m_{PQ}
0	1
0.5	1.5
0.9	1.9
0.99	1.99
0.999	1.999

The tables in the margin show the values of m_{PQ} for several values of x close to 1. The closer Q is to P, the closer x is to 1 and, it appears from the tables, the closer m_{PQ} is to 2. This suggests that the slope of the tangent line t should be $m = 2$.

We say that the slope of the tangent line is the *limit* of the slopes of the secant lines, and we express this symbolically by writing

$$\lim_{Q \to P} m_{PQ} = m \qquad \text{and} \qquad \lim_{x \to 1} \frac{x^2 - 1}{x - 1} = 2$$

Assuming that the slope of the tangent line is indeed 2, we use the point-slope form of the equation of a line (see Appendix B) to write the equation of the tangent line through (1, 1) as

$$y - 1 = 2(x - 1) \qquad \text{or} \qquad y = 2x - 1$$

Figure 3 illustrates the limiting process that occurs in this example. As Q approaches P along the parabola, the corresponding secant lines rotate about P and approach the tangent line t.

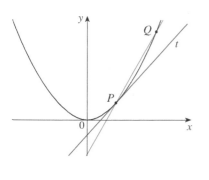
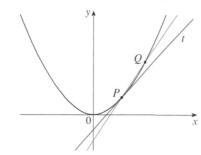
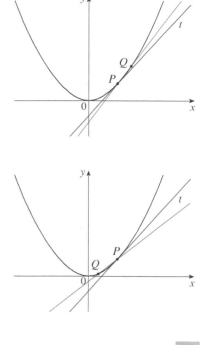

Q approaches P from the right

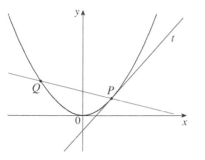
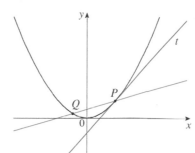

Q approaches P from the left

FIGURE 3

TEC In Visual 2.1 you can see how the process in Figure 3 works for additional functions.

t	Q
0.00	100.00
0.02	81.87
0.04	67.03
0.06	54.88
0.08	44.93
0.10	36.76

Many functions that occur in science are not described by explicit equations; they are defined by experimental data. The next example shows how to estimate the slope of the tangent line to the graph of such a function.

V EXAMPLE 2 Estimating the slope of a tangent line from experimental data The flash unit on a camera operates by storing charge on a capacitor and releasing it suddenly when the flash is set off. The data in the table describe the charge Q remaining on the capacitor (measured in microcoulombs) at time t (measured in seconds after the flash goes off). Use the data to draw the graph of this function and estimate the slope of the tangent line at the point where $t = 0.04$. [*Note:* The slope of the tangent line represents the electric current flowing from the capacitor to the flash bulb (measured in microamperes).]

SOLUTION In Figure 4 we plot the given data and use them to sketch a curve that approximates the graph of the function.

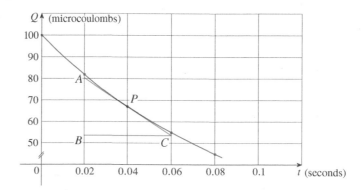

FIGURE 4

Given the points $P(0.04, 67.03)$ and $R(0.00, 100.00)$ on the graph, we find that the slope of the secant line PR is

$$m_{PR} = \frac{100.00 - 67.03}{0.00 - 0.04} = -824.25$$

R	m_{PR}
$(0.00, 100.00)$	-824.25
$(0.02, 81.87)$	-742.00
$(0.06, 54.88)$	-607.50
$(0.08, 44.93)$	-552.50
$(0.10, 36.76)$	-504.50

The table at the left shows the results of similar calculations for the slopes of other secant lines. From this table we would expect the slope of the tangent line at $t = 0.04$ to lie somewhere between -742 and -607.5. In fact, the average of the slopes of the two closest secant lines is

$$\tfrac{1}{2}(-742 - 607.5) = -674.75$$

So, by this method, we estimate the slope of the tangent line to be -675.

The physical meaning of the answer in Example 2 is that the electric current flowing from the capacitor to the flash bulb after 0.04 second is about –670 microamperes.

Another method is to draw an approximation to the tangent line at P and measure the sides of the triangle ABC, as in Figure 4. This gives an estimate of the slope of the tangent line as

$$-\frac{|AB|}{|BC|} \approx -\frac{80.4 - 53.6}{0.06 - 0.02} = -670$$

The Velocity Problem

If you watch the speedometer of a car as you travel in city traffic, you see that the needle doesn't stay still for very long; that is, the velocity of the car is not constant. We assume from watching the speedometer that the car has a definite velocity at each moment, but how is the "instantaneous" velocity defined? Let's investigate the example of a falling ball.

© 2003 Brand X Pictures / Jupiter Images / Fotosearch

The CN Tower in Toronto was the tallest freestanding building in the world for 32 years.

V **EXAMPLE 3**   **Velocity of a falling ball**   Suppose that a ball is dropped from the upper observation deck of the CN Tower in Toronto, 450 m above the ground. Find the velocity of the ball after 5 seconds.

SOLUTION   Through experiments carried out four centuries ago, Galileo discovered that the distance fallen by any freely falling body is proportional to the square of the time it has been falling. (This model for free fall neglects air resistance.) If the distance fallen after t seconds is denoted by $s(t)$ and measured in meters, then Galileo's law is expressed by the equation

$$s(t) = 4.9t^2$$

The difficulty in finding the velocity after 5 s is that we are dealing with a single instant of time ($t = 5$), so no time interval is involved. However, we can approximate the desired quantity by computing the average velocity over the brief time interval of a tenth of a second from $t = 5$ to $t = 5.1$:

$$\text{average velocity} = \frac{\text{change in position}}{\text{time elapsed}}$$

$$= \frac{s(5.1) - s(5)}{0.1}$$

$$= \frac{4.9(5.1)^2 - 4.9(5)^2}{0.1} = 49.49 \text{ m/s}$$

The following table shows the results of similar calculations of the average velocity over successively smaller time periods.

Time interval	Average velocity (m/s)
$5 \leqslant t \leqslant 6$	53.9
$5 \leqslant t \leqslant 5.1$	49.49
$5 \leqslant t \leqslant 5.05$	49.245
$5 \leqslant t \leqslant 5.01$	49.049
$5 \leqslant t \leqslant 5.001$	49.0049

It appears that as we shorten the time period, the average velocity is becoming closer to 49 m/s. The **instantaneous velocity** when $t = 5$ is defined to be the limiting value of these average velocities over shorter and shorter time periods that start at $t = 5$. Thus the (instantaneous) velocity after 5 s is

$$v = 49 \text{ m/s}$$

You may have the feeling that the calculations used in solving this problem are very similar to those used earlier in this section to find tangents. In fact, there is a close connection between the tangent problem and the problem of finding velocities. If we draw the graph of the distance function of the ball (as in Figure 5) and we consider the points $P(a, 4.9a^2)$ and $Q(a + h, 4.9(a + h)^2)$ on the graph, then the slope of the secant line PQ is

$$m_{PQ} = \frac{4.9(a + h)^2 - 4.9a^2}{(a + h) - a}$$

which is the same as the average velocity over the time interval $[a, a + h]$. Therefore the velocity at time $t = a$ (the limit of these average velocities as h approaches 0) must be equal to the slope of the tangent line at P (the limit of the slopes of the secant lines).

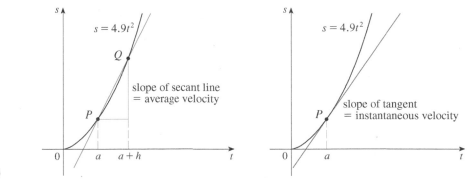

FIGURE 5

Examples 1 and 3 show that in order to solve tangent and velocity problems we must be able to find limits. After studying methods for computing limits in the next four sections, we will return to the problems of finding tangents and velocities in Section 2.6.

2.1 Exercises

1. A tank holds 1000 gallons of water, which drains from the bottom of the tank in half an hour. The values in the table show the volume V of water remaining in the tank (in gallons) after t minutes.

t (min)	5	10	15	20	25	30
V (gal)	694	444	250	111	28	0

(a) If P is the point $(15, 250)$ on the graph of V, find the slopes of the secant lines PQ when Q is the point on the graph with $t = 5, 10, 20, 25,$ and 30.

(b) Estimate the slope of the tangent line at P by averaging the slopes of two secant lines.

(c) Use a graph of the function to estimate the slope of the tangent line at P. (This slope represents the rate at which the water is flowing from the tank after 15 minutes.)

2. A cardiac monitor is used to measure the heart rate of a patient after surgery. It compiles the number of heartbeats after t minutes. When the data in the table are graphed, the slope of the tangent line represents the heart rate in beats per minute.

t (min)	36	38	40	42	44
Heartbeats	2530	2661	2806	2948	3080

The monitor estimates this value by calculating the slope of a secant line. Use the data to estimate the patient's heart rate after 42 minutes using the secant line between the points with the given values of t.

(a) $t = 36$ and $t = 42$ (b) $t = 38$ and $t = 42$
(c) $t = 40$ and $t = 42$ (d) $t = 42$ and $t = 44$

What are your conclusions?

3. The point $P\left(1, \frac{1}{2}\right)$ lies on the curve $y = x/(1 + x)$.

(a) If Q is the point $(x, x/(1 + x))$, use your calculator to find the slope of the secant line PQ (correct to six decimal places) for the following values of x:

(i) 0.5   (ii) 0.9   (iii) 0.99   (iv) 0.999
(v) 1.5   (vi) 1.1   (vii) 1.01   (viii) 1.001

(b) Using the results of part (a), guess the value of the slope of the tangent line to the curve at $P\left(1, \frac{1}{2}\right)$.

(c) Using the slope from part (b), find an equation of the tangent line to the curve at $P\left(1, \frac{1}{2}\right)$.

4. The point $P(0.5, 0)$ lies on the curve $y = \cos \pi x$.

(a) If Q is the point $(x, \cos \pi x)$, use your calculator to find the slope of the secant line PQ (correct to six decimal places) for the following values of x:

(i) 0   (ii) 0.4   (iii) 0.49   (iv) 0.499
(v) 1   (vi) 0.6   (vii) 0.51   (viii) 0.501

(b) Using the results of part (a), guess the value of the slope of the tangent line to the curve at $P(0.5, 0)$.

(c) Using the slope from part (b), find an equation of the tangent line to the curve at $P(0.5, 0)$.

(d) Sketch the curve, two of the secant lines, and the tangent line.

5. If a ball is thrown into the air with a velocity of 40 ft/s, its height in feet t seconds later is given by $y = 40t - 16t^2$.

(a) Find the average velocity for the time period beginning when $t = 2$ and lasting

(i) 0.5 second   (ii) 0.1 second
(iii) 0.05 second   (iv) 0.01 second

(b) Estimate the instantaneous velocity when $t = 2$.

6. If a rock is thrown upward on the planet Mars with a velocity of 10 m/s, its height in meters t seconds later is given by $y = 10t - 1.86t^2$.

(a) Find the average velocity over the given time intervals:

(i) [1, 2]   (ii) [1, 1.5]   (iii) [1, 1.1]
(iv) [1, 1.01]   (v) [1, 1.001]

(b) Estimate the instantaneous velocity when $t = 1$.

7. The table shows the position of a cyclist.

t (seconds)	0	1	2	3	4	5
s (meters)	0	1.4	5.1	10.7	17.7	25.8

(a) Find the average velocity for each time period:

(i) [1, 3]   (ii) [2, 3]   (iii) [3, 5]   (iv) [3, 4]

(b) Use the graph of s as a function of t to estimate the instantaneous velocity when $t = 3$.

8. The displacement (in centimeters) of a particle moving back and forth along a straight line is given by the equation of motion $s = 2 \sin \pi t + 3 \cos \pi t$, where t is measured in seconds.

(a) Find the average velocity during each time period:

(i) [1, 2]   (ii) [1, 1.1]
(iii) [1, 1.01]   (iv) [1, 1.001]

(b) Estimate the instantaneous velocity of the particle when $t = 1$.

9. The point $P(1, 0)$ lies on the curve $y = \sin(10\pi/x)$.

(a) If Q is the point $(x, \sin(10\pi/x))$, find the slope of the secant line PQ (correct to four decimal places) for $x = 2, 1.5, 1.4, 1.3, 1.2, 1.1, 0.5, 0.6, 0.7, 0.8,$ and 0.9. Do the slopes appear to be approaching a limit?

(b) Use a graph of the curve to explain why the slopes of the secant lines in part (a) are not close to the slope of the tangent line at P.

(c) By choosing appropriate secant lines, estimate the slope of the tangent line at P.

⌨ Graphing calculator or computer with graphing software required   **1.** Homework Hints available in TEC

2.2 The Limit of a Function

Having seen in the preceding section how limits arise when we want to find the tangent to a curve or the velocity of an object, we now turn our attention to limits in general and numerical and graphical methods for computing them.

Let's investigate the behavior of the function f defined by $f(x) = x^2 - x + 2$ for values of x near 2. The following table gives values of $f(x)$ for values of x close to 2 but not equal to 2.

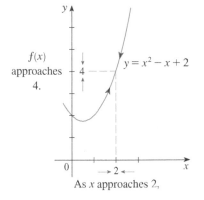

FIGURE 1

x	$f(x)$	x	$f(x)$
1.0	2.000000	3.0	8.000000
1.5	2.750000	2.5	5.750000
1.8	3.440000	2.2	4.640000
1.9	3.710000	2.1	4.310000
1.95	3.852500	2.05	4.152500
1.99	3.970100	2.01	4.030100
1.995	3.985025	2.005	4.015025
1.999	3.997001	2.001	4.003001

From the table and the graph of f (a parabola) shown in Figure 1 we see that when x is close to 2 (on either side of 2), $f(x)$ is close to 4. In fact, it appears that we can make the values of $f(x)$ as close as we like to 4 by taking x sufficiently close to 2. We express this by saying "the limit of the function $f(x) = x^2 - x + 2$ as x approaches 2 is equal to 4." The notation for this is

$$\lim_{x \to 2} (x^2 - x + 2) = 4$$

In general, we use the following notation.

---

1   **Definition**   We write

$$\lim_{x \to a} f(x) = L$$

and say   "the limit of $f(x)$, as x approaches a, equals L"

if we can make the values of $f(x)$ arbitrarily close to L (as close to L as we like) by taking x to be sufficiently close to a (on either side of a) but not equal to a.

Roughly speaking, this says that the values of $f(x)$ tend to get closer and closer to the number L as x gets closer and closer to the number a (from either side of a) but $x \neq a$.

An alternative notation for

$$\lim_{x \to a} f(x) = L$$

is $f(x) \to L$ as $x \to a$

which is usually read "$f(x)$ approaches L as x approaches a."

Notice the phrase "but $x \neq a$" in the definition of limit. This means that in finding the limit of $f(x)$ as x approaches a, we never consider $x = a$. In fact, $f(x)$ need not even be defined when $x = a$. The only thing that matters is how f is defined *near a*.

Figure 2 shows the graphs of three functions. Note that in part (c), $f(a)$ is not defined and in part (b), $f(a) \neq L$. But in each case, regardless of what happens at a, it is true that $\lim_{x \to a} f(x) = L$.

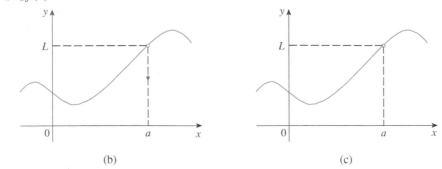

(a)   (b)   (c)

FIGURE 2 $\lim\limits_{x \to a} f(x) = L$ in all three cases

EXAMPLE 1 **Guessing a limit from numerical values**   Guess the value of $\lim\limits_{x \to 1} \dfrac{x-1}{x^2-1}$.

SOLUTION Notice that the function $f(x) = (x-1)/(x^2-1)$ is not defined when $x = 1$, but that doesn't matter because the definition of $\lim_{x \to a} f(x)$ says that we consider values of x that are close to a but not equal to a.

The tables at the left give values of $f(x)$ (correct to six decimal places) for values of x that approach 1 (but are not equal to 1). On the basis of the values in the tables, we make the guess that

$$\lim_{x \to 1} \frac{x-1}{x^2-1} = 0.5$$

$x < 1$	$f(x)$
0.5	0.666667
0.9	0.526316
0.99	0.502513
0.999	0.500250
0.9999	0.500025

$x > 1$	$f(x)$
1.5	0.400000
1.1	0.476190
1.01	0.497512
1.001	0.499750
1.0001	0.499975

Example 1 is illustrated by the graph of f in Figure 3. Now let's change f slightly by giving it the value 2 when $x = 1$ and calling the resulting function g:

$$g(x) = \begin{cases} \dfrac{x-1}{x^2-1} & \text{if } x \neq 1 \\ 2 & \text{if } x = 1 \end{cases}$$

This new function g still has the same limit as x approaches 1. (See Figure 4.)

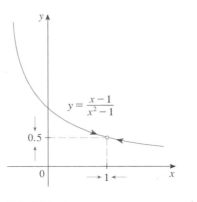

FIGURE 3

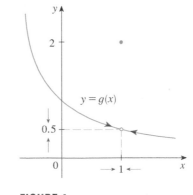

FIGURE 4

EXAMPLE 2 Estimate the value of $\displaystyle\lim_{t \to 0} \frac{\sqrt{t^2 + 9} - 3}{t^2}$.

SOLUTION The table lists values of the function for several values of t near 0.

t	$\dfrac{\sqrt{t^2 + 9} - 3}{t^2}$
± 1.0	0.16228
± 0.5	0.16553
± 0.1	0.16662
± 0.05	0.16666
± 0.01	0.16667

As t approaches 0, the values of the function seem to approach $0.1666666\ldots$ and so we guess that

$$\lim_{t \to 0} \frac{\sqrt{t^2 + 9} - 3}{t^2} = \frac{1}{6}$$

In Example 2 what would have happened if we had taken even smaller values of t? The table in the margin shows the results from one calculator; you can see that something strange seems to be happening.

If you try these calculations on your own calculator you might get different values, but eventually you will get the value 0 if you make t sufficiently small. Does this mean that the answer is really 0 instead of $\frac{1}{6}$? No, the value of the limit is $\frac{1}{6}$, as we will show in the next section. The problem is that the calculator gave false values because $\sqrt{t^2 + 9}$ is very close to 3 when t is small. (In fact, when t is sufficiently small, a calculator's value for $\sqrt{t^2 + 9}$ is $3.000\ldots$ to as many digits as the calculator is capable of carrying.)

Something similar happens when we try to graph the function

$$f(t) = \frac{\sqrt{t^2 + 9} - 3}{t^2}$$

t	$\dfrac{\sqrt{t^2 + 9} - 3}{t^2}$
± 0.0005	0.16800
± 0.0001	0.20000
± 0.00005	0.00000
± 0.00001	0.00000

www.stewartcalculus.com
For a further explanation of why calculators sometimes give false values, click on *Lies My Calculator and Computer Told Me.* In particular, see the section called *The Perils*

of Example 2 on a graphing calculator or computer. Parts (a) and (b) of Figure 5 show quite accurate graphs of f, and when we use the trace mode (if available) we can estimate easily that the limit is about $\frac{1}{6}$. But if we zoom in too much, as in parts (c) and (d), then we get inaccurate graphs, again because of problems with subtraction.

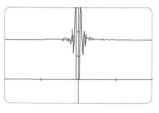 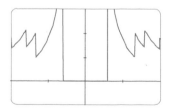

    (a) $[-5, 5]$ by $[-0.1, 0.3]$ (b) $[-0.1, 0.1]$ by $[-0.1, 0.3]$ (c) $[-10^{-6}, 10^{-6}]$ by $[-0.1, 0.3]$ (d) $[-10^{-7}, 10^{-7}]$ by $[-0.1, 0.3]$

FIGURE 5

V   **EXAMPLE 3**   Guess the value of $\lim\limits_{x \to 0} \dfrac{\sin x}{x}$.

SOLUTION   The function $f(x) = (\sin x)/x$ is not defined when $x = 0$. Using a calculator (and remembering that, if $x \in \mathbb{R}$, $\sin x$ means the sine of the angle whose *radian* measure is x), we construct a table of values correct to eight decimal places. From the table at the left and the graph in Figure 6 we guess that

$$\lim_{x \to 0} \frac{\sin x}{x} = 1$$

This guess is in fact correct, as will be proved in Chapter 3 using a geometric argument.

x	$\dfrac{\sin x}{x}$
± 1.0	0.84147098
± 0.5	0.95885108
± 0.4	0.97354586
± 0.3	0.98506736
± 0.2	0.99334665
± 0.1	0.99833417
± 0.05	0.99958339
± 0.01	0.99998333
± 0.005	0.99999583
± 0.001	0.99999983

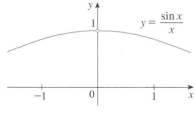

FIGURE 6

V   **EXAMPLE 4**   **A function with oscillating behavior**   Investigate $\lim\limits_{x \to 0} \sin \dfrac{\pi}{x}$.

SOLUTION   Again the function $f(x) = \sin(\pi/x)$ is undefined at 0. Evaluating the function for some small values of x, we get

$$f(1) = \sin \pi = 0 \qquad\qquad f(\tfrac{1}{2}) = \sin 2\pi = 0$$

$$f(\tfrac{1}{3}) = \sin 3\pi = 0 \qquad\qquad f(\tfrac{1}{4}) = \sin 4\pi = 0$$

$$f(0.1) = \sin 10\pi = 0 \qquad\qquad f(0.01) = \sin 100\pi = 0$$

Similarly, $f(0.001) = f(0.0001) = 0$. On the basis of this information we might be tempted to guess that

$$\lim_{x \to 0} \sin \frac{\pi}{x} = 0$$

⊘ but this time our guess is wrong. Note that although $f(1/n) = \sin n\pi = 0$ for any integer n, it is also true that $f(x) = 1$ for infinitely many values of x that approach 0. The graph of f is given in Figure 7.

Computer Algebra Systems

Computer algebra systems (CAS) have commands that compute limits. In order to avoid the types of pitfalls demonstrated in Examples 2, 4, and 5, they don't find limits by numerical experimentation. Instead, they use more sophisticated techniques such as computing infinite series. If you have access to a CAS, use the limit command to compute the limits in the examples of this section and to check your answers in the exercises of this chapter.

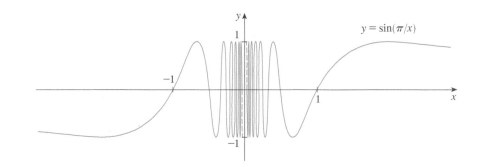

FIGURE 7

The dashed lines near the y-axis indicate that the values of $\sin(\pi/x)$ oscillate between 1 and -1 infinitely often as x approaches 0. (Use a graphing device to graph f and zoom in toward the origin several times. What do you observe?)

Since the values of $f(x)$ do not approach a fixed number as x approaches 0,

$$\lim_{x \to 0} \sin \frac{\pi}{x} \quad \text{does not exist}$$

EXAMPLE 5 Find $\displaystyle\lim_{x \to 0} \left(x^3 + \frac{\cos 5x}{10{,}000} \right)$.

SOLUTION As before, we construct a table of values. From the first table in the margin it appears that

$$\lim_{x \to 0} \left(x^3 + \frac{\cos 5x}{10{,}000} \right) = 0$$

But if we persevere with smaller values of x, the second table suggests that

$$\lim_{x \to 0} \left(x^3 + \frac{\cos 5x}{10{,}000} \right) = 0.000100 = \frac{1}{10{,}000}$$

Later we will see that $\lim_{x \to 0} \cos 5x = 1$; then it follows that the limit is 0.0001.

⊘   Examples 4 and 5 illustrate some of the pitfalls in guessing the value of a limit. It is easy to guess the wrong value if we use inappropriate values of x, but it is difficult to know when to stop calculating values. And, as the discussion after Example 2 shows, sometimes calculators and computers give the wrong values. In the next section, however, we will develop foolproof methods for calculating limits.

▼   **EXAMPLE 6   A limit that does not exist**   The Heaviside function H is defined by

$$H(t) = \begin{cases} 0 & \text{if } t < 0 \\ 1 & \text{if } t \geqslant 0 \end{cases}$$

[This function is named after the electrical engineer Oliver Heaviside (1850–1925) and can be used to describe an electric current that is switched on at time $t = 0$.] Its graph is shown in Figure 8.

As t approaches 0 from the left, $H(t)$ approaches 0. As t approaches 0 from the right, $H(t)$ approaches 1. There is no single number that $H(t)$ approaches as t approaches 0. Therefore, $\lim_{t \to 0} H(t)$ does not exist.

One-Sided Limits

We noticed in Example 6 that $H(t)$ approaches 0 as t approaches 0 from the left and $H(t)$ approaches 1 as t approaches 0 from the right. We indicate this situation symbolically by writing

$$\lim_{t \to 0^-} H(t) = 0 \qquad \text{and} \qquad \lim_{t \to 0^+} H(t) = 1$$

The symbol "$t \to 0^-$" indicates that we consider only values of t that are less than 0. Likewise, "$t \to 0^+$" indicates that we consider only values of t that are greater than 0.

x	$x^3 + \dfrac{\cos 5x}{10{,}000}$
1	1.000028
0.5	0.124920
0.1	0.001088
0.05	0.000222
0.01	0.000101

x	$x^3 + \dfrac{\cos 5x}{10{,}000}$
0.005	0.00010009
0.001	0.00010000

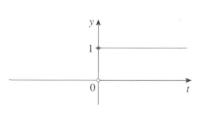

FIGURE 8
The Heaviside function

> **2** **Definition** We write
>
> $$\lim_{x \to a^-} f(x) = L$$
>
> and say the **left-hand limit of** $f(x)$ **as** x **approaches** a [or the **limit of** $f(x)$ **as** x **approaches** a **from the left**] is equal to L if we can make the values of $f(x)$ arbitrarily close to L by taking x to be sufficiently close to a and x less than a.

Notice that Definition 2 differs from Definition 1 only in that we require x to be less than a. Similarly, if we require that x be greater than a, we get "the **right-hand limit of** $f(x)$ **as** x **approaches** a is equal to L" and we write

$$\lim_{x \to a^+} f(x) = L$$

Thus the symbol "$x \to a^+$" means that we consider only $x > a$. These definitions are illustrated in Figure 9.

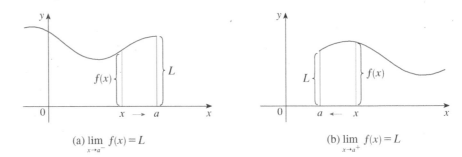

FIGURE 9

(a) $\lim_{x \to a^-} f(x) = L$

(b) $\lim_{x \to a^+} f(x) = L$

By comparing Definition 1 with the definitions of one-sided limits, we see that the following is true.

> **3** $$\lim_{x \to a} f(x) = L \quad \text{if and only if} \quad \lim_{x \to a^-} f(x) = L \quad \text{and} \quad \lim_{x \to a^+} f(x) = L$$

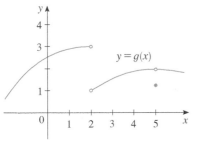

FIGURE 10

V **EXAMPLE 7** **One-sided limits from a graph** The graph of a function g is shown in Figure 10. Use it to state the values (if they exist) of the following:

(a) $\lim_{x \to 2^-} g(x)$ (b) $\lim_{x \to 2^+} g(x)$ (c) $\lim_{x \to 2} g(x)$

(d) $\lim_{x \to 5^-} g(x)$ (e) $\lim_{x \to 5^+} g(x)$ (f) $\lim_{x \to 5} g(x)$

SOLUTION From the graph we see that the values of $g(x)$ approach 3 as x approaches 2 from the left, but they approach 1 as x approaches 2 from the right. Therefore

(a) $\lim_{x \to 2^-} g(x) = 3$ and   (b) $\lim_{x \to 2^+} g(x) = 1$

(c) Since the left and right limits are different, we conclude from (3) that $\lim_{x \to 2} g(x)$ does not exist.

The graph also shows that

(d) $\lim_{x \to 5^-} g(x) = 2$ and   (e) $\lim_{x \to 5^+} g(x) = 2$

(f) This time the left and right limits are the same and so, by (3), we have

$$\lim_{x \to 5} g(x) = 2$$

Despite this fact, notice that $g(5) \neq 2$.

EXAMPLE 8 Find $\lim_{x \to 0} \dfrac{1}{x^2}$ if it exists.

SOLUTION As x becomes close to 0, x^2 also becomes close to 0, and $1/x^2$ becomes very large. (See the table in the margin.) In fact, it appears from the graph of the function $f(x) = 1/x^2$ shown in Figure 11 that the values of $f(x)$ can be made arbitrarily large by taking x close enough to 0. Thus the values of $f(x)$ do not approach a number, so $\lim_{x \to 0} (1/x^2)$ does not exist.

x	$\dfrac{1}{x^2}$
± 1	1
± 0.5	4
± 0.2	25
± 0.1	100
± 0.05	400
± 0.01	10,000
± 0.001	1,000,000

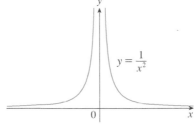

FIGURE 11

At the beginning of this section we considered the function $f(x) = x^2 - x + 2$ and, based on numerical and graphical evidence, we saw that

$$\lim_{x \to 2} (x^2 - x + 2) = 4$$

According to Definition 1, this means that the values of $f(x)$ can be made as close to 4 as we like, provided that we take x sufficiently close to 2. In the following example we use graphical methods to determine just how close is sufficiently close.

EXAMPLE 9 If $f(x) = x^2 - x + 2$, how close to 2 does x have to be to ensure that $f(x)$ is within a distance 0.1 of the number 4?

SOLUTION If the distance from $f(x)$ to 4 is less than 0.1, then $f(x)$ lies between 3.9 and 4.1, so the requirement is that

$$3.9 < x^2 - x + 2 < 4.1$$

Thus we need to determine the values of x such that the curve $y = x^2 - x + 2$ lies between the horizontal lines $y = 3.9$ and $y = 4.1$. We graph the curve and lines near the point $(2, 4)$ in Figure 12. With the cursor, we estimate that the x-coordinate of the point of intersection of the line $y = 3.9$ and the curve $y = x^2 - x + 2$ is about 1.966. Similarly, the curve intersects the line $y = 4.1$ when $x \approx 2.033$. So, rounding to be safe, we conclude that

$$3.9 < x^2 - x + 2 < 4.1 \quad \text{when} \quad 1.97 < x < 2.03$$

Therefore $f(x)$ is within a distance 0.1 of 4 when x is within a distance 0.03 of 2.

The idea behind Example 9 can be used to formulate the precise definition of a limit that is discussed in Appendix D.

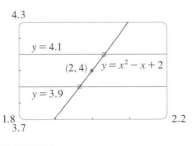

FIGURE 12

2.2 Exercises

1. Explain in your own words what is meant by the equation

$$\lim_{x \to 2} f(x) = 5$$

Is it possible for this statement to be true and yet $f(2) = 3$?
Explain.

2. Explain what it means to say that

$$\lim_{x \to 1^-} f(x) = 3 \quad \text{and} \quad \lim_{x \to 1^+} f(x) = 7$$

In this situation is it possible that $\lim_{x \to 1} f(x)$ exists?
Explain.

3. Use the given graph of f to state the value of each quantity, if it exists. If it does not exist, explain why.
  (a) $\lim\limits_{x \to 1^-} f(x)$ (b) $\lim\limits_{x \to 1^+} f(x)$ (c) $\lim\limits_{x \to 1} f(x)$

  (d) $\lim\limits_{x \to 5} f(x)$ (e) $f(5)$

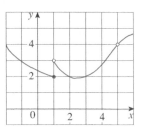

4. For the function f whose graph is given, state the value of each quantity, if it exists. If it does not exist, explain why.
  (a) $\lim\limits_{x \to 0} f(x)$ (b) $\lim\limits_{x \to 3^-} f(x)$ (c) $\lim\limits_{x \to 3^+} f(x)$

  (d) $\lim\limits_{x \to 3} f(x)$ (e) $f(3)$

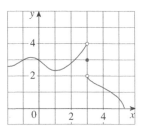

5. For the function g whose graph is given, state the value of each quantity, if it exists. If it does not exist, explain why.
  (a) $\lim\limits_{t \to 0^-} g(t)$ (b) $\lim\limits_{t \to 0^+} g(t)$ (c) $\lim\limits_{t \to 0} g(t)$

  (d) $\lim\limits_{t \to 2^-} g(t)$ (e) $\lim\limits_{t \to 2^+} g(t)$ (f) $\lim\limits_{t \to 2} g(t)$

  (g) $g(2)$ (h) $\lim\limits_{t \to 4} g(t)$

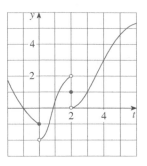

6. For the function h whose graph is given, state the value of each quantity, if it exists. If it does not exist, explain why.
  (a) $\lim\limits_{x \to -3^-} h(x)$ (b) $\lim\limits_{x \to -3^+} h(x)$ (c) $\lim\limits_{x \to -3} h(x)$

  (d) $h(-3)$ (e) $\lim\limits_{x \to 0^-} h(x)$ (f) $\lim\limits_{x \to 0^+} h(x)$

  (g) $\lim\limits_{x \to 0} h(x)$ (h) $h(0)$ (i) $\lim\limits_{x \to 2} h(x)$

  (j) $h(2)$ (k) $\lim\limits_{x \to 5^+} h(x)$ (l) $\lim\limits_{x \to 5^-} h(x)$

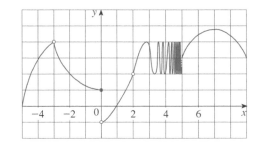

7–8 Sketch the graph of the function and use it to determine the values of a for which $\lim_{x \to a} f(x)$ exists.

7. $f(x) = \begin{cases} 1 + x & \text{if } x < -1 \\ x^2 & \text{if } -1 \leqslant x < 1 \\ 2 - x & \text{if } x \geqslant 1 \end{cases}$

8. $f(x) = \begin{cases} 1 + \sin x & \text{if } x < 0 \\ \cos x & \text{if } 0 \leqslant x \leqslant \pi \\ \sin x & \text{if } x > \pi \end{cases}$

9–11 Use the graph of the function f to state the value of each limit, if it exists. If it does not exist, explain why.
  (a) $\lim\limits_{x \to 0^-} f(x)$ (b) $\lim\limits_{x \to 0^+} f(x)$ (c) $\lim\limits_{x \to 0} f(x)$

9. $f(x) = \dfrac{1}{1 + e^{1/x}}$ **10.** $f(x) = \dfrac{x^2 + x}{\sqrt{x^3 + x^2}}$

Graphing calculator or computer with graphing software required   **1.** Homework Hints available in TEC

11. $f(x) = \dfrac{\sqrt{2 - 2\cos 2x}}{x}$

---

12. A patient receives a 150-mg injection of a drug every 4 hours. The graph shows the amount $f(t)$ of the drug in the bloodstream after t hours. Find

$$\lim_{t \to 12^-} f(t) \qquad \text{and} \qquad \lim_{t \to 12^+} f(t)$$

and explain the significance of these one-sided limits.

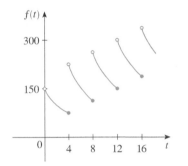

13–16 Sketch the graph of an example of a function f that satisfies all of the given conditions.

13. $\lim_{x \to 0^-} f(x) = -1$, $\quad \lim_{x \to 0^+} f(x) = 2$, $\quad f(0) = 1$

14. $\lim_{x \to 0} f(x) = 1$, $\quad \lim_{x \to 3^-} f(x) = -2$, $\quad \lim_{x \to 3^+} f(x) = 2$,
$f(0) = -1$, $\quad f(3) = 1$

15. $\lim_{x \to 3^+} f(x) = 4$, $\quad \lim_{x \to 3^-} f(x) = 2$, $\quad \lim_{x \to -2} f(x) = 2$,
$f(3) = 3$, $\quad f(-2) = 1$

16. $\lim_{x \to 0^-} f(x) = 2$, $\quad \lim_{x \to 0^+} f(x) = 0$, $\quad \lim_{x \to 4^-} f(x) = 3$,
$\lim_{x \to 4^+} f(x) = 0$, $\quad f(0) = 2$, $\quad f(4) = 1$

17–20 Guess the value of the limit (if it exists) by evaluating the function at the given numbers (correct to six decimal places).

17. $\lim_{x \to 2} \dfrac{x^2 - 2x}{x^2 - x - 2}$, $\quad x = 2.5, 2.1, 2.05, 2.01, 2.005, 2.001,$
$1.9, 1.95, 1.99, 1.995, 1.999$

18. $\lim_{x \to -1} \dfrac{x^2 - 2x}{x^2 - x - 2}$,
$x = 0, -0.5, -0.9, -0.95, -0.99, -0.999,$
$-2, -1.5, -1.1, -1.01, -1.001$

19. $\lim_{t \to 0} \dfrac{e^{5t} - 1}{t}$, $\quad t = \pm 0.5, \pm 0.1, \pm 0.01, \pm 0.001, \pm 0.0001$

20. $\lim_{h \to 0} \dfrac{(2 + h)^5 - 32}{h}$,
$h = \pm 0.5, \pm 0.1, \pm 0.01, \pm 0.001, \pm 0.0001$

21–24 Use a table of values to estimate the value of the limit. If you have a graphing device, use it to confirm your result graphically.

21. $\lim_{x \to 0} \dfrac{\sqrt{x + 4} - 2}{x}$

22. $\lim_{x \to 0} \dfrac{\tan 3x}{\tan 5x}$

23. $\lim_{x \to 1} \dfrac{x^6 - 1}{x^{10} - 1}$

24. $\lim_{x \to 0} \dfrac{9^x - 5^x}{x}$

---

25. (a) By graphing the function $f(x) = (\cos 2x - \cos x)/x^2$ and zooming in toward the point where the graph crosses the y-axis, estimate the value of $\lim_{x \to 0} f(x)$.
(b) Check your answer in part (a) by evaluating $f(x)$ for values of x that approach 0.

26. (a) Estimate the value of

$$\lim_{x \to 0} \dfrac{\sin x}{\sin \pi x}$$

by graphing the function $f(x) = (\sin x)/(\sin \pi x)$. State your answer correct to two decimal places.
(b) Check your answer in part (a) by evaluating $f(x)$ for values of x that approach 0.

27. (a) Estimate the value of the limit $\lim_{x \to 0} (1 + x)^{1/x}$ to five decimal places. Does this number look familiar?
(b) Illustrate part (a) by graphing the function $y = (1 + x)^{1/x}$.

28. The slope of the tangent line to the graph of the exponential function $y = 2^x$ at the point $(0, 1)$ is $\lim_{x \to 0} (2^x - 1)/x$. Estimate the slope to three decimal places.

29. (a) Evaluate the function $f(x) = x^2 - (2^x/1000)$ for $x = 1$, $0.8, 0.6, 0.4, 0.2, 0.1,$ and 0.05, and guess the value of

$$\lim_{x \to 0} \left(x^2 - \dfrac{2^x}{1000} \right)$$

(b) Evaluate $f(x)$ for $x = 0.04, 0.02, 0.01, 0.005, 0.003,$ and 0.001. Guess again.

30. (a) Evaluate $h(x) = (\tan x - x)/x^3$ for $x = 1, 0.5, 0.1, 0.05,$ $0.01,$ and 0.005.
(b) Guess the value of $\lim_{x \to 0} \dfrac{\tan x - x}{x^3}$.
(c) Evaluate $h(x)$ for successively smaller values of x until you finally reach a value of 0 for $h(x)$. Are you still confident that your guess in part (b) is correct? Explain why you eventually obtained 0 values. (In Section 4.5 a method for evaluating the limit will be explained.)
(d) Graph the function h in the viewing rectangle $[-1, 1]$ by $[0, 1]$. Then zoom in toward the point where the graph

crosses the y-axis to estimate the limit of $h(x)$ as x approaches 0. Continue to zoom in until you observe distortions in the graph of h. Compare with the results of part (c).

31. Use a graph to determine how close to 2 we have to take x to ensure that $x^3 - 3x + 4$ is within a distance 0.2 of the number 6. What if we insist that $x^3 - 3x + 4$ be within 0.1 of 6?

32. (a) Use numerical and graphical evidence to guess the value of the limit

$$\lim_{x \to 1} \frac{x^3 - 1}{\sqrt{x} - 1}$$

(b) How close to 1 does x have to be to ensure that the function in part (a) is within a distance 0.5 of its limit?

2.3 Calculating Limits Using the Limit Laws

In Section 2.2 we used calculators and graphs to guess the values of limits, but we saw that such methods don't always lead to the correct answer. In this section we use the following properties of limits, called the *Limit Laws*, to calculate limits.

Limit Laws   Suppose that c is a constant and the limits

$$\lim_{x \to a} f(x) \qquad \text{and} \qquad \lim_{x \to a} g(x)$$

exist. Then

1. $\lim\limits_{x \to a} [f(x) + g(x)] = \lim\limits_{x \to a} f(x) + \lim\limits_{x \to a} g(x)$

2. $\lim\limits_{x \to a} [f(x) - g(x)] = \lim\limits_{x \to a} f(x) - \lim\limits_{x \to a} g(x)$

3. $\lim\limits_{x \to a} [cf(x)] = c \lim\limits_{x \to a} f(x)$

4. $\lim\limits_{x \to a} [f(x)g(x)] = \lim\limits_{x \to a} f(x) \cdot \lim\limits_{x \to a} g(x)$

5. $\lim\limits_{x \to a} \dfrac{f(x)}{g(x)} = \dfrac{\lim\limits_{x \to a} f(x)}{\lim\limits_{x \to a} g(x)} \quad$ if $\lim\limits_{x \to a} g(x) \neq 0$

These five laws can be stated verbally as follows:

Sum Law

1. The limit of a sum is the sum of the limits.

Difference Law

2. The limit of a difference is the difference of the limits.

Constant Multiple Law

3. The limit of a constant times a function is the constant times the limit of the function.

Product Law

4. The limit of a product is the product of the limits.

Quotient Law

5. The limit of a quotient is the quotient of the limits (provided that the limit of the denominator is not 0).

It is easy to believe that these properties are true. For instance, if $f(x)$ is close to L and $g(x)$ is close to M, it is reasonable to conclude that $f(x) + g(x)$ is close to $L + M$. This gives us an intuitive basis for believing that Law 1 is true. All of these laws can be proved using the precise definition of a limit. In Appendix E we give the proof of Law 1.

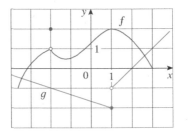

FIGURE 1

EXAMPLE 1 Use the Limit Laws and the graphs of f and g in Figure 1 to evaluate the following limits, if they exist.

(a) $\lim_{x \to -2} [f(x) + 5g(x)]$ (b) $\lim_{x \to 1} [f(x)g(x)]$ (c) $\lim_{x \to 2} \dfrac{f(x)}{g(x)}$

SOLUTION

(a) From the graphs of f and g we see that

$$\lim_{x \to -2} f(x) = 1 \quad \text{and} \quad \lim_{x \to -2} g(x) = -1$$

Therefore we have

$$\lim_{x \to -2} [f(x) + 5g(x)] = \lim_{x \to -2} f(x) + \lim_{x \to -2} [5g(x)] \quad \text{(by Law 1)}$$

$$= \lim_{x \to -2} f(x) + 5 \lim_{x \to -2} g(x) \quad \text{(by Law 3)}$$

$$= 1 + 5(-1) = -4$$

(b) We see that $\lim_{x \to 1} f(x) = 2$. But $\lim_{x \to 1} g(x)$ does not exist because the left and right limits are different:

$$\lim_{x \to 1^-} g(x) = -2 \qquad \lim_{x \to 1^+} g(x) = -1$$

So we can't use Law 4 for the desired limit. But we *can* use Law 4 for the one-sided limits:

$$\lim_{x \to 1^-} [f(x)g(x)] = 2 \cdot (-2) = -4 \qquad \lim_{x \to 1^+} [f(x)g(x)] = 2 \cdot (-1) = -2$$

The left and right limits aren't equal, so $\lim_{x \to 1} [f(x)g(x)]$ does not exist.

(c) The graphs show that

$$\lim_{x \to 2} f(x) \approx 1.4 \quad \text{and} \quad \lim_{x \to 2} g(x) = 0$$

Because the limit of the denominator is 0, we can't use Law 5. The given limit does not exist because the denominator approaches 0 while the numerator approaches a nonzero number. ▬

If we use the Product Law repeatedly with $g(x) = f(x)$, we obtain the following law.

Power Law

6. $\lim_{x \to a} [f(x)]^n = \left[\lim_{x \to a} f(x)\right]^n$ where n is a positive integer

In applying these six limit laws, we need to use two special limits:

7. $\lim_{x \to a} c = c$ **8.** $\lim_{x \to a} x = a$

These limits are obvious from an intuitive point of view (state them in words or draw graphs of $y = c$ and $y = x$).

If we now put $f(x) = x$ in Law 6 and use Law 8, we get another useful special limit.

9. $\lim_{x \to a} x^n = a^n$ where n is a positive integer

A similar limit holds for roots as follows.

---

10. $\lim_{x \to a} \sqrt[n]{x} = \sqrt[n]{a}$ where n is a positive integer

(If n is even, we assume that $a > 0$.)

More generally, we have the following law.

Root Law

---

11. $\lim_{x \to a} \sqrt[n]{f(x)} = \sqrt[n]{\lim_{x \to a} f(x)}$ where n is a positive integer

$\left[\text{If } n \text{ is even, we assume that } \lim_{x \to a} f(x) > 0.\right]$

EXAMPLE 2 Evaluate the following limits and justify each step.

(a) $\lim_{x \to 5} (2x^2 - 3x + 4)$

(b) $\lim_{x \to -2} \dfrac{x^3 + 2x^2 - 1}{5 - 3x}$

SOLUTION

(a) $\quad \lim_{x \to 5} (2x^2 - 3x + 4) = \lim_{x \to 5} (2x^2) - \lim_{x \to 5} (3x) + \lim_{x \to 5} 4$ (by Laws 2 and 1)

$\qquad\qquad\qquad\qquad\qquad = 2 \lim_{x \to 5} x^2 - 3 \lim_{x \to 5} x + \lim_{x \to 5} 4$ (by 3)

$\qquad\qquad\qquad\qquad\qquad = 2(5^2) - 3(5) + 4$ (by 9, 8, and 7)

$\qquad\qquad\qquad\qquad\qquad = 39$

(b) We start by using Law 5, but its use is fully justified only at the final stage when we see that the limits of the numerator and denominator exist and the limit of the denominator is not 0.

$\lim_{x \to -2} \dfrac{x^3 + 2x^2 - 1}{5 - 3x} = \dfrac{\lim\limits_{x \to -2} (x^3 + 2x^2 - 1)}{\lim\limits_{x \to -2} (5 - 3x)}$ (by Law 5)

$\qquad\qquad\qquad\quad = \dfrac{\lim\limits_{x \to -2} x^3 + 2 \lim\limits_{x \to -2} x^2 - \lim\limits_{x \to -2} 1}{\lim\limits_{x \to -2} 5 - 3 \lim\limits_{x \to -2} x}$ (by 1, 2, and 3)

$\qquad\qquad\qquad\quad = \dfrac{(-2)^3 + 2(-2)^2 - 1}{5 - 3(-2)}$ (by 9, 8, and 7)

$\qquad\qquad\qquad\quad = -\dfrac{1}{11}$

Note: If we let $f(x) = 2x^2 - 3x + 4$, then $f(5) = 39$. In other words, we would have gotten the correct answer in Example 2(a) by substituting 5 for x. Similarly, direct substitution provides the correct answer in part (b). The functions in Example 2 are a polynomial and a rational function, respectively, and similar use of the Limit Laws proves that direct substitution always works for such functions (see Exercises 43 and 44). We state this fact as follows.

> **Direct Substitution Property** If f is a polynomial or a rational function and a is in the domain of f, then
>
> $$\lim_{x \to a} f(x) = f(a)$$

Functions with the Direct Substitution Property are called *continuous at a* and will be studied in Section 2.4. However, not all limits can be evaluated by direct substitution, as the following examples show.

EXAMPLE 3 **Direct substitution doesn't always work** Find $\lim\limits_{x \to 1} \dfrac{x^2 - 1}{x - 1}$.

SOLUTION Let $f(x) = (x^2 - 1)/(x - 1)$. We can't find the limit by substituting $x = 1$ because $f(1)$ isn't defined. Nor can we apply the Quotient Law, because the limit of the denominator is 0. Instead, we need to do some preliminary algebra. We factor the numerator as a difference of squares:

$$\frac{x^2 - 1}{x - 1} = \frac{(x - 1)(x + 1)}{x - 1}$$

The numerator and denominator have a common factor of $x - 1$. When we take the limit as x approaches 1, we have $x \neq 1$ and so $x - 1 \neq 0$. Therefore, we can cancel the common factor and compute the limit as follows:

$$\lim_{x \to 1} \frac{x^2 - 1}{x - 1} = \lim_{x \to 1} \frac{(x - 1)(x + 1)}{x - 1}$$

$$= \lim_{x \to 1} (x + 1)$$

$$= 1 + 1 = 2$$

The limit in this example arose in Section 2.1 when we were trying to find the tangent to the parabola $y = x^2$ at the point $(1, 1)$.

Note: In Example 3 we were able to compute the limit by replacing the given function $f(x) = (x^2 - 1)/(x - 1)$ by a simpler function, $g(x) = x + 1$, with the same limit. This is valid because $f(x) = g(x)$ except when $x = 1$, and in computing a limit as x approaches 1 we don't consider what happens when x is actually *equal* to 1. In general, we have the following useful fact.

> If $f(x) = g(x)$ when $x \neq a$, then $\lim\limits_{x \to a} f(x) = \lim\limits_{x \to a} g(x)$, provided the limits exist.

EXAMPLE 4 Find $\lim\limits_{x \to 1} g(x)$ where

$$g(x) = \begin{cases} x + 1 & \text{if } x \neq 1 \\ \pi & \text{if } x = 1 \end{cases}$$

SOLUTION Here g is defined at $x = 1$ and $g(1) = \pi$, but the value of a limit as x approaches 1 does not depend on the value of the function at 1. Since $g(x) = x + 1$ for $x \neq 1$, we have

$$\lim_{x \to 1} g(x) = \lim_{x \to 1} (x + 1) = 2$$

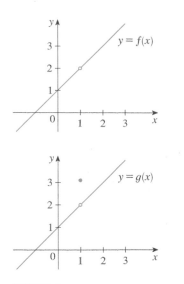

FIGURE 2

The graphs of the functions f (from Example 3) and g (from Example 4)

Note that the values of the functions in Examples 3 and 4 are identical except when $x = 1$ (see Figure 2) and so they have the same limit as x approaches 1.

V **EXAMPLE 5** **Finding a limit by simplifying the function**   Evaluate $\displaystyle\lim_{h \to 0} \frac{(3 + h)^2 - 9}{h}$.

SOLUTION If we define

$$F(h) = \frac{(3 + h)^2 - 9}{h}$$

then, as in Example 3, we can't compute $\lim_{h \to 0} F(h)$ by letting $h = 0$ since $F(0)$ is undefined. But if we simplify $F(h)$ algebraically, we find that

$$F(h) = \frac{(9 + 6h + h^2) - 9}{h} = \frac{6h + h^2}{h} = 6 + h$$

(Recall that we consider only $h \neq 0$ when letting h approach 0.) Thus

$$\lim_{h \to 0} \frac{(3 + h)^2 - 9}{h} = \lim_{h \to 0} (6 + h) = 6$$

EXAMPLE 6 **Calculating a limit by rationalizing**   Find $\displaystyle\lim_{t \to 0} \frac{\sqrt{t^2 + 9} - 3}{t^2}$.

SOLUTION We can't apply the Quotient Law immediately, since the limit of the denominator is 0. Here the preliminary algebra consists of rationalizing the numerator:

$$\lim_{t \to 0} \frac{\sqrt{t^2 + 9} - 3}{t^2} = \lim_{t \to 0} \frac{\sqrt{t^2 + 9} - 3}{t^2} \cdot \frac{\sqrt{t^2 + 9} + 3}{\sqrt{t^2 + 9} + 3}$$

$$= \lim_{t \to 0} \frac{(t^2 + 9) - 9}{t^2 \left(\sqrt{t^2 + 9} + 3\right)} = \lim_{t \to 0} \frac{t^2}{t^2 \left(\sqrt{t^2 + 9} + 3\right)}$$

$$= \lim_{t \to 0} \frac{1}{\sqrt{t^2 + 9} + 3} = \frac{1}{\sqrt{\lim_{t \to 0} (t^2 + 9)} + 3}$$

$$= \frac{1}{3 + 3} = \frac{1}{6}$$

This calculation confirms the guess that we made in Example 2 in Section 2.2.

Some limits are best calculated by first finding the left- and right-hand limits. The following theorem is a reminder of what we discovered in Section 2.2. It says that a two-sided limit exists if and only if both of the one-sided limits exist and are equal.

> **1** **Theorem** $\displaystyle\lim_{x \to a} f(x) = L$ if and only if $\displaystyle\lim_{x \to a^-} f(x) = L = \lim_{x \to a^+} f(x)$

When computing one-sided limits, we use the fact that the Limit Laws also hold for one-sided limits.

EXAMPLE 7   **Finding a limit by calculating left and right limits**   Show that $\lim\limits_{x\to 0}|x| = 0$.

SOLUTION   Recall that

$$|x| = \begin{cases} x & \text{if } x \geqslant 0 \\ -x & \text{if } x < 0 \end{cases}$$

Since $|x| = x$ for $x > 0$, we have

$$\lim_{x\to 0^+}|x| = \lim_{x\to 0^+} x = 0$$

For $x < 0$ we have $|x| = -x$ and so

$$\lim_{x\to 0^-}|x| = \lim_{x\to 0^-}(-x) = 0$$

Therefore, by Theorem 1,

$$\lim_{x\to 0}|x| = 0$$

The result of Example 7 looks plausible from Figure 3.

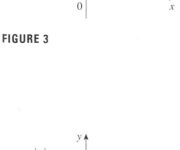

$y = |x|$

FIGURE 3

V   EXAMPLE 8   Prove that $\lim\limits_{x\to 0}\dfrac{|x|}{x}$ does not exist.

SOLUTION

$$\lim_{x\to 0^+}\frac{|x|}{x} = \lim_{x\to 0^+}\frac{x}{x} = \lim_{x\to 0^+} 1 = 1$$

$$\lim_{x\to 0^-}\frac{|x|}{x} = \lim_{x\to 0^-}\frac{-x}{x} = \lim_{x\to 0^-}(-1) = -1$$

Since the right- and left-hand limits are different, it follows from Theorem 1 that $\lim_{x\to 0}|x|/x$ does not exist. The graph of the function $f(x) = |x|/x$ is shown in Figure 4 and supports the one-sided limits that we found.

$y = \dfrac{|x|}{x}$

FIGURE 4

EXAMPLE 9   The **greatest integer function** is defined by $[\![x]\!]$ = the largest integer that is less than or equal to x. (For instance, $[\![4]\!] = 4$, $[\![4.8]\!] = 4$, $[\![\pi]\!] = 3$, $[\![\sqrt{2}\,]\!] = 1$, $[\![-\frac{1}{2}]\!] = -1$.) Show that $\lim_{x\to 3}[\![x]\!]$ does not exist.

Other notations for $[\![x]\!]$ are $[x]$ and $\lfloor x \rfloor$. The greatest integer function is sometimes called the *floor function.*

SOLUTION   The graph of the greatest integer function is shown in Figure 5. Since $[\![x]\!] = 3$ for $3 \leqslant x < 4$, we have

$$\lim_{x\to 3^+}[\![x]\!] = \lim_{x\to 3^+} 3 = 3$$

Since $[\![x]\!] = 2$ for $2 \leqslant x < 3$, we have

$$\lim_{x\to 3^-}[\![x]\!] = \lim_{x\to 3^-} 2 = 2$$

Because these one-sided limits are not equal, $\lim_{x\to 3}[\![x]\!]$ does not exist by Theorem 1.

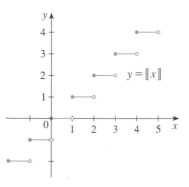

$y = [\![x]\!]$

FIGURE 5
Greatest integer function

The next two theorems give two additional properties of limits. Both can be proved using the precise definition of a limit in Appendix D.

> **2** **Theorem** If $f(x) \leq g(x)$ when x is near a (except possibly at a) and the limits of f and g both exist as x approaches a, then
>
> $$\lim_{x \to a} f(x) \leq \lim_{x \to a} g(x)$$

> **3** **The Squeeze Theorem** If $f(x) \leq g(x) \leq h(x)$ when x is near a (except possibly at a) and
>
> $$\lim_{x \to a} f(x) = \lim_{x \to a} h(x) = L$$
>
> then
>
> $$\lim_{x \to a} g(x) = L$$

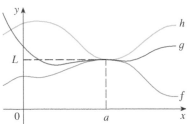

FIGURE 6

The Squeeze Theorem, which is sometimes called the Sandwich Theorem or the Pinching Theorem, is illustrated by Figure 6. It says that if $g(x)$ is squeezed between $f(x)$ and $h(x)$ near a, and if f and h have the same limit L at a, then g is forced to have the same limit L at a.

V EXAMPLE 10 How to squeeze a function   Show that $\displaystyle\lim_{x \to 0} x^2 \sin \frac{1}{x} = 0$.

SOLUTION First note that we **cannot** use

$$\lim_{x \to 0} x^2 \sin \frac{1}{x} = \lim_{x \to 0} x^2 \cdot \lim_{x \to 0} \sin \frac{1}{x}$$

because $\lim_{x \to 0} \sin(1/x)$ does not exist (see Example 4 in Section 2.2).

Instead we apply the Squeeze Theorem, and so we need to find a function f smaller than $g(x) = x^2 \sin(1/x)$ and a function h bigger than g such that both $f(x)$ and $h(x)$ approach 0. To do this we use our knowledge of the sine function. Because the sine of any number lies between -1 and 1, we can write

> **4** $$-1 \leq \sin \frac{1}{x} \leq 1$$

Any inequality remains true when multiplied by a positive number. We know that $x^2 \geq 0$ for all x and so, multiplying each side of the inequalities in (4) by x^2, we get

$$-x^2 \leq x^2 \sin \frac{1}{x} \leq x^2$$

as illustrated by Figure 7. We know that

$$\lim_{x \to 0} x^2 = 0 \qquad \text{and} \qquad \lim_{x \to 0} (-x^2) = 0$$

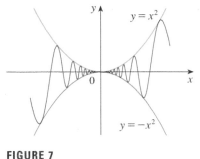

FIGURE 7
$y = x^2 \sin(1/x)$

Taking $f(x) = -x^2$, $g(x) = x^2 \sin(1/x)$, and $h(x) = x^2$ in the Squeeze Theorem, we obtain

$$\lim_{x \to 0} x^2 \sin \frac{1}{x} = 0$$

2.3 Exercises

1. Given that

$$\lim_{x \to 2} f(x) = 4 \qquad \lim_{x \to 2} g(x) = -2 \qquad \lim_{x \to 2} h(x) = 0$$

find the limits that exist. If the limit does not exist, explain why.

(a) $\lim_{x \to 2} [f(x) + 5g(x)]$

(b) $\lim_{x \to 2} [g(x)]^3$

(c) $\lim_{x \to 2} \sqrt{f(x)}$

(d) $\lim_{x \to 2} \dfrac{3f(x)}{g(x)}$

(c) $\lim_{x \to 2} \dfrac{g(x)}{h(x)}$

(f) $\lim_{x \to 2} \dfrac{g(x)h(x)}{f(x)}$

2. The graphs of f and g are given. Use them to evaluate each limit, if it exists. If the limit does not exist, explain why.

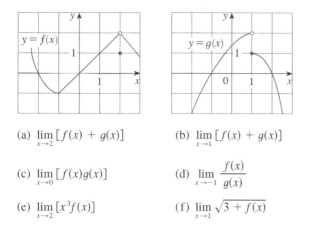

(a) $\lim_{x \to 2} [f(x) + g(x)]$

(b) $\lim_{x \to 1} [f(x) + g(x)]$

(c) $\lim_{x \to 0} [f(x)g(x)]$

(d) $\lim_{x \to -1} \dfrac{f(x)}{g(x)}$

(e) $\lim_{x \to 2} [x^3 f(x)]$

(f) $\lim_{x \to 1} \sqrt{3 + f(x)}$

3–7 Evaluate the limit and justify each step by indicating the appropriate Limit Law(s).

3. $\lim_{x \to -2} (3x^4 + 2x^2 - x + 1)$

4. $\lim_{t \to -1} (t^2 + 1)^3 (t + 3)^5$

5. $\lim_{x \to 8} (1 + \sqrt[3]{x})(2 - 6x^2 + x^3)$

6. $\lim_{u \to -2} \sqrt{u^4 + 3u + 6}$

7. $\lim_{x \to 2} \sqrt{\dfrac{2x^2 + 1}{3x - 2}}$

8. (a) What is wrong with the following equation?

$$\frac{x^2 + x - 6}{x - 2} = x + 3$$

(b) In view of part (a), explain why the equation

$$\lim_{x \to 2} \frac{x^2 + x - 6}{x - 2} = \lim_{x \to 2} (x + 3)$$

is correct.

9–24 Evaluate the limit, if it exists.

9. $\lim_{x \to 5} \dfrac{x^2 - 6x + 5}{x - 5}$

10. $\lim_{x \to 4} \dfrac{x^2 - 4x}{x^2 - 3x - 4}$

11. $\lim_{x \to 5} \dfrac{x^2 - 5x + 6}{x - 5}$

12. $\lim_{x \to -1} \dfrac{2x^2 + 3x + 1}{x^2 - 2x - 3}$

13. $\lim_{t \to -3} \dfrac{t^2 - 9}{2t^2 + 7t + 3}$

14. $\lim_{x \to -1} \dfrac{x^2 - 4x}{x^2 - 3x - 4}$

15. $\lim_{h \to 0} \dfrac{(4 + h)^2 - 16}{h}$

16. $\lim_{h \to 0} \dfrac{(2 + h)^3 - 8}{h}$

17. $\lim_{x \to -2} \dfrac{x + 2}{x^3 + 8}$

18. $\lim_{h \to 0} \dfrac{\sqrt{1 + h} - 1}{h}$

19. $\lim_{x \to -4} \dfrac{\frac{1}{4} + \frac{1}{x}}{4 + x}$

20. $\lim_{x \to -1} \dfrac{x^2 + 2x + 1}{x^4 - 1}$

21. $\lim_{x \to 16} \dfrac{4 - \sqrt{x}}{16x - x^2}$

22. $\lim_{t \to 0} \left(\dfrac{1}{t} - \dfrac{1}{t^2 + t} \right)$

23. $\lim_{t \to 0} \left(\dfrac{1}{t\sqrt{1 + t}} - \dfrac{1}{t} \right)$

24. $\lim_{x \to -4} \dfrac{\sqrt{x^2 + 9} - 5}{x + 4}$

25. (a) Estimate the value of

$$\lim_{x \to 0} \frac{x}{\sqrt{1 + 3x} - 1}$$

by graphing the function $f(x) = x/(\sqrt{1 + 3x} - 1)$.

(b) Make a table of values of $f(x)$ for x close to 0 and guess the value of the limit.

(c) Use the Limit Laws to prove that your guess is correct.

26. (a) Use a graph of

$$f(x) = \frac{\sqrt{3 + x} - \sqrt{3}}{x}$$

to estimate the value of $\lim_{x \to 0} f(x)$ to two decimal places.

(b) Use a table of values of $f(x)$ to estimate the limit to four decimal places.

(c) Use the Limit Laws to find the exact value of the limit.

27. Use the Squeeze Theorem to show that $\lim_{x \to 0} (x^2 \cos 20\pi x) = 0$. Illustrate by graphing the functions $f(x) = -x^2$, $g(x) = x^2 \cos 20\pi x$, and $h(x) = x^2$ on the same screen.

28. Use the Squeeze Theorem to show that

$$\lim_{x \to 0} \sqrt{x^3 + x^2} \sin \frac{\pi}{x} = 0$$

Illustrate by graphing the functions f, g, and h (in the notation of the Squeeze Theorem) on the same screen.

Graphing calculator or computer with graphing software required   **1.** Homework Hints available in TEC

29. If $4x - 9 \le f(x) \le x^2 - 4x + 7$ for $x \ge 0$, find $\lim_{x \to 4} f(x)$.

30. If $2x \le g(x) \le x^4 - x^2 + 2$ for all x, evaluate $\lim_{x \to 1} g(x)$.

31. Prove that $\lim_{x \to 0} x^4 \cos \dfrac{2}{x} = 0$.

32. Prove that $\lim_{x \to 0^+} \sqrt{x}\, e^{\sin(\pi/x)} = 0$.

33–36 Find the limit, if it exists. If the limit does not exist, explain why.

33. $\lim_{x \to 3} (2x + |x - 3|)$

34. $\lim_{x \to -6} \dfrac{2x + 12}{|x + 6|}$

35. $\lim_{x \to 0^-} \left(\dfrac{1}{x} - \dfrac{1}{|x|} \right)$

36. $\lim_{x \to -2} \dfrac{2 - |x|}{2 + x}$

37. Let
$$g(x) = \begin{cases} x & \text{if } x < 1 \\ 3 & \text{if } x = 1 \\ 2 - x^2 & \text{if } 1 < x \le 2 \\ x - 3 & \text{if } x > 2 \end{cases}$$

(a) Evaluate each of the following, if it exists.
   (i) $\lim_{x \to 1^-} g(x)$ (ii) $\lim_{x \to 1} g(x)$ (iii) $g(1)$
   (iv) $\lim_{x \to 2^-} g(x)$ (v) $\lim_{x \to 2^+} g(x)$ (vi) $\lim_{x \to 2} g(x)$
(b) Sketch the graph of g.

38. Let $F(x) = \dfrac{x^2 - 1}{|x - 1|}$.

(a) Find
   (i) $\lim_{x \to 1^+} F(x)$ (ii) $\lim_{x \to 1^-} F(x)$
(b) Does $\lim_{x \to 1} F(x)$ exist?
(c) Sketch the graph of F.

39. (a) If the symbol $[\![\ ]\!]$ denotes the greatest integer function defined in Example 9, evaluate
   (i) $\lim_{x \to -2^+} [\![x]\!]$ (ii) $\lim_{x \to -2} [\![x]\!]$ (iii) $\lim_{x \to -2.4} [\![x]\!]$
(b) If n is an integer, evaluate
   (i) $\lim_{x \to n^-} [\![x]\!]$ (ii) $\lim_{x \to n^+} [\![x]\!]$
(c) For what values of a does $\lim_{x \to a} [\![x]\!]$ exist?

40. Let $f(x) = [\![\cos x]\!]$, $-\pi \le x \le \pi$.
(a) Sketch the graph of f.
(b) Evaluate each limit, if it exists.
   (i) $\lim_{x \to 0} f(x)$ (ii) $\lim_{x \to (\pi/2)^-} f(x)$
   (iii) $\lim_{x \to (\pi/2)^+} f(x)$ (iv) $\lim_{x \to \pi/2} f(x)$
(c) For what values of a does $\lim_{x \to a} f(x)$ exist?

41. If $f(x) = [\![x]\!] + [\![-x]\!]$, show that $\lim_{x \to 2} f(x)$ exists but is not equal to $f(2)$.

42. In the theory of relativity, the Lorentz contraction formula
$$L = L_0 \sqrt{1 - v^2/c^2}$$
expresses the length L of an object as a function of its velocity v with respect to an observer, where L_0 is the length of the object at rest and c is the speed of light. Find $\lim_{v \to c^-} L$ and interpret the result. Why is a left-hand limit necessary?

43. If p is a polynomial, show that $\lim_{x \to a} p(x) = p(a)$.

44. If r is a rational function, use Exercise 43 to show that $\lim_{x \to a} r(x) = r(a)$ for every number a in the domain of r.

45. If $\lim_{x \to 1} \dfrac{f(x) - 8}{x - 1} = 10$, find $\lim_{x \to 1} f(x)$.

46. If $\lim_{x \to 0} \dfrac{f(x)}{x^2} = 5$, find the following limits.
   (a) $\lim_{x \to 0} f(x)$ (b) $\lim_{x \to 0} \dfrac{f(x)}{x}$

47. Show by means of an example that $\lim_{x \to a} [f(x) + g(x)]$ may exist even though neither $\lim_{x \to a} f(x)$ nor $\lim_{x \to a} g(x)$ exists.

48. Show by means of an example that $\lim_{x \to a} [f(x)g(x)]$ may exist even though neither $\lim_{x \to a} f(x)$ nor $\lim_{x \to a} g(x)$ exists.

49. Is there a number a such that
$$\lim_{x \to -2} \frac{3x^2 + ax + a + 3}{x^2 + x - 2}$$
exists? If so, find the value of a and the value of the limit.

50. The figure shows a fixed circle C_1 with equation $(x - 1)^2 + y^2 = 1$ and a shrinking circle C_2 with radius r and center the origin. P is the point $(0, r)$, Q is the upper point of intersection of the two circles, and R is the point of intersection of the line PQ and the x-axis. What happens to R as C_2 shrinks, that is, as $r \to 0^+$?

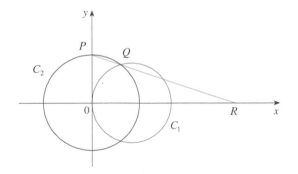

2.4 Continuity

We noticed in Section 2.3 that the limit of a function as x approaches a can often be found simply by calculating the value of the function at a. Functions with this property are called *continuous at a*. We will see that the mathematical definition of continuity corresponds closely with the meaning of the word *continuity* in everyday language. (A continuous process is one that takes place gradually, without interruption or abrupt change.)

---

1 Definition A function f is **continuous at a number a** if

$$\lim_{x \to a} f(x) = f(a)$$

As illustrated in Figure 1, if f is continuous, then the points $(x, f(x))$ on the graph of f approach the point $(a, f(a))$ on the graph. So there is no gap in the curve.

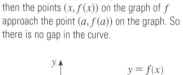
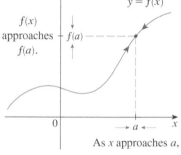

FIGURE 1

Notice that Definition 1 implicitly requires three things if f is continuous at a:

1. $f(a)$ is defined (that is, a is in the domain of f)

2. $\lim_{x \to a} f(x)$ exists

3. $\lim_{x \to a} f(x) = f(a)$

The definition says that f is continuous at a if $f(x)$ approaches $f(a)$ as x approaches a. Thus a continuous function f has the property that a small change in x produces only a small change in $f(x)$. In fact, the change in $f(x)$ can be kept as small as we please by keeping the change in x sufficiently small.

If f is defined near a (in other words, f is defined on an open interval containing a, except perhaps at a), we say that f is **discontinuous at a** (or f has a **discontinuity** at a) if f is not continuous at a.

Physical phenomena are usually continuous. For instance, the displacement or velocity of a vehicle varies continuously with time, as does a person's height. But discontinuities do occur in such situations as electric currents. [See Example 6 in Section 2.2, where the Heaviside function is discontinuous at 0 because $\lim_{t \to 0} H(t)$ does not exist.]

Geometrically, you can think of a function that is continuous at every number in an interval as a function whose graph has no break in it. The graph can be drawn without removing your pen from the paper.

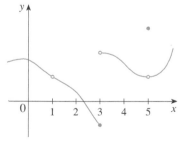

FIGURE 2

EXAMPLE 1 Discontinuities from a graph Figure 2 shows the graph of a function f. At which numbers is f discontinuous? Why?

SOLUTION It looks as if there is a discontinuity when $a = 1$ because the graph has a break there. The official reason that f is discontinuous at 1 is that $f(1)$ is not defined.

The graph also has a break when $a = 3$, but the reason for the discontinuity is different. Here, $f(3)$ is defined, but $\lim_{x \to 3} f(x)$ does not exist (because the left and right limits are different). So f is discontinuous at 3.

What about $a = 5$? Here, $f(5)$ is defined and $\lim_{x \to 5} f(x)$ exists (because the left and right limits are the same). But

$$\lim_{x \to 5} f(x) \neq f(5)$$

So f is discontinuous at 5.

Now let's see how to detect discontinuities when a function is defined by a formula.

V **EXAMPLE 2** **Discontinuities from a formula**   Where are each of the following functions discontinuous?

(a) $f(x) = \dfrac{x^2 - x - 2}{x - 2}$

(b) $f(x) = \begin{cases} \dfrac{1}{x^2} & \text{if } x \neq 0 \\ 1 & \text{if } x = 0 \end{cases}$

(c) $f(x) = \begin{cases} \dfrac{x^2 - x - 2}{x - 2} & \text{if } x \neq 2 \\ 1 & \text{if } x = 2 \end{cases}$

(d) $f(x) = \llbracket x \rrbracket$

SOLUTION

(a) Notice that $f(2)$ is not defined, so f is discontinuous at 2. Later we'll see why f is continuous at all other numbers.

(b) Here $f(0) = 1$ is defined but

$$\lim_{x \to 0} f(x) = \lim_{x \to 0} \frac{1}{x^2}$$

does not exist. (See Example 8 in Section 2.2.) So f is discontinuous at 0.

(c) Here $f(2) = 1$ is defined and

$$\lim_{x \to 2} f(x) = \lim_{x \to 2} \frac{x^2 - x - 2}{x - 2} = \lim_{x \to 2} \frac{(x - 2)(x + 1)}{x - 2} = \lim_{x \to 2} (x + 1) = 3$$

exists. But

$$\lim_{x \to 2} f(x) \neq f(2)$$

so f is not continuous at 2.

(d) The greatest integer function $f(x) = \llbracket x \rrbracket$ has discontinuities at all of the integers because $\lim_{x \to n} \llbracket x \rrbracket$ does not exist if n is an integer. (See Example 9 and Exercise 39 in Section 2.3.)

Figure 3 shows the graphs of the functions in Example 2. In each case the graph can't be drawn without lifting the pen from the paper because a hole or break or jump occurs in the graph. The kind of discontinuity illustrated in parts (a) and (c) is called **removable** because we could remove the discontinuity by redefining f at just the single number 2. [The function $g(x) = x + 1$ is continuous.] The discontinuity in part (b) is called an **infinite discontinuity**. The discontinuities in part (d) are called **jump discontinuities** because the function "jumps" from one value to another.

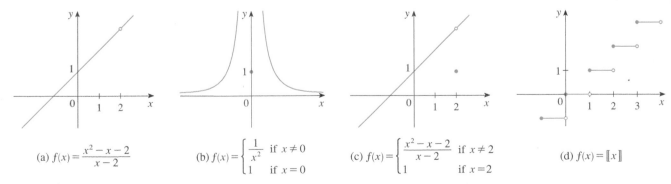

(a) $f(x) = \dfrac{x^2 - x - 2}{x - 2}$

(b) $f(x) = \begin{cases} \dfrac{1}{x^2} & \text{if } x \neq 0 \\ 1 & \text{if } x = 0 \end{cases}$

(c) $f(x) = \begin{cases} \dfrac{x^2 - x - 2}{x - 2} & \text{if } x \neq 2 \\ 1 & \text{if } x = 2 \end{cases}$

(d) $f(x) = \llbracket x \rrbracket$

FIGURE 3 Graphs of the functions in Example 2

---

2 **Definition** A function f is **continuous from the right at a number** a if

$$\lim_{x \to a^+} f(x) = f(a)$$

and f is **continuous from the left at** a if

$$\lim_{x \to a^-} f(x) = f(a)$$

EXAMPLE 3 At each integer n, the function $f(x) = [\![x]\!]$ [see Figure 3(d)] is continuous from the right but discontinuous from the left because

$$\lim_{x \to n^+} f(x) = \lim_{x \to n^+} [\![x]\!] = n = f(n)$$

but

$$\lim_{x \to n^-} f(x) = \lim_{x \to n^-} [\![x]\!] = n - 1 \neq f(n)$$

---

3 **Definition** A function f is **continuous on an interval** if it is continuous at every number in the interval. (If f is defined only on one side of an endpoint of the interval, we understand *continuous* at the endpoint to mean *continuous from the right* or *continuous from the left*.)

EXAMPLE 4 **Continuity from the definition** Show that the function $f(x) = 1 - \sqrt{1 - x^2}$ is continuous on the interval $[-1, 1]$.

SOLUTION If $-1 < a < 1$, then using the Limit Laws, we have

$$\lim_{x \to a} f(x) = \lim_{x \to a} \left(1 - \sqrt{1 - x^2}\right)$$

$$= 1 - \lim_{x \to a} \sqrt{1 - x^2} \qquad \text{(by Laws 2 and 7)}$$

$$= 1 - \sqrt{\lim_{x \to a} (1 - x^2)} \qquad \text{(by 11)}$$

$$= 1 - \sqrt{1 - a^2} \qquad \text{(by 2, 7, and 9)}$$

$$= f(a)$$

Thus, by Definition 1, f is continuous at a if $-1 < a < 1$. Similar calculations show that

$$\lim_{x \to -1^+} f(x) = 1 = f(-1) \qquad \text{and} \qquad \lim_{x \to 1^-} f(x) = 1 = f(1)$$

so f is continuous from the right at -1 and continuous from the left at 1. Therefore, according to Definition 3, f is continuous on $[-1, 1]$.

The graph of f is sketched in Figure 4. It is the lower half of the circle

$$x^2 + (y - 1)^2 = 1$$

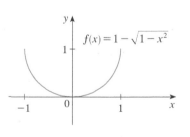

FIGURE 4

Instead of always using Definitions 1, 2, and 3 to verify the continuity of a function as we did in Example 4, it is often convenient to use the next theorem, which shows how to build up complicated continuous functions from simple ones.

> **4** **Theorem** If f and g are continuous at a and c is a constant, then the following functions are also continuous at a:
>
> **1.** $f + g$ **2.** $f - g$ **3.** cf
>
> **4.** fg **5.** $\dfrac{f}{g}$ if $g(a) \neq 0$

PROOF Each of the five parts of this theorem follows from the corresponding Limit Law in Section 2.3. For instance, we give the proof of part 1. Since f and g are continuous at a, we have

$$\lim_{x \to a} f(x) = f(a) \qquad \text{and} \qquad \lim_{x \to a} g(x) = g(a)$$

Therefore

$$
\begin{aligned}
\lim_{x \to a} (f + g)(x) &= \lim_{x \to a} \left[f(x) + g(x) \right] \\
&= \lim_{x \to a} f(x) + \lim_{x \to a} g(x) \qquad \text{(by Law 1)} \\
&= f(a) + g(a) \\
&= (f + g)(a)
\end{aligned}
$$

This shows that $f + g$ is continuous at a.

It follows from Theorem 4 and Definition 3 that if f and g are continuous on an interval, then so are the functions $f + g$, $f - g$, cf, fg, and (if g is never 0) f/g. The following theorem was stated in Section 2.3 as the Direct Substitution Property.

> **5** **Theorem**
> (a) Any polynomial is continuous everywhere; that is, it is continuous on $\mathbb{R} = (-\infty, \infty)$.
> (b) Any rational function is continuous wherever it is defined; that is, it is continuous on its domain.

PROOF
(a) A polynomial is a function of the form

$$P(x) = c_n x^n + c_{n-1} x^{n-1} + \cdots + c_1 x + c_0$$

where $c_0, c_1, \ldots, c_n$ are constants. We know that

$$\lim_{x \to a} c_0 = c_0 \qquad \text{(by Law 7)}$$

and

$$\lim_{x \to a} x^m = a^m \qquad m = 1, 2, \ldots, n \qquad \text{(by 9)}$$

This equation is precisely the statement that the function $f(x) = x^m$ is a continuous function. Thus, by part 3 of Theorem 4, the function $g(x) = cx^m$ is continuous. Since P is a sum of functions of this form and a constant function, it follows from part 1 of Theorem 4 that P is continuous.

(b) A rational function is a function of the form

$$f(x) = \frac{P(x)}{Q(x)}$$

where P and Q are polynomials. The domain of f is $D = \{x \in \mathbb{R} \mid Q(x) \neq 0\}$. We know from part (a) that P and Q are continuous everywhere. Thus, by part 5 of Theorem 4, f is continuous at every number in D.

As an illustration of Theorem 5, observe that the volume of a sphere varies continuously with its radius because the formula $V(r) = \frac{4}{3}\pi r^3$ shows that V is a polynomial function of r. Likewise, if a ball is thrown vertically into the air with a velocity of 50 ft/s, then the height of the ball in feet t seconds later is given by the formula $h = 50t - 16t^2$. Again this is a polynomial function, so the height is a continuous function of the elapsed time.

Knowledge of which functions are continuous enables us to evaluate some limits very quickly, as the following example shows. Compare it with Example 2(b) in Section 2.3.

EXAMPLE 5   **Finding the limit of a continuous function**   Find $\displaystyle\lim_{x \to -2} \frac{x^3 + 2x^2 - 1}{5 - 3x}$.

SOLUTION   The function

$$f(x) = \frac{x^3 + 2x^2 - 1}{5 - 3x}$$

is rational, so by Theorem 5 it is continuous on its domain, which is $\{x \mid x \neq \frac{5}{3}\}$. Therefore

$$\lim_{x \to -2} \frac{x^3 + 2x^2 - 1}{5 - 3x} = \lim_{x \to -2} f(x) = f(-2)$$

$$= \frac{(-2)^3 + 2(-2)^2 - 1}{5 - 3(-2)} = -\frac{1}{11}$$

It turns out that most of the familiar functions are continuous at every number in their domains. For instance, Limit Law 10 (page 106) is exactly the statement that root functions are continuous.

From the appearance of the graphs of the sine and cosine functions (Figure 18 in Section 1.2), we would certainly guess that they are continuous. We know from the definitions of $\sin\theta$ and $\cos\theta$ that the coordinates of the point P in Figure 5 are $(\cos\theta, \sin\theta)$. As $\theta \to 0$, we see that P approaches the point $(1, 0)$ and so $\cos\theta \to 1$ and $\sin\theta \to 0$. Thus

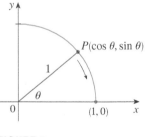

FIGURE 5

Another way to establish the limits in (6) is to use the Squeeze Theorem with the inequality $\sin\theta < \theta$ (for $\theta > 0$), which is proved in Section 3.3.

$$\boxed{6} \qquad \lim_{\theta \to 0} \cos\theta = 1 \qquad \lim_{\theta \to 0} \sin\theta = 0$$

Since $\cos 0 = 1$ and $\sin 0 = 0$, the equations in (6) assert that the cosine and sine functions are continuous at 0. The addition formulas for cosine and sine can then be used to deduce that these functions are continuous everywhere (see Exercises 49 and 50).

It follows from part 5 of Theorem 4 that

$$\tan x = \frac{\sin x}{\cos x}$$

is continuous except where $\cos x = 0$. This happens when x is an odd integer multiple of

$\pi/2$, so $y = \tan x$ has infinite discontinuities when $x = \pm\pi/2, \pm 3\pi/2, \pm 5\pi/2$, and so on (see Figure 6).

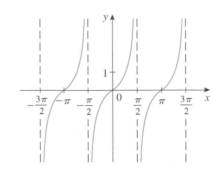

FIGURE 6
$y = \tan x$

In Section 1.5 we defined the exponential function $y = a^x$ so as to fill in the holes in the graph of $y = a^x$ where x is rational. In other words, the very definition of $y = a^x$ makes it a continuous function on $\mathbb{R}$. The inverse function of any continuous one-to-one function is also continuous. (The graph of f^{-1} is obtained by reflecting the graph of f about the line $y = x$. So if the graph of f has no break in it, neither does the graph of f^{-1}.) Therefore the function $y = \log_a x$ is continuous on $(0, \infty)$ because it is the inverse function of $y = a^x$.

---

7 Theorem The following types of functions are continuous at every number in their domains:

polynomials	rational functions
root functions	trigonometric functions
exponential functions	logarithmic functions

EXAMPLE 6   Continuity on intervals

Where is the function $f(x) = \dfrac{\ln x + e^x}{x^2 - 1}$ continuous?

SOLUTION We know from Theorem 7 that the function $y = \ln x$ is continuous for $x > 0$ and $y = e^x$ is continuous on $\mathbb{R}$. Thus, by part 1 of Theorem 4, $y = \ln x + e^x$ is continuous on $(0, \infty)$. The denominator, $y = x^2 - 1$, is a polynomial, so it is continuous everywhere. Therefore, by part 5 of Theorem 4, f is continuous at all positive numbers x except where $x^2 - 1 = 0$. So f is continuous on the intervals $(0, 1)$ and $(1, \infty)$.

EXAMPLE 7   Evaluate $\displaystyle\lim_{x \to \pi} \frac{\sin x}{2 + \cos x}$.

SOLUTION Theorem 7 tells us that $y = \sin x$ is continuous. The function in the denominator, $y = 2 + \cos x$, is the sum of two continuous functions and is therefore continuous. Notice that this function is never 0 because $\cos x \geq -1$ for all x and so $2 + \cos x > 0$ everywhere. Thus the ratio

$$f(x) = \frac{\sin x}{2 + \cos x}$$

is continuous everywhere. Hence, by the definition of a continuous function,

$$\lim_{x \to \pi} \frac{\sin x}{2 + \cos x} = \lim_{x \to \pi} f(x) = f(\pi) = \frac{\sin \pi}{2 + \cos \pi} = \frac{0}{2 - 1} = 0$$

Another way of combining continuous functions f and g to get a new continuous function is to form the composite function $f \circ g$. This fact is a consequence of the following theorem.

This theorem says that a limit symbol can be moved through a function symbol if the function is continuous and the limit exists. In other words, the order of these two symbols can be reversed.

> **8 Theorem** If f is continuous at b and $\lim_{x \to a} g(x) = b$, then $\lim_{x \to a} f(g(x)) = f(b)$. In other words,
>
> $$\lim_{x \to a} f(g(x)) = f\left(\lim_{x \to a} g(x)\right)$$

Intuitively, Theorem 8 is reasonable because if x is close to a, then $g(x)$ is close to b, and since f is continuous at b, if $g(x)$ is close to b, then $f(g(x))$ is close to $f(b)$.

> **9 Theorem** If g is continuous at a and f is continuous at $g(a)$, then the composite function $f \circ g$ given by $(f \circ g)(x) = f(g(x))$ is continuous at a.

This theorem is often expressed informally by saying "a continuous function of a continuous function is a continuous function."

PROOF Since g is continuous at a, we have

$$\lim_{x \to a} g(x) = g(a)$$

Since f is continuous at $b = g(a)$, we can apply Theorem 8 to obtain

$$\lim_{x \to a} f(g(x)) = f(g(a))$$

which is precisely the statement that the function $h(x) = f(g(x))$ is continuous at a; that is, $f \circ g$ is continuous at a.

V EXAMPLE 8 Where are the following functions continuous?
(a) $h(x) = \sin(x^2)$ (b) $F(x) = \ln(1 + \cos x)$

SOLUTION
(a) We have $h(x) = f(g(x))$, where

$$g(x) = x^2 \qquad \text{and} \qquad f(x) = \sin x$$

Now g is continuous on $\mathbb{R}$ since it is a polynomial, and f is also continuous everywhere. Thus $h = f \circ g$ is continuous on $\mathbb{R}$ by Theorem 9.

(b) We know from Theorem 7 that $f(x) = \ln x$ is continuous and $g(x) = 1 + \cos x$ is continuous (because both $y = 1$ and $y = \cos x$ are continuous). Therefore, by Theorem 9, $F(x) = f(g(x))$ is continuous wherever it is defined. Now $\ln(1 + \cos x)$ is defined when $1 + \cos x > 0$. So it is undefined when $\cos x = -1$, and this happens when $x = \pm \pi, \pm 3\pi, \dots$. Thus F has discontinuities when x is an odd multiple of π and is continuous on the intervals between these values (see Figure 7).

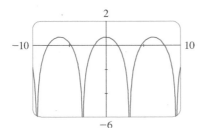

FIGURE 7
$y = \ln(1 + \cos x)$

An important property of continuous functions is expressed by the following theorem, whose proof is found in more advanced books on calculus.

---

10 **The Intermediate Value Theorem**   Suppose that f is continuous on the closed interval $[a, b]$ and let N be any number between $f(a)$ and $f(b)$, where $f(a) \neq f(b)$. Then there exists a number c in (a, b) such that $f(c) = N$.

The Intermediate Value Theorem states that a continuous function takes on every intermediate value between the function values $f(a)$ and $f(b)$. It is illustrated by Figure 8. Note that the value N can be taken on once [as in part (a)] or more than once [as in part (b)].

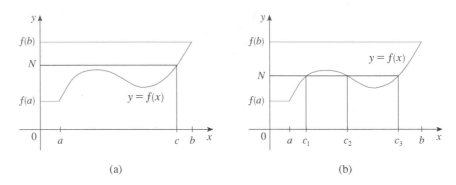

FIGURE 8   (a)   (b)

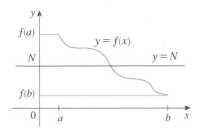

FIGURE 9

If we think of a continuous function as a function whose graph has no hole or break, then it is easy to believe that the Intermediate Value Theorem is true. In geometric terms it says that if any horizontal line $y = N$ is given between $y = f(a)$ and $y = f(b)$ as in Figure 9, then the graph of f can't jump over the line. It must intersect $y = N$ somewhere.

It is important that the function f in Theorem 10 be continuous. The Intermediate Value Theorem is not true in general for discontinuous functions (see Exercise 38).

One use of the Intermediate Value Theorem is in locating roots of equations as in the following example.

V **EXAMPLE 9**   **Using the Intermediate Value Theorem to show the existence of a root**
Show that there is a root of the equation

$$4x^3 - 6x^2 + 3x - 2 = 0$$

between 1 and 2.

SOLUTION   Let $f(x) = 4x^3 - 6x^2 + 3x - 2$. We are looking for a solution of the given equation, that is, a number c between 1 and 2 such that $f(c) = 0$. Therefore, we take $a = 1$, $b = 2$, and $N = 0$ in Theorem 10. We have

$$f(1) = 4 - 6 + 3 - 2 = -1 < 0$$

and

$$f(2) = 32 - 24 + 6 - 2 = 12 > 0$$

Thus $f(1) < 0 < f(2)$; that is, $N = 0$ is a number between $f(1)$ and $f(2)$. Now f is continuous since it is a polynomial, so the Intermediate Value Theorem says there is a number c between 1 and 2 such that $f(c) = 0$. In other words, the equation $4x^3 - 6x^2 + 3x - 2 = 0$ has at least one root c in the interval $(1, 2)$.

In fact, we can locate a root more precisely by using the Intermediate Value Theorem again. Since

$$f(1.2) = -0.128 < 0 \qquad \text{and} \qquad f(1.3) = 0.548 > 0$$

a root must lie between 1.2 and 1.3. A calculator gives, by trial and error,

$$f(1.22) = -0.007008 < 0 \qquad \text{and} \qquad f(1.23) = 0.056068 > 0$$

so a root lies in the interval (1.22, 1.23).

We can use a graphing calculator or computer to illustrate the use of the Intermediate Value Theorem in Example 9. Figure 10 shows the graph of f in the viewing rectangle $[-1, 3]$ by $[-3, 3]$ and you can see that the graph crosses the x-axis between 1 and 2. Figure 11 shows the result of zooming in to the viewing rectangle $[1.2, 1.3]$ by $[-0.2, 0.2]$.

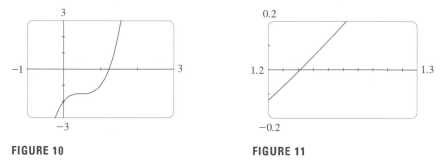

FIGURE 10   **FIGURE 11**

In fact, the Intermediate Value Theorem plays a role in the very way these graphing devices work. A computer calculates a finite number of points on the graph and turns on the pixels that contain these calculated points. It assumes that the function is continuous and takes on all the intermediate values between two consecutive points. The computer therefore connects the pixels by turning on the intermediate pixels.

2.4 Exercises

1. Write an equation that expresses the fact that a function f is continuous at the number 4.

2. If f is continuous on $(-\infty, \infty)$, what can you say about its graph?

3. (a) From the graph of f, state the numbers at which f is discontinuous and explain why.
(b) For each of the numbers stated in part (a), determine whether f is continuous from the right, or from the left, or neither.

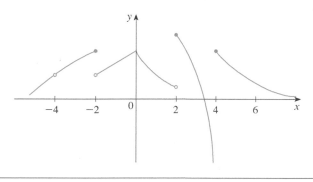

4. From the graph of g, state the intervals on which g is continuous.

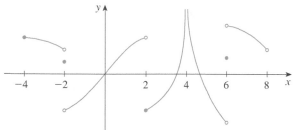

5–8 Sketch the graph of a function f that is continuous except for the stated discontinuity.

5. Discontinuous, but continuous from the right, at 2

6. Discontinuities at -1 and 4, but continuous from the left at -1 and from the right at 4

7. Removable discontinuity at 3, jump discontinuity at 5

8. Neither left nor right continuous at -2, continuous only from the left at 2

Graphing calculator or computer with graphing software required   **1.** Homework Hints available in TEC

9. A parking lot charges $3 for the first hour (or part of an hour) and $2 for each succeeding hour (or part), up to a daily maximum of $10.
   (a) Sketch a graph of the cost of parking at this lot as a function of the time parked there.
   (b) Discuss the discontinuities of this function and their significance to someone who parks in the lot.

10. Explain why each function is continuous or discontinuous.
    (a) The temperature at a specific location as a function of time
    (b) The temperature at a specific time as a function of the distance due west from New York City
    (c) The altitude above sea level as a function of the distance due west from New York City
    (d) The cost of a taxi ride as a function of the distance traveled
    (e) The current in the circuit for the lights in a room as a function of time

11. If f and g are continuous functions with $f(3) = 5$ and $\lim_{x \to 3}[2f(x) - g(x)] = 4$, find $g(3)$.

12–13 Use the definition of continuity and the properties of limits to show that the function is continuous at the given number a.

12. $h(t) = \dfrac{2t - 3t^2}{1 + t^3}$, $a = 1$

13. $f(x) = (x + 2x^3)^4$, $a = -1$

14. Use the definition of continuity and the properties of limits to show that the function $g(x) = 2\sqrt{3 - x}$ is continuous on the interval $(-\infty, 3]$.

15–18 Explain why the function is discontinuous at the given number a. Sketch the graph of the function.

15. $f(x) = \begin{cases} e^x & \text{if } x < 0 \\ x^2 & \text{if } x \geq 0 \end{cases}$ $a = 0$

16. $f(x) = \begin{cases} \dfrac{x^2 - x}{x^2 - 1} & \text{if } x \neq 1 \\ 1 & \text{if } x = 1 \end{cases}$ $a = 1$

17. $f(x) = \begin{cases} \cos x & \text{if } x < 0 \\ 0 & \text{if } x = 0 \\ 1 - x^2 & \text{if } x > 0 \end{cases}$ $a = 0$

18. $f(x) = \begin{cases} \dfrac{2x^2 - 5x - 3}{x - 3} & \text{if } x \neq 3 \\ 6 & \text{if } x = 3 \end{cases}$ $a = 3$

19–24 Explain, using Theorems 4, 5, 7, and 9, why the function is continuous at every number in its domain. State the domain.

19. $R(x) = x^2 + \sqrt{2x - 1}$
20. $G(x) = \sqrt[3]{x}\,(1 + x^3)$
21. $L(t) = e^{-5t}\cos 2\pi t$
22. $h(x) = \dfrac{\sin x}{x + 1}$
23. $G(t) = \ln(t^4 - 1)$
24. $F(x) = \sin(\cos(\sin x))$

25–26 Locate the discontinuities of the function and illustrate by graphing.

25. $y = \dfrac{1}{1 + e^{1/x}}$
26. $y = \ln(\tan^2 x)$

27–30 Use continuity to evaluate the limit.

27. $\lim_{x \to 4} \dfrac{5 + \sqrt{x}}{\sqrt{5 + x}}$
28. $\lim_{x \to \pi} \sin(x + \sin x)$
29. $\lim_{x \to 1} e^{x^2 - x}$
30. $\lim_{x \to 2} (x^3 - 3x + 1)^{-3}$

31–32 Show that f is continuous on $(-\infty, \infty)$.

31. $f(x) = \begin{cases} x^2 & \text{if } x < 1 \\ \sqrt{x} & \text{if } x \geq 1 \end{cases}$

32. $f(x) = \begin{cases} \sin x & \text{if } x < \pi/4 \\ \cos x & \text{if } x \geq \pi/4 \end{cases}$

33. Find the numbers at which the function
$$f(x) = \begin{cases} x + 2 & \text{if } x < 0 \\ e^x & \text{if } 0 \leq x \leq 1 \\ 2 - x & \text{if } x > 1 \end{cases}$$
is discontinuous. At which of these points is f continuous from the right, from the left, or neither? Sketch the graph of f.

34. The gravitational force exerted by the earth on a unit mass at a distance r from the center of the planet is
$$F(r) = \begin{cases} \dfrac{GMr}{R^3} & \text{if } r < R \\ \dfrac{GM}{r^2} & \text{if } r \geq R \end{cases}$$
where M is the mass of the earth, R is its radius, and G is the gravitational constant. Is F a continuous function of r?

35. For what value of the constant c is the function f continuous on $(-\infty, \infty)$?
$$f(x) = \begin{cases} cx^2 + 2x & \text{if } x < 2 \\ x^3 - cx & \text{if } x \geq 2 \end{cases}$$

36. Find the values of a and b that make f continuous everywhere.
$$f(x) = \begin{cases} \dfrac{x^2 - 4}{x - 2} & \text{if } x < 2 \\ ax^2 - bx + 3 & \text{if } 2 \leq x < 3 \\ 2x - a + b & \text{if } x \geq 3 \end{cases}$$

37. Which of the following functions f has a removable discontinuity at a? If the discontinuity is removable, find a function g that agrees with f for $x \neq a$ and is continuous at a.

(a) $f(x) = \dfrac{x^4 - 1}{x - 1}, \quad a = 1$

(b) $f(x) = \dfrac{x^3 - x^2 - 2x}{x - 2}, \quad a = 2$

(c) $f(x) = [\![\sin x]\!], \quad a = \pi$

38. Suppose that a function f is continuous on $[0, 1]$ except at 0.25 and that $f(0) = 1$ and $f(1) = 3$. Let $N = 2$. Sketch two possible graphs of f, one showing that f might not satisfy the conclusion of the Intermediate Value Theorem and one showing that f might still satisfy the conclusion of the Intermediate Value Theorem (even though it doesn't satisfy the hypothesis).

39. If $f(x) = x^2 + 10 \sin x$, show that there is a number c such that $f(c) = 1000$.

40. Suppose f is continuous on $[1, 5]$ and the only solutions of the equation $f(x) = 6$ are $x = 1$ and $x = 4$. If $f(2) = 8$, explain why $f(3) > 6$.

41–44 Use the Intermediate Value Theorem to show that there is a root of the given equation in the specified interval.

41. $x^4 + x - 3 = 0, \quad (1, 2)$ **42.** $\sqrt[3]{x} = 1 - x, \quad (0, 1)$

43. $e^x = 3 - 2x, \quad (0, 1)$ **44.** $\sin x = x^2 - x, \quad (1, 2)$

45–46 (a) Prove that the equation has at least one real root.
(b) Use your calculator to find an interval of length 0.01 that contains a root.

45. $\cos x = x^3$ **46.** $\ln x = 3 - 2x$

47–48 (a) Prove that the equation has at least one real root.
(b) Use your graphing device to find the root correct to three decimal places.

47. $100e^{-x/100} = 0.01x^2$

48. $\sqrt{x - 5} = \dfrac{1}{x + 3}$

49. To prove that sine is continuous we need to show that $\lim_{x \to a} \sin x = \sin a$ for every real number a. If we let $h = x - a$, then $x = a + h$ and $x \to a \iff h \to 0$. So an equivalent statement is that

$$\lim_{h \to 0} \sin(a + h) = \sin a$$

Use (6) to show that this is true.

50. Prove that cosine is a continuous function.

51. Is there a number that is exactly 1 more than its cube?

52. If a and b are positive numbers, prove that the equation

$$\frac{a}{x^3 + 2x^2 - 1} + \frac{b}{x^3 + x - 2} = 0$$

has at least one solution in the interval $(-1, 1)$.

53. Show that the function

$$f(x) = \begin{cases} x^4 \sin(1/x) & \text{if } x \neq 0 \\ 0 & \text{if } x = 0 \end{cases}$$

is continuous on $(-\infty, \infty)$.

54. (a) Show that the absolute value function $F(x) = |x|$ is continuous everywhere.
(b) Prove that if f is a continuous function on an interval, then so is $|f|$.
(c) Is the converse of the statement in part (b) also true? In other words, if $|f|$ is continuous, does it follow that f is continuous? If so, prove it. If not, find a counterexample.

55. A Tibetan monk leaves the monastery at 7:00 AM and takes his usual path to the top of the mountain, arriving at 7:00 PM. The following morning, he starts at 7:00 AM at the top and takes the same path back, arriving at the monastery at 7:00 PM. Use the Intermediate Value Theorem to show that there is a point on the path that the monk will cross at exactly the same time of day on both days.

2.5 Limits Involving Infinity

In this section we investigate the global behavior of functions and, in particular, whether their graphs approach asymptotes, vertical or horizontal.

Infinite Limits

In Example 8 in Section 2.2 we concluded that

$$\lim_{x \to 0} \frac{1}{x^2} \quad \text{does not exist}$$

by observing, from the table of values and the graph of $y = 1/x^2$ in Figure 1, that the values of $1/x^2$ can be made arbitrarily large by taking x close enough to 0. Thus the values of $f(x)$ do not approach a number, so $\lim_{x \to 0} (1/x^2)$ does not exist.

x	$\dfrac{1}{x^2}$
± 1	1
± 0.5	4
± 0.2	25
± 0.1	100
± 0.05	400
± 0.01	10,000
± 0.001	1,000,000

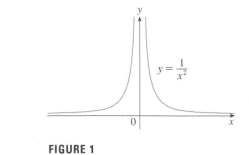

FIGURE 1

To indicate this kind of behavior we use the notation

$$\lim_{x \to 0} \frac{1}{x^2} = \infty$$

⊘ This does not mean that we are regarding ∞ as a number. Nor does it mean that the limit exists. It simply expresses the particular way in which the limit does not exist: $1/x^2$ can be made as large as we like by taking x close enough to 0.

In general, we write symbolically

$$\lim_{x \to a} f(x) = \infty$$

to indicate that the values of $f(x)$ become larger and larger (or "increase without bound") as x approaches a.

A more precise version of Definition 1 is given in Appendix D, Exercise 20.

> **1** **Definition** The notation
>
> $$\lim_{x \to a} f(x) = \infty$$
>
> means that the values of $f(x)$ can be made arbitrarily large (as large as we please) by taking x sufficiently close to a (on either side of a) but not equal to a.

Another notation for $\lim_{x \to a} f(x) = \infty$ is

$$f(x) \to \infty \qquad \text{as} \qquad x \to a$$

Again, the symbol ∞ is not a number, but the expression $\lim_{x \to a} f(x) = \infty$ is often read as

"the limit of $f(x)$, as x approaches a, is infinity"

or "$f(x)$ becomes infinite as x approaches a"

or "$f(x)$ increases without bound as x approaches a"

This definition is illustrated graphically in Figure 2.

Similarly, as shown in Figure 3,

$$\lim_{x \to a} f(x) = -\infty$$

When we say that a number is "large negative," we mean that it is negative but its magnitude (absolute value) is large.

means that the values of $f(x)$ are as large negative as we like for all values of x that are sufficiently close to a, but not equal to a.

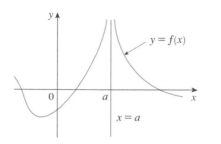

FIGURE 2

$$\lim_{x \to a} f(x) = \infty$$

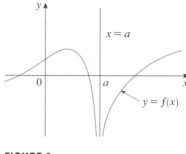

FIGURE 3

$$\lim_{x \to a} f(x) = -\infty$$

The symbol $\lim_{x \to a} f(x) = -\infty$ can be read as "the limit of $f(x)$, as x approaches a, is negative infinity" or "$f(x)$ decreases without bound as x approaches a." As an example we have

$$\lim_{x \to 0} \left(-\frac{1}{x^2} \right) = -\infty$$

Similar definitions can be given for the one-sided infinite limits

$$\lim_{x \to a^-} f(x) = \infty \qquad\qquad \lim_{x \to a^+} f(x) = \infty$$

$$\lim_{x \to a^-} f(x) = -\infty \qquad\qquad \lim_{x \to a^+} f(x) = -\infty$$

remembering that "$x \to a^-$" means that we consider only values of x that are less than a, and similarly "$x \to a^+$" means that we consider only $x > a$. Illustrations of these four cases are given in Figure 4.

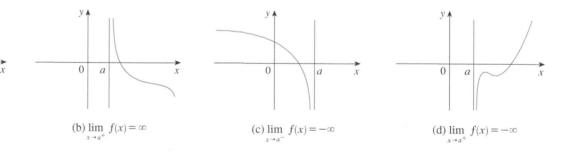

(a) $\lim_{x \to a^-} f(x) = \infty$ (b) $\lim_{x \to a^+} f(x) = \infty$ (c) $\lim_{x \to a^-} f(x) = -\infty$ (d) $\lim_{x \to a^+} f(x) = -\infty$

FIGURE 4

---

2   **Definition**   The line $x = a$ is called a **vertical asymptote** of the curve $y = f(x)$ if at least one of the following statements is true:

$$\lim_{x \to a} f(x) = \infty \qquad \lim_{x \to a^-} f(x) = \infty \qquad \lim_{x \to a^+} f(x) = \infty$$

$$\lim_{x \to a} f(x) = -\infty \qquad \lim_{x \to a^-} f(x) = -\infty \qquad \lim_{x \to a^+} f(x) = -\infty$$

For instance, the y-axis is a vertical asymptote of the curve $y = 1/x^2$ because $\lim_{x \to 0} (1/x^2) = \infty$. In Figure 4 the line $x = a$ is a vertical asymptote in each of the four cases shown.

EXAMPLE 1 **Evaluating one-sided infinite limits** Find $\lim\limits_{x \to 3^+} \dfrac{2x}{x-3}$ and $\lim\limits_{x \to 3^-} \dfrac{2x}{x-3}$.

SOLUTION If x is close to 3 but larger than 3, then the denominator $x - 3$ is a small positive number and $2x$ is close to 6. So the quotient $2x/(x-3)$ is a large *positive* number. Thus, intuitively, we see that

$$\lim_{x \to 3^+} \frac{2x}{x-3} = \infty$$

Likewise, if x is close to 3 but smaller than 3, then $x - 3$ is a small negative number but $2x$ is still a positive number (close to 6). So $2x/(x-3)$ is a numerically large *negative* number. Thus

$$\lim_{x \to 3^-} \frac{2x}{x-3} = -\infty$$

The graph of the curve $y = 2x/(x-3)$ is given in Figure 5. The line $x = 3$ is a vertical asymptote.

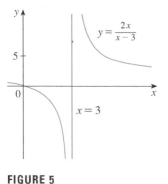

FIGURE 5

Two familiar functions whose graphs have vertical asymptotes are $y = \ln x$ and $y = \tan x$. From Figure 6 we see that

3 $$\lim_{x \to 0^+} \ln x = -\infty$$

and so the line $x = 0$ (the y-axis) is a vertical asymptote. In fact, the same is true for $y = \log_a x$ provided that $a > 1$. (See Figures 11 and 12 in Section 1.6.)

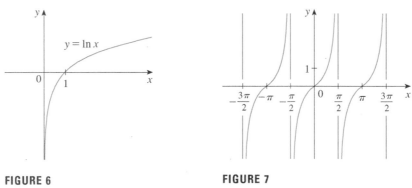

FIGURE 6

FIGURE 7
$y = \tan x$

Figure 7 shows that

$$\lim_{x \to (\pi/2)^-} \tan x = \infty$$

and so the line $x = \pi/2$ is a vertical asymptote. In fact, the lines $x = (2n + 1)\pi/2$, n an integer, are all vertical asymptotes of $y = \tan x$.

EXAMPLE 2 Find $\lim\limits_{x \to 0} \ln(\tan^2 x)$.

PS The problem-solving strategy for Example 2 is *Introduce Something Extra* (see page 83). Here, the something extra, the auxiliary aid, is the new variable t.

SOLUTION We introduce a new variable, $t = \tan^2 x$. Then $t \geqslant 0$ and $t = \tan^2 x \to \tan^2 0 = 0$ as $x \to 0$ because tan is a continuous function. So, by (3), we have

$$\lim_{x \to 0} \ln(\tan^2 x) = \lim_{t \to 0^+} \ln t = -\infty$$

Limits at Infinity

In computing infinite limits, we let x approach a number and the result was that the values of y became arbitrarily large (positive or negative). Here we let x become arbitrarily large (positive or negative) and see what happens to y.

Let's begin by investigating the behavior of the function f defined by

$$f(x) = \frac{x^2 - 1}{x^2 + 1}$$

as x becomes large. The table at the left gives values of this function correct to six decimal places, and the graph of f has been drawn by a computer in Figure 8.

x	$f(x)$
0	-1
± 1	0
± 2	0.600000
± 3	0.800000
± 4	0.882353
± 5	0.923077
± 10	0.980198
± 50	0.999200
± 100	0.999800
± 1000	0.999998

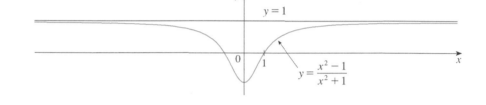

FIGURE 8

As x grows larger and larger you can see that the values of $f(x)$ get closer and closer to 1. In fact, it seems that we can make the values of $f(x)$ as close as we like to 1 by taking x sufficiently large. This situation is expressed symbolically by writing

$$\lim_{x \to \infty} \frac{x^2 - 1}{x^2 + 1} = 1$$

In general, we use the notation

$$\lim_{x \to \infty} f(x) = L$$

to indicate that the values of $f(x)$ approach L as x becomes larger and larger.

A more precise version of Definition 4 is given in Appendix D.

> **4** **Definition** Let f be a function defined on some interval (a, ∞). Then
>
> $$\lim_{x \to \infty} f(x) = L$$
>
> means that the values of $f(x)$ can be made as close to L as we like by taking x sufficiently large.

Another notation for $\lim_{x \to \infty} f(x) = L$ is

$$f(x) \to L \quad \text{as} \quad x \to \infty$$

The symbol ∞ does not represent a number. Nonetheless, the expression $\lim_{x \to \infty} f(x) = L$ is often read as

"the limit of $f(x)$, as x approaches infinity, is L"

or   "the limit of $f(x)$, as x becomes infinite, is L"

or   "the limit of $f(x)$, as x increases without bound, is L"

The meaning of such phrases is given by Definition 4.

Geometric illustrations of Definition 4 are shown in Figure 9. Notice that there are many ways for the graph of f to approach the line $y = L$ (which is called a *horizontal asymptote*) as we look to the far right of each graph.

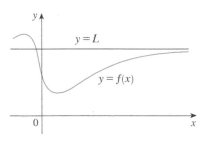
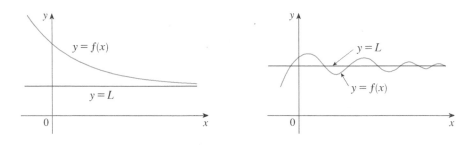

FIGURE 9

Examples illustrating $\lim_{x \to \infty} f(x) = L$

Referring back to Figure 8, we see that for numerically large negative values of x, the values of $f(x)$ are close to 1. By letting x decrease through negative values without bound, we can make $f(x)$ as close to 1 as we like. This is expressed by writing

$$\lim_{x \to -\infty} \frac{x^2 - 1}{x^2 + 1} = 1$$

In general, as shown in Figure 10, the notation

$$\lim_{x \to -\infty} f(x) = L$$

means that the values of $f(x)$ can be made arbitrarily close to L by taking x sufficiently large negative.

Again, the symbol $-\infty$ does not represent a number, but the expression $\lim_{x \to -\infty} f(x) = L$ is often read as

"the limit of $f(x)$, as x approaches negative infinity, is L"

Notice in Figure 10 that the graph approaches the line $y = L$ as we look to the far left of each graph.

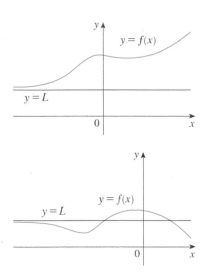

FIGURE 10
Examples illustrating $\lim_{x \to -\infty} f(x) = L$

5	**Definition** The line $y = L$ is called a **horizontal asymptote** of the curve $y = f(x)$ if either

$$\lim_{x \to \infty} f(x) = L \qquad \text{or} \qquad \lim_{x \to -\infty} f(x) = L$$

For instance, the curve illustrated in Figure 8 has the line $y = 1$ as a horizontal asymptote because

$$\lim_{x \to \infty} \frac{x^2 - 1}{x^2 + 1} = 1$$

The curve $y = f(x)$ sketched in Figure 11 has both $y = -1$ and $y = 2$ as horizontal asymptotes because

$$\lim_{x \to \infty} f(x) = -1 \qquad \text{and} \qquad \lim_{x \to -\infty} f(x) = 2$$

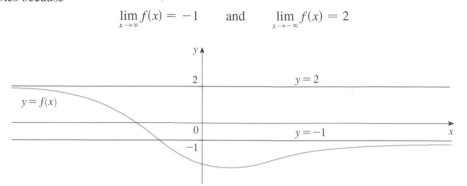

FIGURE 11

EXAMPLE 3 **Infinite limits and asymptotes from a graph** Find the infinite limits, limits at infinity, and asymptotes for the function f whose graph is shown in Figure 12.

SOLUTION We see that the values of $f(x)$ become large as $x \to -1$ from both sides, so

$$\lim_{x \to -1} f(x) = \infty$$

Notice that $f(x)$ becomes large negative as x approaches 2 from the left, but large positive as x approaches 2 from the right. So

$$\lim_{x \to 2^-} f(x) = -\infty \qquad \text{and} \qquad \lim_{x \to 2^+} f(x) = \infty$$

Thus both of the lines $x = -1$ and $x = 2$ are vertical asymptotes.

As x becomes large, it appears that $f(x)$ approaches 4. But as x decreases through negative values, $f(x)$ approaches 2. So

$$\lim_{x \to \infty} f(x) = 4 \qquad \text{and} \qquad \lim_{x \to -\infty} f(x) = 2$$

This means that both $y = 4$ and $y = 2$ are horizontal asymptotes.

EXAMPLE 4 Find $\displaystyle\lim_{x \to \infty} \frac{1}{x}$ and $\displaystyle\lim_{x \to -\infty} \frac{1}{x}$.

SOLUTION Observe that when x is large, $1/x$ is small. For instance,

$$\frac{1}{100} = 0.01 \qquad \frac{1}{10,000} = 0.0001 \qquad \frac{1}{1,000,000} = 0.000001$$

In fact, by taking x large enough, we can make $1/x$ as close to 0 as we please. Therefore, according to Definition 4, we have

$$\lim_{x \to \infty} \frac{1}{x} = 0$$

Similar reasoning shows that when x is large negative, $1/x$ is small negative, so we also have

$$\lim_{x \to -\infty} \frac{1}{x} = 0$$

FIGURE 12

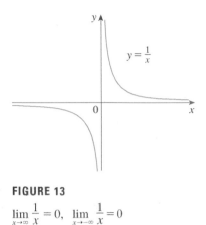

FIGURE 13

$$\lim_{x\to\infty}\frac{1}{x}=0, \quad \lim_{x\to-\infty}\frac{1}{x}=0$$

It follows that the line $y = 0$ (the x-axis) is a horizontal asymptote of the curve $y = 1/x$. (This is an equilateral hyperbola; see Figure 13.)

Most of the Limit Laws that were given in Section 2.3 also hold for limits at infinity. It can be proved that the *Limit Laws listed in Section 2.3 (with the exception of Laws 9 and 10) are also valid if "$x \to a$" is replaced by "$x \to \infty$" or "$x \to -\infty$."* In particular, if we combine Law 6 with the results of Example 4 we obtain the following important rule for calculating limits.

---

6 If n is a positive integer, then

$$\lim_{x\to\infty}\frac{1}{x^n}=0 \qquad \lim_{x\to-\infty}\frac{1}{x^n}=0$$

V **EXAMPLE 5** **A quotient of functions that become large**   Evaluate

$$\lim_{x\to\infty}\frac{3x^2-x-2}{5x^2+4x+1}$$

SOLUTION As x becomes large, both numerator and denominator become large, so it isn't obvious what happens to their ratio. We need to do some preliminary algebra.

To evaluate the limit at infinity of any rational function, we first divide both the numerator and denominator by the highest power of x that occurs in the denominator. (We may assume that $x \neq 0$, since we are interested only in large values of x.) In this case the highest power of x is x^2 and so, using the Limit Laws, we have

$$\lim_{x\to\infty}\frac{3x^2-x-2}{5x^2+4x+1}=\lim_{x\to\infty}\frac{\dfrac{3x^2-x-2}{x^2}}{\dfrac{5x^2+4x+1}{x^2}}=\lim_{x\to\infty}\frac{3-\dfrac{1}{x}-\dfrac{2}{x^2}}{5+\dfrac{4}{x}+\dfrac{1}{x^2}}$$

$$=\frac{\displaystyle\lim_{x\to\infty}\left(3-\frac{1}{x}-\frac{2}{x^2}\right)}{\displaystyle\lim_{x\to\infty}\left(5+\frac{4}{x}+\frac{1}{x^2}\right)}$$

$$=\frac{\displaystyle\lim_{x\to\infty}3-\lim_{x\to\infty}\frac{1}{x}-2\lim_{x\to\infty}\frac{1}{x^2}}{\displaystyle\lim_{x\to\infty}5+4\lim_{x\to\infty}\frac{1}{x}+\lim_{x\to\infty}\frac{1}{x^2}}$$

$$=\frac{3-0-0}{5+0+0} \qquad \text{[by (6)]}$$

$$=\frac{3}{5}$$

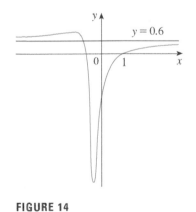

FIGURE 14

$$y=\frac{3x^2-x-2}{5x^2+4x+1}$$

A similar calculation shows that the limit as $x \to -\infty$ is also $\frac{3}{5}$. Figure 14 illustrates the results of these calculations by showing how the graph of the given rational function approaches the horizontal asymptote $y = \frac{3}{5}$.

EXAMPLE 6 **A difference of functions that become large** Compute $\lim\limits_{x \to \infty} \left(\sqrt{x^2 + 1} - x \right)$.

SOLUTION Because both $\sqrt{x^2 + 1}$ and x are large when x is large, it's difficult to see what happens to their difference, so we use algebra to rewrite the function. We first multiply numerator and denominator by the conjugate radical:

$$\lim_{x \to \infty} \left(\sqrt{x^2 + 1} - x \right) = \lim_{x \to \infty} \left(\sqrt{x^2 + 1} - x \right) \frac{\sqrt{x^2 + 1} + x}{\sqrt{x^2 + 1} + x}$$

$$= \lim_{x \to \infty} \frac{(x^2 + 1) - x^2}{\sqrt{x^2 + 1} + x} = \lim_{x \to \infty} \frac{1}{\sqrt{x^2 + 1} + x}$$

Notice that the denominator of this last expression $\left(\sqrt{x^2 + 1} + x \right)$ becomes large as $x \to \infty$ (it's bigger than x). So

$$\lim_{x \to \infty} \left(\sqrt{x^2 + 1} - x \right) = \lim_{x \to \infty} \frac{1}{\sqrt{x^2 + 1} + x} = 0$$

Figure 15 illustrates this result.

We can think of the given function as having a denominator of 1.

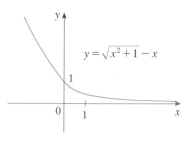

$y = \sqrt{x^2 + 1} - x$

FIGURE 15

The graph of the natural exponential function $y = e^x$ has the line $y = 0$ (the x-axis) as a horizontal asymptote. (The same is true of any exponential function with base $a > 1$.) In fact, from the graph in Figure 16 and the corresponding table of values, we see that

$$\boxed{7} \qquad \boxed{\lim_{x \to -\infty} e^x = 0}$$

Notice that the values of e^x approach 0 very rapidly.

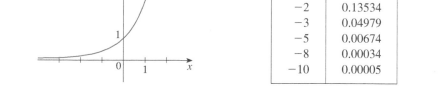

x	e^x
0	1.00000
-1	0.36788
-2	0.13534
-3	0.04979
-5	0.00674
-8	0.00034
-10	0.00005

$y = e^x$

FIGURE 16

EXAMPLE 7 Evaluate $\lim\limits_{x \to 0^-} e^{1/x}$.

SOLUTION If we let $t = 1/x$, we know from Example 4 that $t \to -\infty$ as $x \to 0^-$. Therefore, by (7),

$$\lim_{x \to 0^-} e^{1/x} = \lim_{t \to -\infty} e^t = 0$$

EXAMPLE 8 Evaluate $\lim\limits_{x \to \infty} \sin x$.

SOLUTION As x increases, the values of $\sin x$ oscillate between 1 and -1 infinitely often. Thus $\lim_{x \to \infty} \sin x$ does not exist.

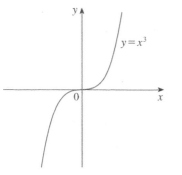

FIGURE 17

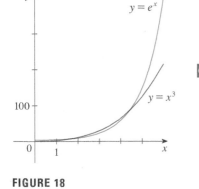

FIGURE 18

Infinite Limits at Infinity

The notation

$$\lim_{x \to \infty} f(x) = \infty$$

is used to indicate that the values of $f(x)$ become large as x becomes large. Similar meanings are attached to the following symbols:

$$\lim_{x \to -\infty} f(x) = \infty \qquad \lim_{x \to \infty} f(x) = -\infty \qquad \lim_{x \to -\infty} f(x) = -\infty$$

From Figures 16 and 17 we see that

$$\lim_{x \to \infty} e^x = \infty \qquad \lim_{x \to \infty} x^3 = \infty \qquad \lim_{x \to -\infty} x^3 = -\infty$$

but, as Figure 18 demonstrates, $y = e^x$ becomes large as $x \to \infty$ at a much faster rate than $y = x^3$.

> **EXAMPLE 9 Finding an infinite limit at infinity** Find $\lim_{x \to \infty} (x^2 - x)$.

⊘ SOLUTION It would be **wrong** to write

$$\lim_{x \to \infty} (x^2 - x) = \lim_{x \to \infty} x^2 - \lim_{x \to \infty} x = \infty - \infty$$

The Limit Laws can't be applied to infinite limits because ∞ is not a number ($\infty - \infty$ can't be defined). However, we *can* write

$$\lim_{x \to \infty} (x^2 - x) = \lim_{x \to \infty} x(x - 1) = \infty$$

because both x and $x - 1$ become arbitrarily large.

> **EXAMPLE 10** Find $\lim_{x \to \infty} \dfrac{x^2 + x}{3 - x}$.

SOLUTION We divide numerator and denominator by x (the highest power of x that occurs in the denominator):

$$\lim_{x \to \infty} \frac{x^2 + x}{3 - x} = \lim_{x \to \infty} \frac{x + 1}{\dfrac{3}{x} - 1} = -\infty$$

because $x + 1 \to \infty$ and $3/x - 1 \to -1$ as $x \to \infty$.

2.5 Exercises

1. Explain in your own words the meaning of each of the following.
 (a) $\lim_{x \to 2} f(x) = \infty$ (b) $\lim_{x \to 1^+} f(x) = -\infty$
 (c) $\lim_{x \to \infty} f(x) = 5$ (d) $\lim_{x \to -\infty} f(x) = 3$

2. (a) Can the graph of $y = f(x)$ intersect a vertical asymptote? Can it intersect a horizontal asymptote? Illustrate by sketching graphs.

 (b) How many horizontal asymptotes can the graph of $y = f(x)$ have? Sketch graphs to illustrate the possibilities.

3. For the function f whose graph is given, state the following.
 (a) $\lim_{x \to 2} f(x)$ (b) $\lim_{x \to -1^-} f(x)$
 (c) $\lim_{x \to -1^+} f(x)$ (d) $\lim_{x \to \infty} f(x)$

Graphing calculator or computer with graphing software required   **1.** Homework Hints available in TEC

(e) $\lim\limits_{x \to -\infty} f(x)$ (f) The equations of the asymptotes

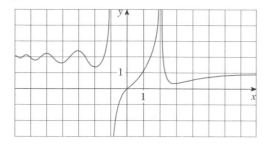

4. For the function g whose graph is given, state the following.

(a) $\lim\limits_{x \to \infty} g(x)$ (b) $\lim\limits_{x \to -\infty} g(x)$

(c) $\lim\limits_{x \to 3} g(x)$ (d) $\lim\limits_{x \to 0} g(x)$

(e) $\lim\limits_{x \to -2^+} g(x)$ (f) The equations of the asymptotes

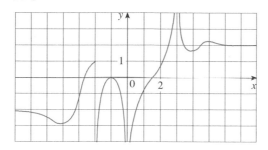

5–10 Sketch the graph of an example of a function f that satisfies all of the given conditions.

5. $\lim\limits_{x \to 0} f(x) = -\infty,$ $\lim\limits_{x \to -\infty} f(x) = 5,$ $\lim\limits_{x \to \infty} f(x) = -5$

6. $\lim\limits_{x \to 2} f(x) = \infty,$ $\lim\limits_{x \to -2^+} f(x) = \infty,$ $\lim\limits_{x \to -2^-} f(x) = -\infty,$
$\lim\limits_{x \to -\infty} f(x) = 0,$ $\lim\limits_{x \to \infty} f(x) = 0,$ $f(0) = 0$

7. $\lim\limits_{x \to 2} f(x) = -\infty,$ $\lim\limits_{x \to \infty} f(x) = \infty,$ $\lim\limits_{x \to -\infty} f(x) = 0,$
$\lim\limits_{x \to 0^+} f(x) = \infty,$ $\lim\limits_{x \to 0^-} f(x) = -\infty$

8. $\lim\limits_{x \to 3^+} f(x) = -\infty,$ $\lim\limits_{x \to 3^-} f(x) = \infty,$ $\lim\limits_{x \to \infty} f(x) = \infty,$ f is odd

9. $f(0) = 3,$ $\lim\limits_{x \to 0^-} f(x) = 4,$ $\lim\limits_{x \to 0^+} f(x) = 2,$
$\lim\limits_{x \to -\infty} f(x) = -\infty,$ $\lim\limits_{x \to 4^-} f(x) = -\infty,$ $\lim\limits_{x \to 4^+} f(x) = \infty,$
$\lim\limits_{x \to \infty} f(x) = 3$

10. $\lim\limits_{x \to 3} f(x) = -\infty,$ $\lim\limits_{x \to \infty} f(x) = 2,$ $f(0) = 0,$ f is even

11. Guess the value of the limit

$$\lim_{x \to \infty} \frac{x^2}{2^x}$$

by evaluating the function $f(x) = x^2/2^x$ for $x = 0, 1, 2, 3,$

4, 5, 6, 7, 8, 9, 10, 20, 50, and 100. Then use a graph of f to support your guess.

12. Determine $\lim\limits_{x \to 1^-} \dfrac{1}{x^3 - 1}$ and $\lim\limits_{x \to 1^+} \dfrac{1}{x^3 - 1}$
   (a) by evaluating $f(x) = 1/(x^3 - 1)$ for values of x that approach 1 from the left and from the right,
   (b) by reasoning as in Example 1, and
   (c) from a graph of f.

13. Use a graph to estimate all the vertical and horizontal asymptotes of the curve

$$y = \frac{x^3}{x^3 - 2x + 1}$$

14. (a) Use a graph of

$$f(x) = \left(1 - \frac{2}{x}\right)^x$$

to estimate the value of $\lim\limits_{x \to \infty} f(x)$ correct to two decimal places.
   (b) Use a table of values of $f(x)$ to estimate the limit to four decimal places.

15–37 Find the limit.

15. $\lim\limits_{x \to 1} \dfrac{2 - x}{(x - 1)^2}$

16. $\lim\limits_{x \to -3^-} \dfrac{x + 2}{x + 3}$

17. $\lim\limits_{x \to 2^+} e^{3/(2 - x)}$

18. $\lim\limits_{x \to \pi^-} \cot x$

19. $\lim\limits_{x \to 3^+} \ln(x^2 - 9)$

20. $\lim\limits_{x \to 2^-} \dfrac{x^2 - 2x}{x^2 - 4x + 4}$

21. $\lim\limits_{x \to 2\pi^-} x \csc x$

22. $\lim\limits_{x \to \infty} \dfrac{3x + 5}{x - 4}$

23. $\lim\limits_{x \to \infty} \dfrac{x^3 + 5x}{2x^3 - x^2 + 4}$

24. $\lim\limits_{t \to -\infty} \dfrac{t^2 + 2}{t^3 + t^2 - 1}$

25. $\lim\limits_{u \to \infty} \dfrac{4u^4 + 5}{(u^2 - 2)(2u^2 - 1)}$

26. $\lim\limits_{x \to \infty} \dfrac{x + 2}{\sqrt{9x^2 + 1}}$

27. $\lim\limits_{x \to \infty} \left(\sqrt{9x^2 + x} - 3x\right)$

28. $\lim\limits_{x \to \infty} \left(\sqrt{x^2 + ax} - \sqrt{x^2 + bx}\right)$

29. $\lim\limits_{x \to \infty} e^{-x^2}$

30. $\lim\limits_{x \to \infty} \sqrt{x^2 + 1}$

31. $\lim\limits_{x \to \infty} \cos x$

32. $\lim\limits_{x \to \infty} \dfrac{\sin^2 x}{x^2}$

33. $\lim\limits_{x \to \infty} (e^{-2x} \cos x)$

34. $\lim\limits_{x \to \infty} \dfrac{e^{3x} - e^{-3x}}{e^{3x} + e^{-3x}}$

35. $\lim\limits_{x \to -\infty} (x^4 + x^5)$

36. $\lim\limits_{x \to (\pi/2)^+} e^{\tan x}$

37. $\lim\limits_{x \to \infty} \dfrac{x + x^3 + x^5}{1 - x^2 + x^4}$

---

38. (a) Graph the function

$$f(x) = \frac{\sqrt{2x^2 + 1}}{3x - 5}$$

How many horizontal and vertical asymptotes do you observe? Use the graph to estimate the values of the limits

$$\lim_{x \to \infty} \frac{\sqrt{2x^2 + 1}}{3x - 5} \quad \text{and} \quad \lim_{x \to -\infty} \frac{\sqrt{2x^2 + 1}}{3x - 5}$$

(b) By calculating values of $f(x)$, give numerical estimates of the limits in part (a).

(c) Calculate the exact values of the limits in part (a). Did you get the same value or different values for these two limits? [In view of your answer to part (a), you might have to check your calculation for the second limit.]

39–42 Find the horizontal and vertical asymptotes of each curve. If you have a graphing device, check your work by graphing the curve and estimating the asymptotes.

39. $y = \dfrac{2x^2 + x - 1}{x^2 + x - 2}$

40. $y = \dfrac{x^2 + 1}{2x^2 - 3x - 2}$

41. $y = \dfrac{x^3 - x}{x^2 - 6x + 5}$

42. $y = \dfrac{2e^x}{e^x - 5}$

43. (a) Estimate the value of

$$\lim_{x \to -\infty} \left(\sqrt{x^2 + x + 1} + x \right)$$

by graphing the function $f(x) = \sqrt{x^2 + x + 1} + x$.

(b) Use a table of values of $f(x)$ to guess the value of the limit.

(c) Prove that your guess is correct.

44. (a) Use a graph of

$$f(x) = \sqrt{3x^2 + 8x + 6} - \sqrt{3x^2 + 3x + 1}$$

to estimate the value of $\lim_{x \to \infty} f(x)$ to one decimal place.

(b) Use a table of values of $f(x)$ to estimate the limit to four decimal places.

(c) Find the exact value of the limit.

45. Estimate the horizontal asymptote of the function

$$f(x) = \frac{3x^3 + 500x^2}{x^3 + 500x^2 + 100x + 2000}$$

by graphing f for $-10 \le x \le 10$. Then calculate the equation of the asymptote by evaluating the limit. How do you explain the discrepancy?

46. (a) Graph the function $f(x) = e^x + \ln|x - 4|$ for $0 \le x \le 5$. Do you think the graph is an accurate representation of f?

(b) How would you get a graph that represents f better?

47. Find a formula for a function f that satisfies the following conditions:

$$\lim_{x \to \pm\infty} f(x) = 0, \quad \lim_{x \to 0} f(x) = -\infty, \quad f(2) = 0,$$

$$\lim_{x \to 3^-} f(x) = \infty, \quad \lim_{x \to 3^+} f(x) = -\infty$$

48. Find a formula for a function that has vertical asymptotes $x = 1$ and $x = 3$ and horizontal asymptote $y = 1$.

49. A function f is a ratio of quadratic functions and has a vertical asymptote $x = 4$ and just one x-intercept, $x = 1$. It is known that f has a removable discontinuity at $x = -1$ and $\lim_{x \to -1} f(x) = 2$. Evaluate

(a) $f(0)$ (b) $\lim\limits_{x \to \infty} f(x)$

50. By the *end behavior* of a function we mean the behavior of its values as $x \to \infty$ and as $x \to -\infty$.

(a) Describe and compare the end behavior of the functions

$$P(x) = 3x^5 - 5x^3 + 2x \qquad Q(x) = 3x^5$$

by graphing both functions in the viewing rectangles $[-2, 2]$ by $[-2, 2]$ and $[-10, 10]$ by $[-10{,}000, 10{,}000]$.

(b) Two functions are said to have the *same end behavior* if their ratio approaches 1 as $x \to \infty$. Show that P and Q have the same end behavior.

51. Let P and Q be polynomials. Find

$$\lim_{x \to \infty} \frac{P(x)}{Q(x)}$$

if the degree of P is (a) less than the degree of Q and (b) greater than the degree of Q.

52. Make a rough sketch of the curve $y = x^n$ (n an integer) for the following five cases:

(i) $n = 0$ (ii) $n > 0$, n odd

(iii) $n > 0$, n even   (iv) $n < 0$, n odd

(v) $n < 0$, n even

Then use these sketches to find the following limits.

(a) $\lim\limits_{x \to 0^+} x^n$ (b) $\lim\limits_{x \to 0^-} x^n$

(c) $\lim\limits_{x \to \infty} x^n$ (d) $\lim\limits_{x \to -\infty} x^n$

53. Find $\lim_{x \to \infty} f(x)$ if, for all $x > 1$,

$$\frac{10e^x - 21}{2e^x} < f(x) < \frac{5\sqrt{x}}{\sqrt{x - 1}}$$

54. In the theory of relativity, the mass of a particle with velocity v is

$$m = \frac{m_0}{\sqrt{1 - v^2/c^2}}$$

where m_0 is the mass of the particle at rest and c is the speed of light. What happens as $v \to c^-$?

55. (a) A tank contains 5000 L of pure water. Brine that contains 30 g of salt per liter of water is pumped into the tank at a rate of 25 L/min. Show that the concentration of salt after t minutes (in grams per liter) is

$$C(t) = \frac{30t}{200 + t}$$

(b) What happens to the concentration as $t \to \infty$?

56. In Chapter 7 we will be able to show, under certain assumptions, that the velocity $v(t)$ of a falling raindrop at time t is

$$v(t) = v^*(1 - e^{-gt/v^*})$$

where g is the acceleration due to gravity and v^* is the *terminal velocity* of the raindrop.
(a) Find $\lim_{t \to \infty} v(t)$.

(b) Graph $v(t)$ if $v^* = 1$ m/s and $g = 9.8$ m/s². How long does it take for the velocity of the raindrop to reach 99% of its terminal velocity?

57. (a) Show that $\lim_{x \to \infty} e^{-x/10} = 0$.
(b) By graphing $y = e^{-x/10}$ and $y = 0.1$ on a common screen, discover how large you need to make x so that $e^{-x/10} < 0.1$.
(c) Can you solve part (b) without using a graphing device?

58. (a) Show that $\lim_{x \to \infty} \dfrac{4x^2 - 5x}{2x^2 + 1} = 2$.

(b) By graphing the function in part (a) and the line $y = 1.9$ on a common screen, find a number N such that

$$\frac{4x^2 - 5x}{2x^2 + 1} > 1.9 \qquad \text{when} \qquad x > N$$

What if 1.9 is replaced by 1.99?

2.6 Derivatives and Rates of Change

The problem of finding the tangent line to a curve and the problem of finding the velocity of an object both involve finding the same type of limit, as we saw in Section 2.1. This special type of limit is called a *derivative* and we will see that it can be interpreted as a rate of change in any of the sciences or engineering.

Tangents

If a curve C has equation $y = f(x)$ and we want to find the tangent line to C at the point $P(a, f(a))$, then we consider a nearby point $Q(x, f(x))$, where $x \neq a$, and compute the slope of the secant line PQ:

$$m_{PQ} = \frac{f(x) - f(a)}{x - a}$$

Then we let Q approach P along the curve C by letting x approach a. If m_{PQ} approaches a number m, then we define the *tangent* t to be the line through P with slope m. (This amounts to saying that the tangent line is the limiting position of the secant line PQ as Q approaches P. See Figure 1.)

---

1 **Definition** The **tangent line** to the curve $y = f(x)$ at the point $P(a, f(a))$ is the line through P with slope

$$m = \lim_{x \to a} \frac{f(x) - f(a)}{x - a}$$

provided that this limit exists.

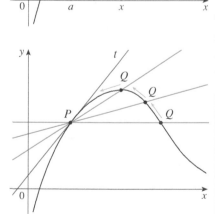

FIGURE 1

In our first example we confirm the guess we made in Example 1 in Section 2.1.

▼ **EXAMPLE 1** **Finding an equation of a tangent**   Find an equation of the tangent line to the parabola $y = x^2$ at the point $P(1, 1)$.

SOLUTION Here we have $a = 1$ and $f(x) = x^2$, so the slope is

$$m = \lim_{x \to 1} \frac{f(x) - f(1)}{x - 1} = \lim_{x \to 1} \frac{x^2 - 1}{x - 1}$$

$$= \lim_{x \to 1} \frac{(x - 1)(x + 1)}{x - 1}$$

$$= \lim_{x \to 1} (x + 1) = 1 + 1 = 2$$

Point-slope form for a line through the point (x_1, y_1) with slope m:
$$y - y_1 = m(x - x_1)$$

Using the point-slope form of the equation of a line, we find that an equation of the tangent line at $(1, 1)$ is

$$y - 1 = 2(x - 1) \qquad \text{or} \qquad y = 2x - 1$$

We sometimes refer to the slope of the tangent line to a curve at a point as the **slope of the curve** at the point. The idea is that if we zoom in far enough toward the point, the curve looks almost like a straight line. Figure 2 illustrates this procedure for the curve $y = x^2$ in Example 1. The more we zoom in, the more the parabola looks like a line. In other words, the curve becomes almost indistinguishable from its tangent line.

TEC Visual 2.6 shows an animation of Figure 2.

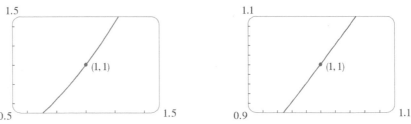

FIGURE 2 Zooming in toward the point $(1, 1)$ on the parabola $y = x^2$

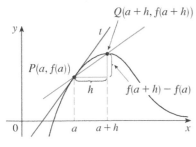

FIGURE 3

There is another expression for the slope of a tangent line that is sometimes easier to use. If $h = x - a$, then $x = a + h$ and so the slope of the secant line PQ is

$$m_{PQ} = \frac{f(a + h) - f(a)}{h}$$

(See Figure 3 where the case $h > 0$ is illustrated and Q is to the right of P. If it happened that $h < 0$, however, Q would be to the left of P.)

Notice that as x approaches a, h approaches 0 (because $h = x - a$) and so the expression for the slope of the tangent line in Definition 1 becomes

2

$$m = \lim_{h \to 0} \frac{f(a + h) - f(a)}{h}$$

EXAMPLE 2 Find an equation of the tangent line to the hyperbola $y = 3/x$ at the point $(3, 1)$.

SOLUTION Let $f(x) = 3/x$. Then the slope of the tangent at $(3, 1)$ is

$$m = \lim_{h \to 0} \frac{f(3+h) - f(3)}{h} = \lim_{h \to 0} \frac{\dfrac{3}{3+h} - 1}{h} = \lim_{h \to 0} \frac{\dfrac{3 - (3+h)}{3+h}}{h}$$

$$= \lim_{h \to 0} \frac{-h}{h(3+h)} = \lim_{h \to 0} -\frac{1}{3+h} = -\frac{1}{3}$$

Therefore an equation of the tangent at the point $(3, 1)$ is

$$y - 1 = -\tfrac{1}{3}(x - 3)$$

which simplifies to

$$x + 3y - 6 = 0$$

The hyperbola and its tangent are shown in Figure 4.

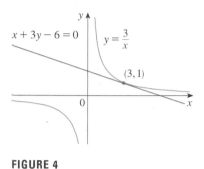

FIGURE 4

Velocities

In Section 2.1 we investigated the motion of a ball dropped from the CN Tower and defined its velocity to be the limiting value of average velocities over shorter and shorter time periods.

In general, suppose an object moves along a straight line according to an equation of motion $s = f(t)$, where s is the displacement (directed distance) of the object from the origin at time t. The function f that describes the motion is called the **position function** of the object. In the time interval from $t = a$ to $t = a + h$ the change in position is $f(a + h) - f(a)$. (See Figure 5.) The average velocity over this time interval is

$$\text{average velocity} = \frac{\text{displacement}}{\text{time}} = \frac{f(a+h) - f(a)}{h}$$

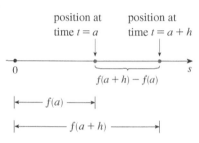

FIGURE 5

which is the same as the slope of the secant line PQ in Figure 6.

Now suppose we compute the average velocities over shorter and shorter time intervals $[a, a + h]$. In other words, we let h approach 0. As in the example of the falling ball, we define the **velocity** (or **instantaneous velocity**) $v(a)$ at time $t = a$ to be the limit of these average velocities:

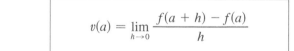

$$\boxed{3} \qquad v(a) = \lim_{h \to 0} \frac{f(a+h) - f(a)}{h}$$

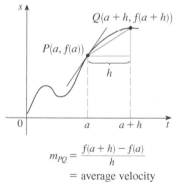

$$m_{PQ} = \frac{f(a+h) - f(a)}{h}$$
$$= \text{average velocity}$$

FIGURE 6

This means that the velocity at time $t = a$ is equal to the slope of the tangent line at P (compare Equations 2 and 3).

Now that we know how to compute limits, let's reconsider the problem of the falling ball.

◢ **EXAMPLE 3** **Velocity of a falling ball** Suppose that a ball is dropped from the upper observation deck of the CN Tower, 450 m above the ground.
(a) What is the velocity of the ball after 5 seconds?
(b) How fast is the ball traveling when it hits the ground?

Recall from Section 2.1: The distance (in meters) fallen after t seconds is $4.9t^2$.

SOLUTION We will need to find the velocity both when $t = 5$ and when the ball hits the ground, so it's efficient to start by finding the velocity at a general time $t = a$. Using the equation of motion $s = f(t) = 4.9t^2$, we have

$$v(a) = \lim_{h \to 0} \frac{f(a + h) - f(a)}{h} = \lim_{h \to 0} \frac{4.9(a + h)^2 - 4.9a^2}{h}$$

$$= \lim_{h \to 0} \frac{4.9(a^2 + 2ah + h^2 - a^2)}{h} = \lim_{h \to 0} \frac{4.9(2ah + h^2)}{h}$$

$$= \lim_{h \to 0} 4.9(2a + h) = 9.8a$$

(a) The velocity after 5 s is $v(5) = (9.8)(5) = 49$ m/s.

(b) Since the observation deck is 450 m above the ground, the ball will hit the ground at the time t_1 when $s(t_1) = 450$, that is,

$$4.9t_1^2 = 450$$

This gives

$$t_1^2 = \frac{450}{4.9} \quad \text{and} \quad t_1 = \sqrt{\frac{450}{4.9}} \approx 9.6 \text{ s}$$

The velocity of the ball as it hits the ground is therefore

$$v(t_1) = 9.8t_1 = 9.8\sqrt{\frac{450}{4.9}} \approx 94 \text{ m/s}$$

Derivatives

We have seen that the same type of limit arises in finding the slope of a tangent line (Equation 2) or the velocity of an object (Equation 3). In fact, limits of the form

$$\lim_{h \to 0} \frac{f(a + h) - f(a)}{h}$$

arise whenever we calculate a rate of change in any of the sciences or engineering, such as a rate of reaction in chemistry or a marginal cost in economics. Since this type of limit occurs so widely, it is given a special name and notation.

---

4   **Definition**   The **derivative of a function f at a number a**, denoted by $f'(a)$, is

$$f'(a) = \lim_{h \to 0} \frac{f(a + h) - f(a)}{h}$$

if this limit exists.

$f'(a)$ is read "f prime of a."

If we write $x = a + h$, then we have $h = x - a$ and h approaches 0 if and only if x approaches a. Therefore an equivalent way of stating the definition of the derivative, as we saw in finding tangent lines, is

5

$$f'(a) = \lim_{x \to a} \frac{f(x) - f(a)}{x - a}$$

V   **EXAMPLE 4   Calculating a derivative at a general number a**   Find the derivative of the function $f(x) = x^2 - 8x + 9$ at the number a.

SOLUTION From Definition 4 we have

$$f'(a) = \lim_{h \to 0} \frac{f(a + h) - f(a)}{h}$$

$$= \lim_{h \to 0} \frac{[(a + h)^2 - 8(a + h) + 9] - [a^2 - 8a + 9]}{h}$$

$$= \lim_{h \to 0} \frac{a^2 + 2ah + h^2 - 8a - 8h + 9 - a^2 + 8a - 9}{h}$$

$$= \lim_{h \to 0} \frac{2ah + h^2 - 8h}{h} = \lim_{h \to 0} (2a + h - 8)$$

$$= 2a - 8$$

We defined the tangent line to the curve $y = f(x)$ at the point $P(a, f(a))$ to be the line that passes through P and has slope m given by Equation 1 or 2. Since, by Definition 4, this is the same as the derivative $f'(a)$, we can now say the following.

> The tangent line to $y = f(x)$ at $(a, f(a))$ is the line through $(a, f(a))$ whose slope is equal to $f'(a)$, the derivative of f at a.

If we use the point-slope form of the equation of a line, we can write an equation of the tangent line to the curve $y = f(x)$ at the point $(a, f(a))$:

$$y - f(a) = f'(a)(x - a)$$

V EXAMPLE 5 Find an equation of the tangent line to the parabola $y = x^2 - 8x + 9$ at the point $(3, -6)$.

SOLUTION From Example 4 we know that the derivative of $f(x) = x^2 - 8x + 9$ at the number a is $f'(a) = 2a - 8$. Therefore the slope of the tangent line at $(3, -6)$ is $f'(3) = 2(3) - 8 = -2$. Thus an equation of the tangent line, shown in Figure 7, is

$$y - (-6) = (-2)(x - 3) \qquad \text{or} \qquad y = -2x$$

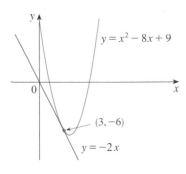

$y = x^2 - 8x + 9$

$(3, -6)$

$y = -2x$

FIGURE 7

Rates of Change

Suppose y is a quantity that depends on another quantity x. Thus y is a function of x and we write $y = f(x)$. If x changes from x_1 to x_2, then the change in x (also called the **increment** of x) is

$$\Delta x = x_2 - x_1$$

and the corresponding change in y is

$$\Delta y = f(x_2) - f(x_1)$$

The difference quotient

$$\frac{\Delta y}{\Delta x} = \frac{f(x_2) - f(x_1)}{x_2 - x_1}$$

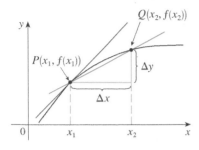

average rate of change $= m_{PQ}$

instantaneous rate of change $=$
          slope of tangent at P

FIGURE 8

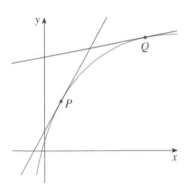

FIGURE 9
The y-values are changing rapidly
at P and slowly at Q.

is called the **average rate of change of y with respect to x** over the interval $[x_1, x_2]$ and can be interpreted as the slope of the secant line PQ in Figure 8.

By analogy with velocity, we consider the average rate of change over smaller and smaller intervals by letting x_2 approach x_1 and therefore letting Δx approach 0. The limit of these average rates of change is called the (**instantaneous**) **rate of change of y with respect to x** at $x = x_1$, which is interpreted as the slope of the tangent to the curve $y = f(x)$ at $P(x_1, f(x_1))$:

$$\boxed{6} \qquad \text{instantaneous rate of change} = \lim_{\Delta x \to 0} \frac{\Delta y}{\Delta x} = \lim_{x_2 \to x_1} \frac{f(x_2) - f(x_1)}{x_2 - x_1}$$

We recognize this limit as being the derivative $f'(x_1)$.

We know that one interpretation of the derivative $f'(a)$ is as the slope of the tangent line to the curve $y = f(x)$ when $x = a$. We now have a second interpretation:

> The derivative $f'(a)$ is the instantaneous rate of change of $y = f(x)$ with respect to x when $x = a$.

The connection with the first interpretation is that if we sketch the curve $y = f(x)$, then the instantaneous rate of change is the slope of the tangent to this curve at the point where $x = a$. This means that when the derivative is large (and therefore the curve is steep, as at the point P in Figure 9), the y-values change rapidly. When the derivative is small, the curve is relatively flat (as at point Q) and the y-values change slowly.

In particular, if $s = f(t)$ is the position function of a particle that moves along a straight line, then $f'(a)$ is the rate of change of the displacement s with respect to the time t. In other words, $f'(a)$ *is the velocity of the particle at time $t = a$*. The **speed** of the particle is the absolute value of the velocity, that is, $|f'(a)|$.

In the next example we discuss the meaning of the derivative of a function that is defined verbally.

▼ EXAMPLE 6 Derivative of a cost function   A manufacturer produces bolts of a fabric with a fixed width. The cost of producing x yards of this fabric is $C = f(x)$ dollars.
(a) What is the meaning of the derivative $f'(x)$? What are its units?
(b) In practical terms, what does it mean to say that $f'(1000) = 9$?
(c) Which do you think is greater, $f'(50)$ or $f'(500)$? What about $f'(5000)$?

SOLUTION
(a) The derivative $f'(x)$ is the instantaneous rate of change of C with respect to x; that is, $f'(x)$ means the rate of change of the production cost with respect to the number of yards produced. (Economists call this rate of change the *marginal cost*. This idea is discussed in more detail in Sections 3.8 and 4.6.)

Because

$$f'(x) = \lim_{\Delta x \to 0} \frac{\Delta C}{\Delta x}$$

the units for $f'(x)$ are the same as the units for the difference quotient $\Delta C/\Delta x$. Since ΔC is measured in dollars and Δx in yards, it follows that the units for $f'(x)$ are dollars per yard.

(b) The statement that $f'(1000) = 9$ means that, after 1000 yards of fabric have been manufactured, the rate at which the production cost is increasing is \$9/yard. (When $x = 1000$, C is increasing 9 times as fast as x.)

Since $\Delta x = 1$ is small compared with $x = 1000$, we could use the approximation

$$f'(1000) \approx \frac{\Delta C}{\Delta x} = \frac{\Delta C}{1} = \Delta C$$

> Here we are assuming that the cost function is well behaved; in other words, $C(x)$ doesn't oscillate rapidly near $x = 1000$.

and say that the cost of manufacturing the 1000th yard (or the 1001st) is about \$9.

(c) The rate at which the production cost is increasing (per yard) is probably lower when $x = 500$ than when $x = 50$ (the cost of making the 500th yard is less than the cost of the 50th yard) because of economies of scale. (The manufacturer makes more efficient use of the fixed costs of production.) So

$$f'(50) > f'(500)$$

But, as production expands, the resulting large-scale operation might become inefficient and there might be overtime costs. Thus it is possible that the rate of increase of costs will eventually start to rise. So it may happen that

$$f'(5000) > f'(500)$$

In the following example we estimate the rate of change of the national debt with respect to time. Here the function is defined not by a formula but by a table of values.

V   **EXAMPLE 7**   **Derivative of a tabular function**   Let $D(t)$ be the US national debt at time t. The table in the margin gives approximate values of this function by providing end of year estimates, in billions of dollars, from 1980 to 2005. Interpret and estimate the value of $D'(1990)$.

t	$D(t)$
1980	930.2
1985	1945.9
1990	3233.3
1995	4974.0
2000	5674.2
2005	7932.7

SOLUTION   The derivative $D'(1990)$ means the rate of change of D with respect to t when $t = 1990$, that is, the rate of increase of the national debt in 1990.

According to Equation 5,

$$D'(1990) = \lim_{t \to 1990} \frac{D(t) - D(1990)}{t - 1990}$$

So we compute and tabulate values of the difference quotient (the average rates of change) as follows.

t	$\dfrac{D(t) - D(1990)}{t - 1990}$
1980	230.31
1985	257.48
1995	348.14
2000	244.09
2005	313.29

From this table we see that $D'(1990)$ lies somewhere between 257.48 and 348.14 billion dollars per year. [Here we are making the reasonable assumption that the debt didn't fluctuate wildly between 1980 and 2000.] We estimate that the rate of increase of the national debt of the United States in 1990 was the average of these two numbers, namely

$$D'(1990) \approx 303 \text{ billion dollars per year}$$

Another method would be to plot the debt function and estimate the slope of the tangent line when $t = 1990$.

A Note on Units

The units for the average rate of change $\Delta D/\Delta t$ are the units for ΔD divided by the units for Δt, namely, billions of dollars per year. The instantaneous rate of change is the limit of the average rates of change, so it is measured in the same units: billions of dollars per year.

In Examples 3, 6, and 7 we saw three specific examples of rates of change: the velocity of an object is the rate of change of displacement with respect to time; marginal cost is the rate of change of production cost with respect to the number of items produced; the rate of change of the debt with respect to time is of interest in economics. Here is a small sample of other rates of change: In physics, the rate of change of work with respect to time is called *power*. Chemists who study a chemical reaction are interested in the rate of change in the concentration of a reactant with respect to time (called the *rate of reaction*). A biologist is interested in the rate of change of the population of a colony of bacteria with respect to time. In fact, the computation of rates of change is important in all of the natural sciences, in engineering, and even in the social sciences. Further examples will be given in Section 3.8.

All these rates of change are derivatives and can therefore be interpreted as slopes of tangents. This gives added significance to the solution of the tangent problem. Whenever we solve a problem involving tangent lines, we are not just solving a problem in geometry. We are also implicitly solving a great variety of problems involving rates of change in science and engineering.

2.6 Exercises

1. A curve has equation $y = f(x)$.
  (a) Write an expression for the slope of the secant line through the points $P(3, f(3))$ and $Q(x, f(x))$.
  (b) Write an expression for the slope of the tangent line at P.

2. Graph the curve $y = e^x$ in the viewing rectangles $[-1, 1]$ by $[0, 2]$, $[-0.5, 0.5]$ by $[0.5, 1.5]$, and $[-0.1, 0.1]$ by $[0.9, 1.1]$. What do you notice about the curve as you zoom in toward the point $(0, 1)$?

3. (a) Find the slope of the tangent line to the parabola $y = 4x - x^2$ at the point $(1, 3)$
    (i) using Definition 1   (ii) using Equation 2
  (b) Find an equation of the tangent line in part (a).
  (c) Graph the parabola and the tangent line. As a check on your work, zoom in toward the point $(1, 3)$ until the parabola and the tangent line are indistinguishable.

4. (a) Find the slope of the tangent line to the curve $y = x - x^3$ at the point $(1, 0)$
    (i) using Definition 1   (ii) using Equation 2
  (b) Find an equation of the tangent line in part (a).
  (c) Graph the curve and the tangent line in successively smaller viewing rectangles centered at $(1, 0)$ until the curve and the line appear to coincide.

5–8 Find an equation of the tangent line to the curve at the given point.

5. $y = 4x - 3x^2$, $(2, -4)$ **6.** $y = x^3 - 3x + 1$, $(2, 3)$

7. $y = \sqrt{x}$, $(1, 1)$ **8.** $y = \dfrac{2x + 1}{x + 2}$, $(1, 1)$

9. (a) Find the slope of the tangent to the curve $y = 3 + 4x^2 - 2x^3$ at the point where $x = a$.

  (b) Find equations of the tangent lines at the points $(1, 5)$ and $(2, 3)$.
  (c) Graph the curve and both tangents on a common screen.

10. (a) Find the slope of the tangent to the curve $y = 1/\sqrt{x}$ at the point where $x = a$.
  (b) Find equations of the tangent lines at the points $(1, 1)$ and $\left(4, \frac{1}{2}\right)$.
  (c) Graph the curve and both tangents on a common screen.

11. (a) A particle starts by moving to the right along a horizontal line; the graph of its position function is shown. When is the particle moving to the right? Moving to the left? Standing still?
  (b) Draw a graph of the velocity function.

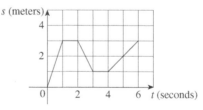

12. Shown are graphs of the position functions of two runners, A and B, who run a 100-m race and finish in a tie.

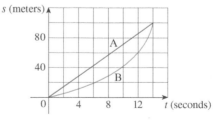

---

1. Homework Hints available in TEC

(a) Describe and compare how the runners run the race.
(b) At what time is the distance between the runners the greatest?
(c) At what time do they have the same velocity?

13. If a ball is thrown into the air with a velocity of 40 ft/s, its height (in feet) after t seconds is given by $y = 40t - 16t^2$. Find the velocity when $t = 2$.

14. If a rock is thrown upward on the planet Mars with a velocity of 10 m/s, its height (in meters) after t seconds is given by $H = 10t - 1.86t^2$.
(a) Find the velocity of the rock after one second.
(b) Find the velocity of the rock when $t = a$.
(c) When will the rock hit the surface?
(d) With what velocity will the rock hit the surface?

15. The displacement (in meters) of a particle moving in a straight line is given by the equation of motion $s = 1/t^2$, where t is measured in seconds. Find the velocity of the particle at times $t = a, t = 1, t = 2,$ and $t = 3$.

16. The displacement (in meters) of a particle moving in a straight line is given by $s = t^2 - 8t + 18$, where t is measured in seconds.
(a) Find the average velocity over each time interval:
    (i) [3, 4]   (ii) [3.5, 4]
    (iii) [4, 5]   (iv) [4, 4.5]
(b) Find the instantaneous velocity when $t = 4$.
(c) Draw the graph of s as a function of t and draw the secant lines whose slopes are the average velocities in part (a) and the tangent line whose slope is the instantaneous velocity in part (b).

17. For the function g whose graph is given, arrange the following numbers in increasing order and explain your reasoning:

$$0 \quad g'(-2) \quad g'(0) \quad g'(2) \quad g'(4)$$

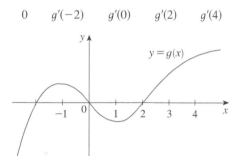

18. Find an equation of the tangent line to the graph of $y = g(x)$ at $x = 5$ if $g(5) = -3$ and $g'(5) = 4$.

19. If an equation of the tangent line to the curve $y = f(x)$ at the point where $a = 2$ is $y = 4x - 5$, find $f(2)$ and $f'(2)$.

20. If the tangent line to $y = f(x)$ at (4, 3) passes through the point (0, 2), find $f(4)$ and $f'(4)$.

21. Sketch the graph of a function f for which $f(0) = 0$, $f'(0) = 3$, $f'(1) = 0$, and $f'(2) = -1$.

22. Sketch the graph of a function g for which $g(0) = g(2) = g(4) = 0$, $g'(1) = g'(3) = 0$, $g'(0) = g'(4) = 1$, $g'(2) = -1$, $\lim_{x \to \infty} g(x) = \infty$, and $\lim_{x \to -\infty} g(x) = -\infty$.

23. If $f(x) = 3x^2 - x^3$, find $f'(1)$ and use it to find an equation of the tangent line to the curve $y = 3x^2 - x^3$ at the point (1, 2).

24. If $g(x) = x^4 - 2$, find $g'(1)$ and use it to find an equation of the tangent line to the curve $y = x^4 - 2$ at the point (1, -1).

25. (a) If $F(x) = 5x/(1 + x^2)$, find $F'(2)$ and use it to find an equation of the tangent line to the curve $y = 5x/(1 + x^2)$ at the point (2, 2).
(b) Illustrate part (a) by graphing the curve and the tangent line on the same screen.

26. (a) If $G(x) = 4x^2 - x^3$, find $G'(a)$ and use it to find equations of the tangent lines to the curve $y = 4x^2 - x^3$ at the points (2, 8) and (3, 9).
(b) Illustrate part (a) by graphing the curve and the tangent lines on the same screen.

27–32 Find $f'(a)$.

27. $f(x) = 3x^2 - 4x + 1$

28. $f(t) = 2t^3 + t$

29. $f(t) = \dfrac{2t + 1}{t + 3}$

30. $f(x) = x^{-2}$

31. $f(x) = \sqrt{1 - 2x}$

32. $f(x) = \dfrac{4}{\sqrt{1 - x}}$

33–38 Each limit represents the derivative of some function f at some number a. State such an f and a in each case.

33. $\lim\limits_{h \to 0} \dfrac{(1 + h)^{10} - 1}{h}$

34. $\lim\limits_{h \to 0} \dfrac{\sqrt[4]{16 + h} - 2}{h}$

35. $\lim\limits_{x \to 5} \dfrac{2^x - 32}{x - 5}$

36. $\lim\limits_{x \to \pi/4} \dfrac{\tan x - 1}{x - \pi/4}$

37. $\lim\limits_{h \to 0} \dfrac{\cos(\pi + h) + 1}{h}$

38. $\lim\limits_{t \to 1} \dfrac{t^4 + t - 2}{t - 1}$

39–40 A particle moves along a straight line with equation of motion $s = f(t)$, where s is measured in meters and t in seconds. Find the velocity and the speed when $t = 5$.

39. $f(t) = 100 + 50t - 4.9t^2$

40. $f(t) = t^{-1} - t$

41. A warm can of soda is placed in a cold refrigerator. Sketch the graph of the temperature of the soda as a function of time. Is the initial rate of change of temperature greater or less than the rate of change after an hour?

42. A roast turkey is taken from an oven when its temperature has reached 185°F and is placed on a table in a room where the temperature is 75°F. The graph shows how the temperature of the turkey decreases and eventually approaches room temperature. By measuring the slope of the tangent, estimate the rate of change of the temperature after an hour.

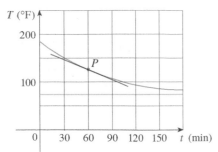

43. The number N of US cellular phone subscribers (in millions) is shown in the table. (Midyear estimates are given.)

t	1996	1998	2000	2002	2004	2006
N	44	69	109	141	182	233

(a) Find the average rate of cell phone growth
    (i) from 2002 to 2006   (ii) from 2002 to 2004
    (iii) from 2000 to 2002
    In each case, include the units.
(b) Estimate the instantaneous rate of growth in 2002 by taking the average of two average rates of change. What are its units?
(c) Estimate the instantaneous rate of growth in 2002 by measuring the slope of a tangent.

44. The number N of locations of a popular coffeehouse chain is given in the table. (The numbers of locations as of June 30 are given.)

Year	2003	2004	2005	2006	2007
N	7225	8569	10,241	12,440	15,011

(a) Find the average rate of growth
    (i) from 2005 to 2007   (ii) from 2005 to 2006
    (iii) from 2004 to 2005
    In each case, include the units.
(b) Estimate the instantaneous rate of growth in 2005 by taking the average of two average rates of change. What are its units?
(c) Estimate the instantaneous rate of growth in 2005 by measuring the slope of a tangent.

45. The cost (in dollars) of producing x units of a certain commodity is $C(x) = 5000 + 10x + 0.05x^2$.
(a) Find the average rate of change of C with respect to x when the production level is changed
    (i) from $x = 100$ to $x = 105$
    (ii) from $x = 100$ to $x = 101$

(b) Find the instantaneous rate of change of C with respect to x when $x = 100$. (This is called the *marginal cost*. Its significance will be explained in Section 3.8.)

46. If a cylindrical tank holds 100,000 gallons of water, which can be drained from the bottom of the tank in an hour, then Torricelli's Law gives the volume V of water remaining in the tank after t minutes as

$$V(t) = 100{,}000\left(1 - \tfrac{1}{60}t\right)^2 \qquad 0 \le t \le 60$$

Find the rate at which the water is flowing out of the tank (the instantaneous rate of change of V with respect to t) as a function of t. What are its units? For times $t = 0$, 10, 20, 30, 40, 50, and 60 min, find the flow rate and the amount of water remaining in the tank. Summarize your findings in a sentence or two. At what time is the flow rate the greatest? The least?

47. The cost of producing x ounces of gold from a new gold mine is $C = f(x)$ dollars.
(a) What is the meaning of the derivative $f'(x)$? What are its units?
(b) What does the statement $f'(800) = 17$ mean?
(c) Do you think the values of $f'(x)$ will increase or decrease in the short term? What about the long term? Explain.

48. The number of bacteria after t hours in a controlled laboratory experiment is $n = f(t)$.
(a) What is the meaning of the derivative $f'(5)$? What are its units?
(b) Suppose there is an unlimited amount of space and nutrients for the bacteria. Which do you think is larger, $f'(5)$ or $f'(10)$? If the supply of nutrients is limited, would that affect your conclusion? Explain.

49. Let $T(t)$ be the temperature (in °F) in Baltimore t hours after midnight on Sept. 26, 2007. The table shows values of this function recorded every two hours. What is the meaning of $T'(10)$? Estimate its value.

t	0	2	4	6	8	10	12	14
T	68	65	63	63	65	76	85	91

50. The quantity (in pounds) of a gourmet ground coffee that is sold by a coffee company at a price of p dollars per pound is $Q = f(p)$.
(a) What is the meaning of the derivative $f'(8)$? What are its units?
(b) Is $f'(8)$ positive or negative? Explain.

51. The quantity of oxygen that can dissolve in water depends on the temperature of the water. (So thermal pollution influences

the oxygen content of water.) The graph shows how oxygen solubility S varies as a function of the water temperature T.
(a) What is the meaning of the derivative $S'(T)$? What are its units?
(b) Estimate the value of $S'(16)$ and interpret it.

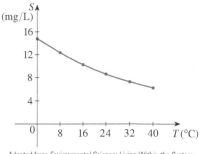

Adapted from *Environmental Science: Living Within the System of Nature*, 2d ed.; by Charles E. Kupchella, © 1989. Reprinted by permission of Prentice-Hall, Inc., Upper Saddle River, NJ.

52. The graph shows the influence of the temperature T on the maximum sustainable swimming speed S of Coho salmon.
(a) What is the meaning of the derivative $S'(T)$? What are its units?

(b) Estimate the values of $S'(15)$ and $S'(25)$ and interpret them.

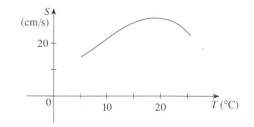

53–54 Determine whether $f'(0)$ exists.

53. $f(x) = \begin{cases} x \sin \dfrac{1}{x} & \text{if } x \neq 0 \\ 0 & \text{if } x = 0 \end{cases}$

54. $f(x) = \begin{cases} x^2 \sin \dfrac{1}{x} & \text{if } x \neq 0 \\ 0 & \text{if } x = 0 \end{cases}$

WRITING PROJECT	**Early Methods for Finding Tangents**

The first person to formulate explicitly the ideas of limits and derivatives was Sir Isaac Newton in the 1660s. But Newton acknowledged that "If I have seen further than other men, it is because I have stood on the shoulders of giants." Two of those giants were Pierre Fermat (1601–1665) and Newton's mentor at Cambridge, Isaac Barrow (1630–1677). Newton was familiar with the methods that these men used to find tangent lines, and their methods played a role in Newton's eventual formulation of calculus.

The following references contain explanations of these methods. Read one or more of the references and write a report comparing the methods of either Fermat or Barrow to modern methods. In particular, use the method of Section 2.6 to find an equation of the tangent line to the curve $y = x^3 + 2x$ at the point $(1, 3)$ and show how either Fermat or Barrow would have solved the same problem. Although you used derivatives and they did not, point out similarities between the methods.

1. Carl Boyer and Uta Merzbach, *A History of Mathematics* (New York: Wiley, 1989), pp. 389, 432.

2. C. H. Edwards, *The Historical Development of the Calculus* (New York: Springer-Verlag, 1979), pp. 124, 132.

3. Howard Eves, *An Introduction to the History of Mathematics*, 6th ed. (New York: Saunders, 1990), pp. 391, 395.

4. Morris Kline, *Mathematical Thought from Ancient to Modern Times* (New York: Oxford University Press, 1972), pp. 344, 346.

2.7   The Derivative as a Function

In the preceding section we considered the derivative of a function f at a fixed number a:

$$\boxed{1} \qquad f'(a) = \lim_{h \to 0} \frac{f(a + h) - f(a)}{h}$$

Here we change our point of view and let the number a vary. If we replace a in Equation 1 by a variable x, we obtain

$$\boxed{2} \qquad \boxed{f'(x) = \lim_{h \to 0} \frac{f(x + h) - f(x)}{h}}$$

Given any number x for which this limit exists, we assign to x the number $f'(x)$. So we can regard f' as a new function, called the **derivative of f** and defined by Equation 2. We know that the value of f' at x, $f'(x)$, can be interpreted geometrically as the slope of the tangent line to the graph of f at the point $(x, f(x))$.

The function f' is called the derivative of f because it has been "derived" from f by the limiting operation in Equation 2. The domain of f' is the set $\{x \mid f'(x) \text{ exists}\}$ and may be smaller than the domain of f.

V   EXAMPLE 1   Derivative of a function given by a graph   The graph of a function f is given in Figure 1. Use it to sketch the graph of the derivative f'.

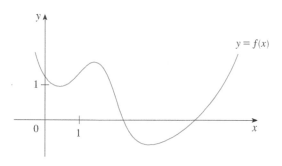

FIGURE 1

SOLUTION   We can estimate the value of the derivative at any value of x by drawing the tangent at the point $(x, f(x))$ and estimating its slope. For instance, for $x = 5$ we draw the tangent at P in Figure 2(a) and estimate its slope to be about $\frac{3}{2}$, so $f'(5) \approx 1.5$. This allows us to plot the point $P'(5, 1.5)$ on the graph of f' directly beneath P. Repeating this procedure at several points, we get the graph shown in Figure 2(b). Notice that the tangents at A, B, and C are horizontal, so the derivative is 0 there and the graph of f' crosses the x-axis at the points A', B', and C', directly beneath A, B, and C. Between A and B the tangents have positive slope, so $f'(x)$ is positive there. But between B and C the tangents have negative slope, so $f'(x)$ is negative there.

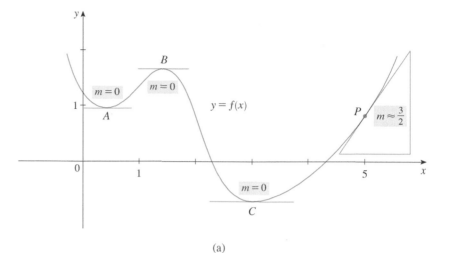

(a)

TEC Visual 2.7 shows an animation of
Figure 2 for several functions.

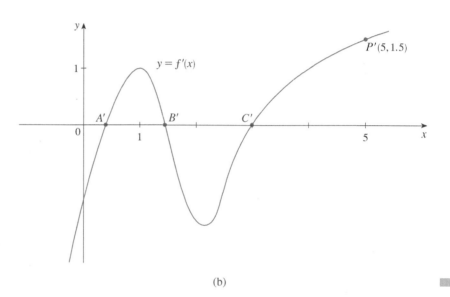

FIGURE 2   (b)

t	$B(t)$
1980	9,847
1982	9,856
1984	9,855
1986	9,862
1988	9,884
1990	9,969
1992	10,046
1994	10,122
1996	10,179
1998	10,217
2000	10,264
2002	10,312
2004	10,348
2006	10,379

If a function is defined by a table of values, then we can construct a table of approximate values of its derivative, as in the next example.

EXAMPLE 2 **Derivative of a function given by a table**   Let $B(t)$ be the population of Belgium at time t. The table at the left gives midyear values of $B(t)$, in thousands, from 1980 to 2006. Construct a table of values for the derivative of this function.

SOLUTION We assume that there were no wild fluctuations in the population between the stated values. Let's start by approximating $B'(1988)$, the rate of increase of the population of Belgium in mid-1988. Since

$$B'(1988) = \lim_{h \to 0} \frac{B(1988 + h) - B(1988)}{h}$$

we have

$$B'(1988) \approx \frac{B(1988 + h) - B(1988)}{h}$$

for small values of h.

For $h = 2$, we get

$$B'(1988) \approx \frac{B(1990) - B(1988)}{2} = \frac{9969 - 9884}{2} = 42.5$$

t	$B'(t)$
1980	4.50
1982	2.00
1984	1.50
1986	7.25
1988	26.75
1990	40.50
1992	38.25
1994	33.25
1996	28.50
1998	22.25
2000	23.75
2002	21.00
2004	11.50
2006	5.00

(This is the average rate of increase between 1988 and 1990.) For $h = -2$, we have

$$B'(1988) \approx \frac{B(1986) - B(1988)}{-2} = \frac{9862 - 9884}{-2} = 11$$

which is the average rate of increase between 1986 and 1988. We get a more accurate approximation if we take the average of these rates of change:

$$B'(1988) \approx \tfrac{1}{2}(42.5 + 11) = 26.75$$

This means that in 1988 the population was increasing at a rate of about 26,750 people per year.

Making similar calculations for the other values (except at the endpoints), we get the table at the left, which shows the approximate values for the derivative.

Figure 3 illustrates Example 2 by showing graphs of the population function $B(t)$ and its derivative $B'(t)$. Notice how the rate of population growth increases to a maximum in 1990 and decreases thereafter.

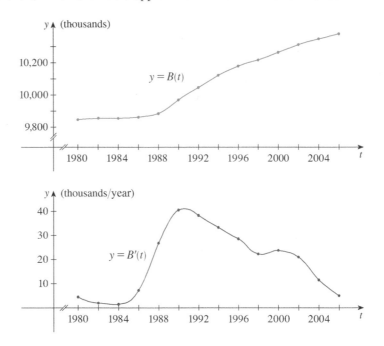

FIGURE 3

V **EXAMPLE 3** **Derivative of a function given by a formula**
(a) If $f(x) = x^3 - x$, find a formula for $f'(x)$.
(b) Illustrate by comparing the graphs of f and f'.

SOLUTION
(a) When using Equation 2 to compute a derivative, we must remember that the variable is h and that x is temporarily regarded as a constant during the calculation of the limit.

$$f'(x) = \lim_{h \to 0} \frac{f(x+h) - f(x)}{h} = \lim_{h \to 0} \frac{[(x+h)^3 - (x+h)] - [x^3 - x]}{h}$$

$$= \lim_{h \to 0} \frac{x^3 + 3x^2h + 3xh^2 + h^3 - x - h - x^3 + x}{h}$$

$$= \lim_{h \to 0} \frac{3x^2h + 3xh^2 + h^3 - h}{h} = \lim_{h \to 0} (3x^2 + 3xh + h^2 - 1) = 3x^2 - 1$$

(b) We use a graphing device to graph f and f' in Figure 4. Notice that $f'(x) = 0$ when f has horizontal tangents and $f'(x)$ is positive when the tangents have positive slope. So these graphs serve as a check on our work in part (a).

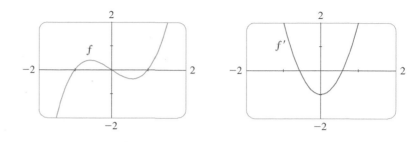

FIGURE 4

EXAMPLE 4 If $f(x) = \sqrt{x}$, find the derivative of f. State the domain of f'.

SOLUTION

$$f'(x) = \lim_{h \to 0} \frac{f(x+h) - f(x)}{h} = \lim_{h \to 0} \frac{\sqrt{x+h} - \sqrt{x}}{h}$$

Here we rationalize the numerator.

$$= \lim_{h \to 0} \left(\frac{\sqrt{x+h} - \sqrt{x}}{h} \cdot \frac{\sqrt{x+h} + \sqrt{x}}{\sqrt{x+h} + \sqrt{x}} \right)$$

$$= \lim_{h \to 0} \frac{(x+h) - x}{h(\sqrt{x+h} + \sqrt{x})} = \lim_{h \to 0} \frac{1}{\sqrt{x+h} + \sqrt{x}}$$

$$= \frac{1}{\sqrt{x} + \sqrt{x}} = \frac{1}{2\sqrt{x}}$$

We see that $f'(x)$ exists if $x > 0$, so the domain of f' is $(0, \infty)$. This is smaller than the domain of f, which is $[0, \infty)$.

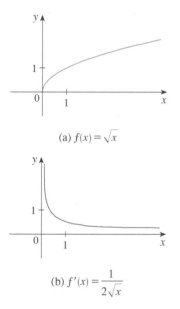

(a) $f(x) = \sqrt{x}$

(b) $f'(x) = \dfrac{1}{2\sqrt{x}}$

FIGURE 5

Let's check to see that the result of Example 4 is reasonable by looking at the graphs of f and f' in Figure 5. When x is close to 0, $\sqrt{x}$ is also close to 0, so $f'(x) = 1/(2\sqrt{x})$ is very large and this corresponds to the steep tangent lines near $(0, 0)$ in Figure 5(a) and the large values of $f'(x)$ just to the right of 0 in Figure 5(b). When x is large, $f'(x)$ is very small and this corresponds to the flatter tangent lines at the far right of the graph of f and the horizontal asymptote of the graph of f'.

EXAMPLE 5 Find f' if $f(x) = \dfrac{1 - x}{2 + x}$.

SOLUTION

$$\frac{\dfrac{a}{b} - \dfrac{c}{d}}{e} = \frac{ad - bc}{bd} \cdot \frac{1}{e}$$

$$f'(x) = \lim_{h \to 0} \frac{f(x+h) - f(x)}{h} = \lim_{h \to 0} \frac{\dfrac{1 - (x+h)}{2 + (x+h)} - \dfrac{1 - x}{2 + x}}{h}$$

$$= \lim_{h \to 0} \frac{(1 - x - h)(2 + x) - (1 - x)(2 + x + h)}{h(2 + x + h)(2 + x)}$$

$$= \lim_{h \to 0} \frac{(2 - x - 2h - x^2 - xh) - (2 - x + h - x^2 - xh)}{h(2 + x + h)(2 + x)}$$

$$= \lim_{h \to 0} \frac{-3h}{h(2 + x + h)(2 + x)} = \lim_{h \to 0} \frac{-3}{(2 + x + h)(2 + x)} = -\frac{3}{(2 + x)^2}$$

Other Notations

If we use the traditional notation $y = f(x)$ to indicate that the independent variable is x and the dependent variable is y, then some common alternative notations for the derivative are as follows:

$$f'(x) = y' = \frac{dy}{dx} = \frac{df}{dx} = \frac{d}{dx} f(x) = Df(x) = D_x f(x)$$

The symbols D and d/dx are called **differentiation operators** because they indicate the operation of **differentiation**, which is the process of calculating a derivative.

The symbol dy/dx, which was introduced by Leibniz, should not be regarded as a ratio (for the time being); it is simply a synonym for $f'(x)$. Nonetheless, it is a very useful and suggestive notation, especially when used in conjunction with increment notation. Referring to Equation 2.6.6, we can rewrite the definition of derivative in Leibniz notation in the form

$$\frac{dy}{dx} = \lim_{\Delta x \to 0} \frac{\Delta y}{\Delta x}$$

If we want to indicate the value of a derivative dy/dx in Leibniz notation at a specific number a, we use the notation

$$\frac{dy}{dx} \bigg|_{x=a} \qquad \text{or} \qquad \frac{dy}{dx} \bigg]_{x=a}$$

which is a synonym for $f'(a)$.

---

3   **Definition**   A function f is **differentiable at** a if $f'(a)$ exists. It is **differentiable on an open interval** (a, b) [or (a, ∞) or $(-\infty, a)$ or $(-\infty, \infty)$] if it is differentiable at every number in the interval.

V   EXAMPLE 6   Where is the function $f(x) = |x|$ differentiable?

SOLUTION   If $x > 0$, then $|x| = x$ and we can choose h small enough that $x + h > 0$ and hence $|x + h| = x + h$. Therefore, for $x > 0$, we have

$$f'(x) = \lim_{h \to 0} \frac{|x + h| - |x|}{h} = \lim_{h \to 0} \frac{(x + h) - x}{h}$$

$$= \lim_{h \to 0} \frac{h}{h} = \lim_{h \to 0} 1 = 1$$

and so f is differentiable for any $x > 0$.

Similarly, for $x < 0$ we have $|x| = -x$ and h can be chosen small enough that $x + h < 0$ and so $|x + h| = -(x + h)$. Therefore, for $x < 0$,

$$f'(x) = \lim_{h \to 0} \frac{|x + h| - |x|}{h} = \lim_{h \to 0} \frac{-(x + h) - (-x)}{h}$$

$$= \lim_{h \to 0} \frac{-h}{h} = \lim_{h \to 0} (-1) = -1$$

and so f is differentiable for any $x < 0$.

For $x = 0$ we have to investigate

$$f'(0) = \lim_{h \to 0} \frac{f(0 + h) - f(0)}{h}$$

$$= \lim_{h \to 0} \frac{|0 + h| - |0|}{h} \quad \text{(if it exists)}$$

Let's compute the left and right limits separately:

$$\lim_{h \to 0^+} \frac{|0 + h| - |0|}{h} = \lim_{h \to 0^+} \frac{|h|}{h} = \lim_{h \to 0^+} \frac{h}{h} = \lim_{h \to 0^+} 1 = 1$$

and $\quad \lim_{h \to 0^-} \frac{|0 + h| - |0|}{h} = \lim_{h \to 0^-} \frac{|h|}{h} = \lim_{h \to 0^-} \frac{-h}{h} = \lim_{h \to 0^-} (-1) = -1$

Since these limits are different, $f'(0)$ does not exist. Thus f is differentiable at all x except 0.

A formula for f' is given by

$$f'(x) = \begin{cases} 1 & \text{if } x > 0 \\ -1 & \text{if } x < 0 \end{cases}$$

and its graph is shown in Figure 6(b). The fact that $f'(0)$ does not exist is reflected geometrically in the fact that the curve $y = |x|$ does not have a tangent line at $(0, 0)$. [See Figure 6(a).]

Both continuity and differentiability are desirable properties for a function to have. The following theorem shows how these properties are related.

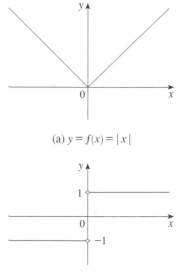

(a) $y = f(x) = |x|$

(b) $y = f'(x)$

FIGURE 6

---

4 **Theorem** If f is differentiable at a, then f is continuous at a.

PROOF To prove that f is continuous at a, we have to show that $\lim_{x \to a} f(x) = f(a)$. We do this by showing that the difference $f(x) - f(a)$ approaches 0 as x approaches a.

The given information is that f is differentiable at a, that is,

$$f'(a) = \lim_{x \to a} \frac{f(x) - f(a)}{x - a}$$

exists (see Equation 2.6.5). To connect the given and the unknown, we divide and multiply $f(x) - f(a)$ by $x - a$ (which we can do when $x \neq a$):

$$f(x) - f(a) = \frac{f(x) - f(a)}{x - a} (x - a)$$

Thus, using the Product Law and (2.6.5), we can write

$$\lim_{x \to a} [f(x) - f(a)] = \lim_{x \to a} \frac{f(x) - f(a)}{x - a} (x - a)$$

$$= \lim_{x \to a} \frac{f(x) - f(a)}{x - a} \cdot \lim_{x \to a} (x - a)$$

$$= f'(a) \cdot 0 = 0$$

To use what we have just proved, we start with $f(x)$ and add and subtract $f(a)$:

$$\lim_{x \to a} f(x) = \lim_{x \to a} [f(a) + (f(x) - f(a))]$$

$$= \lim_{x \to a} f(a) + \lim_{x \to a} [f(x) - f(a)]$$

$$= f(a) + 0 = f(a)$$

Therefore f is continuous at a.

⊘ **Note:** The converse of Theorem 4 is false; that is, there are functions that are continuous but not differentiable. For instance, the function $f(x) = |x|$ is continuous at 0 because

$$\lim_{x \to 0} f(x) = \lim_{x \to 0} |x| = 0 = f(0)$$

(See Example 7 in Section 2.3.) But in Example 6 we showed that f is not differentiable at 0.

How Can a Function Fail to be Differentiable?

We saw that the function $y = |x|$ in Example 6 is not differentiable at 0 and Figure 6(a) shows that its graph changes direction abruptly when $x = 0$. In general, if the graph of a function f has a "corner" or "kink" in it, then the graph of f has no tangent at this point and f is not differentiable there. [In trying to compute $f'(a)$, we find that the left and right limits are different.]

Theorem 4 gives another way for a function not to have a derivative. It says that if f is not continuous at a, then f is not differentiable at a. So at any discontinuity (for instance, a jump discontinuity) f fails to be differentiable.

A third possibility is that the curve has a **vertical tangent line** when $x = a$; that is, f is continuous at a and

$$\lim_{x \to a} |f'(x)| = \infty$$

This means that the tangent lines become steeper and steeper as $x \to a$. Figure 7 shows one way that this can happen; Figure 8(c) shows another. Figure 8 illustrates the three possibilities that we have discussed.

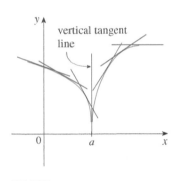

FIGURE 7

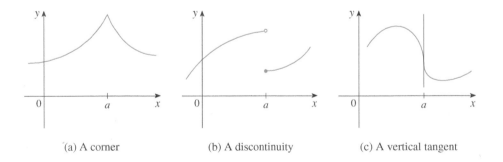

FIGURE 8
Three ways for f not to be differentiable at a

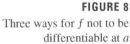

(a) A corner   (b) A discontinuity   (c) A vertical tangent

A graphing calculator or computer provides another way of looking at differentiability. If f is differentiable at a, then when we zoom in toward the point $(a, f(a))$ the graph straightens out and appears more and more like a line. (See Figure 9. We saw a specific example of this in Figure 2 in Section 2.6.) But no matter how much we zoom in toward a point like the ones in Figures 7 and 8(a), we can't eliminate the sharp point or corner (see Figure 10).

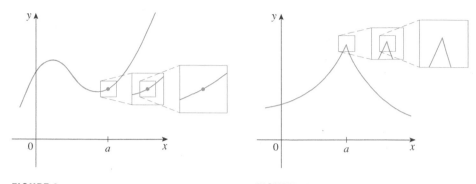

FIGURE 9
f is differentiable at a.

FIGURE 10
f is not differentiable at a.

Higher Derivatives

If f is a differentiable function, then its derivative f' is also a function, so f' may have a derivative of its own, denoted by $(f')' = f''$. This new function f'' is called the **second derivative** of f because it is the derivative of the derivative of f. Using Leibniz notation, we write the second derivative of $y = f(x)$ as

$$\frac{d}{dx}\left(\frac{dy}{dx}\right) = \frac{d^2y}{dx^2}$$

EXAMPLE 7 If $f(x) = x^3 - x$, find and interpret $f''(x)$.

SOLUTION In Example 3 we found that the first derivative is $f'(x) = 3x^2 - 1$. So the second derivative is

$$f''(x) = (f')'(x) = \lim_{h \to 0} \frac{f'(x+h) - f'(x)}{h} = \lim_{h \to 0} \frac{[3(x+h)^2 - 1] - [3x^2 - 1]}{h}$$

$$= \lim_{h \to 0} \frac{3x^2 + 6xh + 3h^2 - 1 - 3x^2 + 1}{h} = \lim_{h \to 0} (6x + 3h) = 6x$$

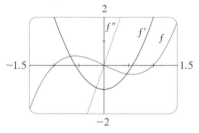

FIGURE 11

TEC In Module 2.7 you can see how changing the coefficients of a polynomial f affects the appearance of the graphs of f, f', and f''.

The graphs of f, f', and f'' are shown in Figure 11.

We can interpret $f''(x)$ as the slope of the curve $y = f'(x)$ at the point $(x, f'(x))$. In other words, it is the rate of change of the slope of the original curve $y = f(x)$.

Notice from Figure 11 that $f''(x)$ is negative when $y = f'(x)$ has negative slope and positive when $y = f'(x)$ has positive slope. So the graphs serve as a check on our calculations.

In general, we can interpret a second derivative as a rate of change of a rate of change. The most familiar example of this is *acceleration,* which we define as follows.

If $s = s(t)$ is the position function of an object that moves in a straight line, we know that its first derivative represents the velocity $v(t)$ of the object as a function of time:

$$v(t) = s'(t) = \frac{ds}{dt}$$

The instantaneous rate of change of velocity with respect to time is called the **acceleration** $a(t)$ of the object. Thus the acceleration function is the derivative of the velocity function and is therefore the second derivative of the position function:

$$a(t) = v'(t) = s''(t)$$

or, in Leibniz notation,

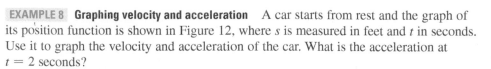

$$a = \frac{dv}{dt} = \frac{d^2s}{dt^2}$$

EXAMPLE 8 **Graphing velocity and acceleration** A car starts from rest and the graph of its position function is shown in Figure 12, where s is measured in feet and t in seconds. Use it to graph the velocity and acceleration of the car. What is the acceleration at $t = 2$ seconds?

SOLUTION By measuring the slope of the graph of $s = f(t)$ at $t = 0, 1, 2, 3, 4,$ and 5, and using the method of Example 1, we plot the graph of the velocity function $v = f'(t)$ in Figure 13. The acceleration when $t = 2$ s is $a = f''(2)$, the slope of the tangent line to the graph of f' when $t = 2$. We estimate the slope of this tangent line to be

$$a(2) = f''(2) = v'(2) \approx \tfrac{27}{3} = 9 \text{ ft/s}^2$$

Similar measurements enable us to graph the acceleration function in Figure 14.

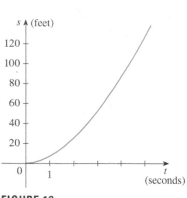

FIGURE 12

Position function of a car

The units for acceleration are feet per second per second, written as ft/s².

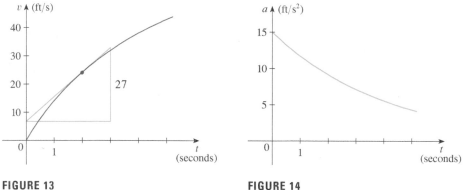

FIGURE 13

Velocity function

FIGURE 14

Acceleration function

The **third derivative** f''' is the derivative of the second derivative: $f''' = (f'')'$. So $f'''(x)$ can be interpreted as the slope of the curve $y = f''(x)$ or as the rate of change of $f''(x)$. If $y = f(x)$, then alternative notations for the third derivative are

$$y''' = f'''(x) = \frac{d}{dx}\left(\frac{d^2y}{dx^2}\right) = \frac{d^3y}{dx^3}$$

The process can be continued. The fourth derivative f'''' is usually denoted by $f^{(4)}$. In general, the nth derivative of f is denoted by $f^{(n)}$ and is obtained from f by differentiating n times. If $y = f(x)$, we write

$$y^{(n)} = f^{(n)}(x) = \frac{d^ny}{dx^n}$$

EXAMPLE 9 If $f(x) = x^3 - x$, find $f'''(x)$ and $f^{(4)}(x)$.

SOLUTION In Example 7 we found that $f''(x) = 6x$. The graph of the second derivative has equation $y = 6x$ and so it is a straight line with slope 6. Since the derivative $f'''(x)$ is the slope of $f''(x)$, we have

$$f'''(x) = 6$$

for all values of x. So f''' is a constant function and its graph is a horizontal line. Therefore, for all values of x,

$$f^{(4)}(x) = 0$$

We can also interpret the third derivative physically in the case where the function is the position function $s = s(t)$ of an object that moves along a straight line. Because

$s''' = (s'')' = a'$, the third derivative of the position function is the derivative of the acceleration function and is called the **jerk**:

$$j = \frac{da}{dt} = \frac{d^3s}{dt^3}$$

Thus the jerk j is the rate of change of acceleration. It is aptly named because a large jerk means a sudden change in acceleration, which causes an abrupt movement in a vehicle.

We have seen that one application of second and third derivatives occurs in analyzing the motion of objects using acceleration and jerk. We will investigate another application of second derivatives in Section 2.8, where we show how knowledge of f'' gives us information about the shape of the graph of f. In Chapter 8 we will see how second and higher derivatives enable us to represent functions as sums of infinite series.

2.7 Exercises

1–2 Use the given graph to estimate the value of each derivative. Then sketch the graph of f'.

1. (a) $f'(-3)$
  (b) $f'(-2)$
  (c) $f'(-1)$
  (d) $f'(0)$
  (e) $f'(1)$
  (f) $f'(2)$
  (g) $f'(3)$

2. (a) $f'(0)$
  (b) $f'(1)$
  (c) $f'(2)$
  (d) $f'(3)$
  (e) $f'(4)$
  (f) $f'(5)$
  (g) $f'(6)$
  (h) $f'(7)$

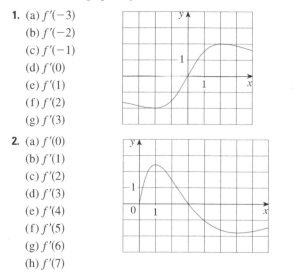

3. Match the graph of each function in (a)–(d) with the graph of its derivative in I–IV. Give reasons for your choices.

(a) (b)

(c) (d)

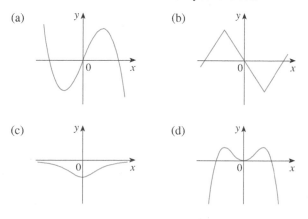

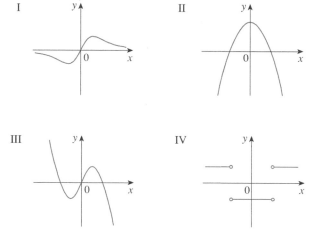

I II

III IV

4–11 Trace or copy the graph of the given function f. (Assume that the axes have equal scales.) Then use the method of Example 1 to sketch the graph of f' below it.

4.

5. **6.**

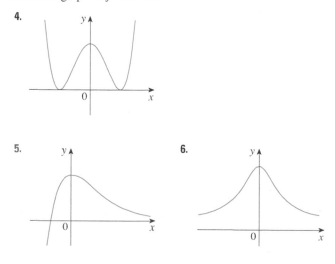

📈 Graphing calculator or computer with graphing software required   **1.** Homework Hints available in TEC

7.

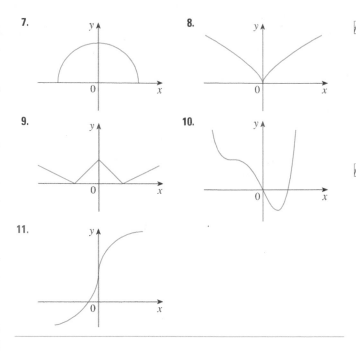

8.

9.

10.

11.

---

12. Shown is the graph of the population function $P(t)$ for yeast cells in a laboratory culture. Use the method of Example 1 to graph the derivative $P'(t)$. What does the graph of P' tell us about the yeast population?

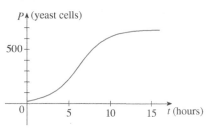

13. The graph shows how the average age of first marriage of Japanese men varied in the last half of the 20th century. Sketch the graph of the derivative function $M'(t)$. During which years was the derivative negative?

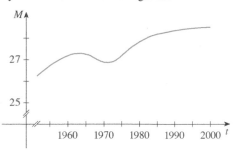

14–16 Make a careful sketch of the graph of f and below it sketch the graph of f' in the same manner as in Exercises 4–11. Can you guess a formula for $f'(x)$ from its graph?

14. $f(x) = \sin x$ **15.** $f(x) = e^x$

16. $f(x) = \ln x$

---

17. Let $f(x) = x^2$.
   (a) Estimate the values of $f'(0)$, $f'(\frac{1}{2})$, $f'(1)$, and $f'(2)$ by using a graphing device to zoom in on the graph of f.
   (b) Use symmetry to deduce the values of $f'(-\frac{1}{2})$, $f'(-1)$, and $f'(-2)$.
   (c) Use the results from parts (a) and (b) to guess a formula for $f'(x)$.
   (d) Use the definition of derivative to prove that your guess in part (c) is correct.

18. Let $f(x) = x^3$.
   (a) Estimate the values of $f'(0)$, $f'(\frac{1}{2})$, $f'(1)$, $f'(2)$, and $f'(3)$ by using a graphing device to zoom in on the graph of f.
   (b) Use symmetry to deduce the values of $f'(-\frac{1}{2})$, $f'(-1)$, $f'(-2)$, and $f'(-3)$.
   (c) Use the values from parts (a) and (b) to graph f'.
   (d) Guess a formula for $f'(x)$.
   (e) Use the definition of derivative to prove that your guess in part (d) is correct.

19–29 Find the derivative of the function using the definition of derivative. State the domain of the function and the domain of its derivative.

19. $f(x) = \frac{1}{2}x - \frac{1}{3}$ **20.** $f(x) = mx + b$

21. $f(t) = 5t - 9t^2$ **22.** $f(x) = 1.5x^2 - x + 3.7$

23. $f(x) = x^2 - 2x^3$ **24.** $f(x) = x + \sqrt{x}$

25. $g(x) = \sqrt{1 + 2x}$ **26.** $f(x) = \dfrac{x^2 - 1}{2x - 3}$

27. $G(t) = \dfrac{4t}{t + 1}$ **28.** $g(t) = \dfrac{1}{\sqrt{t}}$

29. $f(x) = x^4$

30–32 (a) Use the definition of derivative to calculate f'.
(b) Check to see that your answer is reasonable by comparing the graphs of f and f'.

30. $f(x) = x + 1/x$ **31.** $f(x) = x^4 + 2x$

32. $f(t) = t^2 - \sqrt{t}$

---

33. The unemployment rate $U(t)$ varies with time. The table (from the Bureau of Labor Statistics) gives the percentage of unemployed in the US labor force from 1998 to 2007.

t	$U(t)$	t	$U(t)$
1998	4.5	2003	6.0
1999	4.2	2004	5.5
2000	4.0	2005	5.1
2001	4.7	2006	4.6
2002	5.8	2007	4.6

(a) What is the meaning of $U'(t)$? What are its units?
(b) Construct a table of estimated values for $U'(t)$.

34. Let $P(t)$ be the percentage of Americans under the age of 18 at time t. The table gives values of this function in census years from 1950 to 2000.

t	$P(t)$	t	$P(t)$
1950	31.1	1980	28.0
1960	35.7	1990	25.7
1970	34.0	2000	25.7

(a) What is the meaning of $P'(t)$? What are its units?
(b) Construct a table of estimated values for $P'(t)$.
(c) Graph P and P'.
(d) How would it be possible to get more accurate values for $P'(t)$?

35–38 The graph of f is given. State, with reasons, the numbers at which f is not differentiable.

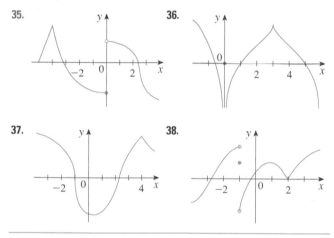

35.   **36.**

37.   **38.**

39. Graph the function $f(x) = x + \sqrt{|x|}$. Zoom in repeatedly, first toward the point $(-1, 0)$ and then toward the origin. What is different about the behavior of f in the vicinity of these two points? What do you conclude about the differentiability of f?

40. Zoom in toward the points $(1, 0)$, $(0, 1)$, and $(-1, 0)$ on the graph of the function $g(x) = (x^2 - 1)^{2/3}$. What do you notice? Account for what you see in terms of the differentiability of g.

41. The figure shows the graphs of f, f', and f''. Identify each curve, and explain your choices.

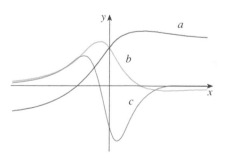

42. The figure shows graphs of f, f', f'', and f'''. Identify each curve, and explain your choices.

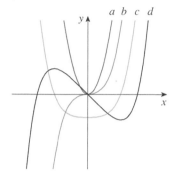

43. The figure shows the graphs of three functions. One is the position function of a car, one is the velocity of the car, and one is its acceleration. Identify each curve, and explain your choices.

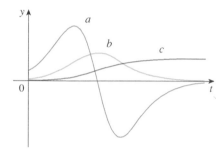

44. The figure shows the graphs of four functions. One is the position function of a car, one is the velocity of the car, one is its acceleration, and one is its jerk. Identify each curve, and explain your choices.

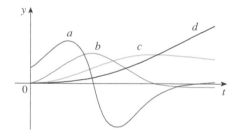

45–46 Use the definition of a derivative to find $f'(x)$ and $f''(x)$. Then graph f, f', and f'' on a common screen and check to see if your answers are reasonable.

45. $f(x) = 3x^2 + 2x + 1$ **46.** $f(x) = x^3 - 3x$

47. If $f(x) = 2x^2 - x^3$, find $f'(x)$, $f''(x)$, $f'''(x)$, and $f^{(4)}(x)$. Graph f, f', f'', and f''' on a common screen. Are the graphs consistent with the geometric interpretations of these derivatives?

48. (a) The graph of a position function of a car is shown, where s is measured in feet and t in seconds. Use it to graph the velocity and acceleration of the car. What is the acceleration at $t = 10$ seconds?

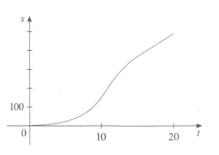

(b) Use the acceleration curve from part (a) to estimate the jerk at $t = 10$ seconds. What are the units for jerk?

49. Let $f(x) = \sqrt[3]{x}$.
(a) If $a \neq 0$, use Equation 2.6.5 to find $f'(a)$.
(b) Show that $f'(0)$ does not exist.
(c) Show that $y = \sqrt[3]{x}$ has a vertical tangent line at $(0, 0)$. (Recall the shape of the graph of f. See Figure 13 in Section 1.2.)

50. (a) If $g(x) = x^{2/3}$, show that $g'(0)$ does not exist.
(b) If $a \neq 0$, find $g'(a)$.

(c) Show that $y = x^{2/3}$ has a vertical tangent line at $(0, 0)$.
(d) Illustrate part (c) by graphing $y = x^{2/3}$.

51. Show that the function $f(x) = |x - 6|$ is not differentiable at 6. Find a formula for f' and sketch its graph.

52. Where is the greatest integer function $f(x) = [\![x]\!]$ not differentiable? Find a formula for f' and sketch its graph.

53. Recall that a function f is called *even* if $f(-x) = f(x)$ for all x in its domain and *odd* if $f(-x) = -f(x)$ for all such x. Prove each of the following.
(a) The derivative of an even function is an odd function.
(b) The derivative of an odd function is an even function.

54. When you turn on a hot-water faucet, the temperature T of the water depends on how long the water has been running.
(a) Sketch a possible graph of T as a function of the time t that has elapsed since the faucet was turned on.
(b) Describe how the rate of change of T with respect to t varies as t increases.
(c) Sketch a graph of the derivative of T.

55. Let ℓ be the tangent line to the parabola $y = x^2$ at the point $(1, 1)$. The *angle of inclination* of ℓ is the angle ϕ that ℓ makes with the positive direction of the x-axis. Calculate ϕ correct to the nearest degree.

2.8 What Does f' Say About f?

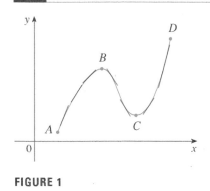

FIGURE 1

Many of the applications of calculus depend on our ability to deduce facts about a function f from information concerning its derivatives. Because $f'(x)$ represents the slope of the curve $y = f(x)$ at the point $(x, f(x))$, it tells us the direction in which the curve proceeds at each point. So it is reasonable to expect that information about $f'(x)$ will provide us with information about $f(x)$.

In particular, to see how the derivative of f can tell us where a function is increasing or decreasing, look at Figure 1. (Increasing functions and decreasing functions were defined in Section 1.1.) Between A and B and between C and D, the tangent lines have positive slope and so $f'(x) > 0$. Between B and C, the tangent lines have negative slope and so $f'(x) < 0$. Thus it appears that f increases when $f'(x)$ is positive and decreases when $f'(x)$ is negative.

It turns out, as we will see in Chapter 4, that what we observed for the function graphed in Figure 1 is always true. We state the general result as follows.

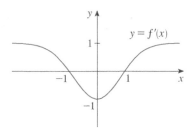

FIGURE 2

If $f'(x) > 0$ on an interval, then f is increasing on that interval.

If $f'(x) < 0$ on an interval, then f is decreasing on that interval.

EXAMPLE 1 **Given a graph of f', what does f look like?**
(a) If it is known that the graph of the derivative f' of a function is as shown in Figure 2, what can we say about f?
(b) If it is known that $f(0) = 0$, sketch a possible graph of f.

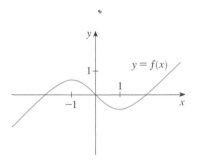

FIGURE 3

SOLUTION

(a) We observe from Figure 2 that $f'(x)$ is negative when $-1 < x < 1$, so the original function f must be decreasing on the interval $(-1, 1)$. Similarly, $f'(x)$ is positive for $x < -1$ and for $x > 1$, so f is increasing on the intervals $(-\infty, -1)$ and $(1, \infty)$. Also note that, since $f'(-1) = 0$ and $f'(1) = 0$, the graph of f has horizontal tangents when $x = \pm 1$.

(b) We use the information from part (a), and the fact that the graph passes through the origin, to sketch a possible graph of f in Figure 3. Notice that $f'(0) = -1$, so we have drawn the curve $y = f(x)$ passing through the origin with a slope of -1. Notice also that $f'(x) \to 1$ as $x \to \pm\infty$ (from Figure 2). So the slope of the curve $y = f(x)$ approaches 1 as x becomes large (positive or negative). That is why we have drawn the graph of f in Figure 3 progressively straighter as $x \to \pm\infty$.

We say that the function f in Example 1 has a **local maximum** at -1 because near $x = -1$ the values of $f(x)$ are at least as big as the neighboring values. Note that $f'(x)$ is positive to the left of -1 and negative just to the right of -1. Similarly, f has a **local minimum** at 1, where the derivative changes from negative to positive. In Chapter 4 we will develop these observations into a general method for finding optimal values of functions.

What Does f'' Say about f?

Let's see how the sign of $f''(x)$ affects the appearance of the graph of f. Since $f'' = (f')'$, we know that if $f''(x)$ is positive, then f' is an increasing function. This says that the slopes of the tangent lines of the curve $y = f(x)$ increase from left to right. Figure 4 shows the graph of such a function. The slope of this curve becomes progressively larger as x increases and we observe that, as a consequence, the curve bends upward. Such a curve is called **concave upward**. In Figure 5, however, $f''(x)$ is negative, which means that f' is decreasing. Thus the slopes of f decrease from left to right and the curve bends downward. This curve is called **concave downward**. We summarize our discussion as follows. (Concavity is discussed in greater detail in Section 4.3.)

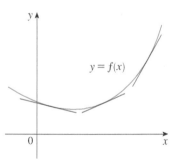

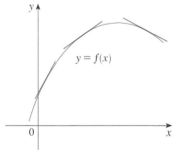

FIGURE 4
Since $f''(x) > 0$, the slopes increase and f is concave upward.

FIGURE 5
Since $f''(x) < 0$, the slopes decrease and f is concave downward.

If $f''(x) > 0$ on an interval, then f is concave upward on that interval.

If $f''(x) < 0$ on an interval, then f is concave downward on that interval.

EXAMPLE 2   Figure 6 shows a population graph for Cyprian honeybees raised in an apiary. How does the rate of population increase change over time? When is this rate highest? Over what intervals is P concave upward or concave downward?

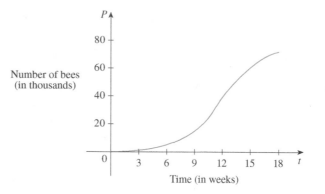

Number of bees
(in thousands)

FIGURE 6

SOLUTION   By looking at the slope of the curve as t increases, we see that the rate of increase of the population is initially very small, then gets larger until it reaches a maximum at about $t = 12$ weeks, and decreases as the population begins to level off. As the population approaches its maximum value of about 75,000 (called the *carrying capacity*), the rate of increase, $P'(t)$, approaches 0. The curve appears to be concave upward on $(0, 12)$ and concave downward on $(12, 18)$.

In Example 2, the population curve changed from concave upward to concave downward at approximately the point $(12, 38,000)$. This point is called an *inflection point* of the curve. The significance of this point is that the rate of population increase has its maximum value there. In general, an **inflection point** is a point where a curve changes its direction of concavity.

V   **EXAMPLE 3**   **Sketching f, given knowledge about f' and f''**   Sketch a possible graph of a function f that satisfies the following conditions:

(i) $f'(x) > 0$ on $(-\infty, 1)$, $f'(x) < 0$ on $(1, \infty)$

(ii) $f''(x) > 0$ on $(-\infty, -2)$ and $(2, \infty)$, $f''(x) < 0$ on $(-2, 2)$

(iii) $\lim_{x \to -\infty} f(x) = -2$, $\lim_{x \to \infty} f(x) = 0$

SOLUTION   Condition (i) tells us that f is increasing on $(-\infty, 1)$ and decreasing on $(1, \infty)$. Condition (ii) says that f is concave upward on $(-\infty, -2)$ and $(2, \infty)$, and concave downward on $(-2, 2)$. From condition (iii) we know that the graph of f has two horizontal asymptotes: $y = -2$ and $y = 0$.

We first draw the horizontal asymptote $y = -2$ as a dashed line (see Figure 7). We then draw the graph of f approaching this asymptote at the far left, increasing to its maximum point at $x = 1$ and decreasing toward the x-axis as $x \to \infty$. We also make sure that the graph has inflection points when $x = -2$ and 2. Notice that the curve bends upward for $x < -2$ and $x > 2$, and bends downward when x is between -2 and 2.

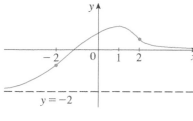

$y = -2$

FIGURE 7

Antiderivatives

In many problems in mathematics and its applications, we are given a function f and we are required to find a function F whose derivative is f. If such a function F exists, we call it an *antiderivative* of f. In other words, an **antiderivative** of f is a function F such that $F' = f$. (In Example 1 we sketched an antiderivative f of the function f'.)

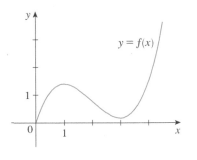

FIGURE 8

EXAMPLE 4   Sketching an antiderivative   Let F be an antiderivative of the function f whose graph is shown in Figure 8.
(a) Where is F increasing or decreasing?
(b) Where is F concave upward or concave downward?
(c) At what values of x does F have an inflection point?
(d) If $F(0) = 1$, sketch the graph of F.
(e) How many antiderivatives does f have?

SOLUTION

(a) We see from Figure 8 that $f(x) > 0$ for all $x > 0$. Since F is an antiderivative of f, we have $F'(x) = f(x)$ and so $F'(x)$ is positive when $x > 0$. This means that F is increasing on $(0, \infty)$.

(b) F is concave upward when $F''(x) > 0$. But $F''(x) = f'(x)$, so F is concave upward when $f'(x) > 0$, that is, when f is increasing. From Figure 8 we see that f is increasing when $0 < x < 1$ and when $x > 3$. So F is concave upward on $(0, 1)$ and $(3, \infty)$. F is concave downward when $F''(x) = f'(x) < 0$, that is, when f is decreasing. So F is concave downward on $(1, 3)$.

(c) F has an inflection point when the direction of concavity changes. From part (b) we know that F changes from concave upward to concave downward at $x = 1$, so F has an inflection point there. F changes from concave downward to concave upward when $x = 3$, so F has another inflection point when $x = 3$.

(d) In sketching the graph of F, we use the information from parts (a), (b), and (c). But, for finer detail, we also bear in mind the meaning of an antiderivative: Because $F'(x) = f(x)$, the slope of $y = F(x)$ at any value of x is equal to the height of $y = f(x)$. (Of course, this is the exact opposite of the procedure we used in Example 1 in Section 2.7 to sketch a derivative.)

Therefore, since $f(0) = 0$, we start drawing the graph of F at the given point $(0, 1)$ with slope 0, always increasing, with upward concavity to $x = 1$, downward concavity to $x = 3$, and upward concavity when $x > 3$. (See Figure 9.) Notice that $f(3) \approx 0.2$, so $y = F(x)$ has a gentle slope at the second inflection point. But we see that the slope becomes steeper when $x > 3$.

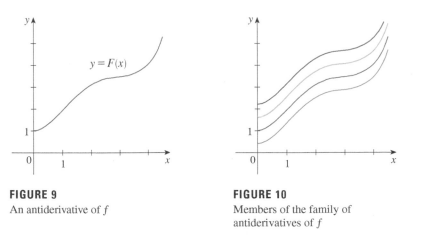

FIGURE 9
An antiderivative of f

FIGURE 10
Members of the family of antiderivatives of f

(e) The antiderivative of f that we sketched in Figure 9 satisfies $F(0) = 1$, so its graph starts at the point $(0, 1)$. But there are many other antiderivatives, whose graphs start at other points on the y-axis. In fact, f has infinitely many antiderivatives; their graphs are obtained from the graph of F by shifting upward or downward as in Figure 10.

2.8 Exercises

1–4 The graph of the *derivative* f' of a function f is shown.
(a) On what intervals is f increasing? Decreasing?
(b) At what values of x does f have a local maximum?
    Local minimum?
(c) If it is known that $f(0) = 0$, sketch a possible graph
    of f.

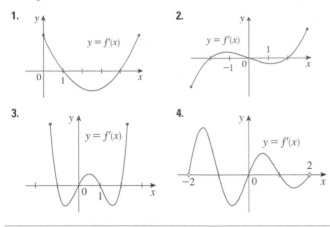

5. Use the given graph of f to estimate the intervals on which the
derivative f' is increasing or decreasing.

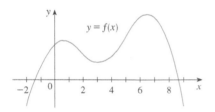

6–7 The graphs of a function f and its derivative f' are shown.
Which is bigger, $f'(-1)$ or $f''(1)$?

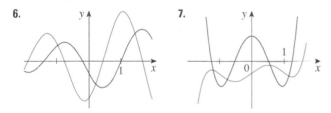

8. (a) Sketch a curve whose slope is always positive and
    increasing.
(b) Sketch a curve whose slope is always positive and
    decreasing.
(c) Give equations for curves with these properties.

9. The president announces that the national deficit is increasing,
but at a decreasing rate. Interpret this statement in terms of a
function and its derivatives.

10. A graph of a population of yeast cells in a new laboratory culture as a function of time is shown.
(a) Describe how the rate of population increase varies.
(b) When is this rate highest?
(c) On what intervals is the population function concave
    upward or downward?
(d) Estimate the coordinates of the inflection point.

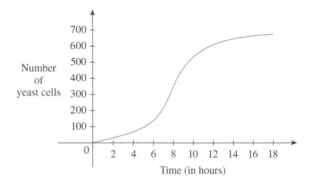

11. The table gives population densities for ring-necked pheasants
(in number of pheasants per acre) on Pelee Island, Ontario.
(a) Describe how the rate of change of population varies.
(b) Estimate the inflection points of the graph. What is the
    significance of these points?

t	1927	1930	1932	1934	1936	1938	1940
$P(t)$	0.1	0.6	2.5	4.6	4.8	3.5	3.0

12. A particle is moving along a horizontal straight line. The graph
of its position function (the distance to the right of a fixed point
as a function of time) is shown.
(a) When is the particle moving toward the right and when is it
    moving toward the left?
(b) When does the particle have positive acceleration and when
    does it have negative acceleration?

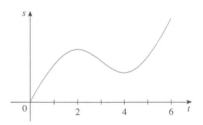

13. Let $K(t)$ be a measure of the knowledge you gain by studying
for a test for t hours. Which do you think is larger, $K(8) - K(7)$
or $K(3) - K(2)$? Is the graph of K concave upward or concave
downward? Why?

 Graphing calculator or computer with graphing software required   **1.** Homework Hints available in TEC

14. Coffee is being poured into the mug shown in the figure at a constant rate (measured in volume per unit time). Sketch a rough graph of the depth of the coffee in the mug as a function of time. Account for the shape of the graph in terms of concavity. What is the significance of the inflection point?

15–16 The graph of the derivative f' of a continuous function f is shown.
(a) On what intervals is f increasing? Decreasing?
(b) At what values of x does f have a local maximum? Local minimum?
(c) On what intervals is f concave upward? Concave downward?
(d) State the x-coordinate(s) of the point(s) of inflection.
(e) Assuming that $f(0) = 0$, sketch a graph of f.

15.

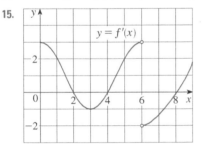

16.

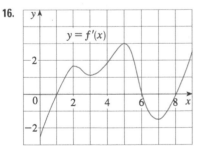

17. Sketch the graph of a function whose first and second derivatives are always negative.

18. Sketch the graph of a function whose first derivative is always negative and whose second derivative is always positive.

19–24 Sketch the graph of a function that satisfies all of the given conditions.

19. $f'(0) = f'(4) = 0$, $f'(x) > 0$ if $x < 0$,
$f'(x) < 0$ if $0 < x < 4$ or if $x > 4$,
$f''(x) > 0$ if $2 < x < 4$, $f''(x) < 0$ if $x < 2$ or $x > 4$

20. $f'(x) > 0$ for all $x \neq 1$, vertical asymptote $x = 1$,
$f''(x) > 0$ if $x < 1$ or $x > 3$, $f''(x) < 0$ if $1 < x < 3$

21. $f'(0) = f'(2) = f'(4) = 0$,
$f'(x) > 0$ if $x < 0$ or $2 < x < 4$,
$f'(x) < 0$ if $0 < x < 2$ or $x > 4$,
$f''(x) > 0$ if $1 < x < 3$, $f''(x) < 0$ if $x < 1$ or $x > 3$

22. $f'(1) = f'(-1) = 0$, $f'(x) < 0$ if $|x| < 1$,
$f'(x) > 0$ if $1 < |x| < 2$, $f'(x) = -1$ if $|x| > 2$,
$f''(x) < 0$ if $-2 < x < 0$, inflection point $(0, 1)$

23. $f'(x) > 0$ if $|x| < 2$, $f'(x) < 0$ if $|x| > 2$,
$f'(-2) = 0$, $\lim_{x \to 2} |f'(x)| = \infty$, $f''(x) > 0$ if $x \neq 2$

24. $f'(x) > 0$ if $|x| < 2$, $f'(x) < 0$ if $|x| > 2$,
$f'(2) = 0$, $\lim_{x \to \infty} f(x) = 1$, $f(-x) = -f(x)$,
$f''(x) < 0$ if $0 < x < 3$, $f''(x) > 0$ if $x > 3$

25. Suppose $f'(x) = xe^{-x^2}$.
(a) On what interval is f increasing? On what interval is f decreasing?
(b) Does f have a maximum value? Minimum value?

26. If $f'(x) = e^{-x^2}$, what can you say about f?

27. Let $f(x) = x^3 - x$. In Examples 3 and 7 in Section 2.7, we showed that $f'(x) = 3x^2 - 1$ and $f''(x) = 6x$. Use these facts to find the following.
(a) The intervals on which f is increasing or decreasing.
(b) The intervals on which f is concave upward or downward.
(c) The inflection point of f.

28. Let $f(x) = x^4 - 2x^2$.
(a) Use the definition of a derivative to find $f'(x)$ and $f''(x)$.
(b) On what intervals is f increasing or decreasing?
(c) On what intervals is f concave upward or concave downward?

29–30 The graph of a function f is shown. Which graph is an antiderivative of f and why?

29.

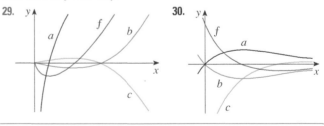

30.

31. The graph of a function is shown in the figure. Make a rough sketch of an antiderivative F, given that $F(0) = 1$.

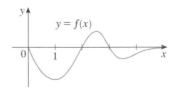

32. The graph of the velocity function of a particle is shown in the figure. Sketch the graph of a position function.

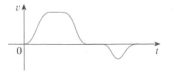

33–34 Draw a graph of f and use it to make a rough sketch of the antiderivative that passes through the origin.

33. $f(x) = \dfrac{\sin x}{1 + x^2}$, $-2\pi \le x \le 2\pi$

34. $f(x) = \sqrt{x^4 - 2x^2 + 2} - 2$, $-3 \le x \le 3$

---

2   Review

Concept Check

1. Explain what each of the following means and illustrate with a sketch.
   (a) $\lim_{x \to a} f(x) = L$
   (b) $\lim_{x \to a^+} f(x) = L$
   (c) $\lim_{x \to a^-} f(x) = L$
   (d) $\lim_{x \to a} f(x) = \infty$
   (e) $\lim_{x \to \infty} f(x) = L$

2. Describe several ways in which a limit can fail to exist. Illustrate with sketches.

3. State the following Limit Laws.
   (a) Sum Law
   (b) Difference Law
   (c) Constant Multiple Law
   (d) Product Law
   (e) Quotient Law
   (f) Power Law
   (g) Root Law

4. What does the Squeeze Theorem say?

5. (a) What does it mean to say that the line $x = a$ is a vertical asymptote of the curve $y = f(x)$? Draw curves to illustrate the various possibilities.
   (b) What does it mean to say that the line $y = L$ is a horizontal asymptote of the curve $y = f(x)$? Draw curves to illustrate the various possibilities.

6. Which of the following curves have vertical asymptotes? Which have horizontal asymptotes?
   (a) $y = x^4$
   (b) $y = \sin x$
   (c) $y = \tan x$
   (d) $y = e^x$
   (e) $y = \ln x$
   (f) $y = 1/x$
   (g) $y = \sqrt{x}$

7. (a) What does it mean for f to be continuous at a?
   (b) What does it mean for f to be continuous on the interval $(-\infty, \infty)$? What can you say about the graph of such a function?

8. What does the Intermediate Value Theorem say?

9. Write an expression for the slope of the tangent line to the curve $y = f(x)$ at the point $(a, f(a))$.

10. Suppose an object moves along a straight line with position $f(t)$ at time t. Write an expression for the instantaneous velocity of the object at time $t = a$. How can you interpret this velocity in terms of the graph of f?

11. If $y = f(x)$ and x changes from x_1 to x_2, write expressions for the following.
   (a) The average rate of change of y with respect to x over the interval $[x_1, x_2]$.
   (b) The instantaneous rate of change of y with respect to x at $x = x_1$.

12. Define the derivative $f'(a)$. Discuss two ways of interpreting this number.

13. Define the second derivative of f. If $f(t)$ is the position function of a particle, how can you interpret the second derivative?

14. (a) What does it mean for f to be differentiable at a?
   (b) What is the relation between the differentiability and continuity of a function?
   (c) Sketch the graph of a function that is continuous but not differentiable at $a = 2$.

15. Describe several ways in which a function can fail to be differentiable. Illustrate with sketches.

16. (a) What does the sign of $f'(x)$ tell us about f?
   (b) What does the sign of $f''(x)$ tell us about f?

17. (a) Define an antiderivative of f.
   (b) What is the antiderivative of a velocity function? What is the antiderivative of an acceleration function?

True-False Quiz

Determine whether the statement is true or false. If it is true, explain why. If it is false, explain why or give an example that disproves the statement.

1. $\lim\limits_{x \to 4}\left(\dfrac{2x}{x-4} - \dfrac{8}{x-4}\right) = \lim\limits_{x \to 4}\dfrac{2x}{x-4} - \lim\limits_{x \to 4}\dfrac{8}{x-4}$

2. $\lim\limits_{x \to 1}\dfrac{x^2+6x-7}{x^2+5x-6} = \dfrac{\lim\limits_{x \to 1}(x^2+6x-7)}{\lim\limits_{x \to 1}(x^2+5x-6)}$

3. $\lim\limits_{x \to 1}\dfrac{x-3}{x^2+2x-4} = \dfrac{\lim\limits_{x \to 1}(x-3)}{\lim\limits_{x \to 1}(x^2+2x-4)}$

4. If $\lim\limits_{x \to 5} f(x) = 2$ and $\lim\limits_{x \to 5} g(x) = 0$, then $\lim\limits_{x \to 5}[f(x)/g(x)]$ does not exist.

5. If $\lim\limits_{x \to 5} f(x) = 0$ and $\lim\limits_{x \to 5} g(x) = 0$, then $\lim\limits_{x \to 5}[f(x)/g(x)]$ does not exist.

6. If $\lim\limits_{x \to 6}[f(x)g(x)]$ exists, then the limit must be $f(6)g(6)$.

7. If p is a polynomial, then $\lim\limits_{x \to b} p(x) = p(b)$.

8. If $\lim\limits_{x \to 0} f(x) = \infty$ and $\lim\limits_{x \to 0} g(x) = \infty$, then $\lim\limits_{x \to 0}[f(x) - g(x)] = 0$.

9. A function can have two different horizontal asymptotes.

10. If f has domain $[0, \infty)$ and has no horizontal asymptote, then $\lim\limits_{x \to \infty} f(x) = \infty$ or $\lim\limits_{x \to \infty} f(x) = -\infty$.

11. If the line $x = 1$ is a vertical asymptote of $y = f(x)$, then f is not defined at 1.

12. If $f(1) > 0$ and $f(3) < 0$, then there exists a number c between 1 and 3 such that $f(c) = 0$.

13. If f is continuous at 5 and $f(5) = 2$ and $f(4) = 3$, then $\lim\limits_{x \to 2} f(4x^2 - 11) = 2$.

14. If f is continuous on $[-1, 1]$ and $f(-1) = 4$ and $f(1) = 3$, then there exists a number r such that $|r| < 1$ and $f(r) = \pi$.

15. If f is continuous at a, then f is differentiable at a.

16. If $f'(r)$ exists, then $\lim\limits_{x \to r} f(x) = f(r)$.

17. $\dfrac{d^2 y}{dx^2} = \left(\dfrac{dy}{dx}\right)^2$

18. If $f(x) > 1$ for all x and $\lim\limits_{x \to 0} f(x)$ exists, then $\lim\limits_{x \to 0} f(x) > 1$.

Exercises

1. The graph of f is given.
(a) Find each limit, or explain why it does not exist.

    (i) $\lim\limits_{x \to 2^+} f(x)$ (ii) $\lim\limits_{x \to -3^+} f(x)$

    (iii) $\lim\limits_{x \to -3} f(x)$ (iv) $\lim\limits_{x \to 4} f(x)$

    (v) $\lim\limits_{x \to 0} f(x)$ (vi) $\lim\limits_{x \to 2^-} f(x)$

    (vii) $\lim\limits_{x \to \infty} f(x)$ (viii) $\lim\limits_{x \to -\infty} f(x)$

(b) State the equations of the horizontal asymptotes.
(c) State the equations of the vertical asymptotes.
(d) At what numbers is f discontinuous? Explain.

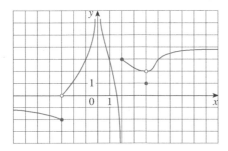

2. Sketch the graph of an example of a function f that satisfies all of the following conditions:

$$\lim\limits_{x \to -\infty} f(x) = -2, \quad \lim\limits_{x \to \infty} f(x) = 0, \quad \lim\limits_{x \to -3} f(x) = \infty,$$

$$\lim\limits_{x \to 3^-} f(x) = -\infty, \quad \lim\limits_{x \to 3^+} f(x) = 2,$$

f is continuous from the right at 3

3–18 Find the limit.

3. $\lim\limits_{x \to 1} e^{x^3 - x}$

4. $\lim\limits_{x \to 3}\dfrac{x^2 - 9}{x^2 + 2x - 3}$

5. $\lim\limits_{x \to -3}\dfrac{x^2 - 9}{x^2 + 2x - 3}$

6. $\lim\limits_{x \to 1^+}\dfrac{x^2 - 9}{x^2 + 2x - 3}$

7. $\lim\limits_{h \to 0}\dfrac{(h-1)^3 + 1}{h}$

8. $\lim\limits_{t \to 2}\dfrac{t^2 - 4}{t^3 - 8}$

9. $\lim\limits_{r \to 9}\dfrac{\sqrt{r}}{(r-9)^4}$

10. $\lim\limits_{v \to 4^+}\dfrac{4 - v}{|4 - v|}$

11. $\lim\limits_{u \to 1}\dfrac{u^4 - 1}{u^3 + 5u^2 - 6u}$

12. $\lim\limits_{x \to 3}\dfrac{\sqrt{x+6} - x}{x^3 - 3x^2}$

13. $\lim\limits_{x \to \pi^-} \ln(\sin x)$

14. $\lim\limits_{x \to -\infty}\dfrac{1 - 2x^2 - x^4}{5 + x - 3x^4}$

15. $\lim\limits_{x \to \infty} \dfrac{\sqrt{x^2 - 9}}{2x - 6}$

16. $\lim\limits_{x \to \infty} e^{x - x^2}$

17. $\lim\limits_{x \to \infty} \left(\sqrt{x^2 + 4x + 1} - x \right)$

18. $\lim\limits_{x \to 1} \left(\dfrac{1}{x - 1} + \dfrac{1}{x^2 - 3x + 2} \right)$

19–20 Use graphs to discover the asymptotes of the curve. Then prove what you have discovered.

19. $y = \dfrac{\cos^2 x}{x^2}$

20. $y = \sqrt{x^2 + x + 1} - \sqrt{x^2 - x}$

21. If $2x - 1 \le f(x) \le x^2$ for $0 < x < 3$, find $\lim\limits_{x \to 1} f(x)$.

22. Prove that $\lim\limits_{x \to 0} x^2 \cos(1/x^2) = 0$.

23. Let

$$f(x) = \begin{cases} \sqrt{-x} & \text{if } x < 0 \\ 3 - x & \text{if } 0 \le x < 3 \\ (x - 3)^2 & \text{if } x > 3 \end{cases}$$

(a) Evaluate each limit, if it exists.

    (i) $\lim\limits_{x \to 0^+} f(x)$ (ii) $\lim\limits_{x \to 0^-} f(x)$ (iii) $\lim\limits_{x \to 0} f(x)$

    (iv) $\lim\limits_{x \to 3^-} f(x)$ (v) $\lim\limits_{x \to 3^+} f(x)$ (vi) $\lim\limits_{x \to 3} f(x)$

(b) Where is f discontinuous?

(c) Sketch the graph of f.

24. Show that each function is continuous on its domain. State the domain.

    (a) $g(x) = \dfrac{\sqrt{x^2 - 9}}{x^2 - 2}$ (b) $h(x) = xe^{\sin x}$

25–26 Use the Intermediate Value Theorem to show that there is a root of the equation in the given interval.

25. $2x^3 + x^2 + 2 = 0$, $(-2, -1)$

26. $e^{-x^2} = x$, $(0, 1)$

27. The displacement (in meters) of an object moving in a straight line is given by $s = 1 + 2t + \frac{1}{4}t^2$, where t is measured in seconds.

(a) Find the average velocity over each time period.

    (i) $[1, 3]$ (ii) $[1, 2]$

    (iii) $[1, 1.5]$ (iv) $[1, 1.1]$

(b) Find the instantaneous velocity when $t = 1$.

28. According to Boyle's Law, if the temperature of a confined gas is held fixed, then the product of the pressure P and the volume V is a constant. Suppose that, for a certain gas, $PV = 800$, where P is measured in pounds per square inch and V is measured in cubic inches.

(a) Find the average rate of change of P as V increases from 200 in^3 to 250 in^3.

(b) Express V as a function of P and show that the instantaneous rate of change of V with respect to P is inversely proportional to the square of P.

29. For the function f whose graph is shown, arrange the following numbers in increasing order:

$$0 \qquad 1 \qquad f'(2) \qquad f'(3) \qquad f'(5) \qquad f''(5)$$

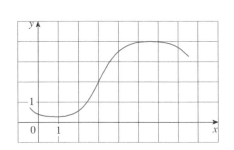

30. (a) Use the definition of a derivative to find $f'(2)$, where $f(x) = x^3 - 2x$.

(b) Find an equation of the tangent line to the curve $y = x^3 - 2x$ at the point $(2, 4)$.

(c) Illustrate part (b) by graphing the curve and the tangent line on the same screen.

31. (a) If $f(x) = e^{-x^2}$, estimate the value of $f'(1)$ graphically and numerically.

(b) Find an approximate equation of the tangent line to the curve $y = e^{-x^2}$ at the point where $x = 1$.

(c) Illustrate part (b) by graphing the curve and the tangent line on the same screen.

32. Find a function f and a number a such that

$$\lim_{h \to 0} \dfrac{(2 + h)^6 - 64}{h} = f'(a)$$

33. The total cost of repaying a student loan at an interest rate of $r\%$ per year is $C = f(r)$.

(a) What is the meaning of the derivative $f'(r)$? What are its units?

(b) What does the statement $f'(10) = 1200$ mean?

(c) Is $f'(r)$ always positive or does it change sign?

34–36 Trace or copy the graph of the function. Then sketch a graph of its derivative directly beneath.

34.

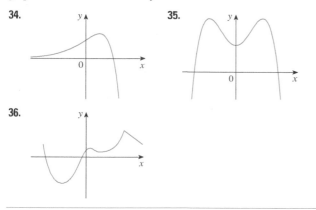

35.

36.

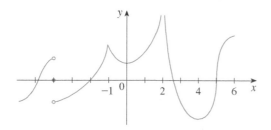

---

37. (a) If $f(x) = \sqrt{3 - 5x}$, use the definition of a derivative to find $f'(x)$.
    (b) Find the domains of f and f'.
    (c) Graph f and f' on a common screen. Compare the graphs to see whether your answer to part (a) is reasonable.

38. (a) Find the asymptotes of the graph of $f(x) = \dfrac{4 - x}{3 + x}$ and use them to sketch the graph.
    (b) Use your graph from part (a) to sketch the graph of f'.
    (c) Use the definition of a derivative to find $f'(x)$.
    (d) Use a graphing device to graph f' and compare with your sketch in part (b).

39. The graph of f is shown. State, with reasons, the numbers at which f is not differentiable.

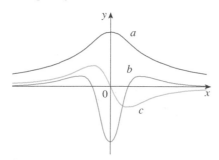

40. The figure shows the graphs of f, f', and f''. Identify each curve, and explain your choices.

41. Let $C(t)$ be the total value of US currency (coins and banknotes) in circulation at time t. The table gives values of this function from 1980 to 2000, as of September 30, in billions of dollars. Interpret and estimate the value of $C'(1990)$.

t	1980	1985	1990	1995	2000
$C(t)$	129.9	187.3	271.9	409.3	568.6

42. The cost of living continues to rise, but at a slower rate. In terms of a function and its derivatives, what does this statement mean?

43. The graph of the *derivative* f' of a function f is given.
    (a) On what intervals is f increasing or decreasing?
    (b) At what values of x does f have a local maximum or minimum?
    (c) Where is f concave upward or downward?
    (d) If $f(0) = 0$, sketch a possible graph of f.

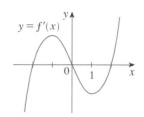

44. The figure shows the graph of the *derivative* f' of a function f.
    (a) Sketch the graph of f''.
    (b) Sketch a possible graph of f.

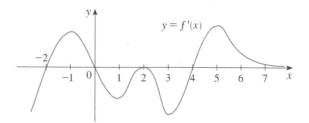

45. Sketch the graph of a function that satisfies the given conditions:

$$f(0) = 0, \quad f'(-2) = f'(1) = f'(9) = 0,$$
$$\lim_{x \to \infty} f(x) = 0, \quad \lim_{x \to 6} f(x) = -\infty,$$
$$f'(x) < 0 \text{ on } (-\infty, -2), (1, 6), \text{ and } (9, \infty),$$
$$f'(x) > 0 \text{ on } (-2, 1) \text{ and } (6, 9),$$
$$f''(x) > 0 \text{ on } (-\infty, 0) \text{ and } (12, \infty),$$
$$f''(x) < 0 \text{ on } (0, 6) \text{ and } (6, 12)$$

46. The *total fertility rate* at time t, denoted by $F(t)$, is an estimate of the average number of children born to each woman (assuming that current birth rates remain constant). The graph of the total fertility rate in the United States shows the fluctuations from 1940 to 1990.
(a) Estimate the values of $F'(1950)$, $F'(1965)$, and $F'(1987)$.
(b) What are the meanings of these derivatives?
(c) Can you suggest reasons for the values of these derivatives?

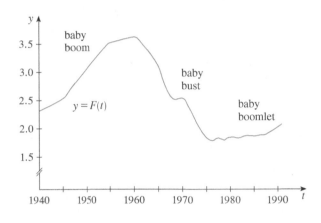

47. A car starts from rest and its distance traveled is recorded in the table in 2-second intervals.

t (seconds)	s (feet)	t (seconds)	s (feet)
0	0	8	180
2	8	10	260
4	40	12	319
6	95	14	373

(a) Estimate the speed after 6 seconds.
(b) Estimate the coordinates of the inflection point of the graph of the position function.
(c) What is the significance of the inflection point?

48. The graph of a function is shown. Sketch the graph of an antiderivative F, given that $F(0) = 0$.

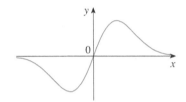

Focus on Problem Solving

In our discussion of the principles of problem solving we considered the problem-solving strategy of *introducing something extra* (see page 83). In the following example we show how this principle is sometimes useful when we evaluate limits. The idea is to change the variable—to introduce a new variable that is related to the original variable—in such a way as to make the problem simpler. Later, in Section 5.5, we will make more extensive use of this general idea.

EXAMPLE 1 Evaluate $\lim\limits_{x \to 0} \dfrac{\sqrt[3]{1 + cx} - 1}{x}$, where c is a constant.

SOLUTION As it stands, this limit looks challenging. In Section 2.3 we evaluated several limits in which both numerator and denominator approached 0. There our strategy was to perform some sort of algebraic manipulation that led to a simplifying cancellation, but here it's not clear what kind of algebra is necessary.

So we introduce a new variable t by the equation

$$t = \sqrt[3]{1 + cx}$$

We also need to express x in terms of t, so we solve this equation:

$$t^3 = 1 + cx \qquad x = \frac{t^3 - 1}{c} \quad (\text{if } c \neq 0)$$

Notice that $x \to 0$ is equivalent to $t \to 1$. This allows us to convert the given limit into one involving the variable t:

$$\lim_{x \to 0} \frac{\sqrt[3]{1 + cx} - 1}{x} = \lim_{t \to 1} \frac{t - 1}{(t^3 - 1)/c}$$

$$= \lim_{t \to 1} \frac{c(t - 1)}{t^3 - 1}$$

The change of variable allowed us to replace a relatively complicated limit by a simpler one of a type that we have seen before. Factoring the denominator as a difference of cubes, we get

$$\lim_{t \to 1} \frac{c(t - 1)}{t^3 - 1} = \lim_{t \to 1} \frac{c(t - 1)}{(t - 1)(t^2 + t + 1)}$$

$$= \lim_{t \to 1} \frac{c}{t^2 + t + 1} = \frac{c}{3}$$

In making the change of variable we had to rule out the case $c = 0$. But if $c = 0$, the function is 0 for all nonzero x and so its limit is 0. Therefore, in all cases, the limit is $c/3$.

Before you look at Example 2, cover up the solution and try it yourself first.

EXAMPLE 2 How many lines are tangent to both of the parabolas $y = -1 - x^2$ and $y = 1 + x^2$? Find the coordinates of the points at which these tangents touch the parabolas.

SOLUTION To gain insight into this problem it is essential to draw a diagram. So we sketch the parabolas $y = 1 + x^2$ (which is the standard parabola $y = x^2$ shifted 1 unit upward) and $y = -1 - x^2$ (which is obtained by reflecting the first parabola about the x-axis). If we try to draw a line tangent to both parabolas, we soon discover that there are only two possibilities, as illustrated in Figure 1.

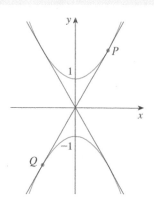

FIGURE 1

Let P be a point at which one of these tangents touches the upper parabola and let a be its x-coordinate. (The choice of notation for the unknown is important. Of course we could have used b or c or x_0 or x_1 instead of a. However, it's not advisable to use x in place of a because that x could be confused with the variable x in the equation of the parabola.) Then, since P lies on the parabola $y = 1 + x^2$, its y-coordinate must be $1 + a^2$. Because of the symmetry shown in Figure 1, the coordinates of the point Q where the tangent touches the lower parabola must be $(-a, -(1 + a^2))$.

To use the given information that the line is a tangent, we equate the slope of the line PQ to the slope of the tangent line at P. We have

$$m_{PQ} = \frac{1 + a^2 - (-1 - a^2)}{a - (-a)} = \frac{1 + a^2}{a}$$

If $f(x) = 1 + x^2$, then the slope of the tangent line at P is $f'(a)$. Using the definition of the derivative as in Section 2.6, we find that $f'(a) = 2a$. Thus the condition that we need to use is that

$$\frac{1 + a^2}{a} = 2a$$

Solving this equation, we get $1 + a^2 = 2a^2$, so $a^2 = 1$ and $a = \pm 1$. Therefore the points are $(1, 2)$ and $(-1, -2)$. By symmetry, the two remaining points are $(-1, 2)$ and $(1, -2)$.

The following problems are meant to test and challenge your problem-solving skills. Some of them require a considerable amount of time to think through, so don't be discouraged if you can't solve them right away. If you get stuck, you might find it helpful to refer to the discussion of the principles of problem solving on page 83.

Problems

1. Evaluate $\lim\limits_{x \to 1} \dfrac{\sqrt[3]{x} - 1}{\sqrt{x} - 1}$.

2. Find numbers a and b such that $\lim\limits_{x \to 0} \dfrac{\sqrt{ax + b} - 2}{x} = 1$.

3. Evaluate $\lim\limits_{x \to 0} \dfrac{|2x - 1| - |2x + 1|}{x}$.

4. The figure shows a point P on the parabola $y = x^2$ and the point Q where the perpendicular bisector of OP intersects the y-axis. As P approaches the origin along the parabola, what happens to Q? Does it have a limiting position? If so, find it.

5. If $[\![x]\!]$ denotes the greatest integer function, find $\lim\limits_{x \to \infty} \dfrac{x}{[\![x]\!]}$.

6. Sketch the region in the plane defined by each of the following equations.
   (a) $[\![x]\!]^2 + [\![y]\!]^2 = 1$ (b) $[\![x]\!]^2 - [\![y]\!]^2 = 3$ (c) $[\![x + y]\!]^2 = 1$ (d) $[\![x]\!] + [\![y]\!] = 1$

7. Find all values of a such that f is continuous on $\mathbb{R}$:

$$f(x) = \begin{cases} x + 1 & \text{if } x \le a \\ x^2 & \text{if } x > a \end{cases}$$

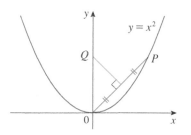

FIGURE FOR PROBLEM 4

8. A **fixed point** of a function f is a number c in its domain such that $f(c) = c$. (The function doesn't move c; it stays fixed.)
   (a) Sketch the graph of a continuous function with domain $[0, 1]$ whose range also lies in $[0, 1]$. Locate a fixed point of f.
   (b) Try to draw the graph of a continuous function with domain $[0, 1]$ and range in $[0, 1]$ that does *not* have a fixed point. What is the obstacle?
   (c) Use the Intermediate Value Theorem to prove that any continuous function with domain $[0, 1]$ and range in $[0, 1]$ must have a fixed point.

9. (a) If we start from $0°$ latitude and proceed in a westerly direction, we can let $T(x)$ denote the temperature at the point x at any given time. Assuming that T is a continuous function of x, show that at any fixed time there are at least two diametrically opposite points on the equator that have exactly the same temperature.
   (b) Does the result in part (a) hold for points lying on any circle on the earth's surface?
   (c) Does the result in part (a) hold for barometric pressure and for altitude above sea level?

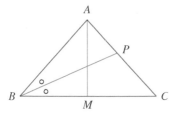

FIGURE FOR PROBLEM 10

10. (a) The figure shows an isosceles triangle ABC with $\angle B = \angle C$. The bisector of angle B intersects the side AC at the point P. Suppose that the base BC remains fixed but the altitude $|AM|$ of the triangle approaches 0, so A approaches the midpoint M of BC. What happens to P during this process? Does it have a limiting position? If so, find it.
   (b) Try to sketch the path traced out by P during this process. Then find an equation of this curve and use this equation to sketch the curve.

11. Find points P and Q on the parabola $y = 1 - x^2$ so that the triangle ABC formed by the x-axis and the tangent lines at P and Q is an equilateral triangle. (See the figure.)

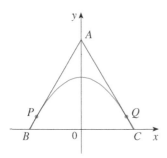

FIGURE FOR PROBLEM 11

12. Water is flowing at a constant rate into a spherical tank. Let $V(t)$ be the volume of water in the tank and $H(t)$ be the height of the water in the tank at time t.
   (a) What are the meanings of $V'(t)$ and $H'(t)$? Are these derivatives positive, negative, or zero?
   (b) Is $V''(t)$ positive, negative, or zero? Explain.
   (c) Let t_1, t_2, and t_3 be the times when the tank is one-quarter full, half full, and three-quarters full, respectively. Are the values $H''(t_1)$, $H''(t_2)$, and $H''(t_3)$ positive, negative, or zero? Why?

13. Suppose f is a function that satisfies the equation

$$f(x + y) = f(x) + f(y) + x^2 y + xy^2$$

for all real numbers x and y. Suppose also that

$$\lim_{x \to 0} \frac{f(x)}{x} = 1$$

   (a) Find $f(0)$.   (b) Find $f'(0)$.   (c) Find $f'(x)$.

14. A car is traveling at night along a highway shaped like a parabola with its vertex at the origin. The car starts at a point 100 m west and 100 m north of the origin and travels in an easterly direction. There is a statue located 100 m east and 50 m north of the origin. At what point on the highway will the car's headlights illuminate the statue?

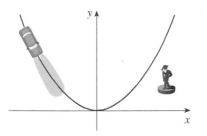

FIGURE FOR PROBLEM 14

15. If $\lim_{x \to a} [f(x) + g(x)] = 2$ and $\lim_{x \to a} [f(x) - g(x)] = 1$, find $\lim_{x \to a} f(x)g(x)$.

16. If f is a differentiable function and $g(x) = xf(x)$, use the definition of a derivative to show that $g'(x) = xf'(x) + f(x)$.

17. Suppose f is a function with the property that $|f(x)| \le x^2$ for all x. Show that $f(0) = 0$. Then show that $f'(0) = 0$.

171

Differentiation Rules

3

We have seen how to interpret derivatives as slopes and rates of change. We have seen how to estimate derivatives of functions given by tables of values. We have learned how to graph derivatives of functions that are defined graphically. We have used the definition of a derivative to calculate the derivatives of functions defined by formulas. But it would be tedious if we always had to use the definition, so in this chapter we develop rules for finding derivatives without having to use the definition directly. These differentiation rules enable us to calculate with relative ease the derivatives of polynomials, rational functions, algebraic functions, exponential and logarithmic functions, and trigonometric and inverse trigonometric functions. We then use these rules to solve problems involving rates of change, tangents to parametric curves, and the approximation of functions.

3.1 | Derivatives of Polynomials and Exponential Functions

In this section we learn how to differentiate constant functions, power functions, polynomials, and exponential functions.

Let's start with the simplest of all functions, the constant function $f(x) = c$. The graph of this function is the horizontal line $y = c$, which has slope 0, so we must have $f'(x) = 0$. (See Figure 1.) A formal proof, from the definition of a derivative, is also easy:

$$f'(x) = \lim_{h \to 0} \frac{f(x + h) - f(x)}{h} = \lim_{h \to 0} \frac{c - c}{h} = \lim_{h \to 0} 0 = 0$$

In Leibniz notation, we write this rule as follows.

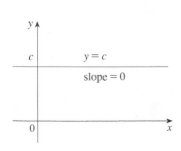

FIGURE 1
The graph of $f(x) = c$ is the line $y = c$, so $f'(x) = 0$.

> **Derivative of a Constant Function**
>
> $$\frac{d}{dx}(c) = 0$$

Power Functions

We next look at the functions $f(x) = x^n$, where n is a positive integer. If $n = 1$, the graph of $f(x) = x$ is the line $y = x$, which has slope 1. (See Figure 2.) So

$$\boxed{1} \qquad \frac{d}{dx}(x) = 1$$

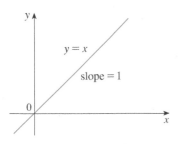

FIGURE 2
The graph of $f(x) = x$ is the line $y = x$, so $f'(x) = 1$.

(You can also verify Equation 1 from the definition of a derivative.) We have already investigated the cases $n = 2$ and $n = 3$. In fact, in Section 2.7 (Exercises 17 and 18) we found that

$$\boxed{2} \qquad \frac{d}{dx}(x^2) = 2x \qquad \frac{d}{dx}(x^3) = 3x^2$$

For $n = 4$ we find the derivative of $f(x) = x^4$ as follows:

$$f'(x) = \lim_{h \to 0} \frac{f(x + h) - f(x)}{h} = \lim_{h \to 0} \frac{(x + h)^4 - x^4}{h}$$

$$= \lim_{h \to 0} \frac{x^4 + 4x^3h + 6x^2h^2 + 4xh^3 + h^4 - x^4}{h}$$

$$= \lim_{h \to 0} \frac{4x^3h + 6x^2h^2 + 4xh^3 + h^4}{h}$$

$$= \lim_{h \to 0} (4x^3 + 6x^2h + 4xh^2 + h^3) = 4x^3$$

Thus

$$\boxed{3} \qquad \frac{d}{dx}(x^4) = 4x^3$$

Comparing the equations in (1), (2), and (3), we see a pattern emerging. It seems to be a reasonable guess that, when n is a positive integer, $(d/dx)(x^n) = nx^{n-1}$. This turns out to be true.

The Power Rule If n is a positive integer, then

$$\frac{d}{dx}(x^n) = nx^{n-1}$$

PROOF If $f(x) = x^n$, then

$$f'(x) = \lim_{h \to 0} \frac{f(x+h) - f(x)}{h} = \lim_{h \to 0} \frac{(x+h)^n - x^n}{h}$$

The Binomial Theorem is given on Reference Page 1.

In finding the derivative of x^4 we had to expand $(x+h)^4$. Here we need to expand $(x+h)^n$ and we use the Binomial Theorem to do so:

$$f'(x) = \lim_{h \to 0} \frac{\left[x^n + nx^{n-1}h + \frac{n(n-1)}{2}x^{n-2}h^2 + \cdots + nxh^{n-1} + h^n \right] - x^n}{h}$$

$$= \lim_{h \to 0} \frac{nx^{n-1}h + \frac{n(n-1)}{2}x^{n-2}h^2 + \cdots + nxh^{n-1} + h^n}{h}$$

$$= \lim_{h \to 0} \left[nx^{n-1} + \frac{n(n-1)}{2}x^{n-2}h + \cdots + nxh^{n-2} + h^{n-1} \right]$$

$$= nx^{n-1}$$

because every term except the first has h as a factor and therefore approaches 0.

We illustrate the Power Rule using various notations in Example 1.

EXAMPLE 1 **Using the Power Rule**
(a) If $f(x) = x^6$, then $f'(x) = 6x^5$. (b) If $y = x^{1000}$, then $y' = 1000x^{999}$.

(c) If $y = t^4$, then $\dfrac{dy}{dt} = 4t^3$. (d) $\dfrac{d}{dr}(r^3) = 3r^2$

What about power functions with negative integer exponents? In Exercise 59 we ask you to verify from the definition of a derivative that

$$\frac{d}{dx}\left(\frac{1}{x}\right) = -\frac{1}{x^2}$$

We can rewrite this equation as

$$\frac{d}{dx}(x^{-1}) = (-1)x^{-2}$$

and so the Power Rule is true when $n = -1$. In fact, we will show in the next section [Exercise 60(c)] that it holds for all negative integers.

What if the exponent is a fraction? In Example 4 in Section 2.7 we found that

$$\frac{d}{dx}\sqrt{x} = \frac{1}{2\sqrt{x}}$$

which can be written as

$$\frac{d}{dx}(x^{1/2}) = \tfrac{1}{2}x^{-1/2}$$

This shows that the Power Rule is true even when $n = \tfrac{1}{2}$. In fact, we will show in Section 3.7 that it is true for all real numbers n.

The Power Rule (General Version)   If n is any real number, then

$$\frac{d}{dx}(x^n) = nx^{n-1}$$

EXAMPLE 2   **The Power Rule for negative and fractional exponents**   Differentiate:

(a) $f(x) = \dfrac{1}{x^2}$

(b) $y = \sqrt[3]{x^2}$

Figure 3 shows the function y in Example 2(b) and its derivative y'. Notice that y is not differentiable at 0 (y' is not defined there). Observe that y' is positive when y increases and is negative when y decreases.

SOLUTION   In each case we rewrite the function as a power of x.

(a) Since $f(x) = x^{-2}$, we use the Power Rule with $n = -2$:

$$f'(x) = \frac{d}{dx}(x^{-2}) = -2x^{-2-1} = -2x^{-3} = -\frac{2}{x^3}$$

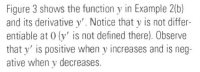

(b)
$$\frac{dy}{dx} = \frac{d}{dx}\left(\sqrt[3]{x^2}\right) = \frac{d}{dx}(x^{2/3}) = \tfrac{2}{3}x^{(2/3)-1} = \tfrac{2}{3}x^{-1/3}$$

FIGURE 3
$y = \sqrt[3]{x^2}$

The Power Rule enables us to find tangent lines without having to resort to the definition of a derivative. It also enables us to find *normal lines*. The **normal line** to a curve C at a point P is the line through P that is perpendicular to the tangent line at P. (In the study of optics, one needs to consider the angle between a light ray and the normal line to a lens.)

■ **EXAMPLE 3**   Find equations of the tangent line and normal line to the curve $y = x\sqrt{x}$ at the point $(1, 1)$. Illustrate by graphing the curve and these lines.

SOLUTION   The derivative of $f(x) = x\sqrt{x} = xx^{1/2} = x^{3/2}$ is

$$f'(x) = \tfrac{3}{2}x^{(3/2)-1} = \tfrac{3}{2}x^{1/2} = \tfrac{3}{2}\sqrt{x}$$

So the slope of the tangent line at $(1, 1)$ is $f'(1) = \tfrac{3}{2}$. Therefore an equation of the tangent line is

$$y - 1 = \tfrac{3}{2}(x - 1) \qquad \text{or} \qquad y = \tfrac{3}{2}x - \tfrac{1}{2}$$

The normal line is perpendicular to the tangent line, so its slope is the negative reciprocal of $\tfrac{3}{2}$, that is, $-\tfrac{2}{3}$. Thus an equation of the normal line is

$$y - 1 = -\tfrac{2}{3}(x - 1) \qquad \text{or} \qquad y = -\tfrac{2}{3}x + \tfrac{5}{3}$$

We graph the curve and its tangent line and normal line in Figure 4.

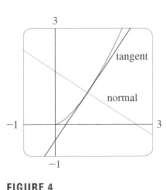

FIGURE 4
$y = x\sqrt{x}$

New Derivatives from Old

When new functions are formed from old functions by addition, subtraction, or multiplication by a constant, their derivatives can be calculated in terms of derivatives of the old functions. In particular, the following formula says that *the derivative of a constant times a function is the constant times the derivative of the function.*

GEOMETRIC INTERPRETATION OF THE CONSTANT MULTIPLE RULE

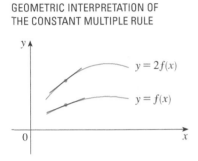

Multiplying by $c = 2$ stretches the graph vertically by a factor of 2. All the rises have been doubled but the runs stay the same. So the slopes are doubled, too.

> **The Constant Multiple Rule** If c is a constant and f is a differentiable function, then
> $$\frac{d}{dx}[cf(x)] = c\frac{d}{dx}f(x)$$

PROOF Let $g(x) = cf(x)$. Then

$$g'(x) = \lim_{h \to 0} \frac{g(x+h) - g(x)}{h} = \lim_{h \to 0} \frac{cf(x+h) - cf(x)}{h}$$

$$= \lim_{h \to 0} c\left[\frac{f(x+h) - f(x)}{h}\right]$$

$$= c\lim_{h \to 0} \frac{f(x+h) - f(x)}{h} \qquad \text{(by Law 3 of limits)}$$

$$= cf'(x)$$

EXAMPLE 4 **Using the Constant Multiple Rule**

(a) $\dfrac{d}{dx}(3x^4) = 3\dfrac{d}{dx}(x^4) = 3(4x^3) = 12x^3$

(b) $\dfrac{d}{dx}(-x) = \dfrac{d}{dx}[(-1)x] = (-1)\dfrac{d}{dx}(x) = -1(1) = -1$

The next rule tells us that *the derivative of a sum of functions is the sum of the derivatives.*

Using prime notation, we can write the Sum Rule as
$$(f + g)' = f' + g'$$

> **The Sum Rule** If f and g are both differentiable, then
> $$\frac{d}{dx}[f(x) + g(x)] = \frac{d}{dx}f(x) + \frac{d}{dx}g(x)$$

PROOF Let $F(x) = f(x) + g(x)$. Then

$$F'(x) = \lim_{h \to 0} \frac{F(x+h) - F(x)}{h}$$

$$= \lim_{h \to 0} \frac{[f(x+h) + g(x+h)] - [f(x) + g(x)]}{h}$$

$$= \lim_{h \to 0} \left[\frac{f(x+h) - f(x)}{h} + \frac{g(x+h) - g(x)}{h}\right]$$

$$= \lim_{h \to 0} \frac{f(x+h) - f(x)}{h} + \lim_{h \to 0} \frac{g(x+h) - g(x)}{h} \qquad \text{(by Law 1)}$$

$$= f'(x) + g'(x)$$

The Sum Rule can be extended to the sum of any number of functions. For instance, using this theorem twice, we get

$$(f + g + h)' = [(f + g) + h]' = (f + g)' + h' = f' + g' + h'$$

By writing $f - g$ as $f + (-1)g$ and applying the Sum Rule and the Constant Multiple Rule, we get the following formula.

The Difference Rule If f and g are both differentiable, then

$$\frac{d}{dx}\,[f(x) - g(x)] = \frac{d}{dx}\,f(x) - \frac{d}{dx}\,g(x)$$

The Constant Multiple Rule, the Sum Rule, and the Difference Rule can be combined with the Power Rule to differentiate any polynomial, as the following examples demonstrate.

EXAMPLE 5 **Differentiating a polynomial**

$$\frac{d}{dx}\,(x^8 + 12x^5 - 4x^4 + 10x^3 - 6x + 5)$$

$$= \frac{d}{dx}\,(x^8) + 12\frac{d}{dx}\,(x^5) - 4\frac{d}{dx}\,(x^4) + 10\frac{d}{dx}\,(x^3) - 6\frac{d}{dx}\,(x) + \frac{d}{dx}\,(5)$$

$$= 8x^7 + 12(5x^4) - 4(4x^3) + 10(3x^2) - 6(1) + 0$$

$$= 8x^7 + 60x^4 - 16x^3 + 30x^2 - 6$$

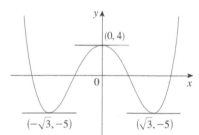

FIGURE 5

The curve $y = x^4 - 6x^2 + 4$ and its horizontal tangents

V **EXAMPLE 6** Find the points on the curve $y = x^4 - 6x^2 + 4$ where the tangent line is horizontal.

SOLUTION Horizontal tangents occur where the derivative is zero. We have

$$\frac{dy}{dx} = \frac{d}{dx}\,(x^4) - 6\frac{d}{dx}\,(x^2) + \frac{d}{dx}\,(4)$$

$$= 4x^3 - 12x + 0 = 4x(x^2 - 3)$$

Thus $dy/dx = 0$ if $x = 0$ or $x^2 - 3 = 0$, that is, $x = \pm\sqrt{3}$. So the given curve has horizontal tangents when $x = 0$, $\sqrt{3}$, and $-\sqrt{3}$. The corresponding points are $(0, 4)$, $(\sqrt{3}, -5)$, and $(-\sqrt{3}, -5)$. (See Figure 5.)

EXAMPLE 7 The equation of motion of a particle is $s = 2t^3 - 5t^2 + 3t + 4$, where s is measured in centimeters and t in seconds. Find the acceleration as a function of time. What is the acceleration after 2 seconds?

SOLUTION The velocity and acceleration are

$$v(t) = \frac{ds}{dt} = 6t^2 - 10t + 3$$

$$a(t) = \frac{dv}{dt} = 12t - 10$$

The acceleration after 2 s is $a(2) = 14 \text{ cm/s}^2$.

Exponential Functions

Let's try to compute the derivative of the exponential function $f(x) = a^x$ using the definition of a derivative:

$$f'(x) = \lim_{h \to 0} \frac{f(x + h) - f(x)}{h} = \lim_{h \to 0} \frac{a^{x+h} - a^x}{h}$$

$$= \lim_{h \to 0} \frac{a^x a^h - a^x}{h} = \lim_{h \to 0} \frac{a^x(a^h - 1)}{h}$$

The factor a^x doesn't depend on h, so we can take it in front of the limit:

$$f'(x) = a^x \lim_{h \to 0} \frac{a^h - 1}{h}$$

Notice that the limit is the value of the derivative of f at 0, that is,

$$\lim_{h \to 0} \frac{a^h - 1}{h} = f'(0)$$

Therefore we have shown that if the exponential function $f(x) = a^x$ is differentiable at 0, then it is differentiable everywhere and

$$\boxed{4} \qquad\qquad f'(x) = f'(0)a^x$$

This equation says that *the rate of change of any exponential function is proportional to the function itself.* (The slope is proportional to the height.)

Numerical evidence for the existence of $f'(0)$ is given in the table at the left for the cases $a = 2$ and $a = 3$. (Values are stated correct to four decimal places.) It appears that the limits exist and

h	$\dfrac{2^h - 1}{h}$	$\dfrac{3^h - 1}{h}$
0.1	0.7177	1.1612
0.01	0.6956	1.1047
0.001	0.6934	1.0992
0.0001	0.6932	1.0987

$$\text{for } a = 2, \quad f'(0) = \lim_{h \to 0} \frac{2^h - 1}{h} \approx 0.69$$

$$\text{for } a = 3, \quad f'(0) = \lim_{h \to 0} \frac{3^h - 1}{h} \approx 1.10$$

In fact, it can be proved that these limits exist and, correct to six decimal places, the values are

$$\frac{d}{dx}(2^x)\bigg|_{x=0} \approx 0.693147 \qquad \frac{d}{dx}(3^x)\bigg|_{x=0} \approx 1.098612$$

Thus, from Equation 4, we have

$$\boxed{5} \qquad\qquad \frac{d}{dx}(2^x) \approx (0.69)2^x \qquad \frac{d}{dx}(3^x) \approx (1.10)3^x$$

Of all possible choices for the base a in Equation 4, the simplest differentiation formula occurs when $f'(0) = 1$. In view of the estimates of $f'(0)$ for $a = 2$ and $a = 3$, it seems reasonable that there is a number a between 2 and 3 for which $f'(0) = 1$. It is traditional to denote this value by the letter e. (In fact, that is how we introduced e in Section 1.5.) Thus we have the following definition.

In Exercise 1 we will see that e lies between 2.7 and 2.8. Later we will be able to show that, correct to five decimal places,

$$e \approx 2.71828$$

Definition of the Number e

e is the number such that $\quad \lim_{h \to 0} \dfrac{e^h - 1}{h} = 1$

Geometrically, this means that of all the possible exponential functions $y = a^x$, the function $f(x) = e^x$ is the one whose tangent line at $(0, 1)$ has a slope $f'(0)$ that is exactly 1. (See Figures 6 and 7.)

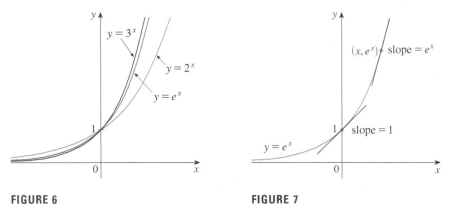

FIGURE 6   **FIGURE 7**

If we put $a = e$ and, therefore, $f'(0) = 1$ in Equation 4, it becomes the following important differentiation formula.

Derivative of the Natural Exponential Function

$$\frac{d}{dx}(e^x) = e^x$$

TEC Visual 3.1 uses the slope-a-scope to illustrate this formula.

Thus the exponential function $f(x) = e^x$ has the property that it is its own derivative. The geometrical significance of this fact is that the slope of a tangent line to the curve $y = e^x$ is equal to the y-coordinate of the point (see Figure 7).

⊵ EXAMPLE 8 If $f(x) = e^x - x$, find f' and f''. Compare the graphs of f and f'.

SOLUTION Using the Difference Rule, we have

$$f'(x) = \frac{d}{dx}(e^x - x) = \frac{d}{dx}(e^x) - \frac{d}{dx}(x) = e^x - 1$$

In Section 2.7 we defined the second derivative as the derivative of f', so

$$f''(x) = \frac{d}{dx}(e^x - 1) = \frac{d}{dx}(e^x) - \frac{d}{dx}(1) = e^x$$

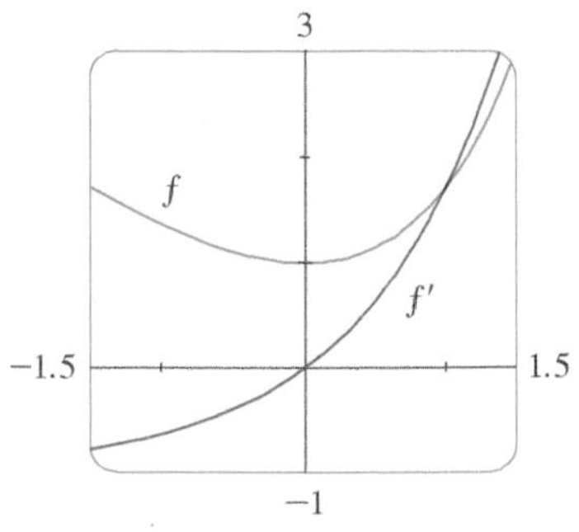

The function f and its derivative f' are graphed in Figure 8. Notice that f has a horizontal tangent when $x = 0$; this corresponds to the fact that $f'(0) = 0$. Notice also that, for $x > 0$, $f'(x)$ is positive and f is increasing. When $x < 0$, $f'(x)$ is negative and f is decreasing.

FIGURE 8

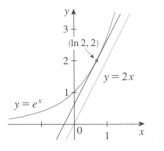

FIGURE 9

EXAMPLE 9 At what point on the curve $y = e^x$ is the tangent line parallel to the line $y = 2x$?

SOLUTION Since $y = e^x$, we have $y' = e^x$. Let the x-coordinate of the point in question be a. Then the slope of the tangent line at that point is e^a. This tangent line will be parallel to the line $y = 2x$ if it has the same slope, that is, 2. Equating slopes, we get

$$e^a = 2 \quad \Rightarrow \quad a = \ln 2$$

Therefore the required point is $(a, e^a) = (\ln 2, 2)$. (See Figure 9.)

3.1 Exercises

1. (a) How is the number e defined?
   (b) Use a calculator to estimate the values of the limits

$$\lim_{h \to 0} \frac{2.7^h - 1}{h} \quad \text{and} \quad \lim_{h \to 0} \frac{2.8^h - 1}{h}$$

   correct to two decimal places. What can you conclude about the value of e?

2. (a) Sketch, by hand, the graph of the function $f(x) = e^x$, paying particular attention to how the graph crosses the y-axis. What fact allows you to do this?
   (b) What types of functions are $f(x) = e^x$ and $g(x) = x^e$? Compare the differentiation formulas for f and g.
   (c) Which of the two functions in part (b) grows more rapidly when x is large?

3–26 Differentiate the function.

3. $f(x) = 186.5$

4. $f(x) = \sqrt{30}$

5. $f(t) = 2 - \frac{2}{3}t$

6. $F(x) = \frac{3}{4}x^8$

7. $f(x) = x^3 - 4x + 6$

8. $f(t) = \frac{1}{2}t^6 - 3t^4 + t$

9. $f(t) = \frac{1}{4}(t^4 + 8)$

10. $h(x) = (x - 2)(2x + 3)$

11. $A(s) = -\dfrac{12}{s^5}$

12. $B(y) = cy^{-6}$

13. $g(t) = 2t^{-3/4}$

14. $h(t) = \sqrt[4]{t} - 4e^t$

15. $y = 3e^x + \dfrac{4}{\sqrt[3]{x}}$

16. $y = \sqrt{x}\,(x - 1)$

17. $F(x) = \left(\frac{1}{2}x\right)^5$

18. $f(x) = \dfrac{x^2 - 3x + 1}{x^2}$

19. $y = \dfrac{x^2 + 4x + 3}{\sqrt{x}}$

20. $g(u) = \sqrt{2}\,u + \sqrt{3u}$

21. $y = 4\pi^2$

22. $y = ae^v + \dfrac{b}{v} + \dfrac{c}{v^2}$

23. $u = \sqrt[5]{t} + 4\sqrt{t^5}$

24. $v = \left(\sqrt{x} + \dfrac{1}{\sqrt[3]{x}}\right)^2$

25. $z = \dfrac{A}{y^{10}} + Be^y$

26. $y = e^{x+1} + 1$

27–28 Find an equation of the tangent line to the curve at the given point.

27. $y = \sqrt[4]{x}$, $(1, 1)$

28. $y = x^4 + 2x^2 - x$, $(1, 2)$

29–30 Find equations of the tangent line and normal line to the curve at the given point.

29. $y = x^4 + 2e^x$, $(0, 2)$

30. $y = (1 + 2x)^2$, $(1, 9)$

31–32 Find an equation of the tangent line to the curve at the given point. Illustrate by graphing the curve and the tangent line on the same screen.

31. $y = 3x^2 - x^3$, $(1, 2)$

32. $y = x - \sqrt{x}$, $(1, 0)$

33–36 Find $f'(x)$. Compare the graphs of f and f' and use them to explain why your answer is reasonable.

33. $f(x) = e^x - 5x$

34. $f(x) = 3x^5 - 20x^3 + 50x$

35. $f(x) = 3x^{15} - 5x^3 + 3$

36. $f(x) = x + \dfrac{1}{x}$

37–38 Estimate the value of $f'(a)$ by zooming in on the graph of f. Then differentiate f to find the exact value of $f'(a)$ and compare with your estimate.

37. $f(x) = 3x^2 - x^3$, $a = 1$

38. $f(x) = 1/\sqrt{x}$, $a = 4$

Graphing calculator or computer with graphing software required   **1.** Homework Hints available in TEC

39. (a) Use a graphing calculator or computer to graph the function $f(x) = x^4 - 3x^3 - 6x^2 + 7x + 30$ in the viewing rectangle $[-3, 5]$ by $[-10, 50]$.
   (b) Using the graph in part (a) to estimate slopes, make a rough sketch, by hand, of the graph of f'. (See Example 1 in Section 2.7.)
   (c) Calculate $f'(x)$ and use this expression, with a graphing device, to graph f'. Compare with your sketch in part (b).

40. (a) Use a graphing calculator or computer to graph the function $g(x) = e^x - 3x^2$ in the viewing rectangle $[-1, 4]$ by $[-8, 8]$.
   (b) Using the graph in part (a) to estimate slopes, make a rough sketch, by hand, of the graph of g'. (See Example 1 in Section 2.7.)
   (c) Calculate $g'(x)$ and use this expression, with a graphing device, to graph g'. Compare with your sketch in part (b).

41–42 Find the first and second derivatives of the function.

41. $f(x) = 10x^{10} + 5x^5 - x$ **42.** $G(r) = \sqrt{r} + \sqrt[3]{r}$

43–44 Find the first and second derivatives of the function. Check to see that your answers are reasonable by comparing the graphs of f, f', and f''.

43. $f(x) = 2x - 5x^{3/4}$ **44.** $f(x) = e^x - x^3$

45. The equation of motion of a particle is $s = t^3 - 3t$, where s is in meters and t is in seconds. Find
   (a) the velocity and acceleration as functions of t,
   (b) the acceleration after 2 s, and
   (c) the acceleration when the velocity is 0.

46. The equation of motion of a particle is $s = t^4 - 2t^3 + t^2 - t$, where s is in meters and t is in seconds.
   (a) Find the velocity and acceleration as functions of t.
   (b) Find the acceleration after 1 s.
   (c) Graph the position, velocity, and acceleration functions on the same screen.

47. On what interval is the function $f(x) = 5x - e^x$ increasing?

48. On what interval is the function $f(x) = x^3 - 4x^2 + 5x$ concave upward?

49. Find the points on the curve $y = 2x^3 + 3x^2 - 12x + 1$ where the tangent is horizontal.

50. For what values of x does the graph of $f(x) = x^3 + 3x^2 + x + 3$ have a horizontal tangent?

51. Show that the curve $y = 6x^3 + 5x - 3$ has no tangent line with slope 4.

52. Find an equation of the tangent line to the curve $y = x\sqrt{x}$ that is parallel to the line $y = 1 + 3x$.

53. Find equations of both lines that are tangent to the curve $y = 1 + x^3$ and parallel to the line $12x - y = 1$.

54. At what point on the curve $y = 1 + 2e^x - 3x$ is the tangent line parallel to the line $3x - y = 5$? Illustrate by graphing the curve and both lines.

55. Find an equation of the normal line to the parabola $y = x^2 - 5x + 4$ that is parallel to the line $x - 3y = 5$.

56. Where does the normal line to the parabola $y = x - x^2$ at the point $(1, 0)$ intersect the parabola a second time? Illustrate with a sketch.

57. Draw a diagram to show that there are two tangent lines to the parabola $y = x^2$ that pass through the point $(0, -4)$. Find the coordinates of the points where these tangent lines intersect the parabola.

58. (a) Find equations of both lines through the point $(2, -3)$ that are tangent to the parabola $y = x^2 + x$.
   (b) Show that there is no line through the point $(2, 7)$ that is tangent to the parabola. Then draw a diagram to see why.

59. Use the definition of a derivative to show that if $f(x) = 1/x$, then $f'(x) = -1/x^2$. (This proves the Power Rule for the case $n = -1$.)

60. Find the nth derivative of each function by calculating the first few derivatives and observing the pattern that occurs.
   (a) $f(x) = x^n$ (b) $f(x) = 1/x$

61. Find a second-degree polynomial P such that $P(2) = 5$, $P'(2) = 3$, and $P''(2) = 2$.

62. The equation $y'' + y' - 2y = x^2$ is called a **differential equation** because it involves an unknown function y and its derivatives y' and y''. Find constants A, B, and C such that the function $y = Ax^2 + Bx + C$ satisfies this equation. (Differential equations will be studied in detail in Chapter 7.)

63. (a) In Section 2.8 we defined an antiderivative of f to be a function F such that $F' = f$. Try to guess a formula for an antiderivative of $f(x) = x^2$. Then check your answer by differentiating it. How many antiderivatives does f have?
   (b) Find antiderivatives for $f(x) = x^3$ and $f(x) = x^4$.
   (c) Find an antiderivative for $f(x) = x^n$, where $n \neq -1$. Check by differentiation.

64. Use the result of Exercise 63(c) to find an antiderivative of each function.
   (a) $f(x) = \sqrt{x}$ (b) $f(x) = e^x + 8x^3$

65. Find the parabola with equation $y = ax^2 + bx$ whose tangent line at $(1, 1)$ has equation $y = 3x - 2$.

66. Suppose the curve $y = x^4 + ax^3 + bx^2 + cx + d$ has a tangent line when $x = 0$ with equation $y = 2x + 1$ and a tangent line when $x = 1$ with equation $y = 2 - 3x$. Find the values of a, b, c, and d.

67. Find a cubic function $y = ax^3 + bx^2 + cx + d$ whose graph has horizontal tangents at the points $(-2, 6)$ and $(2, 0)$.

68. Find the value of c such that the line $y = \frac{3}{2}x + 6$ is tangent to the curve $y = c\sqrt{x}$.

69. For what values of a and b is the line $2x + y = b$ tangent to the parabola $y = ax^2$ when $x = 2$?

70. A tangent line is drawn to the hyperbola $xy = c$ at a point P.
  (a) Show that the midpoint of the line segment cut from this tangent line by the coordinate axes is P.
  (b) Show that the triangle formed by the tangent line and the coordinate axes always has the same area, no matter where P is located on the hyperbola.

71. Evaluate $\displaystyle\lim_{x \to 1} \frac{x^{1000} - 1}{x - 1}$.

72. Draw a diagram showing two perpendicular lines that intersect on the y-axis and are both tangent to the parabola $y = x^2$. Where do these lines intersect?

73. If $c > \frac{1}{2}$, how many lines through the point $(0, c)$ are normal lines to the parabola $y = x^2$? What if $c \le \frac{1}{2}$?

74. Sketch the parabolas $y = x^2$ and $y = x^2 - 2x + 2$. Do you think there is a line that is tangent to both curves? If so, find its equation. If not, why not?

APPLIED PROJECT | **Building a Better Roller Coaster**

Suppose you are asked to design the first ascent and drop for a new roller coaster. By studying photographs of your favorite coasters, you decide to make the slope of the ascent 0.8 and the slope of the drop -1.6. You decide to connect these two straight stretches $y = L_1(x)$ and $y = L_2(x)$ with part of a parabola $y = f(x) = ax^2 + bx + c$, where x and $f(x)$ are measured in feet. For the track to be smooth there can't be abrupt changes in direction, so you want the linear segments L_1 and L_2 to be tangent to the parabola at the transition points P and Q. (See the figure.) To simplify the equations, you decide to place the origin at P.

1. (a) Suppose the horizontal distance between P and Q is 100 ft. Write equations in a, b, and c that will ensure that the track is smooth at the transition points.
  (b) Solve the equations in part (a) for a, b, and c to find a formula for $f(x)$.
  (c) Plot L_1, f, and L_2 to verify graphically that the transitions are smooth.
  (d) Find the difference in elevation between P and Q.

2. The solution in Problem 1 might *look* smooth, but it might not *feel* smooth because the piecewise defined function [consisting of $L_1(x)$ for $x < 0$, $f(x)$ for $0 \le x \le 100$, and $L_2(x)$ for $x > 100$] doesn't have a continuous second derivative. So you decide to improve the design by using a quadratic function $q(x) = ax^2 + bx + c$ only on the interval $10 \le x \le 90$ and connecting it to the linear functions by means of two cubic functions:

$$g(x) = kx^3 + lx^2 + mx + n \qquad 0 \le x < 10$$

$$h(x) = px^3 + qx^2 + rx + s \qquad 90 < x \le 100$$

  (a) Write a system of equations in 11 unknowns that ensure that the functions and their first two derivatives agree at the transition points.
  (b) Solve the equations in part (a) with a computer algebra system to find formulas for $q(x)$, $g(x)$, and $h(x)$.
  (c) Plot L_1, g, q, h, and L_2, and compare with the plot in Problem 1(c).

Graphing calculator or computer with graphing software required

CAS Computer algebra system required

3.2 The Product and Quotient Rules

The formulas of this section enable us to differentiate new functions formed from old functions by multiplication or division.

The Product Rule

By analogy with the Sum and Difference Rules, one might be tempted to guess, as Leibniz did three centuries ago, that the derivative of a product is the product of the derivatives. We can see, however, that this guess is wrong by looking at a particular example. Let $f(x) = x$

and $g(x) = x^2$. Then the Power Rule gives $f'(x) = 1$ and $g'(x) = 2x$. But $(fg)(x) = x^3$, so $(fg)'(x) = 3x^2$. Thus $(fg)' \neq f'g'$. The correct formula was discovered by Leibniz (soon after his false start) and is called the Product Rule.

Before stating the Product Rule, let's see how we might discover it. We start by assuming that $u = f(x)$ and $v = g(x)$ are both positive differentiable functions. Then we can interpret the product uv as an area of a rectangle (see Figure 1). If x changes by an amount Δx, then the corresponding changes in u and v are

$$\Delta u = f(x + \Delta x) - f(x) \qquad \Delta v = g(x + \Delta x) - g(x)$$

and the new value of the product, $(u + \Delta u)(v + \Delta v)$, can be interpreted as the area of the large rectangle in Figure 1 (provided that Δu and Δv happen to be positive).

The change in the area of the rectangle is

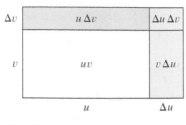

FIGURE 1

The geometry of the Product Rule

$$\boxed{1} \qquad \Delta(uv) = (u + \Delta u)(v + \Delta v) - uv = u\,\Delta v + v\,\Delta u + \Delta u\,\Delta v$$

$$= \text{the sum of the three shaded areas}$$

If we divide by Δx, we get

$$\frac{\Delta(uv)}{\Delta x} = u\,\frac{\Delta v}{\Delta x} + v\,\frac{\Delta u}{\Delta x} + \Delta u\,\frac{\Delta v}{\Delta x}$$

Recall that in Leibniz notation the definition of a derivative can be written as

$$\frac{dy}{dx} = \lim_{\Delta x \to 0} \frac{\Delta y}{\Delta x}$$

If we now let $\Delta x \to 0$, we get the derivative of uv:

$$\frac{d}{dx}(uv) = \lim_{\Delta x \to 0} \frac{\Delta(uv)}{\Delta x} = \lim_{\Delta x \to 0} \left(u\,\frac{\Delta v}{\Delta x} + v\,\frac{\Delta u}{\Delta x} + \Delta u\,\frac{\Delta v}{\Delta x} \right)$$

$$= u \lim_{\Delta x \to 0} \frac{\Delta v}{\Delta x} + v \lim_{\Delta x \to 0} \frac{\Delta u}{\Delta x} + \left(\lim_{\Delta x \to 0} \Delta u \right)\left(\lim_{\Delta x \to 0} \frac{\Delta v}{\Delta x} \right)$$

$$= u\,\frac{dv}{dx} + v\,\frac{du}{dx} + 0 \cdot \frac{dv}{dx}$$

$$\boxed{2} \qquad \frac{d}{dx}(uv) = u\,\frac{dv}{dx} + v\,\frac{du}{dx}$$

(Notice that $\Delta u \to 0$ as $\Delta x \to 0$ since f is differentiable and therefore continuous.)

Although we started by assuming (for the geometric interpretation) that all the quantities are positive, we notice that Equation 1 is always true. (The algebra is valid whether u, v, Δu, and Δv are positive or negative.) So we have proved Equation 2, known as the Product Rule, for all differentiable functions u and v.

In prime notation:

$$(fg)' = fg' + gf'$$

The Product Rule If f and g are both differentiable, then

$$\frac{d}{dx}[f(x)g(x)] = f(x)\,\frac{d}{dx}[g(x)] + g(x)\,\frac{d}{dx}[f(x)]$$

In words, the Product Rule says that *the derivative of a product of two functions is the first function times the derivative of the second function plus the second function times the derivative of the first function.*

EXAMPLE 1 **Using the Product Rule**
(a) If $f(x) = xe^x$, find $f'(x)$.
(b) Find the nth derivative, $f^{(n)}(x)$.

SOLUTION
(a) By the Product Rule, we have

$$f'(x) = \frac{d}{dx}(xe^x)$$

$$= x\frac{d}{dx}(e^x) + e^x\frac{d}{dx}(x)$$

$$= xe^x + e^x \cdot 1 = (x + 1)e^x$$

Figure 2 shows the graphs of the function f of Example 1 and its derivative f'. Notice that $f'(x)$ is positive when f is increasing and negative when f is decreasing.

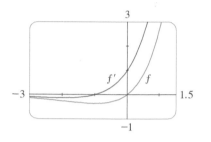

FIGURE 2

(b) Using the Product Rule a second time, we get

$$f''(x) = \frac{d}{dx}[(x + 1)e^x]$$

$$= (x + 1)\frac{d}{dx}(e^x) + e^x\frac{d}{dx}(x + 1)$$

$$= (x + 1)e^x + e^x \cdot 1 = (x + 2)e^x$$

Further applications of the Product Rule give

$$f'''(x) = (x + 3)e^x \qquad f^{(4)}(x) = (x + 4)e^x$$

In fact, each successive differentiation adds another term e^x, so

$$f^{(n)}(x) = (x + n)e^x$$

In Example 2, a and b are constants. It is customary in mathematics to use letters near the beginning of the alphabet to represent constants and letters near the end of the alphabet to represent variables.

EXAMPLE 2 **Differentiating a function with arbitrary constants**
Differentiate the function $f(t) = \sqrt{t}\,(a + bt)$.

SOLUTION 1   Using the Product Rule, we have

$$f'(t) = \sqrt{t}\,\frac{d}{dt}(a + bt) + (a + bt)\frac{d}{dt}\left(\sqrt{t}\right)$$

$$= \sqrt{t} \cdot b + (a + bt) \cdot \tfrac{1}{2}t^{-1/2}$$

$$= b\sqrt{t} + \frac{a + bt}{2\sqrt{t}} = \frac{a + 3bt}{2\sqrt{t}}$$

SOLUTION 2   If we first use the laws of exponents to rewrite $f(t)$, then we can proceed directly without using the Product Rule.

$$f(t) = a\sqrt{t} + bt\sqrt{t} = at^{1/2} + bt^{3/2}$$

$$f'(t) = \tfrac{1}{2}at^{-1/2} + \tfrac{3}{2}bt^{1/2}$$

which is equivalent to the answer given in Solution 1.

Example 2 shows that it is sometimes easier to simplify a product of functions before differentiating than to use the Product Rule. In Example 1, however, the Product Rule is the only possible method.

EXAMPLE 3 If $f(x) = \sqrt{x}\, g(x)$, where $g(4) = 2$ and $g'(4) = 3$, find $f'(4)$.

SOLUTION Applying the Product Rule, we get

$$f'(x) = \frac{d}{dx}\left[\sqrt{x}\, g(x)\right] = \sqrt{x}\,\frac{d}{dx}\left[g(x)\right] + g(x)\,\frac{d}{dx}\left[\sqrt{x}\,\right]$$

$$= \sqrt{x}\, g'(x) + g(x) \cdot \tfrac{1}{2}x^{-1/2} = \sqrt{x}\, g'(x) + \frac{g(x)}{2\sqrt{x}}$$

So
$$f'(4) = \sqrt{4}\, g'(4) + \frac{g(4)}{2\sqrt{4}} = 2 \cdot 3 + \frac{2}{2 \cdot 2} = 6.5$$

V **EXAMPLE 4** **Interpreting the terms in the Product Rule** A telephone company wants to estimate the number of new residential phone lines that it will need to install during the upcoming month. At the beginning of January the company had 100,000 subscribers, each of whom had 1.2 phone lines, on average. The company estimated that its subscribership was increasing at the rate of 1000 monthly. By polling its existing subscribers, the company found that each intended to install an average of 0.01 new phone lines by the end of January. Estimate the number of new lines the company will have to install in January by calculating the rate of increase of lines at the beginning of the month.

SOLUTION Let $s(t)$ be the number of subscribers and let $n(t)$ be the number of phone lines per subscriber at time t, where t is measured in months and $t = 0$ corresponds to the beginning of January. Then the total number of lines is given by

$$L(t) = s(t)n(t)$$

and we want to find $L'(0)$. According to the Product Rule, we have

$$L'(t) = \frac{d}{dt}\left[s(t)n(t)\right] = s(t)\,\frac{d}{dt}\,n(t) + n(t)\,\frac{d}{dt}\,s(t)$$

We are given that $s(0) = 100{,}000$ and $n(0) = 1.2$. The company's estimates concerning rates of increase are that $s'(0) \approx 1000$ and $n'(0) \approx 0.01$. Therefore

$$L'(0) = s(0)n'(0) + n(0)s'(0)$$

$$\approx 100{,}000 \cdot 0.01 + 1.2 \cdot 1000 = 2200$$

The company will need to install approximately 2200 new phone lines in January.

Notice that the two terms arising from the Product Rule come from different sources—old subscribers and new subscribers. One contribution to L' is the number of existing subscribers (100,000) times the rate at which they order new lines (about 0.01 per subscriber monthly). A second contribution is the average number of lines per subscriber (1.2 at the beginning of the month) times the rate of increase of subscribers (1000 monthly).

The Quotient Rule

We find a rule for differentiating the quotient of two differentiable functions $u = f(x)$ and $v = g(x)$ in much the same way that we found the Product Rule. If x, u, and v change by amounts Δx, Δu, and Δv, then the corresponding change in the quotient u/v is

$$\Delta\left(\frac{u}{v}\right) = \frac{u + \Delta u}{v + \Delta v} - \frac{u}{v} = \frac{(u + \Delta u)v - u(v + \Delta v)}{v(v + \Delta v)} = \frac{v\,\Delta u - u\,\Delta v}{v(v + \Delta v)}$$

so

$$\frac{d}{dx}\left(\frac{u}{v}\right) = \lim_{\Delta x \to 0} \frac{\Delta(u/v)}{\Delta x} = \lim_{\Delta x \to 0} \frac{v\dfrac{\Delta u}{\Delta x} - u\dfrac{\Delta v}{\Delta x}}{v(v + \Delta v)}$$

As $\Delta x \to 0$, $\Delta v \to 0$ also, because $v = g(x)$ is differentiable and therefore continuous. Thus, using the Limit Laws, we get

$$\frac{d}{dx}\left(\frac{u}{v}\right) = \frac{v \lim\limits_{\Delta x \to 0} \dfrac{\Delta u}{\Delta x} - u \lim\limits_{\Delta x \to 0} \dfrac{\Delta v}{\Delta x}}{v \lim\limits_{\Delta x \to 0}(v + \Delta v)} = \frac{v\dfrac{du}{dx} - u\dfrac{dv}{dx}}{v^2}$$

In prime notation:

$$\left(\frac{f}{g}\right)' = \frac{gf' - fg'}{g^2}$$

The Quotient Rule If f and g are differentiable, then

$$\frac{d}{dx}\left[\frac{f(x)}{g(x)}\right] = \frac{g(x)\dfrac{d}{dx}[f(x)] - f(x)\dfrac{d}{dx}[g(x)]}{[g(x)]^2}$$

In words, the Quotient Rule says that the *derivative of a quotient is the denominator times the derivative of the numerator minus the numerator times the derivative of the denominator, all divided by the square of the denominator.*

The Quotient Rule and the other differentiation formulas enable us to compute the derivative of any rational function, as the next example illustrates.

We can use a graphing device to check that the answer to Example 5 is plausible. Figure 3 shows the graphs of the function of Example 5 and its derivative. Notice that when y grows rapidly (near -2), y' is large. And when y grows slowly, y' is near 0.

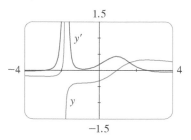

FIGURE 3

▼ **EXAMPLE 5** **Using the Quotient Rule** Let $y = \dfrac{x^2 + x - 2}{x^3 + 6}$. Then

$$y' = \frac{(x^3 + 6)\dfrac{d}{dx}(x^2 + x - 2) - (x^2 + x - 2)\dfrac{d}{dx}(x^3 + 6)}{(x^3 + 6)^2}$$

$$= \frac{(x^3 + 6)(2x + 1) - (x^2 + x - 2)(3x^2)}{(x^3 + 6)^2}$$

$$= \frac{(2x^4 + x^3 + 12x + 6) - (3x^4 + 3x^3 - 6x^2)}{(x^3 + 6)^2}$$

$$= \frac{-x^4 - 2x^3 + 6x^2 + 12x + 6}{(x^3 + 6)^2}$$

▼ **EXAMPLE 6** Find an equation of the tangent line to the curve $y = e^x/(1 + x^2)$ at the point $\left(1, \frac{1}{2}e\right)$.

SOLUTION According to the Quotient Rule, we have

$$\frac{dy}{dx} = \frac{(1 + x^2)\dfrac{d}{dx}(e^x) - e^x\dfrac{d}{dx}(1 + x^2)}{(1 + x^2)^2}$$

$$= \frac{(1 + x^2)e^x - e^x(2x)}{(1 + x^2)^2} = \frac{e^x(1 - x)^2}{(1 + x^2)^2}$$

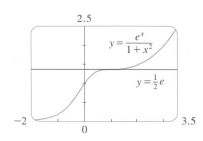

FIGURE 4

So the slope of the tangent line at $\left(1, \frac{1}{2}e\right)$ is

$$\left.\frac{dy}{dx}\right|_{x=1} = 0$$

This means that the tangent line at $\left(1, \frac{1}{2}e\right)$ is horizontal and its equation is $y = \frac{1}{2}e$. [See Figure 4. Notice that the function is increasing and crosses its tangent line at $\left(1, \frac{1}{2}e\right)$.]

Note: Don't use the Quotient Rule *every* time you see a quotient. Sometimes it's easier to rewrite a quotient first to put it in a form that is simpler for the purpose of differentiation. For instance, although it is possible to differentiate the function

$$F(x) = \frac{3x^2 + 2\sqrt{x}}{x}$$

using the Quotient Rule, it is much easier to perform the division first and write the function as

$$F(x) = 3x + 2x^{-1/2}$$

before differentiating.

We summarize the differentiation formulas we have learned so far as follows.

Table of Differentiation Formulas

$\dfrac{d}{dx}(c) = 0$	$\dfrac{d}{dx}(x^n) = nx^{n-1}$	$\dfrac{d}{dx}(e^x) = e^x$
$(cf)' = cf'$	$(f + g)' = f' + g'$	$(f - g)' = f' - g'$
$(fg)' = fg' + gf'$	$\left(\dfrac{f}{g}\right)' = \dfrac{gf' - fg'}{g^2}$	

3.2 Exercises

1. Find the derivative of $f(x) = (1 + 2x^2)(x - x^2)$ in two ways: by using the Product Rule and by performing the multiplication first. Do your answers agree?

2. Find the derivative of the function

$$F(x) = \frac{x^4 - 5x^3 + \sqrt{x}}{x^2}$$

in two ways: by using the Quotient Rule and by simplifying first. Show that your answers are equivalent. Which method do you prefer?

3–24 Differentiate.

3. $f(x) = (x^3 + 2x)e^x$

4. $g(x) = \sqrt{x}\, e^x$

5. $y = \dfrac{e^x}{x^2}$

6. $y = \dfrac{e^x}{1 + x}$

7. $g(x) = \dfrac{3x - 1}{2x + 1}$

8. $f(t) = \dfrac{2t}{4 + t^2}$

9. $F(y) = \left(\dfrac{1}{y^2} - \dfrac{3}{y^4}\right)(y + 5y^3)$

10. $R(t) = (t + e^t)(3 - \sqrt{t})$

11. $y = \dfrac{x^3}{1 - x^2}$

12. $y = \dfrac{x + 1}{x^3 + x - 2}$

13. $y = \dfrac{t^2 + 2}{t^4 - 3t^2 + 1}$

14. $y = \dfrac{t}{(t - 1)^2}$

⌂ Graphing calculator or computer with graphing software required   **1.** Homework Hints available in TEC

15. $y = (r^2 - 2r)e^r$

16. $y = \dfrac{1}{s + ke^s}$

17. $y = \dfrac{v^3 - 2v\sqrt{v}}{v}$

18. $z = w^{3/2}(w + ce^w)$

19. $f(t) = \dfrac{2t}{2 + \sqrt{t}}$

20. $g(t) = \dfrac{t - \sqrt{t}}{t^{1/3}}$

21. $f(x) = \dfrac{A}{B + Ce^x}$

22. $f(x) = \dfrac{1 - xe^x}{x + e^x}$

23. $f(x) = \dfrac{x}{x + \dfrac{c}{x}}$

24. $f(x) = \dfrac{ax + b}{cx + d}$

25–28 Find $f'(x)$ and $f''(x)$.

25. $f(x) = x^4 e^x$

26. $f(x) = x^{5/2} e^x$

27. $f(x) = \dfrac{x^2}{1 + 2x}$

28. $f(x) = \dfrac{x}{x^2 - 1}$

29–30 Find an equation of the tangent line to the given curve at the specified point.

29. $y = \dfrac{2x}{x + 1}$, $(1, 1)$

30. $y = \dfrac{e^x}{x}$, $(1, e)$

31–32 Find equations of the tangent line and normal line to the given curve at the specified point.

31. $y = 2xe^x$, $(0, 0)$

32. $y = \dfrac{\sqrt{x}}{x + 1}$, $(4, 0.4)$

---

33. (a) The curve $y = 1/(1 + x^2)$ is called a **witch of Maria Agnesi**. Find an equation of the tangent line to this curve at the point $\left(-1, \frac{1}{2}\right)$.

(b) Illustrate part (a) by graphing the curve and the tangent line on the same screen.

34. (a) The curve $y = x/(1 + x^2)$ is called a **serpentine**. Find an equation of the tangent line to this curve at the point $(3, 0.3)$.

(b) Illustrate part (a) by graphing the curve and the tangent line on the same screen.

35. (a) If $f(x) = (x^3 - x)e^x$, find $f'(x)$.

(b) Check to see that your answer to part (a) is reasonable by comparing the graphs of f and f'.

36. (a) If $f(x) = e^x/(2x^2 + x + 1)$, find $f'(x)$.

(b) Check to see that your answer to part (a) is reasonable by comparing the graphs of f and f'.

37. (a) If $f(x) = (x^2 - 1)/(x^2 + 1)$, find $f'(x)$ and $f''(x)$.

(b) Check to see that your answers to part (a) are reasonable by comparing the graphs of f, f', and f''.

38. (a) If $f(x) = (x^2 - 1)e^x$, find $f'(x)$ and $f''(x)$.

(b) Check to see that your answers to part (a) are reasonable by comparing the graphs of f, f', and f''.

39. If $f(x) = x^2/(1 + x)$, find $f''(1)$.

40. If $g(x) = x/e^x$, find $g^{(n)}(x)$.

41. Suppose that $f(5) = 1$, $f'(5) = 6$, $g(5) = -3$, and $g'(5) = 2$. Find the following values.

(a) $(fg)'(5)$ (b) $(f/g)'(5)$

(c) $(g/f)'(5)$

42. Suppose that $f(2) = -3$, $g(2) = 4$, $f'(2) = -2$, and $g'(2) = 7$. Find $h'(2)$.

(a) $h(x) = 5f(x) - 4g(x)$ (b) $h(x) = f(x)g(x)$

(c) $h(x) = \dfrac{f(x)}{g(x)}$ (d) $h(x) = \dfrac{g(x)}{1 + f(x)}$

43. If $f(x) = e^x g(x)$, where $g(0) = 2$ and $g'(0) = 5$, find $f'(0)$.

44. If $h(2) = 4$ and $h'(2) = -3$, find

$$\frac{d}{dx}\left(\frac{h(x)}{x}\right)\bigg|_{x=2}$$

45. If f and g are the functions whose graphs are shown, let $u(x) = f(x)g(x)$ and $v(x) = f(x)/g(x)$.

(a) Find $u'(1)$.   (b) Find $v'(5)$.

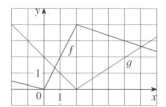

46. Let $P(x) = F(x)G(x)$ and $Q(x) = F(x)/G(x)$, where F and G are the functions whose graphs are shown.

(a) Find $P'(2)$.   (b) Find $Q'(7)$.

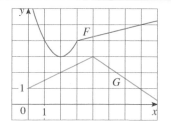

47. If g is a differentiable function, find an expression for the derivative of each of the following functions.

(a) $y = xg(x)$ (b) $y = \dfrac{x}{g(x)}$ (c) $y = \dfrac{g(x)}{x}$

48. If f is a differentiable function, find an expression for the derivative of each of the following functions.

(a) $y = x^2 f(x)$ (b) $y = \dfrac{f(x)}{x^2}$

(c) $y = \dfrac{x^2}{f(x)}$ (d) $y = \dfrac{1 + xf(x)}{\sqrt{x}}$

49. In this exercise we estimate the rate at which the total personal income is rising in the Richmond-Petersburg, Virginia, metropolitan area. In 1999, the population of this area was 961,400, and the population was increasing at roughly 9200 people per year. The average annual income was \$30,593 per capita, and this average was increasing at about \$1400 per year (a little above the national average of about \$1225 yearly). Use the Product Rule and these figures to estimate the rate at which total personal income was rising in the Richmond-Petersburg area in 1999. Explain the meaning of each term in the Product Rule.

50. A manufacturer produces bolts of a fabric with a fixed width. The quantity q of this fabric (measured in yards) that is sold is a function of the selling price p (in dollars per yard), so we can write $q = f(p)$. Then the total revenue earned with selling price p is $R(p) = pf(p)$.
 (a) What does it mean to say that $f(20) = 10{,}000$ and $f'(20) = -350$?
 (b) Assuming the values in part (a), find $R'(20)$ and interpret your answer.

51. On what interval is the function $f(x) = x^3 e^x$ increasing?

52. On what interval is the function $f(x) = x^2 e^x$ concave downward?

53. How many tangent lines to the curve $y = x/(x + 1)$ pass through the point $(1, 2)$? At which points do these tangent lines touch the curve?

54. Find equations of the tangent lines to the curve

$$y = \frac{x - 1}{x + 1}$$

that are parallel to the line $x - 2y = 2$.

55. Find $R'(0)$, where

$$R(x) = \frac{x - 3x^3 + 5x^5}{1 + 3x^3 + 6x^6 + 9x^9}$$

Hint: Instead of finding $R'(x)$ first, let $f(x)$ be the numerator and $g(x)$ the denominator of $R(x)$ and compute $R'(0)$ from $f(0)$, $f'(0)$, $g(0)$, and $g'(0)$.

56. Use the method of Exercise 55 to compute $Q'(0)$, where

$$Q(x) = \frac{1 + x + x^2 + xe^x}{1 - x + x^2 - xe^x}$$

57. (a) Use the Product Rule twice to prove that if f, g, and h are differentiable, then $(fgh)' = f'gh + fg'h + fgh'$.
 (b) Taking $f = g = h$ in part (a), show that

$$\frac{d}{dx}[f(x)]^3 = 3[f(x)]^2 f'(x)$$

 (c) Use part (b) to differentiate $y = e^{3x}$.

58. (a) If $F(x) = f(x)g(x)$, where f and g have derivatives of all orders, show that $F'' = f''g + 2f'g' + fg''$.
 (b) Find similar formulas for F''' and $F^{(4)}$.
 (c) Guess a formula for $F^{(n)}$.

59. Find expressions for the first five derivatives of $f(x) = x^2 e^x$. Do you see a pattern in these expressions? Guess a formula for $f^{(n)}(x)$ and prove it using mathematical induction.

60. (a) If g is differentiable, the **Reciprocal Rule** says that

$$\frac{d}{dx}\left[\frac{1}{g(x)}\right] = -\frac{g'(x)}{[g(x)]^2}$$

Use the Quotient Rule to prove the Reciprocal Rule.
 (b) Use the Reciprocal Rule to differentiate the function in Exercise 16.
 (c) Use the Reciprocal Rule to verify that the Power Rule is valid for negative integers, that is,

$$\frac{d}{dx}(x^{-n}) = -nx^{-n-1}$$

for all positive integers n.

3.3   Derivatives of Trigonometric Functions

A review of the trigonometric functions is given in Appendix C.

Before starting this section, you might need to review the trigonometric functions. In particular, it is important to remember that when we talk about the function f defined for all real numbers x by

$$f(x) = \sin x$$

it is understood that $\sin x$ means the sine of the angle whose *radian* measure is x. A similar convention holds for the other trigonometric functions cos, tan, csc, sec, and cot. Recall from Section 2.4 that all of the trigonometric functions are continuous at every number in their domains.

If we sketch the graph of the function $f(x) = \sin x$ and use the interpretation of $f'(x)$ as the slope of the tangent to the sine curve in order to sketch the graph of f' (see Exercise 14 in Section 2.7), then it looks as if the graph of f' may be the same as the cosine curve (see Figure 1).

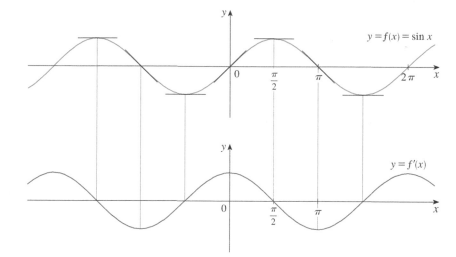

TEC Visual 3.3 shows an animation of Figure 1.

FIGURE 1

Let's try to confirm our guess that if $f(x) = \sin x$, then $f'(x) = \cos x$. From the definition of a derivative, we have

$$f'(x) = \lim_{h \to 0} \frac{f(x + h) - f(x)}{h} = \lim_{h \to 0} \frac{\sin(x + h) - \sin x}{h}$$

We have used the addition formula for sine. See Appendix C.

$$= \lim_{h \to 0} \frac{\sin x \cos h + \cos x \sin h - \sin x}{h}$$

$$= \lim_{h \to 0} \left[\frac{\sin x \cos h - \sin x}{h} + \frac{\cos x \sin h}{h} \right]$$

$$= \lim_{h \to 0} \left[\sin x \left(\frac{\cos h - 1}{h} \right) + \cos x \left(\frac{\sin h}{h} \right) \right]$$

$$\boxed{1} \qquad = \lim_{h \to 0} \sin x \cdot \lim_{h \to 0} \frac{\cos h - 1}{h} + \lim_{h \to 0} \cos x \cdot \lim_{h \to 0} \frac{\sin h}{h}$$

Two of these four limits are easy to evaluate. Since we regard x as a constant when computing a limit as $h \to 0$, we have

$$\lim_{h \to 0} \sin x = \sin x \qquad \text{and} \qquad \lim_{h \to 0} \cos x = \cos x$$

The limit of $(\sin h)/h$ is not so obvious. In Example 3 in Section 2.2 we made the guess, on the basis of numerical and graphical evidence, that

$$\boxed{2} \qquad \boxed{\lim_{\theta \to 0} \frac{\sin \theta}{\theta} = 1}$$

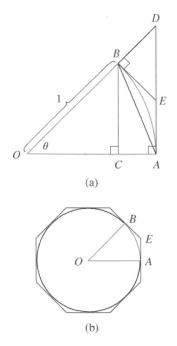

(a)

(b)

FIGURE 2

We now use a geometric argument to prove Equation 2. Assume first that θ lies between 0 and $\pi/2$. Figure 2(a) shows a sector of a circle with center O, central angle θ, and radius 1. BC is drawn perpendicular to OA. By the definition of radian measure, we have arc $AB = \theta$. Also $|BC| = |OB| \sin \theta = \sin \theta$. From the diagram we see that

$$|BC| < |AB| < \text{arc } AB$$

Therefore $\qquad\qquad \sin \theta < \theta \qquad$ so $\qquad \dfrac{\sin \theta}{\theta} < 1$

Let the tangent lines at A and B intersect at E. You can see from Figure 2(b) that the circumference of a circle is smaller than the length of a circumscribed polygon, and so arc $AB < |AE| + |EB|$. Thus

$$\begin{aligned}
\theta = \text{arc } AB &< |AE| + |EB| \\
&< |AE| + |ED| \\
&= |AD| = |OA| \tan \theta \\
&= \tan \theta
\end{aligned}$$

Therefore we have

$$\theta < \frac{\sin \theta}{\cos \theta}$$

so $\qquad\qquad\qquad \cos \theta < \dfrac{\sin \theta}{\theta} < 1$

We know that $\lim_{\theta \to 0} 1 = 1$ and $\lim_{\theta \to 0} \cos \theta = 1$, so by the Squeeze Theorem, we have

$$\lim_{\theta \to 0^+} \frac{\sin \theta}{\theta} = 1$$

But the function $(\sin \theta)/\theta$ is an even function, so its right and left limits must be equal. Hence, we have

$$\lim_{\theta \to 0} \frac{\sin \theta}{\theta} = 1$$

so we have proved Equation 2.

We can deduce the value of the remaining limit in (1) as follows:

We multiply numerator and denominator by $\cos \theta + 1$ in order to put the function in a form in which we can use the limits we know.

$$\begin{aligned}
\lim_{\theta \to 0} \frac{\cos \theta - 1}{\theta} &= \lim_{\theta \to 0} \left(\frac{\cos \theta - 1}{\theta} \cdot \frac{\cos \theta + 1}{\cos \theta + 1} \right) = \lim_{\theta \to 0} \frac{\cos^2 \theta - 1}{\theta (\cos \theta + 1)} \\
&= \lim_{\theta \to 0} \frac{-\sin^2 \theta}{\theta (\cos \theta + 1)} = -\lim_{\theta \to 0} \left(\frac{\sin \theta}{\theta} \cdot \frac{\sin \theta}{\cos \theta + 1} \right) \\
&= -\lim_{\theta \to 0} \frac{\sin \theta}{\theta} \cdot \lim_{\theta \to 0} \frac{\sin \theta}{\cos \theta + 1} \\
&= -1 \cdot \left(\frac{0}{1 + 1} \right) = 0 \qquad \text{(by Equation 2)}
\end{aligned}$$

$$\boxed{3} \qquad \lim_{\theta \to 0} \frac{\cos \theta - 1}{\theta} = 0$$

If we now put the limits (2) and (3) in (1), we get

$$f'(x) = \lim_{h \to 0} \sin x \cdot \lim_{h \to 0} \frac{\cos h - 1}{h} + \lim_{h \to 0} \cos x \cdot \lim_{h \to 0} \frac{\sin h}{h}$$

$$= (\sin x) \cdot 0 + (\cos x) \cdot 1 = \cos x$$

So we have proved the formula for the derivative of the sine function:

$$\boxed{4} \qquad \frac{d}{dx} (\sin x) = \cos x$$

V **EXAMPLE 1** Differentiate $y = x^2 \sin x$.

Figure 3 shows the graphs of the function of Example 1 and its derivative. Notice that $y' = 0$ whenever y has a horizontal tangent.

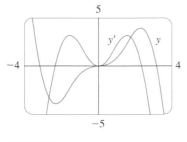

FIGURE 3

SOLUTION Using the Product Rule and Formula 4, we have

$$\frac{dy}{dx} = x^2 \frac{d}{dx} (\sin x) + \sin x \frac{d}{dx} (x^2)$$

$$= x^2 \cos x + 2x \sin x$$

Using the same methods as in the proof of Formula 4, one can prove (see Exercise 18) that

$$\boxed{5} \qquad \frac{d}{dx} (\cos x) = -\sin x$$

The tangent function can also be differentiated by using the definition of a derivative, but it is easier to use the Quotient Rule together with Formulas 4 and 5:

$$\frac{d}{dx} (\tan x) = \frac{d}{dx} \left(\frac{\sin x}{\cos x} \right)$$

$$= \frac{\cos x \dfrac{d}{dx} (\sin x) - \sin x \dfrac{d}{dx} (\cos x)}{\cos^2 x}$$

$$= \frac{\cos x \cdot \cos x - \sin x (-\sin x)}{\cos^2 x}$$

$$= \frac{\cos^2 x + \sin^2 x}{\cos^2 x}$$

$$= \frac{1}{\cos^2 x} = \sec^2 x$$

6

$$\frac{d}{dx} (\tan x) = \sec^2 x$$

The derivatives of the remaining trigonometric functions, csc, sec, and cot, can also be found easily using the Quotient Rule (see Exercises 15–17). We collect all the differentiation formulas for trigonometric functions in the following table. Remember that they are valid only when x is measured in radians.

> **Derivatives of Trigonometric Functions**
>
> $$\frac{d}{dx} (\sin x) = \cos x \qquad\qquad \frac{d}{dx} (\csc x) = -\csc x \cot x$$
>
> $$\frac{d}{dx} (\cos x) = -\sin x \qquad\qquad \frac{d}{dx} (\sec x) = \sec x \tan x$$
>
> $$\frac{d}{dx} (\tan x) = \sec^2 x \qquad\qquad \frac{d}{dx} (\cot x) = -\csc^2 x$$

When you memorize this table, it is helpful to notice that the minus signs go with the derivatives of the "cofunctions," that is, cosine, cosecant, and cotangent.

EXAMPLE 2 Differentiate $f(x) = \dfrac{\sec x}{1 + \tan x}$. For what values of x does the graph of f have a horizontal tangent?

SOLUTION The Quotient Rule gives

$$f'(x) = \frac{(1 + \tan x) \dfrac{d}{dx} (\sec x) - \sec x \dfrac{d}{dx} (1 + \tan x)}{(1 + \tan x)^2}$$

$$= \frac{(1 + \tan x) \sec x \tan x - \sec x \cdot \sec^2 x}{(1 + \tan x)^2}$$

$$= \frac{\sec x (\tan x + \tan^2 x - \sec^2 x)}{(1 + \tan x)^2}$$

$$= \frac{\sec x (\tan x - 1)}{(1 + \tan x)^2}$$

In simplifying the answer we have used the identity $\tan^2 x + 1 = \sec^2 x$.

Since $\sec x$ is never 0, we see that $f'(x) = 0$ when $\tan x = 1$, and this occurs when $x = n\pi + \pi/4$, where n is an integer (see Figure 4).

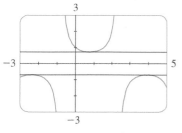

FIGURE 4

The horizontal tangents in Example 2

Trigonometric functions are often used in modeling real-world phenomena. In particular, vibrations, waves, elastic motions, and other quantities that vary in a periodic manner can be described using trigonometric functions. In the following example we discuss an instance of simple harmonic motion.

V **EXAMPLE 3** **Analyzing the motion of a spring** An object at the end of a vertical spring is stretched 4 cm beyond its rest position and released at time $t = 0$. (See Figure 5 and note that the downward direction is positive.) Its position at time t is

$$s = f(t) = 4 \cos t$$

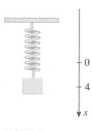

FIGURE 5

Find the velocity and acceleration at time t and use them to analyze the motion of the object.

SOLUTION The velocity and acceleration are

$$v = \frac{ds}{dt} = \frac{d}{dt}(4\cos t) = 4\frac{d}{dt}(\cos t) = -4\sin t$$

$$a = \frac{dv}{dt} = \frac{d}{dt}(-4\sin t) = -4\frac{d}{dt}(\sin t) = -4\cos t$$

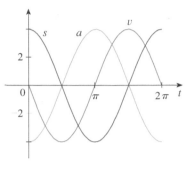

FIGURE 6

The object oscillates from the lowest point ($s = 4$ cm) to the highest point ($s = -4$ cm). The period of the oscillation is 2π, the period of $\cos t$.

The speed is $|v| = 4|\sin t|$, which is greatest when $|\sin t| = 1$, that is, when $\cos t = 0$. So the object moves fastest as it passes through its equilibrium position ($s = 0$). Its speed is 0 when $\sin t = 0$, that is, at the high and low points.

The acceleration $a = -4\cos t = 0$ when $s = 0$. It has greatest magnitude at the high and low points. See the graphs in Figure 6.

EXAMPLE 4 **Finding a high-order derivative from a pattern**
Find the 27th derivative of $\cos x$.

SOLUTION The first few derivatives of $f(x) = \cos x$ are as follows:

$$f'(x) = -\sin x$$
$$f''(x) = -\cos x$$
$$f'''(x) = \sin x$$
$$f^{(4)}(x) = \cos x$$
$$f^{(5)}(x) = -\sin x$$

PS Look for a pattern.

We see that the successive derivatives occur in a cycle of length 4 and, in particular, $f^{(n)}(x) = \cos x$ whenever n is a multiple of 4. Therefore

$$f^{(24)}(x) = \cos x$$

and, differentiating three more times, we have

$$f^{(27)}(x) = \sin x$$

3.3 Exercises

1–14 Differentiate.

1. $f(x) = 3x^2 - 2\cos x$

2. $y = 2\csc x + 5\cos x$

3. $f(x) = \sin x + \frac{1}{2}\cot x$

4. $f(x) = \sqrt{x}\,\sin x$

5. $y = \sec\theta\tan\theta$

6. $g(\theta) = e^\theta(\tan\theta - \theta)$

7. $y = c\cos t + t^2\sin t$

8. $f(t) = \dfrac{\cot t}{e^t}$

9. $y = \dfrac{x}{2 - \tan x}$

10. $y = \dfrac{1 + \sin x}{x + \cos x}$

11. $f(\theta) = \dfrac{\sec\theta}{1 + \sec\theta}$

12. $y = \dfrac{1 - \sec x}{\tan x}$

13. $f(x) = xe^x\csc x$

14. $y = x^2\sin x\tan x$

15. Prove that $\dfrac{d}{dx}(\csc x) = -\csc x\cot x$.

16. Prove that $\dfrac{d}{dx}(\sec x) = \sec x\tan x$.

⌂ Graphing calculator or computer with graphing software required   **1.** Homework Hints available in TEC

17. Prove that $\dfrac{d}{dx}(\cot x) = -\csc^2 x$.

18. Prove, using the definition of derivative, that if $f(x) = \cos x$, then $f'(x) = -\sin x$.

19–22 Find an equation of the tangent line to the curve at the given point.

19. $y = \sec x$, $(\pi/3, 2)$ **20.** $y = e^x \cos x$, $(0, 1)$

21. $y = x + \cos x$, $(0, 1)$ **22.** $y = \dfrac{1}{\sin x + \cos x}$, $(0, 1)$

---

23. (a) Find an equation of the tangent line to the curve
  $y = 2x \sin x$ at the point $(\pi/2, \pi)$.
  (b) Illustrate part (a) by graphing the curve and the tangent line on the same screen.

24. (a) Find an equation of the tangent line to the curve
  $y = 3x + 6 \cos x$ at the point $(\pi/3, \pi + 3)$.
  (b) Illustrate part (a) by graphing the curve and the tangent line on the same screen.

25. (a) If $f(x) = \sec x - x$, find $f'(x)$.
  (b) Check to see that your answer to part (a) is reasonable by graphing both f and f' for $|x| < \pi/2$.

26. (a) If $f(x) = e^x \cos x$, find $f'(x)$ and $f''(x)$.
  (b) Check to see that your answers to part (a) are reasonable by graphing f, f', and f''.

27. If $H(\theta) = \theta \sin \theta$, find $H'(\theta)$ and $H''(\theta)$.

28. If $f(t) = \csc t$, find $f''(\pi/6)$.

29. (a) Use the Quotient Rule to differentiate the function

$$f(x) = \frac{\tan x - 1}{\sec x}$$

  (b) Simplify the expression for $f(x)$ by writing it in terms of $\sin x$ and $\cos x$, and then find $f'(x)$.
  (c) Show that your answers to parts (a) and (b) are equivalent.

30. Suppose $f(\pi/3) = 4$ and $f'(\pi/3) = -2$, and let
  $g(x) = f(x) \sin x$ and $h(x) = (\cos x)/f(x)$. Find
  (a) $g'(\pi/3)$ (b) $h'(\pi/3)$

31–32 For what values of x does the graph of f have a horizontal tangent?

31. $f(x) = x + 2 \sin x$ **32.** $f(x) = e^x \cos x$

---

33. Let $f(x) = x - 2 \sin x$, $0 \le x \le 2\pi$. On what interval is f increasing?

34. Let $f(x) = 2x - \tan x$, $-\pi/2 < x < \pi/2$. On what interval is f concave downward?

35. A mass on a spring vibrates horizontally on a smooth level surface (see the figure). Its equation of motion is $x(t) = 8 \sin t$, where t is in seconds and x in centimeters.
  (a) Find the velocity and acceleration at time t.
  (b) Find the position, velocity, and acceleration of the mass at time $t = 2\pi/3$. In what direction is it moving at that time?

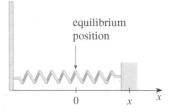

36. An elastic band is hung on a hook and a mass is hung on the lower end of the band. When the mass is pulled downward and then released, it vibrates vertically. The equation of motion is $s = 2 \cos t + 3 \sin t$, $t \ge 0$, where s is measured in centimeters and t in seconds. (Take the positive direction to be downward.)
  (a) Find the velocity and acceleration at time t.
  (b) Graph the velocity and acceleration functions.
  (c) When does the mass pass through the equilibrium position for the first time?
  (d) How far from its equilibrium position does the mass travel?
  (e) When is the speed the greatest?

37. A ladder 10 ft long rests against a vertical wall. Let θ be the angle between the top of the ladder and the wall and let x be the distance from the bottom of the ladder to the wall. If the bottom of the ladder slides away from the wall, how fast does x change with respect to θ when $\theta = \pi/3$?

38. An object with weight W is dragged along a horizontal plane by a force acting along a rope attached to the object. If the rope makes an angle θ with the plane, then the magnitude of the force is

$$F = \frac{\mu W}{\mu \sin \theta + \cos \theta}$$

where μ is a constant called the *coefficient of friction*.
  (a) Find the rate of change of F with respect to θ.
  (b) When is this rate of change equal to 0?
  (c) If $W = 50$ lb and $\mu = 0.6$, draw the graph of F as a function of θ and use it to locate the value of θ for which $dF/d\theta = 0$. Is the value consistent with your answer to part (b)?

39–40 Find the given derivative by finding the first few derivatives and observing the pattern that occurs.

39. $\dfrac{d^{99}}{dx^{99}}(\sin x)$ **40.** $\dfrac{d^{35}}{dx^{35}}(x \sin x)$

41. Find constants A and B such that the function $y = A \sin x + B \cos x$ satisfies the differential equation $y'' + y' - 2y = \sin x$.

42. (a) Use the substitution $\theta = 5x$ to evaluate

$$\lim_{x \to 0} \frac{\sin 5x}{x}$$

(b) Use part (a) and the definition of a derivative to find

$$\frac{d}{dx}(\sin 5x)$$

43–45 Use Formula 2 and trigonometric identities to evaluate the limit.

43. $\lim\limits_{t \to 0} \dfrac{\tan 6t}{\sin 2t}$

44. $\lim\limits_{x \to 0} \dfrac{\sin 3x \sin 5x}{x^2}$

45. $\lim\limits_{\theta \to 0} \dfrac{\sin \theta}{\theta + \tan \theta}$

46. (a) Evaluate $\lim\limits_{x \to \infty} x \sin \dfrac{1}{x}$.

(b) Evaluate $\lim\limits_{x \to 0} x \sin \dfrac{1}{x}$.

(c) Illustrate parts (a) and (b) by graphing $y = x \sin(1/x)$.

47. Differentiate each trigonometric identity to obtain a new (or familiar) identity.

(a) $\tan x = \dfrac{\sin x}{\cos x}$ (b) $\sec x = \dfrac{1}{\cos x}$

(c) $\sin x + \cos x = \dfrac{1 + \cot x}{\csc x}$

48. A semicircle with diameter PQ sits on an isosceles triangle PQR to form a region shaped like a two-dimensional ice-cream cone, as shown in the figure. If $A(\theta)$ is the area of the semicircle and $B(\theta)$ is the area of the triangle, find

$$\lim_{\theta \to 0^+} \frac{A(\theta)}{B(\theta)}$$

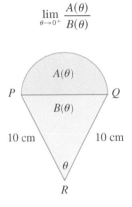

49. The figure shows a circular arc of length s and a chord of length d, both subtended by a central angle θ. Find

$$\lim_{\theta \to 0^+} \frac{s}{d}$$

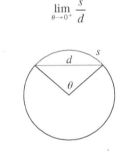

50. Let $f(x) = \dfrac{x}{\sqrt{1 - \cos 2x}}$.

(a) Graph f. What type of discontinuity does it appear to have at 0?

(b) Calculate the left and right limits of f at 0. Do these values confirm your answer to part (a)?

3.4 The Chain Rule

Suppose you are asked to differentiate the function

$$F(x) = \sqrt{x^2 + 1}$$

The differentiation formulas you learned in the previous sections of this chapter do not enable you to calculate $F'(x)$.

Observe that F is a composite function. In fact, if we let $y = f(u) = \sqrt{u}$ and let $u = g(x) = x^2 + 1$, then we can write $y = F(x) = f(g(x))$, that is, $F = f \circ g$. We know how to differentiate both f and g, so it would be useful to have a rule that tells us how to find the derivative of $F = f \circ g$ in terms of the derivatives of f and g.

It turns out that the derivative of the composite function $f \circ g$ is the product of the derivatives of f and g. This fact is one of the most important of the differentiation rules and is

See Section 1.3 for a review of composite functions.

called the *Chain Rule*. It seems plausible if we interpret derivatives as rates of change. Regard du/dx as the rate of change of u with respect to x, dy/du as the rate of change of y with respect to u, and dy/dx as the rate of change of y with respect to x. If u changes twice as fast as x and y changes three times as fast as u, then it seems reasonable that y changes six times as fast as x, and so we expect that

$$\frac{dy}{dx} = \frac{dy}{du}\frac{du}{dx}$$

> **The Chain Rule** If g is differentiable at x and f is differentiable at $g(x)$, then the composite function $F = f \circ g$ defined by $F(x) = f(g(x))$ is differentiable at x and F' is given by the product
>
> $$F'(x) = f'(g(x)) \cdot g'(x)$$
>
> In Leibniz notation, if $y = f(u)$ and $u = g(x)$ are both differentiable functions, then
>
> $$\frac{dy}{dx} = \frac{dy}{du}\frac{du}{dx}$$

James Gregory

The first person to formulate the Chain Rule was the Scottish mathematician James Gregory (1638–1675), who also designed the first practical reflecting telescope. Gregory discovered the basic ideas of calculus at about the same time as Newton. He became the first Professor of Mathematics at the University of St. Andrews and later held the same position at the University of Edinburgh. But one year after accepting that position he died at the age of 36.

COMMENTS ON THE PROOF OF THE CHAIN RULE   Let Δu be the change in u corresponding to a change of Δx in x, that is,

$$\Delta u = g(x + \Delta x) - g(x)$$

Then the corresponding change in y is

$$\Delta y = f(u + \Delta u) - f(u)$$

It is tempting to write

$$\frac{dy}{dx} = \lim_{\Delta x \to 0} \frac{\Delta y}{\Delta x}$$

$$\boxed{1} \qquad = \lim_{\Delta x \to 0} \frac{\Delta y}{\Delta u} \cdot \frac{\Delta u}{\Delta x}$$

$$= \lim_{\Delta x \to 0} \frac{\Delta y}{\Delta u} \cdot \lim_{\Delta x \to 0} \frac{\Delta u}{\Delta x}$$

$$= \lim_{\Delta u \to 0} \frac{\Delta y}{\Delta u} \cdot \lim_{\Delta x \to 0} \frac{\Delta u}{\Delta x} \qquad \text{(Note that } \Delta u \to 0 \text{ as } \Delta x \to 0 \text{ since } g \text{ is continuous.)}$$

$$= \frac{dy}{du}\frac{du}{dx}$$

The only flaw in this reasoning is that in (1) it might happen that $\Delta u = 0$ (even when $\Delta x \neq 0$) and, of course, we can't divide by 0. Nonetheless, this reasoning does at least *suggest* that the Chain Rule is true. A full proof of the Chain Rule is given at the end of this section.

The Chain Rule can be written either in the prime notation

$$\boxed{2} \qquad (f \circ g)'(x) = f'(g(x)) \cdot g'(x)$$

or, if $y = f(u)$ and $u = g(x)$, in Leibniz notation:

$$\boxed{3} \qquad\qquad \frac{dy}{dx} = \frac{dy}{du}\frac{du}{dx}$$

Equation 3 is easy to remember because if dy/du and du/dx were quotients, then we could cancel du. Remember, however, that du has not been defined and du/dx should not be thought of as an actual quotient.

EXAMPLE 1 Using the Chain Rule Find $F'(x)$ if $F(x) = \sqrt{x^2 + 1}$.

SOLUTION 1 (using Equation 2): At the beginning of this section we expressed F as $F(x) = (f \circ g)(x) = f(g(x))$ where $f(u) = \sqrt{u}$ and $g(x) = x^2 + 1$. Since

$$f'(u) = \tfrac{1}{2}u^{-1/2} = \frac{1}{2\sqrt{u}} \qquad \text{and} \qquad g'(x) = 2x$$

we have
$$F'(x) = f'(g(x)) \cdot g'(x)$$

$$= \frac{1}{2\sqrt{x^2 + 1}} \cdot 2x = \frac{x}{\sqrt{x^2 + 1}}$$

SOLUTION 2 (using Equation 3): If we let $u = x^2 + 1$ and $y = \sqrt{u}$, then

$$F'(x) = \frac{dy}{du}\frac{du}{dx} = \frac{1}{2\sqrt{u}}(2x) = \frac{1}{2\sqrt{x^2 + 1}}(2x) = \frac{x}{\sqrt{x^2 + 1}}$$

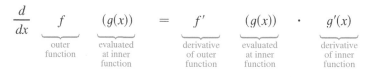

When using Formula 3 we should bear in mind that dy/dx refers to the derivative of y when y is considered as a function of x (called the *derivative of y with respect to x*), whereas dy/du refers to the derivative of y when considered as a function of u (the derivative of y with respect to u). For instance, in Example 1, y can be considered as a function of x $\left(y = \sqrt{x^2 + 1}\right)$ and also as a function of u $\left(y = \sqrt{u}\right)$. Note that

$$\frac{dy}{dx} = F'(x) = \frac{x}{\sqrt{x^2 + 1}} \qquad \text{whereas} \qquad \frac{dy}{du} = f'(u) = \frac{1}{2\sqrt{u}}$$

Note: In using the Chain Rule we work from the outside to the inside. Formula 2 says that *we differentiate the outer function f [at the inner function $g(x)$] and then we multiply by the derivative of the inner function.*

$$\underset{}{\frac{d}{dx}} \quad \underset{\substack{\text{outer} \\ \text{function}}}{f} \quad \underset{\substack{\text{evaluated} \\ \text{at inner} \\ \text{function}}}{(g(x))} \quad = \quad \underset{\substack{\text{derivative} \\ \text{of outer} \\ \text{function}}}{f'} \quad \underset{\substack{\text{evaluated} \\ \text{at inner} \\ \text{function}}}{(g(x))} \quad \cdot \quad \underset{\substack{\text{derivative} \\ \text{of inner} \\ \text{function}}}{g'(x)}$$

▣ EXAMPLE 2 Differentiate (a) $y = \sin(x^2)$ and (b) $y = \sin^2 x$.

SOLUTION

(a) If $y = \sin(x^2)$, then the outer function is the sine function and the inner function is the squaring function, so the Chain Rule gives

$$\frac{dy}{dx} = \underset{}{\frac{d}{dx}} \quad \underset{\substack{\text{outer} \\ \text{function}}}{\sin} \quad \underset{\substack{\text{evaluated} \\ \text{at inner} \\ \text{function}}}{(x^2)} \quad = \quad \underset{\substack{\text{derivative} \\ \text{of outer} \\ \text{function}}}{\cos} \quad \underset{\substack{\text{evaluated} \\ \text{at inner} \\ \text{function}}}{(x^2)} \quad \cdot \quad \underset{\substack{\text{derivative} \\ \text{of inner} \\ \text{function}}}{2x}$$

$$= 2x \cos(x^2)$$

(b) Note that $\sin^2 x = (\sin x)^2$. Here the outer function is the squaring function and the inner function is the sine function. So

$$\frac{dy}{dx} = \frac{d}{dx}\underbrace{(\sin x)^2}_{\substack{\text{inner} \\ \text{function}}} = \underbrace{2}_{\substack{\text{derivative} \\ \text{of outer} \\ \text{function}}} \cdot \underbrace{(\sin x)}_{\substack{\text{evaluated} \\ \text{at inner} \\ \text{function}}} \cdot \underbrace{\cos x}_{\substack{\text{derivative} \\ \text{of inner} \\ \text{function}}}$$

See Reference Page 2 or Appendix C.

The answer can be left as $2 \sin x \cos x$ or written as $\sin 2x$ (by a trigonometric identity known as the double-angle formula).

In Example 2(a) we combined the Chain Rule with the rule for differentiating the sine function. In general, if $y = \sin u$, where u is a differentiable function of x, then, by the Chain Rule,

$$\frac{dy}{dx} = \frac{dy}{du}\frac{du}{dx} = \cos u \frac{du}{dx}$$

Thus

$$\frac{d}{dx}(\sin u) = \cos u \frac{du}{dx}$$

In a similar fashion, all of the formulas for differentiating trigonometric functions can be combined with the Chain Rule.

Let's make explicit the special case of the Chain Rule where the outer function f is a power function. If $y = [g(x)]^n$, then we can write $y = f(u) = u^n$ where $u = g(x)$. By using the Chain Rule and then the Power Rule, we get

$$\frac{dy}{dx} = \frac{dy}{du}\frac{du}{dx} = nu^{n-1}\frac{du}{dx} = n[g(x)]^{n-1}g'(x)$$

> **4** **The Power Rule Combined with the Chain Rule** If n is any real number and $u = g(x)$ is differentiable, then
>
> $$\frac{d}{dx}(u^n) = nu^{n-1}\frac{du}{dx}$$
>
> Alternatively, $\quad\dfrac{d}{dx}[g(x)]^n = n[g(x)]^{n-1} \cdot g'(x)$

Notice that the derivative in Example 1 could be calculated by taking $n = \frac{1}{2}$ in Rule 4.

EXAMPLE 3 **Using the Chain Rule with the Power Rule** Differentiate $y = (x^3 - 1)^{100}$.

SOLUTION Taking $u = g(x) = x^3 - 1$ and $n = 100$ in (4), we have

$$\frac{dy}{dx} = \frac{d}{dx}(x^3 - 1)^{100} = 100(x^3 - 1)^{99}\frac{d}{dx}(x^3 - 1)$$
$$= 100(x^3 - 1)^{99} \cdot 3x^2 = 300x^2(x^3 - 1)^{99}$$

V **EXAMPLE 4** Find $f'(x)$ if $f(x) = \dfrac{1}{\sqrt[3]{x^2 + x + 1}}$.

SOLUTION First rewrite f: $f(x) = (x^2 + x + 1)^{-1/3}$. Thus

$$f'(x) = -\tfrac{1}{3}(x^2 + x + 1)^{-4/3}\frac{d}{dx}(x^2 + x + 1)$$

$$= -\tfrac{1}{3}(x^2 + x + 1)^{-4/3}(2x + 1)$$

EXAMPLE 5 Find the derivative of the function

$$g(t) = \left(\frac{t - 2}{2t + 1}\right)^9$$

SOLUTION Combining the Power Rule, Chain Rule, and Quotient Rule, we get

$$g'(t) = 9\left(\frac{t - 2}{2t + 1}\right)^8 \frac{d}{dt}\left(\frac{t - 2}{2t + 1}\right)$$

$$= 9\left(\frac{t - 2}{2t + 1}\right)^8 \frac{(2t + 1) \cdot 1 - 2(t - 2)}{(2t + 1)^2} = \frac{45(t - 2)^8}{(2t + 1)^{10}}$$

EXAMPLE 6 **Using the Product Rule and the Chain Rule**
Differentiate $y = (2x + 1)^5(x^3 - x + 1)^4$.

The graphs of the functions y and y' in Example 6 are shown in Figure 1. Notice that y' is large when y increases rapidly and $y' = 0$ when y has a horizontal tangent. So our answer appears to be reasonable.

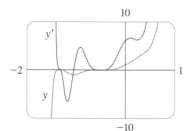

FIGURE 1

SOLUTION In this example we must use the Product Rule before using the Chain Rule:

$$\frac{dy}{dx} = (2x + 1)^5 \frac{d}{dx}(x^3 - x + 1)^4 + (x^3 - x + 1)^4 \frac{d}{dx}(2x + 1)^5$$

$$= (2x + 1)^5 \cdot 4(x^3 - x + 1)^3 \frac{d}{dx}(x^3 - x + 1)$$

$$+ (x^3 - x + 1)^4 \cdot 5(2x + 1)^4 \frac{d}{dx}(2x + 1)$$

$$= 4(2x + 1)^5(x^3 - x + 1)^3(3x^2 - 1) + 5(x^3 - x + 1)^4(2x + 1)^4 \cdot 2$$

Noticing that each term has the common factor $2(2x + 1)^4(x^3 - x + 1)^3$, we could factor it out and write the answer as

$$\frac{dy}{dx} = 2(2x + 1)^4(x^3 - x + 1)^3(17x^3 + 6x^2 - 9x + 3)$$

EXAMPLE 7 Differentiate $y = e^{\sin x}$.

SOLUTION Here the inner function is $g(x) = \sin x$ and the outer function is the exponential function $f(x) = e^x$. So, by the Chain Rule,

$$\frac{dy}{dx} = \frac{d}{dx}(e^{\sin x}) = e^{\sin x}\frac{d}{dx}(\sin x) = e^{\sin x}\cos x$$

We can use the Chain Rule to differentiate an exponential function with any base $a > 0$. Recall from Section 1.6 that $a = e^{\ln a}$. So

$$a^x = (e^{\ln a})^x = e^{(\ln a)x}$$

and the Chain Rule gives

$$\frac{d}{dx}\,(a^x) = \frac{d}{dx}\,(e^{(\ln a)x}) = e^{(\ln a)x}\,\frac{d}{dx}\,(\ln a)x$$

$$= e^{(\ln a)x} \cdot \ln a = a^x \ln a$$

because $\ln a$ is a constant. So we have the formula

Don't confuse Formula 5 (where x is the *exponent*) with the Power Rule (where x is the *base*):

$$\frac{d}{dx}\,(x^n) = nx^{n-1}$$

5

$$\boxed{\frac{d}{dx}\,(a^x) = a^x \ln a}$$

In particular, if $a = 2$, we get

6

$$\frac{d}{dx}\,(2^x) = 2^x \ln 2$$

In Section 3.1 we gave the estimate

$$\frac{d}{dx}\,(2^x) \approx (0.69)2^x$$

This is consistent with the exact formula (6) because $\ln 2 \approx 0.693147$.

The reason for the name "Chain Rule" becomes clear when we make a longer chain by adding another link. Suppose that $y = f(u)$, $u = g(x)$, and $x = h(t)$, where f, g, and h are differentiable functions. Then, to compute the derivative of y with respect to t, we use the Chain Rule twice:

$$\frac{dy}{dt} = \frac{dy}{dx}\,\frac{dx}{dt} = \frac{dy}{du}\,\frac{du}{dx}\,\frac{dx}{dt}$$

▼ EXAMPLE 8   Using the Chain Rule twice   If $f(x) = \sin(\cos(\tan x))$, then

$$f'(x) = \cos(\cos(\tan x))\,\frac{d}{dx}\,\cos(\tan x)$$

$$= \cos(\cos(\tan x))[-\sin(\tan x)]\,\frac{d}{dx}\,(\tan x)$$

$$= -\cos(\cos(\tan x))\,\sin(\tan x)\,\sec^2 x$$

Notice that we used the Chain Rule twice.

EXAMPLE 9   Differentiate $y = e^{\sec 3\theta}$.

SOLUTION   The outer function is the exponential function, the middle function is the secant function, and the inner function is the tripling function. So we have

$$\frac{dy}{d\theta} = e^{\sec 3\theta}\,\frac{d}{d\theta}\,(\sec 3\theta)$$

$$= e^{\sec 3\theta}\,\sec 3\theta\,\tan 3\theta\,\frac{d}{d\theta}\,(3\theta)$$

$$= 3e^{\sec 3\theta}\,\sec 3\theta\,\tan 3\theta$$

Tangents to Parametric Curves

In Section 1.7 we discussed curves defined by parametric equations

$$x = f(t) \qquad y = g(t)$$

The Chain Rule helps us find tangent lines to such curves. Suppose f and g are differentiable functions and we want to find the tangent line at a point on the curve $x = f(t)$, $y = g(t)$ where y is also a differentiable function of x. Then the Chain Rule gives

$$\frac{dy}{dt} = \frac{dy}{dx} \cdot \frac{dx}{dt}$$

If $dx/dt \neq 0$, we can solve for dy/dx:

If we think of the curve as being traced out by a moving particle, then dy/dt and dx/dt are the vertical and horizontal velocities of the particle and Formula 7 says that the slope of the tangent is the ratio of these velocities.

$$\boxed{7} \qquad \frac{dy}{dx} = \frac{\dfrac{dy}{dt}}{\dfrac{dx}{dt}} \qquad \text{if} \quad \frac{dx}{dt} \neq 0$$

Equation 7 (which you can remember by thinking of canceling the dt's) enables us to find the slope dy/dx of the tangent to a parametric curve without having to eliminate the parameter t. We see from (7) that the curve has a horizontal tangent when $dy/dt = 0$ (provided that $dx/dt \neq 0$) and it has a vertical tangent when $dx/dt = 0$ (provided that $dy/dt \neq 0$).

EXAMPLE 10 Find an equation of the tangent line to the parametric curve

$$x = 2 \sin 2t \quad y = 2 \sin t$$

at the point $\left(\sqrt{3}, 1\right)$. Where does this curve have horizontal or vertical tangents?

SOLUTION At the point with parameter value t, the slope is

$$\frac{dy}{dx} = \frac{\dfrac{dy}{dt}}{\dfrac{dx}{dt}} = \frac{\dfrac{d}{dt}(2 \sin t)}{\dfrac{d}{dt}(2 \sin 2t)}$$

$$= \frac{2 \cos t}{2(\cos 2t)(2)} = \frac{\cos t}{2 \cos 2t}$$

The point $\left(\sqrt{3}, 1\right)$ corresponds to the parameter value $t = \pi/6$, so the slope of the tangent at that point is

$$\frac{dy}{dx}\bigg|_{t=\pi/6} = \frac{\cos(\pi/6)}{2\cos(\pi/3)} = \frac{\sqrt{3}/2}{2\left(\frac{1}{2}\right)} = \frac{\sqrt{3}}{2}$$

An equation of the tangent line is therefore

$$y - 1 = \frac{\sqrt{3}}{2}\left(x - \sqrt{3}\right) \qquad \text{or} \qquad y = \frac{\sqrt{3}}{2}x - \frac{1}{2}$$

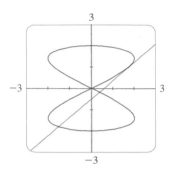

FIGURE 2

Figure 2 shows the curve and its tangent line. The tangent line is horizontal when $dy/dx = 0$, which occurs when $\cos t = 0$ (and $\cos 2t \neq 0$), that is, when $t = \pi/2$ or $3\pi/2$. (Note that the entire curve is given by $0 \leq t \leq 2\pi$.) Thus the curve has horizontal tangents at the points $(0, 2)$ and $(0, -2)$, which we could have guessed from Figure 2.

The tangent is vertical when $dx/dt = 4 \cos 2t = 0$ (and $\cos t \neq 0$), that is, when $t = \pi/4, 3\pi/4, 5\pi/4,$ or $7\pi/4$. The corresponding four points on the curve are $(\pm 2, \pm\sqrt{2})$. If we look again at Figure 2, we see that our answer appears to be reasonable.

How to Prove the Chain Rule

Recall that if $y = f(x)$ and x changes from a to $a + \Delta x$, we defined the increment of y as

$$\Delta y = f(a + \Delta x) - f(a)$$

According to the definition of a derivative, we have

$$\lim_{\Delta x \to 0} \frac{\Delta y}{\Delta x} = f'(a)$$

So if we denote by ε the difference between the difference quotient and the derivative, we obtain

$$\lim_{\Delta x \to 0} \varepsilon = \lim_{\Delta x \to 0} \left(\frac{\Delta y}{\Delta x} - f'(a) \right) = f'(a) - f'(a) = 0$$

But

$$\varepsilon = \frac{\Delta y}{\Delta x} - f'(a) \quad \Rightarrow \quad \Delta y = f'(a)\,\Delta x + \varepsilon\,\Delta x$$

If we define ε to be 0 when $\Delta x = 0$, then ε becomes a continuous function of Δx. Thus, for a differentiable function f, we can write

$$\boxed{8} \qquad \Delta y = f'(a)\,\Delta x + \varepsilon\,\Delta x \qquad \text{where} \quad \varepsilon \to 0 \text{ as } \Delta x \to 0$$

and ε is a continuous function of Δx. This property of differentiable functions is what enables us to prove the Chain Rule.

PROOF OF THE CHAIN RULE   Suppose $u = g(x)$ is differentiable at a and $y = f(u)$ is differentiable at $b = g(a)$. If Δx is an increment in x and Δu and Δy are the corresponding increments in u and y, then we can use Equation 8 to write

$$\boxed{9} \qquad \Delta u = g'(a)\,\Delta x + \varepsilon_1\,\Delta x = [g'(a) + \varepsilon_1]\,\Delta x$$

where $\varepsilon_1 \to 0$ as $\Delta x \to 0$. Similarly

$$\boxed{10} \qquad \Delta y = f'(b)\,\Delta u + \varepsilon_2\,\Delta u = [f'(b) + \varepsilon_2]\,\Delta u$$

where $\varepsilon_2 \to 0$ as $\Delta u \to 0$. If we now substitute the expression for Δu from Equation 9 into Equation 10, we get

$$\Delta y = [f'(b) + \varepsilon_2][g'(a) + \varepsilon_1]\,\Delta x$$

so

$$\frac{\Delta y}{\Delta x} = [f'(b) + \varepsilon_2][g'(a) + \varepsilon_1]$$

As $\Delta x \to 0$, Equation 9 shows that $\Delta u \to 0$. So both $\varepsilon_1 \to 0$ and $\varepsilon_2 \to 0$ as $\Delta x \to 0$.

Therefore

$$\frac{dy}{dx} = \lim_{\Delta x \to 0} \frac{\Delta y}{\Delta x} = \lim_{\Delta x \to 0} \left[f'(b) + \varepsilon_2 \right] \left[g'(a) + \varepsilon_1 \right]$$

$$= f'(b)g'(a) = f'(g(a))g'(a)$$

This proves the Chain Rule.

3.4 Exercises

1–6 Write the composite function in the form $f(g(x))$. [Identify the inner function $u = g(x)$ and the outer function $y = f(u)$.] Then find the derivative dy/dx.

1. $y = \sqrt[3]{1 + 4x}$

2. $y = (2x^3 + 5)^4$

3. $y = \tan \pi x$

4. $y = \sin(\cot x)$

5. $y = e^{\sqrt{x}}$

6. $y = \sqrt{2 - e^x}$

7–36 Find the derivative of the function.

7. $F(x) = (x^4 + 3x^2 - 2)^5$

8. $F(x) = (4x - x^2)^{100}$

9. $F(x) = \sqrt{1 - 2x}$

10. $f(x) = (1 + x^4)^{2/3}$

11. $f(z) = \dfrac{1}{z^2 + 1}$

12. $f(t) = \sqrt[3]{1 + \tan t}$

13. $y = \cos(a^3 + x^3)$

14. $y = a^3 + \cos^3 x$

15. $h(t) = t^3 - 3^t$

16. $y = 3 \cot(n\theta)$

17. $y = xe^{-kx}$

18. $y = e^{-2t} \cos 4t$

19. $y = (2x - 5)^4 (8x^2 - 5)^{-3}$

20. $h(t) = (t^4 - 1)^3 (t^3 + 1)^4$

21. $y = e^{x \cos x}$

22. $y = 10^{1 - x^2}$

23. $y = \left(\dfrac{x^2 + 1}{x^2 - 1} \right)^3$

24. $G(y) = \left(\dfrac{y^2}{y + 1} \right)^5$

25. $y = \sec^2 x + \tan^2 x$

26. $y = \dfrac{e^u - e^{-u}}{e^u + e^{-u}}$

27. $y = \dfrac{r}{\sqrt{r^2 + 1}}$

28. $y = e^{k \tan \sqrt{x}}$

29. $y = \sin(\tan 2x)$

30. $f(t) = \sqrt{\dfrac{t}{t^2 + 4}}$

31. $y = 2^{\sin \pi x}$

32. $y = \sin(\sin(\sin x))$

33. $y = \cot^2(\sin \theta)$

34. $y = \sqrt{x + \sqrt{x + \sqrt{x}}}$

35. $y = \cos \sqrt{\sin(\tan \pi x)}$

36. $y = 2^{3^{x^2}}$

37–40 Find y' and y''.

37. $y = \cos(x^2)$

38. $y = \cos^2 x$

39. $y = e^{\alpha x} \sin \beta x$

40. $y = e^{e^x}$

41–44 Find an equation of the tangent line to the curve at the given point.

41. $y = (1 + 2x)^{10}$, $\quad (0, 1)$

42. $y = \sqrt{1 + x^3}$, $\quad (2, 3)$

43. $y = \sin(\sin x)$, $\quad (\pi, 0)$

44. $y = \sin x + \sin^2 x$, $\quad (0, 0)$

45. (a) Find an equation of the tangent line to the curve $y = 2/(1 + e^{-x})$ at the point $(0, 1)$.
(b) Illustrate part (a) by graphing the curve and the tangent line on the same screen.

46. (a) The curve $y = |x|/\sqrt{2 - x^2}$ is called a *bullet-nose curve*. Find an equation of the tangent line to this curve at the point $(1, 1)$.
(b) Illustrate part (a) by graphing the curve and the tangent line on the same screen.

47. (a) If $f(x) = x\sqrt{2 - x^2}$, find $f'(x)$.
(b) Check to see that your answer to part (a) is reasonable by comparing the graphs of f and f'.

48. The function $f(x) = \sin(x + \sin 2x)$, $0 \le x \le \pi$, arises in applications to frequency modulation (FM) synthesis.
(a) Use a graph of f produced by a graphing device to make a rough sketch of the graph of f'.
(b) Calculate $f'(x)$ and use this expression, with a graphing device, to graph f'. Compare with your sketch in part (a).

49. Find all points on the graph of the function $f(x) = 2 \sin x + \sin^2 x$ at which the tangent line is horizontal.

50. Find the x-coordinates of all points on the curve $y = \sin 2x - 2 \sin x$ at which the tangent line is horizontal.

51. If $F(x) = f(g(x))$, where $f(-2) = 8$, $f'(-2) = 4$, $f'(5) = 3$, $g(5) = -2$, and $g'(5) = 6$, find $F'(5)$.

52. If $h(x) = \sqrt{4 + 3f(x)}$, where $f(1) = 7$ and $f'(1) = 4$, find $h'(1)$.

Graphing calculator or computer with graphing software required   CAS Computer algebra system required   **1.** Homework Hints available in TEC

53. A table of values for f, g, f', and g' is given.

x	$f(x)$	$g(x)$	$f'(x)$	$g'(x)$
1	3	2	4	6
2	1	8	5	7
3	7	2	7	9

(a) If $h(x) = f(g(x))$, find $h'(1)$.
(b) If $H(x) = g(f(x))$, find $H'(1)$.

54. Let f and g be the functions in Exercise 53.
(a) If $F(x) = f(f(x))$, find $F'(2)$.
(b) If $G(x) = g(g(x))$, find $G'(3)$.

55. If f and g are the functions whose graphs are shown, let $u(x) = f(g(x))$, $v(x) = g(f(x))$, and $w(x) = g(g(x))$. Find each derivative, if it exists. If it does not exist, explain why.
(a) $u'(1)$ (b) $v'(1)$ (c) $w'(1)$

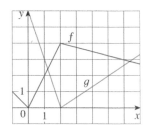

56. If f is the function whose graph is shown, let $h(x) = f(f(x))$ and $g(x) = f(x^2)$. Use the graph of f to estimate the value of each derivative.
(a) $h'(2)$ (b) $g'(2)$

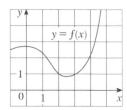

57. Use the table to estimate the value of $h'(0.5)$, where $h(x) = f(g(x))$.

x	0	0.1	0.2	0.3	0.4	0.5	0.6
$f(x)$	12.6	14.8	18.4	23.0	25.9	27.5	29.1
$g(x)$	0.58	0.40	0.37	0.26	0.17	0.10	0.05

58. If $g(x) = f(f(x))$, use the table to estimate the value of $g'(1)$.

x	0.0	0.5	1.0	1.5	2.0	2.5
$f(x)$	1.7	1.8	2.0	2.4	3.1	4.4

59. Suppose f is differentiable on $\mathbb{R}$. Let $F(x) = f(e^x)$ and $G(x) = e^{f(x)}$. Find expressions for (a) $F'(x)$ and (b) $G'(x)$.

60. Suppose f is differentiable on $\mathbb{R}$ and α is a real number. Let $F(x) = f(x^\alpha)$ and $G(x) = [f(x)]^\alpha$. Find expressions for (a) $F'(x)$ and (b) $G'(x)$.

61. Let $r(x) = f(g(h(x)))$, where $h(1) = 2$, $g(2) = 3$, $h'(1) = 4$, $g'(2) = 5$, and $f'(3) = 6$. Find $r'(1)$.

62. If g is a twice differentiable function and $f(x) = xg(x^2)$, find f'' in terms of g, g', and g''.

63. If $F(x) = f(3f(4f(x)))$, where $f(0) = 0$ and $f'(0) = 2$, find $F'(0)$.

64. If $F(x) = f(xf(xf(x)))$, where $f(1) = 2$, $f(2) = 3$, $f'(1) = 4$, $f'(2) = 5$, and $f'(3) = 6$, find $F'(1)$.

65. Show that the function $y = e^{2x}(A \cos 3x + B \sin 3x)$ satisfies the differential equation $y'' - 4y' + 13y = 0$.

66. For what values of r does the function $y = e^{rx}$ satisfy the differential equation $y'' - 4y' + y = 0$?

67. Find the 50th derivative of $y = \cos 2x$.

68. Find the 1000th derivative of $f(x) = xe^{-x}$.

69. The displacement of a particle on a vibrating string is given by the equation
$$s(t) = 10 + \tfrac{1}{4} \sin(10\pi t)$$
where s is measured in centimeters and t in seconds. Find the velocity of the particle after t seconds.

70. If the equation of motion of a particle is given by $s = A \cos(\omega t + \delta)$, the particle is said to undergo *simple harmonic motion*.
(a) Find the velocity of the particle at time t.
(b) When is the velocity 0?

71. A Cepheid variable star is a star whose brightness alternately increases and decreases. The most easily visible such star is Delta Cephei, for which the interval between times of maximum brightness is 5.4 days. The average brightness of this star is 4.0 and its brightness changes by ± 0.35. In view of these data, the brightness of Delta Cephei at time t, where t is measured in days, has been modeled by the function
$$B(t) = 4.0 + 0.35 \sin\!\left(\frac{2\pi t}{5.4}\right)$$
(a) Find the rate of change of the brightness after t days.
(b) Find, correct to two decimal places, the rate of increase after one day.

72. In Example 4 in Section 1.3 we arrived at a model for the length of daylight (in hours) in Philadelphia on the tth day of the year:
$$L(t) = 12 + 2.8 \sin\!\left[\frac{2\pi}{365}(t - 80)\right]$$
Use this model to compare how the number of hours of daylight is increasing in Philadelphia on March 21 and May 21.

73. The motion of a spring that is subject to a frictional force or a damping force (such as a shock absorber in a car) is often modeled by the product of an exponential function and a sine or cosine function. Suppose the equation of motion of a point on such a spring is

$$s(t) = 2e^{-1.5t} \sin 2\pi t$$

where s is measured in centimeters and t in seconds. Find the velocity after t seconds and graph both the position and velocity functions for $0 \leqslant t \leqslant 2$.

74. Under certain circumstances a rumor spreads according to the equation

$$p(t) = \frac{1}{1 + ae^{-kt}}$$

where $p(t)$ is the proportion of the population that knows the rumor at time t and a and k are positive constants. [In Section 7.5 we will see that this is a reasonable equation for $p(t)$.]
(a) Find $\lim_{t \to \infty} p(t)$.
(b) Find the rate of spread of the rumor.
(c) Graph p for the case $a = 10$, $k = 0.5$ with t measured in hours. Use the graph to estimate how long it will take for 80% of the population to hear the rumor.

75. A particle moves along a straight line with displacement $s(t)$, velocity $v(t)$, and acceleration $a(t)$. Show that

$$a(t) = v(t) \frac{dv}{ds}$$

Explain the difference between the meanings of the derivatives dv/dt and dv/ds.

76. Air is being pumped into a spherical weather balloon. At any time t, the volume of the balloon is $V(t)$ and its radius is $r(t)$.
(a) What do the derivatives dV/dr and dV/dt represent?
(b) Express dV/dt in terms of dr/dt.

77. The flash unit on a camera operates by storing charge on a capacitor and releasing it suddenly when the flash is set off. The following data describe the charge Q remaining on the capacitor (measured in microcoulombs, μC) at time t (measured in seconds).

t	0.00	0.02	0.04	0.06	0.08	0.10
Q	100.00	81.87	67.03	54.88	44.93	36.76

(a) Use a graphing calculator or computer to find an exponential model for the charge.
(b) The derivative $Q'(t)$ represents the electric current (measured in microamperes, μA) flowing from the capacitor to the flash bulb. Use part (a) to estimate the current when $t = 0.04$ s. Compare with the result of Example 2 in Section 2.1.

78. The table gives the US population from 1790 to 1860.

Year	Population	Year	Population
1790	3,929,000	1830	12,861,000
1800	5,308,000	1840	17,063,000
1810	7,240,000	1850	23,192,000
1820	9,639,000	1860	31,443,000

(a) Use a graphing calculator or computer to fit an exponential function to the data. Graph the data points and the exponential model. How good is the fit?
(b) Estimate the rates of population growth in 1800 and 1850 by averaging slopes of secant lines.
(c) Use the exponential model in part (a) to estimate the rates of growth in 1800 and 1850. Compare these estimates with the ones in part (b).
(d) Use the exponential model to predict the population in 1870. Compare with the actual population of 38,558,000. Can you explain the discrepancy?

79–81 Find an equation of the tangent line to the curve at the point corresponding to the given value of the parameter.

79. $x = t^4 + 1$, $\quad y = t^3 + t$; $\quad t = -1$

80. $x = \cos \theta + \sin 2\theta$, $\quad y = \sin \theta + \cos 2\theta$; $\quad \theta = 0$

81. $x = e^{\sqrt{t}}$, $\quad y = t - \ln t^2$; $\quad t = 1$

82–83 Find the points on the curve where the tangent is horizontal or vertical. If you have a graphing device, graph the curve to check your work.

82. $x = 2t^3 + 3t^2 - 12t$, $\quad y = 2t^3 + 3t^2 + 1$

83. $x = 10 - t^2$, $\quad y = t^3 - 12t$

84. Show that the curve with parametric equations $x = \sin t$, $y = \sin(t + \sin t)$ has two tangent lines at the origin and find their equations. Illustrate by graphing the curve and its tangents.

85. A curve C is defined by the parametric equations $x = t^2$, $y = t^3 - 3t$.
(a) Show that C has two tangents at the point $(3, 0)$ and find their equations.
(b) Find the points on C where the tangent is horizontal or vertical.
(c) Illustrate parts (a) and (b) by graphing C and the tangent lines.

86. The cycloid $x = r(\theta - \sin \theta)$, $y = r(1 - \cos \theta)$ was discussed in Example 7 in Section 1.7.
(a) Find an equation of the tangent to the cycloid at the point where $\theta = \pi/3$.
(b) At what points is the tangent horizontal? Where is it vertical?
(c) Graph the cycloid and its tangent lines for the case $r = 1$.

CAS **87.** Computer algebra systems have commands that differentiate functions, but the form of the answer may not be convenient and so further commands may be necessary to simplify the answer.
(a) Use a CAS to find the derivative in Example 5 and compare with the answer in that example. Then use the simplify command and compare again.
(b) Use a CAS to find the derivative in Example 6. What happens if you use the simplify command? What happens if you use the factor command? Which form of the answer would be best for locating horizontal tangents?

CAS **88.** (a) Use a CAS to differentiate the function

$$f(x) = \sqrt{\frac{x^4 - x + 1}{x^4 + x + 1}}$$

and to simplify the result.
(b) Where does the graph of f have horizontal tangents?
(c) Graph f and f' on the same screen. Are the graphs consistent with your answer to part (b)?

89. (a) If n is a positive integer, prove that

$$\frac{d}{dx}(\sin^n x \cos nx) = n \sin^{n-1} x \cos(n+1)x$$

(b) Find a formula for the derivative of $y = \cos^n x \cos nx$ that is similar to the one in part (a).

90. Find equations of the tangents to the curve $x = 3t^2 + 1$, $y = 2t^3 + 1$ that pass through the point $(4, 3)$.

91. Use the Chain Rule to show that if θ is measured in degrees, then

$$\frac{d}{d\theta}(\sin \theta) = \frac{\pi}{180} \cos \theta$$

(This gives one reason for the convention that radian measure is always used when dealing with trigonometric functions in calculus: The differentiation formulas would not be as simple if we used degree measure.)

92. (a) Write $|x| = \sqrt{x^2}$ and use the Chain Rule to show that

$$\frac{d}{dx}|x| = \frac{x}{|x|}$$

(b) If $f(x) = |\sin x|$, find $f'(x)$ and sketch the graphs of f and f'. Where is f not differentiable?
(c) If $g(x) = \sin|x|$, find $g'(x)$ and sketch the graphs of g and g'. Where is g not differentiable?

93. If $y = f(u)$ and $u = g(x)$, where f and g are twice differentiable functions, show that

$$\frac{d^2y}{dx^2} = \frac{d^2y}{du^2}\left(\frac{du}{dx}\right)^2 + \frac{dy}{du}\frac{d^2u}{dx^2}$$

94. Assume that a snowball melts so that its volume decreases at a rate proportional to its surface area. If it takes three hours for the snowball to decrease to half its original volume, how much longer will it take for the snowball to melt completely?

LABORATORY PROJECT ▦ **Bézier Curves**

Bézier curves are used in computer-aided design and are named after the French mathematician Pierre Bézier (1910–1999), who worked in the automotive industry. A cubic Bézier curve is determined by four *control points*, $P_0(x_0, y_0)$, $P_1(x_1, y_1)$, $P_2(x_2, y_2)$, and $P_3(x_3, y_3)$, and is defined by the parametric equations

$$x = x_0(1-t)^3 + 3x_1t(1-t)^2 + 3x_2t^2(1-t) + x_3t^3$$

$$y = y_0(1-t)^3 + 3y_1t(1-t)^2 + 3y_2t^2(1-t) + y_3t^3$$

where $0 \le t \le 1$. Notice that when $t = 0$ we have $(x, y) = (x_0, y_0)$ and when $t = 1$ we have $(x, y) = (x_3, y_3)$, so the curve starts at P_0 and ends at P_3.

1. Graph the Bézier curve with control points $P_0(4, 1)$, $P_1(28, 48)$, $P_2(50, 42)$, and $P_3(40, 5)$. Then, on the same screen, graph the line segments P_0P_1, P_1P_2, and P_2P_3. (Exercise 29 in Section 1.7 shows how to do this.) Notice that the middle control points P_1 and P_2 don't lie on the curve; the curve starts at P_0, heads toward P_1 and P_2 without reaching them, and ends at P_3.

2. From the graph in Problem 1, it appears that the tangent at P_0 passes through P_1 and the tangent at P_3 passes through P_2. Prove it.

▦ Graphing calculator or computer with graphing software required

3. Try to produce a Bézier curve with a loop by changing the second control point in Problem 1.

4. Some laser printers use Bézier curves to represent letters and other symbols. Experiment with control points until you find a Bézier curve that gives a reasonable representation of the letter C.

5. More complicated shapes can be represented by piecing together two or more Bézier curves. Suppose the first Bézier curve has control points P_0, P_1, P_2, P_3 and the second one has control points P_3, P_4, P_5, P_6. If we want these two pieces to join together smoothly, then the tangents at P_3 should match and so the points P_2, P_3, and P_4 all have to lie on this common tangent line. Using this principle, find control points for a pair of Bézier curves that represent the letter S.

APPLIED PROJECT | **Where Should a Pilot Start Descent?**

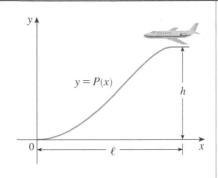

$y = P(x)$

An approach path for an aircraft landing is shown in the figure and satisfies the following conditions:

(i) The cruising altitude is h when descent starts at a horizontal distance ℓ from touchdown at the origin.

(ii) The pilot must maintain a constant horizontal speed v throughout descent.

(iii) The absolute value of the vertical acceleration should not exceed a constant k (which is much less than the acceleration due to gravity).

1. Find a cubic polynomial $P(x) = ax^3 + bx^2 + cx + d$ that satisfies condition (i) by imposing suitable conditions on $P(x)$ and $P'(x)$ at the start of descent and at touchdown.

2. Use conditions (ii) and (iii) to show that

$$\frac{6hv^2}{\ell^2} \le k$$

3. Suppose that an airline decides not to allow vertical acceleration of a plane to exceed $k = 860$ mi/h^2. If the cruising altitude of a plane is 35,000 ft and the speed is 300 mi/h, how far away from the airport should the pilot start descent?

4. Graph the approach path if the conditions stated in Problem 3 are satisfied.

Graphing calculator or computer with graphing software required

---

3.5 Implicit Differentiation

The functions that we have met so far can be described by expressing one variable explicitly in terms of another variable—for example,

$$y = \sqrt{x^3 + 1} \qquad \text{or} \qquad y = x \sin x$$

or, in general, $y = f(x)$. Some functions, however, are defined implicitly by a relation between x and y such as

$$\boxed{1} \qquad\qquad\qquad x^2 + y^2 = 25$$

or

$$\boxed{2} \qquad x^3 + y^3 = 6xy$$

In some cases it is possible to solve such an equation for y as an explicit function (or several functions) of x. For instance, if we solve Equation 1 for y, we get $y = \pm\sqrt{25 - x^2}$, so two of the functions determined by the implicit Equation 1 are $f(x) = \sqrt{25 - x^2}$ and $g(x) = -\sqrt{25 - x^2}$. The graphs of f and g are the upper and lower semicircles of the circle $x^2 + y^2 = 25$. (See Figure 1.)

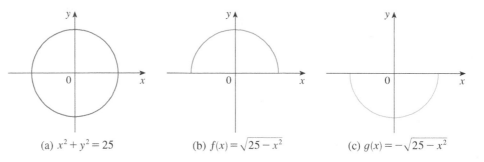

FIGURE 1

(a) $x^2 + y^2 = 25$ (b) $f(x) = \sqrt{25 - x^2}$ (c) $g(x) = -\sqrt{25 - x^2}$

It's not easy to solve Equation 2 for y explicitly as a function of x by hand. (A computer algebra system has no trouble, but the expressions it obtains are very complicated.) Nonetheless, (2) is the equation of a curve called the **folium of Descartes** shown in Figure 2 and it implicitly defines y as several functions of x. The graphs of three such functions are shown in Figure 3. When we say that f is a function defined implicitly by Equation 2, we mean that the equation

$$x^3 + [f(x)]^3 = 6xf(x)$$

is true for all values of x in the domain of f.

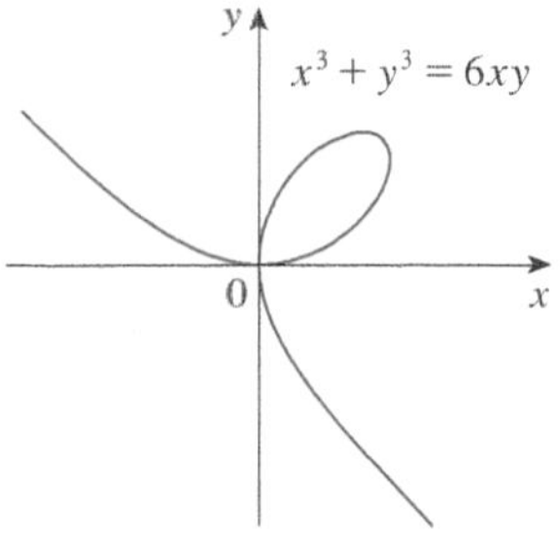

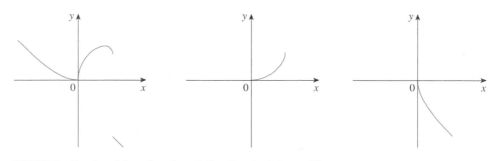

FIGURE 2 The folium of Descartes

FIGURE 3 Graphs of three functions defined by the folium of Descartes

Fortunately, we don't need to solve an equation for y in terms of x in order to find the derivative of y. Instead we can use the method of **implicit differentiation**. This consists of differentiating both sides of the equation with respect to x and then solving the resulting equation for y'. In the examples and exercises of this section it is always assumed that the given equation determines y implicitly as a differentiable function of x so that the method of implicit differentiation can be applied.

V   **EXAMPLE 1**   **Finding a tangent line implicitly**

(a) If $x^2 + y^2 = 25$, find $\dfrac{dy}{dx}$.

(b) Find an equation of the tangent to the circle $x^2 + y^2 = 25$ at the point $(3, 4)$.

SOLUTION 1

(a) Differentiate both sides of the equation $x^2 + y^2 = 25$:

$$\frac{d}{dx}(x^2 + y^2) = \frac{d}{dx}(25)$$

$$\frac{d}{dx}(x^2) + \frac{d}{dx}(y^2) = 0$$

Remembering that y is a function of x and using the Chain Rule, we have

$$\frac{d}{dx}(y^2) = \frac{d}{dy}(y^2)\frac{dy}{dx} = 2y\frac{dy}{dx}$$

Thus
$$2x + 2y\frac{dy}{dx} = 0$$

Now we solve this equation for dy/dx:

$$\frac{dy}{dx} = -\frac{x}{y}$$

(b) At the point $(3, 4)$ we have $x = 3$ and $y = 4$, so

$$\frac{dy}{dx} = -\frac{3}{4}$$

An equation of the tangent to the circle at $(3, 4)$ is therefore

$$y - 4 = -\tfrac{3}{4}(x - 3) \qquad \text{or} \qquad 3x + 4y = 25$$

SOLUTION 2

(b) Solving the equation $x^2 + y^2 = 25$, we get $y = \pm\sqrt{25 - x^2}$. The point $(3, 4)$ lies on the upper semicircle $y = \sqrt{25 - x^2}$ and so we consider the function $f(x) = \sqrt{25 - x^2}$. Differentiating f using the Chain Rule, we have

$$f'(x) = \tfrac{1}{2}(25 - x^2)^{-1/2}\frac{d}{dx}(25 - x^2)$$

$$= \tfrac{1}{2}(25 - x^2)^{-1/2}(-2x) = -\frac{x}{\sqrt{25 - x^2}}$$

Example 1 illustrates that even when it is possible to solve an equation explicitly for y in terms of x, it may be easier to use implicit differentiation.

So
$$f'(3) = -\frac{3}{\sqrt{25 - 3^2}} = -\frac{3}{4}$$

and, as in Solution 1, an equation of the tangent is $3x + 4y = 25$.

Note 1: The expression $dy/dx = -x/y$ in Solution 1 gives the derivative in terms of both x and y. It is correct no matter which function y is determined by the given equation. For instance, for $y = f(x) = \sqrt{25 - x^2}$ we have

$$\frac{dy}{dx} = -\frac{x}{y} = -\frac{x}{\sqrt{25 - x^2}}$$

whereas for $y = g(x) = -\sqrt{25 - x^2}$ we have

$$\frac{dy}{dx} = -\frac{x}{y} = -\frac{x}{-\sqrt{25 - x^2}} = \frac{x}{\sqrt{25 - x^2}}$$

V **EXAMPLE 2**

(a) Find y' if $x^3 + y^3 = 6xy$.

(b) Find the tangent to the folium of Descartes $x^3 + y^3 = 6xy$ at the point $(3, 3)$.

(c) At what point in the first quadrant is the tangent line horizontal?

SOLUTION

(a) Differentiating both sides of $x^3 + y^3 = 6xy$ with respect to x, regarding y as a function of x, and using the Chain Rule on the term y^3 and the Product Rule on the term $6xy$, we get

$$3x^2 + 3y^2y' = 6xy' + 6y$$

or

$$x^2 + y^2y' = 2xy' + 2y$$

We now solve for y':

$$y^2y' - 2xy' = 2y - x^2$$

$$(y^2 - 2x)y' = 2y - x^2$$

$$y' = \frac{2y - x^2}{y^2 - 2x}$$

(b) When $x = y = 3$,

$$y' = \frac{2 \cdot 3 - 3^2}{3^2 - 2 \cdot 3} = -1$$

and a glance at Figure 4 confirms that this is a reasonable value for the slope at $(3, 3)$. So an equation of the tangent to the folium at $(3, 3)$ is

$$y - 3 = -1(x - 3) \qquad \text{or} \qquad x + y = 6$$

(c) The tangent line is horizontal if $y' = 0$. Using the expression for y' from part (a), we see that $y' = 0$ when $2y - x^2 = 0$ (provided that $y^2 - 2x \neq 0$). Substituting $y = \frac{1}{2}x^2$ in the equation of the curve, we get

$$x^3 + \left(\tfrac{1}{2}x^2\right)^3 = 6x\left(\tfrac{1}{2}x^2\right)$$

which simplifies to $x^6 = 16x^3$. Since $x \neq 0$ in the first quadrant, we have $x^3 = 16$. If $x = 16^{1/3} = 2^{4/3}$, then $y = \frac{1}{2}(2^{8/3}) = 2^{5/3}$. Thus the tangent is horizontal at $(2^{4/3}, 2^{5/3})$, which is approximately $(2.5198, 3.1748)$. Looking at Figure 5, we see that our answer is reasonable. ▬

Note 2: There is a formula for the three roots of a cubic equation that is like the quadratic formula but much more complicated. If we use this formula (or a computer algebra system) to solve the equation $x^3 + y^3 = 6xy$ for y in terms of x, we get three functions determined by the equation:

$$y = f(x) = \sqrt[3]{-\tfrac{1}{2}x^3 + \sqrt{\tfrac{1}{4}x^6 - 8x^3}} + \sqrt[3]{-\tfrac{1}{2}x^3 - \sqrt{\tfrac{1}{4}x^6 - 8x^3}}$$

and

$$y = \tfrac{1}{2}\left[-f(x) \pm \sqrt{-3}\left(\sqrt[3]{-\tfrac{1}{2}x^3 + \sqrt{\tfrac{1}{4}x^6 - 8x^3}} - \sqrt[3]{-\tfrac{1}{2}x^3 - \sqrt{\tfrac{1}{4}x^6 - 8x^3}}\right)\right]$$

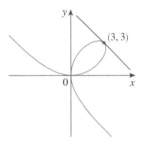

FIGURE 4

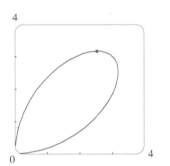

FIGURE 5

The Norwegian mathematician Niels Abel proved in 1824 that no general formula can be given for the roots of a fifth-degree equation in terms of radicals. Later the French mathematician Evariste Galois proved that it is impossible to find a general formula for the roots of an nth-degree equation (in terms of algebraic operations on the coefficients) if n is any integer larger than 4.

(These are the three functions whose graphs are shown in Figure 3.) You can see that the method of implicit differentiation saves an enormous amount of work in cases such as this. Moreover, implicit differentiation works just as easily for equations such as

$$y^5 + 3x^2y^2 + 5x^4 = 12$$

for which it is *impossible* to find a similar expression for y in terms of x.

EXAMPLE 3 Find y' if $\sin(x + y) = y^2 \cos x$.

SOLUTION Differentiating implicitly with respect to x and remembering that y is a function of x, we get

$$\cos(x + y) \cdot (1 + y') = y^2(-\sin x) + (\cos x)(2yy')$$

(Note that we have used the Chain Rule on the left side and the Product Rule and Chain Rule on the right side.) If we collect the terms that involve y', we get

$$\cos(x + y) + y^2 \sin x = (2y \cos x)y' - \cos(x + y) \cdot y'$$

So

$$y' = \frac{y^2 \sin x + \cos(x + y)}{2y \cos x - \cos(x + y)}$$

Figure 6, drawn with the implicit-plotting command of a computer algebra system, shows part of the curve $\sin(x + y) = y^2 \cos x$. As a check on our calculation, notice that $y' = -1$ when $x = y = 0$ and it appears from the graph that the slope is approximately -1 at the origin.

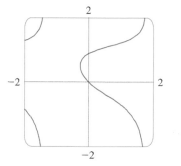

FIGURE 6

Figures 7, 8, and 9 show three more curves produced by a computer algebra system with an implicit-plotting command. In Exercises 37–38 you will have an opportunity to create and examine unusual curves of this nature.

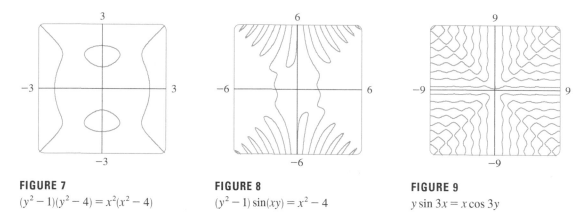

FIGURE 7
$(y^2 - 1)(y^2 - 4) = x^2(x^2 - 4)$

FIGURE 8
$(y^2 - 1)\sin(xy) = x^2 - 4$

FIGURE 9
$y \sin 3x = x \cos 3y$

EXAMPLE 4 **Finding a second derivative implicitly** Find y'' if $x^4 + y^4 = 16$.

SOLUTION Differentiating the equation implicitly with respect to x, we get

$$4x^3 + 4y^3y' = 0$$

Solving for y' gives

3

$$y' = -\frac{x^3}{y^3}$$

Figure 10 shows the graph of the curve $x^4 + y^4 = 16$ of Example 4. Notice that it's a stretched and flattened version of the circle $x^2 + y^2 = 4$. For this reason it's sometimes called a *fat circle*. It starts out very steep on the left but quickly becomes very flat. This can be seen from the expression

$$y' = -\frac{x^3}{y^3} = -\left(\frac{x}{y}\right)^3$$

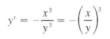
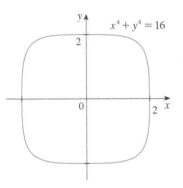

FIGURE 10

To find y'' we differentiate this expression for y' using the Quotient Rule and remembering that y is a function of x:

$$y'' = \frac{d}{dx}\left(-\frac{x^3}{y^3}\right) = -\frac{y^3 \, (d/dx)(x^3) - x^3 \, (d/dx)(y^3)}{(y^3)^2}$$

$$= -\frac{y^3 \cdot 3x^2 - x^3(3y^2 y')}{y^6}$$

If we now substitute Equation 3 into this expression, we get

$$y'' = -\frac{3x^2 y^3 - 3x^3 y^2 \left(-\dfrac{x^3}{y^3}\right)}{y^6}$$

$$= -\frac{3(x^2 y^4 + x^6)}{y^7} = -\frac{3x^2(y^4 + x^4)}{y^7}$$

But the values of x and y must satisfy the original equation $x^4 + y^4 = 16$. So the answer simplifies to

$$y'' = -\frac{3x^2(16)}{y^7} = -48\frac{x^2}{y^7}$$

3.5 Exercises

1–2
(a) Find y' by implicit differentiation.
(b) Solve the equation explicitly for y and differentiate to get y' in terms of x.
(c) Check that your solutions to parts (a) and (b) are consistent by substituting the expression for y into your solution for part (a).

1. $xy + 2x + 3x^2 = 4$ **2.** $\cos x + \sqrt{y} = 5$

3–16 Find dy/dx by implicit differentiation.

3. $x^3 + y^3 = 1$ **4.** $2\sqrt{x} + \sqrt{y} = 3$

5. $x^2 + xy - y^2 = 4$ **6.** $2x^3 + x^2y - xy^3 = 2$

7. $x^4(x + y) = y^2(3x - y)$ **8.** $y^5 + x^2y^3 = 1 + ye^{x^2}$

9. $x^2y^2 + x \sin y = 4$ **10.** $1 + x = \sin(xy^2)$

11. $4 \cos x \sin y = 1$ **12.** $y \sin(x^2) = x \sin(y^2)$

13. $e^{x/y} = x - y$ **14.** $\tan(x - y) = \dfrac{y}{1 + x^2}$

15. $e^y \cos x = 1 + \sin(xy)$ **16.** $\sin x + \cos y = \sin x \cos y$

---

17. If $f(x) + x^2[f(x)]^3 = 10$ and $f(1) = 2$, find $f'(1)$.

18. If $g(x) + x \sin g(x) = x^2$, find $g'(0)$.

19–20 Regard y as the independent variable and x as the dependent variable and use implicit differentiation to find dx/dy.

19. $x^4y^2 - x^3y + 2xy^3 = 0$ **20.** $y \sec x = x \tan y$

21–28 Use implicit differentiation to find an equation of the tangent line to the curve at the given point.

21. $y \sin 2x = x \cos 2y$, $(\pi/2, \pi/4)$

22. $\sin(x + y) = 2x - 2y$, (π, π)

23. $x^2 + xy + y^2 = 3$, $(1, 1)$ (ellipse)

24. $x^2 + 2xy - y^2 + x = 2$, $(1, 2)$ (hyperbola)

25. $x^2 + y^2 = (2x^2 + 2y^2 - x)^2$ **26.** $x^{2/3} + y^{2/3} = 4$
    $\left(0, \frac{1}{2}\right)$ $(-3\sqrt{3}, 1)$
    (cardioid)   (astroid)

---

27. $2(x^2 + y^2)^2 = 25(x^2 - y^2)$
(3, 1)
(lemniscate)

28. $y^2(y^2 - 4) = x^2(x^2 - 5)$
(0, −2)
(devil's curve)

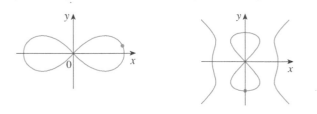

29. (a) The curve with equation $y^2 = 5x^4 - x^2$ is called a **kampyle of Eudoxus**. Find an equation of the tangent line to this curve at the point (1, 2).

(b) Illustrate part (a) by graphing the curve and the tangent line on a common screen. (If your graphing device will graph implicitly defined curves, then use that capability. If not, you can still graph this curve by graphing its upper and lower halves separately.)

30. (a) The curve with equation $y^2 = x^3 + 3x^2$ is called the **Tschirnhausen cubic**. Find an equation of the tangent line to this curve at the point (1, −2).

(b) At what points does this curve have horizontal tangents?

(c) Illustrate parts (a) and (b) by graphing the curve and the tangent lines on a common screen.

31–34 Find y'' by implicit differentiation.

31. $9x^2 + y^2 = 9$

32. $\sqrt{x} + \sqrt{y} = 1$

33. $x^3 + y^3 = 1$

34. $x^4 + y^4 = a^4$

35. If $xy + e^y = e$, find the value of y'' at the point where $x = 0$.

36. If $x^2 + xy + y^3 = 1$, find the value of y''' at the point where $x = 1$.

CAS **37.** Fanciful shapes can be created by using the implicit plotting capabilities of computer algebra systems.

(a) Graph the curve with equation

$$y(y^2 - 1)(y - 2) = x(x - 1)(x - 2)$$

At how many points does this curve have horizontal tangents? Estimate the x-coordinates of these points.

(b) Find equations of the tangent lines at the points (0, 1) and (0, 2).

(c) Find the exact x-coordinates of the points in part (a).

(d) Create even more fanciful curves by modifying the equation in part (a).

CAS **38.** (a) The curve with equation

$$2y^3 + y^2 - y^5 = x^4 - 2x^3 + x^2$$

has been likened to a bouncing wagon. Use a computer algebra system to graph this curve and discover why.

(b) At how many points does this curve have horizontal tangent lines? Find the x-coordinates of these points.

39. Find the points on the lemniscate in Exercise 27 where the tangent is horizontal.

40. Show by implicit differentiation that the tangent to the ellipse

$$\frac{x^2}{a^2} + \frac{y^2}{b^2} = 1$$

at the point (x_0, y_0) is

$$\frac{x_0 x}{a^2} + \frac{y_0 y}{b^2} = 1$$

41–44 Two curves are **orthogonal** if their tangent lines are perpendicular at each point of intersection. Show that the given families of curves are **orthogonal trajectories** of each other, that is, every curve in one family is orthogonal to every curve in the other family. Sketch both families of curves on the same axes.

41. $x^2 + y^2 = r^2$, $ax + by = 0$

42. $x^2 + y^2 = ax$, $x^2 + y^2 = by$

43. $y = cx^2$, $x^2 + 2y^2 = k$

44. $y = ax^3$, $x^2 + 3y^2 = b$

45. Show that the ellipse $x^2/a^2 + y^2/b^2 = 1$ and the hyperbola $x^2/A^2 - y^2/B^2 = 1$ are orthogonal trajectories if $A^2 < a^2$ and $a^2 - b^2 = A^2 + B^2$ (so the ellipse and hyperbola have the same foci).

46. Find the value of the number a such that the families of curves $y = (x + c)^{-1}$ and $y = a(x + k)^{1/3}$ are orthogonal trajectories.

47. (a) The *van der Waals equation* for n moles of a gas is

$$\left(P + \frac{n^2 a}{V^2}\right)(V - nb) = nRT$$

where P is the pressure, V is the volume, and T is the temperature of the gas. The constant R is the universal gas constant and a and b are positive constants that are characteristic of a particular gas. If T remains constant, use implicit differentiation to find dV/dP.

(b) Find the rate of change of volume with respect to pressure of 1 mole of carbon dioxide at a volume of $V = 10$ L and a pressure of $P = 2.5$ atm. Use $a = 3.592$ L^2-atm/mole^2 and $b = 0.04267$ L/mole.

48. (a) Use implicit differentiation to find y' if $x^2 + xy + y^2 + 1 = 0$.

CAS (b) Plot the curve in part (a). What do you see? Prove that what you see is correct.

(c) In view of part (b), what can you say about the expression for y' that you found in part (a)?

49. Show, using implicit differentiation, that any tangent line at a point P to a circle with center O is perpendicular to the radius OP.

50. Show that the sum of the x- and y-intercepts of any tangent line to the curve $\sqrt{x} + \sqrt{y} = \sqrt{c}$ is equal to c.

51. The equation $x^2 - xy + y^2 = 3$ represents a "rotated ellipse," that is, an ellipse whose axes are not parallel to the coordinate axes. Find the points at which this ellipse crosses the x-axis and show that the tangent lines at these points are parallel.

52. (a) Where does the normal line to the ellipse $x^2 - xy + y^2 = 3$ at the point $(-1, 1)$ intersect the ellipse a second time?
(b) Illustrate part (a) by graphing the ellipse and the normal line.

53. Find all points on the curve $x^2y^2 + xy = 2$ where the slope of the tangent line is -1.

54. Find equations of both the tangent lines to the ellipse $x^2 + 4y^2 = 36$ that pass through the point $(12, 3)$.

55. The **Bessel function** of order 0, $y = J(x)$, satisfies the differential equation $xy'' + y' + xy = 0$ for all values of x and its value at 0 is $J(0) = 1$.
(a) Find $J'(0)$.
(b) Use implicit differentiation to find $J''(0)$.

56. The figure shows a lamp located three units to the right of the y-axis and a shadow created by the elliptical region $x^2 + 4y^2 \le 5$. If the point $(-5, 0)$ is on the edge of the shadow, how far above the x-axis is the lamp located?

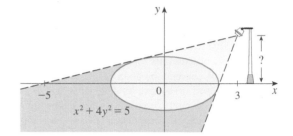

$x^2 + 4y^2 = 5$

3.6   Inverse Trigonometric Functions and Their Derivatives

Recall from Section 1.6 that the only functions that have inverse functions are one-to-one functions. Trigonometric functions, however, are not one-to-one and so they don't have inverse functions. But we can make them one-to-one by restricting their domains and we will see that the inverses of these restricted trigonometric functions play a major role in integral calculus.

You can see from Figure 1 that the sine function $y = \sin x$ is not one-to-one (use the Horizontal Line Test). But the function $f(x) = \sin x$, $-\pi/2 \le x \le \pi/2$, *is* one-to-one (see Figure 2). The inverse function of this restricted sine function f exists and is denoted by $\sin^{-1}$ or $\arcsin$. It is called the **inverse sine function** or the **arcsine function**.

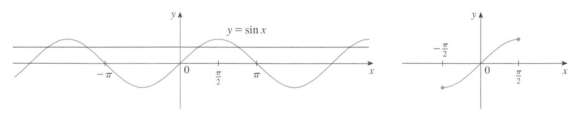

FIGURE 1

FIGURE 2 $y = \sin x$, $-\frac{\pi}{2} \le x \le \frac{\pi}{2}$

Since the definition of an inverse function says that

$$f^{-1}(x) = y \iff f(y) = x$$

we have

$$\sin^{-1}x = y \iff \sin y = x \quad \text{and} \quad -\frac{\pi}{2} \le y \le \frac{\pi}{2}$$

⊘ $\sin^{-1}x \ne \dfrac{1}{\sin x}$

Thus, if $-1 \le x \le 1$, $\sin^{-1}x$ is the number between $-\pi/2$ and $\pi/2$ whose sine is x.

EXAMPLE 1 Evaluate (a) $\sin^{-1}(\frac{1}{2})$ and (b) $\tan(\arcsin \frac{1}{3})$.

SOLUTION
(a) We have

$$\sin^{-1}(\tfrac{1}{2}) = \frac{\pi}{6}$$

because $\sin(\pi/6) = \frac{1}{2}$ and $\pi/6$ lies between $-\pi/2$ and $\pi/2$.

(b) Let $\theta = \arcsin \frac{1}{3}$, so $\sin \theta = \frac{1}{3}$. Then we can draw a right triangle with angle θ as in Figure 3 and deduce from the Pythagorean Theorem that the third side has length $\sqrt{9-1} = 2\sqrt{2}$. This enables us to read from the triangle that

$$\tan(\arcsin \tfrac{1}{3}) = \tan \theta = \frac{1}{2\sqrt{2}}$$

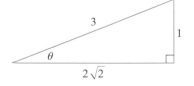

FIGURE 3

The cancellation equations for inverse functions become, in this case,

$$\sin^{-1}(\sin x) = x \quad \text{for } -\frac{\pi}{2} \le x \le \frac{\pi}{2}$$

$$\sin(\sin^{-1}x) = x \quad \text{for } -1 \le x \le 1$$

The inverse sine function, $\sin^{-1}$, has domain $[-1, 1]$ and range $[-\pi/2, \pi/2]$, and its graph, shown in Figure 4, is obtained from that of the restricted sine function (Figure 2) by reflection about the line $y = x$. We know that the sine function f is continuous, so the inverse sine function is also continuous.

We can use implicit differentiation to find the derivative of the inverse sine function, assuming that it is differentiable. (The differentiability is certainly plausible from its graph in Figure 4.)

Let $y = \sin^{-1}x$. Then $\sin y = x$ and $-\pi/2 \le y \le \pi/2$. Differentiating $\sin y = x$ implicitly with respect to x, we obtain

$$\cos y \frac{dy}{dx} = 1$$

and

$$\frac{dy}{dx} = \frac{1}{\cos y}$$

Now $\cos y \ge 0$ since $-\pi/2 \le y \le \pi/2$, so

$$\cos y = \sqrt{1 - \sin^2 y} = \sqrt{1 - x^2}$$

Therefore

$$\frac{dy}{dx} = \frac{1}{\cos y} = \frac{1}{\sqrt{1 - x^2}}$$

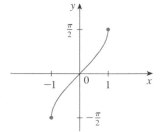

FIGURE 4
$y = \sin^{-1}x = \arcsin x$

The same method can be used to find a formula for the derivative of *any* inverse function. See Exercise 41.

$\boxed{1}$

$$\frac{d}{dx}(\sin^{-1}x) = \frac{1}{\sqrt{1 - x^2}} \qquad -1 < x < 1$$

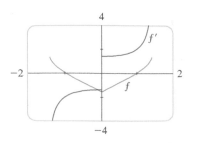

FIGURE 5

The graphs of the function f of Example 2 and its derivative are shown in Figure 5. Notice that f is not differentiable at 0 and this is consistent with the fact that the graph of f' makes a sudden jump at $x = 0$.

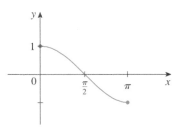

FIGURE 6
$y = \cos x,\ 0 \le x \le \pi$

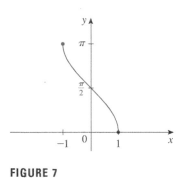

FIGURE 7
$y = \cos^{-1} x = \arccos x$

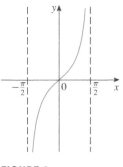

FIGURE 8
$y = \tan x,\ -\frac{\pi}{2} < x < \frac{\pi}{2}$

 **EXAMPLE 2** If $f(x) = \sin^{-1}(x^2 - 1)$, find (a) the domain of f, (b) $f'(x)$, and (c) the domain of f'.

SOLUTION

(a) Since the domain of the inverse sine function is $[-1, 1]$, the domain of f is

$$\{x \mid -1 \le x^2 - 1 \le 1\} = \{x \mid 0 \le x^2 \le 2\}$$
$$= \{x \mid |x| \le \sqrt{2}\,\} = \left[-\sqrt{2}, \sqrt{2}\,\right]$$

(b) Combining Formula 1 with the Chain Rule, we have

$$f'(x) = \frac{1}{\sqrt{1 - (x^2 - 1)^2}}\, \frac{d}{dx}\,(x^2 - 1)$$

$$= \frac{1}{\sqrt{1 - (x^4 - 2x^2 + 1)}}\, 2x = \frac{2x}{\sqrt{2x^2 - x^4}}$$

(c) The domain of f' is

$$\{x \mid -1 < x^2 - 1 < 1\} = \{x \mid 0 < x^2 < 2\}$$
$$= \{x \mid 0 < |x| < \sqrt{2}\,\} = (-\sqrt{2}, 0) \cup (0, \sqrt{2}\,)$$

The **inverse cosine function** is handled similarly. The restricted cosine function $f(x) = \cos x$, $0 \le x \le \pi$, is one-to-one (see Figure 6) and so it has an inverse function denoted by $\cos^{-1}$ or arccos.

$$\cos^{-1} x = y \iff \cos y = x \quad \text{and} \quad 0 \le y \le \pi$$

The inverse cosine function, $\cos^{-1}$, has domain $[-1, 1]$ and range $[0, \pi]$ and is a continuous function whose graph is shown in Figure 7. Its derivative is given by

2
$$\frac{d}{dx}\,(\cos^{-1} x) = -\frac{1}{\sqrt{1 - x^2}} \qquad -1 < x < 1$$

Formula 2 can be proved by the same method as for Formula 1 and is left as Exercise 15.

The tangent function can be made one-to-one by restricting it to the interval $(-\pi/2, \pi/2)$. Thus the **inverse tangent function** is defined as the inverse of the function $f(x) = \tan x$, $-\pi/2 < x < \pi/2$, as shown in Figure 8. It is denoted by $\tan^{-1}$ or arctan.

$$\tan^{-1} x = y \iff \tan y = x \quad \text{and} \quad -\frac{\pi}{2} < y < \frac{\pi}{2}$$

EXAMPLE 3 Simplify the expression $\cos(\tan^{-1} x)$.

SOLUTION 1 Let $y = \tan^{-1} x$. Then $\tan y = x$ and $-\pi/2 < y < \pi/2$. We want to find $\cos y$ but, since $\tan y$ is known, it is easier to find $\sec y$ first.

Since $\qquad \sec^2 y = 1 + \tan^2 y = 1 + x^2$

we have $\qquad \sec y = \sqrt{1 + x^2} \qquad$ (since sec $y > 0$ for $-\pi/2 < y < \pi/2$)

Thus $\qquad \cos(\tan^{-1}x) = \cos y = \dfrac{1}{\sec y} = \dfrac{1}{\sqrt{1 + x^2}}$

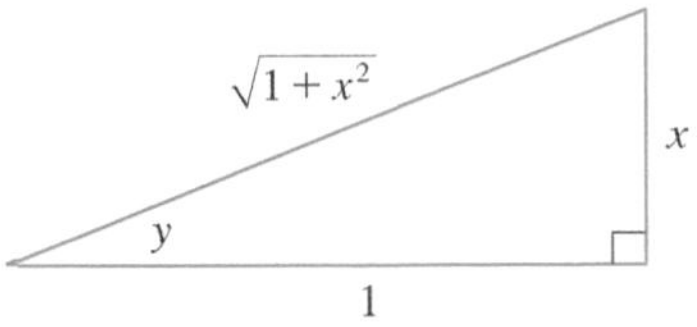

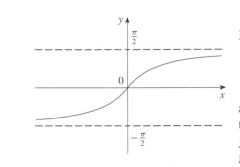

FIGURE 9

SOLUTION 2 Instead of using trigonometric identities as in Solution 1, it is perhaps easier to use a diagram. If $y = \tan^{-1}x$, then $\tan y = x$, and we can read from Figure 9 (which illustrates the case $y > 0$) that

$$\cos(\tan^{-1}x) = \cos y = \frac{1}{\sqrt{1 + x^2}}$$

The inverse tangent function, $\tan^{-1} = \arctan$, has domain $\mathbb{R}$ and range $(-\pi/2, \pi/2)$. Its graph is shown in Figure 10.

We know that

$$\lim_{x \to (\pi/2)^-} \tan x = \infty \qquad \text{and} \qquad \lim_{x \to -(\pi/2)^+} \tan x = -\infty$$

and so the lines $x = \pm\pi/2$ are vertical asymptotes of the graph of tan. Since the graph of $\tan^{-1}$ is obtained by reflecting the graph of the restricted tangent function about the line $y = x$, it follows that the lines $y = \pi/2$ and $y = -\pi/2$ are horizontal asymptotes of the graph of $\tan^{-1}$. This fact is expressed by the following limits:

FIGURE 10

$y = \tan^{-1} x = \arctan x$

$$\boxed{3} \qquad \lim_{x \to \infty} \tan^{-1}x = \frac{\pi}{2} \qquad \lim_{x \to -\infty} \tan^{-1}x = -\frac{\pi}{2}$$

EXAMPLE 4 Evaluate $\displaystyle\lim_{x \to 2^+} \arctan\left(\dfrac{1}{x - 2}\right)$.

SOLUTION If we let $t = 1/(x - 2)$, we know that $t \to \infty$ as $x \to 2^+$. Therefore, by the second equation in (3), we have

$$\lim_{x \to 2^+} \arctan\left(\frac{1}{x - 2}\right) = \lim_{t \to \infty} \arctan t = \frac{\pi}{2}$$

The formula for the derivative of the arctangent function is derived in a way that is similar to the method we used for arcsine. If $y = \tan^{-1}x$, then $\tan y = x$. Differentiating this latter equation implicitly with respect to x, we have

$$\sec^2 y \, \frac{dy}{dx} = 1$$

and so $\qquad \dfrac{dy}{dx} = \dfrac{1}{\sec^2 y} = \dfrac{1}{1 + \tan^2 y} = \dfrac{1}{1 + x^2}$

$$\boxed{4} \qquad \frac{d}{dx}(\tan^{-1}x) = \frac{1}{1 + x^2}$$

EXAMPLE 5 Differentiate (a) $y = \dfrac{1}{\tan^{-1}x}$ and (b) $f(x) = x \arctan\sqrt{x}$.

SOLUTION

(a)
$$\frac{dy}{dx} = \frac{d}{dx}(\tan^{-1}x)^{-1} = -(\tan^{-1}x)^{-2}\frac{d}{dx}(\tan^{-1}x)$$

$$= -\frac{1}{(\tan^{-1}x)^2(1+x^2)}$$

(b) Using the Product Rule and the Chain Rule, we have

Recall that arctan x is an alternative notation for $\tan^{-1}x$.

$$f'(x) = x\frac{1}{1+(\sqrt{x})^2}\left(\tfrac{1}{2}x^{-1/2}\right) + \arctan\sqrt{x}$$

$$= \frac{\sqrt{x}}{2(1+x)} + \arctan\sqrt{x}$$

The inverse trigonometric functions that occur most frequently are the ones that we have just discussed. The differentiation formulas for the remaining inverse trigonometric functions can be found on Reference Page 5, Formulas 22–24.

3.6 Exercises

1–8 Find the exact value of each expression.

1. (a) $\sin^{-1}(\sqrt{3}/2)$ (b) $\cos^{-1}(-1)$

2. (a) $\tan^{-1}(1/\sqrt{3})$ (b) $\sec^{-1}2$

3. (a) $\arctan 1$ (b) $\sin^{-1}(1/\sqrt{2})$

4. (a) $\tan^{-1}(\tan 3\pi/4)$ (b) $\cos(\arcsin\tfrac{1}{2})$

5. $\tan(\sin^{-1}(\tfrac{2}{3}))$ 6. $\csc(\arccos\tfrac{3}{5})$

7. $\sin(2\tan^{-1}\sqrt{2})$ 8. $\cos(\tan^{-1}2 + \tan^{-1}3)$

9. Prove that $\cos(\sin^{-1}x) = \sqrt{1-x^2}$.

10–12 Simplify the expression.

10. $\tan(\sin^{-1}x)$ 11. $\sin(\tan^{-1}x)$

12. $\cos(2\tan^{-1}x)$

13–14 Graph the given functions on the same screen. How are these graphs related?

13. $y = \sin x$, $-\pi/2 \le x \le \pi/2$; $y = \sin^{-1}x$; $y = x$

14. $y = \tan x$, $-\pi/2 < x < \pi/2$; $y = \tan^{-1}x$; $y = x$

15. Prove Formula 2 by the same method as for Formula 1.

16. (a) Prove that $\sin^{-1}x + \cos^{-1}x = \pi/2$.
    (b) Use part (a) to prove Formula 2.

17–29 Find the derivative of the function. Simplify where possible.

17. $y = (\tan^{-1}x)^2$ 18. $y = \tan^{-1}(x^2)$

19. $y = \sin^{-1}(2x+1)$ 20. $F(\theta) = \arcsin\sqrt{\sin\theta}$

21. $G(x) = \sqrt{1-x^2}\arccos x$ 22. $f(x) = x\ln(\arctan x)$

23. $y = \cos^{-1}(e^{2x})$ 24. $y = \tan^{-1}(x - \sqrt{1+x^2})$

25. $y = \arctan(\cos\theta)$ 26. $y = \cos^{-1}(\sin^{-1}t)$

27. $y = x\sin^{-1}x + \sqrt{1-x^2}$ 28. $y = \arctan\sqrt{\dfrac{1-x}{1+x}}$

29. $y = \arccos\left(\dfrac{b + a\cos x}{a + b\cos x}\right)$, $0 \le x \le \pi$, $a > b > 0$

30–31 Find the derivative of the function. Find the domains of the function and its derivative.

30. $f(x) = \arcsin(e^x)$ 31. $g(x) = \cos^{-1}(3 - 2x)$

32. Find y' if $\tan^{-1}(xy) = 1 + x^2y$.

33. If $g(x) = x\sin^{-1}(x/4) + \sqrt{16 - x^2}$, find $g'(2)$.

34. Find an equation of the tangent line to the curve $y = 3\arccos(x/2)$ at the point $(1, \pi)$.

35–36 Find $f'(x)$. Check that your answer is reasonable by comparing the graphs of f and f'.

35. $f(x) = \sqrt{1 - x^2}\arcsin x$ 36. $f(x) = \arctan(x^2 - x)$

Graphing calculator or computer with graphing software required   **1.** Homework Hints available in TEC

37–40 Find the limit.

37. $\lim\limits_{x \to -1^+} \sin^{-1}x$

38. $\lim\limits_{x \to \infty} \arccos\left(\dfrac{1 + x^2}{1 + 2x^2}\right)$

39. $\lim\limits_{x \to \infty} \arctan(e^x)$

40. $\lim\limits_{x \to 0^+} \tan^{-1}(\ln x)$

41. (a) Suppose f is a one-to-one differentiable function and its inverse function f^{-1} is also differentiable. Use implicit differentiation to show that

$$(f^{-1})'(x) = \frac{1}{f'(f^{-1}(x))}$$

provided that the denominator is not 0.
(b) If $f(4) = 5$ and $f'(4) = \frac{2}{3}$, find $(f^{-1})'(5)$.

42. (a) Show that $f(x) = 2x + \cos x$ is one-to-one.
(b) What is the value of $f^{-1}(1)$?
(c) Use the formula from Exercise 41(a) to find $(f^{-1})'(1)$.

43. Use the formula from Exercise 41(a) to prove
(a) Formula 1   (b) Formula 4

44. (a) Sketch the graph of the function $f(x) = \sin(\sin^{-1}x)$.
(b) Sketch the graph of the function $g(x) = \sin^{-1}(\sin x)$, $x \in \mathbb{R}$.
(c) Show that $g'(x) = \dfrac{\cos x}{|\cos x|}$.
(d) Sketch the graph of $h(x) = \cos^{-1}(\sin x)$, $x \in \mathbb{R}$, and find its derivative.

3.7 Derivatives of Logarithmic Functions

In this section we use implicit differentiation to find the derivatives of the logarithmic functions $y = \log_a x$ and, in particular, the natural logarithmic function $y = \ln x$. (It can be proved that logarithmic functions are differentiable; this is certainly plausible from their graphs. See Figure 4 in Section 1.6 for the graphs of the logarithmic functions.)

1
$$\frac{d}{dx}(\log_a x) = \frac{1}{x \ln a}$$

PROOF Let $y = \log_a x$. Then

$$a^y = x$$

Differentiating this equation implicitly with respect to x, using Formula 3.4.5, we get

Formula 3.4.5 says that
$$\frac{d}{dx}(a^x) = a^x \ln a$$

$$a^y(\ln a)\frac{dy}{dx} = 1$$

and so
$$\frac{dy}{dx} = \frac{1}{a^y \ln a} = \frac{1}{x \ln a}$$

If we put $a = e$ in Formula 1, then the factor $\ln a$ on the right side becomes $\ln e = 1$ and we get the formula for the derivative of the natural logarithmic function $\log_e x = \ln x$:

2
$$\frac{d}{dx}(\ln x) = \frac{1}{x}$$

By comparing Formulas 1 and 2, we see one of the main reasons that natural logarithms (logarithms with base e) are used in calculus: The differentiation formula is simplest when $a = e$ because $\ln e = 1$.

V **EXAMPLE 1** Differentiate $y = \ln(x^3 + 1)$.

SOLUTION To use the Chain Rule, we let $u = x^3 + 1$. Then $y = \ln u$, so

$$\frac{dy}{dx} = \frac{dy}{du}\frac{du}{dx} = \frac{1}{u}\frac{du}{dx} = \frac{1}{x^3 + 1}(3x^2) = \frac{3x^2}{x^3 + 1}$$

In general, if we combine Formula 2 with the Chain Rule as in Example 1, we get

$$\boxed{3}\qquad \boxed{\frac{d}{dx}(\ln u) = \frac{1}{u}\frac{du}{dx}} \quad\text{or}\quad \boxed{\frac{d}{dx}[\ln g(x)] = \frac{g'(x)}{g(x)}}$$

EXAMPLE 2 Find $\dfrac{d}{dx}\ln(\sin x)$.

SOLUTION Using (3), we have

$$\frac{d}{dx}\ln(\sin x) = \frac{1}{\sin x}\frac{d}{dx}(\sin x) = \frac{1}{\sin x}\cos x = \cot x$$

EXAMPLE 3 Differentiate $f(x) = \sqrt{\ln x}$.

SOLUTION This time the logarithm is the inner function, so the Chain Rule gives

$$f'(x) = \tfrac{1}{2}(\ln x)^{-1/2}\frac{d}{dx}(\ln x) = \frac{1}{2\sqrt{\ln x}}\cdot\frac{1}{x} = \frac{1}{2x\sqrt{\ln x}}$$

EXAMPLE 4 **Differentiating a logarithm with base 10** Differentiate $f(x) = \log_{10}(2 + \sin x)$.

SOLUTION Using Formula 1 with $a = 10$, we have

$$f'(x) = \frac{d}{dx}\log_{10}(2 + \sin x)$$

$$= \frac{1}{(2 + \sin x)\ln 10}\frac{d}{dx}(2 + \sin x)$$

$$= \frac{\cos x}{(2 + \sin x)\ln 10}$$

Figure 1 shows the graph of the function f of Example 5 together with the graph of its derivative. It gives a visual check on our calculation. Notice that $f'(x)$ is large negative when f is rapidly decreasing.

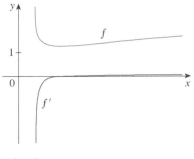

FIGURE 1

EXAMPLE 5 **Simplifying before differentiating** Find $\dfrac{d}{dx}\ln\dfrac{x + 1}{\sqrt{x - 2}}$.

SOLUTION 1

$$\frac{d}{dx}\ln\frac{x + 1}{\sqrt{x - 2}} = \frac{1}{\dfrac{x + 1}{\sqrt{x - 2}}}\frac{d}{dx}\frac{x + 1}{\sqrt{x - 2}}$$

$$= \frac{\sqrt{x - 2}}{x + 1}\frac{\sqrt{x - 2}\cdot 1 - (x + 1)(\tfrac{1}{2})(x - 2)^{-1/2}}{x - 2}$$

$$= \frac{x - 2 - \tfrac{1}{2}(x + 1)}{(x + 1)(x - 2)}$$

$$= \frac{x - 5}{2(x + 1)(x - 2)}$$

SOLUTION 2 If we first simplify the given function using the laws of logarithms, then the differentiation becomes easier:

$$\frac{d}{dx} \ln \frac{x + 1}{\sqrt{x - 2}} = \frac{d}{dx} \left[\ln(x + 1) - \tfrac{1}{2} \ln(x - 2)\right]$$

$$= \frac{1}{x + 1} - \frac{1}{2}\left(\frac{1}{x - 2}\right)$$

(This answer can be left as written, but if we used a common denominator we would see that it gives the same answer as in Solution 1.)

Figure 2 shows the graph of the function $f(x) = \ln|x|$ in Example 6 and its derivative $f'(x) = 1/x$. Notice that when x is small, the graph of $y = \ln|x|$ is steep and so $f'(x)$ is large (positive or negative).

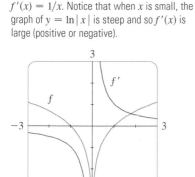

FIGURE 2

V EXAMPLE 6 Find $f'(x)$ if $f(x) = \ln|x|$.

SOLUTION Since

$$f(x) = \begin{cases} \ln x & \text{if } x > 0 \\ \ln(-x) & \text{if } x < 0 \end{cases}$$

it follows that

$$f'(x) = \begin{cases} \dfrac{1}{x} & \text{if } x > 0 \\ \dfrac{1}{-x}(-1) = \dfrac{1}{x} & \text{if } x < 0 \end{cases}$$

Thus $f'(x) = 1/x$ for all $x \neq 0$.

The result of Example 6 is worth remembering:

$$\frac{d}{dx} \ln|x| = \frac{1}{x}$$

Logarithmic Differentiation

The calculation of derivatives of complicated functions involving products, quotients, or powers can often be simplified by taking logarithms. The method used in the following example is called **logarithmic differentiation**.

EXAMPLE 7 **Logarithmic differentiation** Differentiate $y = \dfrac{x^{3/4}\sqrt{x^2 + 1}}{(3x + 2)^5}$.

SOLUTION We take logarithms of both sides of the equation and use the Laws of Logarithms to simplify:

$$\ln y = \tfrac{3}{4} \ln x + \tfrac{1}{2} \ln(x^2 + 1) - 5 \ln(3x + 2)$$

Differentiating implicitly with respect to x gives

$$\frac{1}{y}\frac{dy}{dx} = \frac{3}{4} \cdot \frac{1}{x} + \frac{1}{2} \cdot \frac{2x}{x^2 + 1} - 5 \cdot \frac{3}{3x + 2}$$

Solving for dy/dx, we get

$$\frac{dy}{dx} = y\left(\frac{3}{4x} + \frac{x}{x^2 + 1} - \frac{15}{3x + 2}\right)$$

If we hadn't used logarithmic differentiation in Example 7, we would have had to use both the Quotient Rule and the Product Rule. The resulting calculation would have been horrendous.

Because we have an explicit expression for y, we can substitute and write

$$\frac{dy}{dx} = \frac{x^{3/4}\sqrt{x^2 + 1}}{(3x + 2)^5}\left(\frac{3}{4x} + \frac{x}{x^2 + 1} - \frac{15}{3x + 2}\right)$$

Steps in Logarithmic Differentiation

1. Take natural logarithms of both sides of an equation $y = f(x)$ and use the Laws of Logarithms to simplify.

2. Differentiate implicitly with respect to x.

3. Solve the resulting equation for y'.

If $f(x) < 0$ for some values of x, then $\ln f(x)$ is not defined, but we can write $|y| = |f(x)|$ and use Equation 4. We illustrate this procedure by proving the general version of the Power Rule, as promised in Section 3.1.

The Power Rule   If n is any real number and $f(x) = x^n$, then

$$f'(x) = nx^{n-1}$$

If $x = 0$, we can show that $f'(0) = 0$ for $n > 1$ directly from the definition of a derivative.

PROOF Let $y = x^n$ and use logarithmic differentiation:

$$\ln|y| = \ln|x|^n = n\ln|x| \qquad x \neq 0$$

Therefore

$$\frac{y'}{y} = \frac{n}{x}$$

Hence

$$y' = n\frac{y}{x} = n\frac{x^n}{x} = nx^{n-1}$$

⊘   You should distinguish carefully between the Power Rule $[(x^n)' = nx^{n-1}]$, where the base is variable and the exponent is constant, and the rule for differentiating exponential functions $[(a^x)' = a^x \ln a]$, where the base is constant and the exponent is variable.

In general there are four cases for exponents and bases:

1. $\dfrac{d}{dx}(a^b) = 0$ (a and b are constants)

2. $\dfrac{d}{dx}[f(x)]^b = b[f(x)]^{b-1}f'(x)$

3. $\dfrac{d}{dx}[a^{g(x)}] = a^{g(x)}(\ln a)g'(x)$

4. To find $(d/dx)[f(x)]^{g(x)}$, logarithmic differentiation can be used, as in the next example.

V **EXAMPLE 8** **What to do if both base and exponent contain x** Differentiate $y = x^{\sqrt{x}}$.

SOLUTION 1 Using logarithmic differentiation, we have

$$\ln y = \ln x^{\sqrt{x}} = \sqrt{x}\,\ln x$$

$$\frac{y'}{y} = \sqrt{x} \cdot \frac{1}{x} + (\ln x)\,\frac{1}{2\sqrt{x}}$$

$$y' = y\left(\frac{1}{\sqrt{x}} + \frac{\ln x}{2\sqrt{x}}\right) = x^{\sqrt{x}}\left(\frac{2 + \ln x}{2\sqrt{x}}\right)$$

SOLUTION 2 Another method is to write $x^{\sqrt{x}} = (e^{\ln x})^{\sqrt{x}}$:

$$\frac{d}{dx}\left(x^{\sqrt{x}}\right) = \frac{d}{dx}\left(e^{\sqrt{x}\,\ln x}\right) = e^{\sqrt{x}\,\ln x}\,\frac{d}{dx}\left(\sqrt{x}\,\ln x\right)$$

$$= x^{\sqrt{x}}\left(\frac{2 + \ln x}{2\sqrt{x}}\right) \qquad \text{(as in Solution 1)}$$

Figure 3 illustrates Example 8 by showing the graphs of $f(x) = x^{\sqrt{x}}$ and its derivative.

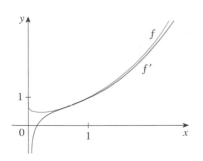

FIGURE 3

The Number e as a Limit

We have shown that if $f(x) = \ln x$, then $f'(x) = 1/x$. Thus $f'(1) = 1$. We now use this fact to express the number e as a limit.

From the definition of a derivative as a limit, we have

$$f'(1) = \lim_{h \to 0} \frac{f(1 + h) - f(1)}{h} = \lim_{x \to 0} \frac{f(1 + x) - f(1)}{x}$$

$$= \lim_{x \to 0} \frac{\ln(1 + x) - \ln 1}{x} = \lim_{x \to 0} \frac{1}{x}\ln(1 + x)$$

$$= \lim_{x \to 0} \ln(1 + x)^{1/x}$$

Because $f'(1) = 1$, we have

$$\lim_{x \to 0} \ln(1 + x)^{1/x} = 1$$

Then, by Theorem 2.4.8 and the continuity of the exponential function, we have

$$e = e^1 = e^{\lim_{x \to 0} \ln(1+x)^{1/x}} = \lim_{x \to 0} e^{\ln(1+x)^{1/x}} = \lim_{x \to 0}(1 + x)^{1/x}$$

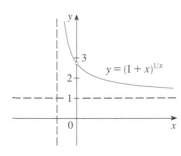

FIGURE 4

x	$(1 + x)^{1/x}$
0.1	2.59374246
0.01	2.70481383
0.001	2.71692393
0.0001	2.71814593
0.00001	2.71826824
0.000001	2.71828047
0.0000001	2.71828169
0.00000001	2.71828181

5
$$\boxed{e = \lim_{x \to 0}(1 + x)^{1/x}}$$

Formula 5 is illustrated by the graph of the function $y = (1 + x)^{1/x}$ in Figure 4 and a table of values for small values of x. This illustrates the fact that, correct to seven decimal places,

$$e \approx 2.7182818$$

If we put $n = 1/x$ in Formula 5, then $n \to \infty$ as $x \to 0^+$ and so an alternative expression for e is

$$\boxed{6} \qquad \boxed{e = \lim_{n \to \infty} \left(1 + \frac{1}{n}\right)^n}$$

3.7 Exercises

1. Explain why the natural logarithmic function $y = \ln x$ is used much more frequently in calculus than the other logarithmic functions $y = \log_a x$.

2–20 Differentiate the function.

2. $f(x) = x \ln x - x$

3. $f(x) = \sin(\ln x)$

4. $f(x) = \ln(\sin^2 x)$

5. $f(x) = \log_2(1 - 3x)$

6. $f(x) = \log_5(xe^x)$

7. $f(x) = \sqrt[5]{\ln x}$

8. $f(x) = \ln \sqrt[5]{x}$

9. $f(x) = \sin x \ln(5x)$

10. $f(t) = \dfrac{1 + \ln t}{1 - \ln t}$

11. $F(t) = \ln \dfrac{(2t + 1)^3}{(3t - 1)^4}$

12. $h(x) = \ln\left(x + \sqrt{x^2 - 1}\right)$

13. $g(x) = \ln\left(x\sqrt{x^2 - 1}\right)$

14. $F(y) = y \ln(1 + e^y)$

15. $y = \ln|2 - x - 5x^2|$

16. $H(z) = \ln \sqrt{\dfrac{a^2 - z^2}{a^2 + z^2}}$

17. $y = \ln(e^{-x} + xe^{-x})$

18. $y = [\ln(1 + e^x)]^2$

19. $y = 2x \log_{10} \sqrt{x}$

20. $y = \log_2(e^{-x} \cos \pi x)$

21–22 Find y' and y''.

21. $y = x^2 \ln(2x)$

22. $y = \dfrac{\ln x}{x^2}$

23–24 Differentiate f and find the domain of f.

23. $f(x) = \dfrac{x}{1 - \ln(x - 1)}$

24. $f(x) = \ln \ln \ln x$

25–27 Find an equation of the tangent line to the curve at the given point.

25. $y = \ln(x^2 - 3x + 1)$, $(3, 0)$

26. $y = \ln(x^3 - 7)$, $(2, 0)$

27. $y = \ln\left(xe^{x^2}\right)$, $(1, 1)$

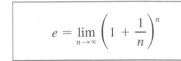 **28.** Find equations of the tangent lines to the curve $y = (\ln x)/x$ at the points $(1, 0)$ and $(e, 1/e)$. Illustrate by graphing the curve and its tangent lines.

29. (a) On what interval is $f(x) = x \ln x$ decreasing?
(b) On what interval is f concave upward?

30. If $f(x) = \sin x + \ln x$, find $f'(x)$. Check that your answer is reasonable by comparing the graphs of f and f'.

31. Let $f(x) = cx + \ln(\cos x)$. For what value of c is $f'(\pi/4) = 6$?

32. Let $f(x) = \log_a(3x^2 - 2)$. For what value of a is $f'(1) = 3$?

33–42 Use logarithmic differentiation to find the derivative of the function.

33. $y = (2x + 1)^5(x^4 - 3)^6$

34. $y = \sqrt{x}\, e^{x^2}(x^2 + 1)^{10}$

35. $y = \dfrac{\sin^2 x \tan^4 x}{(x^2 + 1)^2}$

36. $y = \sqrt[4]{\dfrac{x^2 + 1}{x^2 - 1}}$

37. $y = x^x$

38. $y = x^{\cos x}$

39. $y = (\cos x)^x$

40. $y = \sqrt{x}^{\,x}$

41. $y = (\tan x)^{1/x}$

42. $y = (\sin x)^{\ln x}$

43. Find y' if $y = \ln(x^2 + y^2)$.

44. Find y' if $x^y = y^x$.

45. Find a formula for $f^{(n)}(x)$ if $f(x) = \ln(x - 1)$.

46. Find $\dfrac{d^9}{dx^9}(x^8 \ln x)$.

47. Use the definition of derivative to prove that

$$\lim_{x \to 0} \frac{\ln(1 + x)}{x} = 1$$

48. Show that $\displaystyle\lim_{n \to \infty} \left(1 + \frac{x}{n}\right)^n = e^x$ for any $x > 0$.

| **Hyperbolic Functions**

Certain combinations of the exponential functions e^x and e^{-x} arise so frequently in mathematics and its applications that they deserve to be given special names. This project explores the properties of functions called **hyperbolic functions**. The **hyperbolic sine**, **hyperbolic cosine**, **hyperbolic tangent**, and **hyperbolic secant** functions are defined as follows:

$$\sinh x = \frac{e^x - e^{-x}}{2} \qquad \cosh x = \frac{e^x + e^{-x}}{2}$$

$$\tanh x = \frac{\sinh x}{\cosh x} \qquad \operatorname{sech} x = \frac{1}{\cosh x}$$

The reason for the names of these functions is that they are related to the hyperbola in much the same way that the trigonometric functions are related to the circle.

1. (a) Sketch, by hand, the graphs of the functions $y = \frac{1}{2}e^x$ and $y = \frac{1}{2}e^{-x}$ on the same axes and use graphical addition to draw the graph of cosh.

   (b) Check the accuracy of your sketch in part (a) by using a graphing calculator or computer to graph $y = \cosh x$. What are the domain and range of this function?

2. The most famous application of hyperbolic functions is the use of hyperbolic cosine to describe the shape of a hanging wire. It can be proved that if a heavy flexible cable (such as a telephone or power line) is suspended between two points at the same height, then it takes the shape of a curve with equation $y = a \cosh(x/a)$ called a *catenary*. (The Latin word *catena* means "chain.") Graph several members of the family of functions $y = a \cosh(x/a)$. How does the graph change as a varies?

3. Graph sinh and tanh. Judging from their graphs, which of the functions sinh, cosh, and tanh are even? Which are odd? Use the definitions to prove your assertions.

4. Prove the identity $\cosh^2 x - \sinh^2 x = 1$.

5. Graph the curve with parametric equations $x = \cosh t$, $y = \sinh t$. Can you identify this curve?

6. Prove the identity $\sinh(x + y) = \sinh x \cosh y + \cosh x \sinh y$.

7. The identities in Problems 4 and 6 are similar to well-known trigonometric identities. Try to discover other hyperbolic identities by using known trigonometric identities (Reference Page 2) as your inspiration.

8. The differentiation formulas for the hyperbolic functions are analogous to those for the trigonometric functions, but the signs are sometimes different.

   (a) Show that $\dfrac{d}{dx}(\sinh x) = \cosh x$.

   (b) Discover formulas for the derivatives of $y = \cosh x$ and $y = \tanh x$.

9. (a) Explain why sinh is a one-to-one function.

   (b) Find a formula for the derivative of the inverse hyperbolic sine function $y = \sinh^{-1} x$. [*Hint:* How did we find the derivative of $y = \sin^{-1} x$?]

   (c) Show that $\sinh^{-1} x = \ln\left(x + \sqrt{x^2 + 1}\right)$.

   (d) Use the result of part (c) to find the derivative of $\sinh^{-1} x$. Compare with your answer to part (b).

10. (a) Explain why tanh is a one-to-one function.

    (b) Find a formula for the derivative of the inverse hyperbolic tangent function $y = \tanh^{-1} x$.

    (c) Show that $\tanh^{-1} x = \frac{1}{2}\ln\left(\dfrac{1 + x}{1 - x}\right)$.

    (d) Use the result of part (c) to find the derivative of $\tanh^{-1} x$. Compare with your answer to part (b).

11. At what point on the curve $y = \cosh x$ does the tangent have slope 1?

Graphing calculator or computer with graphing software required

3.8   Rates of Change in the Natural and Social Sciences

We know that if $y = f(x)$, then the derivative dy/dx can be interpreted as the rate of change of y with respect to x. In this section we examine some of the applications of this idea to physics, chemistry, biology, economics, and other sciences.

Let's recall from Section 2.6 the basic idea behind rates of change. If x changes from x_1 to x_2, then the change in x is

$$\Delta x = x_2 - x_1$$

and the corresponding change in y is

$$\Delta y = f(x_2) - f(x_1)$$

The difference quotient

$$\frac{\Delta y}{\Delta x} = \frac{f(x_2) - f(x_1)}{x_2 - x_1}$$

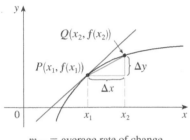

m_{PQ} = average rate of change
$m = f'(x_1)$ = instantaneous rate of change

FIGURE 1

is the **average rate of change of y with respect to x** over the interval $[x_1, x_2]$ and can be interpreted as the slope of the secant line PQ in Figure 1. Its limit as $\Delta x \to 0$ is the derivative $f'(x_1)$, which can therefore be interpreted as the **instantaneous rate of change of y with respect to x** or the slope of the tangent line at $P(x_1, f(x_1))$. Using Leibniz notation, we write the process in the form

$$\frac{dy}{dx} = \lim_{\Delta x \to 0} \frac{\Delta y}{\Delta x}$$

Whenever the function $y = f(x)$ has a specific interpretation in one of the sciences, its derivative will have a specific interpretation as a rate of change. (As we discussed in Section 2.6, the units for dy/dx are the units for y divided by the units for x.) We now look at some of these interpretations in the natural and social sciences.

Physics

If $s = f(t)$ is the position function of a particle that is moving in a straight line, then $\Delta s/\Delta t$ represents the average velocity over a time period Δt, and $v = ds/dt$ represents the instantaneous **velocity** (the rate of change of displacement with respect to time). The instantaneous rate of change of velocity with respect to time is **acceleration**: $a(t) = v'(t) = s''(t)$. This was discussed in Sections 2.6 and 2.7, but now that we know the differentiation formulas, we are able to solve problems involving the motion of objects more easily.

V   EXAMPLE 1   Analyzing the motion of a particle   The position of a particle is given by the equation

$$s = f(t) = t^3 - 6t^2 + 9t$$

where t is measured in seconds and s in meters.
(a) Find the velocity at time t.
(b) What is the velocity after 2 s? After 4 s?
(c) When is the particle at rest?
(d) When is the particle moving forward (that is, in the positive direction)?
(e) Draw a diagram to represent the motion of the particle.
(f) Find the total distance traveled by the particle during the first five seconds.
(g) Find the acceleration at time t and after 4 s.

(h) Graph the position, velocity, and acceleration functions for $0 \leqslant t \leqslant 5$.
(i) When is the particle speeding up? When is it slowing down?

SOLUTION

(a) The velocity function is the derivative of the position function.

$$s = f(t) = t^3 - 6t^2 + 9t$$

$$v(t) = \frac{ds}{dt} = 3t^2 - 12t + 9$$

(b) The velocity after 2 s means the instantaneous velocity when $t = 2$, that is,

$$v(2) = \frac{ds}{dt}\bigg|_{t=2} = 3(2)^2 - 12(2) + 9 = -3 \text{ m/s}$$

The velocity after 4 s is

$$v(4) = 3(4)^2 - 12(4) + 9 = 9 \text{ m/s}$$

(c) The particle is at rest when $v(t) = 0$, that is,

$$3t^2 - 12t + 9 = 3(t^2 - 4t + 3) = 3(t - 1)(t - 3) = 0$$

and this is true when $t = 1$ or $t = 3$. Thus the particle is at rest after 1 s and after 3 s.

(d) The particle moves in the positive direction when $v(t) > 0$, that is,

$$3t^2 - 12t + 9 = 3(t - 1)(t - 3) > 0$$

This inequality is true when both factors are positive ($t > 3$) or when both factors are negative ($t < 1$). Thus the particle moves in the positive direction in the time intervals $t < 1$ and $t > 3$. It moves backward (in the negative direction) when $1 < t < 3$.

(e) Using the information from part (d) we make a schematic sketch in Figure 2 of the motion of the particle back and forth along a line (the s-axis).

(f) Because of what we learned in parts (d) and (e), we need to calculate the distances traveled during the time intervals [0, 1], [1, 3], and [3, 5] separately.
    The distance traveled in the first second is

$$|f(1) - f(0)| = |4 - 0| = 4 \text{ m}$$

From $t = 1$ to $t = 3$ the distance traveled is

$$|f(3) - f(1)| = |0 - 4| = 4 \text{ m}$$

From $t = 3$ to $t = 5$ the distance traveled is

$$|f(5) - f(3)| = |20 - 0| = 20 \text{ m}$$

The total distance is $4 + 4 + 20 = 28$ m.

(g) The acceleration is the derivative of the velocity function:

$$a(t) = \frac{d^2s}{dt^2} = \frac{dv}{dt} = 6t - 12$$

$$a(4) = 6(4) - 12 = 12 \text{ m/s}^2$$

(h) Figure 3 shows the graphs of s, v, and a.

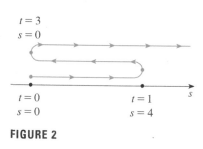

$t = 3$
$s = 0$

$t = 0$ $t = 1$
$s = 0$ $s = 4$

FIGURE 2

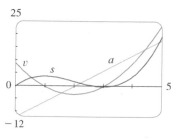

25

v s a

0   5

-12

FIGURE 3

(i) The particle speeds up when the velocity is positive and increasing (v and a are both positive) and also when the velocity is negative and decreasing (v and a are both negative). In other words, the particle speeds up when the velocity and acceleration have the same sign. (The particle is pushed in the same direction it is moving.) From Figure 3 we see that this happens when $1 < t < 2$ and when $t > 3$. The particle slows down when v and a have opposite signs, that is, when $0 \leqslant t < 1$ and when $2 < t < 3$. Figure 4 summarizes the motion of the particle.

TEC In Module 3.8 you can see an animation of Figure 4 with an expression for s that you can choose yourself.

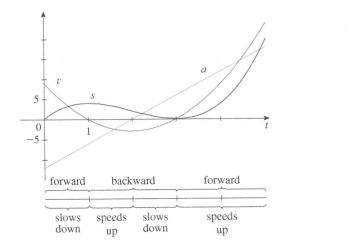

FIGURE 4

EXAMPLE 2   Linear density   If a rod or piece of wire is homogeneous, then its linear density is uniform and is defined as the mass per unit length ($\rho = m/l$) and measured in kilograms per meter. Suppose, however, that the rod is not homogeneous but that its mass measured from its left end to a point x is $m = f(x)$, as shown in Figure 5.

FIGURE 5   This part of the rod has mass $f(x)$.

The mass of the part of the rod that lies between $x = x_1$ and $x = x_2$ is given by $\Delta m = f(x_2) - f(x_1)$, so the average density of that part of the rod is

$$\text{average density} = \frac{\Delta m}{\Delta x} = \frac{f(x_2) - f(x_1)}{x_2 - x_1}$$

If we now let $\Delta x \to 0$ (that is, $x_2 \to x_1$), we are computing the average density over smaller and smaller intervals. The **linear density** ρ at x_1 is the limit of these average densities as $\Delta x \to 0$; that is, the linear density is the rate of change of mass with respect to length. Symbolically,

$$\rho = \lim_{\Delta x \to 0} \frac{\Delta m}{\Delta x} = \frac{dm}{dx}$$

Thus the linear density of the rod is the derivative of mass with respect to length.

For instance, if $m = f(x) = \sqrt{x}$, where x is measured in meters and m in kilograms, then the average density of the part of the rod given by $1 \leq x \leq 1.2$ is

$$\frac{\Delta m}{\Delta x} = \frac{f(1.2) - f(1)}{1.2 - 1} = \frac{\sqrt{1.2} - 1}{0.2} \approx 0.48 \text{ kg/m}$$

while the density right at $x = 1$ is

$$\rho = \frac{dm}{dx}\bigg|_{x=1} = \frac{1}{2\sqrt{x}}\bigg|_{x=1} = 0.50 \text{ kg/m}$$

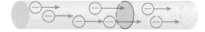

FIGURE 6

■ **EXAMPLE 3** **Current is the derivative of charge**   A current exists whenever electric charges move. Figure 6 shows part of a wire and electrons moving through a plane surface, shaded red. If ΔQ is the net charge that passes through this surface during a time period Δt, then the average current during this time interval is defined as

$$\text{average current} = \frac{\Delta Q}{\Delta t} = \frac{Q_2 - Q_1}{t_2 - t_1}$$

If we take the limit of this average current over smaller and smaller time intervals, we get what is called the **current** I at a given time t_1:

$$I = \lim_{\Delta t \to 0} \frac{\Delta Q}{\Delta t} = \frac{dQ}{dt}$$

Thus the current is the rate at which charge flows through a surface. It is measured in units of charge per unit time (often coulombs per second, called amperes).

Velocity, density, and current are not the only rates of change that are important in physics. Others include power (the rate at which work is done), the rate of heat flow, temperature gradient (the rate of change of temperature with respect to position), and the rate of decay of a radioactive substance in nuclear physics.

Chemistry

EXAMPLE 4 **Rate of reaction**   A chemical reaction results in the formation of one or more substances (called *products*) from one or more starting materials (called *reactants*). For instance, the "equation"

$$2H_2 + O_2 \rightarrow 2H_2O$$

indicates that two molecules of hydrogen and one molecule of oxygen form two molecules of water. Let's consider the reaction

$$A + B \rightarrow C$$

where A and B are the reactants and C is the product. The **concentration** of a reactant A is the number of moles ($1 \text{ mole} = 6.022 \times 10^{23}$ molecules) per liter and is denoted by [A]. The concentration varies during a reaction, so [A], [B], and [C] are all functions of time (t). The average rate of reaction of the product C over a time interval $t_1 \leqslant t \leqslant t_2$ is

$$\frac{\Delta[C]}{\Delta t} = \frac{[C](t_2) - [C](t_1)}{t_2 - t_1}$$

But chemists are more interested in the **instantaneous rate of reaction**, which is obtained by taking the limit of the average rate of reaction as the time interval Δt approaches 0:

$$\text{rate of reaction} = \lim_{\Delta t \to 0} \frac{\Delta[C]}{\Delta t} = \frac{d[C]}{dt}$$

Since the concentration of the product increases as the reaction proceeds, the derivative $d[C]/dt$ will be positive, and so the rate of reaction of C is positive. The concentrations of the reactants, however, decrease during the reaction, so, to make the rates of reaction of A and B positive numbers, we put minus signs in front of the derivatives $d[A]/dt$ and $d[B]/dt$. Since [A] and [B] each decrease at the same rate that [C] increases, we have

$$\text{rate of reaction} = \frac{d[C]}{dt} = -\frac{d[A]}{dt} = -\frac{d[B]}{dt}$$

More generally, it turns out that for a reaction of the form

$$a\text{A} + b\text{B} \to c\text{C} + d\text{D}$$

we have

$$-\frac{1}{a}\frac{d[A]}{dt} = -\frac{1}{b}\frac{d[B]}{dt} = \frac{1}{c}\frac{d[C]}{dt} = \frac{1}{d}\frac{d[D]}{dt}$$

The rate of reaction can be determined from data and graphical methods. In some cases there are explicit formulas for the concentrations as functions of time, which enable us to compute the rate of reaction (see Exercise 22).

EXAMPLE 5   **Compressibility**   One of the quantities of interest in thermodynamics is compressibility. If a given substance is kept at a constant temperature, then its volume V depends on its pressure P. We can consider the rate of change of volume with respect to pressure—namely, the derivative dV/dP. As P increases, V decreases, so $dV/dP < 0$. The **compressibility** is defined by introducing a minus sign and dividing this derivative by the volume V:

$$\text{isothermal compressibility} = \beta = -\frac{1}{V}\frac{dV}{dP}$$

Thus β measures how fast, per unit volume, the volume of a substance decreases as the pressure on it increases at constant temperature.

For instance, the volume V (in cubic meters) of a sample of air at 25°C was found to be related to the pressure P (in kilopascals) by the equation

$$V = \frac{5.3}{P}$$

The rate of change of V with respect to P when $P = 50$ kPa is

$$\left.\frac{dV}{dP}\right|_{P=50} = \left.-\frac{5.3}{P^2}\right|_{P=50}$$

$$= -\frac{5.3}{2500} = -0.00212 \text{ m}^3/\text{kPa}$$

The compressibility at that pressure is

$$\beta = \left.-\frac{1}{V}\frac{dV}{dP}\right|_{P=50} = \frac{0.00212}{\dfrac{5.3}{50}} = 0.02 \text{ (m}^3/\text{kPa)/m}^3$$

Biology

EXAMPLE 6 **Rate of growth of a population**   Let $n = f(t)$ be the number of individuals in an animal or plant population at time t. The change in the population size between the times $t = t_1$ and $t = t_2$ is $\Delta n = f(t_2) - f(t_1)$, and so the average rate of growth during the time period $t_1 \leqslant t \leqslant t_2$ is

$$\text{average rate of growth} = \frac{\Delta n}{\Delta t} = \frac{f(t_2) - f(t_1)}{t_2 - t_1}$$

The **instantaneous rate of growth** is obtained from this average rate of growth by letting the time period Δt approach 0:

$$\text{growth rate} = \lim_{\Delta t \to 0} \frac{\Delta n}{\Delta t} = \frac{dn}{dt}$$

Strictly speaking, this is not quite accurate because the actual graph of a population function $n = f(t)$ would be a step function that is discontinuous whenever a birth or death occurs and therefore not differentiable. However, for a large animal or plant population, we can replace the graph by a smooth approximating curve as in Figure 7.

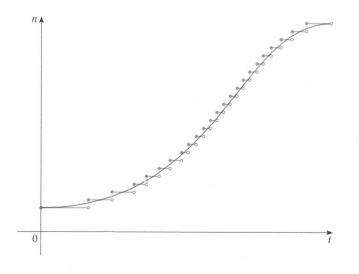

FIGURE 7

A smooth curve approximating
a growth function

To be more specific, consider a population of bacteria in a homogeneous nutrient medium. Suppose that by sampling the population at certain intervals it is determined that the population doubles every hour. If the initial population is n_0 and the time t is measured in hours, then

$$f(1) = 2f(0) = 2n_0$$

$$f(2) = 2f(1) = 2^2 n_0$$

$$f(3) = 2f(2) = 2^3 n_0$$

and, in general,

$$f(t) = 2^t n_0$$

The population function is $n = n_0 2^t$.

In Section 3.4 we showed that

$$\frac{d}{dx}(a^x) = a^x \ln a$$

So the rate of growth of the bacteria population at time t is

$$\frac{dn}{dt} = \frac{d}{dt}(n_0 2^t) = n_0 2^t \ln 2$$

For example, suppose that we start with an initial population of $n_0 = 100$ bacteria. Then the rate of growth after 4 hours is

$$\left.\frac{dn}{dt}\right|_{t=4} = 100 \cdot 2^4 \ln 2 = 1600 \ln 2 \approx 1109$$

This means that, after 4 hours, the bacteria population is growing at a rate of about 1109 bacteria per hour.

EXAMPLE 7   **Blood flow**   When we consider the flow of blood through a blood vessel, such as a vein or artery, we can model the shape of the blood vessel by a cylindrical tube with radius R and length l as illustrated in Figure 8.

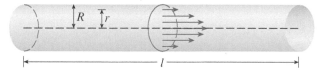

FIGURE 8
Blood flow in an artery

Because of friction at the walls of the tube, the velocity v of the blood is greatest along the central axis of the tube and decreases as the distance r from the axis increases until v becomes 0 at the wall. The relationship between v and r is given by the **law of laminar flow** discovered by the French physician Jean-Louis-Marie Poiseuille in 1840. This law states that

For more detailed information, see W. Nichols and M. O'Rourke (eds.), *McDonald's Blood Flow in Arteries: Theoretic, Experimental, and Clinical Principles,* 5th ed. (New York, 2005).

$$\boxed{1} \qquad v = \frac{P}{4\eta l}(R^2 - r^2)$$

where η is the viscosity of the blood and P is the pressure difference between the ends of the tube. If P and l are constant, then v is a function of r with domain $[0, R]$.

The average rate of change of the velocity as we move from $r = r_1$ outward to $r = r_2$ is given by

$$\frac{\Delta v}{\Delta r} = \frac{v(r_2) - v(r_1)}{r_2 - r_1}$$

and if we let $\Delta r \to 0$, we obtain the **velocity gradient**, that is, the instantaneous rate of change of velocity with respect to r:

$$\text{velocity gradient} = \lim_{\Delta r \to 0} \frac{\Delta v}{\Delta r} = \frac{dv}{dr}$$

Using Equation 1, we obtain

$$\frac{dv}{dr} = \frac{P}{4\eta l}(0 - 2r) = -\frac{Pr}{2\eta l}$$

For one of the smaller human arteries we can take $\eta = 0.027$, $R = 0.008$ cm, $l = 2$ cm, and $P = 4000$ dynes/cm^2, which gives

$$v = \frac{4000}{4(0.027)2}(0.000064 - r^2)$$

$$\approx 1.85 \times 10^4(6.4 \times 10^{-5} - r^2)$$

At $r = 0.002$ cm the blood is flowing at a speed of

$$v(0.002) \approx 1.85 \times 10^4(64 \times 10^{-6} - 4 \times 10^{-6})$$

$$= 1.11 \text{ cm/s}$$

and the velocity gradient at that point is

$$\left.\frac{dv}{dr}\right|_{r=0.002} = -\frac{4000(0.002)}{2(0.027)2} \approx -74 \text{ (cm/s)/cm}$$

To get a feeling for what this statement means, let's change our units from centimeters to micrometers (1 cm = 10,000 μm). Then the radius of the artery is 80 μm. The velocity at the central axis is 11,850 μm/s, which decreases to 11,110 μm/s at a distance of $r = 20$ μm. The fact that $dv/dr = -74$ $(\mu$m/s)/μm means that, when $r = 20$ μm, the velocity is decreasing at a rate of about 74 μm/s for each micrometer that we proceed away from the center.

Economics

V **EXAMPLE 8** **Marginal cost** Suppose $C(x)$ is the total cost that a company incurs in producing x units of a certain commodity. The function C is called a **cost function**. If the number of items produced is increased from x_1 to x_2, then the additional cost is $\Delta C = C(x_2) - C(x_1)$, and the average rate of change of the cost is

$$\frac{\Delta C}{\Delta x} = \frac{C(x_2) - C(x_1)}{x_2 - x_1} = \frac{C(x_1 + \Delta x) - C(x_1)}{\Delta x}$$

The limit of this quantity as $\Delta x \to 0$, that is, the instantaneous rate of change of cost with respect to the number of items produced, is called the **marginal cost** by economists:

$$\text{marginal cost} = \lim_{\Delta x \to 0} \frac{\Delta C}{\Delta x} = \frac{dC}{dx}$$

[Since x often takes on only integer values, it may not make literal sense to let Δx approach 0, but we can always replace $C(x)$ by a smooth approximating function as in Example 6.]

Taking $\Delta x = 1$ and n large (so that Δx is small compared to n), we have

$$C'(n) \approx C(n + 1) - C(n)$$

Thus the marginal cost of producing n units is approximately equal to the cost of producing one more unit, the $(n + 1)$st unit.

It is often appropriate to represent a total cost function by a polynomial

$$C(x) = a + bx + cx^2 + dx^3$$

where a represents the overhead cost (rent, heat, maintenance) and the other terms represent the cost of raw materials, labor, and so on. (The cost of raw materials may be proportional to x, but labor costs might depend partly on higher powers of x because of overtime costs and inefficiencies involved in large-scale operations.)

For instance, suppose a company has estimated that the cost (in dollars) of producing x items is

$$C(x) = 10{,}000 + 5x + 0.01x^2$$

Then the marginal cost function is

$$C'(x) = 5 + 0.02x$$

The marginal cost at the production level of 500 items is

$$C'(500) = 5 + 0.02(500) = \$15/\text{item}$$

This gives the rate at which costs are increasing with respect to the production level when $x = 500$ and predicts the cost of the 501st item.

The actual cost of producing the 501st item is

$$C(501) - C(500) = [10{,}000 + 5(501) + 0.01(501)^2]$$
$$- [10{,}000 + 5(500) + 0.01(500)^2]$$
$$= \$15.01$$

Notice that $C'(500) \approx C(501) - C(500)$.

Economists also study marginal demand, marginal revenue, and marginal profit, which are the derivatives of the demand, revenue, and profit functions. These will be considered in Chapter 4 after we have developed techniques for finding the maximum and minimum values of functions.

Other Sciences

Rates of change occur in all the sciences. A geologist is interested in knowing the rate at which an intruded body of molten rock cools by conduction of heat into surrounding rocks. An engineer wants to know the rate at which water flows into or out of a reservoir. An urban geographer is interested in the rate of change of the population density in a city as the distance from the city center increases. A meteorologist is concerned with the rate of change of atmospheric pressure with respect to height (see Exercise 17 in Section 7.4).

In psychology, those interested in learning theory study the so-called learning curve, which graphs the performance $P(t)$ of someone learning a skill as a function of the training time t. Of particular interest is the rate at which performance improves as time passes, that is, dP/dt.

In sociology, differential calculus is used in analyzing the spread of rumors (or innovations or fads or fashions). If $p(t)$ denotes the proportion of a population that knows a rumor by time t, then the derivative dp/dt represents the rate of spread of the rumor (see Exercise 74 in Section 3.4).

A Single Idea, Many Interpretations

Velocity, density, current, power, and temperature gradient in physics; rate of reaction and compressibility in chemistry; rate of growth and blood velocity gradient in biology; marginal cost and marginal profit in economics; rate of heat flow in geology; rate of improvement of performance in psychology; rate of spread of a rumor in sociology—these are all special cases of a single mathematical concept, the derivative.

This is an illustration of the fact that part of the power of mathematics lies in its abstractness. A single abstract mathematical concept (such as the derivative) can have different interpretations in each of the sciences. When we develop the properties of the mathematical concept once and for all, we can then turn around and apply these results to all of the sciences. This is much more efficient than developing properties of special concepts in each separate science. The French mathematician Joseph Fourier (1768–1830) put it succinctly: "Mathematics compares the most diverse phenomena and discovers the secret analogies that unite them."

3.8 Exercises

1–4 A particle moves according to a law of motion $s = f(t)$, $t \geq 0$, where t is measured in seconds and s in feet.
(a) Find the velocity at time t.
(b) What is the velocity after 3 s?
(c) When is the particle at rest?
(d) When is the particle moving in the positive direction?
(e) Find the total distance traveled during the first 8 s.
(f) Draw a diagram like Figure 2 to illustrate the motion of the particle.
(g) Find the acceleration at time t and after 3 s.
(h) Graph the position, velocity, and acceleration functions for $0 \leq t \leq 8$.
(i) When is the particle speeding up? When is it slowing down?

1. $f(t) = t^3 - 12t^2 + 36t$ **2.** $f(t) = 0.01t^4 - 0.04t^3$

3. $f(t) = \cos(\pi t/4), \quad t \leq 10$ **4.** $f(t) = te^{-t/2}$

5. Graphs of the *velocity* functions of two particles are shown, where t is measured in seconds. When is each particle speeding up? When is it slowing down? Explain.

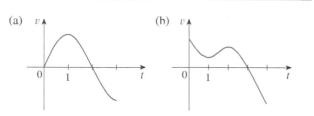

6. Graphs of the *position* functions of two particles are shown, where t is measured in seconds. When is each particle speeding up? When is it slowing down? Explain.

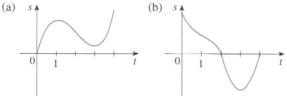

7. The position function of a particle is given by $s = t^3 - 4.5t^2 - 7t, t \geq 0$.
(a) When does the particle reach a velocity of 5 m/s?

⌂ Graphing calculator or computer with graphing software required   **1.** Homework Hints available in TEC

(b) When is the acceleration 0? What is the significance of this value of t?

8. If a ball is given a push so that it has an initial velocity of 5 m/s down a certain inclined plane, then the distance it has rolled after t seconds is $s = 5t + 3t^2$.
(a) Find the velocity after 2 s.
(b) How long does it take for the velocity to reach 35 m/s?

9. If a stone is thrown vertically upward from the surface of the moon with a velocity of 10 m/s, its height (in meters) after t seconds is $h = 10t - 0.83t^2$.
(a) What is the velocity of the stone after 3 s?
(b) What is the velocity of the stone after it has risen 25 m?

10. If a ball is thrown vertically upward with a velocity of 80 ft/s, then its height after t seconds is $s = 80t - 16t^2$.
(a) What is the maximum height reached by the ball?
(b) What is the velocity of the ball when it is 96 ft above the ground on its way up? On its way down?

11. (a) A company makes computer chips from square wafers of silicon. It wants to keep the side length of a wafer very close to 15 mm and it wants to know how the area $A(x)$ of a wafer changes when the side length x changes. Find $A'(15)$ and explain its meaning in this situation.
(b) Show that the rate of change of the area of a square with respect to its side length is half its perimeter. Try to explain geometrically why this is true by drawing a square whose side length x is increased by an amount Δx. How can you approximate the resulting change in area ΔA if Δx is small?

12. (a) Sodium chlorate crystals are easy to grow in the shape of cubes by allowing a solution of water and sodium chlorate to evaporate slowly. If V is the volume of such a cube with side length x, calculate dV/dx when $x = 3$ mm and explain its meaning.
(b) Show that the rate of change of the volume of a cube with respect to its edge length is equal to half the surface area of the cube. Explain geometrically why this result is true by arguing by analogy with Exercise 11(b).

13. (a) Find the average rate of change of the area of a circle with respect to its radius r as r changes from
(i) 2 to 3   (ii) 2 to 2.5   (iii) 2 to 2.1
(b) Find the instantaneous rate of change when $r = 2$.
(c) Show that the rate of change of the area of a circle with respect to its radius (at any r) is equal to the circumference of the circle. Try to explain geometrically why this is true by drawing a circle whose radius is increased by an amount Δr. How can you approximate the resulting change in area ΔA if Δr is small?

14. A stone is dropped into a lake, creating a circular ripple that travels outward at a speed of 60 cm/s. Find the rate at which the area within the circle is increasing after (a) 1 s, (b) 3 s, and (c) 5 s. What can you conclude?

15. A spherical balloon is being inflated. Find the rate of increase of the surface area ($S = 4\pi r^2$) with respect to the radius r when r is (a) 1 ft, (b) 2 ft, and (c) 3 ft. What conclusion can you make?

16. (a) The volume of a growing spherical cell is $V = \frac{4}{3}\pi r^3$, where the radius r is measured in micrometers (1 μm $= 10^{-6}$ m). Find the average rate of change of V with respect to r when r changes from
(i) 5 to 8 μm   (ii) 5 to 6 μm   (iii) 5 to 5.1 μm
(b) Find the instantaneous rate of change of V with respect to r when $r = 5$ μm.
(c) Show that the rate of change of the volume of a sphere with respect to its radius is equal to its surface area. Explain geometrically why this result is true. Argue by analogy with Exercise 13(c).

17. The mass of the part of a metal rod that lies between its left end and a point x meters to the right is $3x^2$ kg. Find the linear density (see Example 2) when x is (a) 1 m, (b) 2 m, and (c) 3 m. Where is the density the highest? The lowest?

18. If a tank holds 5000 gallons of water, which drains from the bottom of the tank in 40 minutes, then Torricelli's Law gives the volume V of water remaining in the tank after t minutes as

$$V = 5000\left(1 - \tfrac{1}{40}t\right)^2 \qquad 0 \leq t \leq 40$$

Find the rate at which water is draining from the tank after (a) 5 min, (b) 10 min, (c) 20 min, and (d) 40 min. At what time is the water flowing out the fastest? The slowest? Summarize your findings.

19. The quantity of charge Q in coulombs (C) that has passed through a point in a wire up to time t (measured in seconds) is given by $Q(t) = t^3 - 2t^2 + 6t + 2$. Find the current when (a) $t = 0.5$ s and (b) $t = 1$ s. [See Example 3. The unit of current is an ampere (1 A $= 1$ C/s).] At what time is the current lowest?

20. Newton's Law of Gravitation says that the magnitude F of the force exerted by a body of mass m on a body of mass M is

$$F = \frac{GmM}{r^2}$$

where G is the gravitational constant and r is the distance between the bodies.
(a) Find dF/dr and explain its meaning. What does the minus sign indicate?
(b) Suppose it is known that the earth attracts an object with a force that decreases at the rate of 2 N/km when $r = 20{,}000$ km. How fast does this force change when $r = 10{,}000$ km?

21. Boyle's Law states that when a sample of gas is compressed at a constant temperature, the product of the pressure and the volume remains constant: $PV = C$.
(a) Find the rate of change of volume with respect to pressure.

(b) A sample of gas is in a container at low pressure and is steadily compressed at constant temperature for 10 minutes. Is the volume decreasing more rapidly at the beginning or the end of the 10 minutes? Explain.

(c) Prove that the isothermal compressibility (see Example 5) is given by $\beta = 1/P$.

22. If, in Example 4, one molecule of the product C is formed from one molecule of the reactant A and one molecule of the reactant B, and the initial concentrations of A and B have a common value $[A] = [B] = a$ moles/L, then

$$[C] = a^2 kt/(akt + 1)$$

where k is a constant.

(a) Find the rate of reaction at time t.

(b) Show that if $x = [C]$, then

$$\frac{dx}{dt} = k(a - x)^2$$

(c) What happens to the concentration as $t \to \infty$?

(d) What happens to the rate of reaction as $t \to \infty$?

(e) What do the results of parts (c) and (d) mean in practical terms?

23. In Example 6 we considered a bacteria population that doubles every hour. Suppose that another population of bacteria triples every hour and starts with 400 bacteria. Find an expression for the number n of bacteria after t hours and use it to estimate the rate of growth of the bacteria population after 2.5 hours.

24. The number of yeast cells in a laboratory culture increases rapidly initially but levels off eventually. The population is modeled by the function

$$n = f(t) = \frac{a}{1 + be^{-0.7t}}$$

where t is measured in hours. At time $t = 0$ the population is 20 cells and is increasing at a rate of 12 cells/hour. Find the values of a and b. According to this model, what happens to the yeast population in the long run?

25. The table gives the population of the world in the 20th century.

Year	Population (in millions)	Year	Population (in millions)
1900	1650	1960	3040
1910	1750	1970	3710
1920	1860	1980	4450
1930	2070	1990	5280
1940	2300	2000	6080
1950	2560		

(a) Estimate the rate of population growth in 1920 and in 1980 by averaging the slopes of two secant lines.

(b) Use a graphing calculator or computer to find a cubic function (a third-degree polynomial) that models the data.

(c) Use your model in part (b) to find a model for the rate of population growth in the 20th century.

(d) Use part (c) to estimate the rates of growth in 1920 and 1980. Compare with your estimates in part (a).

(e) Estimate the rate of growth in 1985.

26. The table shows how the average age of first marriage of Japanese women varied in the last half of the 20th century.

t	$A(t)$	t	$A(t)$
1950	23.0	1980	25.2
1955	23.8	1985	25.5
1960	24.4	1990	25.9
1965	24.5	1995	26.3
1970	24.2	2000	27.0
1975	24.7		

(a) Use a graphing calculator or computer to model these data with a fourth-degree polynomial.

(b) Use part (a) to find a model for $A'(t)$.

(c) Estimate the rate of change of marriage age for women in 1990.

(d) Graph the data points and the models for A and A'.

27. Refer to the law of laminar flow given in Example 7. Consider a blood vessel with radius 0.01 cm, length 3 cm, pressure difference 3000 dynes/cm^2, and viscosity $\eta = 0.027$.

(a) Find the velocity of the blood along the centerline $r = 0$, at radius $r = 0.005$ cm, and at the wall $r = R = 0.01$ cm.

(b) Find the velocity gradient at $r = 0$, $r = 0.005$, and $r = 0.01$.

(c) Where is the velocity the greatest? Where is the velocity changing most?

28. The frequency of vibrations of a vibrating violin string is given by

$$f = \frac{1}{2L}\sqrt{\frac{T}{\rho}}$$

where L is the length of the string, T is its tension, and ρ is its linear density. [See Chapter 11 in D. E. Hall, *Musical Acoustics*, 3rd ed. (Pacific Grove, CA, 2002).]

(a) Find the rate of change of the frequency with respect to
   (i) the length (when T and ρ are constant),
   (ii) the tension (when L and ρ are constant), and
   (iii) the linear density (when L and T are constant).

(b) The pitch of a note (how high or low the note sounds) is determined by the frequency f. (The higher the frequency, the higher the pitch.) Use the signs of the derivatives in part (a) to determine what happens to the pitch of a note
   (i) when the effective length of a string is decreased by placing a finger on the string so a shorter portion of the string vibrates,
   (ii) when the tension is increased by turning a tuning peg,
   (iii) when the linear density is increased by switching to another string.

29. The cost, in dollars, of producing x yards of a certain fabric is

$$C(x) = 1200 + 12x - 0.1x^2 + 0.0005x^3$$

(a) Find the marginal cost function.
(b) Find $C'(200)$ and explain its meaning. What does it predict?
(c) Compare $C'(200)$ with the cost of manufacturing the 201st yard of fabric.

30. The cost function for production of a commodity is

$$C(x) = 339 + 25x - 0.09x^2 + 0.0004x^3$$

(a) Find and interpret $C'(100)$.
(b) Compare $C'(100)$ with the cost of producing the 101st item.

31. If $p(x)$ is the total value of the production when there are x workers in a plant, then the *average productivity* of the workforce at the plant is

$$A(x) = \frac{p(x)}{x}$$

(a) Find $A'(x)$. Why does the company want to hire more workers if $A'(x) > 0$?
(b) Show that $A'(x) > 0$ if $p'(x)$ is greater than the average productivity.

32. If R denotes the reaction of the body to some stimulus of strength x, the *sensitivity* S is defined to be the rate of change of the reaction with respect to x. A particular example is that when the brightness x of a light source is increased, the eye reacts by decreasing the area R of the pupil. The experimental formula

$$R = \frac{40 + 24x^{0.4}}{1 + 4x^{0.4}}$$

has been used to model the dependence of R on x when R is measured in square millimeters and x is measured in appropriate units of brightness.
(a) Find the sensitivity.
(b) Illustrate part (a) by graphing both R and S as functions of x. Comment on the values of R and S at low levels of brightness. Is this what you would expect?

33. The gas law for an ideal gas at absolute temperature T (in kelvins), pressure P (in atmospheres), and volume V (in liters) is $PV = nRT$, where n is the number of moles of the gas and $R = 0.0821$ is the gas constant. Suppose that, at a certain instant, $P = 8.0$ atm and is increasing at a rate of 0.10 atm/min and $V = 10$ L and is decreasing at a rate of 0.15 L/min. Find the rate of change of T with respect to time at that instant if $n = 10$ mol.

34. In a fish farm, a population of fish is introduced into a pond and harvested regularly. A model for the rate of change of the fish population is given by the equation

$$\frac{dP}{dt} = r_0\left(1 - \frac{P(t)}{P_c}\right)P(t) - \beta P(t)$$

where r_0 is the birth rate of the fish, P_c is the maximum population that the pond can sustain (called the *carrying capacity*), and β is the percentage of the population that is harvested.
(a) What value of dP/dt corresponds to a stable population?
(b) If the pond can sustain 10,000 fish, the birth rate is 5%, and the harvesting rate is 4%, find the stable population level.
(c) What happens if β is raised to 5%?

35. In the study of ecosystems, *predator-prey models* are often used to study the interaction between species. Consider populations of tundra wolves, given by $W(t)$, and caribou, given by $C(t)$, in northern Canada. The interaction has been modeled by the equations

$$\frac{dC}{dt} = aC - bCW \qquad \frac{dW}{dt} = -cW + dCW$$

(a) What values of dC/dt and dW/dt correspond to stable populations?
(b) How would the statement "The caribou go extinct" be represented mathematically?
(c) Suppose that $a = 0.05$, $b = 0.001$, $c = 0.05$, and $d = 0.0001$. Find all population pairs (C, W) that lead to stable populations. According to this model, is it possible for the two species to live in balance or will one or both species become extinct?

3.9 Linear Approximations and Differentials

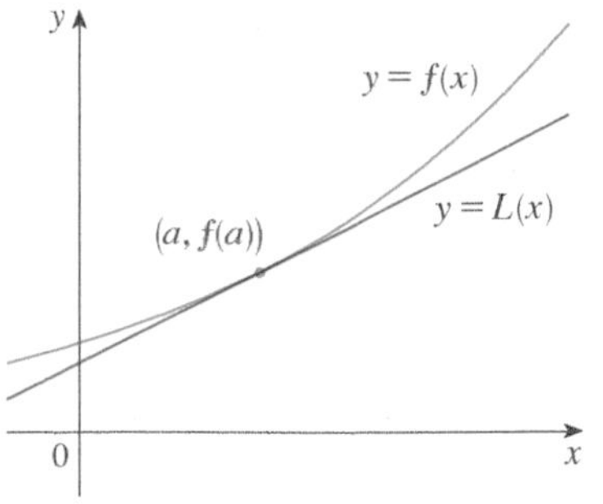

FIGURE 1

We have seen that a curve lies very close to its tangent line near the point of tangency. In fact, by zooming in toward a point on the graph of a differentiable function, we noticed that the graph looks more and more like its tangent line. (See Figure 2 in Section 2.6.) This observation is the basis for a method of finding approximate values of functions.

The idea is that it might be easy to calculate a value $f(a)$ of a function, but difficult (or even impossible) to compute nearby values of f. So we settle for the easily computed values of the linear function L whose graph is the tangent line of f at $(a, f(a))$. (See Figure 1.)

In other words, we use the tangent line at $(a, f(a))$ as an approximation to the curve $y = f(x)$ when x is near a. An equation of this tangent line is

$$y = f(a) + f'(a)(x - a)$$

and the approximation

$$\boxed{1} \qquad\qquad f(x) \approx f(a) + f'(a)(x - a)$$

is called the **linear approximation** or **tangent line approximation** of f at a. The linear function whose graph is this tangent line, that is,

$$\boxed{2} \qquad\qquad L(x) = f(a) + f'(a)(x - a)$$

is called the **linearization** of f at a.

The following example is typical of situations in which we use a linear approximation to predict the future behavior of a function given by empirical data.

☑ EXAMPLE 1 **Predicting from a linear approximation** Suppose that after you stuff a turkey its temperature is 50°F and you then put it in a 325°F oven. After an hour the meat thermometer indicates that the temperature of the turkey is 93°F and after two hours it indicates 129°F. Predict the temperature of the turkey after three hours.

SOLUTION If $T(t)$ represents the temperature of the turkey after t hours, we are given that $T(0) = 50$, $T(1) = 93$, and $T(2) = 129$. In order to make a linear approximation with $a = 2$, we need an estimate for the derivative $T'(2)$. Because

$$T'(2) = \lim_{t \to 2} \frac{T(t) - T(2)}{t - 2}$$

we could estimate $T'(2)$ by the difference quotient with $t = 1$:

$$T'(2) \approx \frac{T(1) - T(2)}{1 - 2} = \frac{93 - 129}{-1} = 36$$

This amounts to approximating the instantaneous rate of temperature change by the average rate of change between $t = 1$ and $t = 2$, which is 36°F/h. With this estimate, the linear approximation (1) for the temperature after 3 h is

$$T(3) \approx T(2) + T'(2)(3 - 2)$$
$$\approx 129 + 36 \cdot 1 = 165$$

So the predicted temperature after three hours is 165°F.

We obtain a more accurate estimate for $T'(2)$ by plotting the given data, as in Figure 2, and estimating the slope of the tangent line at $t = 2$ to be

$$T'(2) \approx 33$$

Then our linear approximation becomes

$$T(3) \approx T(2) + T'(2) \cdot 1 \approx 129 + 33 = 162$$

and our improved estimate for the temperature is 162°F.

Because the temperature curve lies below the tangent line, it appears that the actual temperature after three hours will be somewhat less than 162°F, perhaps closer to 160°F.

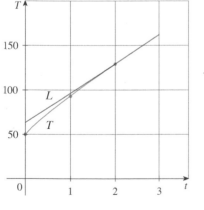

FIGURE 2

☑ EXAMPLE 2 Find the linearization of the function $f(x) = \sqrt{x + 3}$ at $a = 1$ and use it to approximate the numbers $\sqrt{3.98}$ and $\sqrt{4.05}$. Are these approximations overestimates or underestimates?

SOLUTION The derivative of $f(x) = (x + 3)^{1/2}$ is

$$f'(x) = \tfrac{1}{2}(x + 3)^{-1/2} = \frac{1}{2\sqrt{x + 3}}$$

and so we have $f(1) = 2$ and $f'(1) = \tfrac{1}{4}$. Putting these values into Equation 2, we see that the linearization is

$$L(x) = f(1) + f'(1)(x - 1) = 2 + \tfrac{1}{4}(x - 1) = \frac{7}{4} + \frac{x}{4}$$

The corresponding linear approximation (1) is

$$\sqrt{x + 3} \approx \frac{7}{4} + \frac{x}{4} \qquad \text{(when } x \text{ is near 1)}$$

In particular, we have

$$\sqrt{3.98} \approx \tfrac{7}{4} + \tfrac{0.98}{4} = 1.995 \qquad \text{and} \qquad \sqrt{4.05} \approx \tfrac{7}{4} + \tfrac{1.05}{4} = 2.0125$$

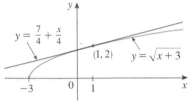

$y = \frac{7}{4} + \frac{x}{4}$

$(1, 2)$ $y = \sqrt{x + 3}$

-3 0 1

FIGURE 3

The linear approximation is illustrated in Figure 3. We see that, indeed, the tangent line approximation is a good approximation to the given function when x is near 1. We also see that our approximations are overestimates because the tangent line lies above the curve.

Of course, a calculator could give us approximations for $\sqrt{3.98}$ and $\sqrt{4.05}$, but the linear approximation gives an approximation *over an entire interval*.

In the following table we compare the estimates from the linear approximation in Example 2 with the true values. Notice from this table, and also from Figure 3, that the tangent line approximation gives good estimates when x is close to 1 but the accuracy of the approximation deteriorates when x is farther away from 1.

	x	From $L(x)$	Actual value
$\sqrt{3.9}$	0.9	1.975	1.97484176 ...
$\sqrt{3.98}$	0.98	1.995	1.99499373 ...
$\sqrt{4}$	1	2	2.00000000 ...
$\sqrt{4.05}$	1.05	2.0125	2.01246117 ...
$\sqrt{4.1}$	1.1	2.025	2.02484567 ...
$\sqrt{5}$	2	2.25	2.23606797 ...
$\sqrt{6}$	3	2.5	2.44948974 ...

How good is the approximation that we obtained in Example 2? The next example shows that by using a graphing calculator or computer we can determine an interval throughout which a linear approximation provides a specified accuracy.

EXAMPLE 3 **Accuracy of a linear approximation**   For what values of x is the linear approximation

$$\sqrt{x + 3} \approx \frac{7}{4} + \frac{x}{4}$$

accurate to within 0.5? What about accuracy to within 0.1?

SOLUTION Accuracy to within 0.5 means that the functions should differ by less than 0.5:

$$\left| \sqrt{x + 3} - \left(\frac{7}{4} + \frac{x}{4} \right) \right| < 0.5$$

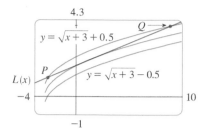

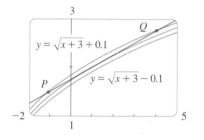

FIGURE 4

FIGURE 5

Equivalently, we could write

$$\sqrt{x + 3} - 0.5 < \frac{7}{4} + \frac{x}{4} < \sqrt{x + 3} + 0.5$$

This says that the linear approximation should lie between the curves obtained by shifting the curve $y = \sqrt{x + 3}$ upward and downward by an amount 0.5. Figure 4 shows the tangent line $y = (7 + x)/4$ intersecting the upper curve $y = \sqrt{x + 3} + 0.5$ at P and Q. Zooming in and using the cursor, we estimate that the x-coordinate of P is about -2.66 and the x-coordinate of Q is about 8.66. Thus we see from the graph that the approximation

$$\sqrt{x + 3} \approx \frac{7}{4} + \frac{x}{4}$$

is accurate to within 0.5 when $-2.6 < x < 8.6$. (We have rounded to be safe.)

Similarly, from Figure 5 we see that the approximation is accurate to within 0.1 when $-1.1 < x < 3.9$.

Applications to Physics

Linear approximations are often used in physics. In analyzing the consequences of an equation, a physicist sometimes needs to simplify a function by replacing it with its linear approximation. For instance, in deriving a formula for the period of a pendulum, physics textbooks obtain the expression $a_T = -g \sin \theta$ for tangential acceleration and then replace $\sin \theta$ by θ with the remark that $\sin \theta$ is very close to θ if θ is not too large. [See, for example, *Physics: Calculus,* 2d ed., by Eugene Hecht (Pacific Grove, CA, 2000), p. 431.] You can verify that the linearization of the function $f(x) = \sin x$ at $a = 0$ is $L(x) = x$ and so the linear approximation at 0 is

$$\sin x \approx x$$

(see Exercise 34). So, in effect, the derivation of the formula for the period of a pendulum uses the tangent line approximation for the sine function.

Another example occurs in the theory of optics, where light rays that arrive at shallow angles relative to the optical axis are called *paraxial rays*. In paraxial (or Gaussian) optics, both $\sin \theta$ and $\cos \theta$ are replaced by their linearizations. In other words, the linear approximations

$$\sin \theta \approx \theta \qquad \text{and} \qquad \cos \theta \approx 1$$

are used because θ is close to 0. The results of calculations made with these approximations became the basic theoretical tool used to design lenses. [See *Optics,* 4th ed., by Eugene Hecht (San Francisco, 2002), p. 154.]

In Section 8.8 we will present several other applications of the idea of linear approximations to physics.

Differentials

The ideas behind linear approximations are sometimes formulated in the terminology and notation of *differentials*. If $y = f(x)$, where f is a differentiable function, then the **differential** dx is an independent variable; that is, dx can be given the value of any real number. The **differential** dy is then defined in terms of dx by the equation

If $dx \neq 0$, we can divide both sides of Equation 3 by dx to obtain

$$\frac{dy}{dx} = f'(x)$$

We have seen similar equations before, but now the left side can genuinely be interpreted as a ratio of differentials.

$$\boxed{3} \qquad dy = f'(x)\, dx$$

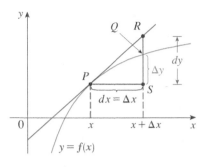

FIGURE 6

So dy is a dependent variable; it depends on the values of x and dx. If dx is given a specific value and x is taken to be some specific number in the domain of f, then the numerical value of dy is determined.

The geometric meaning of differentials is shown in Figure 6. Let $P(x, f(x))$ and $Q(x + \Delta x, f(x + \Delta x))$ be points on the graph of f and let $dx = \Delta x$. The corresponding change in y is

$$\Delta y = f(x + \Delta x) - f(x)$$

The slope of the tangent line PR is the derivative $f'(x)$. Thus the directed distance from S to R is $f'(x)\,dx = dy$. Therefore dy represents the amount that the tangent line rises or falls (the change in the linearization), whereas Δy represents the amount that the curve $y = f(x)$ rises or falls when x changes by an amount dx. Notice from Figure 6 that the approximation $\Delta y \approx dy$ becomes better as Δx becomes smaller.

If we let $dx = x - a$, then $x = a + dx$ and we can rewrite the linear approximation (1) in the notation of differentials:

$$f(a + dx) \approx f(a) + dy$$

For instance, for the function $f(x) = \sqrt{x + 3}$ in Example 2, we have

$$dy = f'(x)\,dx = \frac{dx}{2\sqrt{x + 3}}$$

If $a = 1$ and $dx = \Delta x = 0.05$, then

$$dy = \frac{0.05}{2\sqrt{1 + 3}} = 0.0125$$

and

$$\sqrt{4.05} = f(1.05) \approx f(1) + dy = 2.0125$$

just as we found in Example 2.

Our final example illustrates the use of differentials in estimating the errors that occur because of approximate measurements.

▶ EXAMPLE 4 The radius of a sphere was measured and found to be 21 cm with a possible error in measurement of at most 0.05 cm. What is the maximum error in using this value of the radius to compute the volume of the sphere?

SOLUTION If the radius of the sphere is r, then its volume is $V = \frac{4}{3}\pi r^3$. If the error in the measured value of r is denoted by $dr = \Delta r$, then the corresponding error in the calculated value of V is ΔV, which can be approximated by the differential

$$dV = 4\pi r^2\,dr$$

When $r = 21$ and $dr = 0.05$, this becomes

$$dV = 4\pi(21)^2 0.05 \approx 277$$

The maximum error in the calculated volume is about 277 cm³.

Note: Although the possible error in Example 4 may appear to be rather large, a better picture of the error is given by the **relative error**, which is computed by dividing the error by the total volume:

$$\frac{\Delta V}{V} \approx \frac{dV}{V} = \frac{4\pi r^2\, dr}{\frac{4}{3}\pi r^3} = 3\,\frac{dr}{r}$$

Thus the relative error in the volume is about three times the relative error in the radius. In Example 4 the relative error in the radius is approximately $dr/r = 0.05/21 \approx 0.0024$ and it produces a relative error of about 0.007 in the volume. The errors could also be expressed as **percentage errors** of 0.24% in the radius and 0.7% in the volume.

3.9 Exercises

1. The turkey in Example 1 is removed from the oven when its temperature reaches 185°F and is placed on a table in a room where the temperature is 75°F. After 10 minutes the temperature of the turkey is 172°F and after 20 minutes it is 160°F. Use a linear approximation to predict the temperature of the turkey after half an hour. Do you think your prediction is an overestimate or an underestimate? Why?

2. Atmospheric pressure P decreases as altitude h increases. At a temperature of 15°C, the pressure is 101.3 kilopascals (kPa) at sea level, 87.1 kPa at $h = 1$ km, and 74.9 kPa at $h = 2$ km. Use a linear approximation to estimate the atmospheric pressure at an altitude of 3 km.

3. The graph indicates how Australia's population is aging by showing the past and projected percentage of the population aged 65 and over. Use a linear approximation to predict the percentage of the population that will be 65 and over in the years 2040 and 2050. Do you think your predictions are too high or too low? Why?

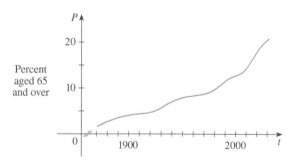

4. The table shows the population of Nepal (in millions) as of June 30 of the given year. Use a linear approximation to estimate the population at midyear in 1989. Use another linear approximation to predict the population in 2010.

t	1985	1990	1995	2000	2005
$N(t)$	17.04	19.33	21.91	24.70	27.68

5–8 Find the linearization $L(x)$ of the function at a.

5. $f(x) = x^4 + 3x^2$, $a = -1$

6. $f(x) = \ln x$, $a = 1$

7. $f(x) = \cos x$, $a = \pi/2$

8. $f(x) = x^{3/4}$, $a = 16$

9. Find the linear approximation of the function $f(x) = \sqrt{1-x}$ at $a = 0$ and use it to approximate the numbers $\sqrt{0.9}$ and $\sqrt{0.99}$. Illustrate by graphing f and the tangent line.

10. Find the linear approximation of the function $g(x) = \sqrt[3]{1+x}$ at $a = 0$ and use it to approximate the numbers $\sqrt[3]{0.95}$ and $\sqrt[3]{1.1}$. Illustrate by graphing g and the tangent line.

11–14 Verify the given linear approximation at $a = 0$. Then determine the values of x for which the linear approximation is accurate to within 0.1.

11. $\sqrt[3]{1-x} \approx 1 - \frac{1}{3}x$

12. $\tan x \approx x$

13. $1/(1+2x)^4 \approx 1 - 8x$

14. $e^x \approx 1 + x$

15–18 Use a linear approximation (or differentials) to estimate the given number.

15. $(2.001)^5$

16. $e^{-0.015}$

17. $(8.06)^{2/3}$

18. $1/1002$

19–21 Explain, in terms of linear approximations or differentials, why the approximation is reasonable.

19. $\sec 0.08 \approx 1$

20. $(1.01)^6 \approx 1.06$

21. $\ln 1.05 \approx 0.05$

22. Let
$$f(x) = (x-1)^2 \qquad g(x) = e^{-2x}$$
and
$$h(x) = 1 + \ln(1-2x)$$

(a) Find the linearizations of f, g, and h at $a = 0$. What do you notice? How do you explain what happened?

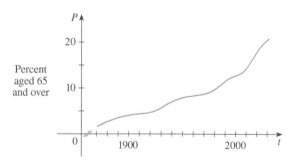 Graphing calculator or computer with graphing software required   **1.** Homework Hints available in TEC

(b) Graph f, g, and h and their linear approximations. For which function is the linear approximation best? For which is it worst? Explain.

23–24 Find the differential of each function.

23. (a) $y = \dfrac{u+1}{u-1}$ 　　　　　　(b) $y = (1 + r^3)^{-2}$

24. (a) $y = e^{\tan \pi t}$ 　　　　　　(b) $y = \sqrt{1 + \ln z}$

25. Let $y = e^{x/10}$.
(a) Find the differential dy.
(b) Evaluate dy and Δy if $x = 0$ and $dx = 0.1$.

26. Let $y = \sqrt{x}$.
(a) Find the differential dy.
(b) Evaluate dy and Δy if $x = 1$ and $dx = \Delta x = 1$.
(c) Sketch a diagram like Figure 6 showing the line segments with lengths dx, dy, and Δy.

27. The edge of a cube was found to be 30 cm with a possible error in measurement of 0.1 cm. Use differentials to estimate the maximum possible error, relative error, and percentage error in computing (a) the volume of the cube and (b) the surface area of the cube.

28. The radius of a circular disk is given as 24 cm with a maximum error in measurement of 0.2 cm.
(a) Use differentials to estimate the maximum error in the calculated area of the disk.
(b) What is the relative error? What is the percentage error?

29. The circumference of a sphere was measured to be 84 cm with a possible error of 0.5 cm.
(a) Use differentials to estimate the maximum error in the calculated surface area. What is the relative error?
(b) Use differentials to estimate the maximum error in the calculated volume. What is the relative error?

30. Use differentials to estimate the amount of paint needed to apply a coat of paint 0.05 cm thick to a hemispherical dome with diameter 50 m.

31. (a) Use differentials to find a formula for the approximate volume of a thin cylindrical shell with height h, inner radius r, and thickness Δr.
(b) What is the error involved in using the formula from part (a)?

32. One side of a right triangle is known to be 20 cm long and the opposite angle is measured as 30°, with a possible error of $\pm 1°$.
(a) Use differentials to estimate the error in computing the length of the hypotenuse.
(b) What is the percentage error?

33. When blood flows along a blood vessel, the flux F (the volume of blood per unit time that flows past a given point) is proportional to the fourth power of the radius R of the blood vessel:

$$F = kR^4$$

(This is known as Poiseuille's Law; we will show why it is true in Section 6.7.) A partially clogged artery can be expanded by an operation called angioplasty, in which a balloon-tipped catheter is inflated inside the artery in order to widen it and restore the normal blood flow.

Show that the relative change in F is about four times the relative change in R. How will a 5% increase in the radius affect the flow of blood?

34. On page 431 of *Physics: Calculus,* 2d ed., by Eugene Hecht (Pacific Grove, CA, 2000), in the course of deriving the formula $T = 2\pi\sqrt{L/g}$ for the period of a pendulum of length L, the author obtains the equation $a_T = -g \sin \theta$ for the tangential acceleration of the bob of the pendulum. He then says, "for small angles, the value of θ in radians is very nearly the value of $\sin \theta$; they differ by less than 2% out to about 20°."
(a) Verify the linear approximation at 0 for the sine function:

$$\sin x \approx x$$

(b) Use a graphing device to determine the values of x for which $\sin x$ and x differ by less than 2%. Then verify Hecht's statement by converting from radians to degrees.

35. Suppose that the only information we have about a function f is that $f(1) = 5$ and the graph of its *derivative* is as shown.
(a) Use a linear approximation to estimate $f(0.9)$ and $f(1.1)$.
(b) Are your estimates in part (a) too large or too small? Explain.

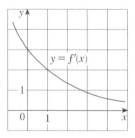

36. Suppose that we don't have a formula for $g(x)$ but we know that $g(2) = -4$ and $g'(x) = \sqrt{x^2 + 5}$ for all x.
(a) Use a linear approximation to estimate $g(1.95)$ and $g(2.05)$.
(b) Are your estimates in part (a) too large or too small? Explain.

LABORATORY PROJECT ◰ **Taylor Polynomials**

The tangent line approximation $L(x)$ is the best first-degree (linear) approximation to $f(x)$ near $x = a$ because $f(x)$ and $L(x)$ have the same rate of change (derivative) at a. For a better approximation than a linear one, let's try a second-degree (quadratic) approximation $P(x)$. In other words, we approximate a curve by a parabola instead of by a straight line. To make sure that the approximation is a good one, we stipulate the following:

    (i) $P(a) = f(a)$ (P and f should have the same value at a.)

    (ii) $P'(a) = f'(a)$ (P and f should have the same rate of change at a.)

    (iii) $P''(a) = f''(a)$ (The slopes of P and f should change at the same rate at a.)

1. Find the quadratic approximation $P(x) = A + Bx + Cx^2$ to the function $f(x) = \cos x$ that satisfies conditions (i), (ii), and (iii) with $a = 0$. Graph P, f, and the linear approximation $L(x) = 1$ on a common screen. Comment on how well the functions P and L approximate f.

2. Determine the values of x for which the quadratic approximation $f(x) \approx P(x)$ in Problem 1 is accurate to within 0.1. [*Hint:* Graph $y = P(x)$, $y = \cos x - 0.1$, and $y = \cos x + 0.1$ on a common screen.]

3. To approximate a function f by a quadratic function P near a number a, it is best to write P in the form

$$P(x) = A + B(x - a) + C(x - a)^2$$

Show that the quadratic function that satisfies conditions (i), (ii), and (iii) is

$$P(x) = f(a) + f'(a)(x - a) + \tfrac{1}{2}f''(a)(x - a)^2$$

4. Find the quadratic approximation to $f(x) = \sqrt{x + 3}$ near $a = 1$. Graph f, the quadratic approximation, and the linear approximation from Example 3 in Section 3.9 on a common screen. What do you conclude?

5. Instead of being satisfied with a linear or quadratic approximation to $f(x)$ near $x = a$, let's try to find better approximations with higher-degree polynomials. We look for an nth-degree polynomial

$$T_n(x) = c_0 + c_1(x - a) + c_2(x - a)^2 + c_3(x - a)^3 + \cdots + c_n(x - a)^n$$

such that T_n and its first n derivatives have the same values at $x = a$ as f and its first n derivatives. By differentiating repeatedly and setting $x = a$, show that these conditions are satisfied if $c_0 = f(a)$, $c_1 = f'(a)$, $c_2 = \tfrac{1}{2}f''(a)$, and in general

$$c_k = \frac{f^{(k)}(a)}{k!}$$

where $k! = 1 \cdot 2 \cdot 3 \cdot 4 \cdot \cdots \cdot k$. The resulting polynomial

$$T_n(x) = f(a) + f'(a)(x - a) + \frac{f''(a)}{2!}(x - a)^2 + \cdots + \frac{f^{(n)}(a)}{n!}(x - a)^n$$

is called the ***n*th-degree Taylor polynomial of f centered at a.**

6. Find the 8th-degree Taylor polynomial centered at $a = 0$ for the function $f(x) = \cos x$. Graph f together with the Taylor polynomials T_2, T_4, T_6, T_8 in the viewing rectangle $[-5, 5]$ by $[-1.4, 1.4]$ and comment on how well they approximate f.

◰ Graphing calculator or computer with graphing software required

3   Review

Concept Check

1. State each differentiation rule both in symbols and in words.
   (a) The Power Rule   (b) The Constant Multiple Rule
   (c) The Sum Rule   (d) The Difference Rule
   (e) The Product Rule   (f) The Quotient Rule
   (g) The Chain Rule

2. State the derivative of each function.
   (a) $y = x^n$ (b) $y = e^x$ (c) $y = a^x$
   (d) $y = \ln x$ (e) $y = \log_a x$ (f) $y = \sin x$
   (g) $y = \cos x$ (h) $y = \tan x$ (i) $y = \csc x$
   (j) $y = \sec x$ (k) $y = \cot x$ (l) $y = \sin^{-1} x$
   (m) $y = \cos^{-1} x$ (n) $y = \tan^{-1} x$

3. (a) How is the number e defined?
   (b) Express e as a limit.

(c) Why is the natural exponential function $y = e^x$ used more often in calculus than the other exponential functions $y = a^x$?
(d) Why is the natural logarithmic function $y = \ln x$ used more often in calculus than the other logarithmic functions $y = \log_a x$?

4. (a) Explain how implicit differentiation works. When should you use it?
   (b) Explain how logarithmic differentiation works. When should you use it?

5. How do you find the slope of a tangent line to a parametric curve $x = f(t)$, $y = g(t)$?

6. Write an expression for the linearization of f at a.

True-False Quiz

Determine whether the statement is true or false. If it is true, explain why. If it is false, explain why or give an example that disproves the statement.

1. If f and g are differentiable, then
$$\frac{d}{dx}[f(x) + g(x)] = f'(x) + g'(x)$$

2. If f and g are differentiable, then
$$\frac{d}{dx}[f(x)g(x)] = f'(x)g'(x)$$

3. If f and g are differentiable, then
$$\frac{d}{dx}[f(g(x))] = f'(g(x))g'(x)$$

4. If f is differentiable, then $\dfrac{d}{dx}\sqrt{f(x)} = \dfrac{f'(x)}{2\sqrt{f(x)}}$.

5. If f is differentiable, then $\dfrac{d}{dx}f(\sqrt{x}) = \dfrac{f'(x)}{2\sqrt{x}}$.

6. If $y = e^2$, then $y' = 2e$.

7. $\dfrac{d}{dx}(10^x) = x10^{x-1}$

8. $\dfrac{d}{dx}(\ln 10) = \dfrac{1}{10}$

9. $\dfrac{d}{dx}(\tan^2 x) = \dfrac{d}{dx}(\sec^2 x)$

10. $\dfrac{d}{dx}|x^2 + x| = |2x + 1|$

11. If $g(x) = x^5$, then $\displaystyle\lim_{x \to 2}\dfrac{g(x) - g(2)}{x - 2} = 80$.

12. An equation of the tangent line to the parabola $y = x^2$ at $(-2, 4)$ is $y - 4 = 2x(x + 2)$.

Exercises

1–36 Calculate y'.

1. $y = (x^4 - 3x^2 + 5)^3$

2. $y = \cos(\tan x)$

3. $y = \sqrt{x} + \dfrac{1}{\sqrt[3]{x^4}}$

4. $y = \dfrac{3x - 2}{\sqrt{2x + 1}}$

5. $y = 2x\sqrt{x^2 + 1}$

6. $y = \dfrac{e^x}{1 + x^2}$

7. $y = e^{\sin 2\theta}$

8. $y = e^{-t}(t^2 - 2t + 2)$

9. $y = \dfrac{t}{1 - t^2}$

10. $y = e^{mx}\cos nx$

11. $y = \dfrac{e^{1/x}}{x^2}$

12. $y = (\arcsin 2x)^2$

13. $xy^4 + x^2 y = x + 3y$

14. $y = \ln(\csc 5x)$

15. $y = \dfrac{\sec 2\theta}{1 + \tan 2\theta}$

16. $x^2 \cos y + \sin 2y = xy$

⌨ Graphing calculator or computer with graphing software required

17. $y = e^{cx}(c \sin x - \cos x)$

18. $y = \ln(x^2 e^x)$

19. $y = \log_5(1 + 2x)$

20. $y = (\ln x)^{\cos x}$

21. $\sin(xy) = x^2 - y$

22. $y = \sqrt{t \ln(t^4)}$

23. $y = 3^{x \ln x}$

24. $xe^y = y - 1$

25. $y = \ln \sin x - \frac{1}{2} \sin^2 x$

26. $y = \dfrac{(x^2 + 1)^4}{(2x + 1)^3(3x - 1)^5}$

27. $y = x \tan^{-1}(4x)$

28. $y = e^{\cos x} + \cos(e^x)$

29. $y = \ln|\sec 5x + \tan 5x|$

30. $y = 10^{\tan \pi\theta}$

31. $y = \tan^2(\sin \theta)$

32. $y = \ln \left| \dfrac{x^2 - 4}{2x + 5} \right|$

33. $y = \sin(\tan \sqrt{1 + x^3})$

34. $y = \arctan(\arcsin \sqrt{x})$

35. $y = \cos(e^{\sqrt{\tan 3x}})$

36. $y = \sin^2(\cos \sqrt{\sin \pi x})$

---

37. If $f(t) = \sqrt{4t + 1}$, find $f''(2)$.

38. If $g(\theta) = \theta \sin \theta$, find $g''(\pi/6)$.

39. If $f(x) = 2^x$, find $f^{(n)}(x)$.

40. Find y'' if $x^6 + y^6 = 1$.

41–44 Find an equation of the tangent to the curve at the given point.

41. $y = 4 \sin^2 x$, $(\pi/6, 1)$

42. $y = \dfrac{x^2 - 1}{x^2 + 1}$, $(0, -1)$

43. $x = \ln t$, $y = t^2 + 1$, $(0, 2)$

44. $x = t^3 - 2t^2 + t + 1$, $y = t^2 + t$, $(1, 0)$

45–46 Find equations of the tangent line and normal line to the curve at the given point.

45. $y = (2 + x)e^{-x}$, $(0, 2)$

46. $x^2 + 4xy + y^2 = 13$, $(2, 1)$

---

47. (a) If $f(x) = x\sqrt{5 - x}$, find $f'(x)$.
  (b) Find equations of the tangent lines to the curve $y = x\sqrt{5 - x}$ at the points $(1, 2)$ and $(4, 4)$.
  (c) Illustrate part (b) by graphing the curve and tangent lines on the same screen.
  (d) Check to see that your answer to part (a) is reasonable by comparing the graphs of f and f'.

48. (a) If $f(x) = 4x - \tan x$, $-\pi/2 < x < \pi/2$, find f' and f''.
  (b) Check to see that your answers to part (a) are reasonable by comparing the graphs of f, f', and f''.

49. If $f(x) = xe^{\sin x}$, find $f'(x)$. Graph f and f' on the same screen and comment.

50. (a) Graph the function $f(x) = x - 2 \sin x$ in the viewing rectangle $[0, 8]$ by $[-2, 8]$.
  (b) On which interval is the average rate of change larger: $[1, 2]$ or $[2, 3]$?

(c) At which value of x is the instantaneous rate of change larger: $x = 2$ or $x = 5$?
(d) Check your visual estimates in part (c) by computing $f'(x)$ and comparing the numerical values of $f'(2)$ and $f'(5)$.

51. Suppose that $h(x) = f(x)g(x)$ and $F(x) = f(g(x))$, where $f(2) = 3$, $g(2) = 5$, $g'(2) = 4$, $f'(2) = -2$, and $f'(5) = 11$. Find (a) $h'(2)$ and (b) $F'(2)$.

52. If f and g are the functions whose graphs are shown, let $P(x) = f(x)g(x)$, $Q(x) = f(x)/g(x)$, and $C(x) = f(g(x))$. Find (a) $P'(2)$, (b) $Q'(2)$, and (c) $C'(2)$.

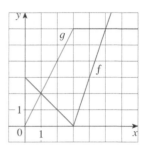

53–60 Find f' in terms of g'.

53. $f(x) = x^2 g(x)$

54. $f(x) = g(x^2)$

55. $f(x) = [g(x)]^2$

56. $f(x) = g(g(x))$

57. $f(x) = g(e^x)$

58. $f(x) = e^{g(x)}$

59. $f(x) = \ln|g(x)|$

60. $f(x) = g(\ln x)$

61–62 Find h' in terms of f' and g'.

61. $h(x) = \dfrac{f(x)g(x)}{f(x) + g(x)}$

62. $h(x) = f(g(\sin 4x))$

---

63. At what point on the curve $y = [\ln(x + 4)]^2$ is the tangent horizontal?

64. (a) Find an equation of the tangent to the curve $y = e^x$ that is parallel to the line $x - 4y = 1$.
  (b) Find an equation of the tangent to the curve $y = e^x$ that passes through the origin.

65. Find the points on the ellipse $x^2 + 2y^2 = 1$ where the tangent line has slope 1.

66. (a) On what interval is the function $f(x) = (\ln x)/x$ increasing?
  (b) On what interval is f concave upward?

67. Find a parabola $y = ax^2 + bx + c$ that passes through the point $(1, 4)$ and whose tangent lines at $x = -1$ and $x = 5$ have slopes 6 and -2, respectively.

68. A particle moves on a vertical line so that its coordinate at time t is $y = t^3 - 12t + 3$, $t \geq 0$.
  (a) Find the velocity and acceleration functions.
  (b) When is the particle moving upward and when is it moving downward?

(c) Find the distance that the particle travels in the time interval $0 \leqslant t \leqslant 3$.

(d) Graph the position, velocity, and acceleration functions for $0 \leqslant t \leqslant 3$.

(e) When is the particle speeding up? When is it slowing down?

69. An equation of motion of the form $s = Ae^{-ct}\cos(\omega t + \delta)$ represents damped oscillation of an object. Find the velocity and acceleration of the object.

70. A particle moves along a horizontal line so that its coordinate at time t is $x = \sqrt{b^2 + c^2 t^2}$, $t \geqslant 0$, where b and c are positive constants.

(a) Find the velocity and acceleration functions.

(b) Show that the particle always moves in the positive direction.

71. The mass of part of a wire is $x\left(1 + \sqrt{x}\,\right)$ kilograms, where x is measured in meters from one end of the wire. Find the linear density of the wire when $x = 4$ m.

72. The volume of a right circular cone is $V = \frac{1}{3}\pi r^2 h$, where r is the radius of the base and h is the height.

(a) Find the rate of change of the volume with respect to the height if the radius is constant.

(b) Find the rate of change of the volume with respect to the radius if the height is constant.

73. The cost, in dollars, of producing x units of a certain commodity is

$$C(x) = 920 + 2x - 0.02x^2 + 0.00007x^3$$

(a) Find the marginal cost function.

(b) Find $C'(100)$ and explain its meaning.

(c) Compare $C'(100)$ with the cost of producing the 101st item.

(d) For what value of x does C have an inflection point? What is the significance of this value of x?

74. The function $C(t) = K(e^{-at} - e^{-bt})$, where a, b, and K are positive constants and $b > a$, is used to model the concentration at time t of a drug injected into the bloodstream.

(a) Show that $\lim_{t \to \infty} C(t) = 0$.

(b) Find $C'(t)$, the rate at which the drug is cleared from circulation.

(c) When is this rate equal to 0?

75. (a) Find the linearization of $f(x) = \sqrt[3]{1 + 3x}$ at $a = 0$. State the corresponding linear approximation and use it to give an approximate value for $\sqrt[3]{1.03}$.

(b) Determine the values of x for which the linear approximation given in part (a) is accurate to within 0.1.

76. A window has the shape of a square surmounted by a semicircle. The base of the window is measured as having width 60 cm with a possible error in measurement of 0.1 cm. Use differentials to estimate the maximum error possible in computing the area of the window.

77. Express the limit

$$\lim_{\theta \to \pi/3} \frac{\cos \theta - 0.5}{\theta - \pi/3}$$

as a derivative and thus evaluate it.

78. Find $f'(x)$ if it is known that

$$\frac{d}{dx}[f(2x)] = x^2$$

79. Evaluate $\lim_{x \to 0} \dfrac{\sqrt{1 + \tan x} - \sqrt{1 + \sin x}}{x^3}$.

80. Show that the length of the portion of any tangent line to the astroid $x^{2/3} + y^{2/3} = a^{2/3}$ cut off by the coordinate axes is constant.

Focus on Problem Solving

Before you look at the solution of the following example, cover it up and first try to solve the problem yourself. It might help to consult the principles of problem solving on page 83.

EXAMPLE For what values of c does the equation $\ln x = cx^2$ have exactly one solution?

SOLUTION One of the most important principles of problem solving is to draw a diagram, even if the problem as stated doesn't explicitly mention a geometric situation. Our present problem can be reformulated geometrically as follows: For what values of c does the curve $y = \ln x$ intersect the curve $y = cx^2$ in exactly one point?

Let's start by graphing $y = \ln x$ and $y = cx^2$ for various values of c. We know that, for $c \neq 0$, $y = cx^2$ is a parabola that opens upward if $c > 0$ and downward if $c < 0$. Figure 1 shows the parabolas $y = cx^2$ for several positive values of c. Most of them don't intersect $y = \ln x$ at all and one intersects twice. We have the feeling that there must be a value of c (somewhere between 0.1 and 0.3) for which the curves intersect exactly once, as in Figure 2.

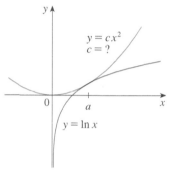

FIGURE 1

FIGURE 2

To find that particular value of c, we let a be the x-coordinate of the single point of intersection. In other words, $\ln a = ca^2$, so a is the unique solution of the given equation. We see from Figure 2 that the curves just touch, so they have a common tangent line when $x = a$. That means the curves $y = \ln x$ and $y = cx^2$ have the same slope when $x = a$. Therefore

$$\frac{1}{a} = 2ca$$

Solving the equations $\ln a = ca^2$ and $1/a = 2ca$, we get

$$\ln a = ca^2 = c \cdot \frac{1}{2c} = \frac{1}{2}$$

Thus $a = e^{1/2}$ and

$$c = \frac{\ln a}{a^2} = \frac{\ln e^{1/2}}{e} = \frac{1}{2e}$$

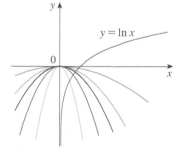

FIGURE 3

For negative values of c we have the situation illustrated in Figure 3: All parabolas $y = cx^2$ with negative values of c intersect $y = \ln x$ exactly once. And let's not forget about $c = 0$: The curve $y = 0x^2 = 0$ is just the x-axis, which intersects $y = \ln x$ exactly once.

To summarize, the required values of c are $c = 1/(2e)$ and $c \leq 0$.

1. The figure shows a circle with radius 1 inscribed in the parabola $y = x^2$. Find the center of the circle.

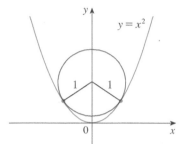

2. Find the point where the curves $y = x^3 - 3x + 4$ and $y = 3(x^2 - x)$ are tangent to each other, that is, have a common tangent line. Illustrate by sketching both curves and the common tangent.

3. Show that the tangent lines to the parabola $y = ax^2 + bx + c$ at any two points with x-coordinates p and q must intersect at a point whose x-coordinate is halfway between p and q.

4. Show that

$$\frac{d}{dx}\left(\frac{\sin^2 x}{1 + \cot x} + \frac{\cos^2 x}{1 + \tan x}\right) = -\cos 2x$$

5. If $f(x) = \lim\limits_{t \to x} \dfrac{\sec t - \sec x}{t - x}$, find the value of $f'(\pi/4)$.

6. If f is differentiable at a, where $a > 0$, evaluate the following limit in terms of $f'(a)$:

$$\lim_{x \to a} \frac{f(x) - f(a)}{\sqrt{x} - \sqrt{a}}$$

7. The figure shows a rotating wheel with radius 40 cm and a connecting rod AP with length 1.2 m. The pin P slides back and forth along the x-axis as the wheel rotates counterclockwise at a rate of 360 revolutions per minute.
  (a) Find the angular velocity of the connecting rod, $d\alpha/dt$, in radians per second, when $\theta = \pi/3$.
  (b) Express the distance $x = |OP|$ in terms of θ.
  (c) Find an expression for the velocity of the pin P in terms of θ.

8. Tangent lines T_1 and T_2 are drawn at two points P_1 and P_2 on the parabola $y = x^2$ and they intersect at a point P. Another tangent line T is drawn at a point between P_1 and P_2; it intersects T_1 at Q_1 and T_2 at Q_2. Show that

$$\frac{|PQ_1|}{|PP_1|} + \frac{|PQ_2|}{|PP_2|} = 1$$

9. Show that

$$\frac{d^n}{dx^n}(e^{ax} \sin bx) = r^n e^{ax} \sin(bx + n\theta)$$

where a and b are positive numbers, $r^2 = a^2 + b^2$, and $\theta = \tan^{-1}(b/a)$.

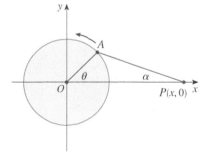

FIGURE FOR PROBLEM 7

---

10. Find the values of the constants a and b such that

$$\lim_{x \to 0} \frac{\sqrt[3]{ax + b} - 2}{x} = \frac{5}{12}$$

11. Let T and N be the tangent and normal lines to the ellipse $x^2/9 + y^2/4 = 1$ at any point P on the ellipse in the first quadrant. Let x_T and y_T be the x- and y-intercepts of T and x_N and y_N be the intercepts of N. As P moves along the ellipse in the first quadrant (but not on the axes), what values can x_T, y_T, x_N, and y_N take on? First try to guess the answers just by looking at the figure. Then use calculus to solve the problem and see how good your intuition is.

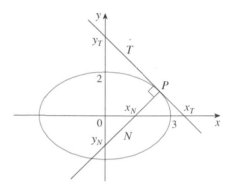

12. If f and g are differentiable functions with $f(0) = g(0) = 0$ and $g'(0) \neq 0$, show that

$$\lim_{x \to 0} \frac{f(x)}{g(x)} = \frac{f'(0)}{g'(0)}$$

13. If

$$y = \frac{x}{\sqrt{a^2 - 1}} - \frac{2}{\sqrt{a^2 - 1}} \arctan \frac{\sin x}{a + \sqrt{a^2 - 1} + \cos x}$$

show that $y' = \dfrac{1}{a + \cos x}$.

14. For which positive numbers a is it true that $a^x \geqslant 1 + x$ for all x?

15. For what value of k does the equation $e^{2x} = k\sqrt{x}$ have exactly one solution?

CAS 16. (a) The cubic function $f(x) = x(x - 2)(x - 6)$ has three distinct zeros: 0, 2, and 6. Graph f and its tangent lines at the *average* of each pair of zeros. What do you notice?
   (b) Suppose the cubic function $f(x) = (x - a)(x - b)(x - c)$ has three distinct zeros: a, b, and c. Prove, with the help of a computer algebra system, that a tangent line drawn at the average of the zeros a and b intersects the graph of f at the third zero.

17. (a) Use the identity for $\tan(x - y)$ (see Equation 14b in Appendix C) to show that if two lines L_1 and L_2 intersect at an angle α, then

$$\tan \alpha = \frac{m_2 - m_1}{1 + m_1 m_2}$$

where m_1 and m_2 are the slopes of L_1 and L_2, respectively.
   (b) The **angle between the curves** C_1 and C_2 at a point of intersection P is defined to be the angle between the tangent lines to C_1 and C_2 at P (if these tangent lines exist). Use part (a) to find, correct to the nearest degree, the angle between each pair of curves at each point of intersection.
     (i) $y = x^2$ and $y = (x - 2)^2$
     (ii) $x^2 - y^2 = 3$ and $x^2 - 4x + y^2 + 3 = 0$

18. Let $P(x_1, y_1)$ be a point on the parabola $y^2 = 4px$ with focus $F(p, 0)$. Let α be the angle between the parabola and the line segment FP, and let β be the angle between the horizontal line $y = y_1$ and the parabola as in the figure. Prove that $\alpha = \beta$. (Thus, by a principle of geometrical optics, light from a source placed at F will be reflected along a line parallel to the x-axis. This explains why *paraboloids*, the surfaces obtained by rotating parabolas about their axes, are used as the shape of some automobile headlights and mirrors for telescopes.)

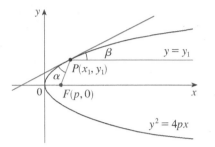

19. Suppose that we replace the parabolic mirror of Problem 18 by a spherical mirror. Although the mirror has no focus, we can show the existence of an *approximate* focus. In the figure, C is a semicircle with center O. A ray of light coming in toward the mirror parallel to the axis along the line PQ will be reflected to the point R on the axis so that $\angle PQO = \angle OQR$ (the angle of incidence is equal to the angle of reflection). What happens to the point R as P is taken closer and closer to the axis?

20. Given an ellipse $x^2/a^2 + y^2/b^2 = 1$, where $a \neq b$, find the equation of the set of all points from which there are two tangents to the curve whose slopes are (a) reciprocals and (b) negative reciprocals.

21. Find the two points on the curve $y = x^4 - 2x^2 - x$ that have a common tangent line.

22. Suppose that three points on the parabola $y = x^2$ have the property that their normal lines intersect at a common point. Show that the sum of their x-coordinates is 0.

23. A *lattice point* in the plane is a point with integer coordinates. Suppose that circles with radius r are drawn using all lattice points as centers. Find the smallest value of r such that any line with slope $\frac{2}{5}$ intersects some of these circles.

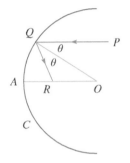

FIGURE FOR PROBLEM 19

Applications of Differentiation

4

We have already investigated some of the applications of derivatives, but now that we know the differentiation rules we are in a better position to pursue the applications of differentiation in greater depth. We show how to analyze the behavior of families of functions, how to solve related rates problems (how to calculate rates that we can't measure from those that we can), and how to find the maximum or minimum value of a quantity. In particular, we will be able to investigate the optimal shape of a can and to explain the location of rainbows in the sky.

4.1 Related Rates

If we are pumping air into a balloon, both the volume and the radius of the balloon are increasing and their rates of increase are related to each other. But it is much easier to measure directly the rate of increase of the volume than the rate of increase of the radius.

In a related rates problem the idea is to compute the rate of change of one quantity in terms of the rate of change of another quantity (which may be more easily measured). The procedure is to find an equation that relates the two quantities and then use the Chain Rule to differentiate both sides with respect to time.

V   EXAMPLE 1   Inflating a balloon   Air is being pumped into a spherical balloon so that its volume increases at a rate of 100 cm³/s. How fast is the radius of the balloon increasing when the diameter is 50 cm?

SOLUTION   We start by identifying two things:

the *given information:*

the rate of increase of the volume of air is 100 cm³/s

and the *unknown:*

the rate of increase of the radius when the diameter is 50 cm

In order to express these quantities mathematically, we introduce some suggestive *notation:*

Let V be the volume of the balloon and let r be its radius.

The key thing to remember is that rates of change are derivatives. In this problem, the volume and the radius are both functions of the time t. The rate of increase of the volume with respect to time is the derivative dV/dt, and the rate of increase of the radius is dr/dt. We can therefore restate the given and the unknown as follows:

$$\text{Given:} \qquad \frac{dV}{dt} = 100 \text{ cm}^3/\text{s}$$

$$\text{Unknown:} \qquad \frac{dr}{dt} \quad \text{when } r = 25 \text{ cm}$$

In order to connect dV/dt and dr/dt, we first relate V and r by the formula for the volume of a sphere:

$$V = \tfrac{4}{3}\pi r^3$$

In order to use the given information, we differentiate each side of this equation with respect to t. To differentiate the right side, we need to use the Chain Rule:

$$\frac{dV}{dt} = \frac{dV}{dr}\frac{dr}{dt} = 4\pi r^2 \frac{dr}{dt}$$

Now we solve for the unknown quantity:

$$\frac{dr}{dt} = \frac{1}{4\pi r^2}\frac{dV}{dt}$$

PS   According to the Principles of Problem Solving discussed on page 83, the first step is to understand the problem. This includes reading the problem carefully, identifying the given and the unknown, and introducing suitable notation.

PS   The second stage of problem solving is to think of a plan for connecting the given and the unknown.

Notice that, although dV/dt is constant, dr/dt is *not* constant.

SECTION 4.1 RELATED RATES 257

If we put $r = 25$ and $dV/dt = 100$ in this equation, we obtain

$$\frac{dr}{dt} = \frac{1}{4\pi(25)^2}\,100 = \frac{1}{25\pi}$$

The radius of the balloon is increasing at the rate of $1/(25\pi) \approx 0.0127$ cm/s.

EXAMPLE 2   **The sliding ladder problem**   A ladder 10 ft long rests against a vertical wall. If the bottom of the ladder slides away from the wall at a rate of 1 ft/s, how fast is the top of the ladder sliding down the wall when the bottom of the ladder is 6 ft from the wall?

SOLUTION   We first draw a diagram and label it as in Figure 1. Let x feet be the distance from the bottom of the ladder to the wall and y feet the distance from the top of the ladder to the ground. Note that x and y are both functions of t (time, measured in seconds).

We are given that $dx/dt = 1$ ft/s and we are asked to find dy/dt when $x = 6$ ft (see Figure 2). In this problem, the relationship between x and y is given by the Pythagorean Theorem:

$$x^2 + y^2 = 100$$

Differentiating each side with respect to t using the Chain Rule, we have

$$2x\frac{dx}{dt} + 2y\frac{dy}{dt} = 0$$

and solving this equation for the desired rate, we obtain

$$\frac{dy}{dt} = -\frac{x}{y}\frac{dx}{dt}$$

When $x = 6$, the Pythagorean Theorem gives $y = 8$ and so, substituting these values and $dx/dt = 1$, we have

$$\frac{dy}{dt} = -\frac{6}{8}(1) = -\frac{3}{4} \text{ ft/s}$$

The fact that dy/dt is negative means that the distance from the top of the ladder to the ground is *decreasing* at a rate of $\frac{3}{4}$ ft/s. In other words, the top of the ladder is sliding down the wall at a rate of $\frac{3}{4}$ ft/s.

EXAMPLE 3   **Filling a tank**   A water tank has the shape of an inverted circular cone with base radius 2 m and height 4 m. If water is being pumped into the tank at a rate of 2 m³/min, find the rate at which the water level is rising when the water is 3 m deep.

SOLUTION   We first sketch the cone and label it as in Figure 3. Let V, r, and h be the volume of the water, the radius of the surface, and the height of the water at time t, where t is measured in minutes.

We are given that $dV/dt = 2$ m³/min and we are asked to find dh/dt when h is 3 m. The quantities V and h are related by the equation

$$V = \tfrac{1}{3}\pi r^2 h$$

but it is very useful to express V as a function of h alone. In order to eliminate r, we use the similar triangles in Figure 3 to write

$$\frac{r}{h} = \frac{2}{4} \qquad r = \frac{h}{2}$$

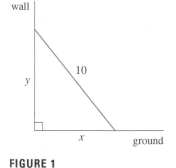

wall

y

10

x

ground

FIGURE 1

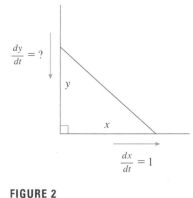

$\frac{dy}{dt} = ?$

y

x

$\frac{dx}{dt} = 1$

FIGURE 2

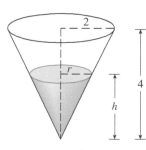

2

r

4

h

FIGURE 3

and the expression for V becomes

$$V = \frac{1}{3}\pi\left(\frac{h}{2}\right)^2 h = \frac{\pi}{12}h^3$$

Now we can differentiate each side with respect to t:

$$\frac{dV}{dt} = \frac{\pi}{4}h^2\frac{dh}{dt}$$

so

$$\frac{dh}{dt} = \frac{4}{\pi h^2}\frac{dV}{dt}$$

Substituting $h = 3$ m and $dV/dt = 2$ m³/min, we have

$$\frac{dh}{dt} = \frac{4}{\pi(3)^2}\cdot 2 = \frac{8}{9\pi}$$

The water level is rising at a rate of $8/(9\pi) \approx 0.28$ m/min.

PS Look back: What have we learned from Examples 1–3 that will help us solve future problems?

⊘ **Warning:** A common error is to substitute the given numerical information (for quantities that vary with time) too early. This should be done only *after* the differentiation. (Step 7 follows Step 6.) For instance, in Example 3 we dealt with general values of h until we finally substituted $h = 3$ at the last stage. (If we had put $h = 3$ earlier, we would have gotten $dV/dt = 0$, which is clearly wrong.)

Problem Solving Strategy   It is useful to recall some of the problem-solving principles from page 83 and adapt them to related rates in light of our experience in Examples 1–3:

1. Read the problem carefully.

2. Draw a diagram if possible.

3. Introduce notation. Assign symbols to all quantities that are functions of time.

4. Express the given information and the required rate in terms of derivatives.

5. Write an equation that relates the various quantities of the problem. If necessary, use the geometry of the situation to eliminate one of the variables by substitution (as in Example 3).

6. Use the Chain Rule to differentiate both sides of the equation with respect to t.

7. Substitute the given information into the resulting equation and solve for the unknown rate.

The following examples are further illustrations of the strategy.

▼ **EXAMPLE 4**   Car A is traveling west at 50 mi/h and car B is traveling north at 60 mi/h. Both are headed for the intersection of the two roads. At what rate are the cars approaching each other when car A is 0.3 mi and car B is 0.4 mi from the intersection?

SOLUTION We draw Figure 4, where C is the intersection of the roads. At a given time t, let x be the distance from car A to C, let y be the distance from car B to C, and let z be the distance between the cars, where x, y, and z are measured in miles.

We are given that $dx/dt = -50$ mi/h and $dy/dt = -60$ mi/h. (The derivatives are negative because x and y are decreasing.) We are asked to find dz/dt. The equation that relates x, y, and z is given by the Pythagorean Theorem:

$$z^2 = x^2 + y^2$$

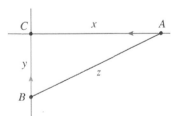

FIGURE 4

Differentiating each side with respect to t, we have

$$2z\frac{dz}{dt} = 2x\frac{dx}{dt} + 2y\frac{dy}{dt}$$

$$\frac{dz}{dt} = \frac{1}{z}\left(x\frac{dx}{dt} + y\frac{dy}{dt}\right)$$

When $x = 0.3$ mi and $y = 0.4$ mi, the Pythagorean Theorem gives $z = 0.5$ mi, so

$$\frac{dz}{dt} = \frac{1}{0.5}[0.3(-50) + 0.4(-60)]$$

$$= -78 \text{ mi/h}$$

The cars are approaching each other at a rate of 78 mi/h.

V **EXAMPLE 5** A man walks along a straight path at a speed of 4 ft/s. A searchlight is located on the ground 20 ft from the path and is kept focused on the man. At what rate is the searchlight rotating when the man is 15 ft from the point on the path closest to the searchlight?

SOLUTION We draw Figure 5 and let x be the distance from the man to the point on the path closest to the searchlight. We let θ be the angle between the beam of the searchlight and the perpendicular to the path.

We are given that $dx/dt = 4$ ft/s and are asked to find $d\theta/dt$ when $x = 15$. The equation that relates x and θ can be written from Figure 5:

$$\frac{x}{20} = \tan\theta \qquad x = 20\tan\theta$$

Differentiating each side with respect to t, we get

$$\frac{dx}{dt} = 20\sec^2\theta\frac{d\theta}{dt}$$

so

$$\frac{d\theta}{dt} = \frac{1}{20}\cos^2\theta\frac{dx}{dt}$$

$$= \frac{1}{20}\cos^2\theta\,(4) = \frac{1}{5}\cos^2\theta$$

When $x = 15$, the length of the beam is 25, so $\cos\theta = \frac{4}{5}$ and

$$\frac{d\theta}{dt} = \frac{1}{5}\left(\frac{4}{5}\right)^2 = \frac{16}{125} = 0.128$$

The searchlight is rotating at a rate of 0.128 rad/s.

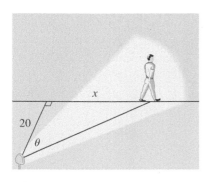

FIGURE 5

4.1 Exercises

1. If V is the volume of a cube with edge length x and the cube expands as time passes, find dV/dt in terms of dx/dt.

2. (a) If A is the area of a circle with radius r and the circle expands as time passes, find dA/dt in terms of dr/dt.
   (b) Suppose oil spills from a ruptured tanker and spreads in a circular pattern. If the radius of the oil spill increases at a constant rate of 1 m/s, how fast is the area of the spill increasing when the radius is 30 m?

3. Each side of a square is increasing at a rate of 6 cm/s. At what rate is the area of the square increasing when the area of the square is 16 cm²?

4. The length of a rectangle is increasing at a rate of 8 cm/s and its width is increasing at a rate of 3 cm/s. When the length is 20 cm and the width is 10 cm, how fast is the area of the rectangle increasing?

5. A cylindrical tank with radius 5 m is being filled with water at a rate of 3 m³/min. How fast is the height of the water increasing?

6. The radius of a sphere is increasing at a rate of 4 mm/s. How fast is the volume increasing when the diameter is 80 mm?

7. Suppose $y = \sqrt{2x + 1}$, where x and y are functions of t.
   (a) If $dx/dt = 3$, find dy/dt when $x = 4$.
   (b) If $dy/dt = 5$, find dx/dt when $x = 12$.

8. If $x^2 + y^2 = 25$ and $dy/dt = 6$, find dx/dt when $y = 4$.

9. If $z^2 = x^2 + y^2$, $dx/dt = 2$, and $dy/dt = 3$, find dz/dt when $x = 5$ and $y = 12$.

10. A particle moves along the curve $y = \sqrt{1 + x^3}$. As it reaches the point $(2, 3)$, the y-coordinate is increasing at a rate of 4 cm/s. How fast is the x-coordinate of the point changing at that instant?

11–14
(a) What quantities are given in the problem?
(b) What is the unknown?
(c) Draw a picture of the situation for any time t.
(d) Write an equation that relates the quantities.
(e) Finish solving the problem.

11. If a snowball melts so that its surface area decreases at a rate of 1 cm²/min, find the rate at which the diameter decreases when the diameter is 10 cm.

12. At noon, ship A is 150 km west of ship B. Ship A is sailing east at 35 km/h and ship B is sailing north at 25 km/h. How fast is the distance between the ships changing at 4:00 PM?

13. A plane flying horizontally at an altitude of 1 mi and a speed of 500 mi/h passes directly over a radar station. Find the rate at which the distance from the plane to the station is increasing when it is 2 mi away from the station.

14. A street light is mounted at the top of a 15-ft-tall pole. A man 6 ft tall walks away from the pole with a speed of 5 ft/s along a straight path. How fast is the tip of his shadow moving when he is 40 ft from the pole?

15. Two cars start moving from the same point. One travels south at 60 mi/h and the other travels west at 25 mi/h. At what rate is the distance between the cars increasing two hours later?

16. A spotlight on the ground shines on a wall 12 m away. If a man 2 m tall walks from the spotlight toward the building at a speed of 1.6 m/s, how fast is the length of his shadow on the building decreasing when he is 4 m from the building?

17. A man starts walking north at 4 ft/s from a point P. Five minutes later a woman starts walking south at 5 ft/s from a point 500 ft due east of P. At what rate are the people moving apart 15 min after the woman starts walking?

18. A baseball diamond is a square with side 90 ft. A batter hits the ball and runs toward first base with a speed of 24 ft/s.
   (a) At what rate is his distance from second base decreasing when he is halfway to first base?
   (b) At what rate is his distance from third base increasing at the same moment?

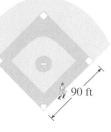

19. The altitude of a triangle is increasing at a rate of 1 cm/min while the area of the triangle is increasing at a rate of 2 cm²/min. At what rate is the base of the triangle changing when the altitude is 10 cm and the area is 100 cm²?

20. A boat is pulled into a dock by a rope attached to the bow of the boat and passing through a pulley on the dock that is 1 m higher than the bow of the boat. If the rope is pulled in at a rate of 1 m/s, how fast is the boat approaching the dock when it is 8 m from the dock?

21. At noon, ship A is 100 km west of ship B. Ship A is sailing south at 35 km/h and ship B is sailing north at 25 km/h. How fast is the distance between the ships changing at 4:00 PM?

---

22. A particle is moving along the curve $y = \sqrt{x}$. As the particle passes through the point $(4, 2)$, its x-coordinate increases at a rate of 3 cm/s. How fast is the distance from the particle to the origin changing at this instant?

23. The top of a ladder slides down a vertical wall at a rate of 0.15 m/s. At the moment when the bottom of the ladder is 3 m from the wall, it slides away from the wall at a rate of 0.2 m/s. How long is the ladder?

24. How fast is the angle between the ladder and the ground changing in Example 2 when the bottom of the ladder is 6 ft from the wall?

25. Two carts, A and B, are connected by a rope 39 ft long that passes over a pulley P (see the figure). The point Q is on the floor 12 ft directly beneath P and between the carts. Cart A is being pulled away from Q at a speed of 2 ft/s. How fast is cart B moving toward Q at the instant when cart A is 5 ft from Q?

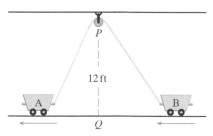

26. Water is leaking out of an inverted conical tank at a rate of 10,000 cm³/min at the same time that water is being pumped into the tank at a constant rate. The tank has height 6 m and the diameter at the top is 4 m. If the water level is rising at a rate of 20 cm/min when the height of the water is 2 m, find the rate at which water is being pumped into the tank.

27. A trough is 10 ft long and its ends have the shape of isosceles triangles that are 3 ft across at the top and have a height of 1 ft. If the trough is being filled with water at a rate of 12 ft³/min, how fast is the water level rising when the water is 6 inches deep?

28. A swimming pool is 20 ft wide, 40 ft long, 3 ft deep at the shallow end, and 9 ft deep at its deepest point. A cross-section is shown in the figure. If the pool is being filled at a rate of 0.8 ft³/min, how fast is the water level rising when the depth at the deepest point is 5 ft?

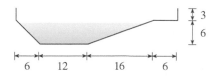

29. Gravel is being dumped from a conveyor belt at a rate of 30 ft³/min, and its coarseness is such that it forms a pile in the shape of a cone whose base diameter and height are always

equal. How fast is the height of the pile increasing when the pile is 10 ft high?

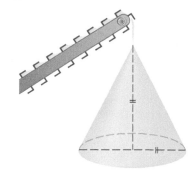

30. A kite 100 ft above the ground moves horizontally at a speed of 8 ft/s. At what rate is the angle between the string and the horizontal decreasing when 200 ft of string has been let out?

31. Two sides of a triangle are 4 m and 5 m in length and the angle between them is increasing at a rate of 0.06 rad/s. Find the rate at which the area of the triangle is increasing when the angle between the sides of fixed length is $\pi/3$.

32. Two sides of a triangle have lengths 12 m and 15 m. The angle between them is increasing at a rate of 2°/min. How fast is the length of the third side increasing when the angle between the sides of fixed length is 60°?

33. Boyle's Law states that when a sample of gas is compressed at a constant temperature, the pressure P and volume V satisfy the equation $PV = C$, where C is a constant. Suppose that at a certain instant the volume is 600 cm³, the pressure is 150 kPa, and the pressure is increasing at a rate of 20 kPa/min. At what rate is the volume decreasing at this instant?

34. When air expands adiabatically (without gaining or losing heat), its pressure P and volume V are related by the equation $PV^{1.4} = C$, where C is a constant. Suppose that at a certain instant the volume is 400 cm³ and the pressure is 80 kPa and is decreasing at a rate of 10 kPa/min. At what rate is the volume increasing at this instant?

35. If two resistors with resistances R_1 and R_2 are connected in parallel, as in the figure, then the total resistance R, measured in ohms (Ω), is given by

$$\frac{1}{R} = \frac{1}{R_1} + \frac{1}{R_2}$$

If R_1 and R_2 are increasing at rates of 0.3 Ω/s and 0.2 Ω/s, respectively, how fast is R changing when $R_1 = 80\ \Omega$ and $R_2 = 100\ \Omega$?

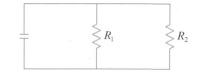

36. Brain weight B as a function of body weight W in fish has been modeled by the power function $B = 0.007W^{2/3}$, where B and W are measured in grams. A model for body weight as a function of body length L (measured in centimeters) is $W = 0.12L^{2.53}$. If, over 10 million years, the average length of a certain species of fish evolved from 15 cm to 20 cm at a constant rate, how fast was this species' brain growing when the average length was 18 cm?

37. A television camera is positioned 4000 ft from the base of a rocket launching pad. The angle of elevation of the camera has to change at the correct rate in order to keep the rocket in sight. Also, the mechanism for focusing the camera has to take into account the increasing distance from the camera to the rising rocket. Let's assume the rocket rises vertically and its speed is 600 ft/s when it has risen 3000 ft.

(a) How fast is the distance from the television camera to the rocket changing at that moment?

(b) If the television camera is always kept aimed at the rocket, how fast is the camera's angle of elevation changing at that same moment?

38. A lighthouse is located on a small island 3 km away from the nearest point P on a straight shoreline and its light makes four revolutions per minute. How fast is the beam of light moving along the shoreline when it is 1 km from P?

39. A plane flies horizontally at an altitude of 5 km and passes directly over a tracking telescope on the ground. When the angle of elevation is $\pi/3$, this angle is decreasing at a rate of $\pi/6$ rad/min. How fast is the plane traveling at that time?

40. A Ferris wheel with a radius of 10 m is rotating at a rate of one revolution every 2 minutes. How fast is a rider rising when his seat is 16 m above ground level?

41. A plane flying with a constant speed of 300 km/h passes over a ground radar station at an altitude of 1 km and climbs at an angle of 30°. At what rate is the distance from the plane to the radar station increasing a minute later?

42. Two people start from the same point. One walks east at 3 mi/h and the other walks northeast at 2 mi/h. How fast is the distance between the people changing after 15 minutes?

43. A runner sprints around a circular track of radius 100 m at a constant speed of 7 m/s. The runner's friend is standing at a distance 200 m from the center of the track. How fast is the distance between the friends changing when the distance between them is 200 m?

44. The minute hand on a watch is 8 mm long and the hour hand is 4 mm long. How fast is the distance between the tips of the hands changing at one o'clock?

4.2   **Maximum and Minimum Values**

Some of the most important applications of differential calculus are *optimization problems,* in which we are required to find the optimal (best) way of doing something. Here are examples of such problems that we will solve in this chapter:

- What is the shape of a can that minimizes manufacturing costs?

- What is the maximum acceleration of a space shuttle? (This is an important question to the astronauts who have to withstand the effects of acceleration.)

- What is the radius of a contracted windpipe that expels air most rapidly during a cough?

- At what angle should blood vessels branch so as to minimize the energy expended by the heart in pumping blood?

These problems can be reduced to finding the maximum or minimum values of a function. Let's first explain exactly what we mean by maximum and minimum values.

We see that the highest point on the graph of the function f shown in Figure 1 is the point $(3, 5)$. In other words, the largest value of f is $f(3) = 5$. Likewise, the smallest value is $f(6) = 2$. We say that $f(3) = 5$ is the *absolute maximum* of f and $f(6) = 2$ is the *absolute minimum*. In general, we use the following definition.

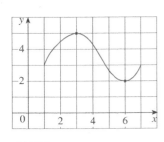

FIGURE 1

> **1**   **Definition** Let c be a number in the domain D of a function f. Then $f(c)$ is the
>
> - **absolute maximum** value of f on D if $f(c) \geq f(x)$ for all x in D.
> - **absolute minimum** value of f on D if $f(c) \leq f(x)$ for all x in D.

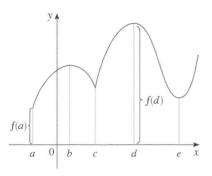

FIGURE 2
Abs min $f(a)$, abs max $f(d)$
loc min $f(c)$, $f(e)$, loc max $f(b)$, $f(d)$

An absolute maximum or minimum is sometimes called a **global** maximum or minimum. The maximum and minimum values of f are called **extreme values** of f.

Figure 2 shows the graph of a function f with absolute maximum at d and absolute minimum at a. Note that $(d, f(d))$ is the highest point on the graph and $(a, f(a))$ is the lowest point. In Figure 2, if we consider only values of x near b [for instance, if we restrict our attention to the interval (a, c)], then $f(b)$ is the largest of those values of $f(x)$ and is called a *local maximum value* of f. Likewise, $f(c)$ is called a *local minimum value* of f because $f(c) \leq f(x)$ for x near c [in the interval (b, d), for instance]. The function f also has a local minimum at e. In general, we have the following definition.

---

2 **Definition** The number $f(c)$ is a

- **local maximum** value of f if $f(c) \geq f(x)$ when x is near c.
- **local minimum** value of f if $f(c) \leq f(x)$ when x is near c.

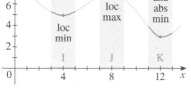

FIGURE 3

In Definition 2 (and elsewhere), if we say that something is true **near** c, we mean that it is true on some open interval containing c. For instance, in Figure 3 we see that $f(4) = 5$ is a local minimum because it's the smallest value of f on the interval I. It's not the absolute minimum because $f(x)$ takes smaller values when x is near 12 (in the interval K, for instance). In fact $f(12) = 3$ is both a local minimum and the absolute minimum. Similarly, $f(8) = 7$ is a local maximum, but not the absolute maximum because f takes larger values near 1.

EXAMPLE 1 **A function with infinitely many extreme values**
The function $f(x) = \cos x$ takes on its (local and absolute) maximum value of 1 infinitely many times, since $\cos 2n\pi = 1$ for any integer n and $-1 \leq \cos x \leq 1$ for all x. Likewise, $\cos(2n + 1)\pi = -1$ is its minimum value, where n is any integer.

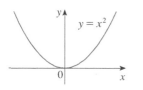

FIGURE 4
Minimum value 0, no maximum

EXAMPLE 2 **A function with a minimum value but no maximum value**
If $f(x) = x^2$, then $f(x) \geq f(0)$ because $x^2 \geq 0$ for all x. Therefore $f(0) = 0$ is the absolute (and local) minimum value of f. This corresponds to the fact that the origin is the lowest point on the parabola $y = x^2$. (See Figure 4.) However, there is no highest point on the parabola and so this function has no maximum value.

EXAMPLE 3 **A function with no maximum or minimum**   From the graph of the function $f(x) = x^3$, shown in Figure 5, we see that this function has neither an absolute maximum value nor an absolute minimum value. In fact, it has no local extreme values either.

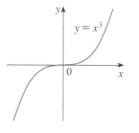

FIGURE 5
No minimum, no maximum

◤ **EXAMPLE 4** **A maximum at an endpoint**   The graph of the function

$$f(x) = 3x^4 - 16x^3 + 18x^2 \qquad -1 \leq x \leq 4$$

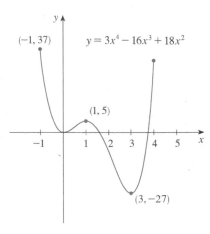

FIGURE 6

is shown in Figure 6. You can see that $f(1) = 5$ is a local maximum, whereas the absolute maximum is $f(-1) = 37$. (This absolute maximum is not a local maximum because it occurs at an endpoint.) Also, $f(0) = 0$ is a local minimum and $f(3) = -27$ is both a local and an absolute minimum. Note that f has neither a local nor an absolute maximum at $x = 4$.

We have seen that some functions have extreme values, whereas others do not. The following theorem gives conditions under which a function is guaranteed to possess extreme values.

> **3** **The Extreme Value Theorem** If f is continuous on a closed interval $[a, b]$, then f attains an absolute maximum value $f(c)$ and an absolute minimum value $f(d)$ at some numbers c and d in $[a, b]$.

The Extreme Value Theorem is illustrated in Figure 7. Note that an extreme value can be taken on more than once. Although the Extreme Value Theorem is intuitively very plausible, it is difficult to prove and so we omit the proof.

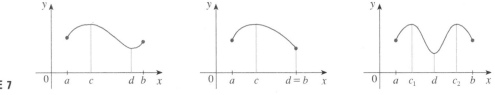

FIGURE 7

Figures 8 and 9 show that a function need not possess extreme values if either hypothesis (continuity or closed interval) is omitted from the Extreme Value Theorem.

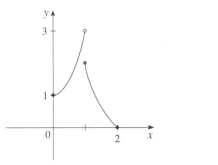

FIGURE 8
This function has minimum value $f(2) = 0$, but no maximum value.

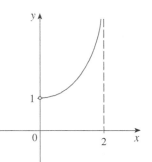

FIGURE 9
This continuous function g has no maximum or minimum.

The function f whose graph is shown in Figure 8 is defined on the closed interval $[0, 2]$ but has no maximum value. [Notice that the range of f is $[0, 3)$. The function takes on values arbitrarily close to 3, but never actually attains the value 3.] This does not contradict the Extreme Value Theorem because f is not continuous. [Nonetheless, a discontinuous function *could* have maximum and minimum values. See Exercise 13(b).]

The function g shown in Figure 9 is continuous on the open interval $(0, 2)$ but has neither a maximum nor a minimum value. [The range of g is $(1, \infty)$. The function takes on arbitrarily large values.] This does not contradict the Extreme Value Theorem because the interval $(0, 2)$ is not closed.

The Extreme Value Theorem says that a continuous function on a closed interval has a maximum value and a minimum value, but it does not tell us how to find these extreme values. We start by looking for local extreme values.

Figure 10 shows the graph of a function f with a local maximum at c and a local minimum at d. It appears that at the maximum and minimum points the tangent lines are horizontal and therefore each has slope 0. We know that the derivative is the slope of the tangent line, so it appears that $f'(c) = 0$ and $f'(d) = 0$. The following theorem says that this is always true for differentiable functions.

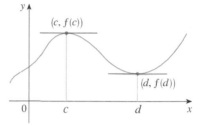

FIGURE 10

Fermat

Fermat's Theorem is named after Pierre Fermat (1601–1665), a French lawyer who took up mathematics as a hobby. Despite his amateur status, Fermat was one of the two inventors of analytic geometry (Descartes was the other). His methods for finding tangents to curves and maximum and minimum values (before the invention of limits and derivatives) made him a forerunner of Newton in the creation of differential calculus.

4 **Fermat's Theorem** If f has a local maximum or minimum at c, and if $f'(c)$ exists, then $f'(c) = 0$.

Our intuition suggests that Fermat's Theorem is true. A rigorous proof, using the definition of a derivative, is given in Appendix E.

Although Fermat's Theorem is very useful, we have to guard against reading too much into it. If $f(x) = x^3$, then $f'(x) = 3x^2$, so $f'(0) = 0$. But f has no maximum or minimum at 0, as you can see from its graph in Figure 11. The fact that $f'(0) = 0$ simply means that the curve $y = x^3$ has a horizontal tangent at $(0, 0)$. Instead of having a maximum or minimum at $(0, 0)$, the curve crosses its horizontal tangent there.

Thus, when $f'(c) = 0$, f doesn't necessarily have a maximum or minimum at c. (In other words, the converse of Fermat's Theorem is false in general.)

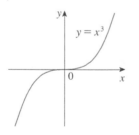

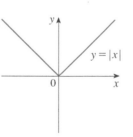

FIGURE 11
If $f(x) = x^3$, then $f'(0) = 0$ but f has no maximum or minimum.

FIGURE 12
If $f(x) = |x|$, then $f(0) = 0$ is a minimum value, but $f'(0)$ does not exist.

We should bear in mind that there may be an extreme value where $f'(c)$ does not exist. For instance, the function $f(x) = |x|$ has its (local and absolute) minimum value at 0 (see Figure 12), but that value cannot be found by setting $f'(x) = 0$ because, as was shown in Example 6 in Section 2.7, $f'(0)$ does not exist.

Fermat's Theorem does suggest that we should at least *start* looking for extreme values of f at the numbers c where $f'(c) = 0$ or where $f'(c)$ does not exist. Such numbers are given a special name.

> **5** **Definition** A **critical number** of a function f is a number c in the domain of f such that either $f'(c) = 0$ or $f'(c)$ does not exist.

Figure 13 shows a graph of the function f in Example 5. It supports our answer because there is a horizontal tangent when $x = 1.5$ and a vertical tangent when $x = 0$.

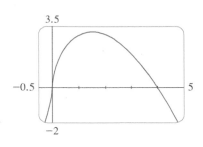

FIGURE 13

EXAMPLE 5 Find the critical numbers of $f(x) = x^{3/5}(4 - x)$.

SOLUTION The Product Rule gives

$$f'(x) = x^{3/5}(-1) + \tfrac{3}{5}x^{-2/5}(4 - x) = -x^{3/5} + \frac{3(4 - x)}{5x^{2/5}}$$

$$= \frac{-5x + 3(4 - x)}{5x^{2/5}} = \frac{12 - 8x}{5x^{2/5}}$$

[The same result could be obtained by first writing $f(x) = 4x^{3/5} - x^{8/5}$.] Therefore $f'(x) = 0$ if $12 - 8x = 0$, that is, $x = \tfrac{3}{2}$, and $f'(x)$ does not exist when $x = 0$. Thus the critical numbers are $\tfrac{3}{2}$ and 0.

In terms of critical numbers, Fermat's Theorem can be rephrased as follows (compare Definition 5 with Theorem 4):

> **6** If f has a local maximum or minimum at c, then c is a critical number of f.

To find an absolute maximum or minimum of a continuous function on a closed interval, we note that either it is local [in which case it occurs at a critical number by (6)] or it occurs at an endpoint of the interval. Thus the following three-step procedure always works.

> **The Closed Interval Method** To find the *absolute* maximum and minimum values of a continuous function f on a closed interval $[a, b]$:
>
> **1.** Find the values of f at the critical numbers of f in (a, b).
>
> **2.** Find the values of f at the endpoints of the interval.
>
> **3.** The largest of the values from Steps 1 and 2 is the absolute maximum value; the smallest of these values is the absolute minimum value.

We can estimate maximum and minimum values very easily using a graphing calculator or a computer with graphing software. But, as Example 6 shows, calculus is needed to find the *exact* values.

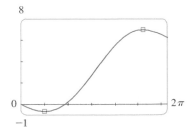

FIGURE 14

EXAMPLE 6 **Finding extreme values on a closed interval**
(a) Use a graphing device to estimate the absolute minimum and maximum values of the function $f(x) = x - 2 \sin x$, $0 \leqslant x \leqslant 2\pi$.
(b) Use calculus to find the exact minimum and maximum values.

SOLUTION
(a) Figure 14 shows a graph of f in the viewing rectangle $[0, 2\pi]$ by $[-1, 8]$. By moving the cursor close to the maximum point, we see that the y-coordinates don't change very much in the vicinity of the maximum. The absolute maximum value is about 6.97 and it occurs when $x \approx 5.2$. Similarly, by moving the cursor close to the minimum point, we see that the absolute minimum value is about -0.68 and it occurs when $x \approx 1.0$. It is possible to get more accurate estimates by zooming in toward the maximum and minimum points, but instead let's use calculus.

(b) The function $f(x) = x - 2 \sin x$ is continuous on $[0, 2\pi]$. Since $f'(x) = 1 - 2 \cos x$, we have $f'(x) = 0$ when $\cos x = \frac{1}{2}$ and this occurs when $x = \pi/3$ or $5\pi/3$. The values of f at these critical numbers are

$$f(\pi/3) = \frac{\pi}{3} - 2 \sin \frac{\pi}{3} = \frac{\pi}{3} - \sqrt{3} \approx -0.684853$$

and
$$f(5\pi/3) = \frac{5\pi}{3} - 2 \sin \frac{5\pi}{3} = \frac{5\pi}{3} + \sqrt{3} \approx 6.968039$$

The values of f at the endpoints are

$$f(0) = 0 \qquad \text{and} \qquad f(2\pi) = 2\pi \approx 6.28$$

Comparing these four numbers and using the Closed Interval Method, we see that the absolute minimum value is $f(\pi/3) = \pi/3 - \sqrt{3}$ and the absolute maximum value is $f(5\pi/3) = 5\pi/3 + \sqrt{3}$. The values from part (a) serve as a check on our work. ▬

NASA

EXAMPLE 7 The Hubble Space Telescope was deployed on April 24, 1990, by the space shuttle *Discovery*. A model for the velocity of the shuttle during this mission, from liftoff at $t = 0$ until the solid rocket boosters were jettisoned at $t = 126$ s, is given by

$$v(t) = 0.001302t^3 - 0.09029t^2 + 23.61t - 3.083$$

(in feet per second). Using this model, estimate the absolute maximum and minimum values of the *acceleration* of the shuttle between liftoff and the jettisoning of the boosters.

SOLUTION We are asked for the extreme values not of the given velocity function, but rather of the acceleration function. So we first need to differentiate to find the acceleration:

$$a(t) = v'(t) = \frac{d}{dt}(0.001302t^3 - 0.09029t^2 + 23.61t - 3.083)$$

$$= 0.003906t^2 - 0.18058t + 23.61$$

We now apply the Closed Interval Method to the continuous function a on the interval $0 \leqslant t \leqslant 126$. Its derivative is

$$a'(t) = 0.007812t - 0.18058$$

The only critical number occurs when $a'(t) = 0$:

$$t_1 = \frac{0.18058}{0.007812} \approx 23.12$$

Evaluating $a(t)$ at the critical number and at the endpoints, we have

$$a(0) = 23.61 \qquad a(t_1) \approx 21.52 \qquad a(126) \approx 62.87$$

So the maximum acceleration is about 62.87 ft/s² and the minimum acceleration is about 21.52 ft/s². ▬

4.2 Exercises

1. Explain the difference between an absolute minimum and a local minimum.

2. Suppose f is a continuous function defined on a closed interval $[a, b]$.
   (a) What theorem guarantees the existence of an absolute maximum value and an absolute minimum value for f?
   (b) What steps would you take to find those maximum and minimum values?

3–4 For each of the numbers a, b, c, d, r, and s, state whether the function whose graph is shown has an absolute maximum or minimum, a local maximum or minimum, or neither a maximum nor a minimum.

3.
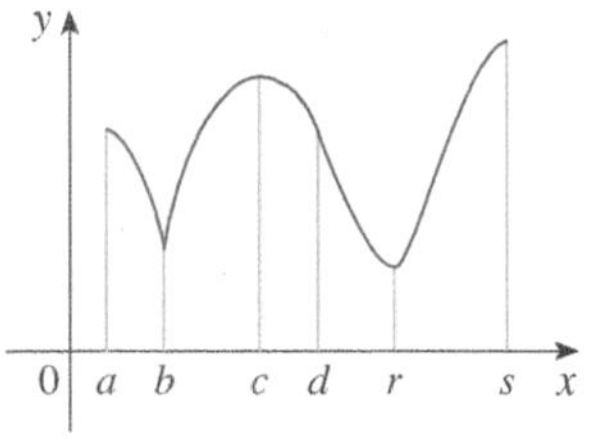

4.
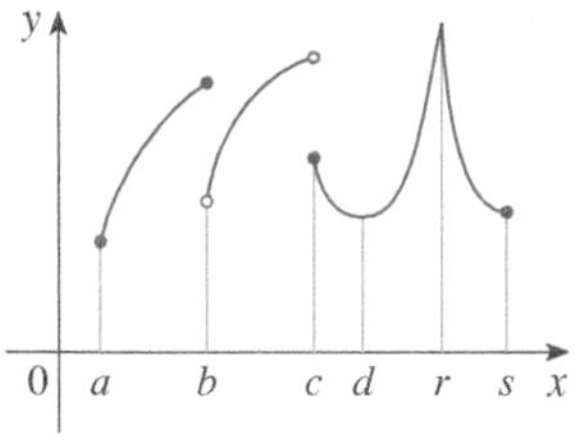

5–6 Use the graph to state the absolute and local maximum and minimum values of the function.

5.
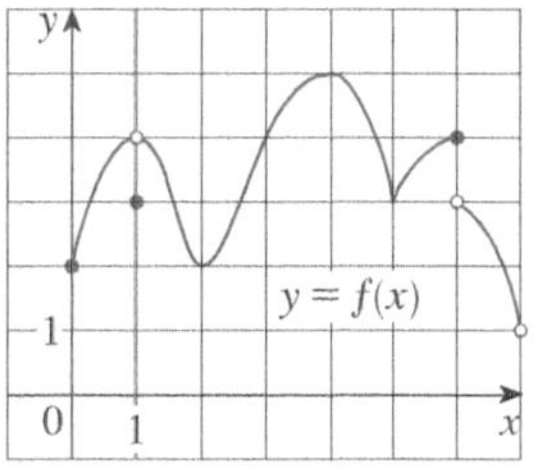

6.
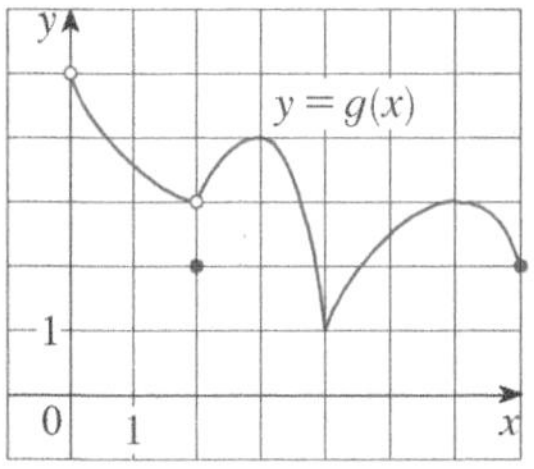

7–10 Sketch the graph of a function f that is continuous on $[1, 5]$ and has the given properties.

7. Absolute minimum at 2, absolute maximum at 3, local minimum at 4

8. Absolute minimum at 1, absolute maximum at 5, local maximum at 2, local minimum at 4

9. Absolute maximum at 5, absolute minimum at 2, local maximum at 3, local minima at 2 and 4

10. f has no local maximum or minimum, but 2 and 4 are critical numbers

11. (a) Sketch the graph of a function that has a local maximum at 2 and is differentiable at 2.
   (b) Sketch the graph of a function that has a local maximum at 2 and is continuous but not differentiable at 2.
   (c) Sketch the graph of a function that has a local maximum at 2 and is not continuous at 2.

12. (a) Sketch the graph of a function on $[-1, 2]$ that has an absolute maximum but no local maximum.
   (b) Sketch the graph of a function on $[-1, 2]$ that has a local maximum but no absolute maximum.

13. (a) Sketch the graph of a function on $[-1, 2]$ that has an absolute maximum but no absolute minimum.
   (b) Sketch the graph of a function on $[-1, 2]$ that is discontinuous but has both an absolute maximum and an absolute minimum.

14. (a) Sketch the graph of a function that has two local maxima, one local minimum, and no absolute minimum.
   (b) Sketch the graph of a function that has three local minima, two local maxima, and seven critical numbers.

15–22 Sketch the graph of f by hand and use your sketch to find the absolute and local maximum and minimum values of f. (Use the graphs and transformations of Sections 1.2 and 1.3.)

15. $f(x) = \frac{1}{2}(3x - 1), \quad x \leqslant 3$

16. $f(x) = 2 - \frac{1}{3}x, \quad x \geqslant -2$

17. $f(x) = x^2, \quad 0 < x < 2$

18. $f(x) = e^x$

19. $f(x) = \ln x, \quad 0 < x \leqslant 2$

20. $f(t) = \cos t, \quad -3\pi/2 \leqslant t \leqslant 3\pi/2$

21. $f(x) = 1 - \sqrt{x}$

22. $f(x) = \begin{cases} 4 - x^2 & \text{if } -2 \leqslant x < 0 \\ 2x - 1 & \text{if } 0 \leqslant x \leqslant 2 \end{cases}$

23–38 Find the critical numbers of the function.

23. $f(x) = 4 + \frac{1}{3}x - \frac{1}{2}x^2$

24. $f(x) = x^3 + 6x^2 - 15x$

25. $f(x) = x^3 + 3x^2 - 24x$

26. $f(x) = x^3 + x^2 + x$

27. $s(t) = 3t^4 + 4t^3 - 6t^2$

28. $g(t) = |3t - 4|$

29. $g(y) = \dfrac{y - 1}{y^2 - y + 1}$

30. $h(p) = \dfrac{p - 1}{p^2 + 4}$

31. $h(t) = t^{3/4} - 2t^{1/4}$

32. $g(x) = x^{1/3} - x^{-2/3}$

33. $F(x) = x^{4/5}(x - 4)^2$

34. $g(\theta) = 4\theta - \tan\theta$

35. $f(\theta) = 2\cos\theta + \sin^2\theta$

36. $h(t) = 3t - \arcsin t$

37. $f(x) = x^2 e^{-3x}$

38. $f(x) = x^{-2}\ln x$

Graphing calculator or computer with graphing software required   1. Homework Hints available in TEC

39–40 A formula for the *derivative* of a function f is given. How many critical numbers does f have?

39. $f'(x) = 5e^{-0.1|x|} \sin x - 1$ **40.** $f'(x) = \dfrac{100 \cos^2 x}{10 + x^2} - 1$

41–54 Find the absolute maximum and absolute minimum values of f on the given interval.

41. $f(x) = 12 + 4x - x^2$, $[0, 5]$

42. $f(x) = 5 + 54x - 2x^3$, $[0, 4]$

43. $f(x) = 2x^3 - 3x^2 - 12x + 1$, $[-2, 3]$

44. $f(x) = x^3 - 6x^2 + 9x + 2$, $[-1, 4]$

45. $f(x) = x^4 - 2x^2 + 3$, $[-2, 3]$

46. $f(x) = (x^2 - 1)^3$, $[-1, 2]$

47. $f(t) = t\sqrt{4 - t^2}$, $[-1, 2]$

48. $f(x) = \dfrac{x^2 - 4}{x^2 + 4}$, $[-4, 4]$

49. $f(x) = xe^{-x^2/8}$, $[-1, 4]$

50. $f(x) = x - \ln x$, $\left[\frac{1}{2}, 2\right]$

51. $f(x) = \ln(x^2 + x + 1)$, $[-1, 1]$

52. $f(x) = x - 2 \tan^{-1}x$, $[0, 4]$

53. $f(t) = 2\cos t + \sin 2t$, $[0, \pi/2]$

54. $f(t) = t + \cot(t/2)$, $[\pi/4, 7\pi/4]$

---

55. If a and b are positive numbers, find the maximum value of $f(x) = x^a(1 - x)^b$, $0 \le x \le 1$.

56. Use a graph to estimate the critical numbers of $f(x) = |x^3 - 3x^2 + 2|$ correct to one decimal place.

57–60
(a) Use a graph to estimate the absolute maximum and minimum values of the function to two decimal places.
(b) Use calculus to find the exact maximum and minimum values.

57. $f(x) = x^5 - x^3 + 2$, $-1 \le x \le 1$

58. $f(x) = e^{x^3 - x}$, $-1 \le x \le 0$

59. $f(x) = x\sqrt{x - x^2}$

60. $f(x) = x - 2\cos x$, $-2 \le x \le 0$

---

61. Between 0°C and 30°C, the volume V (in cubic centimeters) of 1 kg of water at a temperature T is given approximately by the formula

$$V = 999.87 - 0.06426T + 0.0085043T^2 - 0.0000679T^3$$

Find the temperature at which water has its maximum density.

62. An object with weight W is dragged along a horizontal plane by a force acting along a rope attached to the object. If the rope makes an angle θ with the plane, then the magnitude of the force is

$$F = \frac{\mu W}{\mu \sin \theta + \cos \theta}$$

where μ is a positive constant called the *coefficient of friction* and where $0 \le \theta \le \pi/2$. Show that F is minimized when $\tan \theta = \mu$.

63. A model for the US average price of a pound of white sugar from 1993 to 2003 is given by the function

$$S(t) = -0.00003237t^5 + 0.0009037t^4 - 0.008956t^3$$
$$+ 0.03629t^2 - 0.04458t + 0.4074$$

where t is measured in years since August of 1993. Estimate the times when sugar was cheapest and most expensive during the period 1993–2003.

64. On May 7, 1992, the space shuttle *Endeavour* was launched on mission STS-49, the purpose of which was to install a new perigee kick motor in an Intelsat communications satellite. The table gives the velocity data for the shuttle between liftoff and the jettisoning of the solid rocket boosters.

Event	Time (s)	Velocity (ft/s)
Launch	0	0
Begin roll maneuver	10	185
End roll maneuver	15	319
Throttle to 89%	20	447
Throttle to 67%	32	742
Throttle to 104%	59	1325
Maximum dynamic pressure	62	1445
Solid rocket booster separation	125	4151

(a) Use a graphing calculator or computer to find the cubic polynomial that best models the velocity of the shuttle for the time interval $t \in [0, 125]$. Then graph this polynomial.
(b) Find a model for the acceleration of the shuttle and use it to estimate the maximum and minimum values of the acceleration during the first 125 seconds.

65. When a foreign object lodged in the trachea (windpipe) forces a person to cough, the diaphragm thrusts upward causing an increase in pressure in the lungs. This is accompanied by a contraction of the trachea, making a narrower channel for the expelled air to flow through. For a given amount of air to escape in a fixed time, it must move faster through the narrower channel than the wider one. The greater the velocity of the airstream, the greater the force on the foreign object. X rays show that the radius of the circular tracheal tube contracts to about two-thirds of its normal radius during a cough. According to a mathematical model of coughing, the velocity v of the airstream is related to the radius r of the trachea by the equation

$$v(r) = k(r_0 - r)r^2 \qquad \tfrac{1}{2}r_0 \leqslant r \leqslant r_0$$

where k is a constant and r_0 is the normal radius of the trachea. The restriction on r is due to the fact that the tracheal wall stiffens under pressure and a contraction greater than $\tfrac{1}{2}r_0$ is prevented (otherwise the person would suffocate).

(a) Determine the value of r in the interval $\left[\tfrac{1}{2}r_0, r_0\right]$ at which v has an absolute maximum. How does this compare with experimental evidence?

(b) What is the absolute maximum value of v on the interval?

(c) Sketch the graph of v on the interval $[0, r_0]$.

66. A cubic function is a polynomial of degree 3; that is, it has the form $f(x) = ax^3 + bx^2 + cx + d$, where $a \neq 0$.

(a) Show that a cubic function can have two, one, or no critical number(s). Give examples and sketches to illustrate the three possibilities.

(b) How many local extreme values can a cubic function have?

APPLIED PROJECT   The Calculus of Rainbows

Rainbows are created when raindrops scatter sunlight. They have fascinated mankind since ancient times and have inspired attempts at scientific explanation since the time of Aristotle. In this project we use the ideas of Descartes and Newton to explain the shape, location, and colors of rainbows.

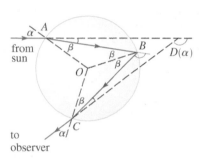

Formation of the primary rainbow

1. The figure shows a ray of sunlight entering a spherical raindrop at A. Some of the light is reflected, but the line AB shows the path of the part that enters the drop. Notice that the light is refracted toward the normal line AO and in fact Snell's Law says that $\sin \alpha = k \sin \beta$, where α is the angle of incidence, β is the angle of refraction, and $k \approx \tfrac{4}{3}$ is the index of refraction for water. At B some of the light passes through the drop and is refracted into the air, but the line BC shows the part that is reflected. (The angle of incidence equals the angle of reflection.) When the ray reaches C, part of it is reflected, but for the time being we are more interested in the part that leaves the raindrop at C. (Notice that it is refracted away from the normal line.) The *angle of deviation* $D(\alpha)$ is the amount of clockwise rotation that the ray has undergone during this three-stage process. Thus

$$D(\alpha) = (\alpha - \beta) + (\pi - 2\beta) + (\alpha - \beta) = \pi + 2\alpha - 4\beta$$

Show that the minimum value of the deviation is $D(\alpha) \approx 138°$ and occurs when $\alpha \approx 59.4°$.

The significance of the minimum deviation is that when $\alpha \approx 59.4°$ we have $D'(\alpha) \approx 0$, so $\Delta D/\Delta \alpha \approx 0$. This means that many rays with $\alpha \approx 59.4°$ become deviated by approximately the same amount. It is the *concentration* of rays coming from near the direction of minimum deviation that creates the brightness of the primary rainbow. The following figure shows that the angle of elevation from the observer up to the highest point on the rainbow is $180° - 138° = 42°$. (This angle is called the *rainbow angle*.)

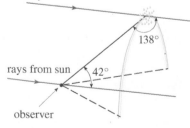

2. Problem 1 explains the location of the primary rainbow, but how do we explain the colors? Sunlight comprises a range of wavelengths, from the red range through orange, yellow, green, blue, indigo, and violet. As Newton discovered in his prism experiments of 1666, the index of refraction is different for each color. (The effect is called *dispersion.*) For red light the refractive index is $k \approx 1.3318$ whereas for violet light it is $k \approx 1.3435$. By repeating the calculation of Problem 1 for these values of k, show that the rainbow angle is about 42.3° for the red bow and 40.6° for the violet bow. So the rainbow really consists of seven individual bows corresponding to the seven colors.

3. Perhaps you have seen a fainter secondary rainbow above the primary bow. That results from the part of a ray that enters a raindrop and is refracted at A, reflected twice (at B and C), and refracted as it leaves the drop at D (see the figure at the left). This time the deviation angle $D(\alpha)$ is the total amount of counterclockwise rotation that the ray undergoes in this four-stage process. Show that

$$D(\alpha) = 2\alpha - 6\beta + 2\pi$$

and $D(\alpha)$ has a minimum value when

$$\cos\alpha = \sqrt{\frac{k^2 - 1}{8}}$$

Taking $k = \frac{4}{3}$, show that the minimum deviation is about 129° and so the rainbow angle for the secondary rainbow is about 51°, as shown in the following figure.

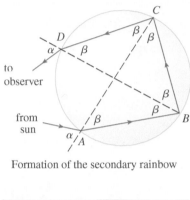

Formation of the secondary rainbow

© C. Donald Ahrens

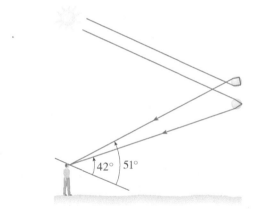

4. Show that the colors in the secondary rainbow appear in the opposite order from those in the primary rainbow.

4.3 Derivatives and the Shapes of Curves

In Section 2.8 we discussed how the signs of the first and second derivatives $f'(x)$ and $f''(x)$ influence the shape of the graph of f. Here we revisit those facts, giving an indication of why they are true and using them, together with the differentiation formulas of Chapter 3, to explain the shapes of graphs.

We start with a fact, known as the Mean Value Theorem, that will be useful not only for present purposes but also for explaining why some of the other basic results of calculus are true.

Lagrange and the
Mean Value Theorem

The Mean Value Theorem was first formulated by Joseph-Louis Lagrange (1736–1813), born in Italy of a French father and an Italian mother. He was a child prodigy and became a professor in Turin at the age of 19. Lagrange made great contributions to number theory, theory of functions, theory of equations, and analytical and celestial mechanics. In particular, he applied calculus to the analysis of the stability of the solar system. At the invitation of Frederick the Great, he succeeded Euler at the Berlin Academy and, when Frederick died, Lagrange accepted King Louis XVI's invitation to Paris, where he was given apartments in the Louvre and became a professor at the Ecole Polytechnique. He was a kind and quiet man, living only for science.

The Mean Value Theorem If f is a differentiable function on the interval $[a, b]$, then there exists a number c between a and b such that

$$\boxed{1} \qquad f'(c) = \frac{f(b) - f(a)}{b - a} \qquad .$$

or, equivalently,

$$\boxed{2} \qquad f(b) - f(a) = f'(c)(b - a)$$

We can see that this theorem is reasonable by interpreting it geometrically. Figures 1 and 2 show the points $A(a, f(a))$ and $B(b, f(b))$ on the graphs of two differentiable functions.

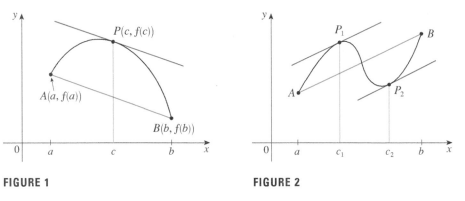

FIGURE 1   **FIGURE 2**

The slope of the secant line AB is

$$m_{AB} = \frac{f(b) - f(a)}{b - a}$$

which is the same expression as on the right side of Equation 1. Since $f'(c)$ is the slope of the tangent line at the point $(c, f(c))$, the Mean Value Theorem, in the form given by Equation 1, says that there is at least one point $P(c, f(c))$ on the graph where the slope of the tangent line is the same as the slope of the secant line AB. In other words, there is a point P where the tangent line is parallel to the secant line AB. It seems clear that there is one such point P in Figure 1 and two such points P_1 and P_2 in Figure 2. Because our intuition tells us that the Mean Value Theorem is true, we take it as the starting point for the development of the main facts of calculus. (When calculus is developed from first principles, however, the Mean Value Theorem is proved as a consequence of the axioms that define the real number system.)

▼ **EXAMPLE 1** **What the Mean Value Theorem says about velocity**   If an object moves in a straight line with position function $s = f(t)$, then the average velocity between $t = a$ and $t = b$ is

$$\frac{f(b) - f(a)}{b - a}$$

and the velocity at $t = c$ is $f'(c)$. Thus the Mean Value Theorem (in the form of Equation 1) tells us that at some time $t = c$ between a and b the instantaneous velocity $f'(c)$ is equal to that average velocity. For instance, if a car traveled 180 km in 2 hours, then the speedometer must have read 90 km/h at least once.

The main significance of the Mean Value Theorem is that it enables us to obtain information about a function from information about its derivative. Our immediate use of this principle is to prove the basic facts concerning increasing and decreasing functions. (See Exercises 63 and 64 for another use.)

Increasing and Decreasing Functions

In Section 1.1 we defined increasing functions and decreasing functions and in Section 2.8 we observed from graphs that a function with a positive derivative is increasing. We now deduce this fact from the Mean Value Theorem.

Let's abbreviate the name of this test to the I/D Test.

> **Increasing/Decreasing Test**
>
> (a) If $f'(x) > 0$ on an interval, then f is increasing on that interval.
>
> (b) If $f'(x) < 0$ on an interval, then f is decreasing on that interval.

PROOF

(a) Let x_1 and x_2 be any two numbers in the interval with $x_1 < x_2$. According to the definition of an increasing function (page 21) we have to show that $f(x_1) < f(x_2)$.

Because we are given that $f'(x) > 0$, we know that f is differentiable on $[x_1, x_2]$. So, by the Mean Value Theorem, there is a number c between x_1 and x_2 such that

$$\boxed{3} \qquad f(x_2) - f(x_1) = f'(c)(x_2 - x_1)$$

Now $f'(c) > 0$ by assumption and $x_2 - x_1 > 0$ because $x_1 < x_2$. Thus the right side of Equation 3 is positive, and so

$$f(x_2) - f(x_1) > 0 \qquad \text{or} \qquad f(x_1) < f(x_2)$$

This shows that f is increasing.

Part (b) is proved similarly. ⬜

EXAMPLE 2 Find where the function $f(x) = 3x^4 - 4x^3 - 12x^2 + 5$ is increasing and where it is decreasing.

SOLUTION $\qquad f'(x) = 12x^3 - 12x^2 - 24x = 12x(x - 2)(x + 1)$

To use the I/D Test we have to know where $f'(x) > 0$ and where $f'(x) < 0$. This depends on the signs of the three factors of $f'(x)$, namely, $12x$, $x - 2$, and $x + 1$. We divide the real line into intervals whose endpoints are the critical numbers -1, 0, and 2 and arrange our work in a chart. A plus sign indicates that the given expression is positive, and a minus sign indicates that it is negative. The last column of the chart gives the conclusion based on the I/D Test. For instance, $f'(x) < 0$ for $0 < x < 2$, so f is decreasing on $(0, 2)$. (It would also be true to say that f is decreasing on the closed interval $[0, 2]$.)

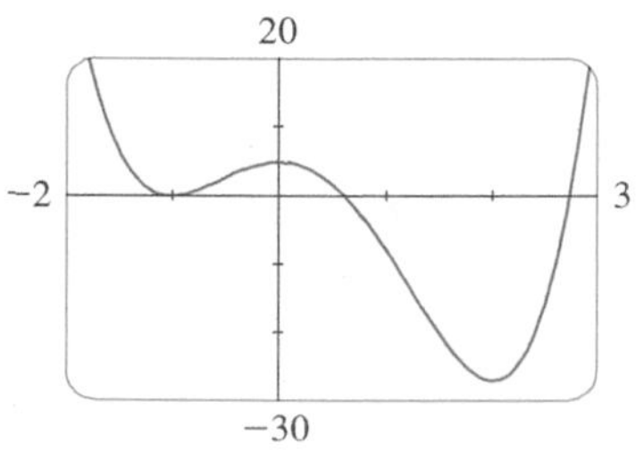

Interval	$12x$	$x - 2$	$x + 1$	$f'(x)$	f
$x < -1$	$-$	$-$	$-$	$-$	decreasing on $(-\infty, -1)$
$-1 < x < 0$	$-$	$-$	$+$	$+$	increasing on $(-1, 0)$
$0 < x < 2$	$+$	$-$	$+$	$-$	decreasing on $(0, 2)$
$x > 2$	$+$	$+$	$+$	$+$	increasing on $(2, \infty)$

FIGURE 3

The graph of f shown in Figure 3 confirms the information in the chart. ∎

Recall from Section 4.2 that if f has a local maximum or minimum at c, then c must be a critical number of f (by Fermat's Theorem), but not every critical number gives rise to a maximum or a minimum. We therefore need a test that will tell us whether or not f has a local maximum or minimum at a critical number.

You can see from Figure 3 that $f(0) = 5$ is a local maximum value of f because f increases on $(-1, 0)$ and decreases on $(0, 2)$. Or, in terms of derivatives, $f'(x) > 0$ for $-1 < x < 0$ and $f'(x) < 0$ for $0 < x < 2$. In other words, the sign of $f'(x)$ changes from positive to negative at 0. This observation is the basis of the following test.

The First Derivative Test Suppose that c is a critical number of a continuous function f.

(a) If f' changes from positive to negative at c, then f has a local maximum at c.

(b) If f' changes from negative to positive at c, then f has a local minimum at c.

(c) If f' does not change sign at c (for example, if f' is positive on both sides of c or negative on both sides), then f has no local maximum or minimum at c.

The First Derivative Test is a consequence of the I/D Test. In part (a), for instance, since the sign of $f'(x)$ changes from positive to negative at c, f is increasing to the left of c and decreasing to the right of c. It follows that f has a local maximum at c.

It is easy to remember the First Derivative Test by visualizing diagrams such as those in Figure 4.

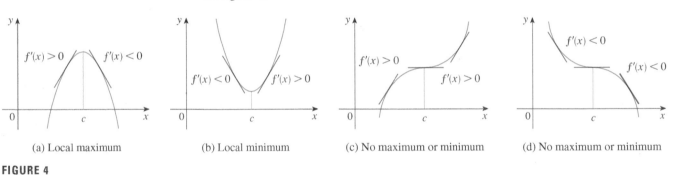

(a) Local maximum   (b) Local minimum   (c) No maximum or minimum   (d) No maximum or minimum

FIGURE 4

V EXAMPLE 3 Find the local minimum and maximum values of the function f in Example 2.

SOLUTION From the chart in the solution to Example 2 we see that $f'(x)$ changes from negative to positive at -1, so $f(-1) = 0$ is a local minimum value by the First Derivative Test. Similarly, f' changes from negative to positive at 2, so $f(2) = -27$ is also a local minimum value. As previously noted, $f(0) = 5$ is a local maximum value because $f'(x)$ changes from positive to negative at 0. ∎

Concavity

Let's recall the definition of concavity from Section 2.8.

A function (or its graph) is called **concave upward** on an interval I if f' is an increasing function on I. It is called **concave downward** on I if f' is decreasing on I.

Notice in Figure 5 that the slopes of the tangent lines increase from left to right on the interval (a, b), so f' is increasing and f is concave upward (abbreviated CU) on (a, b). [It can be proved that this is equivalent to saying that the graph of f lies above all of its tangent lines on (a, b).] Similarly, the slopes of the tangent lines decrease from left to right on (b, c), so f' is decreasing and f is concave downward (CD) on (b, c).

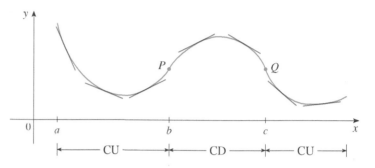

FIGURE 5

A point where a curve changes its direction of concavity is called an **inflection point**. The curve in Figure 5 changes from concave upward to concave downward at P and from concave downward to concave upward at Q, so both P and Q are inflection points.

Because $f'' = (f')'$, we know that if $f''(x)$ is positive, then f' is an increasing function and so f is concave upward. Similarly, if $f''(x)$ is negative, then f' is decreasing and f is concave downward. Thus we have the following test for concavity.

Concavity Test

(a) If $f''(x) > 0$ for all x in I, then the graph of f is concave upward on I.

(b) If $f''(x) < 0$ for all x in I, then the graph of f is concave downward on I.

In view of the Concavity Test, there is a point of inflection at any point where the second derivative changes sign. A consequence of the Concavity Test is the following test for maximum and minimum values.

The Second Derivative Test   Suppose f'' is continuous near c.

(a) If $f'(c) = 0$ and $f''(c) > 0$, then f has a local minimum at c.

(b) If $f'(c) = 0$ and $f''(c) < 0$, then f has a local maximum at c.

For instance, part (a) is true because $f''(x) > 0$ near c and so f is concave upward near c. This means that the graph of f lies *above* its horizontal tangent at c and so f has a local minimum at c. (See Figure 6.)

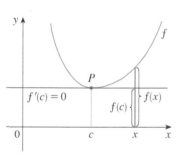

FIGURE 6
$f''(c) > 0$, f is concave upward

V EXAMPLE 4   Analyzing a curve using derivatives   Discuss the curve $y = x^4 - 4x^3$ with respect to concavity, points of inflection, and local maxima and minima. Use this information to sketch the curve.

SOLUTION If $f(x) = x^4 - 4x^3$, then

$$f'(x) = 4x^3 - 12x^2 = 4x^2(x - 3)$$
$$f''(x) = 12x^2 - 24x = 12x(x - 2)$$

To find the critical numbers we set $f'(x) = 0$ and obtain $x = 0$ and $x = 3$. To use the Second Derivative Test we evaluate f'' at these critical numbers:

$$f''(0) = 0 \qquad f''(3) = 36 > 0$$

Since $f'(3) = 0$ and $f''(3) > 0$, $f(3) = -27$ is a local minimum. Since $f''(0) = 0$, the Second Derivative Test gives no information about the critical number 0. But since $f'(x) < 0$ for $x < 0$ and also for $0 < x < 3$, the First Derivative Test tells us that f does not have a local maximum or minimum at 0.

Since $f''(x) = 0$ when $x = 0$ or 2, we divide the real line into intervals with these numbers as endpoints and complete the following chart.

Interval	$f''(x) = 12x(x-2)$	Concavity
$(-\infty, 0)$	$+$	upward
$(0, 2)$	$-$	downward
$(2, \infty)$	$+$	upward

The point $(0, 0)$ is an inflection point since the curve changes from concave upward to concave downward there. Also $(2, -16)$ is an inflection point since the curve changes from concave downward to concave upward there.

Using the local minimum, the intervals of concavity, and the inflection points, we sketch the curve in Figure 7.

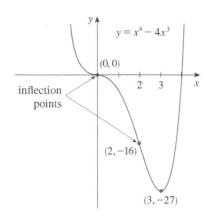

FIGURE 7

Note: The Second Derivative Test is inconclusive when $f''(c) = 0$. In other words, at such a point there might be a maximum, there might be a minimum, or there might be neither (as in Example 4). This test also fails when $f''(c)$ does not exist. In such cases the First Derivative Test must be used. In fact, even when both tests apply, the First Derivative Test is often the easier one to use.

EXAMPLE 5 Sketch the graph of the function $f(x) = x^{2/3}(6 - x)^{1/3}$.

SOLUTION Calculation of the first two derivatives gives

Use the differentiation rules to check these calculations.

$$f'(x) = \frac{4 - x}{x^{1/3}(6 - x)^{2/3}} \qquad f''(x) = \frac{-8}{x^{4/3}(6 - x)^{5/3}}$$

Since $f'(x) = 0$ when $x = 4$ and $f'(x)$ does not exist when $x = 0$ or $x = 6$, the critical numbers are 0, 4, and 6.

Interval	$4 - x$	$x^{1/3}$	$(6 - x)^{2/3}$	$f'(x)$	f
$x < 0$	$+$	$-$	$+$	$-$	decreasing on $(-\infty, 0)$
$0 < x < 4$	$+$	$+$	$+$	$+$	increasing on $(0, 4)$
$4 < x < 6$	$-$	$+$	$+$	$-$	decreasing on $(4, 6)$
$x > 6$	$-$	$+$	$+$	$-$	decreasing on $(6, \infty)$

To find the local extreme values we use the First Derivative Test. Since f' changes from negative to positive at 0, $f(0) = 0$ is a local minimum. Since f' changes from positive to negative at 4, $f(4) = 2^{5/3}$ is a local maximum. The sign of f' does not change at 6, so there is no minimum or maximum there. (The Second Derivative Test could be used at 4 but not at 0 or 6 since f'' does not exist at either of these numbers.)

Looking at the expression for $f''(x)$ and noting that $x^{4/3} \geq 0$ for all x, we have $f''(x) < 0$ for $x < 0$ and for $0 < x < 6$ and $f''(x) > 0$ for $x > 6$. So f is concave downward on $(-\infty, 0)$ and $(0, 6)$ and concave upward on $(6, \infty)$, and the only inflection point is $(6, 0)$. The graph is sketched in Figure 8. Note that the curve has vertical tangents at $(0, 0)$ and $(6, 0)$ because $|f'(x)| \to \infty$ as $x \to 0$ and as $x \to 6$.

Try reproducing the graph in Figure 8 with a graphing calculator or computer. Some machines produce the complete graph, some produce only the portion to the right of the y-axis, and some produce only the portion between $x = 0$ and $x = 6$. For an explanation and cure, see Example 7 in Section 1.4. An equivalent expression that gives the correct graph is

$$y = (x^2)^{1/3} \cdot \frac{6 - x}{|6 - x|} |6 - x|^{1/3}$$

FIGURE 8

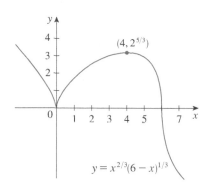

$$y = x^{2/3}(6 - x)^{1/3}$$

EXAMPLE 6 Use the first and second derivatives of $f(x) = e^{1/x}$, together with asymptotes, to sketch its graph.

SOLUTION Notice that the domain of f is $\{x \mid x \neq 0\}$, so we check for vertical asymptotes by computing the left and right limits as $x \to 0$. As $x \to 0^+$, we know that $t = 1/x \to \infty$, so

$$\lim_{x \to 0^+} e^{1/x} = \lim_{t \to \infty} e^t = \infty$$

and this shows that $x = 0$ is a vertical asymptote. As $x \to 0^-$, we have $t = 1/x \to -\infty$, so

$$\lim_{x \to 0^-} e^{1/x} = \lim_{t \to -\infty} e^t = 0$$

As $x \to \pm\infty$, we have $1/x \to 0$ and so

$$\lim_{x \to \pm\infty} e^{1/x} = e^0 = 1$$

TEC In Module 4.3 you can practice using information about f', f'', and asymptotes to determine the shape of the graph of f.

This shows that $y = 1$ is a horizontal asymptote.

Now let's compute the derivative. The Chain Rule gives

$$f'(x) = -\frac{e^{1/x}}{x^2}$$

www.stewartcalculus.com

If you click on *Additional Topics*, you will see
Summary of Curve Sketching

The guidelines given there summarize all the information you need to make a sketch of a curve that conveys its most important aspects. Examples and exercises provide you with additional practice.

Since $e^{1/x} > 0$ and $x^2 > 0$ for all $x \neq 0$, we have $f'(x) < 0$ for all $x \neq 0$. Thus f is decreasing on $(-\infty, 0)$ and on $(0, \infty)$. There is no critical number, so the function has no local maximum or minimum. The second derivative is

$$f''(x) = -\frac{x^2 e^{1/x}(-1/x^2) - e^{1/x}(2x)}{x^4} = \frac{e^{1/x}(2x + 1)}{x^4}$$

Since $e^{1/x} > 0$ and $x^4 > 0$, we have $f''(x) > 0$ when $x > -\frac{1}{2}$ ($x \neq 0$) and $f''(x) < 0$ when $x < -\frac{1}{2}$. So the curve is concave downward on $\left(-\infty, -\frac{1}{2}\right)$ and concave upward on $\left(-\frac{1}{2}, 0\right)$ and on $(0, \infty)$. The inflection point is $\left(-\frac{1}{2}, e^{-2}\right)$.

To sketch the graph of f we first draw the horizontal asymptote $y = 1$ (as a dashed line), together with the parts of the curve near the asymptotes in a preliminary sketch [Figure 9(a)]. These parts reflect the information concerning limits and the fact that f is decreasing on both $(-\infty, 0)$ and $(0, \infty)$. Notice that we have indicated that $f(x) \to 0$ as $x \to 0^-$ even though $f(0)$ does not exist. In Figure 9(b) we finish the sketch by incorporating the information concerning concavity and the inflection point. In Figure 9(c) we check our work with a graphing device.

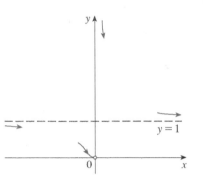
(a) Preliminary sketch

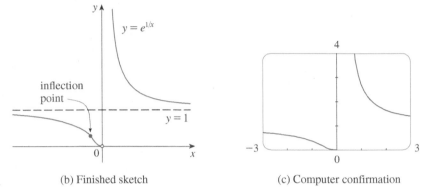
(b) Finished sketch

(c) Computer confirmation

FIGURE 9

EXAMPLE 7 **When does a bee population grow fastest?** A population of honeybees raised in an apiary started with 50 bees at time $t = 0$ and was modeled by the function

$$P(t) = \frac{75{,}200}{1 + 1503e^{-0.5932t}}$$

where t is the time in weeks, $0 \le t \le 25$. Use a graph to estimate the time at which the bee population was growing fastest. Then use derivatives to give a more accurate estimate.

SOLUTION The population grows fastest when the population curve $y = P(t)$ has the steepest tangent line. From the graph of P in Figure 10, we estimate that the steepest tangent occurs when $t \approx 12$, so the bee population was growing most rapidly after about 12 weeks.

For a better estimate we calculate the derivative $P'(t)$, which is the rate of increase of the bee population:

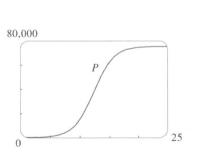

FIGURE 10

$$P'(t) = -\frac{67{,}046{,}785.92e^{-0.5932t}}{(1 + 1503e^{-0.5932t})^2}$$

We graph P' in Figure 11 and observe that P' has its maximum value when $t \approx 12.3$.

To get a still better estimate we note that f' has its maximum value when f' changes from increasing to decreasing. This happens when f changes from concave upward to concave downward, that is, when f has an inflection point. So we ask a CAS to compute the second derivative:

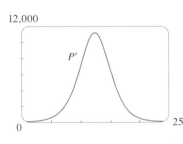

FIGURE 11

$$P''(t) \approx \frac{119555093144e^{-1.1864t}}{(1 + 1503e^{-0.5932t})^3} - \frac{39772153e^{-0.5932t}}{(1 + 1503e^{-0.5932t})^2}$$

We could plot this function to see where it changes from positive to negative, but instead let's have the CAS solve the equation $P''(t) = 0$. It gives the answer $t \approx 12.3318$.

Our final example is concerned with *families* of functions. This means that the functions in the family are related to each other by a formula that contains one or more arbitrary constants. Each value of the constant gives rise to a member of the family and the idea is to see how the graph of the function changes as the constant changes.

EXAMPLE 8 Investigate the family of functions given by $f(x) = cx + \sin x$. What features do the members of this family have in common? How do they differ?

SOLUTION The derivative is $f'(x) = c + \cos x$. If $c > 1$, then $f'(x) > 0$ for all x (since $\cos x \geq -1$), so f is always increasing. If $c = 1$, then $f'(x) = 0$ when x is an odd multiple of π, but f just has horizontal tangents there and is still an increasing function. Similarly, if $c \leq -1$, then f is always decreasing. If $-1 < c < 1$, then the equation $c + \cos x = 0$ has infinitely many solutions $[x = 2n\pi \pm \cos^{-1}(-c)]$ and f has infinitely many minima and maxima.

The second derivative is $f''(x) = -\sin x$, which is negative when $0 < x < \pi$ and, in general, when $2n\pi < x < (2n + 1)\pi$, where n is any integer. Thus *all* members of the family are concave downward on $(0, \pi)$, $(2\pi, 3\pi)$, ... and concave upward on $(\pi, 2\pi)$, $(3\pi, 4\pi)$, ... This is illustrated by several members of the family in Figure 12.

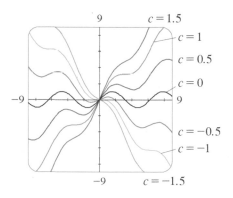

FIGURE 12

4.3   Exercises

1. Use the graph of f to estimate the values of c that satisfy the conclusion of the Mean Value Theorem for the interval $[0, 8]$.

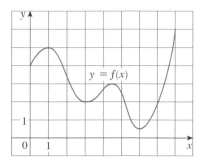

2. Use the given graph of f to find the following.
   (a) The open intervals on which f is concave upward
   (b) The open intervals on which f is concave downward

(c) The coordinates of the points of inflection

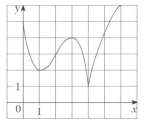

3. Suppose you are given a formula for a function f.
   (a) How do you determine where f is increasing or decreasing?
   (b) How do you determine where the graph of f is concave upward or concave downward?
   (c) How do you locate inflection points?

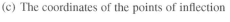 Graphing calculator or computer with graphing software required   CAS Computer algebra system required   **1.** Homework Hints available in TEC

4. (a) State the First Derivative Test.
(b) State the Second Derivative Test. Under what circumstances is it inconclusive? What do you do if it fails?

5. In each part state the x-coordinates of the inflection points of f. Give reasons for your answers.
(a) The curve is the graph of f.
(b) The curve is the graph of f'.
(c) The curve is the graph of f''.

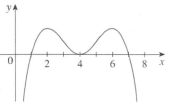

6. The graph of the first derivative f' of a function f is shown.
(a) On what intervals is f increasing? Explain.
(b) At what values of x does f have a local maximum or minimum? Explain.
(c) On what intervals is f concave upward or concave downward? Explain.
(d) What are the x-coordinates of the inflection points of f? Why?

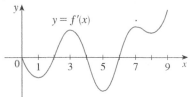

7–16
(a) Find the intervals on which f is increasing or decreasing.
(b) Find the local maximum and minimum values of f.
(c) Find the intervals of concavity and the inflection points.

7. $f(x) = 2x^3 + 3x^2 - 36x$

8. $f(x) = 4x^3 + 3x^2 - 6x + 1$

9. $f(x) = x^4 - 2x^2 + 3$ **10.** $f(x) = \dfrac{x^2}{x^2 + 3}$

11. $f(x) = \sin x + \cos x, \quad 0 \le x \le 2\pi$

12. $f(x) = \cos^2 x - 2 \sin x, \quad 0 \le x \le 2\pi$

13. $f(x) = e^{2x} + e^{-x}$ **14.** $f(x) = x^2 \ln x$

15. $f(x) = (\ln x)/\sqrt{x}$ **16.** $f(x) = \sqrt{x}\,e^{-x}$

17–18 Find the local maximum and minimum values of f using both the First and Second Derivative Tests. Which method do you prefer?

17. $f(x) = x + \sqrt{1 - x}$ **18.** $f(x) = \dfrac{x}{x^2 + 4}$

19. Suppose f'' is continuous on $(-\infty, \infty)$.
(a) If $f'(2) = 0$ and $f''(2) = -5$, what can you say about f?
(b) If $f'(6) = 0$ and $f''(6) = 0$, what can you say about f?

20. (a) Find the critical numbers of $f(x) = x^4(x - 1)^3$.
(b) What does the Second Derivative Test tell you about the behavior of f at these critical numbers?
(c) What does the First Derivative Test tell you?

21–32
(a) Find the intervals of increase or decrease.
(b) Find the local maximum and minimum values.
(c) Find the intervals of concavity and the inflection points.
(d) Use the information from parts (a)–(c) to sketch the graph. Check your work with a graphing device if you have one.

21. $f(x) = 2x^3 - 3x^2 - 12x$ **22.** $f(x) = 2 + 3x - x^3$

23. $f(x) = 2 + 2x^2 - x^4$ **24.** $g(x) = 200 + 8x^3 + x^4$

25. $h(x) = (x + 1)^5 - 5x - 2$ **26.** $h(x) = x^5 - 2x^3 + x$

27. $A(x) = x\sqrt{x + 3}$ **28.** $B(x) = 3x^{2/3} - x$

29. $C(x) = x^{1/3}(x + 4)$ **30.** $f(x) = \ln(x^4 + 27)$

31. $f(\theta) = 2 \cos \theta + \cos^2\theta, \quad 0 \le \theta \le 2\pi$

32. $f(t) = t + \cos t, \quad -2\pi \le t \le 2\pi$

33–40
(a) Find the vertical and horizontal asymptotes.
(b) Find the intervals of increase or decrease.
(c) Find the local maximum and minimum values.
(d) Find the intervals of concavity and the inflection points.
(e) Use the information from parts (a)–(d) to sketch the graph of f.

33. $f(x) = \dfrac{x^2}{x^2 - 1}$ **34.** $f(x) = \dfrac{x^2}{(x - 2)^2}$

35. $f(x) = \sqrt{x^2 + 1} - x$

36. $f(x) = x \tan x, \quad -\pi/2 < x < \pi/2$

37. $f(x) = \ln(1 - \ln x)$ **38.** $f(x) = \dfrac{e^x}{1 + e^x}$

39. $f(x) = e^{-1/(x+1)}$ **40.** $f(x) = e^{\arctan x}$

41. Suppose the derivative of a function f is $f'(x) = (x + 1)^2(x - 3)^5(x - 6)^4$. On what interval is f increasing?

42. Use the methods of this section to sketch the curve $y = x^3 - 3a^2x + 2a^3$, where a is a positive constant. What do the members of this family of curves have in common? How do they differ from each other?

43–44
(a) Use a graph of f to estimate the maximum and minimum values. Then find the exact values.
(b) Estimate the value of x at which f increases most rapidly. Then find the exact value.

43. $f(x) = \dfrac{x + 1}{\sqrt{x^2 + 1}}$ **44.** $f(x) = x^2 e^{-x}$

45–46
(a) Use a graph of f to give a rough estimate of the intervals of concavity and the coordinates of the points of inflection.
(b) Use a graph of f'' to give better estimates.

45. $f(x) = \cos x + \frac{1}{2} \cos 2x, \quad 0 \leqslant x \leqslant 2\pi$

46. $f(x) = x^3(x - 2)^4$

CAS **47–48** Estimate the intervals of concavity to one decimal place by using a computer algebra system to compute and graph f''.

47. $f(x) = \dfrac{x^4 + x^3 + 1}{\sqrt{x^2 + x + 1}}$ **48.** $f(x) = \dfrac{x^2 \tan^{-1} x}{1 + x^3}$

49. Let $f(t)$ be the temperature at time t where you live and suppose that at time $t = 3$ you feel uncomfortably hot. How do you feel about the given data in each case?
(a) $f'(3) = 2, \quad f''(3) = 4$
(b) $f'(3) = 2, \quad f''(3) = -4$
(c) $f'(3) = -2, \quad f''(3) = 4$
(d) $f'(3) = -2, \quad f''(3) = -4$

50. Suppose $f(3) = 2$, $f'(3) = \frac{1}{2}$, and $f'(x) > 0$ and $f''(x) < 0$ for all x.
(a) Sketch a possible graph for f.
(b) How many solutions does the equation $f(x) = 0$ have? Why?
(c) Is it possible that $f'(2) = \frac{1}{3}$? Why?

51–52 Find dy/dx and d^2y/dx^2. For which values of t is the parametric curve concave upward?

51. $x = t^3 - 12t, \quad y = t^2 - 1$

52. $x = \cos 2t, \quad y = \cos t, \quad 0 < t < \pi$

53. In the theory of relativity, the mass of a particle is

$$m = \frac{m_0}{\sqrt{1 - v^2/c^2}}$$

where m_0 is the rest mass of the particle, m is the mass when the particle moves with speed v relative to the observer, and c is the speed of light. Sketch the graph of m as a function of v.

54. In the theory of relativity, the energy of a particle is

$$E = \sqrt{m_0^2 c^4 + h^2 c^2/\lambda^2}$$

where m_0 is the rest mass of the particle, λ is its wave length, and h is Planck's constant. Sketch the graph of E as a function of λ. What does the graph say about the energy?

55. The figure shows a beam of length L embedded in concrete walls. If a constant load W is distributed evenly along its length, the beam takes the shape of the deflection curve

$$y = -\frac{W}{24EI}x^4 + \frac{WL}{12EI}x^3 - \frac{WL^2}{24EI}x^2$$

where E and I are positive constants. (E is Young's modulus of elasticity and I is the moment of inertia of a cross-section of the beam.) Sketch the graph of the deflection curve.

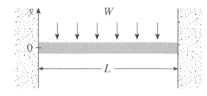

56. Coulomb's Law states that the force of attraction between two charged particles is directly proportional to the product of the charges and inversely proportional to the square of the distance between them. The figure shows particles with charge 1 located at positions 0 and 2 on a coordinate line and a particle with charge -1 at a position x between them. It follows from Coulomb's Law that the net force acting on the middle particle is

$$F(x) = -\frac{k}{x^2} + \frac{k}{(x - 2)^2} \qquad 0 < x < 2$$

where k is a positive constant. Sketch the graph of the net force function. What does the graph say about the force?

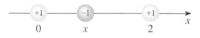

57. A *drug response curve* describes the level of medication in the bloodstream after a drug is administered. A surge function $S(t) = At^p e^{-kt}$ is often used to model the response curve, reflecting an initial surge in the drug level and then a more gradual decline. If, for a particular drug, $A = 0.01$, $p = 4$, $k = 0.07$, and t is measured in minutes, estimate the times corresponding to the inflection points and explain their significance. If you have a graphing device, use it to graph the drug response curve.

58. The family of bell-shaped curves

$$y = \frac{1}{\sigma\sqrt{2\pi}} e^{-(x-\mu)^2/(2\sigma^2)}$$

occurs in probability and statistics, where it is called the *normal density function*. The constant μ is called the *mean* and the positive constant σ is called the *standard deviation*. For simplicity, let's scale the function so as to remove the factor $1/(\sigma\sqrt{2\pi})$ and let's analyze the special case where $\mu = 0$. So we study the function

$$f(x) = e^{-x^2/(2\sigma^2)}$$

(a) Find the asymptote, maximum value, and inflection points of f.
(b) What role does σ play in the shape of the curve?
(c) Illustrate by graphing four members of this family on the same screen.

59. Find a cubic function $f(x) = ax^3 + bx^2 + cx + d$ that has a local maximum value of 3 at $x = -2$ and a local minimum value of 0 at $x = 1$.

60. For what values of the numbers a and b does the function

$$f(x) = axe^{bx^2}$$

have the maximum value $f(2) = 1$?

61. Show that $\tan x > x$ for $0 < x < \pi/2$. [*Hint:* Show that $f(x) = \tan x - x$ is increasing on $(0, \pi/2)$.]

62. (a) Show that $e^x \geq 1 + x$ for $x \geq 0$.
(b) Deduce that $e^x \geq 1 + x + \frac{1}{2}x^2$ for $x \geq 0$.
(c) Use mathematical induction to prove that for $x \geq 0$ and any positive integer n,

$$e^x \geq 1 + x + \frac{x^2}{2!} + \cdots + \frac{x^n}{n!}$$

63. Suppose that $f(0) = -3$ and $f'(x) \leq 5$ for all values of x. The inequality gives a restriction on the rate of growth of f, which then imposes a restriction on the possible values of f. Use the Mean Value Theorem to determine how large $f(4)$ can possibly be.

64. Suppose that $3 \leq f'(x) \leq 5$ for all values of x. Show that $18 \leq f(8) - f(2) \leq 30$.

65. Two runners start a race at the same time and finish in a tie. Prove that at some time during the race they have the same speed. [*Hint:* Consider $f(t) = g(t) - h(t)$, where g and h are the position functions of the two runners.]

66. At 2:00 PM a car's speedometer reads 30 mi/h. At 2:10 PM it reads 50 mi/h. Show that at some time between 2:00 and 2:10 the acceleration is exactly 120 mi/h^2.

67. Show that the curve $y = (1 + x)/(1 + x^2)$ has three points of inflection and they all lie on one straight line.

68. Show that the curves $y = e^{-x}$ and $y = -e^{-x}$ touch the curve $y = e^{-x} \sin x$ at its inflection points.

69. Show that a cubic function (a third-degree polynomial) always has exactly one point of inflection. If its graph has three x-intercepts x_1, x_2, and x_3, show that the x-coordinate of the inflection point is $(x_1 + x_2 + x_3)/3$.

70. For what values of c does the polynomial $P(x) = x^4 + cx^3 + x^2$ have two inflection points? One inflection point? None? Illustrate by graphing P for several values of c. How does the graph change as c decreases?

71. (a) If the function $f(x) = x^3 + ax^2 + bx$ has the local minimum value $-\frac{2}{9}\sqrt{3}$ at $x = 1/\sqrt{3}$, what are the values of a and b?
(b) Which of the tangent lines to the curve in part (a) has the smallest slope?

72. For what values of c is the function

$$f(x) = cx + \frac{1}{x^2 + 3}$$

increasing on $(-\infty, \infty)$?

4.4 Graphing with Calculus *and* Calculators

If you have not already read Section 1.4, you should do so now. In particular, it explains how to avoid some of the pitfalls of graphing devices by choosing appropriate viewing rectangles.

The method we used to sketch curves in the preceding section was a culmination of much of our study of differential calculus. The graph was the final object that we produced. In this section our point of view is completely different. Here we *start* with a graph produced by a graphing calculator or computer and then we refine it. We use calculus to make sure that we reveal all the important aspects of the curve. And with the use of graphing devices we can tackle curves that would be far too complicated to consider without technology. The theme is the *interaction* between calculus and calculators.

EXAMPLE 1 **Discovering hidden behavior**

Graph the polynomial $f(x) = 2x^6 + 3x^5 + 3x^3 - 2x^2$. Use the graphs of f' and f'' to estimate all maximum and minimum points and intervals of concavity.

SOLUTION If we specify a domain but not a range, many graphing devices will deduce a suitable range from the values computed. Figure 1 shows the plot from one such device if we specify that $-5 \leq x \leq 5$. Although this viewing rectangle is useful for showing that the asymptotic behavior (or end behavior) is the same as for $y = 2x^6$, it is obviously hiding some finer detail. So we change to the viewing rectangle $[-3, 2]$ by $[-50, 100]$ shown in Figure 2.

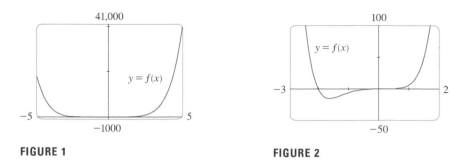

FIGURE 1   **FIGURE 2**

From this graph it appears that there is an absolute minimum value of about -15.33 when $x \approx -1.62$ (by using the cursor) and f is decreasing on $(-\infty, -1.62)$ and increasing on $(-1.62, \infty)$. Also there appears to be a horizontal tangent at the origin and inflection points when $x = 0$ and when x is somewhere between -2 and -1.

Now let's try to confirm these impressions using calculus. We differentiate and get

$$f'(x) = 12x^5 + 15x^4 + 9x^2 - 4x$$

$$f''(x) = 60x^4 + 60x^3 + 18x - 4$$

When we graph f' in Figure 3 we see that $f'(x)$ changes from negative to positive when $x \approx -1.62$; this confirms (by the First Derivative Test) the minimum value that we found earlier. But, perhaps to our surprise, we also notice that $f'(x)$ changes from positive to negative when $x = 0$ and from negative to positive when $x \approx 0.35$. This means that f has a local maximum at 0 and a local minimum when $x \approx 0.35$, but these were hidden in Figure 2. Indeed, if we now zoom in toward the origin in Figure 4, we see what we missed before: a local maximum value of 0 when $x = 0$ and a local minimum value of about -0.1 when $x \approx 0.35$.

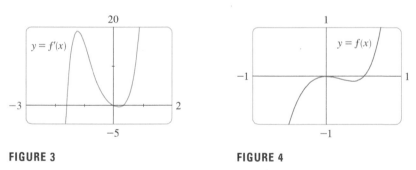

FIGURE 3   **FIGURE 4**

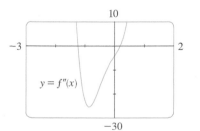

FIGURE 5

What about concavity and inflection points? From Figures 2 and 4 there appear to be inflection points when x is a little to the left of -1 and when x is a little to the right of 0. But it's difficult to determine inflection points from the graph of f, so we graph the second derivative f'' in Figure 5. We see that f'' changes from positive to negative when $x \approx -1.23$ and from negative to positive when $x \approx 0.19$. So, correct to two decimal places, f is concave upward on $(-\infty, -1.23)$ and $(0.19, \infty)$ and concave downward on $(-1.23, 0.19)$. The inflection points are $(-1.23, -10.18)$ and $(0.19, -0.05)$.

We have discovered that no single graph reveals all the important features of this polynomial. But Figures 2 and 4, when taken together, do provide an accurate picture.

V **EXAMPLE 2** Draw the graph of the function

$$f(x) = \frac{x^2 + 7x + 3}{x^2}$$

in a viewing rectangle that contains all the important features of the function. Estimate the maximum and minimum values and the intervals of concavity. Then use calculus to find these quantities exactly.

SOLUTION Figure 6, produced by a computer with automatic scaling, is a disaster. Some graphing calculators use $[-10, 10]$ by $[-10, 10]$ as the default viewing rectangle, so let's try it. We get the graph shown in Figure 7; it's a major improvement.

The y-axis appears to be a vertical asymptote and indeed it is because

$$\lim_{x \to 0} \frac{x^2 + 7x + 3}{x^2} = \infty$$

Figure 7 also allows us to estimate the x-intercepts: about -0.5 and -6.5. The exact values are obtained by using the quadratic formula to solve the equation $x^2 + 7x + 3 = 0$; we get $x = (-7 \pm \sqrt{37})/2$.

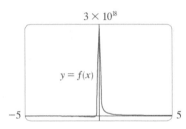

FIGURE 6

FIGURE 7

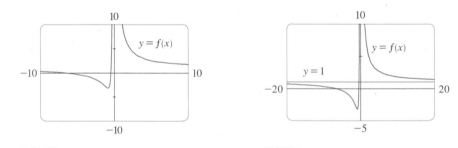

FIGURE 8

To get a better look at horizontal asymptotes, we change to the viewing rectangle $[-20, 20]$ by $[-5, 10]$ in Figure 8. It appears that $y = 1$ is the horizontal asymptote and this is easily confirmed:

$$\lim_{x \to \pm\infty} \frac{x^2 + 7x + 3}{x^2} = \lim_{x \to \pm\infty} \left(1 + \frac{7}{x} + \frac{3}{x^2} \right) = 1$$

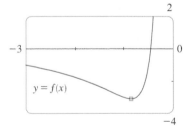

FIGURE 9

To estimate the minimum value we zoom in to the viewing rectangle $[-3, 0]$ by $[-4, 2]$ in Figure 9. The cursor indicates that the absolute minimum value is about -3.1 when $x \approx -0.9$, and we see that the function decreases on $(-\infty, -0.9)$ and $(0, \infty)$ and increases on $(-0.9, 0)$. The exact values are obtained by differentiating:

$$f'(x) = -\frac{7}{x^2} - \frac{6}{x^3} = -\frac{7x + 6}{x^3}$$

This shows that $f'(x) > 0$ when $-\frac{6}{7} < x < 0$ and $f'(x) < 0$ when $x < -\frac{6}{7}$ and when $x > 0$. The exact minimum value is $f\left(-\frac{6}{7}\right) = -\frac{37}{12} \approx -3.08$.

Figure 9 also shows that an inflection point occurs somewhere between $x = -1$ and $x = -2$. We could estimate it much more accurately using the graph of the second derivative, but in this case it's just as easy to find exact values. Since

$$f''(x) = \frac{14}{x^3} + \frac{18}{x^4} = \frac{2(7x + 9)}{x^4}$$

we see that $f''(x) > 0$ when $x > -\frac{9}{7}$ ($x \neq 0$). So f is concave upward on $\left(-\frac{9}{7}, 0\right)$ and $(0, \infty)$ and concave downward on $\left(-\infty, -\frac{9}{7}\right)$. The inflection point is $\left(-\frac{9}{7}, -\frac{71}{27}\right)$.

The analysis using the first two derivatives shows that Figure 8 displays all the major aspects of the curve.

▼ EXAMPLE 3 One graph isn't always enough

Graph the function $f(x) = \dfrac{x^2(x+1)^3}{(x-2)^2(x-4)^4}$.

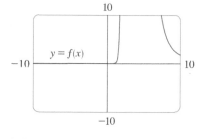

FIGURE 10

SOLUTION Drawing on our experience with a rational function in Example 2, let's start by graphing f in the viewing rectangle $[-10, 10]$ by $[-10, 10]$. From Figure 10 we have the feeling that we are going to have to zoom in to see some finer detail and also zoom out to see the larger picture. But, as a guide to intelligent zooming, let's first take a close look at the expression for $f(x)$. Because of the factors $(x-2)^2$ and $(x-4)^4$ in the denominator, we expect $x = 2$ and $x = 4$ to be the vertical asymptotes. Indeed

$$\lim_{x \to 2} \frac{x^2(x+1)^3}{(x-2)^2(x-4)^4} = \infty \quad \text{and} \quad \lim_{x \to 4} \frac{x^2(x+1)^3}{(x-2)^2(x-4)^4} = \infty$$

To find the horizontal asymptotes, we divide numerator and denominator by x^6:

$$\frac{x^2(x+1)^3}{(x-2)^2(x-4)^4} = \frac{\dfrac{x^2}{x^3} \cdot \dfrac{(x+1)^3}{x^3}}{\dfrac{(x-2)^2}{x^2} \cdot \dfrac{(x-4)^4}{x^4}} = \frac{\dfrac{1}{x}\left(1 + \dfrac{1}{x}\right)^3}{\left(1 - \dfrac{2}{x}\right)^2 \left(1 - \dfrac{4}{x}\right)^4}$$

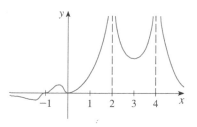

FIGURE 11

This shows that $f(x) \to 0$ as $x \to \pm\infty$, so the x-axis is a horizontal asymptote.

It is also very useful to consider the behavior of the graph near the x-intercepts. Since x^2 is positive, $f(x)$ does not change sign at 0 and so its graph doesn't cross the x-axis at 0. But, because of the factor $(x+1)^3$, the graph does cross the x-axis at -1 and has a horizontal tangent there. Putting all this information together, but without using derivatives, we see that the curve has to look something like the one in Figure 11.

Now that we know what to look for, we zoom in (several times) to produce the graphs in Figures 12 and 13 and zoom out (several times) to get Figure 14.

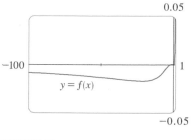

FIGURE 12

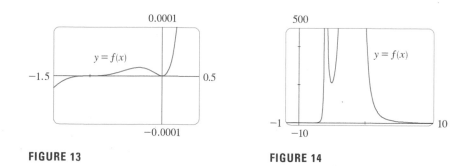

FIGURE 13

FIGURE 14

We can read from these graphs that the absolute minimum is about -0.02 and occurs when $x \approx -20$. There is also a local maximum ≈ 0.00002 when $x \approx -0.3$ and a local minimum ≈ 211 when $x \approx 2.5$. These graphs also show three inflection points near -35, -5, and -1 and two between -1 and 0. To estimate the inflection points closely we would need to graph f'', but to compute f'' by hand is an unreasonable chore. If you have a computer algebra system, then it's easy to do (see Exercise 13).

We have seen that, for this particular function, *three* graphs (Figures 12, 13, and 14) are necessary to convey all the useful information. The only way to display all these features of the function on a single graph is to draw it by hand. Despite the exaggerations and distortions, Figure 11 does manage to summarize the essential nature of the function.

The family of functions

$$f(x) = \sin(x + \sin cx)$$

where c is a constant, occurs in applications to frequency modulation (FM) synthesis. A sine wave is modulated by a wave with a different frequency ($\sin cx$). The case where $c = 2$ is studied in Example 4. Exercise 21 explores another special case.

EXAMPLE 4   Graph the function $f(x) = \sin(x + \sin 2x)$. For $0 \le x \le \pi$, estimate all maximum and minimum values, intervals of increase and decrease, and inflection points.

SOLUTION   We first note that f is periodic with period 2π. Also, f is odd and $|f(x)| \le 1$ for all x. So the choice of a viewing rectangle is not a problem for this function: We start with $[0, \pi]$ by $[-1.1, 1.1]$. (See Figure 15.) It appears that there are three local maximum values and two local minimum values in that window. To confirm this and locate them more accurately, we calculate that

$$f'(x) = \cos(x + \sin 2x) \cdot (1 + 2\cos 2x)$$

and graph both f and f' in Figure 16. Using zoom-in and the First Derivative Test, we find the following approximate values.

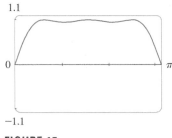

FIGURE 15

Intervals of increase: $(0, 0.6), (1.0, 1.6), (2.1, 2.5)$

Intervals of decrease: $(0.6, 1.0), (1.6, 2.1), (2.5, \pi)$

Local maximum values: $f(0.6) \approx 1, f(1.6) \approx 1, f(2.5) \approx 1$

Local minimum values: $f(1.0) \approx 0.94, f(2.1) \approx 0.94$

The second derivative is

$$f''(x) = -(1 + 2\cos 2x)^2 \sin(x + \sin 2x) - 4\sin 2x \cos(x + \sin 2x)$$

Graphing both f and f'' in Figure 17, we obtain the following approximate values:

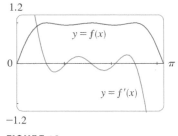

FIGURE 16

Concave upward on: $(0.8, 1.3), (1.8, 2.3)$

Concave downward on: $(0, 0.8), (1.3, 1.8), (2.3, \pi)$

Inflection points: $(0, 0), (0.8, 0.97), (1.3, 0.97), (1.8, 0.97), (2.3, 0.97)$

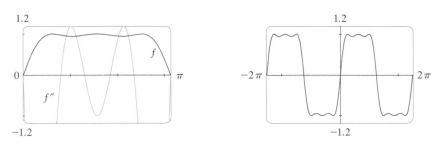

FIGURE 17   **FIGURE 18**

Having checked that Figure 15 does indeed represent f accurately for $0 \le x \le \pi$, we can state that the extended graph in Figure 18 represents f accurately for $-2\pi \le x \le 2\pi$.

▶ EXAMPLE 5   Graphing a family of functions

How does the graph of $f(x) = 1/(x^2 + 2x + c)$ vary as c varies?

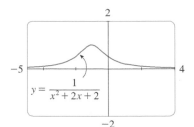

FIGURE 19
$c = 2$

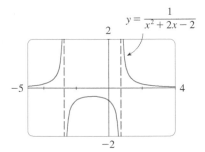

FIGURE 20
$c = -2$

TEC See an animation of Figure 21 in Visual 4.4.

SOLUTION The graphs in Figures 19 and 20 (the special cases $c = 2$ and $c = -2$) show two very different-looking curves. Before drawing any more graphs, let's see what members of this family have in common. Since

$$\lim_{x \to \pm\infty} \frac{1}{x^2 + 2x + c} = 0$$

for any value of c, they all have the x-axis as a horizontal asymptote. A vertical asymptote will occur when $x^2 + 2x + c = 0$. Solving this quadratic equation, we get $x = -1 \pm \sqrt{1 - c}$. When $c > 1$, there is no vertical asymptote (as in Figure 19). When $c = 1$, the graph has a single vertical asymptote $x = -1$ because

$$\lim_{x \to -1} \frac{1}{x^2 + 2x + 1} = \lim_{x \to -1} \frac{1}{(x + 1)^2} = \infty$$

When $c < 1$, there are two vertical asymptotes: $x = -1 \pm \sqrt{1 - c}$ (as in Figure 20).
   Now we compute the derivative:

$$f'(x) = -\frac{2x + 2}{(x^2 + 2x + c)^2}$$

This shows that $f'(x) = 0$ when $x = -1$ (if $c \neq 1$), $f'(x) > 0$ when $x < -1$, and $f'(x) < 0$ when $x > -1$. For $c \geq 1$, this means that f increases on $(-\infty, -1)$ and decreases on $(-1, \infty)$. For $c > 1$, there is an absolute maximum value $f(-1) = 1/(c - 1)$. For $c < 1$, $f(-1) = 1/(c - 1)$ is a local maximum value and the intervals of increase and decrease are interrupted at the vertical asymptotes.
   Figure 21 is a "slide show" displaying five members of the family, all graphed in the viewing rectangle $[-5, 4]$ by $[-2, 2]$. As predicted, $c = 1$ is the value at which a transition takes place from two vertical asymptotes to one, and then to none. As c increases from 1, we see that the maximum point becomes lower; this is explained by the fact that $1/(c - 1) \to 0$ as $c \to \infty$. As c decreases from 1, the vertical asymptotes become more widely separated because the distance between them is $2\sqrt{1 - c}$, which becomes large as $c \to -\infty$. Again, the maximum point approaches the x-axis because $1/(c - 1) \to 0$ as $c \to -\infty$.

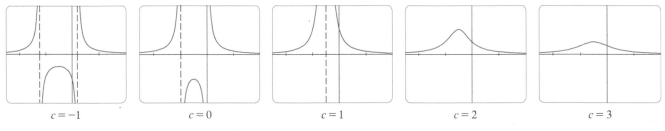

| $c = -1$ | $c = 0$ | $c = 1$ | $c = 2$ | $c = 3$ |

FIGURE 21   The family of functions $f(x) = 1/(x^2 + 2x + c)$

There is clearly no inflection point when $c \leq 1$. For $c > 1$ we calculate that

$$f''(x) = \frac{2(3x^2 + 6x + 4 - c)}{(x^2 + 2x + c)^3}$$

and deduce that inflection points occur when $x = -1 \pm \sqrt{3(c - 1)}/3$. So the inflection points become more spread out as c increases and this seems plausible from the last two parts of Figure 21.

In Section 1.7 we used graphing devices to graph parametric curves and in Section 3.4 we found tangents to parametric curves. But, as our final example shows, we are now in a position to use calculus to ensure that a parameter interval or a viewing rectangle will reveal all the important aspects of a curve.

EXAMPLE 6 Graph the curve with parametric equations

$$x(t) = t^2 + t + 1 \qquad y(t) = 3t^4 - 8t^3 - 18t^2 + 25$$

in a viewing rectangle that displays the important features of the curve. Find the coordinates of the interesting points on the curve.

SOLUTION Figure 22 shows the graph of this curve in the viewing rectangle $[0, 4]$ by $[-20, 60]$. Zooming in toward the point P where the curve intersects itself, we estimate that the coordinates of P are $(1.50, 22.25)$. We estimate that the highest point on the loop has coordinates $(1, 25)$, the lowest point $(1, 18)$, and the leftmost point $(0.75, 21.7)$. To be sure that we have discovered all the interesting aspects of the curve, however, we need to use calculus. From Equation 3.4.7, we have

$$\frac{dy}{dx} = \frac{dy/dt}{dx/dt} = \frac{12t^3 - 24t^2 - 36t}{2t + 1}$$

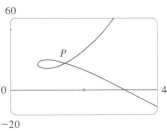

FIGURE 22

The vertical tangent occurs when $dx/dt = 2t + 1 = 0$, that is, $t = -\frac{1}{2}$. So the exact coordinates of the leftmost point of the loop are $x\left(-\frac{1}{2}\right) = 0.75$ and $y\left(-\frac{1}{2}\right) = 21.6875$. Also,

$$\frac{dy}{dt} = 12t(t^2 - 2t - 3) = 12t(t + 1)(t - 3)$$

and so horizontal tangents occur when $t = 0$, -1, and 3. The bottom of the loop corresponds to $t = -1$ and, indeed, its coordinates are $x(-1) = 1$ and $y(-1) = 18$. Similarly, the coordinates of the top of the loop are exactly what we estimated: $x(0) = 1$ and $y(0) = 25$. But what about the parameter value $t = 3$? The corresponding point on the curve has coordinates $x(3) = 13$ and $y(3) = -110$. Figure 23 shows the graph of the curve in the viewing rectangle $[0, 25]$ by $[-120, 80]$. This shows that the point $(13, -110)$ is the lowest point on the curve. We can now be confident that there are no hidden maximum or minimum points.

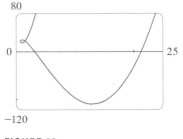

FIGURE 23

4.4 ⊞ Exercises

1–8 Produce graphs of f that reveal all the important aspects of the curve. In particular, you should use graphs of f' and f'' to estimate the intervals of increase and decrease, extreme values, intervals of concavity, and inflection points.

1. $f(x) = 4x^4 - 32x^3 + 89x^2 - 95x + 29$

2. $f(x) = x^6 - 15x^5 + 75x^4 - 125x^3 - x$

3. $f(x) = x^6 - 10x^5 - 400x^4 + 2500x^3$

4. $f(x) = \dfrac{x^2 - 1}{40x^3 + x + 1}$

5. $f(x) = \dfrac{x}{x^3 - x^2 - 4x + 1}$

6. $f(x) = \tan x + 5 \cos x$

7. $f(x) = x^2 - 4x + 7 \cos x, \quad -4 \leqslant x \leqslant 4$

8. $f(x) = \dfrac{e^x}{x^2 - 9}$

9–10 Produce graphs of f that reveal all the important aspects of the curve. Estimate the intervals of increase and decrease and intervals of concavity, and use calculus to find these intervals exactly.

9. $f(x) = 1 + \dfrac{1}{x} + \dfrac{8}{x^2} + \dfrac{1}{x^3}$

10. $f(x) = \dfrac{1}{x^8} - \dfrac{2 \times 10^8}{x^4}$

11–12 Sketch the graph by hand using asymptotes and intercepts, but not derivatives. Then use your sketch as a guide to producing graphs (with a graphing device) that display the major features of the curve. Use these graphs to estimate the maximum and minimum values.

11. $f(x) = \dfrac{(x + 4)(x - 3)^2}{x^4(x - 1)}$

12. $f(x) = \dfrac{(2x + 3)^2(x - 2)^5}{x^3(x - 5)^2}$

[CAS] **13.** If f is the function considered in Example 3, use a computer algebra system to calculate f' and then graph it to confirm that all the maximum and minimum values are as given in the example. Calculate f'' and use it to estimate the intervals of concavity and inflection points.

[CAS] **14.** If f is the function of Exercise 12, find f' and f'' and use their graphs to estimate the intervals of increase and decrease and concavity of f.

[CAS] **15–19** Use a computer algebra system to graph f and to find f' and f''. Use graphs of these derivatives to estimate the intervals of increase and decrease, extreme values, intervals of concavity, and inflection points of f.

15. $f(x) = \dfrac{\sqrt{x}}{x^2 + x + 1}$

16. $f(x) = \dfrac{x^{2/3}}{1 + x + x^4}$

17. $f(x) = \sqrt{x + 5 \sin x}, \quad x \le 20$

18. $f(x) = (x^2 - 1)e^{\arctan x}$

19. $f(x) = \dfrac{1 - e^{1/x}}{1 + e^{1/x}}$

---

20. Graph $f(x) = e^x + \ln|x - 4|$ using as many viewing rectangles as you need to depict the true nature of the function.

21. In Example 4 we considered a member of the family of functions $f(x) = \sin(x + \sin cx)$ that occur in FM synthesis. Here we investigate the function with $c = 3$. Start by graphing f in the viewing rectangle $[0, \pi]$ by $[-1.2, 1.2]$. How many local maximum points do you see? The graph has more than are visible to the naked eye. To discover the hidden maximum and minimum points you will need to examine the graph of f' very carefully. In fact, it helps to look at the graph of f'' at the same time. Find all the maximum and minimum values and inflection points. Then graph f in the viewing rectangle $[-2\pi, 2\pi]$ by $[-1.2, 1.2]$ and comment on symmetry.

22. Use a graph to estimate the coordinates of the leftmost point on the curve $x = t^4 - t^2$, $y = t + \ln t$. Then use calculus to find the exact coordinates.

23–24 Graph the curve in a viewing rectangle that displays all the important aspects of the curve. At what points does the curve have vertical or horizontal tangents?

23. $x = t^4 - 2t^3 - 2t^2$, $\quad y = t^3 - t$

24. $x = t^4 + 4t^3 - 8t^2$, $\quad y = 2t^2 - t$

---

25. Investigate the family of curves given by the parametric equations $x = t^3 - ct$, $y = t^2$. In particular, determine the values of c for which there is a loop and find the point where the curve intersects itself. What happens to the loop as c increases? Find the coordinates of the leftmost and rightmost points of the loop.

26. The family of functions $f(t) = C(e^{-at} - e^{-bt})$, where a, b, and C are positive numbers and $b > a$, has been used to model the concentration of a drug injected into the bloodstream at time $t = 0$. Graph several members of this family. What do they have in common? For fixed values of C and a, discover graphically what happens as b increases. Then use calculus to prove what you have discovered.

27–33 Describe how the graph of f varies as c varies. Graph several members of the family to illustrate the trends that you discover. In particular, you should investigate how maximum and minimum points and inflection points move when c changes. You should also identify any transitional values of c at which the basic shape of the curve changes.

27. $f(x) = x^4 + cx^2$ **28.** $f(x) = x^3 + cx$

29. $f(x) = e^x + ce^{-x}$ **30.** $f(x) = \ln(x^2 + c)$

31. $f(x) = \dfrac{cx}{1 + c^2x^2}$ **32.** $f(x) = \dfrac{1}{(1 - x^2)^2 + cx^2}$

33. $f(x) = cx + \sin x$

---

34. Investigate the family of curves given by the equation $f(x) = x^4 + cx^2 + x$. Start by determining the transitional value of c at which the number of inflection points changes. Then graph several members of the family to see what shapes are possible. There is another transitional value of c at which the number of critical numbers changes. Try to discover it graphically. Then prove what you have discovered.

35. (a) Investigate the family of polynomials given by the equation $f(x) = cx^4 - 2x^2 + 1$. For what values of c does the curve have minimum points?

     (b) Show that the minimum and maximum points of every curve in the family lie on the parabola $y = 1 - x^2$. Illustrate by graphing this parabola and several members of the family.

36. (a) Investigate the family of polynomials given by the equation $f(x) = 2x^3 + cx^2 + 2x$. For what values of c does the curve have maximum and minimum points?

     (b) Show that the minimum and maximum points of every curve in the family lie on the curve $y = x - x^3$. Illustrate by graphing this curve and several members of the family.

4.5 Indeterminate Forms and l'Hospital's Rule

Suppose we are trying to analyze the behavior of the function

$$F(x) = \frac{\ln x}{x - 1}$$

Although F is not defined when $x = 1$, we need to know how F behaves *near* 1. In particular, we would like to know the value of the limit

$$\boxed{1} \qquad \lim_{x \to 1} \frac{\ln x}{x - 1}$$

In computing this limit we can't apply Law 5 of limits (the limit of a quotient is the quotient of the limits, see Section 2.3) because the limit of the denominator is 0. In fact, although the limit in (1) exists, its value is not obvious because both numerator and denominator approach 0 and $\frac{0}{0}$ is not defined.

In general, if we have a limit of the form

$$\lim_{x \to a} \frac{f(x)}{g(x)}$$

where both $f(x) \to 0$ and $g(x) \to 0$ as $x \to a$, then this limit may or may not exist and is called an **indeterminate form of type $\frac{0}{0}$**. We met some limits of this type in Chapter 2. For rational functions, we can cancel common factors:

$$\lim_{x \to 1} \frac{x^2 - x}{x^2 - 1} = \lim_{x \to 1} \frac{x(x - 1)}{(x + 1)(x - 1)} = \lim_{x \to 1} \frac{x}{x + 1} = \frac{1}{2}$$

We used a geometric argument to show that

$$\lim_{x \to 0} \frac{\sin x}{x} = 1$$

But these methods do not work for limits such as (1), so in this section we introduce a systematic method, known as *l'Hospital's Rule*, for the evaluation of indeterminate forms.

Another situation in which a limit is not obvious occurs when we look for a horizontal asymptote of F and need to evaluate the limit

$$\boxed{2} \qquad \lim_{x \to \infty} \frac{\ln x}{x - 1}$$

It isn't obvious how to evaluate this limit because both numerator and denominator become large as $x \to \infty$. There is a struggle between numerator and denominator. If the numerator wins, the limit will be ∞; if the denominator wins, the answer will be 0. Or there may be some compromise, in which case the answer will be some finite positive number.

In general, if we have a limit of the form

$$\lim_{x \to a} \frac{f(x)}{g(x)}$$

where both $f(x) \to \infty$ (or $-\infty$) and $g(x) \to \infty$ (or $-\infty$), then the limit may or may not exist and is called an **indeterminate form of type ∞/∞**. We saw in Section 2.5 that this type of limit can be evaluated for certain functions, including rational functions, by dividing numerator and denominator by the highest power of x that occurs in the denominator. For instance,

$$\lim_{x \to \infty} \frac{x^2 - 1}{2x^2 + 1} = \lim_{x \to \infty} \frac{1 - \dfrac{1}{x^2}}{2 + \dfrac{1}{x^2}} = \frac{1 - 0}{2 + 0} = \frac{1}{2}$$

This method does not work for limits such as (2), but l'Hospital's Rule also applies to this type of indeterminate form.

L'Hospital

L'Hospital's Rule is named after a French noble-man, the Marquis de l'Hospital (1661–1704), but was discovered by a Swiss mathematician, John Bernoulli (1667–1748). You might some-times see l'Hospital spelled as l'Hôpital, but he spelled his own name l'Hospital, as was com-mon in the 17th century. See Exercise 69 for the example that the Marquis used to illustrate his rule. See the project on page 299 for fur-ther historical details.

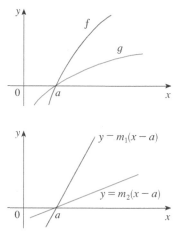

FIGURE 1

Figure 1 suggests visually why l'Hospital's Rule might be true. The first graph shows two differentiable functions f and g, each of which approaches 0 as $x \to a$. If we were to zoom in toward the point $(a, 0)$, the graphs would start to look almost linear. But if the functions actually *were* linear, as in the sec-ond graph, then their ratio would be

$$\frac{m_1(x - a)}{m_2(x - a)} = \frac{m_1}{m_2}$$

which is the ratio of their derivatives. This suggests that

$$\lim_{x \to a} \frac{f(x)}{g(x)} = \lim_{x \to a} \frac{f'(x)}{g'(x)}$$

L'Hospital's Rule Suppose f and g are differentiable and $g'(x) \neq 0$ near a (except possibly at a). Suppose that

$$\lim_{x \to a} f(x) = 0 \qquad \text{and} \qquad \lim_{x \to a} g(x) = 0$$

or that

$$\lim_{x \to a} f(x) = \pm\infty \qquad \text{and} \qquad \lim_{x \to a} g(x) = \pm\infty$$

(In other words, we have an indeterminate form of type $\frac{0}{0}$ or ∞/∞.) Then

$$\lim_{x \to a} \frac{f(x)}{g(x)} = \lim_{x \to a} \frac{f'(x)}{g'(x)}$$

if the limit on the right side exists (or is ∞ or $-\infty$).

Note 1: L'Hospital's Rule says that the limit of a quotient of functions is equal to the limit of the quotient of their derivatives, provided that the given conditions are satisfied. It is especially important to verify the conditions regarding the limits of f and g before using l'Hospital's Rule.

Note 2: L'Hospital's Rule is also valid for one-sided limits and for limits at infinity or negative infinity; that is, "$x \to a$" can be replaced by any of the symbols $x \to a^+$, $x \to a^-$, $x \to \infty$, or $x \to -\infty$.

Note 3: For the special case in which $f(a) = g(a) = 0$, f' and g' are continuous, and $g'(a) \neq 0$, it is easy to see why l'Hospital's Rule is true. In fact, using the alternative form of the definition of a derivative, we have

$$\lim_{x \to a} \frac{f'(x)}{g'(x)} = \frac{f'(a)}{g'(a)} = \frac{\displaystyle\lim_{x \to a} \frac{f(x) - f(a)}{x - a}}{\displaystyle\lim_{x \to a} \frac{g(x) - g(a)}{x - a}} = \lim_{x \to a} \frac{\dfrac{f(x) - f(a)}{x - a}}{\dfrac{g(x) - g(a)}{x - a}}$$

$$= \lim_{x \to a} \frac{f(x) - f(a)}{g(x) - g(a)} = \lim_{x \to a} \frac{f(x)}{g(x)}$$

The general version of l'Hospital's Rule is more difficult; its proof can be found in more advanced books.

⚡ **EXAMPLE 1** **An indeterminate form of type 0/0**   Find $\lim\limits_{x \to 1} \dfrac{\ln x}{x - 1}$.

SOLUTION Since

$$\lim_{x \to 1} \ln x = \ln 1 = 0 \qquad \text{and} \qquad \lim_{x \to 1} (x - 1) = 0$$

we can apply l'Hospital's Rule:

⊘ Notice that when using l'Hospital's Rule we differentiate the numerator and denominator *separately*. We do *not* use the Quotient Rule.

$$\lim_{x \to 1} \frac{\ln x}{x - 1} = \lim_{x \to 1} \frac{\dfrac{d}{dx}(\ln x)}{\dfrac{d}{dx}(x - 1)} = \lim_{x \to 1} \frac{1/x}{1}$$

$$= \lim_{x \to 1} \frac{1}{x} = 1$$

The graph of the function of Example 2 is shown in Figure 2. We have noticed previously that exponential functions grow far more rapidly than power functions, so the result of Example 2 is not unexpected. See also Exercise 63.

⚡ **EXAMPLE 2** **An indeterminate form of type ∞/∞**   Calculate $\lim\limits_{x \to \infty} \dfrac{e^x}{x^2}$.

SOLUTION We have $\lim_{x \to \infty} e^x = \infty$ and $\lim_{x \to \infty} x^2 = \infty$, so l'Hospital's Rule gives

$$\lim_{x \to \infty} \frac{e^x}{x^2} = \lim_{x \to \infty} \frac{\dfrac{d}{dx}(e^x)}{\dfrac{d}{dx}(x^2)} = \lim_{x \to \infty} \frac{e^x}{2x}$$

Since $e^x \to \infty$ and $2x \to \infty$ as $x \to \infty$, the limit on the right side is also indeterminate, but a second application of l'Hospital's Rule gives

$$\lim_{x \to \infty} \frac{e^x}{x^2} = \lim_{x \to \infty} \frac{e^x}{2x} = \lim_{x \to \infty} \frac{e^x}{2} = \infty$$

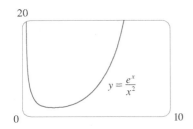

20

$y = \dfrac{e^x}{x^2}$

0   10

FIGURE 2

The graph of the function of Example 3 is shown in Figure 3. We have discussed previously the slow growth of logarithms, so it isn't surprising that this ratio approaches 0 as $x \to \infty$. See also Exercise 64.

⚡ **EXAMPLE 3** Calculate $\lim\limits_{x \to \infty} \dfrac{\ln x}{\sqrt[3]{x}}$.

SOLUTION Since $\ln x \to \infty$ and $\sqrt[3]{x} \to \infty$ as $x \to \infty$, l'Hospital's Rule applies:

$$\lim_{x \to \infty} \frac{\ln x}{\sqrt[3]{x}} = \lim_{x \to \infty} \frac{1/x}{\frac{1}{3} x^{-2/3}}$$

Notice that the limit on the right side is now indeterminate of type $\frac{0}{0}$. But instead of applying l'Hospital's Rule a second time as we did in Example 2, we simplify the expression and see that a second application is unnecessary:

$$\lim_{x \to \infty} \frac{\ln x}{\sqrt[3]{x}} = \lim_{x \to \infty} \frac{1/x}{\frac{1}{3} x^{-2/3}} = \lim_{x \to \infty} \frac{3}{\sqrt[3]{x}} = 0$$

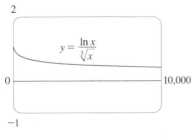

2

$y = \dfrac{\ln x}{\sqrt[3]{x}}$

0   10,000

−1

FIGURE 3

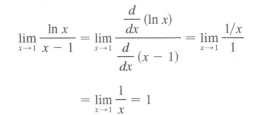

EXAMPLE 4 **Using l'Hospital's Rule three times** Find $\lim\limits_{x \to 0} \dfrac{\tan x - x}{x^3}$.

SOLUTION Noting that both $\tan x - x \to 0$ and $x^3 \to 0$ as $x \to 0$, we use l'Hospital's Rule:

$$\lim_{x \to 0} \frac{\tan x - x}{x^3} = \lim_{x \to 0} \frac{\sec^2 x - 1}{3x^2}$$

Since the limit on the right side is still indeterminate of type $\frac{0}{0}$, we apply l'Hospital's Rule again:

$$\lim_{x \to 0} \frac{\sec^2 x - 1}{3x^2} = \lim_{x \to 0} \frac{2 \sec^2 x \tan x}{6x}$$

Because $\lim_{x \to 0} \sec^2 x = 1$, we simplify the calculation by writing

$$\lim_{x \to 0} \frac{2 \sec^2 x \tan x}{6x} = \frac{1}{3} \lim_{x \to 0} \sec^2 x \cdot \lim_{x \to 0} \frac{\tan x}{x} = \frac{1}{3} \lim_{x \to 0} \frac{\tan x}{x}$$

We can evaluate this last limit either by using l'Hospital's Rule a third time or by writing $\tan x$ as $(\sin x)/(\cos x)$ and making use of our knowledge of trigonometric limits. Putting together all the steps, we get

$$\lim_{x \to 0} \frac{\tan x - x}{x^3} = \lim_{x \to 0} \frac{\sec^2 x - 1}{3x^2} = \lim_{x \to 0} \frac{2 \sec^2 x \tan x}{6x}$$

$$= \frac{1}{3} \lim_{x \to 0} \frac{\tan x}{x} = \frac{1}{3} \lim_{x \to 0} \frac{\sec^2 x}{1} = \frac{1}{3}$$

The graph in Figure 4 gives visual confirmation of the result of Example 4. If we were to zoom in too far, however, we would get an inaccurate graph because $\tan x$ is close to x when x is small. See Exercise 30(d) in Section 2.2.

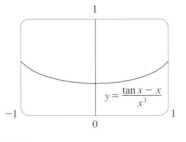

$$y = \frac{\tan x - x}{x^3}$$

FIGURE 4

V **EXAMPLE 5** Find $\lim\limits_{x \to \pi^-} \dfrac{\sin x}{1 - \cos x}$.

SOLUTION If we blindly attempted to use l'Hospital's Rule, we would get

$$\lim_{x \to \pi^-} \frac{\sin x}{1 - \cos x} = \lim_{x \to \pi^-} \frac{\cos x}{\sin x} = -\infty$$

This is **wrong**! Although the numerator $\sin x \to 0$ as $x \to \pi^-$, notice that the denominator $(1 - \cos x)$ does not approach 0, so l'Hospital's Rule can't be applied here.

The required limit is, in fact, easy to find because the function is continuous at π and the denominator is nonzero there:

$$\lim_{x \to \pi^-} \frac{\sin x}{1 - \cos x} = \frac{\sin \pi}{1 - \cos \pi} = \frac{0}{1 - (-1)} = 0$$

Example 5 shows what can go wrong if you use l'Hospital's Rule without thinking. Other limits *can* be found using l'Hospital's Rule but are more easily found by other methods. (See Examples 3 and 5 in Section 2.3, Example 5 in Section 2.5, and the discussion at the beginning of this section.) So when evaluating any limit, you should consider other methods before using l'Hospital's Rule.

Indeterminate Products

If $\lim_{x \to a} f(x) = 0$ and $\lim_{x \to a} g(x) = \infty$ (or $-\infty$), then it isn't clear what the value of $\lim_{x \to a} f(x)g(x)$, if any, will be. There is a struggle between f and g. If f wins, the limit will be 0; if g wins, the answer will be ∞ (or $-\infty$). Or there may be a compromise where the answer is a finite nonzero number. This kind of limit is called an **indeterminate form of type $0 \cdot \infty$**. We can deal with it by writing the product fg as a quotient:

$$fg = \frac{f}{1/g} \qquad \text{or} \qquad fg = \frac{g}{1/f}$$

This converts the given limit into an indeterminate form of type $\frac{0}{0}$ or ∞/∞ so that we can use l'Hospital's Rule.

V   **EXAMPLE 6**   Evaluate $\lim_{x \to 0^+} x \ln x$. Use the knowledge of this limit, together with information from derivatives, to sketch the curve $y = x \ln x$.

SOLUTION   The given limit is indeterminate because, as $x \to 0^+$, the first factor (x) approaches 0 while the second factor $(\ln x)$ approaches $-\infty$. Writing $x = 1/(1/x)$, we have $1/x \to \infty$ as $x \to 0^+$, so l'Hospital's Rule gives

$$\lim_{x \to 0^+} x \ln x = \lim_{x \to 0^+} \frac{\ln x}{1/x} = \lim_{x \to 0^+} \frac{1/x}{-1/x^2} = \lim_{x \to 0^+} (-x) = 0$$

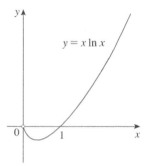

$y = x \ln x$

FIGURE 5

If $f(x) = x \ln x$, then

$$f'(x) = x \cdot \frac{1}{x} + \ln x = 1 + \ln x$$

so $f'(x) = 0$ when $\ln x = -1$, which means that $x = e^{-1}$. In fact, $f'(x) > 0$ when $x > e^{-1}$ and $f'(x) < 0$ when $x < e^{-1}$, so f is increasing on $(1/e, \infty)$ and decreasing on $(0, 1/e)$. Thus, by the First Derivative Test, $f(1/e) = -1/e$ is a local (and absolute) minimum. Also, $f''(x) = 1/x > 0$, so f is concave upward on $(0, \infty)$. We use this information, together with the crucial knowledge that $\lim_{x \to 0^+} f(x) = 0$, to sketch the curve in Figure 5.

Note: In solving Example 6 another possible option would have been to write

$$\lim_{x \to 0^+} x \ln x = \lim_{x \to 0^+} \frac{x}{1/\ln x}$$

This gives an indeterminate form of the type 0/0, but if we apply l'Hospital's Rule we get a more complicated expression than the one we started with. In general, when we rewrite an indeterminate product, we try to choose the option that leads to the simpler limit.

Indeterminate Differences

If $\lim_{x \to a} f(x) = \infty$ and $\lim_{x \to a} g(x) = \infty$, then the limit

$$\lim_{x \to a} [f(x) - g(x)]$$

is called an **indeterminate form of type $\infty - \infty$**. Again there is a contest between f and g. Will the answer be ∞ (f wins) or will it be $-\infty$ (g wins) or will they compromise on a finite number? To find out, we try to convert the difference into a quotient (for instance, by using a common denominator, or rationalization, or factoring out a common factor) so that we have an indeterminate form of type $\frac{0}{0}$ or ∞/∞.

EXAMPLE 7 **An indeterminate form of type $\infty - \infty$** Compute $\lim\limits_{x \to (\pi/2)^-} (\sec x - \tan x)$.

SOLUTION First notice that $\sec x \to \infty$ and $\tan x \to \infty$ as $x \to (\pi/2)^-$, so the limit is indeterminate. Here we use a common denominator:

$$\lim_{x \to (\pi/2)^-} (\sec x - \tan x) = \lim_{x \to (\pi/2)^-} \left(\frac{1}{\cos x} - \frac{\sin x}{\cos x} \right)$$

$$= \lim_{x \to (\pi/2)^-} \frac{1 - \sin x}{\cos x} = \lim_{x \to (\pi/2)^-} \frac{-\cos x}{-\sin x} = 0$$

Note that the use of l'Hospital's Rule is justified because $1 - \sin x \to 0$ and $\cos x \to 0$ as $x \to (\pi/2)^-$.

Indeterminate Powers

Several indeterminate forms arise from the limit

$$\lim_{x \to a} [f(x)]^{g(x)}$$

1. $\lim\limits_{x \to a} f(x) = 0$ and $\lim\limits_{x \to a} g(x) = 0$ type 0^0

2. $\lim\limits_{x \to a} f(x) = \infty$ and $\lim\limits_{x \to a} g(x) = 0$ type ∞^0

3. $\lim\limits_{x \to a} f(x) = 1$ and $\lim\limits_{x \to a} g(x) = \pm\infty$ type 1^∞

Although forms of the type 0^0, ∞^0, and 1^∞ are indeterminate, the form 0^∞ is not indeterminate. (See Exercise 72.)

Each of these three cases can be treated either by taking the natural logarithm:

$$\text{let} \quad y = [f(x)]^{g(x)}, \quad \text{then} \quad \ln y = g(x) \ln f(x)$$

or by writing the function as an exponential:

$$[f(x)]^{g(x)} = e^{g(x) \ln f(x)}$$

(Recall that both of these methods were used in differentiating such functions.) In either method we are led to the indeterminate product $g(x) \ln f(x)$, which is of type $0 \cdot \infty$.

EXAMPLE 8 **An indeterminate form of type 1^∞** Calculate $\lim\limits_{x \to 0^+} (1 + \sin 4x)^{\cot x}$.

SOLUTION First notice that as $x \to 0^+$, we have $1 + \sin 4x \to 1$ and $\cot x \to \infty$, so the given limit is indeterminate. Let

$$y = (1 + \sin 4x)^{\cot x}$$

Then $\ln y = \ln[(1 + \sin 4x)^{\cot x}] = \cot x \ln(1 + \sin 4x)$

so l'Hospital's Rule gives

$$\lim_{x \to 0^+} \ln y = \lim_{x \to 0^+} \frac{\ln(1 + \sin 4x)}{\tan x} = \lim_{x \to 0^+} \frac{\dfrac{4 \cos 4x}{1 + \sin 4x}}{\sec^2 x} = 4$$

So far we have computed the limit of $\ln y$, but what we want is the limit of y. To find this we use the fact that $y = e^{\ln y}$:

$$\lim_{x \to 0^+} (1 + \sin 4x)^{\cot x} = \lim_{x \to 0^+} y = \lim_{x \to 0^+} e^{\ln y} = e^4$$

> **V** **EXAMPLE 9** **An indeterminate form of type 0^0** Find $\lim\limits_{x \to 0^+} x^x$.

SOLUTION Notice that this limit is indeterminate since $0^x = 0$ for any $x > 0$ but $x^0 = 1$ for any $x \neq 0$. We could proceed as in Example 8 or by writing the function as an exponential:

$$x^x = (e^{\ln x})^x = e^{x \ln x}$$

In Example 6 we used l'Hospital's Rule to show that

$$\lim_{x \to 0^+} x \ln x = 0$$

Therefore

$$\lim_{x \to 0^+} x^x = \lim_{x \to 0^+} e^{x \ln x} = e^0 = 1$$

The graph of the function $y = x^x$, $x > 0$, is shown in Figure 6. Notice that although 0^0 is not defined, the values of the function approach 1 as $x \to 0^+$. This confirms the result of Example 9.

FIGURE 6

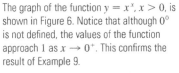

4.5 Exercises

1–4 Given that

$$\lim_{x \to a} f(x) = 0 \qquad \lim_{x \to a} g(x) = 0 \qquad \lim_{x \to a} h(x) = 1$$

$$\lim_{x \to a} p(x) = \infty \qquad \lim_{x \to a} q(x) = \infty$$

which of the following limits are indeterminate forms? For those that are not an indeterminate form, evaluate the limit where possible.

1. (a) $\lim\limits_{x \to a} \dfrac{f(x)}{g(x)}$ (b) $\lim\limits_{x \to a} \dfrac{f(x)}{p(x)}$ (c) $\lim\limits_{x \to a} \dfrac{h(x)}{p(x)}$

    (d) $\lim\limits_{x \to a} \dfrac{p(x)}{f(x)}$ (e) $\lim\limits_{x \to a} \dfrac{p(x)}{q(x)}$

2. (a) $\lim\limits_{x \to a} [f(x)p(x)]$ (b) $\lim\limits_{x \to a} [h(x)p(x)]$

    (c) $\lim\limits_{x \to a} [p(x)q(x)]$

3. (a) $\lim\limits_{x \to a} [f(x) - p(x)]$ (b) $\lim\limits_{x \to a} [p(x) - q(x)]$

    (c) $\lim\limits_{x \to a} [p(x) + q(x)]$

4. (a) $\lim\limits_{x \to a} [f(x)]^{g(x)}$ (b) $\lim\limits_{x \to a} [f(x)]^{p(x)}$ (c) $\lim\limits_{x \to a} [h(x)]^{p(x)}$

    (d) $\lim\limits_{x \to a} [p(x)]^{f(x)}$ (e) $\lim\limits_{x \to a} [p(x)]^{q(x)}$ (f) $\lim\limits_{x \to a} \sqrt[q(x)]{p(x)}$

5–46 Find the limit. Use l'Hospital's Rule where appropriate. If there is a more elementary method, consider using it. If l'Hospital's Rule doesn't apply, explain why.

5. $\lim\limits_{x \to 1} \dfrac{x^2 - 1}{x^2 - x}$

6. $\lim\limits_{x \to 1} \dfrac{x^a - 1}{x^b - 1}$

7. $\lim\limits_{x \to (\pi/2)^+} \dfrac{\cos x}{1 - \sin x}$

8. $\lim\limits_{x \to 0} \dfrac{\sin 4x}{\tan 5x}$

9. $\lim\limits_{t \to 0} \dfrac{e^t - 1}{t^3}$

10. $\lim\limits_{t \to 0} \dfrac{e^{3t} - 1}{t}$

11. $\lim\limits_{x \to \infty} \dfrac{\ln x}{\sqrt{x}}$

12. $\lim\limits_{\theta \to \pi/2} \dfrac{1 - \sin \theta}{\csc \theta}$

13. $\lim\limits_{x \to 0^+} \dfrac{\ln x}{x}$

14. $\lim\limits_{x \to \infty} \dfrac{(\ln x)^2}{x}$

15. $\lim\limits_{x \to 0} \dfrac{\sqrt{1 + 2x} - \sqrt{1 - 4x}}{x}$

16. $\lim\limits_{x \to 1} \dfrac{\ln x}{\sin \pi x}$

17. $\lim\limits_{t \to 0} \dfrac{5^t - 3^t}{t}$

18. $\lim\limits_{u \to \infty} \dfrac{e^{u/10}}{u^3}$

19. $\lim\limits_{x \to 0} \dfrac{e^x - 1 - x}{x^2}$

20. $\lim\limits_{x \to 0} \dfrac{\cos mx - \cos nx}{x^2}$

---

21. $\displaystyle\lim_{x\to1}\frac{1-x+\ln x}{1+\cos \pi x}$

22. $\displaystyle\lim_{x\to0}\frac{x}{\tan^{-1}(4x)}$

23. $\displaystyle\lim_{x\to1}\frac{x^a-ax+a-1}{(x-1)^2}$

24. $\displaystyle\lim_{x\to0}\frac{e^x-e^{-x}-2x}{x-\sin x}$

25. $\displaystyle\lim_{x\to0}\frac{\cos x-1+\frac{1}{2}x^2}{x^4}$

26. $\displaystyle\lim_{x\to a^+}\frac{\cos x \ln(x-a)}{\ln(e^x-e^a)}$

27. $\displaystyle\lim_{x\to\infty} x \sin(\pi/x)$

28. $\displaystyle\lim_{x\to-\infty} x^2 e^x$

29. $\displaystyle\lim_{x\to0}\cot 2x \sin 6x$

30. $\displaystyle\lim_{x\to0^+}\sin x \ln x$

31. $\displaystyle\lim_{x\to\infty} x^3 e^{-x^2}$

32. $\displaystyle\lim_{x\to\infty} x \tan(1/x)$

33. $\displaystyle\lim_{x\to1}\left(\frac{x}{x-1}-\frac{1}{\ln x}\right)$

34. $\displaystyle\lim_{x\to0}(\csc x - \cot x)$

35. $\displaystyle\lim_{x\to\infty}\left(\sqrt{x^2+x}-x\right)$

36. $\displaystyle\lim_{x\to0^+}\left(\cot x - \frac{1}{x}\right)$

37. $\displaystyle\lim_{x\to\infty}(x-\ln x)$

38. $\displaystyle\lim_{x\to\infty}(xe^{1/x}-x)$

39. $\displaystyle\lim_{x\to0^+} x^{x^2}$

40. $\displaystyle\lim_{x\to0^+}(\tan 2x)^x$

41. $\displaystyle\lim_{x\to0}(1-2x)^{1/x}$

42. $\displaystyle\lim_{x\to\infty}\left(1+\frac{a}{x}\right)^{bx}$

43. $\displaystyle\lim_{x\to\infty} x^{1/x}$

44. $\displaystyle\lim_{x\to\infty} x^{(\ln 2)/(1+\ln x)}$

45. $\displaystyle\lim_{x\to0^+}(4x+1)^{\cot x}$

46. $\displaystyle\lim_{x\to1}(2-x)^{\tan(\pi x/2)}$

47–48 Use a graph to estimate the value of the limit. Then use l'Hospital's Rule to find the exact value.

47. $\displaystyle\lim_{x\to\infty}\left(1+\frac{2}{x}\right)^x$

48. $\displaystyle\lim_{x\to0}\frac{5^x-4^x}{3^x-2^x}$

49–50 Illustrate l'Hospital's Rule by graphing both $f(x)/g(x)$ and $f'(x)/g'(x)$ near $x=0$ to see that these ratios have the same limit as $x\to0$. Also, calculate the exact value of the limit.

49. $f(x)=e^x-1,\quad g(x)=x^3+4x$

50. $f(x)=2x\sin x,\quad g(x)=\sec x-1$

51–54 Use l'Hospital's Rule to help find the asymptotes of f. Then use them, together with information from f' and f'', to sketch the graph of f. Check your work with a graphing device.

51. $f(x)=xe^{-x}$

52. $f(x)=e^x/x$

53. $f(x)=(\ln x)/x$

54. $f(x)=xe^{-x^2}$

55–56
(a) Graph the function.
(b) Use l'Hospital's Rule to explain the behavior as $x\to0$.
(c) Estimate the minimum value and intervals of concavity. Then use calculus to find the exact values.

55. $f(x)=x^2\ln x$

56. $f(x)=xe^{1/x}$

CAS **57–58**
(a) Graph the function.
(b) Explain the shape of the graph by computing the limit as $x\to0^+$ or as $x\to\infty$.
(c) Estimate the maximum and minimum values and then use calculus to find the exact values.
(d) Use a graph of f'' to estimate the x-coordinates of the inflection points.

57. $f(x)=x^{1/x}$

58. $f(x)=(\sin x)^{\sin x}$

---

59. Investigate the family of curves given by $f(x)=xe^{-cx}$, where c is a real number. Start by computing the limits as $x\to\pm\infty$. Identify any transitional values of c where the basic shape changes. What happens to the maximum or minimum points and inflection points as c changes? Illustrate by graphing several members of the family.

60. Investigate the family of curves given by $f(x)=x^n e^{-x}$, where n is a positive integer. What features do these curves have in common? How do they differ from one another? In particular, what happens to the maximum and minimum points and inflection points as n increases? Illustrate by graphing several members of the family.

61. What happens if you try to use l'Hospital's Rule to evaluate

$$\lim_{x\to\infty}\frac{x}{\sqrt{x^2+1}}$$

Evaluate the limit using another method.

62. Investigate the family of curves $f(x)=e^x-cx$. In particular, find the limits as $x\to\pm\infty$ and determine the values of c for which f has an absolute minimum. What happens to the minimum points as c increases?

63. Prove that

$$\lim_{x\to\infty}\frac{e^x}{x^n}=\infty$$

for any positive integer n. This shows that the exponential function approaches infinity faster than any power of x.

64. Prove that

$$\lim_{x\to\infty}\frac{\ln x}{x^p}=0$$

for any number $p>0$. This shows that the logarithmic function approaches ∞ more slowly than any power of x.

65. If an initial amount A_0 of money is invested at an interest rate r compounded n times a year, the value of the investment after t years is

$$A = A_0 \left(1 + \frac{r}{n} \right)^{nt}$$

If we let $n \to \infty$, we refer to the *continuous compounding* of interest. Use l'Hospital's Rule to show that if interest is compounded continuously, then the amount after t years is

$$A = A_0 e^{rt}$$

66. If an object with mass m is dropped from rest, one model for its speed v after t seconds, taking air resistance into account, is

$$v = \frac{mg}{c} (1 - e^{-ct/m})$$

where g is the acceleration due to gravity and c is a positive constant. (In Chapter 7 we will be able to deduce this equation from the assumption that the air resistance is proportional to the speed of the object; c is the proportionality constant.)
(a) Calculate $\lim_{t \to \infty} v$. What is the meaning of this limit?
(b) For fixed t, use l'Hospital's Rule to calculate $\lim_{c \to 0^+} v$. What can you conclude about the velocity of a falling object in a vacuum?

67. If an electrostatic field E acts on a liquid or a gaseous polar dielectric, the net dipole moment P per unit volume is

$$P(E) = \frac{e^E + e^{-E}}{e^E - e^{-E}} - \frac{1}{E}$$

Show that $\lim_{E \to 0^+} P(E) = 0$.

68. A metal cable has radius r and is covered by insulation, so that the distance from the center of the cable to the exterior of the insulation is R. The velocity v of an electrical impulse in the cable is

$$v = -c \left(\frac{r}{R} \right)^2 \ln \left(\frac{r}{R} \right)$$

where c is a positive constant. Find the following limits and interpret your answers.
(a) $\lim_{R \to r^+} v$ (b) $\lim_{r \to 0^+} v$

69. The first appearance in print of l'Hospital's Rule was in the book *Analyse des Infiniment Petits* published by the Marquis de l'Hospital in 1696. This was the first calculus *textbook* ever published and the example that the Marquis used in that book to illustrate his rule was to find the limit of the function

$$y = \frac{\sqrt{2a^3x - x^4} - a\sqrt[3]{aax}}{a - \sqrt[4]{ax^3}}$$

as x approaches a, where $a > 0$. (At that time it was common to write aa instead of a^2.) Solve this problem.

70. The figure shows a sector of a circle with central angle θ. Let $A(\theta)$ be the area of the segment between the chord PR and the arc PR. Let $B(\theta)$ be the area of the triangle PQR. Find $\lim_{\theta \to 0^+} A(\theta)/B(\theta)$.

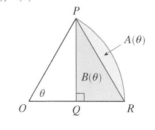

71. Evaluate $\lim_{x \to \infty} \left[x - x^2 \ln \left(\frac{1+x}{x} \right) \right]$.

72. Suppose f is a positive function. If $\lim_{x \to a} f(x) = 0$ and $\lim_{x \to a} g(x) = \infty$, show that

$$\lim_{x \to a} [f(x)]^{g(x)} = 0$$

This shows that 0^∞ is not an indeterminate form.

73. If f' is continuous, $f(2) = 0$, and $f'(2) = 7$, evaluate

$$\lim_{x \to 0} \frac{f(2 + 3x) + f(2 + 5x)}{x}$$

74. For what values of a and b is the following equation true?

$$\lim_{x \to 0} \left(\frac{\sin 2x}{x^3} + a + \frac{b}{x^2} \right) = 0$$

75. If f' is continuous, use l'Hospital's Rule to show that

$$\lim_{h \to 0} \frac{f(x + h) - f(x - h)}{2h} = f'(x)$$

Explain the meaning of this equation with the aid of a diagram.

76. Let

$$f(x) = \begin{cases} |x|^x & \text{if } x \neq 0 \\ 1 & \text{if } x = 0 \end{cases}$$

(a) Show that f is continuous at 0.
(b) Investigate graphically whether f is differentiable at 0 by zooming in several times toward the point $(0, 1)$ on the graph of f.
(c) Show that f is not differentiable at 0. How can you reconcile this fact with the appearance of the graphs in part (b)?

The Origins of l'Hospital's Rule

www.stewartcalculus.com
The Internet is another source of information for this project. Click on *History of Mathematics* for a list of reliable websites.

L'Hospital's Rule was first published in 1696 in the Marquis de l'Hospital's calculus textbook *Analyse des Infiniment Petits,* but the rule was discovered in 1694 by the Swiss mathematician John (Johann) Bernoulli. The explanation is that these two mathematicians had entered into a curious business arrangement whereby the Marquis de l'Hospital bought the rights to Bernoulli's mathematical discoveries. The details, including a translation of l'Hospital's letter to Bernoulli proposing the arrangement, can be found in the book by Eves [1].

Write a report on the historical and mathematical origins of l'Hospital's Rule. Start by providing brief biographical details of both men (the dictionary edited by Gillispie [2] is a good source) and outline the business deal between them. Then give l'Hospital's statement of his rule, which is found in Struik's sourcebook [4] and more briefly in the book of Katz [3]. Notice that l'Hospital and Bernoulli formulated the rule geometrically and gave the answer in terms of differentials. Compare their statement with the version of l'Hospital's Rule given in Section 4.5 and show that the two statements are essentially the same.

1. Howard Eves, *In Mathematical Circles (Volume 2: Quadrants III and IV)* (Boston: Prindle, Weber and Schmidt, 1969), pp. 20–22.
2. C. C. Gillispie, ed., *Dictionary of Scientific Biography* (New York: Scribner's, 1974). See the article on Johann Bernoulli by E. A. Fellmann and J. O. Fleckenstein in Volume II and the article on the Marquis de l'Hospital by Abraham Robinson in Volume VIII.
3. Victor Katz, *A History of Mathematics: An Introduction* (New York: HarperCollins, 1993), p. 484.
4. D. J. Struik, ed., *A Sourcebook in Mathematics, 1200–1800* (Princeton, NJ: Princeton University Press, 1969), pp. 315–316.

4.6 Optimization Problems

The methods we have learned in this chapter for finding extreme values have practical applications in many areas of life. A businessperson wants to minimize costs and maximize profits. A traveler wants to minimize transportation time. Fermat's Principle in optics states that light follows the path that takes the least time. In this section and the next we solve such problems as maximizing areas, volumes, and profits and minimizing distances, times, and costs.

In solving such practical problems the greatest challenge is often to convert the word problem into a mathematical optimization problem by setting up the function that is to be maximized or minimized. Let's recall the problem-solving principles discussed on page 83 and adapt them to this situation:

PS

Steps in Solving Optimization Problems

1. **Understand the Problem**   The first step is to read the problem carefully until it is clearly understood. Ask yourself: What is the unknown? What are the given quantities? What are the given conditions?

2. **Draw a Diagram**   In most problems it is useful to draw a diagram and identify the given and required quantities on the diagram.

3. **Introduce Notation**   Assign a symbol to the quantity that is to be maximized or minimized (let's call it Q for now). Also select symbols $(a, b, c, \ldots, x, y)$ for other unknown quantities and label the diagram with these symbols. It may help to use initials as suggestive symbols—for example, A for area, h for height, t for time.

4. Express Q in terms of some of the other symbols from Step 3.

5. If Q has been expressed as a function of more than one variable in Step 4, use the given information to find relationships (in the form of equations) among these variables. Then use these equations to eliminate all but one of the variables in the expression for Q. Thus Q will be expressed as a function of *one* variable x, say, $Q = f(x)$. Write the domain of this function.

6. Use the methods of Sections 4.2 and 4.3 to find the *absolute* maximum or minimum value of f. In particular, if the domain of f is a closed interval, then the Closed Interval Method in Section 4.2 can be used.

EXAMPLE 1   **Maximizing area**   A farmer has 2400 ft of fencing and wants to fence off a rectangular field that borders a straight river. He needs no fence along the river. What are the dimensions of the field that has the largest area?

PS Understand the problem

PS Analogy: Try special cases

PS Draw diagrams

SOLUTION   In order to get a feeling for what is happening in this problem, let's experiment with some special cases. Figure 1 (not to scale) shows three possible ways of laying out the 2400 ft of fencing.

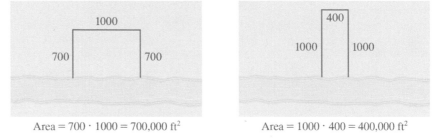

Area = 100 · 2200 = 220,000 ft²   Area = 700 · 1000 = 700,000 ft²   Area = 1000 · 400 = 400,000 ft²

FIGURE 1

We see that when we try shallow, wide fields or deep, narrow fields, we get relatively small areas. It seems plausible that there is some intermediate configuration that produces the largest area.

Figure 2 illustrates the general case. We wish to maximize the area A of the rectangle. Let x and y be the depth and width of the rectangle (in feet). Then we express A in terms of x and y:

PS Introduce notation

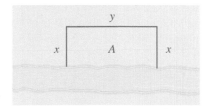

FIGURE 2

$$A = xy$$

We want to express A as a function of just one variable, so we eliminate y by expressing it in terms of x. To do this we use the given information that the total length of the fencing is 2400 ft. Thus

$$2x + y = 2400$$

From this equation we have $y = 2400 - 2x$, which gives

$$A = x(2400 - 2x) = 2400x - 2x^2$$

Note that $x \geq 0$ and $x \leq 1200$ (otherwise $A < 0$). So the function that we wish to maximize is

$$A(x) = 2400x - 2x^2 \qquad 0 \leq x \leq 1200$$

The derivative is $A'(x) = 2400 - 4x$, so to find the critical numbers we solve the equation

$$2400 - 4x = 0$$

which gives $x = 600$. The maximum value of A must occur either at this critical number or at an endpoint of the interval. Since $A(0) = 0$, $A(600) = 720{,}000$, and $A(1200) = 0$, the Closed Interval Method gives the maximum value as $A(600) = 720{,}000$.

[Alternatively, we could have observed that $A''(x) = -4 < 0$ for all x, so A is always concave downward and the local maximum at $x = 600$ must be an absolute maximum.]

Thus the rectangular field should be 600 ft deep and 1200 ft wide. ∎

▼ EXAMPLE 2 Minimizing cost A cylindrical can is to be made to hold 1 L of oil. Find the dimensions that will minimize the cost of the metal to manufacture the can.

SOLUTION Draw the diagram as in Figure 3, where r is the radius and h the height (both in centimeters). In order to minimize the cost of the metal, we minimize the total surface area of the cylinder (top, bottom, and sides). From Figure 4 we see that the sides are made from a rectangular sheet with dimensions $2\pi r$ and h. So the surface area is

$$A = 2\pi r^2 + 2\pi r h$$

FIGURE 3

To eliminate h we use the fact that the volume is given as 1 L, which we take to be 1000 cm³. Thus

$$\pi r^2 h = 1000$$

which gives $h = 1000/(\pi r^2)$. Substitution of this into the expression for A gives

$$A = 2\pi r^2 + 2\pi r\left(\frac{1000}{\pi r^2}\right) = 2\pi r^2 + \frac{2000}{r}$$

Therefore the function that we want to minimize is

$$A(r) = 2\pi r^2 + \frac{2000}{r} \qquad r > 0$$

Area $2(\pi r^2)$ Area $(2\pi r)h$

FIGURE 4

To find the critical numbers, we differentiate:

$$A'(r) = 4\pi r - \frac{2000}{r^2} = \frac{4(\pi r^3 - 500)}{r^2}$$

In the Applied Project on page 311 we investigate the most economical shape for a can by taking into account other manufacturing costs.

Then $A'(r) = 0$ when $\pi r^3 = 500$, so the only critical number is $r = \sqrt[3]{500/\pi}$.

Since the domain of A is $(0, \infty)$, we can't use the argument of Example 1 concerning endpoints. But we can observe that $A'(r) < 0$ for $r < \sqrt[3]{500/\pi}$ and $A'(r) > 0$ for $r > \sqrt[3]{500/\pi}$, so A is decreasing for *all* r to the left of the critical number and increasing for *all* r to the right. Thus $r = \sqrt[3]{500/\pi}$ must give rise to an *absolute* minimum.

[Alternatively, we could argue that $A(r) \to \infty$ as $r \to 0^+$ and $A(r) \to \infty$ as $r \to \infty$, so there must be a minimum value of $A(r)$, which must occur at the critical number. See Figure 5.]

The value of h corresponding to $r = \sqrt[3]{500/\pi}$ is

$$h = \frac{1000}{\pi r^2} = \frac{1000}{\pi(500/\pi)^{2/3}} = 2\sqrt[3]{\frac{500}{\pi}} = 2r$$

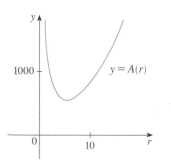

FIGURE 5

Thus, to minimize the cost of the can, the radius should be $\sqrt[3]{500/\pi}$ cm and the height should be equal to twice the radius, namely, the diameter. ∎

Note 1: The argument used in Example 2 to justify the absolute minimum is a variant of the First Derivative Test (which applies only to *local* maximum or minimum values) and is stated here for future reference.

> **First Derivative Test for Absolute Extreme Values** Suppose that c is a critical number of a continuous function f defined on an interval.
>
> (a) If $f'(x) > 0$ for all $x < c$ and $f'(x) < 0$ for all $x > c$, then $f(c)$ is the absolute maximum value of f.
>
> (b) If $f'(x) < 0$ for all $x < c$ and $f'(x) > 0$ for all $x > c$, then $f(c)$ is the absolute minimum value of f.

Note 2: An alternative method for solving optimization problems is to use implicit differentiation. Let's look at Example 2 again to illustrate the method. We work with the same equations

$$A = 2\pi r^2 + 2\pi rh \qquad \pi r^2 h = 1000$$

but instead of eliminating h, we differentiate both equations implicitly with respect to r:

$$A' = 4\pi r + 2\pi h + 2\pi rh' \qquad 2\pi rh + \pi r^2 h' = 0$$

The minimum occurs at a critical number, so we set $A' = 0$, simplify, and arrive at the equations

$$2r + h + rh' = 0 \qquad 2h + rh' = 0$$

and subtraction gives $2r - h = 0$, or $h = 2r$.

◼ EXAMPLE 3 Find the point on the parabola $y^2 = 2x$ that is closest to the point $(1, 4)$.

SOLUTION The distance between the point $(1, 4)$ and the point (x, y) is

$$d = \sqrt{(x - 1)^2 + (y - 4)^2}$$

(See Figure 6.) But if (x, y) lies on the parabola, then $x = \frac{1}{2}y^2$, so the expression for d becomes

$$d = \sqrt{\left(\tfrac{1}{2}y^2 - 1\right)^2 + (y - 4)^2}$$

(Alternatively, we could have substituted $y = \sqrt{2x}$ to get d in terms of x alone.) Instead of minimizing d, we minimize its square:

$$d^2 = f(y) = \left(\tfrac{1}{2}y^2 - 1\right)^2 + (y - 4)^2$$

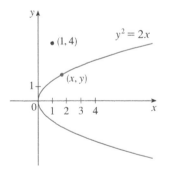

FIGURE 6

(You should convince yourself that the minimum of d occurs at the same point as the minimum of d^2, but d^2 is easier to work with.) Differentiating, we obtain

$$f'(y) = 2\left(\tfrac{1}{2}y^2 - 1\right)y + 2(y - 4) = y^3 - 8$$

so $f'(y) = 0$ when $y = 2$. Observe that $f'(y) < 0$ when $y < 2$ and $f'(y) > 0$ when $y > 2$, so by the First Derivative Test for Absolute Extreme Values, the absolute minimum occurs when $y = 2$. (Or we could simply say that because of the geometric nature of the problem, it's obvious that there is a closest point but not a farthest point.) The corresponding value of x is $x = \frac{1}{2}y^2 = 2$. Thus the point on $y^2 = 2x$ closest to $(1, 4)$ is $(2, 2)$.   ◼

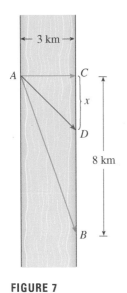

FIGURE 7

EXAMPLE 4 Minimizing time A man launches his boat from point A on a bank of a straight river, 3 km wide, and wants to reach point B, 8 km downstream on the opposite bank, as quickly as possible (see Figure 7). He could row his boat directly across the river to point C and then run to B, or he could row directly to B, or he could row to some point D between C and B and then run to B. If he can row 6 km/h and run 8 km/h, where should he land to reach B as soon as possible? (We assume that the speed of the water is negligible compared with the speed at which the man rows.)

SOLUTION If we let x be the distance from C to D, then the running distance is $|DB| = 8 - x$ and the Pythagorean Theorem gives the rowing distance as $|AD| = \sqrt{x^2 + 9}$. We use the equation

$$\text{time} = \frac{\text{distance}}{\text{rate}}$$

Then the rowing time is $\sqrt{x^2 + 9}/6$ and the running time is $(8 - x)/8$, so the total time T as a function of x is

$$T(x) = \frac{\sqrt{x^2 + 9}}{6} + \frac{8 - x}{8}$$

The domain of this function T is $[0, 8]$. Notice that if $x = 0$, he rows to C and if $x = 8$, he rows directly to B. The derivative of T is

$$T'(x) = \frac{x}{6\sqrt{x^2 + 9}} - \frac{1}{8}$$

Thus, using the fact that $x \geqslant 0$, we have

$$T'(x) = 0 \iff \frac{x}{6\sqrt{x^2 + 9}} = \frac{1}{8} \iff 4x = 3\sqrt{x^2 + 9}$$

$$\iff 16x^2 = 9(x^2 + 9) \iff 7x^2 = 81$$

$$\iff x = \frac{9}{\sqrt{7}}$$

The only critical number is $x = 9/\sqrt{7}$. To see whether the minimum occurs at this critical number or at an endpoint of the domain $[0, 8]$, we evaluate T at all three points:

$$T(0) = 1.5 \qquad T\left(\frac{9}{\sqrt{7}}\right) = 1 + \frac{\sqrt{7}}{8} \approx 1.33 \qquad T(8) = \frac{\sqrt{73}}{6} \approx 1.42$$

Since the smallest of these values of T occurs when $x = 9/\sqrt{7}$, the absolute minimum value of T must occur there. Figure 8 illustrates this calculation by showing the graph of T.

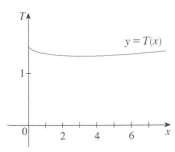

FIGURE 8

Thus the man should land the boat at a point $9/\sqrt{7}$ km (≈ 3.4 km) downstream from his starting point.

V EXAMPLE 5 Find the area of the largest rectangle that can be inscribed in a semicircle of radius r.

SOLUTION 1 Let's take the semicircle to be the upper half of the circle $x^2 + y^2 = r^2$ with center the origin. Then the word *inscribed* means that the rectangle has two vertices on the semicircle and two vertices on the x-axis as shown in Figure 9.

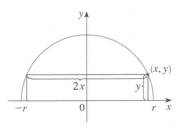

FIGURE 9

Let (x, y) be the vertex that lies in the first quadrant. Then the rectangle has sides of lengths $2x$ and y, so its area is

$$A = 2xy$$

To eliminate y we use the fact that (x, y) lies on the circle $x^2 + y^2 = r^2$ and so $y = \sqrt{r^2 - x^2}$. Thus

$$A = 2x\sqrt{r^2 - x^2}$$

The domain of this function is $0 \le x \le r$. Its derivative is

$$A' = 2\sqrt{r^2 - x^2} - \frac{2x^2}{\sqrt{r^2 - x^2}} = \frac{2(r^2 - 2x^2)}{\sqrt{r^2 - x^2}}$$

which is 0 when $2x^2 = r^2$, that is, $x = r/\sqrt{2}$ (since $x \ge 0$). This value of x gives a maximum value of A since $A(0) = 0$ and $A(r) = 0$. Therefore the area of the largest inscribed rectangle is

$$A\left(\frac{r}{\sqrt{2}}\right) = 2\frac{r}{\sqrt{2}}\sqrt{r^2 - \frac{r^2}{2}} = r^2$$

SOLUTION 2   A simpler solution is possible if we think of using an angle as a variable. Let θ be the angle shown in Figure 10. Then the area of the rectangle is

$$A(\theta) = (2r\cos\theta)(r\sin\theta) = r^2(2\sin\theta\,\cos\theta) = r^2\sin 2\theta$$

We know that $\sin 2\theta$ has a maximum value of 1 and it occurs when $2\theta = \pi/2$. So $A(\theta)$ has a maximum value of r^2 and it occurs when $\theta = \pi/4$.

Notice that this trigonometric solution doesn't involve differentiation. In fact, we didn't need to use calculus at all. ▄

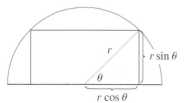

$r\sin\theta$

$r\cos\theta$

FIGURE 10

Applications to Business and Economics

In Section 3.8 we introduced the idea of marginal cost. Recall that if $C(x)$, the **cost function**, is the cost of producing x units of a certain product, then the **marginal cost** is the rate of change of C with respect to x. In other words, the marginal cost function is the derivative, $C'(x)$, of the cost function.

Now let's consider marketing. Let $p(x)$ be the price per unit that the company can charge if it sells x units. Then p is called the **demand function** (or **price function**) and we would expect it to be a decreasing function of x. If x units are sold and the price per unit is $p(x)$, then the total revenue is

$$R(x) = xp(x)$$

and R is called the **revenue function**. The derivative R' of the revenue function is called the **marginal revenue function** and is the rate of change of revenue with respect to the number of units sold.

If x units are sold, then the total profit is

$$P(x) = R(x) - C(x)$$

and P is called the **profit function**. The **marginal profit function** is P', the derivative of the profit function. In Exercises 43–48 you are asked to use the marginal cost, revenue, and profit functions to minimize costs and maximize revenues and profits.

V EXAMPLE 6 **Maximizing revenue** A store has been selling 200 DVD burners a week at $350 each. A market survey indicates that for each $10 rebate offered to buyers, the number of units sold will increase by 20 a week. Find the demand function and the revenue function. How large a rebate should the store offer to maximize its revenue?

SOLUTION If x is the number of DVD burners sold per week, then the weekly increase in sales is $x - 200$. For each increase of 20 units sold, the price is decreased by $10. So for each additional unit sold, the decrease in price will be $\frac{1}{20} \times 10$ and the demand function is

$$p(x) = 350 - \tfrac{10}{20}(x - 200) = 450 - \tfrac{1}{2}x$$

The revenue function is

$$R(x) = xp(x) = 450x - \tfrac{1}{2}x^2$$

Since $R'(x) = 450 - x$, we see that $R'(x) = 0$ when $x = 450$. This value of x gives an absolute maximum by the First Derivative Test (or simply by observing that the graph of R is a parabola that opens downward). The corresponding price is

$$p(450) = 450 - \tfrac{1}{2}(450) = 225$$

and the rebate is $350 - 225 = 125$. Therefore, to maximize revenue, the store should offer a rebate of $125. ▬

4.6 Exercises

1. Consider the following problem: Find two numbers whose sum is 23 and whose product is a maximum.
(a) Make a table of values, like the following one, so that the sum of the numbers in the first two columns is always 23. On the basis of the evidence in your table, estimate the answer to the problem.

First number	Second number	Product
1	22	22
2	21	42
3	20	60
.	.	.
.	.	.
.	.	.

(b) Use calculus to solve the problem and compare with your answer to part (a).

2. Find two numbers whose difference is 100 and whose product is a minimum.

3. Find two positive numbers whose product is 100 and whose sum is a minimum.

4. The sum of two positive numbers is 16. What is the smallest possible value of the sum of their squares?

5. Find the dimensions of a rectangle with perimeter 100 m whose area is as large as possible.

6. Find the dimensions of a rectangle with area 1000 m² whose perimeter is as small as possible.

7. A model used for the yield Y of an agricultural crop as a function of the nitrogen level N in the soil (measured in appropriate units) is

$$Y = \frac{kN}{1 + N^2}$$

where k is a positive constant. What nitrogen level gives the best yield?

8. The rate (in mg carbon/m³/h) at which photosynthesis takes place for a species of phytoplankton is modeled by the function

$$P = \frac{100I}{I^2 + I + 4}$$

where I is the light intensity (measured in thousands of foot-candles). For what light intensity is P a maximum?

⌂ Graphing calculator or computer with graphing software required   CAS Computer algebra system required   **1.** Homework Hints available in TEC

9. Consider the following problem: A farmer with 750 ft of fencing wants to enclose a rectangular area and then divide it into four pens with fencing parallel to one side of the rectangle. What is the largest possible total area of the four pens?

(a) Draw several diagrams illustrating the situation, some with shallow, wide pens and some with deep, narrow pens. Find the total areas of these configurations. Does it appear that there is a maximum area? If so, estimate it.

(b) Draw a diagram illustrating the general situation. Introduce notation and label the diagram with your symbols.

(c) Write an expression for the total area.

(d) Use the given information to write an equation that relates the variables.

(e) Use part (d) to write the total area as a function of one variable.

(f) Finish solving the problem and compare the answer with your estimate in part (a).

10. Consider the following problem: A box with an open top is to be constructed from a square piece of cardboard, 3 ft wide, by cutting out a square from each of the four corners and bending up the sides. Find the largest volume that such a box can have.

(a) Draw several diagrams to illustrate the situation, some short boxes with large bases and some tall boxes with small bases. Find the volumes of several such boxes. Does it appear that there is a maximum volume? If so, estimate it.

(b) Draw a diagram illustrating the general situation. Introduce notation and label the diagram with your symbols.

(c) Write an expression for the volume.

(d) Use the given information to write an equation that relates the variables.

(e) Use part (d) to write the volume as a function of one variable.

(f) Finish solving the problem and compare the answer with your estimate in part (a).

11. If 1200 cm² of material is available to make a box with a square base and an open top, find the largest possible volume of the box.

12. A box with a square base and open top must have a volume of 32,000 cm³. Find the dimensions of the box that minimize the amount of material used.

13. (a) Show that of all the rectangles with a given area, the one with smallest perimeter is a square.
(b) Show that of all the rectangles with a given perimeter, the one with greatest area is a square.

14. A rectangular storage container with an open top is to have a volume of 10 m³. The length of its base is twice the width. Material for the base costs $10 per square meter. Material for the sides costs $6 per square meter. Find the cost of materials for the cheapest such container.

15. Find the points on the ellipse $4x^2 + y^2 = 4$ that are farthest away from the point $(1, 0)$.

16. Find, correct to two decimal places, the coordinates of the point on the curve $y = \tan x$ that is closest to the point $(1, 1)$.

17. Find the dimensions of the rectangle of largest area that can be inscribed in an equilateral triangle of side L if one side of the rectangle lies on the base of the triangle.

18. Find the dimensions of the rectangle of largest area that has its base on the x-axis and its other two vertices above the x-axis and lying on the parabola $y = 8 - x^2$.

19. A right circular cylinder is inscribed in a sphere of radius r. Find the largest possible volume of such a cylinder.

20. Find the area of the largest rectangle that can be inscribed in the ellipse $x^2/a^2 + y^2/b^2 = 1$.

21. Find the dimensions of the isosceles triangle of largest area that can be inscribed in a circle of radius r.

22. A cylindrical can without a top is made to contain V cm³ of liquid. Find the dimensions that will minimize the cost of the metal to make the can.

23. A Norman window has the shape of a rectangle surmounted by a semicircle. (Thus the diameter of the semicircle is equal to the width of the rectangle. See Exercise 58 on page 24.) If the perimeter of the window is 30 ft, find the dimensions of the window so that the greatest possible amount of light is admitted.

24. A right circular cylinder is inscribed in a cone with height h and base radius r. Find the largest possible volume of such a cylinder.

25. A piece of wire 10 m long is cut into two pieces. One piece is bent into a square and the other is bent into an equilateral triangle. How should the wire be cut so that the total area enclosed is (a) a maximum? (b) A minimum?

26. A fence 8 ft tall runs parallel to a tall building at a distance of 4 ft from the building. What is the length of the shortest ladder that will reach from the ground over the fence to the wall of the building?

27. A cone-shaped drinking cup is made from a circular piece of paper of radius R by cutting out a sector and joining the edges CA and CB. Find the maximum capacity of such a cup.

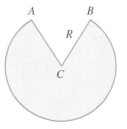

28. A cone-shaped paper drinking cup is to be made to hold 27 cm³ of water. Find the height and radius of the cup that will use the smallest amount of paper.

29. A cone with height h is inscribed in a larger cone with height H so that its vertex is at the center of the base of the larger cone. Show that the inner cone has maximum volume when $h = \frac{1}{3}H$.

30. The graph shows the fuel consumption c of a car (measured in gallons per hour) as a function of the speed v of the car. At very low speeds the engine runs inefficiently, so initially c decreases as the speed increases. But at high speeds the fuel consumption increases. You can see that $c(v)$ is minimized for this car when $v \approx 30$ mi/h. However, for fuel efficiency, what must be minimized is not the consumption in gallons per hour but rather the fuel consumption in gallons *per mile.* Let's call this consumption G. Using the graph, estimate the speed at which G has its minimum value.

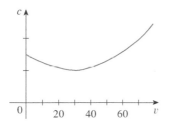

31. If a resistor of R ohms is connected across a battery of E volts with internal resistance r ohms, then the power (in watts) in the external resistor is

$$P = \frac{E^2 R}{(R + r)^2}$$

If E and r are fixed but R varies, what is the maximum value of the power?

32. For a fish swimming at a speed v relative to the water, the energy expenditure per unit time is proportional to v^3. It is believed that migrating fish try to minimize the total energy required to swim a fixed distance. If the fish are swimming against a current u ($u < v$), then the time required to swim a distance L is $L/(v - u)$ and the total energy E required to swim the distance is given by

$$E(v) = av^3 \cdot \frac{L}{v - u}$$

where a is the proportionality constant.
(a) Determine the value of v that minimizes E.
(b) Sketch the graph of E.

Note: This result has been verified experimentally; migrating fish swim against a current at a speed 50% greater than the current speed.

33. In a beehive, each cell is a regular hexagonal prism, open at one end with a trihedral angle at the other end as in the figure. It is believed that bees form their cells in such a way as to

minimize the surface area for a given volume, thus using the least amount of wax in cell construction. Examination of these cells has shown that the measure of the apex angle θ is amazingly consistent. Based on the geometry of the cell, it can be shown that the surface area S is given by

$$S = 6sh - \tfrac{3}{2}s^2 \cot \theta + \left(3s^2\sqrt{3}/2\right) \csc \theta$$

where s, the length of the sides of the hexagon, and h, the height, are constants.
(a) Calculate $dS/d\theta$.
(b) What angle should the bees prefer?
(c) Determine the minimum surface area of the cell (in terms of s and h).
Note: Actual measurements of the angle θ in beehives have been made, and the measures of these angles seldom differ from the calculated value by more than 2°.

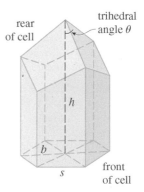

34. A boat leaves a dock at 2:00 PM and travels due south at a speed of 20 km/h. Another boat has been heading due east at 15 km/h and reaches the same dock at 3:00 PM. At what time were the two boats closest together?

35. An oil refinery is located on the north bank of a straight river that is 2 km wide. A pipeline is to be constructed from the refinery to storage tanks located on the south bank of the river 6 km east of the refinery. The cost of laying pipe is $400,000/km over land to a point P on the north bank and $800,000/km under the river to the tanks. To minimize the cost of the pipeline, where should P be located?

36. Suppose the refinery in Exercise 35 is located 1 km north of the river. Where should P be located?

37. The illumination of an object by a light source is directly proportional to the strength of the source and inversely proportional to the square of the distance from the source. If two light sources, one three times as strong as the other, are placed 10 ft apart, where should an object be placed on the line between the sources so as to receive the least illumination?

38. A woman at a point A on the shore of a circular lake with radius 2 mi wants to arrive at the point C diametrically opposite A on the other side of the lake in the shortest possible time (see the figure). She can walk at the rate of 4 mi/h and row a boat at 2 mi/h. How should she proceed?

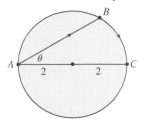

39. Find an equation of the line through the point $(3, 5)$ that cuts off the least area from the first quadrant.

40. At which points on the curve $y = 1 + 40x^3 - 3x^5$ does the tangent line have the largest slope?

41. What is the shortest possible length of the line segment that is cut off by the first quadrant and is tangent to the curve $y = 3/x$ at some point?

42. What is the smallest possible area of the triangle that is cut off by the first quadrant and whose hypotenuse is tangent to the parabola $y = 4 - x^2$ at some point?

43. (a) If $C(x)$ is the cost of producing x units of a commodity, then the **average cost** per unit is $c(x) = C(x)/x$. Show that if the average cost is a minimum, then the marginal cost equals the average cost.
(b) If $C(x) = 16{,}000 + 200x + 4x^{3/2}$, in dollars, find (i) the cost, average cost, and marginal cost at a production level of 1000 units; (ii) the production level that will minimize the average cost; and (iii) the minimum average cost.

44. (a) Show that if the profit $P(x)$ is a maximum, then the marginal revenue equals the marginal cost.
(b) If $C(x) = 16{,}000 + 500x - 1.6x^2 + 0.004x^3$ is the cost function and $p(x) = 1700 - 7x$ is the demand function, find the production level that will maximize profit.

45. A baseball team plays in a stadium that holds 55,000 spectators. With ticket prices at $10, the average attendance had been 27,000. When ticket prices were lowered to $8, the average attendance rose to 33,000.
(a) Find the demand function, assuming that it is linear.
(b) How should ticket prices be set to maximize revenue?

46. During the summer months Terry makes and sells necklaces on the beach. Last summer he sold the necklaces for $10 each and his sales averaged 20 per day. When he increased the price by $1, he found that the average decreased by two sales per day.
(a) Find the demand function, assuming that it is linear.
(b) If the material for each necklace costs Terry $6, what should the selling price be to maximize his profit?

47. A manufacturer has been selling 1000 television sets a week at $450 each. A market survey indicates that for each $10 rebate offered to the buyer, the number of sets sold will increase by 100 per week.
(a) Find the demand function.
(b) How large a rebate should the company offer the buyer in order to maximize its revenue?

(c) If its weekly cost function is $C(x) = 68{,}000 + 150x$, how should the manufacturer set the size of the rebate in order to maximize its profit?

48. The manager of a 100-unit apartment complex knows from experience that all units will be occupied if the rent is $800 per month. A market survey suggests that, on average, one additional unit will remain vacant for each $10 increase in rent. What rent should the manager charge to maximize revenue?

49. Let a and b be positive numbers. Find the length of the shortest line segment that is cut off by the first quadrant and passes through the point (a, b).

CAS **50.** The frame for a kite is to be made from six pieces of wood. The four exterior pieces have been cut with the lengths indicated in the figure. To maximize the area of the kite, how long should the diagonal pieces be?

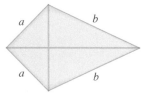

51. Let v_1 be the velocity of light in air and v_2 the velocity of light in water. According to Fermat's Principle, a ray of light will travel from a point A in the air to a point B in the water by a path ACB that minimizes the time taken. Show that

$$\frac{\sin \theta_1}{\sin \theta_2} = \frac{v_1}{v_2}$$

where θ_1 (the angle of incidence) and θ_2 (the angle of refraction) are as shown. This equation is known as Snell's Law.

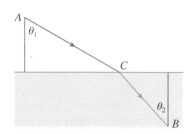

52. Two vertical poles PQ and ST are secured by a rope PRS going from the top of the first pole to a point R on the ground between the poles and then to the top of the second pole as in the figure. Show that the shortest length of such a rope occurs when $\theta_1 = \theta_2$.

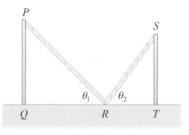

53. The upper right-hand corner of a piece of paper, 12 in. by 8 in., as in the figure, is folded over to the bottom edge. How would you fold it so as to minimize the length of the fold? In other words, how would you choose x to minimize y?

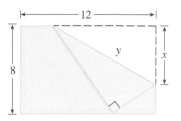

54. A steel pipe is being carried down a hallway 9 ft wide. At the end of the hall there is a right-angled turn into a narrower hallway 6 ft wide. What is the length of the longest pipe that can be carried horizontally around the corner?

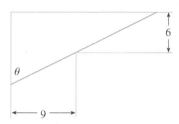

55. Find the maximum area of a rectangle that can be circumscribed about a given rectangle with length L and width W. [*Hint:* Express the area as a function of an angle θ.]

56. A rain gutter is to be constructed from a metal sheet of width 30 cm by bending up one-third of the sheet on each side through an angle θ. How should θ be chosen so that the gutter will carry the maximum amount of water?

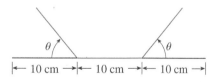

57. Where should the point P be chosen on the line segment AB so as to maximize the angle θ?

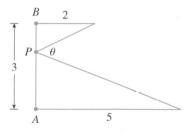

58. A painting in an art gallery has height h and is hung so that its lower edge is a distance d above the eye of an observer (as in the figure). How far from the wall should the observer stand to get the best view? (In other words, where should the observer stand so as to maximize the angle θ subtended at his eye by the painting?)

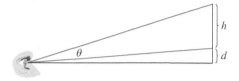

59. Ornithologists have determined that some species of birds tend to avoid flights over large bodies of water during daylight hours. It is believed that more energy is required to fly over water than over land because air generally rises over land and falls over water during the day. A bird with these tendencies is released from an island that is 5 km from the nearest point B on a straight shoreline, flies to a point C on the shoreline, and then flies along the shoreline to its nesting area D. Assume that the bird instinctively chooses a path that will minimize its energy expenditure. Points B and D are 13 km apart.
(a) In general, if it takes 1.4 times as much energy to fly over water as it does over land, to what point C should the bird fly in order to minimize the total energy expended in returning to its nesting area?
(b) Let W and L denote the energy (in joules) per kilometer flown over water and land, respectively. What would a large value of the ratio W/L mean in terms of the bird's flight? What would a small value mean? Determine the ratio W/L corresponding to the minimum expenditure of energy.
(c) What should the value of W/L be in order for the bird to fly directly to its nesting area D? What should the value of W/L be for the bird to fly to B and then along the shore to D?
(d) If the ornithologists observe that birds of a certain species reach the shore at a point 4 km from B, how many times more energy does it take a bird to fly over water than over land?

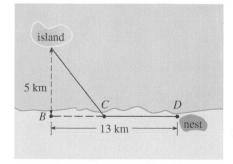

60. The blood vascular system consists of blood vessels (arteries, arterioles, capillaries, and veins) that convey blood from the heart to the organs and back to the heart. This system should work so as to minimize the energy expended by the heart in pumping the blood. In particular, this energy is reduced when the resistance of the blood is lowered. One of Poiseuille's

Laws gives the resistance R of the blood as

$$R = C \frac{L}{r^4}$$

where L is the length of the blood vessel, r is the radius, and C is a positive constant determined by the viscosity of the blood. (Poiseuille established this law experimentally, but it also follows from Equation 6.7.2.) The figure shows a main blood vessel with radius r_1 branching at an angle θ into a smaller vessel with radius r_2.

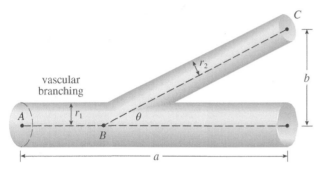

(a) Use Poiseuille's Law to show that the total resistance of the blood along the path ABC is

$$R = C\left(\frac{a - b\cot\theta}{r_1^4} + \frac{b\csc\theta}{r_2^4}\right)$$

where a and b are the distances shown in the figure.

(b) Prove that this resistance is minimized when

$$\cos\theta = \frac{r_2^4}{r_1^4}$$

(c) Find the optimal branching angle (correct to the nearest degree) when the radius of the smaller blood vessel is two-thirds the radius of the larger vessel.

61. The speeds of sound c_1 in an upper layer and c_2 in a lower layer of rock and the thickness h of the upper layer can be determined by seismic exploration if the speed of sound in the lower layer is greater than the speed in the upper layer. A dynamite charge is detonated at a point P and the transmitted signals are recorded at a point Q, which is a distance D from P. The first signal to arrive at Q travels along the surface and takes T_1 seconds. The next signal travels from P to a point R, from R to S in the lower layer, and then to Q, taking T_2 seconds. The third signal is reflected off the lower layer at the midpoint O of RS and takes T_3 seconds to reach Q.

(a) Express T_1, T_2, and T_3 in terms of D, h, c_1, c_2, and θ.

(b) Show that T_2 is a minimum when $\sin\theta = c_1/c_2$.

(c) Suppose that $D = 1$ km, $T_1 = 0.26$ s, $T_2 = 0.32$ s, and $T_3 = 0.34$ s. Find c_1, c_2, and h.

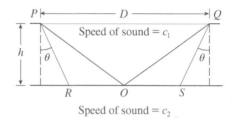

Note: Geophysicists use this technique when studying the structure of the earth's crust, whether searching for oil or examining fault lines.

62. Two light sources of identical strength are placed 10 m apart. An object is to be placed at a point P on a line ℓ parallel to the line joining the light sources and at a distance d meters from it (see the figure). We want to locate P on ℓ so that the intensity of illumination is minimized. We need to use the fact that the intensity of illumination for a single source is directly proportional to the strength of the source and inversely proportional to the square of the distance from the source.

(a) Find an expression for the intensity $I(x)$ at the point P.

(b) If $d = 5$ m, use graphs of $I(x)$ and $I'(x)$ to show that the intensity is minimized when $x = 5$ m, that is, when P is at the midpoint of ℓ.

(c) If $d = 10$ m, show that the intensity (perhaps surprisingly) is *not* minimized at the midpoint.

(d) Somewhere between $d = 5$ m and $d = 10$ m there is a transitional value of d at which the point of minimal illumination abruptly changes. Estimate this value of d by graphical methods. Then find the exact value of d.

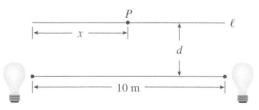

| **APPLIED PROJECT** | **The Shape of a Can** |

Discs cut from squares

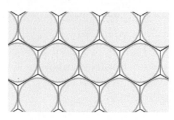

Discs cut from hexagons

In this project we investigate the most economical shape for a can. We first interpret this to mean that the volume V of a cylindrical can is given and we need to find the height h and radius r that minimize the cost of the metal to make the can (see the figure). If we disregard any waste metal in the manufacturing process, then the problem is to minimize the surface area of the cylinder. We solved this problem in Example 2 in Section 4.6 and we found that $h = 2r$; that is, the height should be the same as the diameter. But if you go to your cupboard or your supermarket with a ruler, you will discover that the height is usually greater than the diameter and the ratio h/r varies from 2 up to about 3.8. Let's see if we can explain this phenomenon.

1. The material for the cans is cut from sheets of metal. The cylindrical sides are formed by bending rectangles; these rectangles are cut from the sheet with little or no waste. But if the top and bottom discs are cut from squares of side $2r$ (as in the figure), this leaves considerable waste metal, which may be recycled but has little or no value to the can makers. If this is the case, show that the amount of metal used is minimized when

$$\frac{h}{r} = \frac{8}{\pi} \approx 2.55$$

2. A more efficient packing of the discs is obtained by dividing the metal sheet into hexagons and cutting the circular lids and bases from the hexagons (see the figure). Show that if this strategy is adopted, then

$$\frac{h}{r} = \frac{4\sqrt{3}}{\pi} \approx 2.21$$

3. The values of h/r that we found in Problems 1 and 2 are a little closer to the ones that actually occur on supermarket shelves, but they still don't account for everything. If we look more closely at some real cans, we see that the lid and the base are formed from discs with radius larger than r that are bent over the ends of the can. If we allow for this we would increase h/r. More significantly, in addition to the cost of the metal we need to incorporate the manufacturing of the can into the cost. Let's assume that most of the expense is incurred in joining the sides to the rims of the cans. If we cut the discs from hexagons as in Problem 2, then the total cost is proportional to

$$4\sqrt{3}\, r^2 + 2\pi r h + k(4\pi r + h)$$

where k is the reciprocal of the length that can be joined for the cost of one unit area of metal. Show that this expression is minimized when

$$\frac{\sqrt[3]{V}}{k} = \sqrt[3]{\frac{\pi h}{r}} \cdot \frac{2\pi - h/r}{\pi h/r - 4\sqrt{3}}$$

4. Plot $\sqrt[3]{V}/k$ as a function of $x = h/r$ and use your graph to argue that when a can is large or joining is cheap, we should make h/r approximately 2.21 (as in Problem 2). But when the can is small or joining is costly, h/r should be substantially larger.

5. Our analysis shows that large cans should be almost square but small cans should be tall and thin. Take a look at the relative shapes of the cans in a supermarket. Is our conclusion usually true in practice? Are there exceptions? Can you suggest reasons why small cans are not always tall and thin?

⌂ Graphing calculator or computer with graphing software required

4.7 Newton's Method

Suppose that a car dealer offers to sell you a car for $18,000 or for payments of $375 per month for five years. You would like to know what monthly interest rate the dealer is, in effect, charging you. To find the answer, you have to solve the equation

$$\boxed{1} \qquad 48x(1 + x)^{60} - (1 + x)^{60} + 1 = 0$$

(The details are explained in Exercise 33.) How would you solve such an equation?

For a quadratic equation $ax^2 + bx + c = 0$ there is a well-known formula for the roots. For third- and fourth-degree equations there are also formulas for the roots, but they are extremely complicated. If f is a polynomial of degree 5 or higher, there is no such formula (see the note on page 213). Likewise, there is no formula that will enable us to find the exact roots of a transcendental equation such as $\cos x = x$.

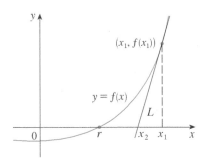

FIGURE 1

Try to solve Equation 1 using the numerical rootfinder on your calculator or computer. Some machines are not able to solve it. Others are successful but require you to specify a starting point for the search.

We can find an *approximate* solution to Equation 1 by plotting the left side of the equation. Using a graphing device, and after experimenting with viewing rectangles, we produce the graph in Figure 1.

We see that in addition to the solution $x = 0$, which doesn't interest us, there is a solution between 0.007 and 0.008. Zooming in shows that the root is approximately 0.0076. If we need more accuracy we could zoom in repeatedly, but that becomes tiresome. A faster alternative is to use a numerical rootfinder on a calculator or computer algebra system. If we do so, we find that the root, correct to nine decimal places, is 0.007628603.

How do those numerical rootfinders work? They use a variety of methods, but most of them make some use of **Newton's method**, also called the **Newton-Raphson method**. We will explain how this method works, partly to show what happens inside a calculator or computer, and partly as an application of the idea of linear approximation.

The geometry behind Newton's method is shown in Figure 2, where the root that we are trying to find is labeled r. We start with a first approximation x_1, which is obtained by guessing, or from a rough sketch of the graph of f, or from a computer-generated graph of f. Consider the tangent line L to the curve $y = f(x)$ at the point $(x_1, f(x_1))$ and look at the x-intercept of L, labeled x_2. The idea behind Newton's method is that the tangent line is close to the curve and so its x-intercept, x_2, is close to the x-intercept of the curve (namely, the root r that we are seeking). Because the tangent is a line, we can easily find its x-intercept.

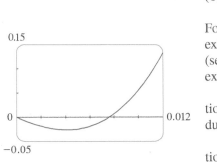

FIGURE 2

To find a formula for x_2 in terms of x_1 we use the fact that the slope of L is $f'(x_1)$, so its equation is

$$y - f(x_1) = f'(x_1)(x - x_1)$$

Since the x-intercept of L is x_2, we set $y = 0$ and obtain

$$0 - f(x_1) = f'(x_1)(x_2 - x_1)$$

If $f'(x_1) \neq 0$, we can solve this equation for x_2:

$$x_2 = x_1 - \frac{f(x_1)}{f'(x_1)}$$

We use x_2 as a second approximation to r.

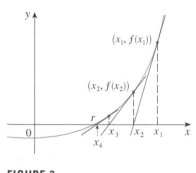

FIGURE 3

Next we repeat this procedure with x_1 replaced by the second approximation x_2, using the tangent line at $(x_2, f(x_2))$. This gives a third approximation:

$$x_3 = x_2 - \frac{f(x_2)}{f'(x_2)}$$

If we keep repeating this process, we obtain a sequence of approximations $x_1, x_2, x_3, x_4, \ldots$ as shown in Figure 3. In general, if the nth approximation is x_n and $f'(x_n) \neq 0$, then the next approximation is given by

$$\boxed{2} \qquad \boxed{\; x_{n+1} = x_n - \frac{f(x_n)}{f'(x_n)} \;}$$

Sequences were briefly introduced in *A Preview of Calculus* on page 6. A more thorough discussion starts in Section 8.1.

If the numbers x_n become closer and closer to r as n becomes large, then we say that the sequence *converges* to r and we write

$$\lim_{n \to \infty} x_n = r$$

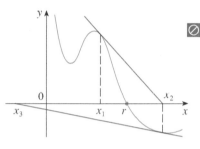

FIGURE 4

⊘ Although the sequence of successive approximations converges to the desired root for functions of the type illustrated in Figure 3, in certain circumstances the sequence may not converge. For example, consider the situation shown in Figure 4. You can see that x_2 is a worse approximation than x_1. This is likely to be the case when $f'(x_1)$ is close to 0. It might even happen that an approximation (such as x_3 in Figure 4) falls outside the domain of f. Then Newton's method fails and a better initial approximation x_1 should be chosen. See Exercises 25–27 for specific examples in which Newton's method works very slowly or does not work at all.

V **EXAMPLE 1** Starting with $x_1 = 2$, find the third approximation x_3 to the root of the equation $x^3 - 2x - 5 = 0$.

SOLUTION We apply Newton's method with

$$f(x) = x^3 - 2x - 5 \qquad \text{and} \qquad f'(x) = 3x^2 - 2$$

TEC In Module 4.7 you can investigate how Newton's Method works for several functions and what happens when you change x_1.

Newton himself used this equation to illustrate his method and he chose $x_1 = 2$ after some experimentation because $f(1) = -6$, $f(2) = -1$, and $f(3) = 16$. Equation 2 becomes

$$x_{n+1} = x_n - \frac{x_n^3 - 2x_n - 5}{3x_n^2 - 2}$$

With $n = 1$ we have

$$x_2 = x_1 - \frac{x_1^3 - 2x_1 - 5}{3x_1^2 - 2}$$

$$= 2 - \frac{2^3 - 2(2) - 5}{3(2)^2 - 2} = 2.1$$

Figure 5 shows the geometry behind the first step in Newton's method in Example 1. Since $f'(2) = 10$, the tangent line to $y = x^3 - 2x - 5$ at $(2, -1)$ has equation $y = 10x - 21$ so its x-intercept is $x_2 = 2.1$.

Then with $n = 2$ we obtain

$$x_3 = x_2 - \frac{x_2^3 - 2x_2 - 5}{3x_2^2 - 2} = 2.1 - \frac{(2.1)^3 - 2(2.1) - 5}{3(2.1)^2 - 2} \approx 2.0946$$

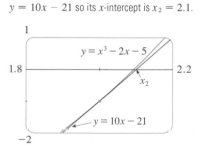

It turns out that this third approximation $x_3 \approx 2.0946$ is accurate to four decimal places.

FIGURE 5

Suppose that we want to achieve a given accuracy, say to eight decimal places, using Newton's method. How do we know when to stop? The rule of thumb that is generally used is that we can stop when successive approximations x_n and x_{n+1} agree to eight decimal places. (A precise statement concerning accuracy in Newton's method will be given in Exercise 33 in Section 8.8.)

Notice that the procedure in going from n to $n + 1$ is the same for all values of n. (It is called an *iterative* process.) This means that Newton's method is particularly convenient for use with a programmable calculator or a computer.

V EXAMPLE 2 Use Newton's method to find $\sqrt[6]{2}$ correct to eight decimal places.

SOLUTION First we observe that finding $\sqrt[6]{2}$ is equivalent to finding the positive root of the equation

$$x^6 - 2 = 0$$

so we take $f(x) = x^6 - 2$. Then $f'(x) = 6x^5$ and Formula 2 (Newton's method) becomes

$$x_{n+1} = x_n - \frac{x_n^6 - 2}{6x_n^5}$$

If we choose $x_1 = 1$ as the initial approximation, then we obtain

$$x_2 \approx 1.16666667$$
$$x_3 \approx 1.12644368$$
$$x_4 \approx 1.12249707$$
$$x_5 \approx 1.12246205$$
$$x_6 \approx 1.12246205$$

Since x_5 and x_6 agree to eight decimal places, we conclude that

$$\sqrt[6]{2} \approx 1.12246205$$

to eight decimal places.

V EXAMPLE 3 Find, correct to six decimal places, the root of the equation $\cos x = x$.

SOLUTION We first rewrite the equation in standard form:

$$\cos x - x = 0$$

Therefore we let $f(x) = \cos x - x$. Then $f'(x) = -\sin x - 1$, so Formula 2 becomes

$$x_{n+1} = x_n - \frac{\cos x_n - x_n}{-\sin x_n - 1} = x_n + \frac{\cos x_n - x_n}{\sin x_n + 1}$$

In order to guess a suitable value for x_1 we sketch the graphs of $y = \cos x$ and $y = x$ in Figure 6. It appears that they intersect at a point whose x-coordinate is somewhat less than 1, so let's take $x_1 = 1$ as a convenient first approximation. Then, remembering to put our calculator in radian mode, we get

$$x_2 \approx 0.75036387$$
$$x_3 \approx 0.73911289$$
$$x_4 \approx 0.73908513$$
$$x_5 \approx 0.73908513$$

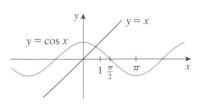

FIGURE 6

Since x_4 and x_5 agree to six decimal places (eight, in fact), we conclude that the root of the equation, correct to six decimal places, is 0.739085.

Instead of using the rough sketch in Figure 6 to get a starting approximation for Newton's method in Example 3, we could have used the more accurate graph that a calculator or computer provides. Figure 7 suggests that we use $x_1 = 0.75$ as the initial approximation. Then Newton's method gives

$$x_2 \approx 0.73911114 \qquad x_3 \approx 0.73908513 \qquad x_4 \approx 0.73908513$$

and so we obtain the same answer as before, but with one fewer step.

You might wonder why we bother at all with Newton's method if a graphing device is available. Isn't it easier to zoom in repeatedly and find the roots as we did in Section 1.4? If only one or two decimal places of accuracy are required, then indeed Newton's method is inappropriate and a graphing device suffices. But if six or eight decimal places are required, then repeated zooming becomes tiresome. It is usually faster and more efficient to use a computer and Newton's method in tandem—the graphing device to get started and Newton's method to finish.

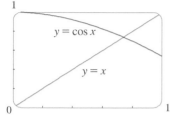

FIGURE 7

4.7 Exercises

1. The figure shows the graph of a function f. Suppose that Newton's method is used to approximate the root r of the equation $f(x) = 0$ with initial approximation $x_1 = 1$.
(a) Draw the tangent lines that are used to find x_2 and x_3, and estimate the numerical values of x_2 and x_3.
(b) Would $x_1 = 5$ be a better first approximation? Explain.

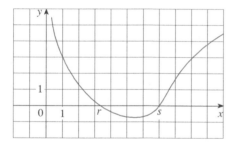

2. Follow the instructions for Exercise 1(a) but use $x_1 = 9$ as the starting approximation for finding the root s.

3. Suppose the line $y = 5x - 4$ is tangent to the curve $y = f(x)$ when $x = 3$. If Newton's method is used to locate a root of the equation $f(x) = 0$ and the initial approximation is $x_1 = 3$, find the second approximation x_2.

4. For each initial approximation, determine graphically what happens if Newton's method is used for the function whose graph is shown.
(a) $x_1 = 0$ (b) $x_1 = 1$ (c) $x_1 = 3$
(d) $x_1 = 4$ (e) $x_1 = 5$

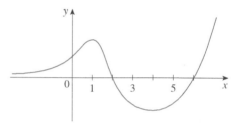

5–8 Use Newton's method with the specified initial approximation x_1 to find x_3, the third approximation to the root of the given equation. (Give your answer to four decimal places.)

5. $x^3 + 2x - 4 = 0$, $x_1 = 1$

6. $\frac{1}{3}x^3 + \frac{1}{2}x^2 + 3 = 0$, $x_1 = -3$

7. $x^5 - x - 1 = 0$, $x_1 = 1$

8. $x^5 + 2 = 0$, $x_1 = -1$

9. Use Newton's method with initial approximation $x_1 = -1$ to find x_2, the second approximation to the root of the equation $x^3 + x + 3 = 0$. Explain how the method works by first graphing the function and its tangent line at $(-1, 1)$.

10. Use Newton's method with initial approximation $x_1 = 1$ to find x_2, the second approximation to the root of the equation $x^4 - x - 1 = 0$. Explain how the method works by first graphing the function and its tangent line at $(1, -1)$.

Graphing calculator or computer with graphing software required   **1.** Homework Hints available in TEC

11–12 Use Newton's method to approximate the given number correct to eight decimal places.

11. $\sqrt[5]{20}$

12. $\sqrt[100]{100}$

13–16 Use Newton's method to find all roots of the equation correct to six decimal places.

13. $x^4 = 1 + x$

14. $e^x = 3 - 2x$

15. $(x - 2)^2 = \ln x$

16. $\dfrac{1}{x} = 1 + x^3$

17–22 Use Newton's method to find all the roots of the equation correct to eight decimal places. Start by drawing a graph to find initial approximations.

17. $x^6 - x^5 - 6x^4 - x^2 + x + 10 = 0$

18. $x^2(4 - x^2) = \dfrac{4}{x^2 + 1}$

19. $x^2\sqrt{2 - x - x^2} = 1$

20. $3 \sin(x^2) = 2x$

21. $4e^{-x^2} \sin x = x^2 - x + 1$

22. $e^{\arctan x} = \sqrt{x^3 + 1}$

---

23. (a) Apply Newton's method to the equation $x^2 - a = 0$ to derive the following square-root algorithm (used by the ancient Babylonians to compute $\sqrt{a}$):

$$x_{n+1} = \frac{1}{2}\left(x_n + \frac{a}{x_n}\right)$$

(b) Use part (a) to compute $\sqrt{1000}$ correct to six decimal places.

24. (a) Apply Newton's method to the equation $1/x - a = 0$ to derive the following reciprocal algorithm:

$$x_{n+1} = 2x_n - ax_n^2$$

(This algorithm enables a computer to find reciprocals without actually dividing.)

(b) Use part (a) to compute $1/1.6984$ correct to six decimal places.

25. Explain why Newton's method doesn't work for finding the root of the equation $x^3 - 3x + 6 = 0$ if the initial approximation is chosen to be $x_1 = 1$.

26. (a) Use Newton's method with $x_1 = 1$ to find the root of the equation $x^3 - x = 1$ correct to six decimal places.

(b) Solve the equation in part (a) using $x_1 = 0.6$ as the initial approximation.

(c) Solve the equation in part (a) using $x_1 = 0.57$. (You definitely need a programmable calculator for this part.)

(d) Graph $f(x) = x^3 - x - 1$ and its tangent lines at $x_1 = 1$, 0.6, and 0.57 to explain why Newton's method is so sensitive to the value of the initial approximation.

27. Explain why Newton's method fails when applied to the equation $\sqrt[3]{x} = 0$ with any initial approximation $x_1 \neq 0$. Illustrate your explanation with a sketch.

28. Use Newton's method to find the absolute maximum value of the function $f(x) = x \cos x$, $0 \leqslant x \leqslant \pi$, correct to six decimal places.

29. Use Newton's method to find the coordinates of the inflection point of the curve $y = e^{\cos x}$, $0 \leqslant x \leqslant \pi$, correct to six decimal places.

30. Of the infinitely many lines that are tangent to the curve $y = -\sin x$ and pass through the origin, there is one that has the largest slope. Use Newton's method to find the slope of that line correct to six decimal places.

31. Use Newton's method to find the coordinates, correct to six decimal places, of the point on the parabola $y = (x - 1)^2$ that is closest to the origin.

32. In the figure, the length of the chord AB is 4 cm and the length of the arc AB is 5 cm. Find the central angle θ, in radians, correct to four decimal places. Then give the answer to the nearest degree.

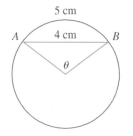

33. A car dealer sells a new car for $18,000. He also offers to sell the same car for payments of $375 per month for five years. What monthly interest rate is this dealer charging?

To solve this problem you will need to use the formula for the present value A of an annuity consisting of n equal payments of size R with interest rate i per time period:

$$A = \frac{R}{i}[1 - (1 + i)^{-n}]$$

Replacing i by x, show that

$$48x(1 + x)^{60} - (1 + x)^{60} + 1 = 0$$

Use Newton's method to solve this equation.

34. The figure shows the sun located at the origin and the earth at the point $(1, 0)$. (The unit here is the distance between the centers of the earth and the sun, called an *astronomical unit:* 1 AU $\approx 1.496 \times 10^8$ km.) There are five locations $L_1, L_2, L_3, L_4,$ and L_5 in this plane of rotation of the earth about the sun where a satellite remains motionless with respect to the earth because the forces acting on the satellite (including the gravitational attractions of the earth and the sun) balance each other. These locations are called *libration points.*

(A solar research satellite has been placed at one of these libration points.) If m_1 is the mass of the sun, m_2 is the mass of the earth, and $r = m_2/(m_1 + m_2)$, it turns out that the x-coordinate of L_1 is the unique root of the fifth-degree equation

$$p(x) = x^5 - (2 + r)x^4 + (1 + 2r)x^3 - (1 - r)x^2$$
$$+ 2(1 - r)x + r - 1 = 0$$

and the x-coordinate of L_2 is the root of the equation

$$p(x) - 2rx^2 = 0$$

Using the value $r \approx 3.04042 \times 10^{-6}$, find the locations of the libration points (a) L_1 and (b) L_2.

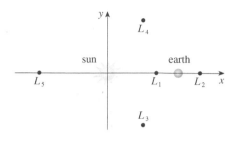

4.8 Antiderivatives

A physicist who knows the velocity of a particle might wish to know its position at a given time. An engineer who can measure the variable rate at which water is leaking from a tank wants to know the amount leaked over a certain time period. A biologist who knows the rate at which a bacteria population is increasing might want to deduce what the size of the population will be at some future time. In each case, the problem is to find a function F whose derivative is a known function f. If such a function F exists, it is called an *antiderivative* of f.

> **Definition**   A function F is called an **antiderivative** of f on an interval I if $F'(x) = f(x)$ for all x in I.

In Section 2.8 we introduced the idea of an antiderivative and we learned how to sketch the graph of an antiderivative of f if we are given the graph of f. Now that we know the differentiation formulas, we are in a position to find explicit expressions for antiderivatives. For instance, let $f(x) = x^2$. It isn't difficult to discover an antiderivative of f if we keep the Power Rule in mind. In fact, if $F(x) = \frac{1}{3}x^3$, then $F'(x) = x^2 = f(x)$. But the function $G(x) = \frac{1}{3}x^3 + 100$ also satisfies $G'(x) = x^2$. Therefore both F and G are antiderivatives of f. Indeed, any function of the form $H(x) = \frac{1}{3}x^3 + C$, where C is a constant, is an antiderivative of f. The following theorem says that f has no other antiderivative. A proof of Theorem 1, using the Mean Value Theorem, is outlined in Exercise 55.

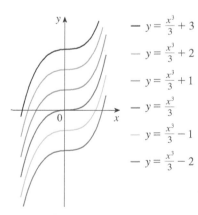

$$- \ y = \frac{x^3}{3} + 3$$

$$- \ y = \frac{x^3}{3} + 2$$

$$- \ y = \frac{x^3}{3} + 1$$

$$- \ y = \frac{x^3}{3}$$

$$- \ y = \frac{x^3}{3} - 1$$

$$- \ y = \frac{x^3}{3} - 2$$

> **1**   **Theorem**   If F is an antiderivative of f on an interval I, then the most general antiderivative of f on I is
>
> $$F(x) + C$$
>
> where C is an arbitrary constant.

FIGURE 1
Members of the family of antiderivatives of $f(x) = x^2$

Going back to the function $f(x) = x^2$, we see that the general antiderivative of f is $\frac{1}{3}x^3 + C$. By assigning specific values to the constant C, we obtain a family of functions whose graphs are vertical translates of one another (see Figure 1). This makes sense because each curve must have the same slope at any given value of x.

EXAMPLE 1 Find the most general antiderivative of each of the following functions.
(a) $f(x) = \sin x$ (b) $f(x) = 1/x$ (c) $f(x) = x^n, \quad n \neq -1$

SOLUTION

(a) If $F(x) = -\cos x$, then $F'(x) = \sin x$, so an antiderivative of $\sin x$ is $-\cos x$. By Theorem 1, the most general antiderivative is $G(x) = -\cos x + C$.

(b) Recall from Section 3.7 that

$$\frac{d}{dx}(\ln x) = \frac{1}{x}$$

So on the interval $(0, \infty)$ the general antiderivative of $1/x$ is $\ln x + C$. We also learned that

$$\frac{d}{dx}(\ln|x|) = \frac{1}{x}$$

for all $x \neq 0$. Theorem 1 then tells us that the general antiderivative of $f(x) = 1/x$ is $\ln|x| + C$ on any interval that doesn't contain 0. In particular, this is true on each of the intervals $(-\infty, 0)$ and $(0, \infty)$. So the general antiderivative of f is

$$F(x) = \begin{cases} \ln x + C_1 & \text{if } x > 0 \\ \ln(-x) + C_2 & \text{if } x < 0 \end{cases}$$

(c) We use the Power Rule to discover an antiderivative of x^n. In fact, if $n \neq -1$, then

$$\frac{d}{dx}\left(\frac{x^{n+1}}{n+1}\right) = \frac{(n+1)x^n}{n+1} = x^n$$

Thus the general antiderivative of $f(x) = x^n$ is

$$F(x) = \frac{x^{n+1}}{n+1} + C$$

This is valid for $n \geq 0$ since then $f(x) = x^n$ is defined on an interval. If n is negative (but $n \neq -1$), it is valid on any interval that doesn't contain 0.

As in Example 1, every differentiation formula, when read from right to left, gives rise to an antidifferentiation formula. In Table 2 we list some particular antiderivatives. Each formula in the table is true because the derivative of the function in the right column appears in the left column. In particular, the first formula says that the antiderivative of a constant times a function is the constant times the antiderivative of the function. The second formula says that the antiderivative of a sum is the sum of the antiderivatives. (We use the notation $F' = f$, $G' = g$.)

2 **Table of Antidifferentiation Formulas**

To obtain the most general antiderivative from the particular ones in Table 2, we have to add a constant (or constants), as in Example 1.

Function	Particular antiderivative	Function	Particular antiderivative
$cf(x)$	$cF(x)$	$\sin x$	$-\cos x$
$f(x) + g(x)$	$F(x) + G(x)$	$\sec^2 x$	$\tan x$
$x^n \ (n \neq -1)$	$\dfrac{x^{n+1}}{n+1}$	$\sec x \tan x$	$\sec x$
$1/x$	$\ln|x|$	$\dfrac{1}{\sqrt{1-x^2}}$	$\sin^{-1}x$
e^x	e^x	$\dfrac{1}{1+x^2}$	$\tan^{-1}x$
$\cos x$	$\sin x$		

EXAMPLE 2 **Finding a function, given its derivative** Find all functions g such that

$$g'(x) = 4 \sin x + \frac{2x^5 - \sqrt{x}}{x}$$

SOLUTION We first rewrite the given function as follows:

$$g'(x) = 4 \sin x + \frac{2x^5}{x} - \frac{\sqrt{x}}{x} = 4 \sin x + 2x^4 - \frac{1}{\sqrt{x}}$$

Thus we want to find an antiderivative of

$$g'(x) = 4 \sin x + 2x^4 - x^{-1/2}$$

Using the formulas in Table 2 together with Theorem 1, we obtain

$$g(x) = 4(-\cos x) + 2\frac{x^5}{5} - \frac{x^{1/2}}{\frac{1}{2}} + C$$

$$= -4 \cos x + \tfrac{2}{5}x^5 - 2\sqrt{x} + C$$

In applications of calculus it is very common to have a situation as in Example 2, where it is required to find a function, given knowledge about its derivatives. An equation that involves the derivatives of a function is called a **differential equation**. These will be studied in some detail in Chapter 7, but for the present we can solve some elementary differential equations. The general solution of a differential equation involves an arbitrary constant (or constants) as in Example 2. However, there may be some extra conditions given that will determine the constants and therefore uniquely specify the solution.

Figure 2 shows the graphs of the function f' in Example 3 and its antiderivative f. Notice that $f'(x) > 0$, so f is always increasing. Also notice that when f' has a maximum or minimum, f appears to have an inflection point. So the graph serves as a check on our calculation.

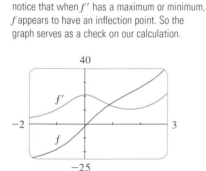

FIGURE 2

EXAMPLE 3 Find f if $f'(x) = e^x + 20(1 + x^2)^{-1}$ and $f(0) = -2$.

SOLUTION The general antiderivative of

$$f'(x) = e^x + \frac{20}{1 + x^2}$$

is $$f(x) = e^x + 20 \tan^{-1}x + C$$

To determine C we use the fact that $f(0) = -2$:

$$f(0) = e^0 + 20 \tan^{-1} 0 + C = -2$$

Thus we have $C = -2 - 1 = -3$, so the particular solution is

$$f(x) = e^x + 20 \tan^{-1}x - 3$$

V **EXAMPLE 4** **Finding a function, given its second derivative**
Find f if $f''(x) = 12x^2 + 6x - 4$, $f(0) = 4$, and $f(1) = 1$.

SOLUTION The general antiderivative of $f''(x) = 12x^2 + 6x - 4$ is

$$f'(x) = 12\frac{x^3}{3} + 6\frac{x^2}{2} - 4x + C = 4x^3 + 3x^2 - 4x + C$$

Using the antidifferentiation rules once more, we find that

$$f(x) = 4\frac{x^4}{4} + 3\frac{x^3}{3} - 4\frac{x^2}{2} + Cx + D = x^4 + x^3 - 2x^2 + Cx + D$$

To determine C and D we use the given conditions that $f(0) = 4$ and $f(1) = 1$. Since $f(0) = 0 + D = 4$, we have $D = 4$. Since

$$f(1) = 1 + 1 - 2 + C + 4 = 1$$

we have $C = -3$. Therefore the required function is

$$f(x) = x^4 + x^3 - 2x^2 - 3x + 4$$

Rectilinear Motion

Antidifferentiation is particularly useful in analyzing the motion of an object moving in a straight line. Recall that if the object has position function $s = f(t)$, then the velocity function is $v(t) = s'(t)$. This means that the position function is an antiderivative of the velocity function. Likewise, the acceleration function is $a(t) = v'(t)$, so the velocity function is an antiderivative of the acceleration. If the acceleration and the initial values $s(0)$ and $v(0)$ are known, then the position function can be found by antidifferentiating twice.

▼ EXAMPLE 5 Finding position, given acceleration   A particle moves in a straight line and has acceleration given by $a(t) = 6t + 4$. Its initial velocity is $v(0) = -6$ cm/s and its initial displacement is $s(0) = 9$ cm. Find its position function $s(t)$.

SOLUTION Since $v'(t) = a(t) = 6t + 4$, antidifferentiation gives

$$v(t) = 6\frac{t^2}{2} + 4t + C = 3t^2 + 4t + C$$

Note that $v(0) = C$. But we are given that $v(0) = -6$, so $C = -6$ and

$$v(t) = 3t^2 + 4t - 6$$

Since $v(t) = s'(t)$, s is the antiderivative of v:

$$s(t) = 3\frac{t^3}{3} + 4\frac{t^2}{2} - 6t + D = t^3 + 2t^2 - 6t + D$$

This gives $s(0) = D$. We are given that $s(0) = 9$, so $D = 9$ and the required position function is

$$s(t) = t^3 + 2t^2 - 6t + 9$$

An object near the surface of the earth is subject to a gravitational force that produces a downward acceleration denoted by g. For motion close to the ground we may assume that g is constant, its value being about 9.8 m/s^2 (or 32 ft/s^2).

EXAMPLE 6   A ball is thrown upward with a speed of 48 ft/s from the edge of a cliff 432 ft above the ground. Find its height above the ground t seconds later. When does it reach its maximum height? When does it hit the ground?

SOLUTION The motion is vertical and we choose the positive direction to be upward. At time t the distance above the ground is $s(t)$ and the velocity $v(t)$ is decreasing. Therefore the acceleration must be negative and we have

$$a(t) = \frac{dv}{dt} = -32$$

Taking antiderivatives, we have

$$v(t) = -32t + C$$

To determine C we use the given information that $v(0) = 48$. This gives $48 = 0 + C$, so

$$v(t) = -32t + 48$$

The maximum height is reached when $v(t) = 0$, that is, after 1.5 s. Since $s'(t) = v(t)$, we antidifferentiate again and obtain

$$s(t) = -16t^2 + 48t + D$$

Using the fact that $s(0) = 432$, we have $432 = 0 + D$ and so

$$s(t) = -16t^2 + 48t + 432$$

Figure 3 shows the position function of the ball in Example 6. The graph corroborates the conclusions we reached: The ball reaches its maximum height after 1.5 s and hits the ground after 6.9 s.

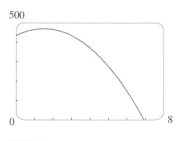

FIGURE 3

The expression for $s(t)$ is valid until the ball hits the ground. This happens when $s(t) = 0$, that is, when

$$-16t^2 + 48t + 432 = 0$$

or, equivalently,

$$t^2 - 3t - 27 = 0$$

Using the quadratic formula to solve this equation, we get

$$t = \frac{3 \pm 3\sqrt{13}}{2}$$

We reject the solution with the minus sign since it gives a negative value for t. Therefore the ball hits the ground after $3(1 + \sqrt{13})/2 \approx 6.9$ s.

4.8 Exercises

1–16 Find the most general antiderivative of the function. (Check your answer by differentiation.)

1. $f(x) = \frac{1}{2} + \frac{3}{4}x^2 - \frac{4}{5}x^3$

2. $f(x) = 8x^9 - 3x^6 + 12x^3$

3. $f(x) = (x + 1)(2x - 1)$

4. $f(x) = x(2 - x)^2$

5. $f(x) = 5x^{1/4} - 7x^{3/4}$

6. $f(x) = 2x + 3x^{1.7}$

7. $f(x) = 6\sqrt{x} - \sqrt[6]{x}$

8. $f(x) = \sqrt[4]{x^3} + \sqrt[3]{x^4}$

9. $f(x) = \dfrac{10}{x^9}$

10. $g(x) = \dfrac{5 - 4x^3 + 2x^6}{x^6}$

11. $f(u) = \dfrac{u^4 + 3\sqrt{u}}{u^2}$

12. $f(x) = 3e^x + 7\sec^2 x$

13. $g(\theta) = \cos\theta - 5\sin\theta$

14. $f(x) = 2\sqrt{x} + 6\cos x$

15. $f(x) = \dfrac{x^5 - x^3 + 2x}{x^4}$

16. $f(x) = \dfrac{2 + x^2}{1 + x^2}$

17–18 Find the antiderivative F of f that satisfies the given condition. Check your answer by comparing the graphs of f and F.

17. $f(x) = 5x^4 - 2x^5$, $\quad F(0) = 4$

18. $f(x) = 4 - 3(1 + x^2)^{-1}$, $\quad F(1) = 0$

19–36 Find f.

19. $f''(x) = 6x + 12x^2$

20. $f''(x) = 2 + x^3 + x^6$

21. $f''(x) = \frac{2}{3}x^{2/3}$

22. $f''(x) = 6x + \sin x$

23. $f'(x) = 1 - 6x$, $\quad f(0) = 8$

24. $f'(x) = 8x^3 + 12x + 3$, $\quad f(1) = 6$

25. $f'(x) = \sqrt{x}\,(6 + 5x)$, $\quad f(1) = 10$

26. $f'(x) = 2x - 3/x^4$, $\quad x > 0$, $\quad f(1) = 3$

27. $f'(t) = 2\cos t + \sec^2 t$, $\quad -\pi/2 < t < \pi/2$, $\quad f(\pi/3) = 4$

28. $f'(x) = 4/\sqrt{1 - x^2}$, $\quad f(\frac{1}{2}) = 1$

29. $f''(x) = -2 + 12x - 12x^2$, $\quad f(0) = 4$, $\quad f'(0) = 12$

30. $f''(x) = 8x^3 + 5$, $\quad f(1) = 0$, $\quad f'(1) = 8$

31. $f''(\theta) = \sin\theta + \cos\theta$, $\quad f(0) = 3$, $\quad f'(0) = 4$

32. $f''(t) = 3/\sqrt{t}$, $\quad f(4) = 20$, $\quad f'(4) = 7$

33. $f''(x) = 2 - 12x$, $\quad f(0) = 9$, $\quad f(2) = 15$

34. $f''(t) = 2e^t + 3\sin t$, $\quad f(0) = 0$, $\quad f(\pi) = 0$

35. $f''(x) = 2 + \cos x$, $\quad f(0) = -1$, $\quad f(\pi/2) = 0$

36. $f'''(x) = \cos x$, $\quad f(0) = 1$, $\quad f'(0) = 2$, $\quad f''(0) = 3$

⊞ Graphing calculator or computer with graphing software required   **1.** Homework Hints available in TEC

37. Given that the graph of f passes through the point $(1, 6)$ and that the slope of its tangent line at $(x, f(x))$ is $2x + 1$, find $f(2)$.

38. Find a function f such that $f'(x) = x^3$ and the line $x + y = 0$ is tangent to the graph of f.

39. The graph of f' is shown in the figure. Sketch the graph of f if f is continuous and $f(0) = -1$.

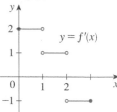

40. (a) Use a graphing device to graph $f(x) = e^x - 2x$.
   (b) Starting with the graph in part (a), sketch a rough graph of the antiderivative F that satisfies $F(0) = 1$.
   (c) Use the rules of this section to find an expression for $F(x)$.
   (d) Graph F using the expression in part (c). Compare with your sketch in part (b).

41. A particle moves along a straight line with velocity function $v(t) = \sin t - \cos t$ and its initial displacement is $s(0) = 0$ m. Find its position function $s(t)$.

42. A particle moves with acceleration function $a(t) = 5 + 4t - 2t^2$. Its initial velocity is $v(0) = 3$ m/s and its initial displacement is $s(0) = 10$ m. Find its position after t seconds.

43. A stone is dropped from the upper observation deck (the Space Deck) of the CN Tower, 450 m above the ground.
   (a) Find the distance of the stone above ground level at time t.
   (b) How long does it take the stone to reach the ground?
   (c) With what velocity does it strike the ground?
   (d) If the stone is thrown downward with a speed of 5 m/s, how long does it take to reach the ground?

44. Show that for motion in a straight line with constant acceleration a, initial velocity v_0, and initial displacement s_0, the displacement after time t is
$$s = \tfrac{1}{2}at^2 + v_0 t + s_0$$

45. An object is projected upward with initial velocity v_0 meters per second from a point s_0 meters above the ground. Show that
$$[v(t)]^2 = v_0^2 - 19.6[s(t) - s_0]$$

46. Two balls are thrown upward from the edge of the cliff in Example 6. The first is thrown with a speed of 48 ft/s and the other is thrown a second later with a speed of 24 ft/s. Do the balls ever pass each other?

47. A company estimates that the marginal cost (in dollars per item) of producing x items is $1.92 - 0.002x$. If the cost of producing one item is \$562, find the cost of producing 100 items.

48. The linear density of a rod of length 1 m is given by $\rho(x) = 1/\sqrt{x}$, in grams per centimeter, where x is measured in centimeters from one end of the rod. Find the mass of the rod.

49. A stone was dropped off a cliff and hit the ground with a speed of 120 ft/s. What is the height of the cliff?

50. A car is traveling at 50 mi/h when the brakes are fully applied, producing a constant deceleration of 22 ft/s^2. What is the distance traveled before the car comes to a stop?

51. What constant acceleration is required to increase the speed of a car from 30 mi/h to 50 mi/h in 5 s?

52. A car braked with a constant deceleration of 16 ft/s^2, producing skid marks measuring 200 ft before coming to a stop. How fast was the car traveling when the brakes were first applied?

53. A car is traveling at 100 km/h when the driver sees an accident 80 m ahead and slams on the brakes. What constant deceleration is required to stop the car in time to avoid a pileup?

54. If a diver of mass m stands at the end of a diving board with length L and linear density ρ, then the board takes on the shape of a curve $y = f(x)$, where
$$EIy'' = mg(L - x) + \tfrac{1}{2}\rho g(L - x)^2$$
E and I are positive constants that depend on the material of the board and $g\ (< 0)$ is the acceleration due to gravity.
   (a) Find an expression for the shape of the curve.
   (b) Use $f(L)$ to estimate the distance below the horizontal at the end of the board.

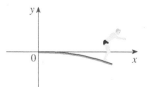

55. To prove Theorem 1, let F and G be any two antiderivatives of f on I and let $H = G - F$.
   (a) If x_1 and x_2 are any two numbers in I with $x_1 < x_2$, apply the Mean Value Theorem on the interval $[x_1, x_2]$ to show that $H(x_1) = H(x_2)$. Why does this show that H is a constant function?
   (b) Deduce Theorem 1 from the result of part (a).

56. Since raindrops grow as they fall, their surface area increases and therefore the resistance to their falling increases. A raindrop has an initial downward velocity of 10 m/s and its downward acceleration is
$$a = \begin{cases} 9 - 0.9t & \text{if } 0 \leqslant t \leqslant 10 \\ 0 & \text{if } t > 10 \end{cases}$$

If the raindrop is initially 500 m above the ground, how long does it take to fall?

57. A high-speed bullet train accelerates and decelerates at the rate of 4 ft/s². Its maximum cruising speed is 90 mi/h.
(a) What is the maximum distance the train can travel if it accelerates from rest until it reaches its cruising speed and then runs at that speed for 15 minutes?
(b) Suppose that the train starts from rest and must come to a complete stop in 15 minutes. What is the maximum distance it can travel under these conditions?
(c) Find the minimum time that the train takes to travel between two consecutive stations that are 45 miles apart.

(d) The trip from one station to the next takes 37.5 minutes. How far apart are the stations?

58. A model rocket is fired vertically upward from rest. Its acceleration for the first three seconds is $a(t) = 60t$, at which time the fuel is exhausted and it becomes a freely "falling" body. Fourteen seconds later, the rocket's parachute opens, and the (downward) velocity slows linearly to -18 ft/s in 5 s. The rocket then "floats" to the ground at that rate.
(a) Determine the position function s and the velocity function v (for all times t). Sketch the graphs of s and v.
(b) At what time does the rocket reach its maximum height, and what is that height?
(c) At what time does the rocket land?

4 Review

Concept Check

1. Explain the difference between an absolute maximum and a local maximum. Illustrate with a sketch.

2. (a) What does the Extreme Value Theorem say?
(b) Explain how the Closed Interval Method works.

3. (a) State Fermat's Theorem.
(b) Define a critical number of f.

4. State the Mean Value Theorem and give a geometric interpretation.

5. (a) State the Increasing/Decreasing Test.
(b) What does it mean to say that f is concave upward on an interval I?
(c) State the Concavity Test.
(d) What are inflection points? How do you find them?

6. (a) State the First Derivative Test.
(b) State the Second Derivative Test.
(c) What are the relative advantages and disadvantages of these tests?

7. (a) What does l'Hospital's Rule say?
(b) How can you use l'Hospital's Rule if you have a product $f(x)g(x)$ where $f(x) \to 0$ and $g(x) \to \infty$ as $x \to a$?

(c) How can you use l'Hospital's Rule if you have a difference $f(x) - g(x)$ where $f(x) \to \infty$ and $g(x) \to \infty$ as $x \to a$?
(d) How can you use l'Hospital's Rule if you have a power $[f(x)]^{g(x)}$ where $f(x) \to 0$ and $g(x) \to 0$ as $x \to a$?

8. If you have a graphing calculator or computer, why do you need calculus to graph a function?

9. (a) Given an initial approximation x_1 to a root of the equation $f(x) = 0$, explain geometrically, with a diagram, how the second approximation x_2 in Newton's method is obtained.
(b) Write an expression for x_2 in terms of x_1, $f(x_1)$, and $f'(x_1)$.
(c) Write an expression for x_{n+1} in terms of x_n, $f(x_n)$, and $f'(x_n)$.
(d) Under what circumstances is Newton's method likely to fail or to work very slowly?

10. (a) What is an antiderivative of a function f?
(b) Suppose F_1 and F_2 are both antiderivatives of f on an interval I. How are F_1 and F_2 related?

True-False Quiz

Determine whether the statement is true or false. If it is true, explain why. If it is false, explain why or give an example that disproves the statement.

1. If $f'(c) = 0$, then f has a local maximum or minimum at c.

2. If f has an absolute minimum value at c, then $f'(c) = 0$.

3. If f is continuous on (a, b), then f attains an absolute maximum value $f(c)$ and an absolute minimum value $f(d)$ at some numbers c and d in (a, b).

4. If f is differentiable and $f(-1) = f(1)$, then there is a number c such that $|c| < 1$ and $f'(c) = 0$.

5. If $f'(x) < 0$ for $1 < x < 6$, then f is decreasing on $(1, 6)$.

6. If $f''(2) = 0$, then $(2, f(2))$ is an inflection point of the curve $y = f(x)$.

7. If $f'(x) = g'(x)$ for $0 < x < 1$, then $f(x) = g(x)$ for $0 < x < 1$.

8. There exists a function f such that $f(1) = -2$, $f(3) = 0$, and $f'(x) > 1$ for all x.

9. There exists a function f such that $f(x) > 0$, $f'(x) < 0$, and $f''(x) > 0$ for all x.

10. There exists a function f such that $f(x) < 0$, $f'(x) < 0$, and $f''(x) > 0$ for all x.

11. If f and g are increasing on an interval I, then $f + g$ is increasing on I.

12. If f and g are increasing on an interval I, then $f - g$ is increasing on I.

13. If f and g are increasing on an interval I, then fg is increasing on I.

14. If f and g are positive increasing functions on an interval I, then fg is increasing on I.

15. If f is increasing and $f(x) > 0$ on I, then $g(x) = 1/f(x)$ is decreasing on I.

16. If f is even, then f' is even.

17. If f is periodic, then f' is periodic.

18. The most general antiderivative of $f(x) = x^{-2}$ is

$$F(x) = -\frac{1}{x} + C$$

19. If $f'(x)$ exists and is nonzero for all x, then $f(1) \neq f(0)$.

20. $\lim\limits_{x \to 0} \dfrac{x}{e^x} = 1$

Exercises

1–6 Find the local and absolute extreme values of the function on the given interval.

1. $f(x) = x^3 - 6x^2 + 9x + 1$, $\quad [2, 4]$

2. $f(x) = x\sqrt{1 - x}$, $\quad [-1, 1]$

3. $f(x) = \dfrac{3x - 4}{x^2 + 1}$, $\quad [-2, 2]$

4. $f(x) = (x^2 + 2x)^3$, $\quad [-2, 1]$

5. $f(x) = x + \sin 2x$, $\quad [0, \pi]$

6. $f(x) = (\ln x)/x^2$, $\quad [1, 3]$

7–14
(a) Find the vertical and horizontal asymptotes, if any.
(b) Find the intervals of increase or decrease.
(c) Find the local maximum and minimum values.
(d) Find the intervals of concavity and the inflection points.
(e) Use the information from parts (a)–(d) to sketch the graph of f. Check your work with a graphing device.

7. $f(x) = 2 - 2x - x^3$

8. $f(x) = x^4 + 4x^3$

9. $f(x) = x + \sqrt{1 - x}$

10. $f(x) = \dfrac{1}{1 - x^2}$

11. $y = \sin^2 x - 2\cos x$

12. $y = e^{2x - x^2}$

13. $y = e^x + e^{-3x}$

14. $y = \ln(x^2 - 1)$

15–18 Produce graphs of f that reveal all the important aspects of the curve. Use graphs of f' and f'' to estimate the intervals of increase and decrease, extreme values, intervals of concavity, and inflection points. In Exercise 15 use calculus to find these quantities exactly.

15. $f(x) = \dfrac{x^2 - 1}{x^3}$

16. $f(x) = \dfrac{x^3 - x}{x^2 + x + 3}$

17. $f(x) = 3x^6 - 5x^5 + x^4 - 5x^3 - 2x^2 + 2$

18. $f(x) = x^2 + 6.5\sin x$, $\quad -5 \leqslant x \leqslant 5$

19. Graph $f(x) = e^{-1/x^2}$ in a viewing rectangle that shows all the main aspects of this function. Estimate the inflection points. Then use calculus to find them exactly.

20. (a) Graph the function $f(x) = 1/(1 + e^{1/x})$.
(b) Explain the shape of the graph by computing the limits of $f(x)$ as x approaches ∞, $-\infty$, 0^+, and 0^-.
(c) Use the graph of f to estimate the coordinates of the inflection points.
(d) Use your CAS to compute and graph f''.
(e) Use the graph in part (d) to estimate the inflection points more accurately.

21–22 Use the graphs of f, f', and f'' to estimate the x-coordinates of the maximum and minimum points and inflection points of f.

21. $f(x) = \dfrac{\cos^2 x}{\sqrt{x^2 + x + 1}}$, $\quad -\pi \leqslant x \leqslant \pi$

22. $f(x) = e^{-0.1x} \ln(x^2 - 1)$

23. Investigate the family of functions $f(x) = \ln(\sin x + C)$. What features do the members of this family have in common? How do they differ? For which values of C is f continuous on $(-\infty, \infty)$? For which values of C does f have no graph at all? What happens as $C \to \infty$?

24. Investigate the family of functions $f(x) = cxe^{-cx^2}$. What happens to the maximum and minimum points and the inflection points as c changes? Illustrate your conclusions by graphing several members of the family.

25. For what values of the constants a and b is $(1, 6)$ a point of inflection of the curve $y = x^3 + ax^2 + bx + 1$?

Graphing calculator or computer with graphing software required   CAS   Computer algebra system required

26. Let $g(x) = f(x^2)$, where f is twice differentiable for all x, $f'(x) > 0$ for all $x \neq 0$, and f is concave downward on $(-\infty, 0)$ and concave upward on $(0, \infty)$.
(a) At what numbers does g have an extreme value?
(b) Discuss the concavity of g.

27–34 Evaluate the limit.

27. $\displaystyle\lim_{x \to 0} \frac{\tan \pi x}{\ln(1 + x)}$

28. $\displaystyle\lim_{x \to 0} \frac{1 - \cos x}{x^2 + x}$

29. $\displaystyle\lim_{x \to 0} \frac{e^{4x} - 1 - 4x}{x^2}$

30. $\displaystyle\lim_{x \to \infty} \frac{e^{4x} - 1 - 4x}{x^2}$

31. $\displaystyle\lim_{x \to \infty} x^3 e^{-x}$

32. $\displaystyle\lim_{x \to 0^+} x^2 \ln x$

33. $\displaystyle\lim_{x \to 1^+} \left(\frac{x}{x - 1} - \frac{1}{\ln x} \right)$

34. $\displaystyle\lim_{x \to (\pi/2)^-} (\tan x)^{\cos x}$

35. The angle of elevation of the sun is decreasing at a rate of 0.25 rad/h. How fast is the shadow cast by a 400-ft-tall building increasing when the angle of elevation of the sun is $\pi/6$?

36. A paper cup has the shape of a cone with height 10 cm and radius 3 cm (at the top). If water is poured into the cup at a rate of 2 cm³/s, how fast is the water level rising when the water is 5 cm deep?

37. A balloon is rising at a constant speed of 5 ft/s. A boy is cycling along a straight road at a speed of 15 ft/s. When he passes under the balloon, it is 45 ft above him. How fast is the distance between the boy and the balloon increasing 3 s later?

38. A waterskier skis over the ramp shown in the figure at a speed of 30 ft/s. How fast is she rising as she leaves the ramp?

39. Find two positive integers such that the sum of the first number and four times the second number is 1000 and the product of the numbers is as large as possible.

40. Find the point on the hyperbola $xy = 8$ that is closest to the point $(3, 0)$.

41. Find the smallest possible area of an isosceles triangle that is circumscribed about a circle of radius r.

42. Find the volume of the largest circular cone that can be inscribed in a sphere of radius r.

43. In $\triangle ABC$, D lies on AB, $|CD| = 5$ cm, $|AD| = 4$ cm, $|BD| = 4$ cm, and $CD \perp AB$. Where should a point P be chosen on CD so that the sum $|PA| + |PB| + |PC|$ is a minimum? What if $|CD| = 2$ cm?

44. An observer stands at a point P, one unit away from a track. Two runners start at the point S in the figure and run along the track. One runner runs three times as fast as the other. Find the maximum value of the observer's angle of sight θ between the runners. [*Hint:* Maximize $\tan \theta$.]

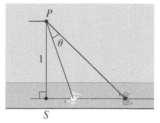

45. The velocity of a wave of length L in deep water is

$$v = K \sqrt{\frac{L}{C} + \frac{C}{L}}$$

where K and C are known positive constants. What is the length of the wave that gives the minimum velocity?

46. A metal storage tank with volume V is to be constructed in the shape of a right circular cylinder surmounted by a hemisphere. What dimensions will require the least amount of metal?

47. A hockey team plays in an arena with a seating capacity of 15,000 spectators. With the ticket price set at $12, average attendance at a game has been 11,000. A market survey indicates that for each dollar the ticket price is lowered, average attendance will increase by 1000. How should the owners of the team set the ticket price to maximize their revenue from ticket sales?

48. A manufacturer determines that the cost of making x units of a commodity is $C(x) = 1800 + 25x - 0.2x^2 + 0.001x^3$ and the demand function is $p(x) = 48.2 - 0.03x$.
(a) Graph the cost and revenue functions and use the graphs to estimate the production level for maximum profit.
(b) Use calculus to find the production level for maximum profit.
(c) Estimate the production level that minimizes the average cost.

49. Use Newton's method to find the absolute maximum value of the function $f(t) = \cos t + t - t^2$ correct to eight decimal places.

50. Use Newton's method to find all roots of the equation $\sin x = x^2 - 3x + 1$ correct to six decimal places.

51–52 Find the most general antiderivative of the function.

51. $f(x) = e^x - (2/\sqrt{x})$

52. $g(t) = (1 + t)/\sqrt{t}$

53–56 Find $f(x)$.

53. $f'(t) = 2t - 3 \sin t, \quad f(0) = 5$

54. $f'(u) = \dfrac{u^2 + \sqrt{u}}{u}, \quad f(1) = 3$

55. $f''(x) = 1 - 6x + 48x^2$, $f(0) = 1$, $f'(0) = 2$

56. $f''(x) = 2x^3 + 3x^2 - 4x + 5$, $f(0) = 2$, $f(1) = 0$

57–58 A particle is moving with the given data. Find the position of the particle.

57. $v(t) = 2t - 1/(1 + t^2)$, $s(0) = 1$

58. $a(t) = \sin t + 3 \cos t$, $s(0) = 0$, $v(0) = 2$

---

59. (a) If $f(x) = 0.1e^x + \sin x$, $-4 \le x \le 4$, use a graph of f to sketch a rough graph of the antiderivative F of f that satisfies $F(0) = 0$.
  (b) Find an expression for $F(x)$.
  (c) Graph F using the expression in part (b). Compare with your sketch in part (a).

60. Sketch the graph of a continuous, even function f such that $f(0) = 0$, $f'(x) = 2x$ if $0 < x < 1$, $f'(x) = -1$ if $1 < x < 3$, and $f'(x) = 1$ if $x > 3$.

61. A canister is dropped from a helicopter 500 m above the ground. Its parachute does not open, but the canister has been designed to withstand an impact velocity of 100 m/s. Will it burst?

62. Investigate the family of curves given by

$$f(x) = x^4 + x^3 + cx^2$$

In particular you should determine the transitional value of c at which the number of critical numbers changes and the transitional value at which the number of inflection points changes. Illustrate the various possible shapes with graphs.

63. A rectangular beam will be cut from a cylindrical log of radius 10 inches.
  (a) Show that the beam of maximal cross-sectional area is a square.
  (b) Four rectangular planks will be cut from the four sections of the log that remain after cutting the square beam. Determine the dimensions of the planks that will have maximal cross-sectional area.
  (c) Suppose that the strength of a rectangular beam is proportional to the product of its width and the square of its depth. Find the dimensions of the strongest beam that can be cut from the cylindrical log.

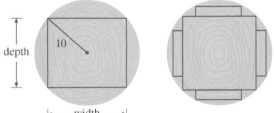

64. If a projectile is fired with an initial velocity v at an angle of inclination θ from the horizontal, then its trajectory, neglecting air resistance, is the parabola

$$y = (\tan \theta)x - \frac{g}{2v^2 \cos^2\theta} x^2 \qquad 0 \le \theta \le \frac{\pi}{2}$$

  (a) Suppose the projectile is fired from the base of a plane that is inclined at an angle α, $\alpha > 0$, from the horizontal, as shown in the figure. Show that the range of the projectile, measured up the slope, is given by

$$R(\theta) = \frac{2v^2 \cos \theta \, \sin(\theta - \alpha)}{g \cos^2\alpha}$$

  (b) Determine θ so that R is a maximum.
  (c) Suppose the plane is at an angle α *below* the horizontal. Determine the range R in this case, and determine the angle at which the projectile should be fired to maximize R.

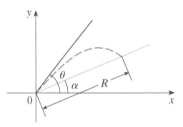

65. A light is to be placed atop a pole of height h feet to illuminate a busy traffic circle, which has a radius of 40 ft. The intensity of illumination I at any point P on the circle is directly proportional to the cosine of the angle θ (see the figure) and inversely proportional to the square of the distance d from the source.
  (a) How tall should the light pole be to maximize I?
  (b) Suppose that the light pole is h feet tall and that a woman is walking away from the base of the pole at the rate of 4 ft/s. At what rate is the intensity of the light at the point on her back 4 ft above the ground decreasing when she reaches the outer edge of the traffic circle?

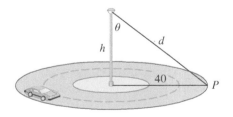

Focus on Problem Solving

One of the most important principles of problem solving is *analogy* (see page 83). If you are having trouble getting started on a problem, it is sometimes helpful to start by solving a similar, but simpler, problem. The following example illustrates the principle. Cover up the solution and try solving it yourself first.

EXAMPLE If x, y, and z are positive numbers, prove that

$$\frac{(x^2 + 1)(y^2 + 1)(z^2 + 1)}{xyz} \geq 8$$

SOLUTION It may be difficult to get started on this problem. (Some students have tackled it by multiplying out the numerator, but that just creates a mess.) Let's try to think of a similar, simpler problem. When several variables are involved, it's often helpful to think of an analogous problem with fewer variables. In the present case we can reduce the number of variables from three to one and prove the analogous inequality

$$\boxed{1} \qquad\qquad \frac{x^2 + 1}{x} \geq 2 \qquad \text{for } x > 0$$

In fact, if we are able to prove (1), then the desired inequality follows because

$$\frac{(x^2 + 1)(y^2 + 1)(z^2 + 1)}{xyz} = \left(\frac{x^2 + 1}{x}\right)\left(\frac{y^2 + 1}{y}\right)\left(\frac{z^2 + 1}{z}\right) \geq 2 \cdot 2 \cdot 2 = 8$$

The key to proving (1) is to recognize that it is a disguised version of a minimum problem. If we let

$$f(x) = \frac{x^2 + 1}{x} = x + \frac{1}{x} \qquad x > 0$$

then $f'(x) = 1 - (1/x^2)$, so $f'(x) = 0$ when $x = 1$. Also, $f'(x) < 0$ for $0 < x < 1$ and $f'(x) > 0$ for $x > 1$. Therefore the absolute minimum value of f is $f(1) = 2$. This means that

$$\frac{x^2 + 1}{x} \geq 2 \qquad \text{for all positive values of } x$$

and, as previously mentioned, the given inequality follows by multiplication.

The inequality in (1) could also be proved without calculus. In fact, if $x > 0$, we have

$$\frac{x^2 + 1}{x} \geq 2 \quad \Longleftrightarrow \quad x^2 + 1 \geq 2x \quad \Longleftrightarrow \quad x^2 - 2x + 1 \geq 0$$

$$\Longleftrightarrow \quad (x - 1)^2 \geq 0$$

Because the last inequality is obviously true, the first one is true too.

PS **Look Back**

What have we learned from the solution to this example?

- To solve a problem involving several variables, it might help to solve a similar problem with just one variable.

- When trying to prove an inequality, it might help to think of it as a maximum or minimum problem.

1. If a rectangle has its base on the *x*-axis and two vertices on the curve $y = e^{-x^2}$, show that the rectangle has the largest possible area when the two vertices are at the points of inflection of the curve.

2. Show that $|\sin x - \cos x| \leq \sqrt{2}$ for all *x*.

3. Show that, for all positive values of *x* and *y*,

$$\frac{e^{x+y}}{xy} \geq e^2$$

4. Show that $x^2 y^2 (4 - x^2)(4 - y^2) \leq 16$ for all numbers *x* and *y* such that $|x| \leq 2$ and $|y| \leq 2$.

5. Does the function $f(x) = e^{10|x-2|-x^2}$ have an absolute maximum? If so, find it. What about an absolute minimum?

6. Find the point on the parabola $y = 1 - x^2$ at which the tangent line cuts from the first quadrant the triangle with the smallest area.

7. Find the highest and lowest points on the curve $x^2 + xy + y^2 = 12$.

8. An arc *PQ* of a circle subtends a central angle θ as in the figure. Let $A(\theta)$ be the area between the chord *PQ* and the arc *PQ*. Let $B(\theta)$ be the area between the tangent lines *PR*, *QR*, and the arc. Find

$$\lim_{\theta \to 0^+} \frac{A(\theta)}{B(\theta)}$$

9. If *a*, *b*, *c*, and *d* are constants such that

$$\lim_{x \to 0} \frac{ax^2 + \sin bx + \sin cx + \sin dx}{3x^2 + 5x^4 + 7x^6} = 8$$

find the value of the sum $a + b + c + d$.

10. Sketch the region in the plane consisting of all points (x, y) such that

$$2xy \leq |x - y| \leq x^2 + y^2$$

11. Determine the values of the number *a* for which the function *f* has no critical number:

$$f(x) = (a^2 + a - 6)\cos 2x + (a - 2)x + \cos 1$$

12. For what value of *a* is the following equation true?

$$\lim_{x \to \infty} \left(\frac{x + a}{x - a}\right)^x = e$$

13. For what values of *c* does the curve $y = cx^3 + e^x$ have inflection points?

14. Sketch the set of all points (x, y) such that $|x + y| \leq e^x$.

15. If $P(a, a^2)$ is any point on the parabola $y = x^2$, except for the origin, let *Q* be the point where the normal line intersects the parabola again. Show that the line segment *PQ* has the shortest possible length when $a = 1/\sqrt{2}$.

16. For what values of *c* is there a straight line that intersects the curve

$$y = x^4 + cx^3 + 12x^2 - 5x + 2$$

in four distinct points?

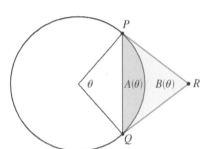

FIGURE FOR PROBLEM 8

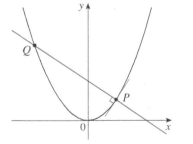

FIGURE FOR PROBLEM 15

17. The line $y = mx + b$ intersects the parabola $y = x^2$ in points A and B. (See the figure.) Find the point P on the arc AOB of the parabola that maximizes the area of the triangle PAB.

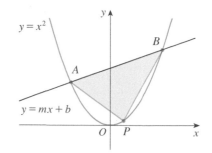

18. $ABCD$ is a square piece of paper with sides of length 1 m. A quarter-circle is drawn from B to D with center A. The piece of paper is folded along EF, with E on AB and F on AD, so that A falls on the quarter-circle. Determine the maximum and minimum areas that the triangle AEF can have.

19. In an automobile race along a straight road, car A passed car B twice. Prove that at some time during the race their accelerations were equal.

20. A hemispherical bubble is placed on a spherical bubble of radius 1. A smaller hemispherical bubble is then placed on the first one. This process is continued until n chambers, including the sphere, are formed. (The figure shows the case $n = 4$.) Use mathematical induction to prove that the maximum height of any bubble tower with n chambers is $1 + \sqrt{n}$.

FIGURE FOR PROBLEM 20

21. One of the problems posed by the Marquis de l'Hospital in his calculus textbook *Analyse des Infiniment Petits* concerns a pulley that is attached to the ceiling of a room at a point C by a rope of length r. At another point B on the ceiling, at a distance d from C (where $d > r$), a rope of length ℓ is attached and passed through the pulley at F and connected to a weight W. The weight is released and comes to rest at its equilibrium position D. As l'Hospital argued, this happens when the distance $|ED|$ is maximized. Show that when the system reaches equilibrium, the value of x is

$$\frac{r}{4d}\left(r + \sqrt{r^2 + 8d^2}\right)$$

Notice that this expression is independent of both W and ℓ.

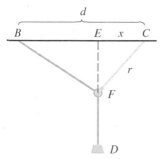

FIGURE FOR PROBLEM 21

22. Given a sphere with radius r, find the height of a pyramid of minimum volume whose base is a square and whose base and triangular faces are all tangent to the sphere. What if the base of the pyramid is a regular n-gon? (A regular n-gon is a polygon with n equal sides and angles.) (Use the fact that the volume of a pyramid is $\frac{1}{3}Ah$, where A is the area of the base.)

23. A container in the shape of an inverted cone has height 16 cm and radius 5 cm at the top. It is partially filled with a liquid that oozes through the sides at a rate proportional to the area of the container that is in contact with the liquid. (The surface area of a cone is $\pi r l$, where r is the radius and l is the slant height.) If we pour the liquid into the container at a rate of 2 cm³/min, then the height of the liquid decreases at a rate of 0.3 cm/min when the height is 10 cm. If our goal is to keep the liquid at a constant height of 10 cm, at what rate should we pour the liquid into the container?

24. A cone of radius r centimeters and height h centimeters is lowered point first at a rate of 1 cm/s into a tall cylinder of radius R centimeters that is partially filled with water. How fast is the water level rising at the instant the cone is completely submerged?

Integrals

5

In Chapter 2 we used the tangent and velocity problems to introduce the derivative, which is the central idea in differential calculus. In much the same way, this chapter starts with the area and distance problems and uses them to formulate the idea of a definite integral, which is the basic concept of integral calculus. We will see in Chapters 6 and 7 how to use the integral to solve problems concerning volumes, lengths of curves, population predictions, cardiac output, forces on a dam, work, consumer surplus, and baseball, among many others.

There is a connection between integral calculus and differential calculus. The Fundamental Theorem of Calculus relates the integral to the derivative, and we will see in this chapter that it greatly simplifies the solution of many problems.

5.1 Areas and Distances

Now is a good time to read (or reread) *A Preview of Calculus* (see page 3). It discusses the unifying ideas of calculus and helps put in perspective where we have been and where we are going.

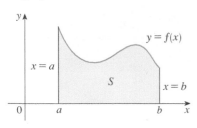

FIGURE 1
$S = \{(x, y) \mid a \leq x \leq b, 0 \leq y \leq f(x)\}$

In this section we discover that in trying to find the area under a curve or the distance traveled by a car, we end up with the same special type of limit.

The Area Problem

We begin by attempting to solve the *area problem:* Find the area of the region S that lies under the curve $y = f(x)$ from a to b. This means that S, illustrated in Figure 1, is bounded by the graph of a continuous function f [where $f(x) \geq 0$], the vertical lines $x = a$ and $x = b$, and the x-axis.

In trying to solve the area problem we have to ask ourselves: What is the meaning of the word *area*? This question is easy to answer for regions with straight sides. For a rectangle, the area is defined as the product of the length and the width. The area of a triangle is half the base times the height. The area of a polygon is found by dividing it into triangles (as in Figure 2) and adding the areas of the triangles.

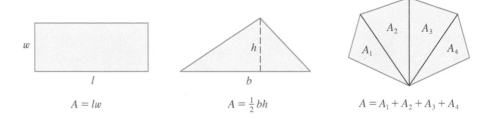

FIGURE 2 $A = lw$ $A = \frac{1}{2}bh$ $A = A_1 + A_2 + A_3 + A_4$

However, it isn't so easy to find the area of a region with curved sides. We all have an intuitive idea of what the area of a region is. But part of the area problem is to make this intuitive idea precise by giving an exact definition of area.

Recall that in defining a tangent we first approximated the slope of the tangent line by slopes of secant lines and then we took the limit of these approximations. We pursue a similar idea for areas. We first approximate the region S by rectangles and then we take the limit of the areas of these rectangles as we increase the number of rectangles. The following example illustrates the procedure.

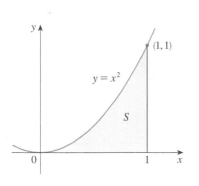

FIGURE 3

V   EXAMPLE 1   Estimating an area   Use rectangles to estimate the area under the parabola $y = x^2$ from 0 to 1 (the parabolic region S illustrated in Figure 3).

SOLUTION   We first notice that the area of S must be somewhere between 0 and 1 because S is contained in a square with side length 1, but we can certainly do better than that. Suppose we divide S into four strips S_1, S_2, S_3, and S_4 by drawing the vertical lines $x = \frac{1}{4}$, $x = \frac{1}{2}$, and $x = \frac{3}{4}$ as in Figure 4(a).

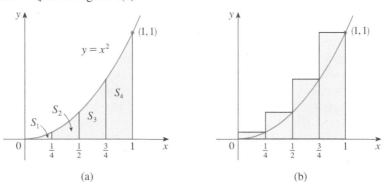

FIGURE 4   (a)   (b)

We can approximate each strip by a rectangle whose base is the same as the strip and whose height is the same as the right edge of the strip [see Figure 4(b)]. In other words, the heights of these rectangles are the values of the function $f(x) = x^2$ at the *right* endpoints of the subintervals $\left[0, \frac{1}{4}\right]$, $\left[\frac{1}{4}, \frac{1}{2}\right]$, $\left[\frac{1}{2}, \frac{3}{4}\right]$, and $\left[\frac{3}{4}, 1\right]$.

Each rectangle has width $\frac{1}{4}$ and the heights are $\left(\frac{1}{4}\right)^2$, $\left(\frac{1}{2}\right)^2$, $\left(\frac{3}{4}\right)^2$, and 1^2. If we let R_4 be the sum of the areas of these approximating rectangles, we get

$$R_4 = \tfrac{1}{4} \cdot \left(\tfrac{1}{4}\right)^2 + \tfrac{1}{4} \cdot \left(\tfrac{1}{2}\right)^2 + \tfrac{1}{4} \cdot \left(\tfrac{3}{4}\right)^2 + \tfrac{1}{4} \cdot 1^2 = \tfrac{15}{32} = 0.46875$$

From Figure 4(b) we see that the area A of S is less than R_4, so

$$A < 0.46875$$

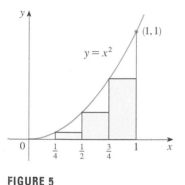

FIGURE 5

Instead of using the rectangles in Figure 4(b) we could use the smaller rectangles in Figure 5 whose heights are the values of f at the *left* endpoints of the subintervals. (The leftmost rectangle has collapsed because its height is 0.) The sum of the areas of these approximating rectangles is

$$L_4 = \tfrac{1}{4} \cdot 0^2 + \tfrac{1}{4} \cdot \left(\tfrac{1}{4}\right)^2 + \tfrac{1}{4} \cdot \left(\tfrac{1}{2}\right)^2 + \tfrac{1}{4} \cdot \left(\tfrac{3}{4}\right)^2 = \tfrac{7}{32} = 0.21875$$

We see that the area of S is larger than L_4, so we have lower and upper estimates for A:

$$0.21875 < A < 0.46875$$

We can repeat this procedure with a larger number of strips. Figure 6 shows what happens when we divide the region S into eight strips of equal width.

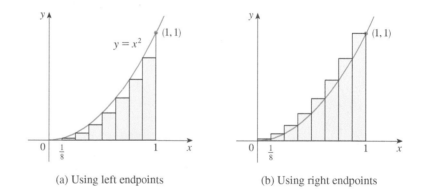

FIGURE 6

Approximating S with eight rectangles

(a) Using left endpoints   (b) Using right endpoints

By computing the sum of the areas of the smaller rectangles (L_8) and the sum of the areas of the larger rectangles (R_8), we obtain better lower and upper estimates for A:

$$0.2734375 < A < 0.3984375$$

So one possible answer to the question is to say that the true area of S lies somewhere between 0.2734375 and 0.3984375.

We could obtain better estimates by increasing the number of strips. The table at the left shows the results of similar calculations (with a computer) using n rectangles whose heights are found with left endpoints (L_n) or right endpoints (R_n). In particular, we see by using 50 strips that the area lies between 0.3234 and 0.3434. With 1000 strips we narrow it down even more: A lies between 0.3328335 and 0.3338335. A good estimate is obtained by averaging these numbers: $A \approx 0.3333335$.

n	L_n	R_n
10	0.2850000	0.3850000
20	0.3087500	0.3587500
30	0.3168519	0.3501852
50	0.3234000	0.3434000
100	0.3283500	0.3383500
1000	0.3328335	0.3338335

From the values in the table in Example 1, it looks as if R_n is approaching $\frac{1}{3}$ as n increases. We confirm this in the next example.

V   EXAMPLE 2   For the region S in Example 1, show that the sum of the areas of the upper approximating rectangles approaches $\frac{1}{3}$, that is,

$$\lim_{n \to \infty} R_n = \frac{1}{3}$$

SOLUTION R_n is the sum of the areas of the n rectangles in Figure 7. Each rectangle has width $1/n$ and the heights are the values of the function $f(x) = x^2$ at the points $1/n, 2/n, 3/n, \ldots, n/n$; that is, the heights are $(1/n)^2, (2/n)^2, (3/n)^2, \ldots, (n/n)^2$. Thus

$$R_n = \frac{1}{n}\left(\frac{1}{n}\right)^2 + \frac{1}{n}\left(\frac{2}{n}\right)^2 + \frac{1}{n}\left(\frac{3}{n}\right)^2 + \cdots + \frac{1}{n}\left(\frac{n}{n}\right)^2$$

$$= \frac{1}{n} \cdot \frac{1}{n^2}(1^2 + 2^2 + 3^2 + \cdots + n^2)$$

$$= \frac{1}{n^3}(1^2 + 2^2 + 3^2 + \cdots + n^2)$$

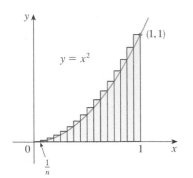

FIGURE 7

Here we need the formula for the sum of the squares of the first n positive integers:

$$\boxed{1} \qquad\qquad 1^2 + 2^2 + 3^2 + \cdots + n^2 = \frac{n(n+1)(2n+1)}{6}$$

Perhaps you have seen this formula before. It is proved in Example 5 in Appendix F. Putting Formula 1 into our expression for R_n, we get

$$R_n = \frac{1}{n^3} \cdot \frac{n(n+1)(2n+1)}{6} = \frac{(n+1)(2n+1)}{6n^2}$$

Here we are computing the limit of the sequence $\{R_n\}$. Sequences and their limits were discussed in *A Preview of Calculus* and will be studied in detail in Section 8.1. The idea is very similar to a limit at infinity (Section 2.5) except that in writing $\lim_{n \to \infty}$ we restrict n to be a positive integer. In particular, we know that

$$\lim_{n \to \infty} \frac{1}{n} = 0$$

When we write $\lim_{n \to \infty} R_n = \frac{1}{3}$ we mean that we can make R_n as close to $\frac{1}{3}$ as we like by taking n sufficiently large.

Thus we have

$$\lim_{n \to \infty} R_n = \lim_{n \to \infty} \frac{(n+1)(2n+1)}{6n^2}$$

$$= \lim_{n \to \infty} \frac{1}{6}\left(\frac{n+1}{n}\right)\left(\frac{2n+1}{n}\right)$$

$$= \lim_{n \to \infty} \frac{1}{6}\left(1 + \frac{1}{n}\right)\left(2 + \frac{1}{n}\right)$$

$$= \frac{1}{6} \cdot 1 \cdot 2 = \frac{1}{3}$$

It can be shown that the lower approximating sums also approach $\frac{1}{3}$, that is,

$$\lim_{n \to \infty} L_n = \frac{1}{3}$$

From Figures 8 and 9 it appears that, as n increases, both L_n and R_n become better and better approximations to the area of S. Therefore we *define* the area A to be the limit of the sums of the areas of the approximating rectangles, that is,

TEC In Visual 5.1 you can create pictures like those in Figures 8 and 9 for other values of n.

$$A = \lim_{n \to \infty} R_n = \lim_{n \to \infty} L_n = \tfrac{1}{3}$$

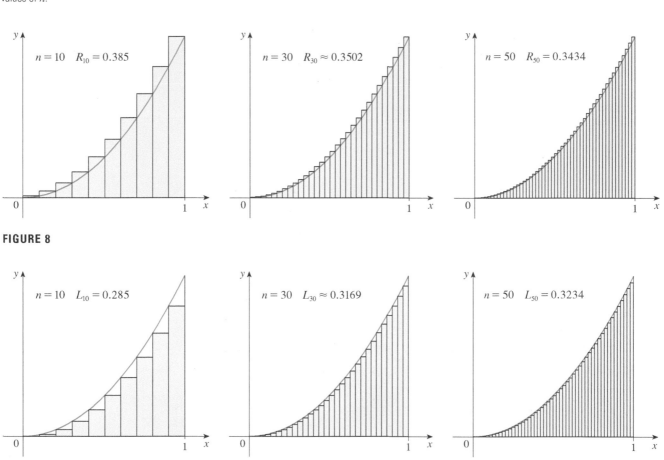

$n = 10$ $R_{10} = 0.385$

$n = 30$ $R_{30} \approx 0.3502$

$n = 50$ $R_{50} = 0.3434$

FIGURE 8

$n = 10$ $L_{10} = 0.285$

$n = 30$ $L_{30} \approx 0.3169$

$n = 50$ $L_{50} = 0.3234$

FIGURE 9   The area is the number that is smaller than all upper sums and larger than all lower sums

Let's apply the idea of Examples 1 and 2 to the more general region S of Figure 1. We start by subdividing S into n strips $S_1, S_2, \ldots, S_n$ of equal width as in Figure 10.

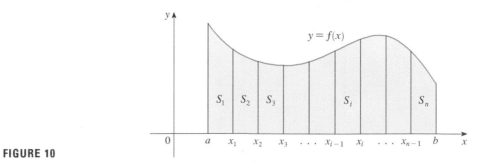

FIGURE 10

The width of the interval $[a, b]$ is $b - a$, so the width of each of the n strips is

$$\Delta x = \frac{b - a}{n}$$

These strips divide the interval $[a, b]$ into n subintervals

$$[x_0, x_1], \quad [x_1, x_2], \quad [x_2, x_3], \quad \ldots, \quad [x_{n-1}, x_n]$$

where $x_0 = a$ and $x_n = b$. The right endpoints of the subintervals are

$$x_1 = a + \Delta x,$$

$$x_2 = a + 2\,\Delta x,$$

$$x_3 = a + 3\,\Delta x,$$

$$\vdots$$

Let's approximate the ith strip S_i by a rectangle with width Δx and height $f(x_i)$, which is the value of f at the right endpoint (see Figure 11). Then the area of the ith rectangle is $f(x_i)\,\Delta x$. What we think of intuitively as the area of S is approximated by the sum of the areas of these rectangles, which is

$$R_n = f(x_1)\,\Delta x + f(x_2)\,\Delta x + \cdots + f(x_n)\,\Delta x$$

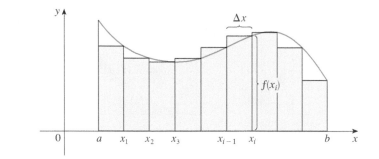

FIGURE 11

Figure 12 shows this approximation for $n = 2, 4, 8$, and 12. Notice that this approximation appears to become better and better as the number of strips increases, that is, as $n \to \infty$. Therefore we define the area A of the region S in the following way.

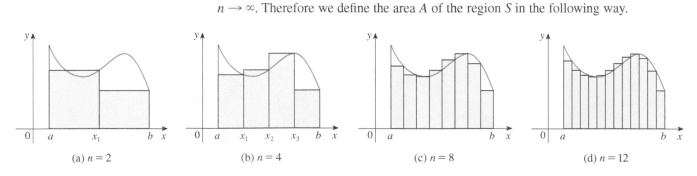

(a) $n = 2$ (b) $n = 4$ (c) $n = 8$ (d) $n = 12$

FIGURE 12

> **2** **Definition** The **area** A of the region S that lies under the graph of the continuous function f is the limit of the sum of the areas of approximating rectangles:
>
> $$A = \lim_{n \to \infty} R_n = \lim_{n \to \infty} \left[f(x_1)\,\Delta x + f(x_2)\,\Delta x + \cdots + f(x_n)\,\Delta x \right]$$

It can be proved that the limit in Definition 2 always exists, since we are assuming that f is continuous. It can also be shown that we get the same value if we use left endpoints:

$$\boxed{3} \qquad A = \lim_{n \to \infty} L_n = \lim_{n \to \infty} \left[f(x_0)\,\Delta x + f(x_1)\,\Delta x + \cdots + f(x_{n-1})\,\Delta x \right]$$

In fact, instead of using left endpoints or right endpoints, we could take the height of the ith rectangle to be the value of f at *any* number x_i^* in the ith subinterval $[x_{i-1}, x_i]$. We call the numbers $x_1^*, x_2^*, \ldots, x_n^*$ the **sample points**. Figure 13 shows approximating rectangles when the sample points are not chosen to be endpoints. So a more general expression for the area of S is

$$\boxed{4} \qquad A = \lim_{n \to \infty} \left[f(x_1^*)\,\Delta x + f(x_2^*)\,\Delta x + \cdots + f(x_n^*)\,\Delta x \right]$$

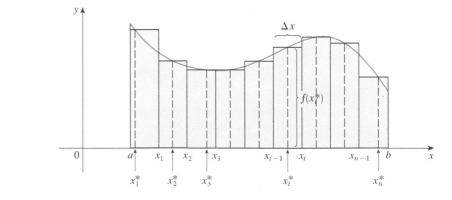

FIGURE 13

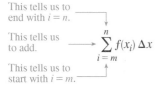

This tells us to end with $i = n$.

This tells us to add.

This tells us to start with $i = m$.

$$\sum_{i=m}^{n} f(x_i)\,\Delta x$$

If you need practice with sigma notation, look at the examples and try some of the exercises in Appendix F.

We often use **sigma notation** to write sums with many terms more compactly. For instance,

$$\sum_{i=1}^{n} f(x_i)\,\Delta x = f(x_1)\,\Delta x + f(x_2)\,\Delta x + \cdots + f(x_n)\,\Delta x$$

So the expressions for area in Equations 2, 3, and 4 can be written as follows:

$$A = \lim_{n \to \infty} \sum_{i=1}^{n} f(x_i)\,\Delta x$$

$$A = \lim_{n \to \infty} \sum_{i=1}^{n} f(x_{i-1})\,\Delta x$$

$$A = \lim_{n \to \infty} \sum_{i=1}^{n} f(x_i^*)\,\Delta x$$

We can also rewrite Formula 1 in the following way:

$$\sum_{i=1}^{n} i^2 = \frac{n(n + 1)(2n + 1)}{6}$$

EXAMPLE 3   **An area expressed as a limit**   Let A be the area of the region that lies under the graph of $f(x) = e^{-x}$ between $x = 0$ and $x = 2$.
(a) Using right endpoints, find an expression for A as a limit. Do not evaluate the limit.
(b) Estimate the area by taking the sample points to be midpoints and using four subintervals and then ten subintervals.

SOLUTION
(a) Since $a = 0$ and $b = 2$, the width of a subinterval is

$$\Delta x = \frac{2 - 0}{n} = \frac{2}{n}$$

So $x_1 = 2/n$, $x_2 = 4/n$, $x_3 = 6/n$, $x_i = 2i/n$, and $x_n = 2n/n$. The sum of the areas of the approximating rectangles is

$$R_n = f(x_1)\,\Delta x + f(x_2)\,\Delta x + \cdots + f(x_n)\,\Delta x$$

$$= e^{-x_1}\,\Delta x + e^{-x_2}\,\Delta x + \cdots + e^{-x_n}\,\Delta x$$

$$= e^{-2/n}\left(\frac{2}{n}\right) + e^{-4/n}\left(\frac{2}{n}\right) + \cdots + e^{-2n/n}\left(\frac{2}{n}\right)$$

According to Definition 2, the area is

$$A = \lim_{n \to \infty} R_n = \lim_{n \to \infty} \frac{2}{n}\left(e^{-2/n} + e^{-4/n} + e^{-6/n} + \cdots + e^{-2n/n}\right)$$

Using sigma notation we could write

$$A = \lim_{n \to \infty} \frac{2}{n} \sum_{i=1}^{n} e^{-2i/n}$$

It is difficult to evaluate this limit directly by hand, but with the aid of a computer algebra system it isn't hard (see Exercise 26). In Section 5.3 we will be able to find A more easily using a different method.

(b) With $n = 4$ the subintervals of equal width $\Delta x = 0.5$ are $[0, 0.5]$, $[0.5, 1]$, $[1, 1.5]$, and $[1.5, 2]$. The midpoints of these subintervals are $x_1^* = 0.25$, $x_2^* = 0.75$, $x_3^* = 1.25$, and $x_4^* = 1.75$, and the sum of the areas of the four approximating rectangles (see Figure 14) is

FIGURE 14

$$M_4 = \sum_{i=1}^{4} f(x_i^*)\,\Delta x$$

$$= f(0.25)\,\Delta x + f(0.75)\,\Delta x + f(1.25)\,\Delta x + f(1.75)\,\Delta x$$

$$= e^{-0.25}(0.5) + e^{-0.75}(0.5) + e^{-1.25}(0.5) + e^{-1.75}(0.5)$$

$$= \tfrac{1}{2}(e^{-0.25} + e^{-0.75} + e^{-1.25} + e^{-1.75}) \approx 0.8557$$

So an estimate for the area is

$$A \approx 0.8557$$

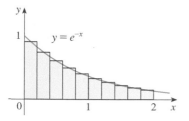

FIGURE 15

With $n = 10$ the subintervals are $[0, 0.2], [0.2, 0.4], \ldots, [1.8, 2]$ and the midpoints are $x_1^* = 0.1$, $x_2^* = 0.3$, $x_3^* = 0.5, \ldots, x_{10}^* = 1.9$. Thus

$$A \approx M_{10} = f(0.1)\,\Delta x + f(0.3)\,\Delta x + f(0.5)\,\Delta x + \cdots + f(1.9)\,\Delta x$$

$$= 0.2(e^{-0.1} + e^{-0.3} + e^{-0.5} + \cdots + e^{-1.9}) \approx 0.8632$$

From Figure 15 it appears that this estimate is better than the estimate with $n = 4$. ▬

The Distance Problem

Now let's consider the *distance problem:* Find the distance traveled by an object during a certain time period if the velocity of the object is known at all times. (In a sense this is the inverse problem of the velocity problem that we discussed in Section 2.1.) If the velocity remains constant, then the distance problem is easy to solve by means of the formula

$$\text{distance} = \text{velocity} \times \text{time}$$

But if the velocity varies, it's not so easy to find the distance traveled. We investigate the problem in the following example.

▾ **EXAMPLE 4** **Estimating a distance** Suppose the odometer on our car is broken and we want to estimate the distance driven over a 30-second time interval. We take speedometer readings every five seconds and record them in the following table:

Time (s)	0	5	10	15	20	25	30
Velocity (mi/h)	17	21	24	29	32	31	28

In order to have the time and the velocity in consistent units, let's convert the velocity readings to feet per second (1 mi/h $= 5280/3600$ ft/s):

Time (s)	0	5	10	15	20	25	30
Velocity (ft/s)	25	31	35	43	47	46	41

During the first five seconds the velocity doesn't change very much, so we can estimate the distance traveled during that time by assuming that the velocity is constant. If we take the velocity during that time interval to be the initial velocity (25 ft/s), then we obtain the approximate distance traveled during the first five seconds:

$$25 \text{ ft/s} \times 5 \text{ s} = 125 \text{ ft}$$

Similarly, during the second time interval the velocity is approximately constant and we take it to be the velocity when $t = 5$ s. So our estimate for the distance traveled from $t = 5$ s to $t = 10$ s is

$$31 \text{ ft/s} \times 5 \text{ s} = 155 \text{ ft}$$

If we add similar estimates for the other time intervals, we obtain an estimate for the total distance traveled:

$$(25 \times 5) + (31 \times 5) + (35 \times 5) + (43 \times 5) + (47 \times 5) + (46 \times 5) = 1135 \text{ ft}$$

We could just as well have used the velocity at the *end* of each time period instead of the velocity at the beginning as our assumed constant velocity. Then our estimate becomes

$$(31 \times 5) + (35 \times 5) + (43 \times 5) + (47 \times 5) + (46 \times 5) + (41 \times 5) = 1215 \text{ ft}$$

If we had wanted a more accurate estimate, we could have taken velocity readings every two seconds, or even every second.

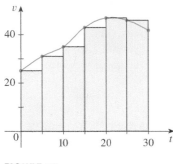

FIGURE 16

Perhaps the calculations in Example 4 remind you of the sums we used earlier to estimate areas. The similarity is explained when we sketch a graph of the velocity function of the car in Figure 16 and draw rectangles whose heights are the initial velocities for each time interval. The area of the first rectangle is $25 \times 5 = 125$, which is also our estimate for the distance traveled in the first five seconds. In fact, the area of each rectangle can be interpreted as a distance because the height represents velocity and the width represents time. The sum of the areas of the rectangles in Figure 16 is $L_6 = 1135$, which is our initial estimate for the total distance traveled.

In general, suppose an object moves with velocity $v = f(t)$, where $a \leq t \leq b$ and $f(t) \geq 0$ (so the object always moves in the positive direction). We take velocity readings at times $t_0 \ (= a), t_1, t_2, \ldots, t_n \ (= b)$ so that the velocity is approximately constant on each subinterval. If these times are equally spaced, then the time between consecutive readings is $\Delta t = (b - a)/n$. During the first time interval the velocity is approximately $f(t_0)$ and so the distance traveled is approximately $f(t_0) \, \Delta t$. Similarly, the distance traveled during the second time interval is about $f(t_1) \, \Delta t$ and the total distance traveled during the time interval $[a, b]$ is approximately

$$f(t_0) \, \Delta t + f(t_1) \, \Delta t + \cdots + f(t_{n-1}) \, \Delta t = \sum_{i=1}^{n} f(t_{i-1}) \, \Delta t$$

If we use the velocity at right endpoints instead of left endpoints, our estimate for the total distance becomes

$$f(t_1) \, \Delta t + f(t_2) \, \Delta t + \cdots + f(t_n) \, \Delta t = \sum_{i=1}^{n} f(t_i) \, \Delta t$$

The more frequently we measure the velocity, the more accurate our estimates become, so it seems plausible that the *exact* distance d traveled is the *limit* of such expressions:

$$\boxed{5} \qquad\qquad d = \lim_{n \to \infty} \sum_{i=1}^{n} f(t_{i-1}) \, \Delta t = \lim_{n \to \infty} \sum_{i=1}^{n} f(t_i) \, \Delta t$$

We will see in Section 5.3 that this is indeed true.

Because Equation 5 has the same form as our expressions for area in Equations 2 and 3, it follows that the distance traveled is equal to the area under the graph of the velocity function. In Chapter 6 we will see that other quantities of interest in the natural and social sciences—such as the work done by a variable force or the cardiac output of the heart—can also be interpreted as the area under a curve. So when we compute areas in this chapter, bear in mind that they can be interpreted in a variety of practical ways.

5.1 Exercises

1. (a) By reading values from the given graph of f, use four rectangles to find a lower estimate and an upper estimate for the area under the given graph of f from $x = 0$ to $x = 8$. In each case sketch the rectangles that you use.
   (b) Find new estimates using eight rectangles in each case.

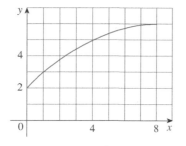

2. (a) Use six rectangles to find estimates of each type for the area under the given graph of f from $x = 0$ to $x = 12$.
   (i) L_6 (sample points are left endpoints)
   (ii) R_6 (sample points are right endpoints)
   (iii) M_6 (sample points are midpoints)
   (b) Is L_6 an underestimate or overestimate of the true area?
   (c) Is R_6 an underestimate or overestimate of the true area?
   (d) Which of the numbers L_6, R_6, or M_6 gives the best estimate? Explain.

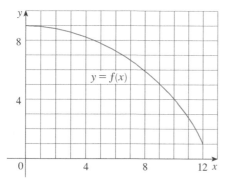

3. (a) Estimate the area under the graph of $f(x) = \cos x$ from $x = 0$ to $x = \pi/2$ using four approximating rectangles and right endpoints. Sketch the graph and the rectangles. Is your estimate an underestimate or an overestimate?
   (b) Repeat part (a) using left endpoints.

4. (a) Estimate the area under the graph of $f(x) = \sqrt{x}$ from $x = 0$ to $x = 4$ using four approximating rectangles and right endpoints. Sketch the graph and the rectangles. Is your estimate an underestimate or an overestimate?
   (b) Repeat part (a) using left endpoints.

5. (a) Estimate the area under the graph of $f(x) = 1 + x^2$ from $x = -1$ to $x = 2$ using three rectangles and right end-

points. Then improve your estimate by using six rectangles. Sketch the curve and the approximating rectangles.
   (b) Repeat part (a) using left endpoints.
   (c) Repeat part (a) using midpoints.
   (d) From your sketches in parts (a)–(c), which appears to be the best estimate?

6. (a) Graph the function $f(x) = x - 2 \ln x$, $1 \leqslant x \leqslant 5$.
   (b) Estimate the area under the graph of f using four approximating rectangles and taking the sample points to be (i) right endpoints and (ii) midpoints. In each case sketch the curve and the rectangles.
   (c) Improve your estimates in part (b) by using eight rectangles.

7–8 With a programmable calculator (or a computer), it is possible to evaluate the expressions for the sums of areas of approximating rectangles, even for large values of n, using looping. (On a TI use the Is> command or a For-EndFor loop, on a Casio use Isz, on an HP or in BASIC use a FOR-NEXT loop.) Compute the sum of the areas of approximating rectangles using equal subintervals and right endpoints for $n = 10, 30, 50$, and 100. Then guess the value of the exact area.

7. The region under $y = x^4$ from 0 to 1

8. The region under $y = \cos x$ from 0 to $\pi/2$

9. Some computer algebra systems have commands that will draw approximating rectangles and evaluate the sums of their areas, at least if x_i^* is a left or right endpoint. (For instance, in Maple use `leftbox`, `rightbox`, `leftsum`, and `rightsum`.)
   (a) If $f(x) = 1/(x^2 + 1)$, $0 \leqslant x \leqslant 1$, find the left and right sums for $n = 10, 30$, and 50.
   (b) Illustrate by graphing the rectangles in part (a).
   (c) Show that the exact area under f lies between 0.780 and 0.791.

10. (a) If $f(x) = \ln x$, $1 \leqslant x \leqslant 4$, use the commands discussed in Exercise 9 to find the left and right sums for $n = 10, 30$, and 50.
   (b) Illustrate by graphing the rectangles in part (a).
   (c) Show that the exact area under f lies between 2.50 and 2.59.

11. The speed of a runner increased steadily during the first three seconds of a race. Her speed at half-second intervals is given in the table. Find lower and upper estimates for the distance that she traveled during these three seconds.

t (s)	0	0.5	1.0	1.5	2.0	2.5	3.0
v (ft/s)	0	6.2	10.8	14.9	18.1	19.4	20.2

Graphing calculator or computer with graphing software required   CAS Computer algebra system required   **1.** Homework Hints available in TEC

12. Speedometer readings for a motorcycle at 12-second intervals are given in the table.
(a) Estimate the distance traveled by the motorcycle during this time period using the velocities at the beginning of the time intervals.
(b) Give another estimate using the velocities at the end of the time periods.
(c) Are your estimates in parts (a) and (b) upper and lower estimates? Explain.

t (s)	0	12	24	36	48	60
v (ft/s)	30	28	25	22	24	27

13. Oil leaked from a tank at a rate of $r(t)$ liters per hour. The rate decreased as time passed and values of the rate at two-hour time intervals are shown in the table. Find lower and upper estimates for the total amount of oil that leaked out.

t (h)	0	2	4	6	8	10
$r(t)$ (L/h)	8.7	7.6	6.8	6.2	5.7	5.3

14. When we estimate distances from velocity data, it is sometimes necessary to use times $t_0, t_1, t_2, t_3, \ldots$ that are not equally spaced. We can still estimate distances using the time periods $\Delta t_i = t_i - t_{i-1}$. For example, on May 7, 1992, the space shuttle *Endeavour* was launched on mission STS-49, the purpose of which was to install a new perigee kick motor in an Intelsat communications satellite. The table, provided by NASA, gives the velocity data for the shuttle between liftoff and the jettisoning of the solid rocket boosters. Use these data to estimate the height above the earth's surface of the *Endeavour,* 62 seconds after liftoff.

Event	Time (s)	Velocity (ft/s)
Launch	0	0
Begin roll maneuver	10	185
End roll maneuver	15	319
Throttle to 89%	20	447
Throttle to 67%	32	742
Throttle to 104%	59	1325
Maximum dynamic pressure	62	1445
Solid rocket booster separation	125	4151

15. The velocity graph of a braking car is shown. Use it to estimate the distance traveled by the car while the brakes are applied.

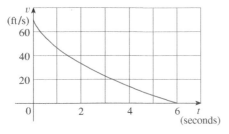

16. The velocity graph of a car accelerating from rest to a speed of 120 km/h over a period of 30 seconds is shown. Estimate the distance traveled during this period.

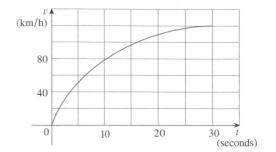

17–19 Use Definition 2 to find an expression for the area under the graph of f as a limit. Do not evaluate the limit.

17. $f(x) = \dfrac{2x}{x^2 + 1}, \quad 1 \le x \le 3$

18. $f(x) = x^2 + \sqrt{1 + 2x}, \quad 4 \le x \le 7$

19. $f(x) = x \cos x, \quad 0 \le x \le \pi/2$

20–21 Determine a region whose area is equal to the given limit. Do not evaluate the limit.

20. $\displaystyle \lim_{n \to \infty} \sum_{i=1}^{n} \frac{2}{n} \left(5 + \frac{2i}{n} \right)^{10}$

21. $\displaystyle \lim_{n \to \infty} \sum_{i=1}^{n} \frac{\pi}{4n} \tan \frac{i\pi}{4n}$

22. (a) Use Definition 2 to find an expression for the area under the curve $y = x^3$ from 0 to 1 as a limit.
(b) The following formula for the sum of the cubes of the first n integers is proved in Appendix F. Use it to evaluate the limit in part (a).

$$1^3 + 2^3 + 3^3 + \cdots + n^3 = \left[\frac{n(n + 1)}{2} \right]^2$$

23. Let A be the area under the graph of an increasing continuous function f from a to b, and let L_n and R_n be the approximations to A with n subintervals using left and right endpoints, respectively.
(a) How are A, L_n, and R_n related?
(b) Show that

$$R_n - L_n = \frac{b - a}{n} [f(b) - f(a)]$$

(c) Deduce that

$$R_n - A < \frac{b - a}{n} [f(b) - f(a)]$$

24. If A is the area under the curve $y = e^x$ from 1 to 3, use Exercise 23 to find a value of n such that $R_n - A < 0.0001$.

25. (a) Express the area under the curve $y = x^5$ from 0 to 2 as a limit.
  (b) Use a computer algebra system to find the sum in your expression from part (a).
  (c) Evaluate the limit in part (a).

26. Find the exact area of the region under the graph of $y = e^{-x}$ from 0 to 2 by using a computer algebra system to evaluate the sum and then the limit in Example 3(a). Compare your answer with the estimate obtained in Example 3(b).

27. Find the exact area under the cosine curve $y = \cos x$ from $x = 0$ to $x = b$, where $0 \leq b \leq \pi/2$. (Use a computer

algebra system both to evaluate the sum and compute the limit.) In particular, what is the area if $b = \pi/2$?

28. (a) Let A_n be the area of a polygon with n equal sides inscribed in a circle with radius r. By dividing the polygon into n congruent triangles with central angle $2\pi/n$, show that

$$A_n = \tfrac{1}{2}nr^2 \sin\left(\frac{2\pi}{n}\right)$$

  (b) Show that $\lim_{n \to \infty} A_n = \pi r^2$. [*Hint:* Use Equation 3.3.2 on page 191.]

5.2 The Definite Integral

We saw in Section 5.1 that a limit of the form

$$\boxed{1} \qquad \lim_{n \to \infty} \sum_{i=1}^{n} f(x_i^*)\,\Delta x = \lim_{n \to \infty} \left[f(x_1^*)\,\Delta x + f(x_2^*)\,\Delta x + \cdots + f(x_n^*)\,\Delta x \right]$$

arises when we compute an area. We also saw that it arises when we try to find the distance traveled by an object. It turns out that this same type of limit occurs in a wide variety of situations even when f is not necessarily a positive function. In Chapter 6 we will see that limits of the form (1) also arise in finding lengths of curves, volumes of solids, centers of mass, force due to water pressure, and work, as well as other quantities. We therefore give this type of limit a special name and notation.

A precise definition of this type of limit is given in Appendix D.

> **2** **Definition of a Definite Integral** If f is a function defined for $a \leq x \leq b$, we divide the interval $[a, b]$ into n subintervals of equal width $\Delta x = (b - a)/n$. We let $x_0 (= a), x_1, x_2, \ldots, x_n (= b)$ be the endpoints of these subintervals and we let $x_1^*, x_2^*, \ldots, x_n^*$ be any **sample points** in these subintervals, so x_i^* lies in the ith subinterval $[x_{i-1}, x_i]$. Then the **definite integral of f from a to b** is
>
> $$\int_a^b f(x)\,dx = \lim_{n \to \infty} \sum_{i=1}^{n} f(x_i^*)\,\Delta x$$
>
> provided that this limit exists. If it does exist, we say that f is **integrable** on $[a, b]$.

Note 1: The symbol $\int$ was introduced by Leibniz and is called an **integral sign**. It is an elongated S and was chosen because an integral is a limit of sums. In the notation $\int_a^b f(x)\,dx$, $f(x)$ is called the **integrand** and a and b are called the **limits of integration**; a is the **lower limit** and b is the **upper limit**. For now, the symbol dx has no meaning by itself; $\int_a^b f(x)\,dx$ is all one symbol. The dx simply indicates that the independent variable is x. The procedure of calculating an integral is called **integration**.

Note 2: The definite integral $\int_a^b f(x)\,dx$ is a number; it does not depend on x. In fact, we could use any letter in place of x without changing the value of the integral:

$$\int_a^b f(x)\,dx = \int_a^b f(t)\,dt = \int_a^b f(r)\,dr$$

Note 3: The sum

$$\sum_{i=1}^{n} f(x_i^*)\,\Delta x$$

that occurs in Definition 2 is called a **Riemann sum** after the German mathematician Bernhard Riemann (1826–1866). So Definition 2 says that the definite integral of an integrable function can be approximated to within any desired degree of accuracy by a Riemann sum.

We know that if f happens to be positive, then the Riemann sum can be interpreted as a sum of areas of approximating rectangles (see Figure 1). By comparing Definition 2 with the definition of area in Section 5.1, we see that the definite integral $\int_a^b f(x)\,dx$ can be interpreted as the area under the curve $y = f(x)$ from a to b. (See Figure 2.)

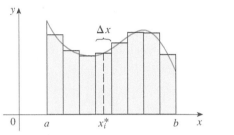

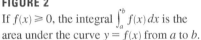

Riemann

Bernhard Riemann received his Ph.D. under the direction of the legendary Gauss at the University of Göttingen and remained there to teach. Gauss, who was not in the habit of praising other mathematicians, spoke of Riemann's "creative, active, truly mathematical mind and gloriously fertile originality." The definition (2) of an integral that we use is due to Riemann. He also made major contributions to the theory of functions of a complex variable, mathematical physics, number theory, and the foundations of geometry. Riemann's broad concept of space and geometry turned out to be the right setting, 50 years later, for Einstein's general relativity theory. Riemann's health was poor throughout his life, and he died of tuberculosis at the age of 39.

FIGURE 1
If $f(x) \geqslant 0$, the Riemann sum $\Sigma f(x_i^*)\,\Delta x$ is the sum of areas of rectangles.

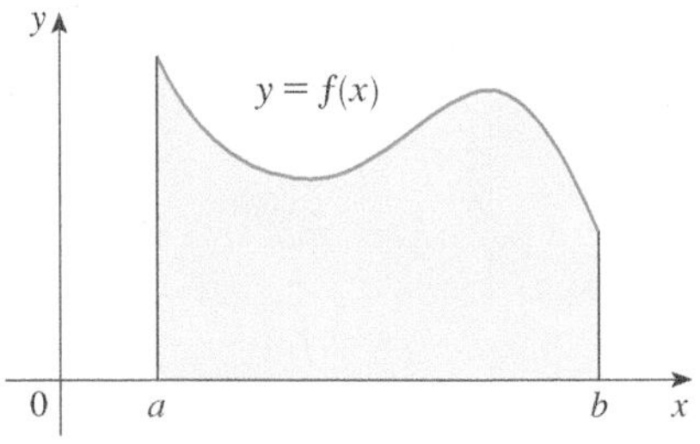

FIGURE 2
If $f(x) \geqslant 0$, the integral $\int_a^b f(x)\,dx$ is the area under the curve $y = f(x)$ from a to b.

If f takes on both positive and negative values, as in Figure 3, then the Riemann sum is the sum of the areas of the rectangles that lie above the x-axis and the *negatives* of the areas of the rectangles that lie below the x-axis (the areas of the blue rectangles *minus* the areas of the gold rectangles). When we take the limit of such Riemann sums, we get the situation illustrated in Figure 4. A definite integral can be interpreted as a **net area**, that is, a difference of areas:

$$\int_a^b f(x)\,dx = A_1 - A_2$$

where A_1 is the area of the region above the x-axis and below the graph of f, and A_2 is the area of the region below the x-axis and above the graph of f.

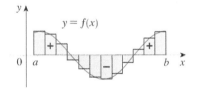

FIGURE 3
$\Sigma f(x_i^*)\,\Delta x$ is an approximation to the net area.

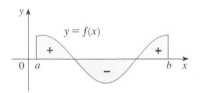

FIGURE 4
$\int_a^b f(x)\,dx$ is the net area.

Note 4: Although we have defined $\int_a^b f(x)\,dx$ by dividing $[a, b]$ into subintervals of equal width, there are situations in which it is advantageous to work with subintervals of unequal width. For instance, in Exercise 14 in Section 5.1 NASA provided velocity data at times that were not equally spaced, but we were still able to estimate the distance traveled. And there are methods for numerical integration that take advantage of unequal subintervals.

If the subinterval widths are $\Delta x_1, \Delta x_2, \ldots, \Delta x_n$, we have to ensure that all these widths approach 0 in the limiting process. This happens if the largest width, $\max \Delta x_i$, approaches 0. So in this case the definition of a definite integral becomes

$$\int_a^b f(x)\,dx = \lim_{\max \Delta x_i \to 0} \sum_{i=1}^{n} f(x_i^*)\,\Delta x_i$$

Note 5: We have defined the definite integral for an integrable function, but not all functions are integrable (see Exercises 55–56). The following theorem shows that the most commonly occurring functions are in fact integrable. It is proved in more advanced courses.

---

3 **Theorem** If f is continuous on $[a, b]$, or if f has only a finite number of jump discontinuities, then f is integrable on $[a, b]$; that is, the definite integral $\int_a^b f(x)\, dx$ exists.

If f is integrable on $[a, b]$, then the limit in Definition 2 exists and gives the same value no matter how we choose the sample points x_i^*. To simplify the calculation of the integral we often take the sample points to be right endpoints. Then $x_i^* = x_i$ and the definition of an integral simplifies as follows.

---

4 **Theorem** If f is integrable on $[a, b]$, then

$$\int_a^b f(x)\, dx = \lim_{n \to \infty} \sum_{i=1}^{n} f(x_i)\, \Delta x$$

where

$$\Delta x = \frac{b - a}{n} \qquad \text{and} \qquad x_i = a + i\, \Delta x$$

EXAMPLE 1   **Writing a limit of Riemann sums as an integral**   Express

$$\lim_{n \to \infty} \sum_{i=1}^{n} (x_i^3 + x_i \sin x_i)\, \Delta x$$

as an integral on the interval $[0, \pi]$.

SOLUTION Comparing the given limit with the limit in Theorem 4, we see that they will be identical if we choose $f(x) = x^3 + x \sin x$. We are given that $a = 0$ and $b = \pi$. Therefore, by Theorem 4, we have

$$\lim_{n \to \infty} \sum_{i=1}^{n} (x_i^3 + x_i \sin x_i)\, \Delta x = \int_0^{\pi} (x^3 + x \sin x)\, dx \qquad \blacksquare$$

Later, when we apply the definite integral to physical situations, it will be important to recognize limits of sums as integrals, as we did in Example 1. When Leibniz chose the notation for an integral, he chose the ingredients as reminders of the limiting process. In general, when we write

$$\lim_{n \to \infty} \sum_{i=1}^{n} f(x_i^*)\, \Delta x = \int_a^b f(x)\, dx$$

we replace $\lim \Sigma$ by $\int$, x_i^* by x, and Δx by dx.

Evaluating Integrals

When we use a limit to evaluate a definite integral, we need to know how to work with sums. The following three equations give formulas for sums of powers of positive integers.

Equation 5 may be familiar to you from a course in algebra. Equations 6 and 7 were discussed in Section 5.1 and are proved in Appendix F.

5

$$\sum_{i=1}^{n} i = \frac{n(n+1)}{2}$$

6

$$\sum_{i=1}^{n} i^2 = \frac{n(n+1)(2n+1)}{6}$$

7

$$\sum_{i=1}^{n} i^3 = \left[\frac{n(n+1)}{2}\right]^2$$

The remaining formulas are simple rules for working with sigma notation:

Formulas 8–11 are proved by writing out each side in expanded form. The left side of Equation 9 is

$$ca_1 + ca_2 + \cdots + ca_n$$

The right side is

$$c(a_1 + a_2 + \cdots + a_n)$$

These are equal by the distributive property. The other formulas are discussed in Appendix F.

8

$$\sum_{i=1}^{n} c = nc$$

9

$$\sum_{i=1}^{n} ca_i = c \sum_{i=1}^{n} a_i$$

10

$$\sum_{i=1}^{n} (a_i + b_i) = \sum_{i=1}^{n} a_i + \sum_{i=1}^{n} b_i$$

11

$$\sum_{i=1}^{n} (a_i - b_i) = \sum_{i=1}^{n} a_i - \sum_{i=1}^{n} b_i$$

EXAMPLE 2   **Evaluating an integral as a limit of Riemann sums**
(a) Evaluate the Riemann sum for $f(x) = x^3 - 6x$, taking the sample points to be right endpoints and $a = 0$, $b = 3$, and $n = 6$.

(b) Evaluate $\int_0^3 (x^3 - 6x)\,dx$.

SOLUTION
(a) With $n = 6$ the interval width is

$$\Delta x = \frac{b-a}{n} = \frac{3-0}{6} = \frac{1}{2}$$

and the right endpoints are $x_1 = 0.5$, $x_2 = 1.0$, $x_3 = 1.5$, $x_4 = 2.0$, $x_5 = 2.5$, and $x_6 = 3.0$. So the Riemann sum is

$$R_6 = \sum_{i=1}^{6} f(x_i)\,\Delta x$$

$$= f(0.5)\,\Delta x + f(1.0)\,\Delta x + f(1.5)\,\Delta x + f(2.0)\,\Delta x + f(2.5)\,\Delta x + f(3.0)\,\Delta x$$

$$= \tfrac{1}{2}(-2.875 - 5 - 5.625 - 4 + 0.625 + 9)$$

$$= -3.9375$$

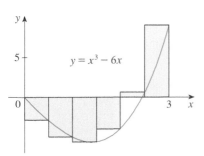

FIGURE 5

Notice that f is not a positive function and so the Riemann sum does not represent a sum of areas of rectangles. But it does represent the sum of the areas of the blue rectangles (above the x-axis) minus the sum of the areas of the gold rectangles (below the x-axis) in Figure 5.

(b) With n subintervals we have

$$\Delta x = \frac{b - a}{n} = \frac{3}{n}$$

Thus $x_0 = 0$, $x_1 = 3/n$, $x_2 = 6/n$, $x_3 = 9/n$, and, in general, $x_i = 3i/n$. Since we are using right endpoints, we can use Theorem 4:

$$\int_0^3 (x^3 - 6x)\,dx = \lim_{n \to \infty} \sum_{i=1}^n f(x_i)\,\Delta x = \lim_{n \to \infty} \sum_{i=1}^n f\left(\frac{3i}{n}\right)\frac{3}{n}$$

In the sum, n is a constant (unlike i), so we can move $3/n$ in front of the Σ sign.

$$= \lim_{n \to \infty} \frac{3}{n} \sum_{i=1}^n \left[\left(\frac{3i}{n}\right)^3 - 6\left(\frac{3i}{n}\right)\right] \qquad \text{(Equation 9 with } c = 3/n)$$

$$= \lim_{n \to \infty} \frac{3}{n} \sum_{i=1}^n \left[\frac{27}{n^3} i^3 - \frac{18}{n} i\right]$$

$$= \lim_{n \to \infty} \left[\frac{81}{n^4} \sum_{i=1}^n i^3 - \frac{54}{n^2} \sum_{i=1}^n i\right] \qquad \text{(Equations 11 and 9)}$$

$$= \lim_{n \to \infty} \left\{\frac{81}{n^4}\left[\frac{n(n+1)}{2}\right]^2 - \frac{54}{n^2}\frac{n(n+1)}{2}\right\} \qquad \text{(Equations 7 and 5)}$$

$$= \lim_{n \to \infty} \left[\frac{81}{4}\left(1 + \frac{1}{n}\right)^2 - 27\left(1 + \frac{1}{n}\right)\right]$$

$$= \frac{81}{4} - 27 = -\frac{27}{4} = -6.75$$

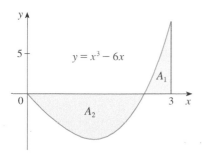

FIGURE 6
$\int_0^3 (x^3 - 6x)\,dx = A_1 - A_2 = -6.75$

This integral can't be interpreted as an area because f takes on both positive and negative values. But it can be interpreted as the difference of areas $A_1 - A_2$, where A_1 and A_2 are shown in Figure 6.

Figure 7 illustrates the calculation by showing the positive and negative terms in the right Riemann sum R_n for $n = 40$. The values in the table show the Riemann sums approaching the exact value of the integral, -6.75, as $n \to \infty$.

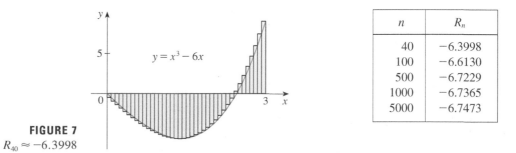

FIGURE 7
$R_{40} \approx -6.3998$

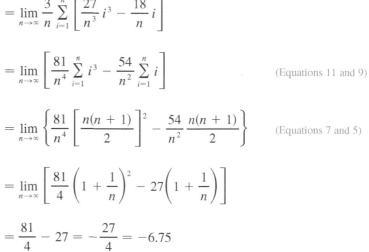

n	R_n
40	-6.3998
100	-6.6130
500	-6.7229
1000	-6.7365
5000	-6.7473

A much simpler method for evaluating the integral in Example 2 will be given in Section 5.3 after we have proved the Evaluation Theorem.

Because $f(x) = e^x$ is positive, the integral in Example 3 represents the area shown in Figure 8.

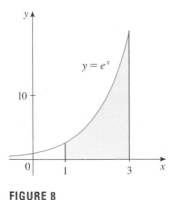

FIGURE 8

A computer algebra system is able to find an explicit expression for this sum because it is a geometric series. The limit could be found using l'Hospital's Rule.

EXAMPLE 3
(a) Set up an expression for $\int_1^3 e^x \, dx$ as a limit of sums.
(b) Use a computer algebra system to evaluate the expression.

SOLUTION
(a) Here we have $f(x) = e^x$, $a = 1$, $b = 3$, and

$$\Delta x = \frac{b - a}{n} = \frac{2}{n}$$

So $x_0 = 1$, $x_1 = 1 + 2/n$, $x_2 = 1 + 4/n$, $x_3 = 1 + 6/n$, and

$$x_i = 1 + \frac{2i}{n}$$

From Theorem 4, we get

$$\int_1^3 e^x \, dx = \lim_{n \to \infty} \sum_{i=1}^{n} f(x_i) \, \Delta x$$

$$= \lim_{n \to \infty} \sum_{i=1}^{n} f\left(1 + \frac{2i}{n}\right) \frac{2}{n}$$

$$= \lim_{n \to \infty} \frac{2}{n} \sum_{i=1}^{n} e^{1 + 2i/n}$$

(b) If we ask a computer algebra system to evaluate the sum and simplify, we obtain

$$\sum_{i=1}^{n} e^{1 + 2i/n} = \frac{e^{(3n+2)/n} - e^{(n+2)/n}}{e^{2/n} - 1}$$

Now we ask the computer algebra system to evaluate the limit:

$$\int_1^3 e^x \, dx = \lim_{n \to \infty} \frac{2}{n} \cdot \frac{e^{(3n+2)/n} - e^{(n+2)/n}}{e^{2/n} - 1} = e^3 - e$$

We will learn a much easier method for the evaluation of integrals in the next section.

V **EXAMPLE 4** **Using geometry to evaluate integrals** Evaluate the following integrals by interpreting each in terms of areas.

(a) $\int_0^1 \sqrt{1 - x^2} \, dx$ 　　　　　　(b) $\int_0^3 (x - 1) \, dx$

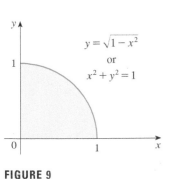

FIGURE 9

SOLUTION
(a) Since $f(x) = \sqrt{1 - x^2} \geqslant 0$, we can interpret this integral as the area under the curve $y = \sqrt{1 - x^2}$ from 0 to 1. But, since $y^2 = 1 - x^2$, we get $x^2 + y^2 = 1$, which shows that the graph of f is the quarter-circle with radius 1 in Figure 9. Therefore

$$\int_0^1 \sqrt{1 - x^2} \, dx = \tfrac{1}{4} \pi (1)^2 = \frac{\pi}{4}$$

(In Section 5.7 we will be able to *prove* that the area of a circle of radius r is πr^2.)

(b) The graph of $y = x - 1$ is the line with slope 1 shown in Figure 10. We compute the integral as the difference of the areas of the two triangles:

$$\int_0^3 (x - 1)\,dx = A_1 - A_2 = \tfrac{1}{2}(2 \cdot 2) - \tfrac{1}{2}(1 \cdot 1) = 1.5$$

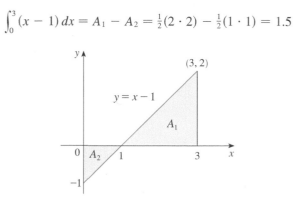

FIGURE 10

The Midpoint Rule

We often choose the sample point x_i^* to be the right endpoint of the ith subinterval because it is convenient for computing the limit. But if the purpose is to find an *approximation* to an integral, it is usually better to choose x_i^* to be the midpoint of the interval, which we denote by $\bar{x}_i$. Any Riemann sum is an approximation to an integral, but if we use midpoints we get the following approximation.

TEC Module 5.2/5.9 shows how the Midpoint Rule estimates improve as n increases.

Midpoint Rule

$$\int_a^b f(x)\,dx \approx \sum_{i=1}^{n} f(\bar{x}_i)\,\Delta x = \Delta x\,[f(\bar{x}_1) + \cdots + f(\bar{x}_n)]$$

where

$$\Delta x = \frac{b - a}{n}$$

and

$$\bar{x}_i = \tfrac{1}{2}(x_{i-1} + x_i) = \text{midpoint of } [x_{i-1}, x_i]$$

V   EXAMPLE 5   Estimating an integral with the Midpoint Rule

Use the Midpoint Rule with $n = 5$ to approximate $\int_1^2 \dfrac{1}{x}\,dx$.

SOLUTION   The endpoints of the five subintervals are 1, 1.2, 1.4, 1.6, 1.8, and 2.0, so the midpoints are 1.1, 1.3, 1.5, 1.7, and 1.9. The width of the subintervals is $\Delta x = (2 - 1)/5 = \tfrac{1}{5}$, so the Midpoint Rule gives

$$\int_1^2 \frac{1}{x}\,dx \approx \Delta x\,[f(1.1) + f(1.3) + f(1.5) + f(1.7) + f(1.9)]$$

$$= \frac{1}{5}\left(\frac{1}{1.1} + \frac{1}{1.3} + \frac{1}{1.5} + \frac{1}{1.7} + \frac{1}{1.9}\right)$$

$$\approx 0.691908$$

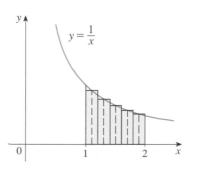

FIGURE 11

Since $f(x) = 1/x > 0$ for $1 \le x \le 2$, the integral represents an area, and the approximation given by the Midpoint Rule is the sum of the areas of the rectangles shown in Figure 11.

At the moment we don't know how accurate the approximation in Example 5 is, but in Section 5.9 we will learn a method for estimating the error involved in using the Midpoint Rule. At that time we will discuss other methods for approximating definite integrals.

If we apply the Midpoint Rule to the integral in Example 2, we get the picture in Figure 12. The approximation $M_{40} \approx -6.7563$ is much closer to the true value -6.75 than the right endpoint approximation, $R_{40} \approx -6.3998$, shown in Figure 7.

 In Visual 5.2 you can compare left, right, and midpoint approximations to the integral in Example 2 for different values of n.

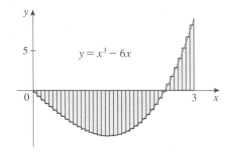

FIGURE 12

$M_{40} \approx -6.7563$

Properties of the Definite Integral

When we defined the definite integral $\int_a^b f(x)\,dx$, we implicitly assumed that $a < b$. But the definition as a limit of Riemann sums makes sense even if $a > b$. Notice that if we reverse a and b, then Δx changes from $(b - a)/n$ to $(a - b)/n$. Therefore

$$\int_b^a f(x)\,dx = -\int_a^b f(x)\,dx$$

If $a = b$, then $\Delta x = 0$ and so

$$\int_a^a f(x)\,dx = 0$$

We now develop some basic properties of integrals that will help us to evaluate integrals in a simple manner. We assume that f and g are continuous functions.

FIGURE 13

$\int_a^b c\,dx = c(b - a)$

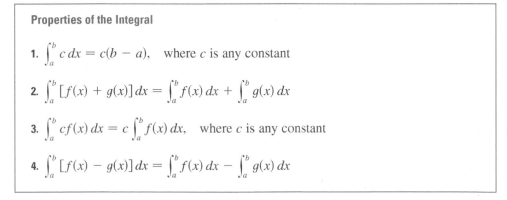

Properties of the Integral

1. $\int_a^b c\,dx = c(b - a)$,   where c is any constant

2. $\int_a^b [f(x) + g(x)]\,dx = \int_a^b f(x)\,dx + \int_a^b g(x)\,dx$

3. $\int_a^b cf(x)\,dx = c \int_a^b f(x)\,dx$,   where c is any constant

4. $\int_a^b [f(x) - g(x)]\,dx = \int_a^b f(x)\,dx - \int_a^b g(x)\,dx$

Property 1 says that the integral of a constant function $f(x) = c$ is the constant times the length of the interval. If $c > 0$ and $a < b$, this is to be expected because $c(b - a)$ is the area of the shaded rectangle in Figure 13.

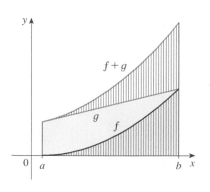

FIGURE 14

$$\int_a^b [f(x) + g(x)]\, dx =$$
$$\int_a^b f(x)\, dx + \int_a^b g(x)\, dx$$

Property 3 seems intuitively reasonable because we know that multiplying a function by a positive number c stretches or shrinks its graph vertically by a factor of c. So it stretches or shrinks each approximating rectangle by a factor c and therefore it has the effect of multiplying the area by c.

Property 2 says that the integral of a sum is the sum of the integrals. For positive functions it says that the area under $f + g$ is the area under f plus the area under g. Figure 14 helps us understand why this is true: In view of how graphical addition works, the corresponding vertical line segments have equal height.

In general, Property 2 follows from Theorem 4 and the fact that the limit of a sum is the sum of the limits:

$$\int_a^b [f(x) + g(x)]\, dx = \lim_{n \to \infty} \sum_{i=1}^{n} [f(x_i) + g(x_i)]\, \Delta x$$

$$= \lim_{n \to \infty} \left[\sum_{i=1}^{n} f(x_i)\, \Delta x + \sum_{i=1}^{n} g(x_i)\, \Delta x \right]$$

$$= \lim_{n \to \infty} \sum_{i=1}^{n} f(x_i)\, \Delta x + \lim_{n \to \infty} \sum_{i=1}^{n} g(x_i)\, \Delta x$$

$$= \int_a^b f(x)\, dx + \int_a^b g(x)\, dx$$

Property 3 can be proved in a similar manner and says that the integral of a constant times a function is the constant times the integral of the function. In other words, a constant (but *only* a constant) can be taken in front of an integral sign. Property 4 is proved by writing $f - g = f + (-g)$ and using Properties 2 and 3 with $c = -1$.

EXAMPLE 6 Use the properties of integrals to evaluate $\int_0^1 (4 + 3x^2)\, dx$.

SOLUTION Using Properties 2 and 3 of integrals, we have

$$\int_0^1 (4 + 3x^2)\, dx = \int_0^1 4\, dx + \int_0^1 3x^2\, dx = \int_0^1 4\, dx + 3 \int_0^1 x^2\, dx$$

We know from Property 1 that

$$\int_0^1 4\, dx = 4(1 - 0) = 4$$

and we found in Example 2 in Section 5.1 that $\int_0^1 x^2\, dx = \frac{1}{3}$. So

$$\int_0^1 (4 + 3x^2)\, dx = \int_0^1 4\, dx + 3 \int_0^1 x^2\, dx$$

$$= 4 + 3 \cdot \tfrac{1}{3} = 5$$

The next property tells us how to combine integrals of the same function over adjacent intervals:

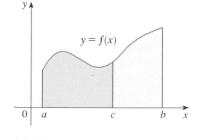

FIGURE 15

5. $$\int_a^c f(x)\, dx + \int_c^b f(x)\, dx = \int_a^b f(x)\, dx$$

This is not easy to prove in general, but for the case where $f(x) \geq 0$ and $a < c < b$ Property 5 can be seen from the geometric interpretation in Figure 15: The area under $y = f(x)$ from a to c plus the area from c to b is equal to the total area from a to b.

V EXAMPLE 7 If it is known that $\int_0^{10} f(x)\,dx = 17$ and $\int_0^8 f(x)\,dx = 12$, find $\int_8^{10} f(x)\,dx$.

SOLUTION By Property 5, we have

$$\int_0^8 f(x)\,dx + \int_8^{10} f(x)\,dx = \int_0^{10} f(x)\,dx$$

so
$$\int_8^{10} f(x)\,dx = \int_0^{10} f(x)\,dx - \int_0^8 f(x)\,dx = 17 - 12 = 5$$

Properties 1–5 are true whether $a < b$, $a = b$, or $a > b$. The following properties, in which we compare sizes of functions and sizes of integrals, are true only if $a \leqslant b$.

Comparison Properties of the Integral

6. If $f(x) \geqslant 0$ for $a \leqslant x \leqslant b$, then $\int_a^b f(x)\,dx \geqslant 0$.

7. If $f(x) \geqslant g(x)$ for $a \leqslant x \leqslant b$, then $\int_a^b f(x)\,dx \geqslant \int_a^b g(x)\,dx$.

8. If $m \leqslant f(x) \leqslant M$ for $a \leqslant x \leqslant b$, then

$$m(b - a) \leqslant \int_a^b f(x)\,dx \leqslant M(b - a)$$

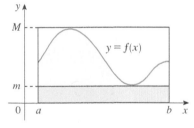

$y = f(x)$

FIGURE 16

If $f(x) \geqslant 0$, then $\int_a^b f(x)\,dx$ represents the area under the graph of f, so the geometric interpretation of Property 6 is simply that areas are positive. (It also follows directly from the definition because all the quantities involved are positive.) Property 7 says that a bigger function has a bigger integral. It follows from Properties 6 and 4 because $f - g \geqslant 0$.

Property 8 is illustrated by Figure 16 for the case where $f(x) \geqslant 0$. If f is continuous we could take m and M to be the absolute minimum and maximum values of f on the interval $[a, b]$. In this case Property 8 says that the area under the graph of f is greater than the area of the rectangle with height m and less than the area of the rectangle with height M.

PROOF OF PROPERTY 8   Since $m \leqslant f(x) \leqslant M$, Property 7 gives

$$\int_a^b m\,dx \leqslant \int_a^b f(x)\,dx \leqslant \int_a^b M\,dx$$

Using Property 1 to evaluate the integrals on the left and right sides, we obtain

$$m(b - a) \leqslant \int_a^b f(x)\,dx \leqslant M(b - a)$$

Property 8 is useful when all we want is a rough estimate of the size of an integral without going to the bother of using the Midpoint Rule.

EXAMPLE 8 Use Property 8 to estimate $\int_0^1 e^{-x^2}\,dx$.

SOLUTION Because $f(x) = e^{-x^2}$ is a decreasing function on $[0, 1]$, its absolute maximum value is $M = f(0) = 1$ and its absolute minimum value is $m = f(1) = e^{-1}$. Thus, by

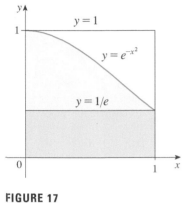

FIGURE 17

Property 8,

$$e^{-1}(1 - 0) \leqslant \int_0^1 e^{-x^2} dx \leqslant 1(1 - 0)$$

or

$$e^{-1} \leqslant \int_0^1 e^{-x^2} dx \leqslant 1$$

Since $e^{-1} \approx 0.3679$, we can write

$$0.367 \leqslant \int_0^1 e^{-x^2} dx \leqslant 1$$

The result of Example 8 is illustrated in Figure 17. The integral is greater than the area of the lower rectangle and less than the area of the square.

5.2   Exercises

1. Evaluate the Riemann sum for $f(x) = 3 - \frac{1}{2}x$, $2 \leqslant x \leqslant 14$, with six subintervals, taking the sample points to be left endpoints. Explain, with the aid of a diagram, what the Riemann sum represents.

2. If $f(x) = x^2 - 2x$, $0 \leqslant x \leqslant 3$, evaluate the Riemann sum with $n = 6$, taking the sample points to be right endpoints. What does the Riemann sum represent? Illustrate with a diagram.

3. If $f(x) = e^x - 2$, $0 \leqslant x \leqslant 2$, find the Riemann sum with $n = 4$ correct to six decimal places, taking the sample points to be midpoints. What does the Riemann sum represent? Illustrate with a diagram.

4. (a) Find the Riemann sum for $f(x) = \sin x$, $0 \leqslant x \leqslant 3\pi/2$, with six terms, taking the sample points to be right endpoints. (Give your answer correct to six decimal places.) Explain what the Riemann sum represents with the aid of a sketch.
   (b) Repeat part (a) with midpoints as sample points.

5. The graph of a function f is given. Estimate $\int_0^8 f(x) dx$ using four subintervals with (a) right endpoints, (b) left endpoints, and (c) midpoints.

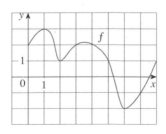

6. The graph of g is shown. Estimate $\int_{-3}^3 g(x) dx$ with six subintervals using (a) right endpoints, (b) left endpoints, and (c) midpoints.

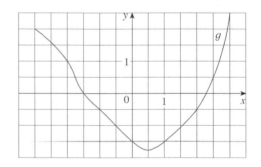

7. A table of values of an increasing function f is shown. Use the table to find lower and upper estimates for $\int_{10}^{30} f(x) dx$.

x	10	14	18	22	26	30
$f(x)$	-12	-6	-2	1	3	8

8. The table gives the values of a function obtained from an experiment. Use them to estimate $\int_3^9 f(x) dx$ using three equal subintervals with (a) right endpoints, (b) left endpoints, and (c) midpoints. If the function is known to be an increasing function, can you say whether your estimates are less than or greater than the exact value of the integral?

x	3	4	5	6	7	8	9
$f(x)$	-3.4	-2.1	-0.6	0.3	0.9	1.4	1.8

⌂ Graphing calculator or computer with graphing software required   CAS Computer algebra system required   **1.** Homework Hints available in TEC

9–12 Use the Midpoint Rule with the given value of n to approximate the integral. Round the answer to four decimal places.

9. $\int_{2}^{10} \sqrt{x^3 + 1}\, dx, \quad n = 4$

10. $\int_{0}^{\pi/2} \cos^4 x\, dx, \quad n = 4$

11. $\int_{0}^{1} \sin(x^2)\, dx, \quad n = 5$

12. $\int_{1}^{5} x^2 e^{-x}\, dx, \quad n = 4$

CAS **13.** If you have a CAS that evaluates midpoint approximations and graphs the corresponding rectangles (use `middlesum` and `middlebox` commands in Maple), check the answer to Exercise 11 and illustrate with a graph. Then repeat with $n = 10$ and $n = 20$.

14. With a programmable calculator or computer (see the instructions for Exercise 7 in Section 5.1), compute the left and right Riemann sums for the function $f(x) = \sin(x^2)$ on the interval $[0, 1]$ with $n = 100$. Explain why these estimates show that

$$0.306 < \int_{0}^{1} \sin(x^2)\, dx < 0.315$$

Deduce that the approximation using the Midpoint Rule with $n = 5$ in Exercise 11 is accurate to two decimal places.

15. Use a calculator or computer to make a table of values of right Riemann sums R_n for the integral $\int_{0}^{\pi} \sin x\, dx$ with $n = 5, 10, 50,$ and 100. What value do these numbers appear to be approaching?

16. Use a calculator or computer to make a table of values of left and right Riemann sums L_n and R_n for the integral $\int_{0}^{2} e^{-x^2}\, dx$ with $n = 5, 10, 50,$ and 100. Between what two numbers must the value of the integral lie? Can you make a similar statement for the integral $\int_{-1}^{2} e^{-x^2}\, dx$? Explain.

17–20 Express the limit as a definite integral on the given interval.

17. $\lim\limits_{n \to \infty} \sum\limits_{i=1}^{n} x_i \ln(1 + x_i^2)\, \Delta x, \quad [2, 6]$

18. $\lim\limits_{n \to \infty} \sum\limits_{i=1}^{n} \dfrac{\cos x_i}{x_i}\, \Delta x, \quad [\pi, 2\pi]$

19. $\lim\limits_{n \to \infty} \sum\limits_{i=1}^{n} \sqrt{2x_i^* + (x_i^*)^2}\, \Delta x, \quad [1, 8]$

20. $\lim\limits_{n \to \infty} \sum\limits_{i=1}^{n} [4 - 3(x_i^*)^2 + 6(x_i^*)^5]\, \Delta x, \quad [0, 2]$

21–25 Use the form of the definition of the integral given in Theorem 4 to evaluate the integral.

21. $\int_{-1}^{5} (1 + 3x)\, dx$

22. $\int_{1}^{4} (x^2 + 2x - 5)\, dx$

23. $\int_{0}^{2} (2 - x^2)\, dx$

24. $\int_{0}^{5} (1 + 2x^3)\, dx$

25. $\int_{1}^{2} x^3\, dx$

---

26. (a) Find an approximation to the integral $\int_{0}^{4} (x^2 - 3x)\, dx$ using a Riemann sum with right endpoints and $n = 8$.
(b) Draw a diagram like Figure 3 to illustrate the approximation in part (a).
(c) Use Theorem 4 to evaluate $\int_{0}^{4} (x^2 - 3x)\, dx$.
(d) Interpret the integral in part (c) as a difference of areas and illustrate with a diagram like Figure 4.

27–28 Express the integral as a limit of Riemann sums. Do not evaluate the limit.

27. $\int_{2}^{6} \dfrac{x}{1 + x^5}\, dx$

28. $\int_{1}^{10} (x - 4 \ln x)\, dx$

CAS **29–30** Express the integral as a limit of sums. Then evaluate, using a computer algebra system to find both the sum and the limit.

29. $\int_{0}^{\pi} \sin 5x\, dx$

30. $\int_{2}^{10} x^6\, dx$

31. The graph of f is shown. Evaluate each integral by interpreting it in terms of areas.

(a) $\int_{0}^{2} f(x)\, dx$

(b) $\int_{0}^{5} f(x)\, dx$

(c) $\int_{5}^{7} f(x)\, dx$

(d) $\int_{0}^{9} f(x)\, dx$

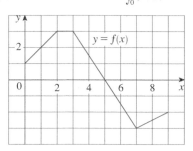

32. The graph of g consists of two straight lines and a semicircle. Use it to evaluate each integral.

(a) $\int_{0}^{2} g(x)\, dx$ (b) $\int_{2}^{6} g(x)\, dx$ (c) $\int_{0}^{7} g(x)\, dx$

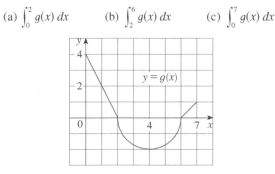

33–38 Evaluate the integral by interpreting it in terms of areas.

33. $\int_0^3 \left(\frac{1}{2} x - 1 \right) dx$

34. $\int_{-2}^2 \sqrt{4 - x^2} \, dx$

35. $\int_{-3}^0 \left(1 + \sqrt{9 - x^2} \right) dx$

36. $\int_{-1}^3 (3 - 2x) \, dx$

37. $\int_{-1}^2 |x| \, dx$

38. $\int_0^{10} |x - 5| \, dx$

39. Evaluate $\int_\pi^\pi \sin^2 x \cos^4 x \, dx$.

40. Given that $\int_0^1 3x \sqrt{x^2 + 4} \, dx = 5\sqrt{5} - 8$, what is $\int_1^0 3u \sqrt{u^2 + 4} \, du$?

41. Write as a single integral in the form $\int_a^b f(x) \, dx$:

$$\int_{-2}^2 f(x) \, dx + \int_2^5 f(x) \, dx - \int_{-2}^{-1} f(x) \, dx$$

42. If $\int_1^5 f(x) \, dx = 12$ and $\int_4^5 f(x) \, dx = 3.6$, find $\int_1^4 f(x) \, dx$.

43. If $\int_0^9 f(x) \, dx = 37$ and $\int_0^9 g(x) \, dx = 16$, find $\int_0^9 [2f(x) + 3g(x)] \, dx$.

44. Find $\int_0^5 f(x) \, dx$ if

$$f(x) = \begin{cases} 3 & \text{for } x < 3 \\ x & \text{for } x \ge 3 \end{cases}$$

45. Use the result of Example 3 to evaluate $\int_1^3 e^{x+2} \, dx$.

46. Use the properties of integrals and the result of Example 3 to evaluate $\int_1^3 (2e^x - 1) \, dx$.

47. For the function f whose graph is shown, list the following quantities in increasing order, from smallest to largest, and explain your reasoning.

(A) $\int_0^8 f(x) \, dx$ (B) $\int_0^3 f(x) \, dx$
(C) $\int_3^8 f(x) \, dx$ (D) $\int_4^8 f(x) \, dx$
(E) $f'(1)$

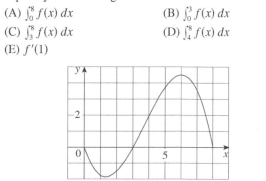

48. If $F(x) = \int_2^x f(t) \, dt$, where f is the function whose graph is given, which of the following values is largest?
(A) $F(0)$ (B) $F(1)$
(C) $F(2)$ (D) $F(3)$
(E) $F(4)$

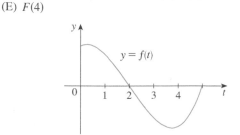

49. Each of the regions A, B, and C bounded by the graph of f and the x-axis has area 3. Find the value of

$$\int_{-4}^2 [f(x) + 2x + 5] \, dx$$

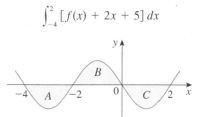

50. Suppose f has absolute minimum value m and absolute maximum value M. Between what two values must $\int_0^2 f(x) \, dx$ lie? Which property of integrals allows you to make your conclusion?

51. Use the properties of integrals to verify that

$$2 \le \int_{-1}^1 \sqrt{1 + x^2} \, dx \le 2\sqrt{2}$$

52. Use Property 8 to estimate the value of the integral

$$\int_0^2 \frac{1}{1 + x^2} \, dx$$

53–54 Express the limit as a definite integral.

53. $\lim\limits_{n \to \infty} \sum\limits_{i=1}^n \frac{i^4}{n^5}$ [*Hint:* Consider $f(x) = x^4$.]

54. $\lim\limits_{n \to \infty} \frac{1}{n} \sum\limits_{i=1}^n \frac{1}{1 + (i/n)^2}$

55. Let $f(x) = 0$ if x is any rational number and $f(x) = 1$ if x is any irrational number. Show that f is not integrable on $[0, 1]$.

56. Let $f(0) = 0$ and $f(x) = 1/x$ if $0 < x \le 1$. Show that f is not integrable on $[0, 1]$. [*Hint:* Show that the first term in the Riemann sum, $f(x_1^*) \, \Delta x$, can be made arbitrarily large.]

5.3   Evaluating Definite Integrals

In Section 5.2 we computed integrals from the definition as a limit of Riemann sums and we saw that this procedure is sometimes long and difficult. Sir Isaac Newton discovered a much simpler method for evaluating integrals and a few years later Leibniz made the same discovery. They realized that they could calculate $\int_a^b f(x)\,dx$ if they happened to know an antiderivative F of f. Their discovery, called the Evaluation Theorem, is part of the Fundamental Theorem of Calculus, which is discussed in the next section.

Evaluation Theorem If f is continuous on the interval $[a, b]$, then

$$\int_a^b f(x)\,dx = F(b) - F(a)$$

where F is any antiderivative of f, that is, $F' = f$.

This theorem states that if we know an antiderivative F of f, then we can evaluate $\int_a^b f(x)\,dx$ simply by subtracting the values of F at the endpoints of the interval $[a, b]$. It is very surprising that $\int_a^b f(x)\,dx$, which was defined by a complicated procedure involving all of the values of $f(x)$ for $a \leqslant x \leqslant b$, can be found by knowing the values of $F(x)$ at only two points, a and b.

For instance, we know from Section 4.8 that an antiderivative of the function $f(x) = x^2$ is $F(x) = \frac{1}{3}x^3$, so the Evaluation Theorem tells us that

$$\int_0^1 x^2\,dx = F(1) - F(0) = \tfrac{1}{3} \cdot 1^3 - \tfrac{1}{3} \cdot 0^3 = \tfrac{1}{3}$$

Comparing this method with the calculation in Example 2 in Section 5.1, where we found the area under the parabola $y = x^2$ from 0 to 1 by computing a limit of sums, we see that the Evaluation Theorem provides us with a simple and powerful method.

Although the Evaluation Theorem may be surprising at first glance, it becomes plausible if we interpret it in physical terms. If $v(t)$ is the velocity of an object and $s(t)$ is its position at time t, then $v(t) = s'(t)$, so s is an antiderivative of v. In Section 5.1 we considered an object that always moves in the positive direction and made the guess that the area under the velocity curve is equal to the distance traveled. In symbols:

$$\int_a^b v(t)\,dt = s(b) - s(a)$$

That is exactly what the Evaluation Theorem says in this context.

PROOF OF THE EVALUATION THEOREM We divide the interval $[a, b]$ into n subintervals with endpoints $x_0 (= a)$, $x_1, x_2, \ldots, x_n (= b)$ and with length $\Delta x = (b - a)/n$. Let F be any antiderivative of f. By subtracting and adding like terms, we can express the total difference in the F values as the sum of the differences over the subintervals:

$$F(b) - F(a) = F(x_n) - F(x_0)$$

$$= F(x_n) - F(x_{n-1}) + F(x_{n-1}) - F(x_{n-2}) + \cdots + F(x_2) - F(x_1) + F(x_1) - F(x_0)$$

$$= \sum_{i=1}^{n} [F(x_i) - F(x_{i-1})]$$

The Mean Value Theorem was discussed in Section 4.3.

Now F is continuous (because it's differentiable) and so we can apply the Mean Value Theorem to F on each subinterval $[x_{i-1}, x_i]$. Thus there exists a number x_i^* between x_{i-1} and x_i such that

$$F(x_i) - F(x_{i-1}) = F'(x_i^*)(x_i - x_{i-1}) = f(x_i^*)\,\Delta x$$

Therefore
$$F(b) - F(a) = \sum_{i=1}^{n} f(x_i^*) \Delta x$$

Now we take the limit of each side of this equation as $n \to \infty$. The left side is a constant and the right side is a Riemann sum for the function f, so

$$F(b) - F(a) = \lim_{n \to \infty} \sum_{i=1}^{n} f(x_i^*) \Delta x = \int_a^b f(x)\, dx$$

When applying the Evaluation Theorem we use the notation

$$F(x)\Big]_a^b = F(b) - F(a)$$

and so we can write

$$\int_a^b f(x)\, dx = F(x)\Big]_a^b \qquad \text{where} \qquad F' = f$$

Other common notations are $F(x)\big|_a^b$ and $[F(x)]_a^b$.

EXAMPLE 1 **Using the Evaluation Theorem** Evaluate $\int_1^3 e^x\, dx$.

SOLUTION An antiderivative of $f(x) = e^x$ is $F(x) = e^x$, so we use the Evaluation Theorem as follows:

$$\int_1^3 e^x\, dx = e^x\Big]_1^3 = e^3 - e$$

If you compare the calculation in Example 1 with the one in Example 3 in Section 5.2, you will see that the Evaluation Theorem gives a *much* shorter method.

In applying the Evaluation Theorem we use a particular antiderivative F of f. It is not necessary to use the most general antiderivative $(e^x + C)$.

EXAMPLE 2 Find the area under the cosine curve from 0 to b, where $0 \le b \le \pi/2$.

SOLUTION Since an antiderivative of $f(x) = \cos x$ is $F(x) = \sin x$, we have

$$A = \int_0^b \cos x\, dx = \sin x\Big]_0^b = \sin b - \sin 0 = \sin b$$

In particular, taking $b = \pi/2$, we have proved that the area under the cosine curve from 0 to $\pi/2$ is $\sin(\pi/2) = 1$. (See Figure 1.)

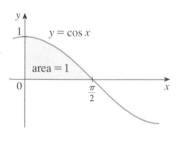

FIGURE 1

When the French mathematician Gilles de Roberval first found the area under the sine and cosine curves in 1635, this was a very challenging problem that required a great deal of ingenuity. If we didn't have the benefit of the Evaluation Theorem, we would have to compute a difficult limit of sums using obscure trigonometric identities (or a computer algebra system as in Exercise 27 in Section 5.1). It was even more difficult for Roberval because the apparatus of limits had not been invented in 1635. But in the 1660s and 1670s, when the Evaluation Theorem was discovered by Newton and Leibniz, such problems became very easy, as you can see from Example 2.

Indefinite Integrals

We need a convenient notation for antiderivatives that makes them easy to work with. Because of the relation given by the Evaluation Theorem between antiderivatives and integrals, the notation $\int f(x)\,dx$ is traditionally used for an antiderivative of f and is called an **indefinite integral**. Thus

$$\int f(x)\,dx = F(x) \qquad \text{means} \qquad F'(x) = f(x)$$

⊘   You should distinguish carefully between definite and indefinite integrals. A definite integral $\int_a^b f(x)\,dx$ is a *number*, whereas an indefinite integral $\int f(x)\,dx$ is a *function* (or family of functions). The connection between them is given by the Evaluation Theorem: If f is continuous on $[a, b]$, then

$$\int_a^b f(x)\,dx = \int f(x)\,dx \Big]_a^b$$

Recall from Section 4.8 that if F is an antiderivative of f on an interval I, then the most general antiderivative of f on I is $F(x) + C$, where C is an arbitrary constant. For instance, the formula

$$\int \frac{1}{x}\,dx = \ln|x| + C$$

is valid (on any interval that doesn't contain 0) because $(d/dx)\ln|x| = 1/x$. So an indefinite integral $\int f(x)\,dx$ can represent either a particular antiderivative of f or an entire *family* of antiderivatives (one for each value of the constant C).

The effectiveness of the Evaluation Theorem depends on having a supply of antiderivatives of functions. We therefore restate the Table of Antidifferentiation Formulas from Section 4.8, together with a few others, in the notation of indefinite integrals. Any formula can be verified by differentiating the function on the right side and obtaining the integrand. For instance,

$$\int \sec^2 x\,dx = \tan x + C \qquad \text{because} \qquad \frac{d}{dx}(\tan x + C) = \sec^2 x$$

---

1   Table of Indefinite Integrals

$$\int [f(x) + g(x)]\,dx = \int f(x)\,dx + \int g(x)\,dx \qquad \int cf(x)\,dx = c\int f(x)\,dx$$

$$\int x^n\,dx = \frac{x^{n+1}}{n+1} + C \quad (n \neq -1) \qquad \int \frac{1}{x}\,dx = \ln|x| + C$$

$$\int e^x\,dx = e^x + C \qquad \int a^x\,dx = \frac{a^x}{\ln a} + C$$

We adopt the convention that when a formula for a general indefinite integral is given, it is valid only on an interval.

$$\int \sin x\,dx = -\cos x + C \qquad \int \cos x\,dx = \sin x + C$$

$$\int \sec^2 x\,dx = \tan x + C \qquad \int \csc^2 x\,dx = -\cot x + C$$

$$\int \sec x \tan x\,dx = \sec x + C \qquad \int \csc x \cot x\,dx = -\csc x + C$$

$$\int \frac{1}{x^2+1}\,dx = \tan^{-1}x + C \qquad \int \frac{1}{\sqrt{1-x^2}}\,dx = \sin^{-1}x + C$$

EXAMPLE 3 Find the general indefinite integral

$$\int (10x^4 - 2\sec^2 x)\, dx$$

SOLUTION Using our convention and Table 1 and properties of integrals, we have

$$\int (10x^4 - 2\sec^2 x)\, dx = 10 \int x^4\, dx - 2 \int \sec^2 x\, dx$$

$$= 10\frac{x^5}{5} - 2\tan x + C$$

$$= 2x^5 - 2\tan x + C$$

You should check this answer by differentiating it.

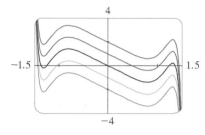

FIGURE 2

The indefinite integral in Example 3 is graphed in Figure 2 for several values of C. Here the value of C is the y-intercept.

EXAMPLE 4 Evaluate $\int_0^3 (x^3 - 6x)\, dx$.

SOLUTION Using the Evaluation Theorem and Table 1, we have

$$\int_0^3 (x^3 - 6x)\, dx = \frac{x^4}{4} - 6\frac{x^2}{2}\bigg]_0^3$$

$$= \left(\tfrac{1}{4}\cdot 3^4 - 3\cdot 3^2\right) - \left(\tfrac{1}{4}\cdot 0^4 - 3\cdot 0^2\right)$$

$$= \tfrac{81}{4} - 27 - 0 + 0 = -6.75$$

Compare this calculation with Example 2(b) in Section 5.2.

V **EXAMPLE 5** **An integral interpreted as a net area**

Find $\int_0^2 \left(2x^3 - 6x + \dfrac{3}{x^2 + 1}\right) dx$ and interpret the result in terms of areas.

SOLUTION The Evaluation Theorem gives

$$\int_0^2 \left(2x^3 - 6x + \frac{3}{x^2 + 1}\right) dx = 2\frac{x^4}{4} - 6\frac{x^2}{2} + 3\tan^{-1}x\bigg]_0^2$$

$$= \tfrac{1}{2}x^4 - 3x^2 + 3\tan^{-1}x\big]_0^2$$

$$= \tfrac{1}{2}(2^4) - 3(2^2) + 3\tan^{-1}2 - 0$$

$$= -4 + 3\tan^{-1}2$$

This is the exact value of the integral. If a decimal approximation is desired, we can use a calculator to approximate $\tan^{-1}2$. Doing so, we get

$$\int_0^2 \left(2x^3 - 6x + \frac{3}{x^2 + 1}\right) dx \approx -0.67855$$

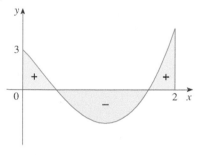

FIGURE 3

Figure 3 shows the graph of the integrand. We know from Section 5.2 that the value of the integral can be interpreted as a net area: the sum of the areas labeled with a plus sign minus the area labeled with a minus sign.

EXAMPLE 6 **Simplifying before integrating**   Evaluate $\displaystyle\int_1^9 \frac{2t^2 + t^2\sqrt{t} - 1}{t^2}\, dt$.

SOLUTION First we need to write the integrand in a simpler form by carrying out the division:

$$\int_1^9 \frac{2t^2 + t^2\sqrt{t} - 1}{t^2}\, dt = \int_1^9 (2 + t^{1/2} - t^{-2})\, dt$$

$$= 2t + \frac{t^{3/2}}{\frac{3}{2}} - \frac{t^{-1}}{-1}\Big]_1^9 = 2t + \tfrac{2}{3}t^{3/2} + \frac{1}{t}\Big]_1^9$$

$$= \left(2 \cdot 9 + \tfrac{2}{3}(9)^{3/2} + \tfrac{1}{9}\right) - \left(2 \cdot 1 + \tfrac{2}{3} \cdot 1^{3/2} + \tfrac{1}{1}\right)$$

$$= 18 + 18 + \tfrac{1}{9} - 2 - \tfrac{2}{3} - 1 = 32\tfrac{4}{9}$$

Applications

The Evaluation Theorem says that if f is continuous on $[a, b]$, then

$$\int_a^b f(x)\, dx = F(b) - F(a)$$

where F is any antiderivative of f. This means that $F' = f$, so the equation can be rewritten as

$$\int_a^b F'(x)\, dx = F(b) - F(a)$$

We know that $F'(x)$ represents the rate of change of $y = F(x)$ with respect to x and $F(b) - F(a)$ is the change in y when x changes from a to b. [Note that y could, for instance, increase, then decrease, then increase again. Although y might change in both directions, $F(b) - F(a)$ represents the *net* change in y.] So we can reformulate the Evaluation Theorem in words as follows.

Net Change Theorem   The integral of a rate of change is the net change:

$$\int_a^b F'(x)\, dx = F(b) - F(a)$$

This principle can be applied to all of the rates of change in the natural and social sciences that we discussed in Section 3.8. Here are a few instances of this idea:

- If $V(t)$ is the volume of water in a reservoir at time t, then its derivative $V'(t)$ is the rate at which water flows into the reservoir at time t. So

$$\int_{t_1}^{t_2} V'(t)\, dt = V(t_2) - V(t_1)$$

  is the change in the amount of water in the reservoir between time t_1 and time t_2.

- If $[C](t)$ is the concentration of the product of a chemical reaction at time t, then the rate of reaction is the derivative $d[C]/dt$. So

$$\int_{t_1}^{t_2} \frac{d[C]}{dt}\, dt = [C](t_2) - [C](t_1)$$

  is the change in the concentration of C from time t_1 to time t_2.

- If the mass of a rod measured from the left end to a point x is $m(x)$, then the linear density is $\rho(x) = m'(x)$. So

$$\int_a^b \rho(x)\,dx = m(b) - m(a)$$

  is the mass of the segment of the rod that lies between $x = a$ and $x = b$.

- If the rate of growth of a population is dn/dt, then

$$\int_{t_1}^{t_2} \frac{dn}{dt}\,dt = n(t_2) - n(t_1)$$

  is the net change in population during the time period from t_1 to t_2. (The population increases when births happen and decreases when deaths occur. The net change takes into account both births and deaths.)

- If $C(x)$ is the cost of producing x units of a commodity, then the marginal cost is the derivative $C'(x)$. So

$$\int_{x_1}^{x_2} C'(x)\,dx = C(x_2) - C(x_1)$$

  is the increase in cost when production is increased from x_1 units to x_2 units.

- If an object moves along a straight line with position function $s(t)$, then its velocity is $v(t) = s'(t)$, so

$$\boxed{2} \qquad \int_{t_1}^{t_2} v(t)\,dt = s(t_2) - s(t_1)$$

  is the net change of position, or *displacement,* of the particle during the time period from t_1 to t_2. In Section 5.1 we guessed that this was true for the case where the object moves in the positive direction, but now we have proved that it is always true.

- If we want to calculate the distance the object travels during the time interval, we have to consider the intervals when $v(t) \geqslant 0$ (the particle moves to the right) and also the intervals when $v(t) \leqslant 0$ (the particle moves to the left). In both cases the distance is computed by integrating $|v(t)|$, the speed. Therefore

$$\boxed{3} \qquad \int_{t_1}^{t_2} |v(t)|\,dt = \text{total distance traveled}$$

Figure 4 shows how both displacement and distance traveled can be interpreted in terms of areas under a velocity curve.

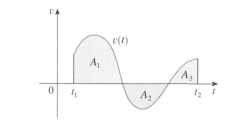

$$\text{displacement} = \int_{t_1}^{t_2} v(t)\,dt = A_1 - A_2 + A_3$$

$$\text{distance} = \int_{t_1}^{t_2} |v(t)|\,dt = A_1 + A_2 + A_3$$

FIGURE 4

- The acceleration of the object is $a(t) = v'(t)$, so

$$\int_{t_1}^{t_2} a(t)\, dt = v(t_2) - v(t_1)$$

is the change in velocity from time t_1 to time t_2.

V   EXAMPLE 7   Displacement versus distance   A particle moves along a line so that its velocity at time t is $v(t) = t^2 - t - 6$ (measured in meters per second).
(a) Find the displacement of the particle during the time period $1 \le t \le 4$.
(b) Find the distance traveled during this time period.

SOLUTION
(a) By Equation 2, the displacement is

$$s(4) - s(1) = \int_1^4 v(t)\, dt = \int_1^4 (t^2 - t - 6)\, dt$$

$$= \left[\frac{t^3}{3} - \frac{t^2}{2} - 6t \right]_1^4 = -\frac{9}{2}$$

This means that the particle's position at time $t = 4$ is 4.5 m to the left of its position at the start of the time period.

(b) Note that $v(t) = t^2 - t - 6 = (t - 3)(t + 2)$ and so $v(t) \le 0$ on the interval $[1, 3]$ and $v(t) \ge 0$ on $[3, 4]$. Thus, from Equation 3, the distance traveled is

To integrate the absolute value of $v(t)$, we use Property 5 of integrals from Section 5.2 to split the integral into two parts, one where $v(t) \le 0$ and one where $v(t) \ge 0$.

$$\int_1^4 |v(t)|\, dt = \int_1^3 [-v(t)]\, dt + \int_3^4 v(t)\, dt$$

$$= \int_1^3 (-t^2 + t + 6)\, dt + \int_3^4 (t^2 - t - 6)\, dt$$

$$= \left[-\frac{t^3}{3} + \frac{t^2}{2} + 6t \right]_1^3 + \left[\frac{t^3}{3} - \frac{t^2}{2} - 6t \right]_3^4$$

$$= \frac{61}{6} \approx 10.17 \text{ m}$$

EXAMPLE 8   Computing energy by integrating power   Figure 5 shows the power consumption in the city of San Francisco for a day in September (P is measured in megawatts; t is measured in hours starting at midnight). Estimate the energy used on that day.

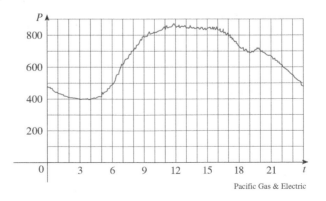

FIGURE 5

Pacific Gas & Electric

SOLUTION Power is the rate of change of energy: $P(t) = E'(t)$. So, by the Net Change Theorem,

$$\int_0^{24} P(t)\, dt = \int_0^{24} E'(t)\, dt = E(24) - E(0)$$

is the total amount of energy used on that day. We approximate the value of the integral using the Midpoint Rule with 12 subintervals and $\Delta t = 2$:

$$\int_0^{24} P(t)\, dt \approx [P(1) + P(3) + P(5) + \cdots + P(21) + P(23)]\,\Delta t$$

$$\approx (440 + 400 + 420 + 620 + 790 + 840 + 850$$

$$+\, 840 + 810 + 690 + 670 + 550)(2)$$

$$= 15{,}840$$

The energy used was approximately 15,840 megawatt-hours.

A note on units

How did we know what units to use for energy in Example 8? The integral $\int_0^{24} P(t)\, dt$ is defined as the limit of sums of terms of the form $P(t_i^*)\,\Delta t$. Now $P(t_i^*)$ is measured in megawatts and Δt is measured in hours, so their product is measured in megawatt-hours. The same is true of the limit. In general, the unit of measurement for $\int_a^b f(x)\, dx$ is the product of the unit for $f(x)$ and the unit for x.

5.3 Exercises

1–30 Evaluate the integral.

1. $\int_{-2}^{3} (x^2 - 3)\, dx$

2. $\int_{1}^{2} x^{-2}\, dx$

3. $\int_{0}^{2} \left(x^4 - \frac{3}{4}x^2 + \frac{2}{3}x - 1\right) dx$

4. $\int_{0}^{1} \left(1 + \frac{1}{2}u^4 - \frac{2}{5}u^9\right) du$

5. $\int_{0}^{1} x^{4/5}\, dx$

6. $\int_{1}^{8} \sqrt[3]{x}\, dx$

7. $\int_{-1}^{0} (2x - e^x)\, dx$

8. $\int_{-5}^{5} e\, dx$

9. $\int_{1}^{2} (1 + 2y)^2\, dy$

10. $\int_{0}^{2} (y - 1)(2y + 1)\, dy$

11. $\int_{1}^{9} \frac{x - 1}{\sqrt{x}}\, dx$

12. $\int_{-1}^{1} t(1 - t)^2\, dt$

13. $\int_{0}^{1} x(\sqrt[3]{x} + \sqrt[4]{x})\, dx$

14. $\int_{0}^{\pi/4} \sec\theta \tan\theta\, d\theta$

15. $\int_{0}^{\pi/4} \sec^2 t\, dt$

16. $\int_{1}^{18} \sqrt{\frac{3}{z}}\, dz$

17. $\int_{1}^{9} \frac{1}{2x}\, dx$

18. $\int_{0}^{5} (2e^x + 4\cos x)\, dx$

19. $\int_{1/2}^{\sqrt{3}/2} \frac{6}{\sqrt{1 - t^2}}\, dt$

20. $\int_{0}^{1} 10^x\, dx$

21. $\int_{-1}^{1} e^{u+1}\, du$

22. $\int_{0}^{1} \frac{4}{t^2 + 1}\, dt$

23. $\int_{1}^{2} \frac{v^3 + 3v^6}{v^4}\, dv$

24. $\int_{0}^{\pi/3} \frac{\sin\theta + \sin\theta \tan^2\theta}{\sec^2\theta}\, d\theta$

25. $\int_{0}^{\pi/4} \frac{1 + \cos^2\theta}{\cos^2\theta}\, d\theta$

26. $\int_{1}^{2} \frac{(x - 1)^3}{x^2}\, dx$

27. $\int_{0}^{1/\sqrt{3}} \frac{t^2 - 1}{t^4 - 1}\, dt$

28. $\int_{0}^{2} |2x - 1|\, dx$

Graphing calculator or computer with graphing software required   **1.** Homework Hints available in TEC

29. $\int_{-1}^{2} (x - 2|x|)\, dx$

30. $\int_{0}^{3\pi/2} |\sin x|\, dx$

31–32 What is wrong with the equation?

31. $\int_{-1}^{3} \frac{1}{x^2}\, dx = \dfrac{x^{-1}}{-1} \bigg]_{-1}^{3} = -\dfrac{4}{3}$

32. $\int_{0}^{\pi} \sec^2 x\, dx = \tan x \big]_{0}^{\pi} = 0$

33–34 Use a graph to give a rough estimate of the area of the region that lies beneath the given curve. Then find the exact area.

33. $y = \sin x,\ 0 \leqslant x \leqslant \pi$

34. $y = \sec^2 x,\ 0 \leqslant x \leqslant \pi/3$

---

35. Use a graph to estimate the x-intercepts of the curve $y = 1 - 2x - 5x^4$. Then use this information to estimate the area of the region that lies under the curve and above the x-axis.

36. Repeat Exercise 35 for the curve $y = (x^2 + 1)^{-1} - x^4$.

37–38 Evaluate the integral and interpret it as a difference of areas. Illustrate with a sketch.

37. $\int_{-1}^{2} x^3\, dx$

38. $\int_{-\pi/2}^{2\pi} \cos x\, dx$

39–40 Verify by differentiation that the formula is correct.

39. $\int \cos^3 x\, dx = \sin x - \tfrac{1}{3}\sin^3 x + C$

40. $\int x \cos x\, dx = x \sin x + \cos x + C$

41–42 Find the general indefinite integral. Illustrate by graphing several members of the family on the same screen.

41. $\int (\cos x + \tfrac{1}{2}x)\, dx$

42. $\int (e^x - 2x^2)\, dx$

43–48 Find the general indefinite integral.

43. $\int (1 - t)(2 + t^2)\, dt$

44. $\int v(v^2 + 2)^2\, dv$

45. $\int (1 + \tan^2\alpha)\, d\alpha$

46. $\int \sec t\,(\sec t + \tan t)\, dt$

47. $\int \dfrac{\sin x}{1 - \sin^2 x}\, dx$

48. $\int \dfrac{\sin 2x}{\sin x}\, dx$

---

49. The area of the region that lies to the right of the y-axis and to the left of the parabola $x = 2y - y^2$ (the shaded region in the figure) is given by the integral $\int_0^2 (2y - y^2)\, dy$. (Turn your head clockwise and think of the region as lying below the curve $x = 2y - y^2$ from $y = 0$ to $y = 2$.) Find the area of the region.

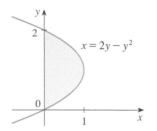

50. The boundaries of the shaded region are the y-axis, the line $y = 1$, and the curve $y = \sqrt[4]{x}$. Find the area of this region by writing x as a function of y and integrating with respect to y (as in Exercise 49).

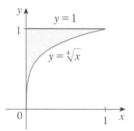

51. If $w'(t)$ is the rate of growth of a child in pounds per year, what does $\int_5^{10} w'(t)\, dt$ represent?

52. The current in a wire is defined as the derivative of the charge: $I(t) = Q'(t)$. (See Example 3 in Section 3.8.) What does $\int_a^b I(t)\, dt$ represent?

53. If oil leaks from a tank at a rate of $r(t)$ gallons per minute at time t, what does $\int_0^{120} r(t)\, dt$ represent?

54. A honeybee population starts with 100 bees and increases at a rate of $n'(t)$ bees per week. What does $100 + \int_0^{15} n'(t)\, dt$ represent?

55. In Section 4.6 we defined the marginal revenue function $R'(x)$ as the derivative of the revenue function $R(x)$, where x is the number of units sold. What does $\int_{1000}^{5000} R'(x)\, dx$ represent?

56. If $f(x)$ is the slope of a trail at a distance of x miles from the start of the trail, what does $\int_3^5 f(x)\, dx$ represent?

57. If x is measured in meters and $f(x)$ is measured in newtons, what are the units for $\int_0^{100} f(x)\, dx$?

58. If the units for x are feet and the units for $a(x)$ are pounds per foot, what are the units for da/dx? What units does $\int_2^8 a(x)\, dx$ have?

59–60 The velocity function (in meters per second) is given for a particle moving along a line. Find (a) the displacement and (b) the distance traveled by the particle during the given time interval.

59. $v(t) = 3t - 5, \quad 0 \le t \le 3$

60. $v(t) = t^2 - 2t - 8, \quad 1 \le t \le 6$

61–62 The acceleration function (in m/s^2) and the initial velocity are given for a particle moving along a line. Find (a) the velocity at time t and (b) the distance traveled during the given time interval.

61. $a(t) = t + 4, \quad v(0) = 5, \quad 0 \le t \le 10$

62. $a(t) = 2t + 3, \quad v(0) = -4, \quad 0 \le t \le 3$

63. The linear density of a rod of length 4 m is given by $\rho(x) = 9 + 2\sqrt{x}$ measured in kilograms per meter, where x is measured in meters from one end of the rod. Find the total mass of the rod.

64. Water flows from the bottom of a storage tank at a rate of $r(t) = 200 - 4t$ liters per minute, where $0 \le t \le 50$. Find the amount of water that flows from the tank during the first 10 minutes.

65. The velocity of a car was read from its speedometer at 10-second intervals and recorded in the table. Use the Midpoint Rule to estimate the distance traveled by the car.

t (s)	v (mi/h)	t (s)	v (mi/h)
0	0	60	56
10	38	70	53
20	52	80	50
30	58	90	47
40	55	100	45
50	51		

66. Suppose that a volcano is erupting and readings of the rate $r(t)$ at which solid materials are spewed into the atmosphere are given in the table. The time t is measured in seconds and the units for $r(t)$ are tonnes (metric tons) per second.

t	0	1	2	3	4	5	6
$r(t)$	2	10	24	36	46	54	60

(a) Give upper and lower estimates for the total quantity $Q(6)$ of erupted materials after 6 seconds.

(b) Use the Midpoint Rule to estimate $Q(6)$.

67. The marginal cost of manufacturing x yards of a certain fabric is $C'(x) = 3 - 0.01x + 0.000006x^2$ (in dollars per yard). Find the increase in cost if the production level is raised from 2000 yards to 4000 yards.

68. Water flows into and out of a storage tank. A graph of the rate of change $r(t)$ of the volume of water in the tank, in liters per day, is shown. If the amount of water in the tank at time $t = 0$ is 25,000 L, use the Midpoint Rule to estimate the amount of water four days later.

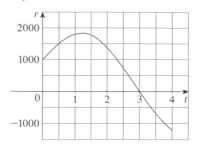

69. Economists use a cumulative distribution called a *Lorenz curve* to describe the distribution of income between households in a given country. Typically, a Lorenz curve is defined on $[0, 1]$ with endpoints $(0, 0)$ and $(1, 1)$, and is continuous, increasing, and concave upward. The points on this curve are determined by ranking all households by income and then computing the percentage of households whose income is less than or equal to a given percentage of the total income of the country. For example, the point $(a/100, b/100)$ is on the Lorenz curve if the bottom $a\%$ of the households receive less than or equal to $b\%$ of the total income. *Absolute equality* of income distribution would occur if the bottom $a\%$ of the households receive $a\%$ of the income, in which case the Lorenz curve would be the line $y = x$. The area between the Lorenz curve and the line $y = x$ measures how much the income distribution differs from absolute equality. The *coefficient of inequality* is the ratio of the area between the Lorenz curve and the line $y = x$ to the area under $y = x$.

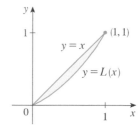

(a) Show that the coefficient of inequality is twice the area between the Lorenz curve and the line $y = x$, that is, show that

$$\text{coefficient of inequality} = 2 \int_0^1 [x - L(x)]\, dx$$

(b) The income distribution for a certain country is represented by the Lorenz curve defined by the equation

$$L(x) = \tfrac{5}{12}x^2 + \tfrac{7}{12}x$$

What is the percentage of total income received by the bottom 50% of the households? Find the coefficient of inequality.

70. On May 7, 1992, the space shuttle *Endeavour* was launched on mission STS-49, the purpose of which was to install a new perigee kick motor in an Intelsat communications satellite. The

table gives the velocity data for the shuttle between liftoff and the jettisoning of the solid rocket boosters.
(a) Use a graphing calculator or computer to model these data by a third-degree polynomial.
(b) Use the model in part (a) to estimate the height reached by the *Endeavour*, 125 seconds after liftoff.

Event	Time (s)	Velocity (ft/s)
Launch	0	0
Begin roll maneuver	10	185
End roll maneuver	15	319
Throttle to 89%	20	447
Throttle to 67%	32	742
Throttle to 104%	59	1325
Maximum dynamic pressure	62	1445
Solid rocket booster separation	125	4151

71. (a) Show that $1 \le \sqrt{1 + x^3} \le 1 + x^3$ for $x \ge 0$.
(b) Show that $1 \le \int_0^1 \sqrt{1 + x^3}\, dx \le 1.25$.

72. (a) Show that $\cos(x^2) \ge \cos x$ for $0 \le x \le 1$.
(b) Deduce that $\int_0^{\pi/6} \cos(x^2)\, dx \ge \frac{1}{2}$.

73. Suppose h is a function such that $h(1) = -2$, $h'(1) = 2$, $h''(1) = 3$, $h(2) = 6$, $h'(2) = 5$, $h''(2) = 13$, and h'' is continuous everywhere. Evaluate $\int_1^2 h''(u)\, du$.

74. The area labeled B is three times the area labeled A. Express b in terms of a.

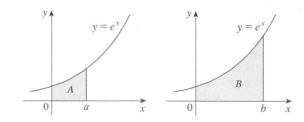

75–76 Evaluate the limit by first recognizing the sum as a Riemann sum for a function defined on $[0, 1]$.

75. $\displaystyle\lim_{n \to \infty} \sum_{i=1}^{n} \frac{i^3}{n^4}$

76. $\displaystyle\lim_{n \to \infty} \frac{1}{n}\left(\sqrt{\frac{1}{n}} + \sqrt{\frac{2}{n}} + \sqrt{\frac{3}{n}} + \cdots + \sqrt{\frac{n}{n}} \right)$

DISCOVERY PROJECT **Area Functions**

1. (a) Draw the line $y = 2t + 1$ and use geometry to find the area under this line, above the t-axis, and between the vertical lines $t = 1$ and $t = 3$.
(b) If $x > 1$, let $A(x)$ be the area of the region that lies under the line $y = 2t + 1$ between $t = 1$ and $t = x$. Sketch this region and use geometry to find an expression for $A(x)$.
(c) Differentiate the area function $A(x)$. What do you notice?

2. (a) If $0 \le x \le \pi$, let $A(x) = \int_0^x \sin t\, dt$. $A(x)$ represents the area of a region. Sketch that region.
(b) Use the Evaluation Theorem to find an expression for $A(x)$.
(c) Find $A'(x)$. What do you notice?
(d) If x is any number between 0 and π, and h is a small positive number, then $A(x + h) - A(x)$ represents the area of a region. Describe and sketch the region.
(e) Draw a rectangle that approximates the region in part (d). By comparing the areas of these two regions, show that

$$\frac{A(x + h) - A(x)}{h} \approx \sin x$$

(f) Use part (e) to give an intuitive explanation for the result of part (c).

3. (a) Draw the graph of the function $f(x) = \cos(x^2)$ in the viewing rectangle $[0, 2]$ by $[-1.25, 1.25]$.
(b) If we define a new function g by

$$g(x) = \int_0^x \cos(t^2)\, dt$$

Graphing calculator or computer with graphing software required

then $g(x)$ is the area under the graph of f from 0 to x [until $f(x)$ becomes negative, at which point $g(x)$ becomes a difference of areas]. Use part (a) to determine the value of x at which $g(x)$ starts to decrease. [Unlike the integral in Problem 2, it is impossible to evaluate the integral defining g to obtain an explicit expression for $g(x)$.]

(c) Use the integration command on your calculator or computer to estimate $g(0.2)$, $g(0.4)$, $g(0.6)$, . . . , $g(1.8)$, $g(2)$. Then use these values to sketch a graph of g.

(d) Use your graph of g from part (c) to sketch the graph of g' using the interpretation of $g'(x)$ as the slope of a tangent line. How does the graph of g' compare with the graph of f?

4. Suppose f is a continuous function on the interval $[a, b]$ and we define a new function g by the equation

$$g(x) = \int_a^x f(t)\, dt$$

Based on your results in Problems 1–3, conjecture an expression for $g'(x)$.

5.4 The Fundamental Theorem of Calculus

The Fundamental Theorem of Calculus is appropriately named because it establishes a connection between the two branches of calculus: differential calculus and integral calculus. Differential calculus arose from the tangent problem, whereas integral calculus arose from a seemingly unrelated problem, the area problem. Newton's mentor at Cambridge, Isaac Barrow (1630–1677), discovered that these two problems are actually closely related. In fact, he realized that differentiation and integration are inverse processes. The Fundamental Theorem of Calculus gives the precise inverse relationship between the derivative and the integral. It was Newton and Leibniz who exploited this relationship and used it to develop calculus into a systematic mathematical method.

The first part of the Fundamental Theorem deals with functions defined by an equation of the form

1

$$g(x) = \int_a^x f(t)\, dt$$

where f is a continuous function on $[a, b]$ and x varies between a and b. Observe that g depends only on x, which appears as the variable upper limit in the integral. If x is a fixed number, then the integral $\int_a^x f(t)\, dt$ is a definite number. If we then let x vary, the number $\int_a^x f(t)\, dt$ also varies and defines a function of x denoted by $g(x)$.

If f happens to be a positive function, then $g(x)$ can be interpreted as the area under the graph of f from a to x, where x can vary from a to b. (Think of g as the "area so far" function; see Figure 1.)

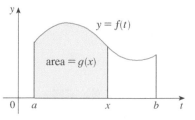

FIGURE 1

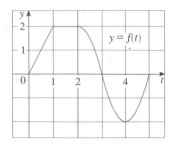

FIGURE 2

EXAMPLE 1   **A function defined as an integral**   If f is the function whose graph is shown in Figure 2 and $g(x) = \int_0^x f(t)\,dt$, find the values of $g(0)$, $g(1)$, $g(2)$, $g(3)$, $g(4)$, and $g(5)$. Then sketch a rough graph of g.

SOLUTION   First we notice that $g(0) = \int_0^0 f(t)\,dt = 0$. From Figure 3 we see that $g(1)$ is the area of a triangle:

$$g(1) = \int_0^1 f(t)\,dt = \tfrac{1}{2}(1 \cdot 2) = 1$$

To find $g(2)$ we again refer to Figure 3 and add to $g(1)$ the area of a rectangle:

$$g(2) = \int_0^2 f(t)\,dt = \int_0^1 f(t)\,dt + \int_1^2 f(t)\,dt = 1 + (1 \cdot 2) = 3$$

We estimate that the area under f from 2 to 3 is about 1.3, so

$$g(3) = g(2) + \int_2^3 f(t)\,dt \approx 3 + 1.3 = 4.3$$

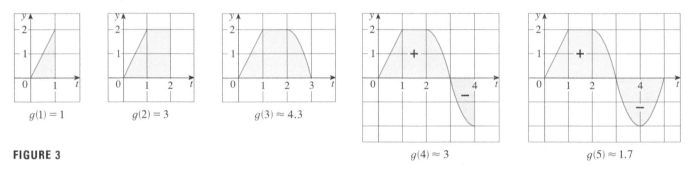

$g(1) = 1$ $\qquad$ $g(2) = 3$ $\qquad$ $g(3) \approx 4.3$ $\qquad$ $g(4) \approx 3$ $\qquad$ $g(5) \approx 1.7$

FIGURE 3

For $t > 3$, $f(t)$ is negative and so we start subtracting areas:

$$g(4) = g(3) + \int_3^4 f(t)\,dt \approx 4.3 + (-1.3) = 3.0$$

$$g(5) = g(4) + \int_4^5 f(t)\,dt \approx 3 + (-1.3) = 1.7$$

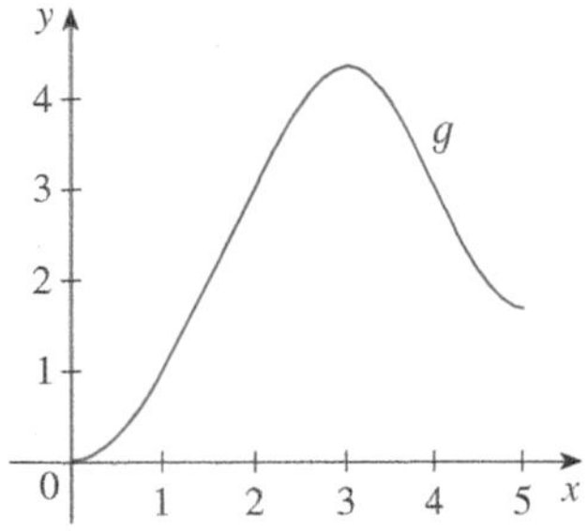

We use these values to sketch the graph of g in Figure 4. Notice that, because $f(t)$ is positive for $t < 3$, we keep adding area for $t < 3$ and so g is increasing up to $x = 3$, where it attains a maximum value. For $x > 3$, g decreases because $f(t)$ is negative.

FIGURE 4

$g(x) = \int_a^x f(t)\,dt$

EXAMPLE 2   If $g(x) = \int_a^x f(t)\,dt$, where $a = 1$ and $f(t) = t^2$, find a formula for $g(x)$ and calculate $g'(x)$.

SOLUTION   In this case we can compute $g(x)$ explicitly using the Evaluation Theorem:

$$g(x) = \int_1^x t^2\,dt = \frac{t^3}{3}\bigg]_1^x = \frac{x^3 - 1}{3}$$

Then $\qquad\qquad$ $g'(x) = \dfrac{d}{dx}\left(\tfrac{1}{3}x^3 - \tfrac{1}{3}\right) = x^2$

For the function in Example 2 notice that $g'(x) = x^2$, that is, $g' = f$. In other words, if g is defined as the integral of f by Equation 1, then g turns out to be an antiderivative of f, at least in this case. And if we sketch the derivative of the function g shown in Figure 4 by estimating slopes of tangents, we get a graph like that of f in Figure 2. So we suspect that $g' = f$ in Example 1 too.

To see why this might be generally true we consider any continuous function f with $f(x) \geq 0$. Then $g(x) = \int_a^x f(t)\, dt$ can be interpreted as the area under the graph of f from a to x, as in Figure 1.

In order to compute $g'(x)$ from the definition of a derivative we first observe that, for $h > 0$, $g(x + h) - g(x)$ is obtained by subtracting areas, so it is the area under the graph of f from x to $x + h$ (the blue area in Figure 5). For small h you can see from the figure that this area is approximately equal to the area of the rectangle with height $f(x)$ and width h:

$$g(x + h) - g(x) \approx hf(x)$$

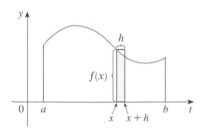

so

$$\frac{g(x + h) - g(x)}{h} \approx f(x)$$

FIGURE 5

Intuitively, we therefore expect that

$$g'(x) = \lim_{h \to 0} \frac{g(x + h) - g(x)}{h} = f(x)$$

The fact that this is true, even when f is not necessarily positive, is the first part of the Fundamental Theorem of Calculus.

We abbreviate the name of this theorem as FTC1. In words, it says that the derivative of a definite integral with respect to its upper limit is the integrand evaluated at the upper limit.

The Fundamental Theorem of Calculus, Part 1 If f is continuous on $[a, b]$, then the function g defined by

$$g(x) = \int_a^x f(t)\, dt \qquad a \leq x \leq b$$

is an antiderivative of f, that is, $g'(x) = f(x)$ for $a < x < b$.

Using Leibniz notation for derivatives, we can write this theorem as

$$\frac{d}{dx} \int_a^x f(t)\, dt = f(x)$$

when f is continuous. Roughly speaking, this equation says that if we first integrate f and then differentiate the result, we get back to the original function f.

It is easy to prove the Fundamental Theorem if we make the assumption that f possesses an antiderivative F. (This is certainly plausible. After all, we sketched graphs of antiderivatives in Section 2.8.) Then, by the Evaluation Theorem,

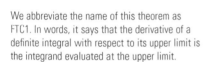 Module 5.4 provides visual evidence for FTC1.

$$\int_a^x f(t)\, dt = F(x) - F(a)$$

for any x between a and b. Therefore

$$\frac{d}{dx} \int_a^x f(t)\, dt = \frac{d}{dx} [F(x) - F(a)] = F'(x) = f(x)$$

as required. At the end of this section we present a proof without the assumption that an antiderivative exists.

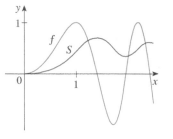

FIGURE 6

$f(x) = \sin(\pi x^2/2)$

$S(x) = \int_0^x \sin(\pi t^2/2)\, dt$

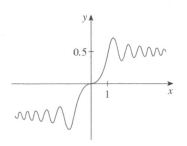

FIGURE 7

The Fresnel function

$S(x) = \int_0^x \sin(\pi t^2/2)\, dt$

V   EXAMPLE 3   Differentiating an integral

Find the derivative of the function $g(x) = \int_0^x \sqrt{1 + t^2}\, dt$.

SOLUTION Since $f(t) = \sqrt{1 + t^2}$ is continuous, Part 1 of the Fundamental Theorem of Calculus gives

$$g'(x) = \sqrt{1 + x^2}$$

EXAMPLE 4   A function from physics   Although a formula of the form $g(x) = \int_a^x f(t)\, dt$ may seem like a strange way of defining a function, books on physics, chemistry, and statistics are full of such functions. For instance, the **Fresnel function**

$$S(x) = \int_0^x \sin(\pi t^2/2)\, dt$$

is named after the French physicist Augustin Fresnel (1788–1827), who is famous for his works in optics. This function first appeared in Fresnel's theory of the diffraction of light waves, but more recently it has been applied to the design of highways.

Part 1 of the Fundamental Theorem tells us how to differentiate the Fresnel function:

$$S'(x) = \sin(\pi x^2/2)$$

This means that we can apply all the methods of differential calculus to analyze S (see Exercise 27).

Figure 6 shows the graphs of $f(x) = \sin(\pi x^2/2)$ and the Fresnel function $S(x) = \int_0^x f(t)\, dt$. A computer was used to graph S by computing the value of this integral for many values of x. It does indeed look as if $S(x)$ is the area under the graph of f from 0 to x [until $x \approx 1.4$ when $S(x)$ becomes a difference of areas]. Figure 7 shows a larger part of the graph of S.

If we now start with the graph of S in Figure 6 and think about what its derivative should look like, it seems reasonable that $S'(x) = f(x)$. [For instance, S is increasing when $f(x) > 0$ and decreasing when $f(x) < 0$.] So this gives a visual confirmation of Part 1 of the Fundamental Theorem of Calculus.

EXAMPLE 5   Combining the Chain Rule with FTC1   Find $\dfrac{d}{dx} \displaystyle\int_1^{x^4} \sec t\, dt$.

SOLUTION Here we have to be careful to use the Chain Rule in conjunction with Part 1 of the Fundamental Theorem. Let $u = x^4$. Then

$$\frac{d}{dx} \int_1^{x^4} \sec t\, dt = \frac{d}{dx} \int_1^{u} \sec t\, dt$$

$$= \frac{d}{du} \left[\int_1^{u} \sec t\, dt \right] \frac{du}{dx} \qquad \text{(by the Chain Rule)}$$

$$= \sec u \, \frac{du}{dx} \qquad\qquad \text{(by FTC1)}$$

$$= \sec(x^4) \cdot 4x^3$$

Differentiation and Integration as Inverse Processes

We now bring together the two parts of the Fundamental Theorem. We regard Part 1 as fundamental because it relates integration and differentiation. But the Evaluation Theorem from Section 5.3 also relates integrals and derivatives, so we rename it as Part 2 of the Fundamental Theorem.

The Fundamental Theorem of Calculus   Suppose f is continuous on $[a, b]$.

1. If $g(x) = \int_a^x f(t)\, dt$, then $g'(x) = f(x)$.

2. $\int_a^b f(x)\, dx = F(b) - F(a)$, where F is any antiderivative of f, that is, $F' = f$.

We noted that Part 1 can be rewritten as

$$\frac{d}{dx} \int_a^x f(t)\, dt = f(x)$$

which says that if f is integrated and then the result is differentiated, we arrive back at the original function f. In Section 5.3 we reformulated Part 2 as the Net Change Theorem:

$$\int_a^b F'(x)\, dx = F(b) - F(a)$$

This version says that if we take a function F, first differentiate it, and then integrate the result, we arrive back at the original function F, but in the form $F(b) - F(a)$. Taken together, the two parts of the Fundamental Theorem of Calculus say that differentiation and integration are inverse processes. Each undoes what the other does.

The Fundamental Theorem of Calculus is unquestionably the most important theorem in calculus and, indeed, it ranks as one of the great accomplishments of the human mind. Before it was discovered, from the time of Eudoxus and Archimedes to the time of Galileo and Fermat, problems of finding areas, volumes, and lengths of curves were so difficult that only a genius could meet the challenge. But now, armed with the systematic method that Newton and Leibniz fashioned out of the Fundamental Theorem, we will see in the chapters to come that these challenging problems are accessible to all of us.

Proof of FTC1

Here we give a proof of Part 1 of the Fundamental Theorem of Calculus without assuming the existence of an antiderivative of f. Let $g(x) = \int_a^x f(t)\, dt$. If x and $x + h$ are in the open interval (a, b), then

$$
\begin{aligned}
g(x + h) - g(x) &= \int_a^{x+h} f(t)\, dt - \int_a^x f(t)\, dt \\
&= \left(\int_a^x f(t)\, dt + \int_x^{x+h} f(t)\, dt \right) - \int_a^x f(t)\, dt \\
&= \int_x^{x+h} f(t)\, dt
\end{aligned}
$$

and so, for $h \neq 0$,

FIGURE 8

$$\boxed{2} \qquad \frac{g(x + h) - g(x)}{h} = \frac{1}{h} \int_x^{x+h} f(t)\, dt$$

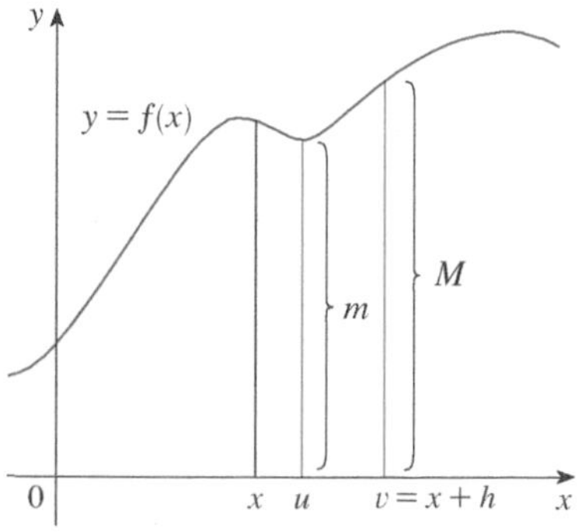

For now let's assume that $h > 0$. Since f is continuous on $[x, x + h]$, the Extreme Value Theorem says that there are numbers u and v in $[x, x + h]$ such that $f(u) = m$ and $f(v) = M$, where m and M are the absolute minimum and maximum values of f on $[x, x + h]$. (See Figure 8.)

By Property 8 of integrals, we have

$$mh \leq \int_x^{x+h} f(t)\, dt \leq Mh$$

that is,

$$f(u)h \leq \int_x^{x+h} f(t)\, dt \leq f(v)h$$

Since $h > 0$, we can divide this inequality by h:

$$f(u) \leq \frac{1}{h} \int_x^{x+h} f(t)\, dt \leq f(v)$$

Now we use Equation 2 to replace the middle part of this inequality:

$$\boxed{3} \qquad\qquad f(u) \leq \frac{g(x+h) - g(x)}{h} \leq f(v)$$

Inequality 3 can be proved in a similar manner for the case where $h < 0$. Now we let $h \to 0$. Then $u \to x$ and $v \to x$, since u and v lie between x and $x + h$. Thus

$$\lim_{h \to 0} f(u) = \lim_{u \to x} f(u) = f(x) \qquad \text{and} \qquad \lim_{h \to 0} f(v) = \lim_{v \to x} f(v) = f(x)$$

because f is continuous at x. We conclude, from (3) and the Squeeze Theorem, that

$$\boxed{4} \qquad\qquad g'(x) = \lim_{h \to 0} \frac{g(x+h) - g(x)}{h} = f(x)$$

If $x = a$ or b, then Equation 4 can be interpreted as a one-sided limit, Then Theorem 2.7.4 (modified for one-sided limits) shows that g is continuous on $[a, b]$. ▭

5.4 Exercises

1. Explain exactly what is meant by the statement that "differentiation and integration are inverse processes."

2. Let $g(x) = \int_0^x f(t)\, dt$, where f is the function whose graph is shown.
   (a) Evaluate $g(x)$ for $x = 0, 1, 2, 3, 4, 5,$ and 6.
   (b) Estimate $g(7)$.
   (c) Where does g have a maximum value? Where does it have a minimum value?
   (d) Sketch a rough graph of g.

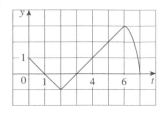

3. Let $g(x) = \int_0^x f(t)\, dt$, where f is the function whose graph is shown.
   (a) Evaluate $g(0), g(1), g(2), g(3),$ and $g(6)$.
   (b) On what interval is g increasing?
   (c) Where does g have a maximum value?
   (d) Sketch a rough graph of g.

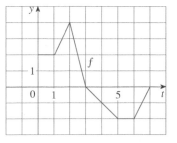

4. Let $g(x) = \int_0^x f(t)\, dt$, where f is the function whose graph is shown.
   (a) Evaluate $g(0)$ and $g(6)$.

(b) Estimate $g(x)$ for $x = 1, 2, 3, 4,$ and 5.
(c) On what interval is g increasing?
(d) Where does g have a maximum value?
(e) Sketch a rough graph of g.
(f) Use the graph in part (e) to sketch the graph of $g'(x)$. Compare with the graph of f.

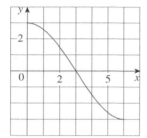

5–6 Sketch the area represented by $g(x)$. Then find $g'(x)$ in two ways: (a) by using Part 1 of the Fundamental Theorem and (b) by evaluating the integral using Part 2 and then differentiating.

5. $g(x) = \displaystyle\int_0^x (1 + t^2)\, dt$

6. $g(x) = \displaystyle\int_0^x \left(1 + \sqrt{t}\right) dt$

7–18 Use Part 1 of the Fundamental Theorem of Calculus to find the derivative of the function.

7. $g(x) = \displaystyle\int_1^x \dfrac{1}{t^3 + 1}\, dt$

8. $g(x) = \displaystyle\int_3^x e^{t^2 - t}\, dt$

9. $g(y) = \displaystyle\int_2^y t^2 \sin t\, dt$

10. $g(r) = \displaystyle\int_0^r \sqrt{x^2 + 4}\, dx$

11. $F(x) = \displaystyle\int_x^\pi \sqrt{1 + \sec t}\, dt$

$\left[\text{Hint: } \displaystyle\int_x^\pi \sqrt{1 + \sec t}\, dt = -\int_\pi^x \sqrt{1 + \sec t}\, dt \right]$

12. $G(x) = \displaystyle\int_x^1 \cos\sqrt{t}\, dt$

13. $h(x) = \displaystyle\int_2^{1/x} \arctan t\, dt$

14. $h(x) = \displaystyle\int_0^{x^2} \sqrt{1 + r^3}\, dr$

15. $y = \displaystyle\int_0^{\tan x} \sqrt{t + \sqrt{t}}\, dt$

16. $y = \displaystyle\int_{e^x}^0 \sin^3 t\, dt$

17. $g(x) = \displaystyle\int_{2x}^{3x} \dfrac{u^2 - 1}{u^2 + 1}\, du$

$\left[\text{Hint: } \displaystyle\int_{2x}^{3x} f(u)\, du = \int_{2x}^0 f(u)\, du + \int_0^{3x} f(u)\, du \right]$

18. $y = \displaystyle\int_{\sin x}^{\cos x} (1 + v^2)^{10}\, dv$

19–20 Let $g(x) = \int_0^x f(t)\, dt$, where f is the function whose graph is shown.
(a) At what values of x do the local maximum and minimum values of g occur?

(b) Where does g attain its absolute maximum value?
(c) On what intervals is g concave downward?
(d) Sketch the graph of g.

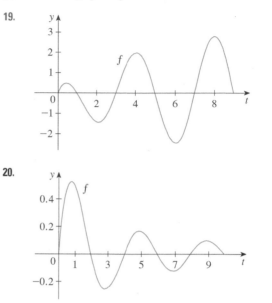

21. If $f(x) = \int_0^x (1 - t^2)e^{t^2}\, dt$, on what interval is f increasing?

22. If $f(x) = \int_0^{\sin x} \sqrt{1 + t^2}\, dt$ and $g(y) = \int_3^y f(x)\, dx$, find $g''(\pi/6)$.

23. On what interval is the curve

$$y = \int_0^x \dfrac{t^2}{t^2 + t + 2}\, dt$$

concave downward?

24. Find the slope of the tangent line to the curve with parametric equations $x = \int_0^t \sqrt{1 + u^3}\, du$, $y = 1 + 2t - t^3$ at the point $(0, 1)$.

25. If $f(1) = 12$, f' is continuous, and $\int_1^4 f'(x)\, dx = 17$, what is the value of $f(4)$?

26. The **error function**

$$\operatorname{erf}(x) = \dfrac{2}{\sqrt{\pi}} \int_0^x e^{-t^2}\, dt$$

is used in probability, statistics, and engineering.
(a) Show that $\int_a^b e^{-t^2}\, dt = \frac{1}{2}\sqrt{\pi}\, [\operatorname{erf}(b) - \operatorname{erf}(a)]$.
(b) Show that the function $y = e^{x^2}\operatorname{erf}(x)$ satisfies the differential equation $y' = 2xy + 2/\sqrt{\pi}$.

27. The Fresnel function S was defined in Example 4 and graphed in Figures 6 and 7.
(a) At what values of x does this function have local maximum values?
(b) On what intervals is the function concave upward?
(c) Use a graph to solve the following equation correct to two decimal places:

$$\int_0^x \sin(\pi t^2/2)\, dt = 0.2$$

CAS **28.** The **sine integral function**

$$Si(x) = \int_0^x \frac{\sin t}{t}\, dt$$

is important in electrical engineering. [The integrand $f(t) = (\sin t)/t$ is not defined when $t = 0$, but we know that its limit is 1 when $t \to 0$. So we define $f(0) = 1$ and this makes f a continuous function everywhere.]
(a) Draw the graph of Si.
(b) At what values of x does this function have local maximum values?
(c) Find the coordinates of the first inflection point to the right of the origin.
(d) Does this function have horizontal asymptotes?
(e) Solve the following equation correct to one decimal place:

$$\int_0^x \frac{\sin t}{t}\, dt = 1$$

29. Find a function f such that $f(1) = 0$ and $f'(x) = 2^x/x$.

30. Let

$$f(x) = \begin{cases} 0 & \text{if } x < 0 \\ x & \text{if } 0 \le x \le 1 \\ 2 - x & \text{if } 1 < x \le 2 \\ 0 & \text{if } x > 2 \end{cases}$$

and

$$g(x) = \int_0^x f(t)\, dt$$

(a) Find an expression for $g(x)$ similar to the one for $f(x)$.
(b) Sketch the graphs of f and g.
(c) Where is f differentiable? Where is g differentiable?

31. Find a function f and a number a such that

$$6 + \int_a^x \frac{f(t)}{t^2}\, dt = 2\sqrt{x}$$

for all $x > 0$.

32. A high-tech company purchases a new computing system whose initial value is V. The system will depreciate at the

rate $f = f(t)$ and will accumulate maintenance costs at the rate $g = g(t)$, where t is the time measured in months. The company wants to determine the optimal time to replace the system.
(a) Let

$$C(t) = \frac{1}{t} \int_0^t [f(s) + g(s)]\, ds$$

Show that the critical numbers of C occur at the numbers t where $C(t) = f(t) + g(t)$.
(b) Suppose that

$$f(t) = \begin{cases} \dfrac{V}{15} - \dfrac{V}{450} t & \text{if } 0 < t \le 30 \\ 0 & \text{if } t > 30 \end{cases}$$

and

$$g(t) = \frac{Vt^2}{12{,}900} \qquad t > 0$$

Determine the length of time T for the total depreciation $D(t) = \int_0^t f(s)\, ds$ to equal the initial value V.
(c) Determine the absolute minimum of C on $(0, T]$.
(d) Sketch the graphs of C and $f + g$ in the same coordinate system, and verify the result in part (a) in this case.

33. A manufacturing company owns a major piece of equipment that depreciates at the (continuous) rate $f = f(t)$, where t is the time measured in months since its last overhaul. Because a fixed cost A is incurred each time the machine is overhauled, the company wants to determine the optimal time T (in months) between overhauls.
(a) Explain why $\int_0^t f(s)\, ds$ represents the loss in value of the machine over the period of time t since the last overhaul.
(b) Let $C = C(t)$ be given by

$$C(t) = \frac{1}{t}\left[A + \int_0^t f(s)\, ds\right]$$

What does C represent and why would the company want to minimize C?
(c) Show that C has a minimum value at the numbers $t = T$ where $C(T) = f(T)$.

WRITING PROJECT **Newton, Leibniz, and the Invention of Calculus**

We sometimes read that the inventors of calculus were Sir Isaac Newton (1642–1727) and Gottfried Wilhelm Leibniz (1646–1716). But we know that the basic ideas behind integration were investigated 2500 years ago by ancient Greeks such as Eudoxus and Archimedes, and methods for finding tangents were pioneered by Pierre Fermat (1601–1665), Isaac Barrow (1630–1677), and others. Barrow—who taught at Cambridge and was a major influence on Newton—was the first to understand the inverse relationship between differentiation and integration. What Newton and Leibniz did was to use this relationship, in the form of the Fundamental Theorem of Calculus, in order to develop calculus into a systematic mathematical discipline. It is in this sense that Newton and Leibniz are credited with the invention of calculus.

Read about the contributions of these men in one or more of the given references and write a report on one of the following three topics. You can include biographical details, but the main thrust of your report should be a description, in some detail, of their methods and notations. In particular, you should consult one of the sourcebooks, which give excerpts from the original publications of Newton and Leibniz, translated from Latin to English.

- The Role of Newton in the Development of Calculus

- The Role of Leibniz in the Development of Calculus

- The Controversy between the Followers of Newton and Leibniz over Priority in the Invention of Calculus

References

1. Carl Boyer and Uta Merzbach, *A History of Mathematics* (New York: Wiley, 1987), Chapter 19.
2. Carl Boyer, *The History of the Calculus and Its Conceptual Development* (New York: Dover, 1959), Chapter V.
3. C. H. Edwards, *The Historical Development of the Calculus* (New York: Springer-Verlag, 1979), Chapters 8 and 9.
4. Howard Eves, *An Introduction to the History of Mathematics,* 6th ed. (New York: Saunders, 1990), Chapter 11.
5. C. C. Gillispie, ed., *Dictionary of Scientific Biography* (New York: Scribner's, 1974). See the article on Leibniz by Joseph Hofmann in Volume VIII and the article on Newton by I. B. Cohen in Volume X.
6. Victor Katz, *A History of Mathematics: An Introduction* (New York: HarperCollins, 1993), Chapter 12.
7. Morris Kline, *Mathematical Thought from Ancient to Modern Times* (New York: Oxford University Press, 1972), Chapter 17.

Sourcebooks

1. John Fauvel and Jeremy Gray, eds., *The History of Mathematics: A Reader* (London: MacMillan Press, 1987), Chapters 12 and 13.
2. D. E. Smith, ed., *A Sourcebook in Mathematics* (New York: Dover, 1959), Chapter V.
3. D. J. Struik, ed., *A Sourcebook in Mathematics, 1200–1800* (Princeton, NJ: Princeton University Press, 1969), Chapter V.

5.5 The Substitution Rule

Because of the Fundamental Theorem, it's important to be able to find antiderivatives. But our antidifferentiation formulas don't tell us how to evaluate integrals such as

$$\boxed{1} \qquad \int 2x\sqrt{1 + x^2}\, dx$$

PS To find this integral we use the problem-solving strategy of *introducing something extra*. Here the "something extra" is a new variable; we change from the variable x to a new variable u. Suppose that we let u be the quantity under the root sign in (1): $u = 1 + x^2$. Then the differential of u is $du = 2x\, dx$. Notice that if the dx in the notation for an integral were to be interpreted as a differential, then the differential $2x\, dx$ would occur in (1) and so,

Differentials were defined in Section 3.9. If $u = f(x)$, then
$$du = f'(x)\, dx$$

formally, without justifying our calculation, we could write

$$\boxed{2} \qquad \int 2x\sqrt{1+x^2}\, dx = \int \sqrt{1+x^2}\ 2x\, dx = \int \sqrt{u}\ du$$

$$= \tfrac{2}{3} u^{3/2} + C = \tfrac{2}{3}(x^2+1)^{3/2} + C$$

But now we can check that we have the correct answer by using the Chain Rule to differentiate the final function of Equation 2:

$$\frac{d}{dx}\left[\tfrac{2}{3}(x^2+1)^{3/2} + C\right] = \tfrac{2}{3}\cdot \tfrac{3}{2}(x^2+1)^{1/2}\cdot 2x = 2x\sqrt{x^2+1}$$

In general, this method works whenever we have an integral that we can write in the form $\int f(g(x))g'(x)\, dx$. Observe that if $F' = f$, then

$$\boxed{3} \qquad \int F'(g(x))g'(x)\, dx = F(g(x)) + C$$

because, by the Chain Rule,

$$\frac{d}{dx}[F(g(x))] = F'(g(x))g'(x)$$

If we make the "change of variable" or "substitution" $u = g(x)$, then from Equation 3 we have

$$\int F'(g(x))g'(x)\, dx = F(g(x)) + C = F(u) + C = \int F'(u)\, du$$

or, writing $F' = f$, we get

$$\int f(g(x))g'(x)\, dx = \int f(u)\, du$$

Thus we have proved the following rule.

---

4 **The Substitution Rule** If $u = g(x)$ is a differentiable function whose range is an interval I and f is continuous on I, then

$$\int f(g(x))g'(x)\, dx = \int f(u)\, du$$

Notice that the Substitution Rule for integration was proved using the Chain Rule for differentiation. Notice also that if $u = g(x)$, then $du = g'(x)\, dx$, so a way to remember the Substitution Rule is to think of dx and du in (4) as differentials.

Thus the Substitution Rule says: **It is permissible to operate with dx and du after integral signs as if they were differentials.**

EXAMPLE 1 **Using the Substitution Rule**   Find $\displaystyle\int x^3 \cos(x^4 + 2)\, dx$.

SOLUTION We make the substitution $u = x^4 + 2$ because its differential is $du = 4x^3\, dx$, which, apart from the constant factor 4, occurs in the integral. Thus, using $x^3\, dx = \tfrac{1}{4}\, du$

and the Substitution Rule, we have

$$\int x^3 \cos(x^4 + 2)\, dx = \int \cos u \cdot \tfrac{1}{4}\, du = \tfrac{1}{4} \int \cos u\, du$$

$$= \tfrac{1}{4} \sin u + C$$

$$= \tfrac{1}{4} \sin(x^4 + 2) + C$$

Check the answer by differentiating it.

Notice that at the final stage we had to return to the original variable x.

The idea behind the Substitution Rule is to replace a relatively complicated integral by a simpler integral. This is accomplished by changing from the original variable x to a new variable u that is a function of x. Thus in Example 1 we replaced the integral $\int x^3 \cos(x^4 + 2)\, dx$ by the simpler integral $\tfrac{1}{4} \int \cos u\, du$.

The main challenge in using the Substitution Rule is to think of an appropriate substitution. You should try to choose u to be some function in the integrand whose differential also occurs (except for a constant factor). This was the case in Example 1. If that is not possible, try choosing u to be some complicated part of the integrand (perhaps the inner function in a composite function). Finding the right substitution is a bit of an art. It's not unusual to guess wrong; if your first guess doesn't work, try another substitution.

EXAMPLE 2   Two possible substitutions   Evaluate $\int \sqrt{2x + 1}\, dx$.

SOLUTION 1 Let $u = 2x + 1$. Then $du = 2\, dx$, so $dx = \tfrac{1}{2}\, du$. Thus the Substitution Rule gives

$$\int \sqrt{2x + 1}\, dx = \int \sqrt{u}\ \cdot \tfrac{1}{2}\, du = \tfrac{1}{2} \int u^{1/2}\, du$$

$$= \frac{1}{2} \cdot \frac{u^{3/2}}{3/2} + C = \tfrac{1}{3} u^{3/2} + C$$

$$= \tfrac{1}{3}(2x + 1)^{3/2} + C$$

SOLUTION 2 Another possible substitution is $u = \sqrt{2x + 1}$. Then

$$du = \frac{dx}{\sqrt{2x + 1}} \qquad \text{so} \qquad dx = \sqrt{2x + 1}\, du = u\, du$$

(Or observe that $u^2 = 2x + 1$, so $2u\, du = 2\, dx$.) Therefore

$$\int \sqrt{2x + 1}\, dx = \int u \cdot u\, du = \int u^2\, du$$

$$= \frac{u^3}{3} + C = \tfrac{1}{3}(2x + 1)^{3/2} + C$$

V   EXAMPLE 3   Find $\displaystyle \int \frac{x}{\sqrt{1 - 4x^2}}\, dx$.

SOLUTION Let $u = 1 - 4x^2$. Then $du = -8x\, dx$, so $x\, dx = -\tfrac{1}{8}\, du$ and

$$\int \frac{x}{\sqrt{1 - 4x^2}}\, dx = -\tfrac{1}{8} \int \frac{1}{\sqrt{u}}\, du = -\tfrac{1}{8} \int u^{-1/2}\, du$$

$$= -\tfrac{1}{8}\left(2\sqrt{u}\right) + C = -\tfrac{1}{4}\sqrt{1 - 4x^2} + C$$

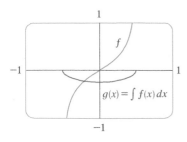

FIGURE 1

The answer to Example 3 could be checked by differentiation, but instead let's check it with a graph. In Figure 1 we have used a computer to graph both the integrand $f(x) = x/\sqrt{1 - 4x^2}$ and its indefinite integral $g(x) = -\frac{1}{4}\sqrt{1 - 4x^2}$ (we take the case $C = 0$). Notice that $g(x)$ decreases when $f(x)$ is negative, increases when $f(x)$ is positive, and has its minimum value when $f(x) = 0$. So it seems reasonable, from the graphical evidence, that g is an antiderivative of f.

EXAMPLE 4 Calculate $\int e^{5x}\, dx$.

SOLUTION If we let $u = 5x$, then $du = 5\, dx$, so $dx = \frac{1}{5}\, du$. Therefore

$$\int e^{5x}\, dx = \frac{1}{5}\int e^u\, du = \frac{1}{5}e^u + C = \frac{1}{5}e^{5x} + C$$

V EXAMPLE 5 Calculate $\int \tan x\, dx$.

SOLUTION First we write tangent in terms of sine and cosine:

$$\int \tan x\, dx = \int \frac{\sin x}{\cos x}\, dx$$

This suggests that we should substitute $u = \cos x$, since then $du = -\sin x\, dx$ and so $\sin x\, dx = -du$:

$$\int \tan x\, dx = \int \frac{\sin x}{\cos x}\, dx = -\int \frac{1}{u}\, du$$

$$= -\ln|u| + C = -\ln|\cos x| + C$$

Since $-\ln|\cos x| = \ln(|\cos x|^{-1}) = \ln(1/|\cos x|) = \ln|\sec x|$, the result of Example 5 can also be written as

$$\int \tan x\, dx = \ln|\sec x| + C$$

Definite Integrals

When evaluating a *definite* integral by substitution, two methods are possible. One method is to evaluate the indefinite integral first and then use the Evaluation Theorem. For instance, using the result of Example 2, we have

$$\int_0^4 \sqrt{2x + 1}\, dx = \int \sqrt{2x + 1}\, dx\Big]_0^4 = \frac{1}{3}(2x + 1)^{3/2}\Big]_0^4$$

$$= \frac{1}{3}(9)^{3/2} - \frac{1}{3}(1)^{3/2} = \frac{1}{3}(27 - 1) = \frac{26}{3}$$

Another method, which is usually preferable, is to change the limits of integration when the variable is changed.

This rule says that when using a substitution in a definite integral, we must put everything in terms of the new variable u, not only x and dx but also the limits of integration. The new limits of integration are the values of u that correspond to $x = a$ and $x = b$.

> **5** **The Substitution Rule for Definite Integrals** If g' is continuous on $[a, b]$ and f is continuous on the range of $u = g(x)$, then
>
> $$\int_a^b f(g(x))g'(x)\, dx = \int_{g(a)}^{g(b)} f(u)\, du$$

PROOF Let F be an antiderivative of f. Then, by (3), $F(g(x))$ is an antiderivative of $f(g(x))g'(x)$, so by the Evaluation Theorem, we have

$$\int_a^b f(g(x))g'(x)\,dx = F(g(x))\Big]_a^b = F(g(b)) - F(g(a))$$

But, applying the Evaluation Theorem a second time, we also have

$$\int_{g(a)}^{g(b)} f(u)\,du = F(u)\Big]_{g(a)}^{g(b)} = F(g(b)) - F(g(a))$$

EXAMPLE 6 **Substitution in a definite integral** Evaluate $\int_0^4 \sqrt{2x+1}\,dx$ using (5).

SOLUTION Using the substitution from Solution 1 of Example 2, we have $u = 2x + 1$ and $dx = \frac{1}{2}\,du$. To find the new limits of integration we note that

$$\text{when } x = 0,\ u = 2(0) + 1 = 1 \qquad \text{and} \qquad \text{when } x = 4,\ u = 2(4) + 1 = 9$$

Therefore

$$\int_0^4 \sqrt{2x+1}\,dx = \int_1^9 \tfrac{1}{2}\sqrt{u}\,du$$

$$= \tfrac{1}{2} \cdot \tfrac{2}{3} u^{3/2}\Big]_1^9$$

$$= \tfrac{1}{3}(9^{3/2} - 1^{3/2}) = \tfrac{26}{3}$$

The geometric interpretation of Example 6 is shown in Figure 2. The substitution $u = 2x + 1$ stretches the interval $[0, 4]$ by a factor of 2 and translates it to the right by 1 unit. The Substitution Rule shows that the two areas are equal.

Observe that when using (5) we do *not* return to the variable x after integrating. We simply evaluate the expression in u between the appropriate values of u.

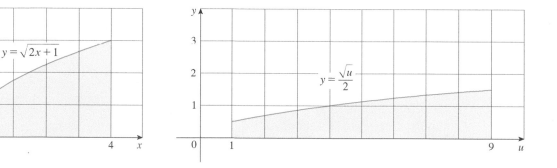

FIGURE 2

The integral given in Example 7 is an abbreviation for

$$\int_1^2 \frac{1}{(3-5x)^2}\,dx$$

EXAMPLE 7 Evaluate $\int_1^2 \frac{dx}{(3-5x)^2}$.

SOLUTION Let $u = 3 - 5x$. Then $du = -5\,dx$, so $dx = -\frac{1}{5}\,du$. When $x = 1$, $u = -2$ and when $x = 2$, $u = -7$. Thus

$$\int_1^2 \frac{dx}{(3-5x)^2} = -\frac{1}{5}\int_{-2}^{-7} \frac{du}{u^2}$$

$$= -\frac{1}{5}\left[-\frac{1}{u}\right]_{-2}^{-7} = \frac{1}{5u}\Big]_{-2}^{-7}$$

$$= \frac{1}{5}\left(-\frac{1}{7} + \frac{1}{2}\right) = \frac{1}{14}$$

Since the function $f(x) = (\ln x)/x$ in Example 8 is positive for $x > 1$, the integral represents the area of the shaded region in Figure 3.

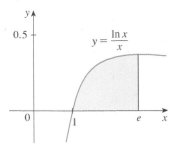

FIGURE 3

 **EXAMPLE 8**   Calculate $\displaystyle\int_1^e \frac{\ln x}{x}\, dx$.

SOLUTION We let $u = \ln x$ because its differential $du = dx/x$ occurs in the integral. When $x = 1$, $u = \ln 1 = 0$; when $x = e$, $u = \ln e = 1$. Thus

$$\int_1^e \frac{\ln x}{x}\, dx = \int_0^1 u\, du = \frac{u^2}{2}\bigg]_0^1 = \frac{1}{2}$$

Symmetry

The next theorem uses the Substitution Rule for Definite Integrals (5) to simplify the calculation of integrals of functions that possess symmetry properties.

---

6 **Integrals of Symmetric Functions**   Suppose f is continuous on $[-a, a]$.

(a) If f is even $[f(-x) = f(x)]$, then $\int_{-a}^a f(x)\, dx = 2\int_0^a f(x)\, dx$.

(b) If f is odd $[f(-x) = -f(x)]$, then $\int_{-a}^a f(x)\, dx = 0$.

PROOF We split the integral in two:

7 $$\int_{-a}^a f(x)\, dx = \int_{-a}^0 f(x)\, dx + \int_0^a f(x)\, dx = -\int_0^{-a} f(x)\, dx + \int_0^a f(x)\, dx$$

In the first integral on the far right side we make the substitution $u = -x$. Then $du = -dx$ and when $x = -a$, $u = a$. Therefore

$$-\int_0^{-a} f(x)\, dx = -\int_0^a f(-u)\,(-du) = \int_0^a f(-u)\, du$$

and so Equation 7 becomes

8 $$\int_{-a}^a f(x)\, dx = \int_0^a f(-u)\, du + \int_0^a f(x)\, dx$$

(a) If f is even, then $f(-u) = f(u)$ so Equation 8 gives

$$\int_{-a}^a f(x)\, dx = \int_0^a f(u)\, du + \int_0^a f(x)\, dx = 2\int_0^a f(x)\, dx$$

(b) If f is odd, then $f(-u) = -f(u)$ and so Equation 8 gives

$$\int_{-a}^a f(x)\, dx = -\int_0^a f(u)\, du + \int_0^a f(x)\, dx = 0$$

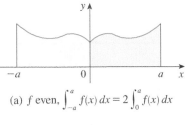

(a) f even, $\int_{-a}^a f(x)\, dx = 2\int_0^a f(x)\, dx$

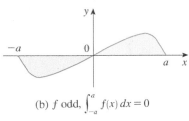

(b) f odd, $\int_{-a}^a f(x)\, dx = 0$

FIGURE 4

Theorem 6 is illustrated by Figure 4. For the case where f is positive and even, part (a) says that the area under $y = f(x)$ from $-a$ to a is twice the area from 0 to a because of symmetry. Recall that an integral $\int_a^b f(x)\, dx$ can be expressed as the area above the x-axis and below $y = f(x)$ minus the area below the axis and above the curve. Thus part (b) says the integral is 0 because the areas cancel.

V   EXAMPLE 9   Integrating an even function   Since $f(x) = x^6 + 1$ satisfies $f(-x) = f(x)$, it is even and so

$$\int_{-2}^{2} (x^6 + 1)\, dx = 2 \int_{0}^{2} (x^6 + 1)\, dx$$

$$= 2\left[\tfrac{1}{7}x^7 + x\right]_0^2 = 2\left(\tfrac{128}{7} + 2\right) = \tfrac{284}{7}$$

EXAMPLE 10   Integrating an odd function   Since $f(x) = (\tan x)/(1 + x^2 + x^4)$ satisfies $f(-x) = -f(x)$, it is odd and so

$$\int_{-1}^{1} \frac{\tan x}{1 + x^2 + x^4}\, dx = 0$$

5.5   Exercises

1–6 Evaluate the integral by making the given substitution.

1. $\displaystyle\int e^{-x}\, dx, \quad u = -x$

2. $\displaystyle\int x^3(2 + x^4)^5\, dx, \quad u = 2 + x^4$

3. $\displaystyle\int x^2\sqrt{x^3 + 1}\, dx, \quad u = x^3 + 1$

4. $\displaystyle\int \frac{dt}{(1 - 6t)^4}, \quad u = 1 - 6t$

5. $\displaystyle\int \cos^3\theta \sin\theta\, d\theta, \quad u = \cos\theta$

6. $\displaystyle\int \frac{\sec^2(1/x)}{x^2}\, dx, \quad u = 1/x$

7–36 Evaluate the indefinite integral.

7. $\displaystyle\int x \sin(x^2)\, dx$

8. $\displaystyle\int x^2(x^3 + 5)^9\, dx$

9. $\displaystyle\int (3x - 2)^{20}\, dx$

10. $\displaystyle\int (3t + 2)^{2.4}\, dt$

11. $\displaystyle\int \sin \pi t\, dt$

12. $\displaystyle\int e^x \cos(e^x)\, dx$

13. $\displaystyle\int \frac{(\ln x)^2}{x}\, dx$

14. $\displaystyle\int \frac{x}{(x^2 + 1)^2}\, dx$

15. $\displaystyle\int \frac{dx}{5 - 3x}$

16. $\displaystyle\int \frac{\sin \sqrt{x}}{\sqrt{x}}\, dx$

17. $\displaystyle\int \frac{a + bx^2}{\sqrt{3ax + bx^3}}\, dx$

18. $\displaystyle\int \frac{z^2}{z^3 + 1}\, dz$

19. $\displaystyle\int e^x\sqrt{1 + e^x}\, dx$

20. $\displaystyle\int \sec 2\theta \tan 2\theta\, d\theta$

21. $\displaystyle\int \frac{\cos x}{\sin^2 x}\, dx$

22. $\displaystyle\int \frac{\tan^{-1}x}{1 + x^2}\, dx$

23. $\displaystyle\int (x^2 + 1)(x^3 + 3x)^4\, dx$

24. $\displaystyle\int \frac{\sin(\ln x)}{x}\, dx$

25. $\displaystyle\int \sqrt{\cot x}\, \csc^2 x\, dx$

26. $\displaystyle\int \frac{\cos(\pi/x)}{x^2}\, dx$

27. $\displaystyle\int \frac{dx}{\sqrt{1 - x^2}\, \sin^{-1} x}$

28. $\displaystyle\int \frac{dt}{\cos^2 t\sqrt{1 + \tan t}}$

29. $\displaystyle\int \sec^3 x \tan x\, dx$

30. $\displaystyle\int x^2\sqrt{2 + x}\, dx$

31. $\displaystyle\int x(2x + 5)^8\, dx$

32. $\displaystyle\int \frac{e^x}{e^x + 1}\, dx$

33. $\displaystyle\int \frac{\sin 2x}{1 + \cos^2 x}\, dx$

34. $\displaystyle\int \frac{\sin x}{1 + \cos^2 x}\, dx$

35. $\displaystyle\int \frac{1 + x}{1 + x^2}\, dx$

36. $\displaystyle\int \frac{x}{1 + x^4}\, dx$

37–40 Evaluate the indefinite integral. Illustrate and check that your answer is reasonable by graphing both the function and its antiderivative (take $C = 0$).

37. $\displaystyle\int x(x^2 - 1)^3\, dx$

38. $\displaystyle\int \tan^2\theta \sec^2\theta\, d\theta$

39. $\displaystyle\int e^{\cos x} \sin x\, dx$

40. $\displaystyle\int \sin x \cos^4 x\, dx$

Graphing calculator or computer with graphing software required   **1.** Homework Hints available in TEC

41–57 Evaluate the definite integral.

41. $\displaystyle\int_0^1 \cos(\pi t/2)\, dt$

42. $\displaystyle\int_0^1 (3t - 1)^{50}\, dt$

43. $\displaystyle\int_0^1 \sqrt[3]{1 + 7x}\, dx$

44. $\displaystyle\int_0^{\sqrt{\pi}} x \cos(x^2)\, dx$

45. $\displaystyle\int_0^1 x^2(1 + 2x^3)^5\, dx$

46. $\displaystyle\int_{1/6}^{1/2} \csc \pi t \, \cot \pi t \, dt$

47. $\displaystyle\int_1^4 \frac{e^{\sqrt{x}}}{\sqrt{x}}\, dx$

48. $\displaystyle\int_0^{\pi/2} \cos x \, \sin(\sin x)\, dx$

49. $\displaystyle\int_{-\pi/4}^{\pi/4} (x^3 + x^4 \tan x)\, dx$

50. $\displaystyle\int_{-\pi/2}^{\pi/2} \frac{x^2 \sin x}{1 + x^6}\, dx$

51. $\displaystyle\int_1^2 x\sqrt{x - 1}\, dx$

52. $\displaystyle\int_0^a x\sqrt{a^2 - x^2}\, dx$

53. $\displaystyle\int_0^1 \frac{e^z + 1}{e^z + z}\, dz$

54. $\displaystyle\int_0^{1/2} \frac{\sin^{-1}x}{\sqrt{1 - x^2}}\, dx$

55. $\displaystyle\int_e^{e^4} \frac{dx}{x\sqrt{\ln x}}$

56. $\displaystyle\int_0^{T/2} \sin(2\pi t/T - \alpha)\, dt$

57. $\displaystyle\int_0^1 \frac{dx}{\left(1 + \sqrt{x}\right)^4}$

---

58. Verify that $f(x) = \sin \sqrt[3]{x}$ is an odd function and use that fact to show that

$$0 \leqslant \int_{-2}^3 \sin \sqrt[3]{x}\, dx \leqslant 1$$

59. Evaluate $\int_{-2}^2 (x + 3)\sqrt{4 - x^2}\, dx$ by writing it as a sum of two integrals and interpreting one of those integrals in terms of an area.

60. Evaluate $\int_0^1 x\sqrt{1 - x^4}\, dx$ by making a substitution and interpreting the resulting integral in terms of an area.

61. Which of the following areas are equal? Why?

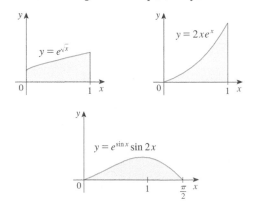

62. A model for the basal metabolism rate, in kcal/h, of a young man is $R(t) = 85 - 0.18 \cos(\pi t/12)$, where t is the time in

hours measured from 5:00 AM. What is the total basal metabolism of this man, $\int_0^{24} R(t)\, dt$, over a 24-hour time period?

63. An oil storage tank ruptures at time $t = 0$ and oil leaks from the tank at a rate of $r(t) = 100e^{-0.01t}$ liters per minute. How much oil leaks out during the first hour?

64. A bacteria population starts with 400 bacteria and grows at a rate of $r(t) = (450.268)e^{1.12567t}$ bacteria per hour. How many bacteria will there be after three hours?

65. Breathing is cyclic and a full respiratory cycle from the beginning of inhalation to the end of exhalation takes about 5 s. The maximum rate of air flow into the lungs is about 0.5 L/s. This explains, in part, why the function $f(t) = \frac{1}{2} \sin(2\pi t/5)$ has often been used to model the rate of air flow into the lungs. Use this model to find the volume of inhaled air in the lungs at time t.

66. Alabama Instruments Company has set up a production line to manufacture a new calculator. The rate of production of these calculators after t weeks is

$$\frac{dx}{dt} = 5000\left(1 - \frac{100}{(t + 10)^2}\right) \text{ calculators/week}$$

(Notice that production approaches 5000 per week as time goes on, but the initial production is lower because of the workers' unfamiliarity with the new techniques.) Find the number of calculators produced from the beginning of the third week to the end of the fourth week.

67. If f is continuous and $\int_0^4 f(x)\, dx = 10$, find $\int_0^2 f(2x)\, dx$.

68. If f is continuous and $\int_0^9 f(x)\, dx = 4$, find $\int_0^3 xf(x^2)\, dx$.

69. If f is continuous on $\mathbb{R}$, prove that

$$\int_a^b f(-x)\, dx = \int_{-b}^{-a} f(x)\, dx$$

For the case where $f(x) \geqslant 0$ and $0 < a < b$, draw a diagram to interpret this equation geometrically as an equality of areas.

70. If f is continuous on $\mathbb{R}$, prove that

$$\int_a^b f(x + c)\, dx = \int_{a+c}^{b+c} f(x)\, dx$$

For the case where $f(x) \geqslant 0$, draw a diagram to interpret this equation geometrically as an equality of areas.

71. If a and b are positive numbers, show that

$$\int_0^1 x^a(1 - x)^b\, dx = \int_0^1 x^b(1 - x)^a\, dx$$

72. (a) If f is continuous, prove that

$$\int_0^{\pi/2} f(\cos x)\, dx = \int_0^{\pi/2} f(\sin x)\, dx$$

(b) Use part (a) to evaluate $\int_0^{\pi/2} \cos^2 x\, dx$ and $\int_0^{\pi/2} \sin^2 x\, dx$.

5.6 Integration by Parts

Every differentiation rule has a corresponding integration rule. For instance, the Substitution Rule for integration corresponds to the Chain Rule for differentiation. The rule that corresponds to the Product Rule for differentiation is called the rule for *integration by parts*.

The Product Rule states that if f and g are differentiable functions, then

$$\frac{d}{dx}[f(x)g(x)] = f(x)g'(x) + g(x)f'(x)$$

In the notation for indefinite integrals this equation becomes

$$\int [f(x)g'(x) + g(x)f'(x)]\, dx = f(x)g(x)$$

or

$$\int f(x)g'(x)\, dx + \int g(x)f'(x)\, dx = f(x)g(x)$$

We can rearrange this equation as

1

$$\int f(x)g'(x)\, dx = f(x)g(x) - \int g(x)f'(x)\, dx$$

Formula 1 is called the **formula for integration by parts**. It is perhaps easier to remember in the following notation. Let $u = f(x)$ and $v = g(x)$. Then the differentials are $du = f'(x)\, dx$ and $dv = g'(x)\, dx$, so, by the Substitution Rule, the formula for integration by parts becomes

2

$$\int u\, dv = uv - \int v\, du$$

EXAMPLE 1 **Integrating by parts** Find $\int x \sin x\, dx$.

SOLUTION USING FORMULA 1 Suppose we choose $f(x) = x$ and $g'(x) = \sin x$. Then $f'(x) = 1$ and $g(x) = -\cos x$. (For g we can choose *any* antiderivative of g'.) Thus, using Formula 1, we have

$$\int x \sin x\, dx = f(x)g(x) - \int g(x)f'(x)\, dx$$

$$= x(-\cos x) - \int (-\cos x)\, dx$$

$$= -x \cos x + \int \cos x\, dx$$

$$= -x \cos x + \sin x + C$$

It's wise to check the answer by differentiating it. If we do so, we get $x \sin x$, as expected.

SOLUTION USING FORMULA 2 Let

$$u = x \qquad dv = \sin x \, dx$$

Then

$$du = dx \qquad v = -\cos x$$

and so

$$\int x \sin x \, dx = \int \overset{u}{\overbrace{x}} \ \overset{dv}{\overbrace{\sin x \, dx}} = \overset{u}{\overbrace{x}} \ \overset{v}{\overbrace{(-\cos x)}} - \int \overset{v}{\overbrace{(-\cos x)}} \ \overset{du}{\overbrace{dx}}$$

$$= -x \cos x + \int \cos x \, dx$$

$$= -x \cos x + \sin x + C$$

Note: Our aim in using integration by parts is to obtain a simpler integral than the one we started with. Thus in Example 1 we started with $\int x \sin x \, dx$ and expressed it in terms of the simpler integral $\int \cos x \, dx$. If we had instead chosen $u = \sin x$ and $dv = x \, dx$, then $du = \cos x \, dx$ and $v = x^2/2$, so integration by parts gives

$$\int x \sin x \, dx = (\sin x) \frac{x^2}{2} - \frac{1}{2} \int x^2 \cos x \, dx$$

Although this is true, $\int x^2 \cos x \, dx$ is a more difficult integral than the one we started with. In general, when deciding on a choice for u and dv, we usually try to choose $u = f(x)$ to be a function that becomes simpler when differentiated (or at least not more complicated) as long as $dv = g'(x) \, dx$ can be readily integrated to give v.

V **EXAMPLE 2** Evaluate $\int \ln x \, dx$.

SOLUTION Here we don't have much choice for u and dv. Let

$$u = \ln x \qquad dv = dx$$

Then

$$du = \frac{1}{x} \, dx \qquad v = x$$

Integrating by parts, we get

$$\int \ln x \, dx = x \ln x - \int x \, \frac{dx}{x}$$

$$= x \ln x - \int dx$$

$$= x \ln x - x + C$$

Integration by parts is effective in this example because the derivative of the function $f(x) = \ln x$ is simpler than f.

V **EXAMPLE 3** **Integrating by parts twice** Find $\int t^2 e^t \, dt$.

SOLUTION Notice that t^2 becomes simpler when differentiated (whereas e^t is unchanged when differentiated or integrated), so we choose

$$u = t^2 \qquad dv = e^t \, dt$$

Then

$$du = 2t \, dt \qquad v = e^t$$

Integration by parts gives

$$\boxed{3} \qquad \int t^2 e^t \, dt = t^2 e^t - 2 \int t e^t \, dt$$

The integral that we obtained, $\int t e^t \, dt$, is simpler than the original integral but is still not obvious. Therefore we use integration by parts a second time, this time with $u = t$ and $dv = e^t \, dt$. Then $du = dt$, $v = e^t$, and

$$\int t e^t \, dt = t e^t - \int e^t \, dt$$
$$= t e^t - e^t + C$$

Putting this in Equation 3, we get

$$\int t^2 e^t \, dt = t^2 e^t - 2 \int t e^t \, dt$$
$$= t^2 e^t - 2(t e^t - e^t + C)$$
$$= t^2 e^t - 2t e^t + 2e^t + C_1 \qquad \text{where } C_1 = -2C$$

V   EXAMPLE 4   Evaluate $\int e^x \sin x \, dx$.

An easier method, using complex numbers, is given in Exercise 50 in Appendix I.

SOLUTION   Neither e^x nor $\sin x$ becomes simpler when differentiated, but we try choosing $u = e^x$ and $dv = \sin x \, dx$ anyway. Then $du = e^x \, dx$ and $v = -\cos x$, so integration by parts gives

$$\boxed{4} \qquad \int e^x \sin x \, dx = -e^x \cos x + \int e^x \cos x \, dx$$

The integral that we have obtained, $\int e^x \cos x \, dx$, is no simpler than the original one, but at least it's no more difficult. Having had success in the preceding example integrating by parts twice, we persevere and integrate by parts again. This time we use $u = e^x$ and $dv = \cos x \, dx$. Then $du = e^x \, dx$, $v = \sin x$, and

$$\boxed{5} \qquad \int e^x \cos x \, dx = e^x \sin x - \int e^x \sin x \, dx$$

At first glance, it appears as if we have accomplished nothing because we have arrived at $\int e^x \sin x \, dx$, which is where we started. However, if we put Equation 5 into Equation 4 we get

$$\int e^x \sin x \, dx = -e^x \cos x + e^x \sin x - \int e^x \sin x \, dx$$

This can be regarded as an equation to be solved for the unknown integral. Adding $\int e^x \sin x \, dx$ to both sides, we obtain

$$2 \int e^x \sin x \, dx = -e^x \cos x + e^x \sin x$$

Dividing by 2 and adding the constant of integration, we get

$$\int e^x \sin x \, dx = \tfrac{1}{2} e^x (\sin x - \cos x) + C$$

Figure 1 illustrates Example 4 by showing the graphs of $f(x) = e^x \sin x$ and $F(x) = \tfrac{1}{2} e^x (\sin x - \cos x)$. As a visual check on our work, notice that $f(x) = 0$ when F has a maximum or minimum.

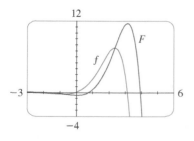

FIGURE 1

If we combine the formula for integration by parts with the Evaluation Theorem, we can evaluate definite integrals by parts. Evaluating both sides of Formula 1 between a and b, assuming f' and g' are continuous, and using the Evaluation Theorem, we obtain

$$\boxed{6 \qquad \int_a^b f(x)g'(x)\,dx = f(x)g(x)\Big]_a^b - \int_a^b g(x)f'(x)\,dx}$$

EXAMPLE 5 **Definite integration by parts** Calculate $\displaystyle\int_0^1 \tan^{-1}x\,dx$.

SOLUTION Let

$$u = \tan^{-1}x \qquad\qquad dv = dx$$

Then

$$du = \frac{dx}{1+x^2} \qquad\qquad v = x$$

So Formula 6 gives

$$\int_0^1 \tan^{-1}x\,dx = x\tan^{-1}x\Big]_0^1 - \int_0^1 \frac{x}{1+x^2}\,dx$$

$$= 1 \cdot \tan^{-1}1 - 0 \cdot \tan^{-1}0 - \int_0^1 \frac{x}{1+x^2}\,dx$$

$$= \frac{\pi}{4} - \int_0^1 \frac{x}{1+x^2}\,dx$$

Since $\tan^{-1}x \geq 0$ for $x \geq 0$, the integral in Example 5 can be interpreted as the area of the region shown in Figure 2.

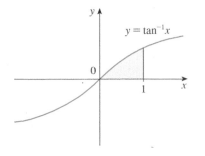

$y = \tan^{-1}x$

FIGURE 2

To evaluate this integral we use the substitution $t = 1 + x^2$ (since u has another meaning in this example). Then $dt = 2x\,dx$, so $x\,dx = \frac{1}{2}\,dt$. When $x = 0$, $t = 1$; when $x = 1$, $t = 2$; so

$$\int_0^1 \frac{x}{1+x^2}\,dx = \frac{1}{2}\int_1^2 \frac{dt}{t} = \frac{1}{2}\ln|t|\Big]_1^2$$

$$= \frac{1}{2}(\ln 2 - \ln 1) = \frac{1}{2}\ln 2$$

Therefore

$$\int_0^1 \tan^{-1}x\,dx = \frac{\pi}{4} - \int_0^1 \frac{x}{1+x^2}\,dx = \frac{\pi}{4} - \frac{\ln 2}{2}$$

EXAMPLE 6 Prove the reduction formula

Equation 7 is called a *reduction formula* because the exponent n has been *reduced* to $n - 1$ and $n - 2$.

$$\boxed{7} \qquad \int \sin^n x\,dx = -\frac{1}{n}\cos x\,\sin^{n-1}x + \frac{n-1}{n}\int \sin^{n-2}x\,dx$$

where $n \geq 2$ is an integer.

SOLUTION Let

$$u = \sin^{n-1}x \qquad\qquad\qquad dv = \sin x\,dx$$

Then

$$du = (n-1)\sin^{n-2}x\,\cos x\,dx \qquad\qquad v = -\cos x$$

so integration by parts gives

$$\int \sin^n x \, dx = -\cos x \sin^{n-1} x + (n-1) \int \sin^{n-2} x \cos^2 x \, dx$$

Since $\cos^2 x = 1 - \sin^2 x$, we have

$$\int \sin^n x \, dx = -\cos x \sin^{n-1} x + (n-1) \int \sin^{n-2} x \, dx - (n-1) \int \sin^n x \, dx$$

As in Example 4, we solve this equation for the desired integral by taking the last term on the right side to the left side. Thus we have

$$n \int \sin^n x \, dx = -\cos x \sin^{n-1} x + (n-1) \int \sin^{n-2} x \, dx$$

or

$$\int \sin^n x \, dx = -\frac{1}{n} \cos x \sin^{n-1} x + \frac{n-1}{n} \int \sin^{n-2} x \, dx$$

The reduction formula (7) is useful because by using it repeatedly we could eventually express $\int \sin^n x \, dx$ in terms of $\int \sin x \, dx$ (if n is odd) or $\int (\sin x)^0 \, dx = \int dx$ (if n is even).

5.6 Exercises

1–2 Evaluate the integral using integration by parts with the indicated choices of u and dv.

1. $\int x^2 \ln x \, dx; \quad u = \ln x, \ dv = x^2 \, dx$

2. $\int \theta \cos \theta \, d\theta; \quad u = \theta, \ dv = \cos \theta \, d\theta$

3–24 Evaluate the integral.

3. $\int x \cos 5x \, dx$

4. $\int x e^{-x} \, dx$

5. $\int r e^{r/2} \, dr$

6. $\int t \sin 2t \, dt$

7. $\int x^2 \sin \pi x \, dx$

8. $\int x^2 \cos mx \, dx$

9. $\int \ln \sqrt[3]{x} \, dx$

10. $\int p^5 \ln p \, dp$

11. $\int \arctan 4t \, dt$

12. $\int \sin^{-1} x \, dx$

13. $\int e^{2\theta} \sin 3\theta \, d\theta$

14. $\int e^{-\theta} \cos 2\theta \, d\theta$

15. $\int_0^\pi t \sin 3t \, dt$

16. $\int_0^1 (x^2 + 1) e^{-x} \, dx$

17. $\int_1^2 \frac{\ln x}{x^2} \, dx$

18. $\int_4^9 \frac{\ln y}{\sqrt{y}} \, dy$

19. $\int_0^1 \frac{y}{e^{2y}} \, dy$

20. $\int_1^{\sqrt{3}} \arctan(1/x) \, dx$

21. $\int_0^{1/2} \cos^{-1} x \, dx$

22. $\int_0^1 \frac{r^3}{\sqrt{4 + r^2}} \, dr$

23. $\int_1^2 (\ln x)^2 \, dx$

24. $\int_0^t e^s \sin(t - s) \, ds$

25–30 First make a substitution and then use integration by parts to evaluate the integral.

25. $\int \cos \sqrt{x} \, dx$

26. $\int t^3 e^{-t^2} \, dt$

Graphing calculator or computer with graphing software required   **1.** Homework Hints available in TEC

27. $\int_{\sqrt{\pi/2}}^{\sqrt{\pi}} \theta^3 \cos(\theta^2)\, d\theta$

28. $\int_0^\pi e^{\cos t} \sin 2t\, dt$

29. $\int x \ln(1 + x)\, dx$

30. $\int \sin(\ln x)\, dx$

31–34 Evaluate the indefinite integral. Illustrate, and check that your answer is reasonable, by graphing both the function and its antiderivative (take $C = 0$).

31. $\int x e^{-2x}\, dx$

32. $\int x^{3/2} \ln x\, dx$

33. $\int x^3 \sqrt{1 + x^2}\, dx$

34. $\int x^2 \sin 2x\, dx$

---

35. (a) Use the reduction formula in Example 6 to show that

$$\int \sin^2 x\, dx = \frac{x}{2} - \frac{\sin 2x}{4} + C$$

(b) Use part (a) and the reduction formula to evaluate $\int \sin^4 x\, dx$.

36. (a) Prove the reduction formula

$$\int \cos^n x\, dx = \frac{1}{n} \cos^{n-1} x \sin x + \frac{n-1}{n} \int \cos^{n-2} x\, dx$$

(b) Use part (a) to evaluate $\int \cos^2 x\, dx$.
(c) Use parts (a) and (b) to evaluate $\int \cos^4 x\, dx$.

37. (a) Use the reduction formula in Example 6 to show that

$$\int_0^{\pi/2} \sin^n x\, dx = \frac{n-1}{n} \int_0^{\pi/2} \sin^{n-2} x\, dx$$

where $n \geqslant 2$ is an integer.
(b) Use part (a) to evaluate $\int_0^{\pi/2} \sin^3 x\, dx$ and $\int_0^{\pi/2} \sin^5 x\, dx$.
(c) Use part (a) to show that, for odd powers of sine,

$$\int_0^{\pi/2} \sin^{2n+1} x\, dx = \frac{2 \cdot 4 \cdot 6 \cdots \cdots 2n}{3 \cdot 5 \cdot 7 \cdots \cdots (2n+1)}$$

38. Prove that, for even powers of sine,

$$\int_0^{\pi/2} \sin^{2n} x\, dx = \frac{1 \cdot 3 \cdot 5 \cdots \cdots (2n-1)}{2 \cdot 4 \cdot 6 \cdots \cdots 2n} \frac{\pi}{2}$$

39–40 Use integration by parts to prove the reduction formula.

39. $\int (\ln x)^n\, dx = x(\ln x)^n - n \int (\ln x)^{n-1}\, dx$

40. $\int x^n e^x\, dx = x^n e^x - n \int x^{n-1} e^x\, dx$

41. Use Exercise 39 to find $\int (\ln x)^3\, dx$.

42. Use Exercise 40 to find $\int x^4 e^x\, dx$.

43. A particle that moves along a straight line has velocity $v(t) = t^2 e^{-t}$ meters per second after t seconds. How far will it travel during the first t seconds?

44. A rocket accelerates by burning its onboard fuel, so its mass decreases with time. Suppose the initial mass of the rocket at liftoff (including its fuel) is m, the fuel is consumed at rate r, and the exhaust gases are ejected with constant velocity v_e (relative to the rocket). A model for the velocity of the rocket at time t is given by the equation

$$v(t) = -gt - v_e \ln \frac{m - rt}{m}$$

where g is the acceleration due to gravity and t is not too large. If $g = 9.8$ m/s^2, $m = 30{,}000$ kg, $r = 160$ kg/s, and $v_e = 3000$ m/s, find the height of the rocket one minute after liftoff.

45. Suppose that $f(1) = 2$, $f(4) = 7$, $f'(1) = 5$, $f'(4) = 3$, and f'' is continuous. Find the value of $\int_1^4 x f''(x)\, dx$.

46. (a) Use integration by parts to show that

$$\int f(x)\, dx = x f(x) - \int x f'(x)\, dx$$

(b) If f and g are inverse functions and f' is continuous, prove that

$$\int_a^b f(x)\, dx = bf(b) - af(a) - \int_{f(a)}^{f(b)} g(y)\, dy$$

[*Hint:* Use part (a) and make the substitution $y = f(x)$.]
(c) In the case where f and g are positive functions and $b > a > 0$, draw a diagram to give a geometric interpretation of part (b).
(d) Use part (b) to evaluate $\int_1^e \ln x\, dx$.

47. If $f(0) = g(0) = 0$ and f'' and g'' are continuous, show that

$$\int_0^a f(x) g''(x)\, dx = f(a) g'(a) - f'(a) g(a) + \int_0^a f''(x) g(x)\, dx$$

48. Let $I_n = \int_0^{\pi/2} \sin^n x\, dx$.
(a) Show that $I_{2n+2} \leqslant I_{2n+1} \leqslant I_{2n}$.
(b) Use Exercise 38 to show that

$$\frac{I_{2n+2}}{I_{2n}} = \frac{2n+1}{2n+2}$$

(c) Use parts (a) and (b) to show that

$$\frac{2n+1}{2n+2} \leqslant \frac{I_{2n+1}}{I_{2n}} \leqslant 1$$

and deduce that $\lim_{n \to \infty} I_{2n+1}/I_{2n} = 1$.

(d) Use part (c) and Exercises 37 and 38 to show that

$$\lim_{n \to \infty} \frac{2}{1} \cdot \frac{2}{3} \cdot \frac{4}{3} \cdot \frac{4}{5} \cdot \frac{6}{5} \cdot \frac{6}{7} \cdot \cdots \cdot \frac{2n}{2n-1} \cdot \frac{2n}{2n+1} = \frac{\pi}{2}$$

This formula is usually written as an infinite product:

$$\frac{\pi}{2} = \frac{2}{1} \cdot \frac{2}{3} \cdot \frac{4}{3} \cdot \frac{4}{5} \cdot \frac{6}{5} \cdot \frac{6}{7} \cdot \cdots$$

and is called the *Wallis product.*

(e) We construct rectangles as follows. Start with a square of area 1 and attach rectangles of area 1 alternately beside or

on top of the previous rectangle (see the figure). Find the limit of the ratios of width to height of these rectangles.

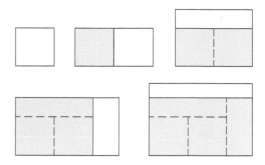

5.7 Additional Techniques of Integration

We have learned the two basic techniques of integration—substitution and parts—in Sections 5.5 and 5.6. Here we discuss briefly methods that are special to particular classes of functions, such as trigonometric functions and rational functions.

Trigonometric Integrals

We can use trigonometric identities to integrate certain combinations of trigonometric functions.

EXAMPLE 1 **An integral with an odd power of cos x**   Evaluate $\int \cos^3 x \, dx$.

SOLUTION We would like to use the Substitution Rule, but simply substituting $u = \cos x$ isn't helpful, since then $du = -\sin x \, dx$. In order to integrate powers of cosine, we would need an extra $\sin x$ factor. (Similarly, a power of sine would require an extra $\cos x$ factor.) Here we separate one cosine factor and convert the remaining $\cos^2 x$ factor to an expression involving sine using the identity $\sin^2 x + \cos^2 x = 1$:

$$\cos^3 x = \cos^2 x \cdot \cos x = (1 - \sin^2 x) \cos x$$

We can then evaluate the integral by substituting $u = \sin x$, so $du = \cos x \, dx$ and

$$\int \cos^3 x \, dx = \int \cos^2 x \cdot \cos x \, dx = \int (1 - \sin^2 x) \cos x \, dx$$

$$= \int (1 - u^2) \, du = u - \tfrac{1}{3} u^3 + C$$

$$= \sin x - \tfrac{1}{3} \sin^3 x + C$$

In general, we try to write an integrand involving powers of sine and cosine in a form where we have only one sine factor (and the remainder of the expression in terms of cosine) or only one cosine factor (and the remainder of the expression in terms of sine). The identity $\sin^2 x + \cos^2 x = 1$ enables us to convert back and forth between even powers of sine and cosine.

If the integrand contains only even powers of both sine and cosine, however, this strategy fails. In this case, we can take advantage of the *half-angle identities*

See Appendix C, Formula 17.

$$\sin^2 x = \tfrac{1}{2}(1 - \cos 2x)$$

and

$$\cos^2 x = \tfrac{1}{2}(1 + \cos 2x)$$

Example 2 shows that the area of the region shown in Figure 1 is $\pi/2$.

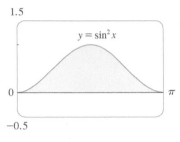

FIGURE 1

V   EXAMPLE 2   An integral with an even power of sin x   Evaluate $\int_0^\pi \sin^2 x \, dx$.

SOLUTION   If we write $\sin^2 x = 1 - \cos^2 x$, the integral is no simpler to evaluate. Using the half-angle formula for $\sin^2 x$, however, we have

$$\int_0^\pi \sin^2 x \, dx = \tfrac{1}{2}\int_0^\pi (1 - \cos 2x) \, dx = \left[\tfrac{1}{2}\left(x - \tfrac{1}{2}\sin 2x\right)\right]_0^\pi$$

$$= \tfrac{1}{2}\left(\pi - \tfrac{1}{2}\sin 2\pi\right) - \tfrac{1}{2}\left(0 - \tfrac{1}{2}\sin 0\right) = \tfrac{1}{2}\pi$$

Notice that we mentally made the substitution $u = 2x$ when integrating $\cos 2x$. Another method for evaluating this integral was given in Exercise 35 in Section 5.6.

We can use a similar strategy to integrate powers of $\tan x$ and $\sec x$ using the identity $\sec^2 x = 1 + \tan^2 x$. (See Exercises 7–10.)

Trigonometric Substitution

A number of practical problems require us to integrate algebraic functions that contain an expression of the form $\sqrt{a^2 - x^2}$, $\sqrt{a^2 + x^2}$, or $\sqrt{x^2 - a^2}$. Sometimes, the best way to perform the integration is to make a trigonometric substitution that gets rid of the root sign.

EXAMPLE 3   Prove that the area of a circle with radius r is πr^2.

SOLUTION   This is, of course, a well-known formula. A long time ago you were *told* that it's true; but the only way to actually *prove* it is by integration.

For simplicity, let's place the circle with its center at the origin, so its equation is $x^2 + y^2 = r^2$. Solving this equation for y, we get

$$y = \pm\sqrt{r^2 - x^2}$$

Because the circle is symmetric with respect to both axes, the total area A is four times the area in the first quadrant (see Figure 2).

The part of the circle in the first quadrant is given by the function

$$y = \sqrt{r^2 - x^2} \qquad 0 \leqslant x \leqslant r$$

and so

$$\tfrac{1}{4}A = \int_0^r \sqrt{r^2 - x^2} \, dx$$

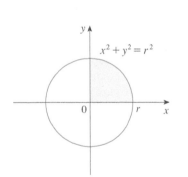

FIGURE 2

To simplify this integral, we would like to make a substitution that turns $r^2 - x^2$ into the square of something. The trigonometric identity $1 - \sin^2\theta = \cos^2\theta$ is useful here. In fact, because

$$r^2 - r^2\sin^2\theta = r^2(1 - \sin^2\theta) = r^2\cos^2\theta$$

we make the substitution

$$x = r\sin\theta$$

This substitution is a bit different from our previous substitutions. Here the old variable x is a function of the new variable θ instead of the other way around. But our substitution $x = r \sin \theta$ is equivalent to saying that $\theta = \sin^{-1}(x/r)$.

Since $0 \leqslant x \leqslant r$, we restrict θ so that $0 \leqslant \theta \leqslant \pi/2$. We have $dx = r \cos \theta \, d\theta$ and

$$\sqrt{r^2 - x^2} = \sqrt{r^2 - r^2 \sin^2\theta} = \sqrt{r^2 \cos^2\theta} = r \cos \theta$$

because $\cos \theta \geqslant 0$ when $0 \leqslant \theta \leqslant \pi/2$. Therefore the Substitution Rule gives

$$\int_0^r \sqrt{r^2 - x^2} \, dx = \int_0^{\pi/2} (r \cos \theta) \, r \cos \theta \, d\theta = r^2 \int_0^{\pi/2} \cos^2\theta \, d\theta$$

This trigonometric integral is similar to the one in Example 2; we integrate $\cos^2\theta$ by means of the identity

$$\cos^2\theta = \tfrac{1}{2}(1 + \cos 2\theta)$$

Here we made the mental substitution $u = 2\theta$.

Thus

$$\tfrac{1}{4}A = r^2 \int_0^{\pi/2} \cos^2\theta \, d\theta = \tfrac{1}{2}r^2 \int_0^{\pi/2} (1 + \cos 2\theta) \, d\theta$$

$$= \tfrac{1}{2}r^2 \Big[\theta + \tfrac{1}{2}\sin 2\theta\Big]_0^{\pi/2} = \tfrac{1}{2}r^2\left(\frac{\pi}{2} + 0 - 0\right)$$

$$= \tfrac{1}{4}\pi r^2$$

We have therefore proved the famous formula $A = \pi r^2$.

www.stewartcalculus.com

For more examples, click on *Trigonometric Substitution* under *Additional Topics*.

Example 3 suggests that if an integrand contains a factor of the form $\sqrt{a^2 - x^2}$, then a trigonometric substitution $x = a \sin \theta$ may be effective. But that doesn't mean that such a substitution is *always* the best method. To evaluate $\int x\sqrt{a^2 - x^2} \, dx$, for instance, a simpler substitution is $u = a^2 - x^2$ because $du = -2x \, dx$.

When an integral contains an expression of the form $\sqrt{a^2 + x^2}$, the substitution $x = a \tan \theta$ should be considered because the identity $1 + \tan^2\theta = \sec^2\theta$ eliminates the root sign. Similarly, if the factor $\sqrt{x^2 - a^2}$ occurs, the substitution $x = a \sec \theta$ is effective.

Partial Fractions

See Appendix G for a more complete treatment of partial fractions.

We integrate rational functions (ratios of polynomials) by expressing them as sums of simpler fractions, called *partial fractions*, that we already know how to integrate. The following example illustrates the simplest case.

EXAMPLE 4 Find $\int \dfrac{5x - 4}{2x^2 + x - 1} \, dx$.

SOLUTION Notice that the denominator can be factored as a product of linear factors:

$$\frac{5x - 4}{2x^2 + x - 1} = \frac{5x - 4}{(x + 1)(2x - 1)}$$

In a case like this, where the numerator has a smaller degree than the denominator, we can write the given rational function as a sum of partial fractions:

$$\frac{5x - 4}{(x + 1)(2x - 1)} = \frac{A}{x + 1} + \frac{B}{2x - 1}$$

where A and B are constants. To find the values of A and B we multiply both sides of this equation by $(x + 1)(2x - 1)$, obtaining

$$5x - 4 = A(2x - 1) + B(x + 1)$$

or

$$5x - 4 = (2A + B)x + (-A + B)$$

The coefficients of x must be equal and the constant terms are also equal. So

$$2A + B = 5 \qquad \text{and} \qquad -A + B = -4$$

Solving this system of linear equations for A and B, we get $A = 3$ and $B = -1$, so

Verify that this equation is correct by taking the fractions on the right side to a common denominator.

$$\frac{5x - 4}{(x + 1)(2x - 1)} = \frac{3}{x + 1} - \frac{1}{2x - 1}$$

Each of the resulting partial fractions is easy to integrate (using the substitutions $u = x + 1$ and $u = 2x - 1$, respectively). So we have

$$\int \frac{5x - 4}{2x^2 + x - 1}\, dx = \int \left(\frac{3}{x + 1} - \frac{1}{2x - 1} \right) dx$$

$$= 3 \ln|x + 1| - \tfrac{1}{2} \ln|2x - 1| + C \qquad \blacksquare$$

Note 1: If the degree in the numerator in Example 4 had been the same as that of the denominator, or higher, we would have had to take the preliminary step of performing a long division. For instance,

$$\frac{2x^3 - 11x^2 - 2x + 2}{2x^2 + x - 1} = x - 6 + \frac{5x - 4}{(x + 1)(2x - 1)}$$

Note 2: If the denominator has more than two linear factors, we need to include a term corresponding to each factor. For example,

$$\frac{x + 6}{x(x - 3)(4x + 5)} = \frac{A}{x} + \frac{B}{x - 3} + \frac{C}{4x + 5}$$

where A, B, and C are constants determined by solving a system of three equations in the unknowns A, B, and C.

Note 3: If a linear factor is repeated, we need to include extra terms in the partial fraction expansion. Here's an example:

$$\frac{x}{(x + 2)^2(x - 1)} = \frac{A}{x + 2} + \frac{B}{(x + 2)^2} + \frac{C}{x - 1}$$

Note 4: When we factor a denominator as far as possible, it might happen that we obtain an irreducible quadratic factor $ax^2 + bx + c$, where the discriminant $b^2 - 4ac$ is negative. Then the corresponding partial fraction is of the form

$$\frac{Ax + B}{ax^2 + bx + c}$$

where A and B are constants to be determined. This term can be integrated by completing the square and using the formula

You can verify Formula 1 by differentiating the right side.

$$\boxed{\textbf{1}}\qquad \int \frac{dx}{x^2 + a^2} = \frac{1}{a}\tan^{-1}\left(\frac{x}{a}\right) + C$$

V **EXAMPLE 5** Evaluate $\displaystyle\int \frac{2x^2 - x + 4}{x^3 + 4x}\,dx$.

SOLUTION Since $x^3 + 4x = x(x^2 + 4)$ can't be factored further, we write

$$\frac{2x^2 - x + 4}{x(x^2 + 4)} = \frac{A}{x} + \frac{Bx + C}{x^2 + 4}$$

Multiplying by $x(x^2 + 4)$, we have

$$2x^2 - x + 4 = A(x^2 + 4) + (Bx + C)x$$
$$= (A + B)x^2 + Cx + 4A$$

Equating coefficients, we obtain

$$A + B = 2 \qquad C = -1 \qquad 4A = 4$$

Thus $A = 1$, $B = 1$, and $C = -1$ and so

$$\int \frac{2x^2 - x + 4}{x^3 + 4x}\,dx = \int \left[\frac{1}{x} + \frac{x - 1}{x^2 + 4}\right]dx$$

In order to integrate the second term we split it into two parts:

$$\int \frac{x - 1}{x^2 + 4}\,dx = \int \frac{x}{x^2 + 4}\,dx - \int \frac{1}{x^2 + 4}\,dx$$

We make the substitution $u = x^2 + 4$ in the first of these integrals so that $du = 2x\,dx$. We evaluate the second integral by means of Formula 1 with $a = 2$:

$$\int \frac{2x^2 - x + 4}{x(x^2 + 4)}\,dx = \int \frac{1}{x}\,dx + \int \frac{x}{x^2 + 4}\,dx - \int \frac{1}{x^2 + 4}\,dx$$

Here we use K for the constant of integration because C has already been used.

$$= \ln|x| + \tfrac{1}{2}\ln(x^2 + 4) - \tfrac{1}{2}\tan^{-1}(x/2) + K$$

www.stewartcalculus.com

Integration is more difficult than differentiation because it's not always easy to recognize which integration technique to use. For advice on integration strategy, click on *Strategy for Integration* under *Additional Topics*.

5.7 Exercises

1–6 Evaluate the integral.

1. $\displaystyle\int \sin^3 x \cos^2 x \, dx$

2. $\displaystyle\int_0^{\pi/2} \cos^5 x \, dx$

3. $\displaystyle\int_{\pi/2}^{3\pi/4} \sin^5 x \cos^3 x \, dx$

4. $\displaystyle\int \sin^3(mx) \, dx$

5. $\displaystyle\int_0^{2\pi} \cos^2(6\theta) \, d\theta$

6. $\displaystyle\int_0^{\pi/2} \sin^2 x \cos^2 x \, dx$

7–8 Use the substitution $u = \sec x$ to evaluate the integral.

7. $\displaystyle\int \tan^3 x \sec x \, dx$

8. $\displaystyle\int \tan^5 x \sec^3 x \, dx$

9–10 Use the substitution $u = \tan x$ to evaluate the integral.

9. $\displaystyle\int_0^{\pi/4} \tan^2 x \sec^4 x \, dx$

10. $\displaystyle\int \tan^4 x \sec^6 x \, dx$

⊞ Graphing calculator or computer with graphing software required   **1.** Homework Hints available in TEC

11. Use the substitution $x = 3 \sin \theta$, $-\pi/2 \leqslant \theta \leqslant \pi/2$, and the identity $\cot^2\theta = \csc^2\theta - 1$ to evaluate

$$\int \frac{\sqrt{9 - x^2}}{x^2}\, dx$$

12. Use the substitution $x = \sec \theta$, where $0 \leqslant \theta < \pi/2$ or $\pi \leqslant \theta < 3\pi/2$, to evaluate

$$\int \frac{\sqrt{x^2 - 1}}{x^4}\, dx$$

13. Use the substitution $x = 2 \tan \theta$, $-\pi/2 < \theta < \pi/2$, to evaluate

$$\int \frac{1}{x^2\sqrt{x^2 + 4}}\, dx$$

14. (a) Verify, by differentiation, that

$$\int \sec^3\theta \, d\theta = \tfrac{1}{2}\bigl(\sec \theta \tan \theta + \ln |\sec \theta + \tan \theta|\bigr) + C$$

(b) Evaluate $\displaystyle\int_0^1 \sqrt{x^2 + 1}\, dx$.

15–18 Evaluate the integral.

15. $\displaystyle\int_{\sqrt{2}}^2 \frac{1}{t^3\sqrt{t^2 - 1}}\, dt$

16. $\displaystyle\int_0^{2\sqrt{3}} \frac{x^3}{\sqrt{16 - x^2}}\, dx$

17. $\displaystyle\int \frac{dx}{x^2\sqrt{4 - x^2}}$

18. $\displaystyle\int \frac{x^3}{\sqrt{x^2 + 1}}\, dx$

19–20 Write out the form of the partial fraction expansion of the function. Do not determine the numerical values of the coefficients.

19. (a) $\dfrac{2x}{(x + 3)(3x + 1)}$

(b) $\dfrac{1}{x^3 + 2x^2 + x}$

20. (a) $\dfrac{x}{x^2 + x - 2}$

(b) $\dfrac{x^2}{x^2 + x + 2}$

21–28 Evaluate the integral.

21. $\displaystyle\int \frac{5x + 1}{(2x + 1)(x - 1)}\, dx$

22. $\displaystyle\int_0^1 \frac{x - 4}{x^2 - 5x + 6}\, dx$

23. $\displaystyle\int_2^3 \frac{1}{x^2 - 1}\, dx$

24. $\displaystyle\int \frac{x^2 + 2x - 1}{x^3 - x}\, dx$

25. $\displaystyle\int \frac{10}{(x - 1)(x^2 + 9)}\, dx$

26. $\displaystyle\int \frac{2x^2 + 5}{(x^2 + 1)(x^2 + 4)}\, dx$

27. $\displaystyle\int \frac{x^3 + x^2 + 2x + 1}{(x^2 + 1)(x^2 + 2)}\, dx$

28. $\displaystyle\int \frac{x^2 - x + 6}{x^3 + 3x}\, dx$

29–32 Use long division to evaluate the integral.

29. $\displaystyle\int \frac{x}{x - 6}\, dx$

30. $\displaystyle\int \frac{r^2}{r + 4}\, dr$

31. $\displaystyle\int \frac{x^3 + 4}{x^2 + 4}\, dx$

32. $\displaystyle\int_0^1 \frac{x^3 - 4x - 10}{x^2 - x - 6}\, dx$

33–34 Make a substitution to express the integrand as a rational function and then evaluate the integral.

33. $\displaystyle\int_9^{16} \frac{\sqrt{x}}{x - 4}\, dx$

34. $\displaystyle\int \frac{dx}{2\sqrt{x + 3} + x}$

35. By completing the square in the quadratic $x^2 + x + 1$ and making a substitution, evaluate

$$\int \frac{dx}{x^2 + x + 1}$$

36. By completing the square in the quadratic $3 - 2x - x^2$ and making a trigonometric substitution, evaluate

$$\int \frac{x}{\sqrt{3 - 2x - x^2}}\, dx$$

5.8 Integration Using Tables and Computer Algebra Systems

In this section we describe how to evaluate integrals using tables and computer algebra systems.

Tables of Integrals

Tables of indefinite integrals are very useful when we are confronted by an integral that is difficult to evaluate by hand and we don't have access to a computer algebra system. A relatively brief table of 120 integrals, categorized by form, is provided on the Reference Pages at the back of the book. More extensive tables are available in *CRC Standard Mathematical Tables and Formulae,* 31st ed. by Daniel Zwillinger (Boca Raton, FL, 2002) (709 entries) or in Gradshteyn and Ryzhik's *Table of Integrals, Series, and Products,* 6e (San Diego,

2000), which contains hundreds of pages of integrals. It should be remembered, however, that integrals do not often occur in exactly the form listed in a table. Usually we need to use the Substitution Rule or algebraic manipulation to transform a given integral into one of the forms in the table.

The Table of Integrals appears on Reference Pages 6–10 at the back of the book.

EXAMPLE 1 Use the Table of Integrals to evaluate $\int_0^2 \dfrac{x^2 + 12}{x^2 + 4}\, dx$.

SOLUTION The only formula in the table that resembles our given integral is entry 17:

$$\int \frac{du}{a^2 + u^2} = \frac{1}{a}\tan^{-1}\frac{u}{a} + C$$

If we perform long division, we get

$$\frac{x^2 + 12}{x^2 + 4} = 1 + \frac{8}{x^2 + 4}$$

Now we can use Formula 17 with $a = 2$:

$$\int_0^2 \frac{x^2 + 12}{x^2 + 4}\, dx = \int_0^2 \left(1 + \frac{8}{x^2 + 4}\right) dx$$

$$= x + 8 \cdot \tfrac{1}{2}\tan^{-1}\frac{x}{2}\bigg]_0^2$$

$$= 2 + 4\tan^{-1}1 = 2 + \pi$$

V EXAMPLE 2 Use the Table of Integrals to find $\int \dfrac{x^2}{\sqrt{5 - 4x^2}}\, dx$.

SOLUTION If we look at the section of the table entitled *Forms involving* $\sqrt{a^2 - u^2}$, we see that the closest entry is number 34:

$$\int \frac{u^2}{\sqrt{a^2 - u^2}}\, du = -\frac{u}{2}\sqrt{a^2 - u^2} + \frac{a^2}{2}\sin^{-1}\left(\frac{u}{a}\right) + C$$

This is not exactly what we have, but we will be able to use it if we first make the substitution $u = 2x$:

$$\int \frac{x^2}{\sqrt{5 - 4x^2}}\, dx = \int \frac{(u/2)^2}{\sqrt{5 - u^2}}\frac{du}{2} = \frac{1}{8}\int \frac{u^2}{\sqrt{5 - u^2}}\, du$$

Then we use Formula 34 with $a^2 = 5$ (so $a = \sqrt{5}$):

$$\int \frac{x^2}{\sqrt{5 - 4x^2}}\, dx = \frac{1}{8}\int \frac{u^2}{\sqrt{5 - u^2}}\, du = \frac{1}{8}\left(-\frac{u}{2}\sqrt{5 - u^2} + \frac{5}{2}\sin^{-1}\frac{u}{\sqrt{5}}\right) + C$$

$$= -\frac{x}{8}\sqrt{5 - 4x^2} + \frac{5}{16}\sin^{-1}\left(\frac{2x}{\sqrt{5}}\right) + C$$

EXAMPLE 3 Use the Table of Integrals to find $\int x^3 \sin x \, dx$.

SOLUTION If we look in the section called *Trigonometric Forms*, we see that none of the entries explicitly includes a u^3 factor. However, we can use the reduction formula in entry 84 with $n = 3$:

$$\int x^3 \sin x \, dx = -x^3 \cos x + 3 \int x^2 \cos x \, dx$$

85. $\displaystyle\int u^n \cos u \, du$

$\displaystyle = u^n \sin u - n \int u^{n-1} \sin u \, du$

We now need to evaluate $\int x^2 \cos x \, dx$. We can use the reduction formula in entry 85 with $n = 2$, followed by entry 82:

$$\int x^2 \cos x \, dx = x^2 \sin x - 2 \int x \sin x \, dx$$

$$= x^2 \sin x - 2(\sin x - x \cos x) + K$$

Combining these calculations, we get

$$\int x^3 \sin x \, dx = -x^3 \cos x + 3x^2 \sin x + 6x \cos x - 6 \sin x + C$$

where $C = 3K$.

V **EXAMPLE 4** Use the Table of Integrals to find $\int x\sqrt{x^2 + 2x + 4} \, dx$.

SOLUTION Since the table gives forms involving $\sqrt{a^2 + x^2}$, $\sqrt{a^2 - x^2}$, and $\sqrt{x^2 - a^2}$, but not $\sqrt{ax^2 + bx + c}$, we first complete the square:

$$x^2 + 2x + 4 = (x + 1)^2 + 3$$

If we make the substitution $u = x + 1$ (so $x = u - 1$), the integrand will involve the pattern $\sqrt{a^2 + u^2}$:

$$\int x\sqrt{x^2 + 2x + 4} \, dx = \int (u - 1)\sqrt{u^2 + 3} \, du$$

$$= \int u\sqrt{u^2 + 3} \, du - \int \sqrt{u^2 + 3} \, du$$

The first integral is evaluated using the substitution $t = u^2 + 3$:

$$\int u\sqrt{u^2 + 3} \, du = \tfrac{1}{2}\int \sqrt{t} \, dt = \tfrac{1}{2} \cdot \tfrac{2}{3}t^{3/2} = \tfrac{1}{3}(u^2 + 3)^{3/2}$$

21. $\displaystyle\int \sqrt{a^2 + u^2} \, du = \frac{u}{2}\sqrt{a^2 + u^2}$

$\displaystyle + \frac{a^2}{2}\ln\!\left(u + \sqrt{a^2 + u^2}\right) + C$

For the second integral we use Formula 21 with $a = \sqrt{3}$:

$$\int \sqrt{u^2 + 3} \, du = \frac{u}{2}\sqrt{u^2 + 3} + \tfrac{3}{2}\ln\!\left(u + \sqrt{u^2 + 3}\right)$$

Thus

$$\int x\sqrt{x^2 + 2x + 4} \, dx$$

$$= \tfrac{1}{3}(x^2 + 2x + 4)^{3/2} - \frac{x + 1}{2}\sqrt{x^2 + 2x + 4} - \tfrac{3}{2}\ln\!\left(x + 1 + \sqrt{x^2 + 2x + 4}\right) + C$$

Computer Algebra Systems

We have seen that the use of tables involves matching the form of the given integrand with the forms of the integrands in the tables. Computers are particularly good at matching patterns. And just as we used substitutions in conjunction with tables, a CAS can perform substitutions that transform a given integral into one that occurs in its stored formulas. So it isn't surprising that computer algebra systems excel at integration. That doesn't mean that integration by hand is an obsolete skill. We will see that a hand computation sometimes produces an indefinite integral in a form that is more convenient than a machine answer.

To begin, let's see what happens when we ask a machine to integrate the relatively simple function $y = 1/(3x - 2)$. Using the substitution $u = 3x - 2$, an easy calculation by hand gives

$$\int \frac{1}{3x - 2}\, dx = \tfrac{1}{3}\ln|3x - 2| + C$$

whereas Derive, Mathematica, and Maple all return the answer

$$\tfrac{1}{3}\ln(3x - 2)$$

The first thing to notice is that computer algebra systems omit the constant of integration. In other words, they produce a *particular* antiderivative, not the most general one. Therefore, when making use of a machine integration, we might have to add a constant. Second, the absolute value signs are omitted in the machine answer. That is fine if our problem is concerned only with values of x greater than $\tfrac{2}{3}$. But if we are interested in other values of x, then we need to insert the absolute value symbol.

In the next example we reconsider the integral of Example 4, but this time we ask a machine for the answer.

EXAMPLE 5 Use a computer algebra system to find $\int x\sqrt{x^2 + 2x + 4}\, dx$.

SOLUTION Maple responds with the answer

$$\tfrac{1}{3}(x^2 + 2x + 4)^{3/2} - \tfrac{1}{4}(2x + 2)\sqrt{x^2 + 2x + 4} - \frac{3}{2}\operatorname{arcsinh}\frac{\sqrt{3}}{3}(1 + x)$$

This looks different from the answer we found in Example 4, but it is equivalent because the third term can be rewritten using the identity

$$\operatorname{arcsinh} x = \ln\left(x + \sqrt{x^2 + 1}\right)$$

This is the formula in Problem 9(c) in the Discovery Project on page 227.

Thus

$$\operatorname{arcsinh}\frac{\sqrt{3}}{3}(1 + x) = \ln\left[\frac{\sqrt{3}}{3}(1 + x) + \sqrt{\tfrac{1}{3}(1 + x)^2 + 1}\right]$$

$$= \ln\frac{1}{\sqrt{3}}\left[1 + x + \sqrt{(1 + x)^2 + 3}\right]$$

$$= \ln\frac{1}{\sqrt{3}} + \ln\left(x + 1 + \sqrt{x^2 + 2x + 4}\right)$$

The resulting extra term $-\tfrac{3}{2}\ln(1/\sqrt{3})$ can be absorbed into the constant of integration.

Mathematica gives the answer

$$\left(\frac{5}{6} + \frac{x}{6} + \frac{x^2}{3}\right)\sqrt{x^2 + 2x + 4} - \frac{3}{2}\operatorname{arcsinh}\left(\frac{1 + x}{\sqrt{3}}\right)$$

Mathematica combined the first two terms of Example 4 (and the Maple result) into a single term by factoring.

Derive gives the answer

$$\tfrac{1}{6}\sqrt{x^2 + 2x + 4}\ (2x^2 + x + 5) - \tfrac{3}{2}\ln\!\left(\sqrt{x^2 + 2x + 4} + x + 1\right)$$

The first term is like the first term in the Mathematica answer, and the second term is identical to the last term in Example 4.

EXAMPLE 6 Use a CAS to evaluate $\int x(x^2 + 5)^8\,dx$.

SOLUTION Maple and Mathematica give the same answer:

$$\tfrac{1}{18}x^{18} + \tfrac{5}{2}x^{16} + 50x^{14} + \tfrac{1750}{3}x^{12} + 4375x^{10} + 21875x^8 + \tfrac{218750}{3}x^6 + 156250x^4 + \tfrac{390625}{2}x^2$$

It's clear that both systems must have expanded $(x^2 + 5)^8$ by the Binomial Theorem and then integrated each term.

If we integrate by hand instead, using the substitution $u = x^2 + 5$, we get

$$\int x(x^2 + 5)^8\,dx = \tfrac{1}{18}(x^2 + 5)^9 + C$$

For most purposes, this is a more convenient form of the answer.

EXAMPLE 7 Use a CAS to find $\int \sin^5 x \cos^2 x\,dx$.

SOLUTION Derive and Maple report the answer

$$-\tfrac{1}{7}\sin^4 x \cos^3 x - \tfrac{4}{35}\sin^2 x \cos^3 x - \tfrac{8}{105}\cos^3 x$$

whereas Mathematica produces

$$-\tfrac{5}{64}\cos x - \tfrac{1}{192}\cos 3x + \tfrac{3}{320}\cos 5x - \tfrac{1}{448}\cos 7x$$

We suspect that there are trigonometric identities which show that these three answers are equivalent. Indeed, if we ask Derive, Maple, and Mathematica to simplify their expressions using trigonometric identities, they ultimately produce the same form of the answer:

$$\int \sin^5 x \cos^2 x\,dx = -\tfrac{1}{3}\cos^3 x + \tfrac{2}{5}\cos^5 x - \tfrac{1}{7}\cos^7 x$$

Can We Integrate All Continuous Functions?

The question arises: Will our basic integration formulas, together with the Substitution Rule, integration by parts, tables of integrals, and computer algebra systems, enable us to find the integral of every continuous function? In particular, can we use these techniques to evaluate $\int e^{x^2}\,dx$? The answer is No, at least not in terms of the functions that we are familiar with.

Most of the functions that we have been dealing with in this book are what are called **elementary functions**. These are the polynomials, rational functions, power functions (x^a), exponential functions (a^x), logarithmic functions, trigonometric and inverse trigonometric functions, and all functions that can be obtained from these by the five operations of addi-

Derive and the TI-89 and TI-92 also give this answer.

tion, subtraction, multiplication, division, and composition. For instance, the function

$$f(x) = \sqrt{\frac{x^2 - 1}{x^3 + 2x - 1}} + \ln(\cos x) - xe^{\sin 2x}$$

is an elementary function.

If f is an elementary function, then f' is an elementary function but $\int f(x)\,dx$ need not be an elementary function. Consider $f(x) = e^{x^2}$. Since f is continuous, its integral exists, and if we define the function F by

$$F(x) = \int_0^x e^{t^2}\,dt$$

then we know from Part 1 of the Fundamental Theorem of Calculus that

$$F'(x) = e^{x^2}$$

Thus $f(x) = e^{x^2}$ has an antiderivative F, but it has been proved that F is not an elementary function. This means that no matter how hard we try, we will never succeed in evaluating $\int e^{x^2}\,dx$ in terms of the functions we know. (In Chapter 8, however, we will see how to express $\int e^{x^2}\,dx$ as an infinite series.) The same can be said of the following integrals:

$$\int \frac{e^x}{x}\,dx \qquad\qquad \int \sin(x^2)\,dx \qquad\qquad \int \cos(e^x)\,dx$$

$$\int \sqrt{x^3 + 1}\,dx \qquad\qquad \int \frac{1}{\ln x}\,dx \qquad\qquad \int \frac{\sin x}{x}\,dx$$

In fact, the majority of elementary functions don't have elementary antiderivatives.

5.8 Exercises

1–22 Use the Table of Integrals on Reference Pages 6–10 to evaluate the integral.

1. $\displaystyle\int \tan^3(\pi x)\,dx$

2. $\displaystyle\int e^{2\theta} \sin 3\theta\,d\theta$

3. $\displaystyle\int \frac{dx}{x^2\sqrt{4x^2 + 9}}$

4. $\displaystyle\int_2^3 \frac{1}{x^2\sqrt{4x^2 - 7}}\,dx$

5. $\displaystyle\int e^{2x}\arctan(e^x)\,dx$

6. $\displaystyle\int \frac{\sqrt{2y^2 - 3}}{y^2}\,dy$

7. $\displaystyle\int_0^\pi x^3 \sin x\,dx$

8. $\displaystyle\int \frac{dx}{2x^3 - 3x^2}$

9. $\displaystyle\int \frac{\tan^3(1/z)}{z^2}\,dz$

10. $\displaystyle\int \sin^{-1}\sqrt{x}\,dx$

11. $\displaystyle\int y\sqrt{6 + 4y - 4y^2}\,dy$

12. $\displaystyle\int x\sin(x^2)\cos(3x^2)\,dx$

13. $\displaystyle\int \sin^2 x \cos x \ln(\sin x)\,dx$

14. $\displaystyle\int \frac{\sin 2\theta}{\sqrt{5 - \sin\theta}}\,d\theta$

15. $\displaystyle\int \frac{e^x}{3 - e^{2x}}\,dx$

16. $\displaystyle\int_0^2 x^3\sqrt{4x^2 - x^4}\,dx$

17. $\displaystyle\int \frac{x^4\,dx}{\sqrt{x^{10} - 2}}$

18. $\displaystyle\int_0^1 x^4 e^{-x}\,dx$

19. $\displaystyle\int \frac{\sqrt{4 + (\ln x)^2}}{x}\,dx$

20. $\displaystyle\int \frac{\sec^2\theta \tan^2\theta}{\sqrt{9 - \tan^2\theta}}\,d\theta$

21. $\displaystyle\int \sqrt{e^{2x} - 1}\,dx$

22. $\displaystyle\int e^t \sin(\alpha t - 3)\,dt$

23. Verify Formula 53 in the Table of Integrals (a) by differentiation and (b) by using the substitution $t = a + bu$.

24. Verify Formula 31 (a) by differentiation and (b) by substituting $u = a\sin\theta$.

CAS **25–32** Use a computer algebra system to evaluate the integral. Compare the answer with the result of using tables. If the answers are not the same, show that they are equivalent.

25. $\displaystyle\int \sec^4 x\,dx$

26. $\displaystyle\int x^2(1 + x^3)^4\,dx$

27. $\displaystyle\int x^2\sqrt{x^2 + 4}\,dx$

28. $\displaystyle\int \frac{dx}{e^x(3e^x + 2)}$

CAS Computer algebra system required   **1.** Homework Hints available in TEC

29. $\int x\sqrt{1 + 2x}\, dx$

30. $\int \sin^4 x\, dx$

31. $\int \tan^5 x\, dx$

32. $\int \dfrac{1}{\sqrt{1 + \sqrt[3]{x}}}\, dx$

[CAS] **33.** (a) Use the table of integrals to evaluate $F(x) = \int f(x)\, dx$, where

$$f(x) = \frac{1}{x\sqrt{1 - x^2}}$$

What is the domain of f and F?

(b) Use a CAS to evaluate $F(x)$. What is the domain of the function F that the CAS produces? Is there a discrepancy between this domain and the domain of the function F that you found in part (a)?

[CAS] **34.** Computer algebra systems sometimes need a helping hand from human beings. Try to evaluate

$$\int (1 + \ln x)\sqrt{1 + (x \ln x)^2}\, dx$$

with a computer algebra system. If it doesn't return an answer, make a substitution that changes the integral into one that the CAS *can* evaluate.

DISCOVERY PROJECT   [CAS] **Patterns in Integrals**

In this project a computer algebra system is used to investigate indefinite integrals of families of functions. By observing the patterns that occur in the integrals of several members of the family, you will first guess, and then prove, a general formula for the integral of any member of the family.

1. (a) Use a computer algebra system to evaluate the following integrals.

   (i) $\displaystyle\int \frac{1}{(x + 2)(x + 3)}\, dx$

   (ii) $\displaystyle\int \frac{1}{(x + 1)(x + 5)}\, dx$

   (iii) $\displaystyle\int \frac{1}{(x + 2)(x - 5)}\, dx$

   (iv) $\displaystyle\int \frac{1}{(x + 2)^2}\, dx$

   (b) Based on the pattern of your responses in part (a), guess the value of the integral

$$\int \frac{1}{(x + a)(x + b)}\, dx$$

   if $a \neq b$. What if $a = b$?

   (c) Check your guess by asking your CAS to evaluate the integral in part (b). Then prove it using partial fractions or by differentiation.

2. (a) Use a computer algebra system to evaluate the following integrals.

   (i) $\displaystyle\int \sin x \cos 2x\, dx$ (ii) $\displaystyle\int \sin 3x \cos 7x\, dx$ (iii) $\displaystyle\int \sin 8x \cos 3x\, dx$

   (b) Based on the pattern of your responses in part (a), guess the value of the integral

$$\int \sin ax \cos bx\, dx$$

   (c) Check your guess with a CAS. Then prove it by differentiation. For what values of a and b is it valid?

3. (a) Use a computer algebra system to evaluate the following integrals.

   (i) $\displaystyle\int \ln x\, dx$ (ii) $\displaystyle\int x \ln x\, dx$ (iii) $\displaystyle\int x^2 \ln x\, dx$

   (iv) $\displaystyle\int x^3 \ln x\, dx$ (v) $\displaystyle\int x^7 \ln x\, dx$

[CAS] Computer algebra system required

(b) Based on the pattern of your responses in part (a), guess the value of

$$\int x^n \ln x \, dx$$

(c) Use integration by parts to prove the conjecture that you made in part (b). For what values of n is it valid?

4. (a) Use a computer algebra system to evaluate the following integrals.

    (i) $\displaystyle\int xe^x \, dx$ (ii) $\displaystyle\int x^2 e^x \, dx$ (iii) $\displaystyle\int x^3 e^x \, dx$

    (iv) $\displaystyle\int x^4 e^x \, dx$ (v) $\displaystyle\int x^5 e^x \, dx$

(b) Based on the pattern of your responses in part (a), guess the value of $\int x^6 e^x \, dx$. Then use your CAS to check your guess.

(c) Based on the patterns in parts (a) and (b), make a conjecture as to the value of the integral

$$\int x^n e^x \, dx$$

    when n is a positive integer.

(d) Use mathematical induction to prove the conjecture you made in part (c).

5.9   Approximate Integration

There are two situations in which it is impossible to find the exact value of a definite integral.

The first situation arises from the fact that in order to evaluate $\int_a^b f(x) \, dx$ using the Evaluation Theorem we need to know an antiderivative of f. Sometimes, however, it is difficult, or even impossible, to find an antiderivative (see Section 5.8). For example, it is impossible to evaluate the following integrals exactly:

$$\int_0^1 e^{x^2} \, dx \qquad \int_{-1}^1 \sqrt{1 + x^3} \, dx$$

The second situation arises when the function is determined from a scientific experiment through instrument readings or collected data. There may be no formula for the function (see Example 5).

In both cases we need to find approximate values of definite integrals. We already know one such method. Recall that the definite integral is defined as a limit of Riemann sums, so any Riemann sum could be used as an approximation to the integral: If we divide $[a, b]$ into n subintervals of equal length $\Delta x = (b - a)/n$, then we have

$$\int_a^b f(x) \, dx \approx \sum_{i=1}^n f(x_i^*) \, \Delta x$$

where x_i^* is any point in the ith subinterval $[x_{i-1}, x_i]$. If x_i^* is chosen to be the left endpoint of the interval, then $x_i^* = x_{i-1}$ and we have

$$\boxed{1} \qquad\qquad \int_a^b f(x) \, dx \approx L_n = \sum_{i=1}^n f(x_{i-1}) \, \Delta x$$

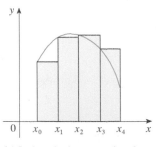

(a) Left endpoint approximation

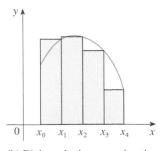

(b) Right endpoint approximation

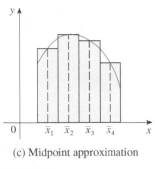

(c) Midpoint approximation

FIGURE 1

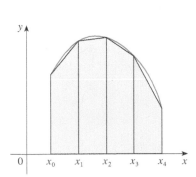

FIGURE 2
Trapezoidal approximation

If $f(x) \geq 0$, then the integral represents an area and (1) represents an approximation of this area by the rectangles shown in Figure 1(a) with $n = 4$. If we choose x_i^* to be the right endpoint, then $x_i^* = x_i$ and we have

$$\boxed{2} \qquad \int_a^b f(x)\, dx \approx R_n = \sum_{i=1}^n f(x_i)\, \Delta x$$

[See Figure 1(b).] The approximations L_n and R_n defined by Equations 1 and 2 are called the **left endpoint approximation** and **right endpoint approximation**, respectively.

In Section 5.2 we also considered the case where x_i^* is chosen to be the midpoint $\bar{x}_i$ of the subinterval $[x_{i-1}, x_i]$. Figure 1(c) shows the midpoint approximation M_n, which appears to be better than either L_n or R_n.

Midpoint Rule

$$\int_a^b f(x)\, dx \approx M_n = \Delta x \left[f(\bar{x}_1) + f(\bar{x}_2) + \cdots + f(\bar{x}_n) \right]$$

where
$$\Delta x = \frac{b - a}{n}$$

and
$$\bar{x}_i = \tfrac{1}{2}(x_{i-1} + x_i) = \text{midpoint of } [x_{i-1}, x_i]$$

Another approximation, called the Trapezoidal Rule, results from averaging the approximations in Equations 1 and 2:

$$\int_a^b f(x)\, dx \approx \frac{1}{2}\left[\sum_{i=1}^n f(x_{i-1})\, \Delta x + \sum_{i=1}^n f(x_i)\, \Delta x \right] = \frac{\Delta x}{2}\left[\sum_{i=1}^n \big(f(x_{i-1}) + f(x_i) \big) \right]$$

$$= \frac{\Delta x}{2}\left[\big(f(x_0) + f(x_1) \big) + \big(f(x_1) + f(x_2) \big) + \cdots + \big(f(x_{n-1}) + f(x_n) \big) \right]$$

$$= \frac{\Delta x}{2}\left[f(x_0) + 2f(x_1) + 2f(x_2) + \cdots + 2f(x_{n-1}) + f(x_n) \right]$$

Trapezoidal Rule

$$\int_a^b f(x)\, dx \approx T_n = \frac{\Delta x}{2}\left[f(x_0) + 2f(x_1) + 2f(x_2) + \cdots + 2f(x_{n-1}) + f(x_n) \right]$$

where $\Delta x = (b - a)/n$ and $x_i = a + i\,\Delta x$.

The reason for the name Trapezoidal Rule can be seen from Figure 2, which illustrates the case with $f(x) \geq 0$ and $n = 4$. The area of the trapezoid that lies above the ith subinterval is

$$\Delta x \left(\frac{f(x_{i-1}) + f(x_i)}{2} \right) = \frac{\Delta x}{2}\left[f(x_{i-1}) + f(x_i) \right]$$

and if we add the areas of all these trapezoids, we get the right side of the Trapezoidal Rule.

EXAMPLE 1 Use (a) the Trapezoidal Rule and (b) the Midpoint Rule with $n = 5$ to approximate the integral $\int_1^2 (1/x)\, dx$.

SOLUTION

(a) With $n = 5$, $a = 1$, and $b = 2$, we have $\Delta x = (2 - 1)/5 = 0.2$, and so the Trapezoidal Rule gives

$$\int_1^2 \frac{1}{x}\, dx \approx T_5 = \frac{0.2}{2}\left[f(1) + 2f(1.2) + 2f(1.4) + 2f(1.6) + 2f(1.8) + f(2) \right]$$

$$= 0.1\left(\frac{1}{1} + \frac{2}{1.2} + \frac{2}{1.4} + \frac{2}{1.6} + \frac{2}{1.8} + \frac{1}{2} \right)$$

$$\approx 0.695635$$

This approximation is illustrated in Figure 3.

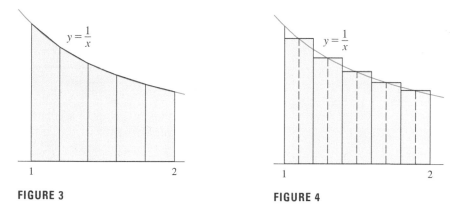

$y = \dfrac{1}{x}$

$y = \dfrac{1}{x}$

FIGURE 3

FIGURE 4

(b) The midpoints of the five subintervals are 1.1, 1.3, 1.5, 1.7, and 1.9, so the Midpoint Rule gives

$$\int_1^2 \frac{1}{x}\, dx \approx \Delta x \left[f(1.1) + f(1.3) + f(1.5) + f(1.7) + f(1.9) \right]$$

$$= \frac{1}{5}\left(\frac{1}{1.1} + \frac{1}{1.3} + \frac{1}{1.5} + \frac{1}{1.7} + \frac{1}{1.9} \right)$$

$$\approx 0.691908$$

This approximation is illustrated in Figure 4.

In Example 1 we deliberately chose an integral whose value can be computed explicitly so that we can see how accurate the Trapezoidal and Midpoint Rules are. By the Fundamental Theorem of Calculus,

$$\int_1^2 \frac{1}{x}\, dx = \ln x \Big]_1^2 = \ln 2 = 0.693147\ldots$$

$\int_a^b f(x)\, dx = \text{approximation} + \text{error}$

The **error** in using an approximation is defined to be the amount that needs to be added to the approximation to make it exact. From the values in Example 1 we see that the errors in the Trapezoidal and Midpoint Rule approximations for $n = 5$ are

$$E_T \approx -0.002488 \qquad \text{and} \qquad E_M \approx 0.001239$$

In general, we have

$$E_T = \int_a^b f(x)\, dx - T_n \qquad \text{and} \qquad E_M = \int_a^b f(x)\, dx - M_n$$

TEC Module 5.2/5.9 allows you to compare approximation methods.

The following tables show the results of calculations similar to those in Example 1, but for $n = 5$, 10, and 20 and for the left and right endpoint approximations as well as the Trapezoidal and Midpoint Rules.

Approximations to $\int_1^2 \dfrac{1}{x}\, dx$

n	L_n	R_n	T_n	M_n
5	0.745635	0.645635	0.695635	0.691908
10	0.718771	0.668771	0.693771	0.692835
20	0.705803	0.680803	0.693303	0.693069

Corresponding errors

n	E_L	E_R	E_T	E_M
5	−0.052488	0.047512	−0.002488	0.001239
10	−0.025624	0.024376	−0.000624	0.000312
20	−0.012656	0.012344	−0.000156	0.000078

We can make several observations from these tables:

1. In all of the methods we get more accurate approximations when we increase the value of n. (But very large values of n result in so many arithmetic operations that we have to beware of accumulated round-off error.)

2. The errors in the left and right endpoint approximations are opposite in sign and appear to decrease by a factor of about 2 when we double the value of n.

It turns out that these observations are true in most cases.

3. The Trapezoidal and Midpoint Rules are much more accurate than the endpoint approximations.

4. The errors in the Trapezoidal and Midpoint Rules are opposite in sign and appear to decrease by a factor of about 4 when we double the value of n.

5. The size of the error in the Midpoint Rule is about half the size of the error in the Trapezoidal Rule.

Figure 5 shows why we can usually expect the Midpoint Rule to be more accurate than the Trapezoidal Rule. The area of a typical rectangle in the Midpoint Rule is the same as the area of the trapezoid $ABCD$ whose upper side is tangent to the graph at P. The area of this trapezoid is closer to the area under the graph than is the area of the trapezoid $AQRD$ used in the Trapezoidal Rule. [The midpoint error (shaded red) is smaller than the trapezoidal error (shaded blue).]

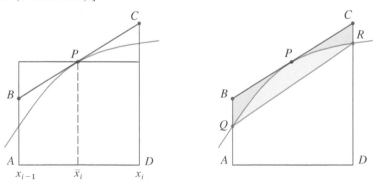

FIGURE 5

These observations are corroborated in the following error estimates, which are proved in books on numerical analysis. Notice that Observation 4 corresponds to the n^2 in each denominator because $(2n)^2 = 4n^2$. The fact that the estimates depend on the size of the second derivative is not surprising if you look at Figure 5, because $f''(x)$ measures how much the graph is curved. [Recall that $f''(x)$ measures how fast the slope of $y = f(x)$ changes.]

> **3** **Error Bounds**   Suppose $|f''(x)| \leq K$ for $a \leq x \leq b$. If E_T and E_M are the errors in the Trapezoidal and Midpoint Rules, then
>
> $$|E_T| \leq \frac{K(b-a)^3}{12n^2} \qquad \text{and} \qquad |E_M| \leq \frac{K(b-a)^3}{24n^2}$$

Let's apply this error estimate to the Trapezoidal Rule approximation in Example 1. If $f(x) = 1/x$, then $f'(x) = -1/x^2$ and $f''(x) = 2/x^3$. Since $1 \leq x \leq 2$, we have $1/x \leq 1$, so

$$|f''(x)| = \left| \frac{2}{x^3} \right| \leq \frac{2}{1^3} = 2$$

Therefore, taking $K = 2$, $a = 1$, $b = 2$, and $n = 5$ in the error estimate (3), we see that

K can be any number larger than all the values of $|f''(x)|$, but smaller values of K give better error bounds.

$$|E_T| \leq \frac{2(2-1)^3}{12(5)^2} = \frac{1}{150} \approx 0.006667$$

Comparing this error estimate of 0.006667 with the actual error of about 0.002488, we see that it can happen that the actual error is substantially less than the upper bound for the error given by (3).

V EXAMPLE 2   How large should we take n in order to guarantee that the Trapezoidal and Midpoint Rule approximations for $\int_1^2 (1/x)\, dx$ are accurate to within 0.0001?

SOLUTION We saw in the preceding calculation that $|f''(x)| \leq 2$ for $1 \leq x \leq 2$, so we can take $K = 2$, $a = 1$, and $b = 2$ in (3). Accuracy to within 0.0001 means that the size of the error should be less than 0.0001. Therefore we choose n so that

$$\frac{2(1)^3}{12n^2} < 0.0001$$

Solving the inequality for n, we get

$$n^2 > \frac{2}{12(0.0001)}$$

It's quite possible that a lower value for n would suffice, but 41 is the smallest value for which the error bound formula can *guarantee* us accuracy to within 0.0001.

or

$$n > \frac{1}{\sqrt{0.0006}} \approx 40.8$$

Thus $n = 41$ will ensure the desired accuracy.

For the same accuracy with the Midpoint Rule we choose n so that

$$\frac{2(1)^3}{24n^2} < 0.0001$$

which gives

$$n > \frac{1}{\sqrt{0.0012}} \approx 29$$

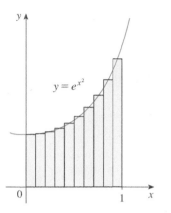

$y = e^{x^2}$

FIGURE 6

V EXAMPLE 3 Estimating the error in using the Midpoint Rule
(a) Use the Midpoint Rule with $n = 10$ to approximate the integral $\int_0^1 e^{x^2}\,dx$.
(b) Give an upper bound for the error involved in this approximation.

SOLUTION
(a) Since $a = 0$, $b = 1$, and $n = 10$, the Midpoint Rule gives

$$\int_0^1 e^{x^2}\,dx \approx \Delta x\,[\,f(0.05) + f(0.15) + \cdots + f(0.85) + f(0.95)\,]$$

$$= 0.1[e^{0.0025} + e^{0.0225} + e^{0.0625} + e^{0.1225} + e^{0.2025} + e^{0.3025}$$

$$+ e^{0.4225} + e^{0.5625} + e^{0.7225} + e^{0.9025}]$$

$$\approx 1.460393$$

Figure 6 illustrates this approximation.

(b) Since $f(x) = e^{x^2}$, we have $f'(x) = 2xe^{x^2}$ and $f''(x) = (2 + 4x^2)e^{x^2}$. Also, since $0 \le x \le 1$, we have $x^2 \le 1$ and so

$$0 \le f''(x) = (2 + 4x^2)e^{x^2} \le 6e$$

Error estimates give upper bounds for the error. They are theoretical, worst-case scenarios. The actual error in this case turns out to be about 0.0023.

Taking $K = 6e$, $a = 0$, $b = 1$, and $n = 10$ in the error estimate (3), we see that an upper bound for the error is

$$\frac{6e(1)^3}{24(10)^2} = \frac{e}{400} \approx 0.007$$

Simpson's Rule

Another rule for approximate integration results from using parabolas instead of straight line segments to approximate a curve. As before, we divide $[a, b]$ into n subintervals of equal length $h = \Delta x = (b - a)/n$, but this time we assume that n is an *even* number. Then on each consecutive pair of intervals we approximate the curve $y = f(x) \ge 0$ by a parabola as shown in Figure 7. If $y_i = f(x_i)$, then $P_i(x_i, y_i)$ is the point on the curve lying above x_i. A typical parabola passes through three consecutive points P_i, P_{i+1}, and P_{i+2}.

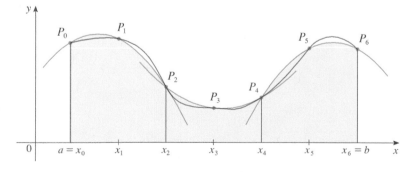

FIGURE 7

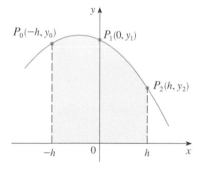

FIGURE 8

To simplify our calculations, we first consider the case where $x_0 = -h$, $x_1 = 0$, and $x_2 = h$. (See Figure 8.) We know that the equation of the parabola through P_0, P_1, and P_2 is of the form $y = Ax^2 + Bx + C$ and so the area under the parabola from $x = -h$ to $x = h$ is

Here we have used Theorem 5.5.6.
Notice that $Ax^2 + C$ is even and Bx is odd.

$$\int_{-h}^{h} (Ax^2 + Bx + C)\, dx = 2\int_{0}^{h} (Ax^2 + C)\, dx$$

$$= 2\left[A\frac{x^3}{3} + Cx \right]_0^h$$

$$= 2\left(A\frac{h^3}{3} + Ch \right) = \frac{h}{3}(2Ah^2 + 6C)$$

But, since the parabola passes through $P_0(-h, y_0)$, $P_1(0, y_1)$, and $P_2(h, y_2)$, we have

$$y_0 = A(-h)^2 + B(-h) + C = Ah^2 - Bh + C$$

$$y_1 = C$$

$$y_2 = Ah^2 + Bh + C$$

and therefore $\qquad\qquad y_0 + 4y_1 + y_2 = 2Ah^2 + 6C$

Thus we can rewrite the area under the parabola as

$$\frac{h}{3}(y_0 + 4y_1 + y_2)$$

Now, by shifting this parabola horizontally we do not change the area under it. This means that the area under the parabola through P_0, P_1, and P_2 from $x = x_0$ to $x = x_2$ in Figure 7 is still

$$\frac{h}{3}(y_0 + 4y_1 + y_2)$$

Similarly, the area under the parabola through P_2, P_3, and P_4 from $x = x_2$ to $x = x_4$ is

$$\frac{h}{3}(y_2 + 4y_3 + y_4)$$

If we compute the areas under all the parabolas in this manner and add the results, we get

$$\int_{a}^{b} f(x)\, dx \approx \frac{h}{3}(y_0 + 4y_1 + y_2) + \frac{h}{3}(y_2 + 4y_3 + y_4) + \cdots + \frac{h}{3}(y_{n-2} + 4y_{n-1} + y_n)$$

$$= \frac{h}{3}(y_0 + 4y_1 + 2y_2 + 4y_3 + 2y_4 + \cdots + 2y_{n-2} + 4y_{n-1} + y_n)$$

Although we have derived this approximation for the case in which $f(x) \geq 0$, it is a reasonable approximation for any continuous function f and is called Simpson's Rule after the English mathematician Thomas Simpson (1710–1761). Note the pattern of coefficients: $1, 4, 2, 4, 2, 4, 2, \ldots, 4, 2, 4, 1$.

Simpson

Thomas Simpson was a weaver who taught
himself mathematics and went on to become
one of the best English mathematicians of the
18th century. What we call Simpson's Rule was
actually known to Cavalieri and Gregory in the
17th century, but Simpson popularized it in his
book *Mathematical Dissertaions* (1743).

Simpson's Rule

$$\int_a^b f(x)\, dx \approx S_n = \frac{\Delta x}{3}\left[f(x_0) + 4f(x_1) + 2f(x_2) + 4f(x_3) + \cdots \right.$$

$$\left. + 2f(x_{n-2}) + 4f(x_{n-1}) + f(x_n) \right]$$

where n is even and $\Delta x = (b - a)/n$.

EXAMPLE 4   Use Simpson's Rule with $n = 10$ to approximate $\int_1^2 (1/x)\, dx$.

SOLUTION   Putting $f(x) = 1/x$, $n = 10$, and $\Delta x = 0.1$ in Simpson's Rule, we obtain

$$\int_1^2 \frac{1}{x}\, dx \approx S_{10}$$

$$= \frac{\Delta x}{3}\left[f(1) + 4f(1.1) + 2f(1.2) + 4f(1.3) + \cdots + 2f(1.8) + 4f(1.9) + f(2) \right]$$

$$= \frac{0.1}{3}\left(\frac{1}{1} + \frac{4}{1.1} + \frac{2}{1.2} + \frac{4}{1.3} + \frac{2}{1.4} + \frac{4}{1.5} + \frac{2}{1.6} + \frac{4}{1.7} + \frac{2}{1.8} + \frac{4}{1.9} + \frac{1}{2} \right)$$

$$\approx 0.693150$$

Notice that, in Example 4, Simpson's Rule gives us a *much* better approximation
($S_{10} \approx 0.693150$) to the true value of the integral ($\ln 2 \approx 0.693147\ldots$) than does the
Trapezoidal Rule ($T_{10} \approx 0.693771$) or the Midpoint Rule ($M_{10} \approx 0.692835$). It turns out
(see Exercise 42) that the approximations in Simpson's Rule are weighted averages of
those in the Trapezoidal and Midpoint Rules:

$$S_{2n} = \tfrac{1}{3} T_n + \tfrac{2}{3} M_n$$

(Recall that E_T and E_M usually have opposite signs and $|E_M|$ is about half the size of $|E_T|$.)

In many applications of calculus we need to evaluate an integral even if no explicit formula is known for y as a function of x. A function may be given graphically or as a table
of values of collected data. If there is evidence that the values are not changing rapidly,
then the Trapezoidal Rule or Simpson's Rule can still be used to find an approximate value
for $\int_a^b y\, dx$, the integral of y with respect to x.

  EXAMPLE 5   **Estimating the amount of transmitted data**   Figure 9 shows data traffic on
the link from the United States to SWITCH, the Swiss academic and research network,
on February 10, 1998. $D(t)$ is the data throughput, measured in megabits per second
(Mb/s). Use Simpson's Rule to estimate the total amount of data transmitted on the link
from midnight to noon on that day.

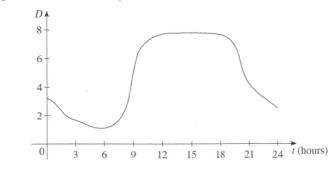

FIGURE 9

SOLUTION Because we want the units to be consistent and $D(t)$ is measured in megabits per second, we convert the units for t from hours to seconds. If we let $A(t)$ be the amount of data (in megabits) transmitted by time t, where t is measured in seconds, then $A'(t) = D(t)$. So, by the Net Change Theorem (see Section 5.3), the total amount of data transmitted by noon (when $t = 12 \times 60^2 = 43{,}200$) is

$$A(43{,}200) = \int_0^{43{,}200} D(t)\, dt$$

We estimate the values of $D(t)$ at hourly intervals from the graph and compile them in the table.

t (hours)	t (seconds)	$D(t)$	t (hours)	t (seconds)	$D(t)$
0	0	3.2	7	25,200	1.3
1	3,600	2.7	8	28,800	2.8
2	7,200	1.9	9	32,400	5.7
3	10,800	1.7	10	36,000	7.1
4	14,400	1.3	11	39,600	7.7
5	18,000	1.0	12	43,200	7.9
6	21,600	1.1			

Then we use Simpson's Rule with $n = 12$ and $\Delta t = 3600$ to estimate the integral:

$$\int_0^{43{,}200} A(t)\, dt \approx \frac{\Delta t}{3} [D(0) + 4D(3600) + 2D(7200) + \cdots + 4D(39{,}600) + D(43{,}200)]$$

$$\approx \frac{3600}{3} [3.2 + 4(2.7) + 2(1.9) + 4(1.7) + 2(1.3) + 4(1.0)$$

$$+ 2(1.1) + 4(1.3) + 2(2.8) + 4(5.7) + 2(7.1) + 4(7.7) + 7.9]$$

$$= 143{,}880$$

Thus the total amount of data transmitted from midnight to noon is about 144,000 megabits, or 144 gigabits.

The table in the margin shows how Simpson's Rule compares with the Midpoint Rule for the integral $\int_1^2 (1/x)\, dx$, whose true value is about 0.69314718. The second table shows how the error E_S in Simpson's Rule decreases by a factor of about 16 when n is doubled. (In Exercises 25 and 26 you are asked to verify this for two additional integrals.) That is consistent with the appearance of n^4 in the denominator of the following error estimate for Simpson's Rule. It is similar to the estimates given in (3) for the Trapezoidal and Midpoint Rules, but it uses the fourth derivative of f.

n	M_n	S_n
4	0.69121989	0.69315453
8	0.69266055	0.69314765
16	0.69302521	0.69314721

n	E_M	E_S
4	0.00192729	−0.00000735
8	0.00048663	−0.00000047
16	0.00012197	−0.00000003

4 **Error Bound for Simpson's Rule** Suppose that $|f^{(4)}(x)| \leq K$ for $a \leq x \leq b$. If E_S is the error involved in using Simpson's Rule, then

$$|E_S| \leq \frac{K(b-a)^5}{180 n^4}$$

EXAMPLE 6 How large should we take n in order to guarantee that the Simpson's Rule approximation for $\int_1^2 (1/x)\, dx$ is accurate to within 0.0001?

SOLUTION If $f(x) = 1/x$, then $f^{(4)}(x) = 24/x^5$. Since $x \geqslant 1$, we have $1/x \leqslant 1$ and so

$$|f^{(4)}(x)| = \left|\frac{24}{x^5}\right| \leqslant 24$$

Many calculators and computer algebra systems have a built-in algorithm that computes an approximation of a definite integral. Some of these machines use Simpson's Rule; others use more sophisticated techniques such as *adaptive numerical integration*. This means that if a function fluctuates much more on a certain part of the interval than it does elsewhere, then that part gets divided into more subintervals. This strategy reduces the number of calculations required to achieve a prescribed accuracy.

Therefore we can take $K = 24$ in (4). Thus, for an error less than 0.0001, we should choose n so that

$$\frac{24(1)^5}{180n^4} < 0.0001$$

This gives

$$n^4 > \frac{24}{180(0.0001)}$$

or

$$n > \frac{1}{\sqrt[4]{0.00075}} \approx 6.04$$

Therefore $n = 8$ (n must be even) gives the desired accuracy. (Compare this with Example 2, where we obtained $n = 41$ for the Trapezoidal Rule and $n = 29$ for the Midpoint Rule.)

EXAMPLE 7 **Estimating the error in using Simpson's Rule**
(a) Use Simpson's Rule with $n = 10$ to approximate the integral $\int_0^1 e^{x^2}\, dx$.
(b) Estimate the error involved in this approximation.

SOLUTION
(a) If $n = 10$, then $\Delta x = 0.1$ and Simpson's Rule gives

$$\int_0^1 e^{x^2}\, dx \approx \frac{\Delta x}{3}[f(0) + 4f(0.1) + 2f(0.2) + \cdots + 2f(0.8) + 4f(0.9) + f(1)]$$

$$= \frac{0.1}{3}[e^0 + 4e^{0.01} + 2e^{0.04} + 4e^{0.09} + 2e^{0.16} + 4e^{0.25} + 2e^{0.36}$$

$$+ 4e^{0.49} + 2e^{0.64} + 4e^{0.81} + e^1]$$

$$\approx 1.462681$$

Figure 10 illustrates the calculation in Example 7. Notice that the parabolic arcs are so close to the graph of $y = e^{x^2}$ that they are practically indistinguishable from it.

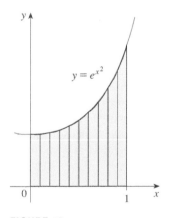

FIGURE 10

(b) The fourth derivative of $f(x) = e^{x^2}$ is

$$f^{(4)}(x) = (12 + 48x^2 + 16x^4)e^{x^2}$$

and so, since $0 \leqslant x \leqslant 1$, we have

$$0 \leqslant f^{(4)}(x) \leqslant (12 + 48 + 16)e^1 = 76e$$

Therefore, putting $K = 76e$, $a = 0$, $b = 1$, and $n = 10$ in (4), we see that the error is at most

$$\frac{76e(1)^5}{180(10)^4} \approx 0.000115$$

(Compare this with Example 3.) Thus, correct to three decimal places, we have

$$\int_0^1 e^{x^2}\, dx \approx 1.463$$

5.9 Exercises

1. Let $I = \int_0^4 f(x)\,dx$, where f is the function whose graph is shown.
  (a) Use the graph to find L_2, R_2, and M_2.
  (b) Are these underestimates or overestimates of I?
  (c) Use the graph to find T_2. How does it compare with I?
  (d) For any value of n, list the numbers L_n, R_n, M_n, T_n, and I in increasing order.

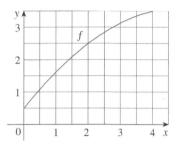

2. The left, right, Trapezoidal, and Midpoint Rule approximations were used to estimate $\int_0^2 f(x)\,dx$, where f is the function whose graph is shown. The estimates were 0.7811, 0.8675, 0.8632, and 0.9540, and the same number of subintervals were used in each case.
  (a) Which rule produced which estimate?
  (b) Between which two approximations does the true value of $\int_0^2 f(x)\,dx$ lie?

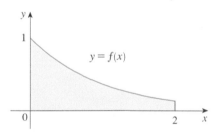

3. Estimate $\int_0^1 \cos(x^2)\,dx$ using (a) the Trapezoidal Rule and (b) the Midpoint Rule, each with $n = 4$. From a graph of the integrand, decide whether your answers are underestimates or overestimates. What can you conclude about the true value of the integral?

4. Draw the graph of $f(x) = \sin\left(\frac{1}{2}x^2\right)$ in the viewing rectangle $[0, 1]$ by $[0, 0.5]$ and let $I = \int_0^1 f(x)\,dx$.
  (a) Use the graph to decide whether L_2, R_2, M_2, and T_2 underestimate or overestimate I.
  (b) For any value of n, list the numbers L_n, R_n, M_n, T_n, and I in increasing order.
  (c) Compute L_5, R_5, M_5, and T_5. From the graph, which do you think gives the best estimate of I?

5–6 Use (a) the Midpoint Rule and (b) Simpson's Rule to approximate the given integral with the specified value of n. (Round your answers to six decimal places.) Compare your results to the actual value to determine the error in each approximation.

5. $\int_0^2 \dfrac{x}{1+x^2}\,dx$, $n = 10$ **6.** $\int_0^\pi x \cos x\,dx$, $n = 4$

7–16 Use (a) the Trapezoidal Rule, (b) the Midpoint Rule, and (c) Simpson's Rule to approximate the given integral with the specified value of n. (Round your answers to six decimal places.)

7. $\int_0^2 \sqrt[4]{1 + x^2}\,dx$, $n = 8$ **8.** $\int_0^{1/2} \sin(x^2)\,dx$, $n = 4$

9. $\int_1^2 \dfrac{\ln x}{1+x}\,dx$, $n = 10$ **10.** $\int_0^3 \dfrac{dt}{1 + t^2 + t^4}$, $n = 6$

11. $\int_0^{1/2} \sin(e^{t/2})\,dt$, $n = 8$ **12.** $\int_0^4 \sqrt{1 + \sqrt{x}}\,dx$, $n = 8$

13. $\int_0^4 e^{\sqrt{t}} \sin t\,dt$, $n = 8$ **14.** $\int_0^4 \cos \sqrt{x}\,dx$, $n = 10$

15. $\int_1^5 \dfrac{\cos x}{x}\,dx$, $n = 8$ **16.** $\int_4^6 \ln(x^3 + 2)\,dx$, $n = 10$

17. (a) Find the approximations T_8 and M_8 for the integral $\int_0^1 \cos(x^2)\,dx$.
  (b) Estimate the errors in the approximations of part (a).
  (c) How large do we have to choose n so that the approximations T_n and M_n to the integral in part (a) are accurate to within 0.0001?

18. (a) Find the approximations T_{10} and M_{10} for $\int_1^2 e^{1/x}\,dx$.
  (b) Estimate the errors in the approximations of part (a).
  (c) How large do we have to choose n so that the approximations T_n and M_n to the integral in part (a) are accurate to within 0.0001?

19. (a) Find the approximations T_{10}, M_{10}, and S_{10} for $\int_0^\pi \sin x\,dx$ and the corresponding errors E_T, E_M, and E_S.
  (b) Compare the actual errors in part (a) with the error estimates given by (3) and (4).
  (c) How large do we have to choose n so that the approximations T_n, M_n, and S_n to the integral in part (a) are accurate to within 0.00001?

20. How large should n be to guarantee that the Simpson's Rule approximation to $\int_0^1 e^{x^2}\,dx$ is accurate to within 0.00001?

21. The trouble with the error estimates is that it is often very difficult to compute four derivatives and obtain a good upper bound K for $|f^{(4)}(x)|$ by hand. But computer algebra systems

---

Graphing calculator or computer with graphing software required   CAS Computer algebra system required   **1.** Homework Hints available in TEC

have no problem computing $f^{(4)}$ and graphing it, so we can easily find a value for K from a machine graph. This exercise deals with approximations to the integral $I = \int_0^{2\pi} f(x)\,dx$, where $f(x) = e^{\cos x}$.

(a) Use a graph to get a good upper bound for $|f''(x)|$.

(b) Use M_{10} to approximate I.

(c) Use part (a) to estimate the error in part (b).

(d) Use the built-in numerical integration capability of your CAS to approximate I.

(e) How does the actual error compare with the error estimate in part (c)?

(f) Use a graph to get a good upper bound for $|f^{(4)}(x)|$.

(g) Use S_{10} to approximate I.

(h) Use part (f) to estimate the error in part (g).

(i) How does the actual error compare with the error estimate in part (h)?

(j) How large should n be to guarantee that the size of the error in using S_n is less than 0.0001?

CAS **22.** Repeat Exercise 21 for the integral $\int_{-1}^{1} \sqrt{4 - x^3}\,dx$.

23–24 Find the approximations L_n, R_n, T_n, and M_n for $n = 5, 10,$ and 20. Then compute the corresponding errors E_L, E_R, E_T, and E_M. (Round your answers to six decimal places. You may wish to use the sum command on a computer algebra system.) What observations can you make? In particular, what happens to the errors when n is doubled?

23. $\int_0^1 xe^x\,dx$ **24.** $\int_1^2 \frac{1}{x^2}\,dx$

25–26 Find the approximations T_n, M_n, and S_n for $n = 6$ and 12. Then compute the corresponding errors E_T, E_M, and E_S. (Round your answers to six decimal places. You may wish to use the sum command on a computer algebra system.) What observations can you make? In particular, what happens to the errors when n is doubled?

25. $\int_0^2 x^4\,dx$ **26.** $\int_1^4 \frac{1}{\sqrt{x}}\,dx$

27. Estimate the area under the graph in the figure by using (a) the Trapezoidal Rule, (b) the Midpoint Rule, and (c) Simpson's Rule, each with $n = 6$.

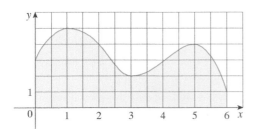

28. A radar gun was used to record the speed of a runner during the first 5 seconds of a race (see the table). Use Simpson's Rule to estimate the distance the runner covered during those 5 seconds.

t (s)	v (m/s)	t (s)	v (m/s)
0	0	3.0	10.51
0.5	4.67	3.5	10.67
1.0	7.34	4.0	10.76
1.5	8.86	4.5	10.81
2.0	9.73	5.0	10.81
2.5	10.22		

29. The graph of the acceleration $a(t)$ of a car measured in ft/s^2 is shown. Use Simpson's Rule to estimate the increase in the velocity of the car during the 6-second time interval.

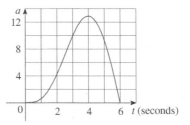

30. Water leaked from a tank at a rate of $r(t)$ liters per hour, where the graph of r is as shown. Use Simpson's Rule to estimate the total amount of water that leaked out during the first 6 hours.

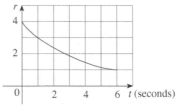

31. The table (supplied by San Diego Gas and Electric) gives the power consumption P in megawatts in San Diego County from midnight to 6:00 AM on a day in December. Use Simpson's Rule to estimate the energy used during that time period. (Use the fact that power is the derivative of energy.)

t	P	t	P
0:00	1814	3:30	1611
0:30	1735	4:00	1621
1:00	1686	4:30	1666
1:30	1646	5:00	1745
2:00	1637	5:30	1886
2:30	1609	6:00	2052
3:00	1604		

32. Shown is the graph of traffic on an Internet service provider's T1 data line from midnight to 8:00 AM. D is the data throughput, measured in megabits per second. Use Simpson's Rule to estimate the total amount of data transmitted during that time period.

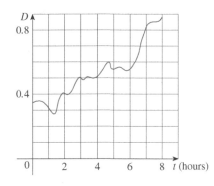

33. (a) Use the Midpoint Rule and the given data to estimate the value of the integral $\int_0^{3.2} f(x)\, dx$.

x	$f(x)$	x	$f(x)$
0.0	6.8	2.0	7.6
0.4	6.5	2.4	8.4
0.8	6.3	2.8	8.8
1.2	6.4	3.2	9.0
1.6	6.9		

(b) If it is known that $-4 \leq f''(x) \leq 1$ for all x, estimate the error involved in the approximation in part (a).

CAS **34.** The figure shows a pendulum with length L that makes a maximum angle θ_0 with the vertical. Using Newton's Second Law, it can be shown that the period T (the time for one complete swing) is given by

$$T = 4\sqrt{\frac{L}{g}} \int_0^{\pi/2} \frac{dx}{\sqrt{1 - k^2 \sin^2 x}}$$

where $k = \sin\left(\frac{1}{2}\theta_0\right)$ and g is the acceleration due to gravity. If $L = 1$ m and $\theta_0 = 42°$, use Simpson's Rule with $n = 10$ to find the period.

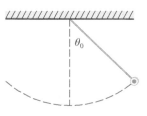

35. The intensity of light with wavelength λ traveling through a diffraction grating with N slits at an angle θ is given by $I(\theta) = N^2 \sin^2 k / k^2$, where $k = (\pi N d \sin\theta)/\lambda$ and d is the distance between adjacent slits. A helium-neon laser with wavelength $\lambda = 632.8 \times 10^{-9}$ m is emitting a narrow band of light, given by $-10^{-6} < \theta < 10^{-6}$, through a grating with 10,000 slits spaced 10^{-4} m apart. Use the Midpoint Rule with $n = 10$ to estimate the total light intensity $\int_{-10^{-6}}^{10^{-6}} I(\theta)\, d\theta$ emerging from the grating.

36. Sketch the graph of a continuous function on $[0, 2]$ for which the right endpoint approximation with $n = 2$ is more accurate than Simpson's Rule.

37. Sketch the graph of a continuous function on $[0, 2]$ for which the Trapezoidal Rule with $n = 2$ is more accurate than the Midpoint Rule.

38. Use the Trapezoidal Rule with $n = 10$ to approximate $\int_0^{20} \cos(\pi x)\, dx$. Compare your result to the actual value. Can you explain the discrepancy?

39. If f is a positive function and $f''(x) < 0$ for $a \leq x \leq b$, show that

$$T_n < \int_a^b f(x)\, dx < M_n$$

40. Show that if f is a polynomial of degree 3 or lower, then Simpson's Rule gives the exact value of $\int_a^b f(x)\, dx$.

41. Show that $\frac{1}{2}(T_n + M_n) = T_{2n}$.

42. Show that $\frac{1}{3}T_n + \frac{2}{3}M_n = S_{2n}$.

5.10 Improper Integrals

In defining a definite integral $\int_a^b f(x)\, dx$ we dealt with a function f defined on a finite interval $[a, b]$ and we assumed that f does not have an infinite discontinuity (see Section 5.2). In this section we extend the concept of a definite integral to the case where the interval is infinite and also to the case where f has an infinite discontinuity in $[a, b]$. In either case the integral is called an *improper* integral. One of the most important applications of this idea, probability distributions, will be studied in Section 6.8.

Type 1: Infinite Intervals

Consider the infinite region S that lies under the curve $y = 1/x^2$, above the x-axis, and to the right of the line $x = 1$. You might think that, since S is infinite in extent, its area must be infinite, but let's take a closer look. The area of the part of S that lies to the left of the line $x = t$ (shaded in Figure 1) is

$$A(t) = \int_1^t \frac{1}{x^2}\,dx = -\frac{1}{x}\bigg]_1^t = 1 - \frac{1}{t}$$

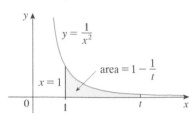

FIGURE 1

Notice that $A(t) < 1$ no matter how large t is chosen.

We also observe that

$$\lim_{t \to \infty} A(t) = \lim_{t \to \infty} \left(1 - \frac{1}{t}\right) = 1$$

The area of the shaded region approaches 1 as $t \to \infty$ (see Figure 2), so we say that the area of the infinite region S is equal to 1 and we write

$$\int_1^\infty \frac{1}{x^2}\,dx = \lim_{t \to \infty} \int_1^t \frac{1}{x^2}\,dx = 1$$

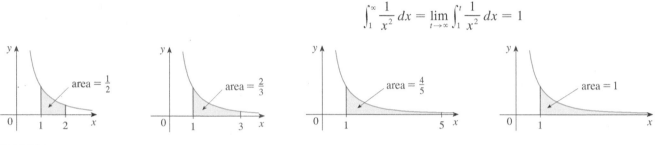

FIGURE 2

Using this example as a guide, we define the integral of f (not necessarily a positive function) over an infinite interval as the limit of integrals over finite intervals.

---

1 **Definition of an Improper Integral of Type 1**

(a) If $\int_a^t f(x)\,dx$ exists for every number $t \geq a$, then

$$\int_a^\infty f(x)\,dx = \lim_{t \to \infty} \int_a^t f(x)\,dx$$

provided this limit exists (as a finite number).

(b) If $\int_t^b f(x)\,dx$ exists for every number $t \leq b$, then

$$\int_{-\infty}^b f(x)\,dx = \lim_{t \to -\infty} \int_t^b f(x)\,dx$$

provided this limit exists (as a finite number).

The improper integrals $\int_a^\infty f(x)\,dx$ and $\int_{-\infty}^b f(x)\,dx$ are called **convergent** if the corresponding limit exists and **divergent** if the limit does not exist.

(c) If both $\int_a^\infty f(x)\,dx$ and $\int_{-\infty}^a f(x)\,dx$ are convergent, then we define

$$\int_{-\infty}^\infty f(x)\,dx = \int_{-\infty}^a f(x)\,dx + \int_a^\infty f(x)\,dx$$

In part (c) any real number a can be used (see Exercise 54).

Any of the improper integrals in Definition 1 can be interpreted as an area provided that f is a positive function. For instance, in case (a) if $f(x) \geqslant 0$ and the integral $\int_a^\infty f(x)\,dx$ is convergent, then we define the area of the region $S = \{(x, y) \mid x \geqslant a, 0 \leqslant y \leqslant f(x)\}$ in Figure 3 to be

$$A(S) = \int_a^\infty f(x)\,dx$$

This is appropriate because $\int_a^\infty f(x)\,dx$ is the limit as $t \to \infty$ of the area under the graph of f from a to t.

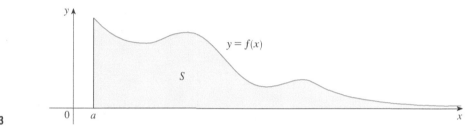

FIGURE 3

V EXAMPLE 1 Determine whether the integral $\int_1^\infty (1/x)\,dx$ is convergent or divergent.

SOLUTION According to part (a) of Definition 1, we have

$$\int_1^\infty \frac{1}{x}\,dx = \lim_{t \to \infty} \int_1^t \frac{1}{x}\,dx = \lim_{t \to \infty} \ln|x|\Big]_1^t$$

$$= \lim_{t \to \infty} (\ln t - \ln 1) = \lim_{t \to \infty} \ln t = \infty$$

The limit does not exist as a finite number and so the improper integral $\int_1^\infty (1/x)\,dx$ is divergent.

Let's compare the result of Example 1 with the example given at the beginning of this section:

$$\int_1^\infty \frac{1}{x^2}\,dx \text{ converges} \qquad \int_1^\infty \frac{1}{x}\,dx \text{ diverges}$$

Geometrically, this says that although the curves $y = 1/x^2$ and $y = 1/x$ look very similar for $x > 0$, the region under $y = 1/x^2$ to the right of $x = 1$ (the shaded region in Figure 4) has finite area whereas the corresponding region under $y = 1/x$ (in Figure 5) has infinite area. Note that both $1/x^2$ and $1/x$ approach 0 as $x \to \infty$ but $1/x^2$ approaches 0 faster than $1/x$. The values of $1/x$ don't decrease fast enough for its integral to have a finite value.

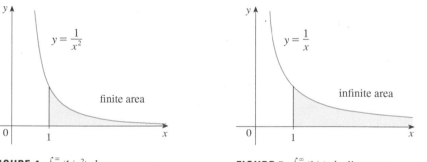

FIGURE 4 $\int_1^\infty (1/x^2)\,dx$ converges

FIGURE 5 $\int_1^\infty (1/x)\,dx$ diverges

EXAMPLE 2 **Using l'Hospital's Rule with an improper integral**   Evaluate $\int_{-\infty}^{0} xe^x\,dx$.

SOLUTION Using part (b) of Definition 1, we have

$$\int_{-\infty}^{0} xe^x\,dx = \lim_{t \to -\infty} \int_{t}^{0} xe^x\,dx$$

We integrate by parts with $u = x$, $dv = e^x\,dx$ so that $du = dx$, $v = e^x$:

$$\int_{t}^{0} xe^x\,dx = xe^x \Big]_{t}^{0} - \int_{t}^{0} e^x\,dx = -te^t - 1 + e^t$$

We know that $e^t \to 0$ as $t \to -\infty$, and by l'Hospital's Rule we have

TEC In Module 5.10 you can investigate visually and numerically whether several improper integrals are convergent or divergent.

$$\lim_{t \to -\infty} te^t = \lim_{t \to -\infty} \frac{t}{e^{-t}} = \lim_{t \to -\infty} \frac{1}{-e^{-t}}$$

$$= \lim_{t \to -\infty} (-e^t) = 0$$

Therefore

$$\int_{-\infty}^{0} xe^x\,dx = \lim_{t \to -\infty} (-te^t - 1 + e^t)$$

$$= -0 - 1 + 0 = -1$$

EXAMPLE 3   Evaluate $\int_{-\infty}^{\infty} \frac{1}{1 + x^2}\,dx$.

SOLUTION It's convenient to choose $a = 0$ in Definition 1(c):

$$\int_{-\infty}^{\infty} \frac{1}{1 + x^2}\,dx = \int_{-\infty}^{0} \frac{1}{1 + x^2}\,dx + \int_{0}^{\infty} \frac{1}{1 + x^2}\,dx$$

We must now evaluate the integrals on the right side separately:

$$\int_{0}^{\infty} \frac{1}{1 + x^2}\,dx = \lim_{t \to \infty} \int_{0}^{t} \frac{dx}{1 + x^2} = \lim_{t \to \infty} \tan^{-1}x \Big]_{0}^{t}$$

$$= \lim_{t \to \infty} (\tan^{-1}t - \tan^{-1}0) = \lim_{t \to \infty} \tan^{-1}t = \frac{\pi}{2}$$

$$\int_{-\infty}^{0} \frac{1}{1 + x^2}\,dx = \lim_{t \to -\infty} \int_{t}^{0} \frac{dx}{1 + x^2} = \lim_{t \to -\infty} \tan^{-1}x \Big]_{t}^{0}$$

$$= \lim_{t \to -\infty} (\tan^{-1}0 - \tan^{-1}t)$$

$$= 0 - \left(-\frac{\pi}{2}\right) = \frac{\pi}{2}$$

Since both of these integrals are convergent, the given integral is convergent and

$$\int_{-\infty}^{\infty} \frac{1}{1 + x^2}\,dx = \frac{\pi}{2} + \frac{\pi}{2} = \pi$$

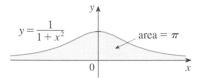

FIGURE 6

Since $1/(1 + x^2) > 0$, the given improper integral can be interpreted as the area of the infinite region that lies under the curve $y = 1/(1 + x^2)$ and above the x-axis (see Figure 6).

EXAMPLE 4   For what values of p is the integral

$$\int_1^\infty \frac{1}{x^p}\, dx$$

convergent?

SOLUTION   We know from Example 1 that if $p = 1$, then the integral is divergent, so let's assume that $p \neq 1$. Then

$$\int_1^\infty \frac{1}{x^p}\, dx = \lim_{t \to \infty} \int_1^t x^{-p}\, dx$$

$$= \lim_{t \to \infty} \frac{x^{-p+1}}{-p + 1} \bigg]_{x=1}^{x=t}$$

$$= \lim_{t \to \infty} \frac{1}{1 - p} \left[\frac{1}{t^{p-1}} - 1 \right]$$

If $p > 1$, then $p - 1 > 0$, so as $t \to \infty$, $t^{p-1} \to \infty$ and $1/t^{p-1} \to 0$. Therefore

$$\int_1^\infty \frac{1}{x^p}\, dx = \frac{1}{p - 1} \qquad \text{if } p > 1$$

and so the integral converges. But if $p < 1$, then $p - 1 < 0$ and so

$$\frac{1}{t^{p-1}} = t^{1-p} \to \infty \qquad \text{as } t \to \infty$$

and the integral diverges.

We summarize the result of Example 4 for future reference:

$$\boxed{2} \qquad \int_1^\infty \frac{1}{x^p}\, dx \quad \text{is convergent if } p > 1 \text{ and divergent if } p \leq 1.$$

Type 2: Discontinuous Integrands

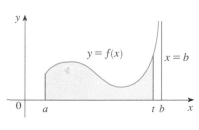

FIGURE 7

Suppose that f is a positive continuous function defined on a finite interval $[a, b)$ but has a vertical asymptote at b. Let S be the unbounded region under the graph of f and above the x-axis between a and b. (For Type 1 integrals, the regions extended indefinitely in a horizontal direction. Here the region is infinite in a vertical direction.) The area of the part of S between a and t (the shaded region in Figure 7) is

$$A(t) = \int_a^t f(x)\, dx$$

If it happens that $A(t)$ approaches a definite number A as $t \to b^-$, then we say that the area of the region S is A and we write

$$\int_a^b f(x)\, dx = \lim_{t \to b^-} \int_a^t f(x)\, dx$$

We use this equation to define an improper integral of Type 2 even when f is not a positive function, no matter what type of discontinuity f has at b.

Parts (b) and (c) of Definition 3 are illustrated in Figures 8 and 9 for the case where $f(x) \geq 0$ and f has vertical asymptotes at a and c, respectively.

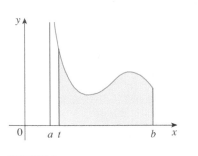

FIGURE 8

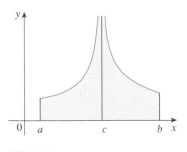

FIGURE 9

---

3   **Definition of an Improper Integral of Type 2**

(a) If f is continuous on $[a, b)$ and is discontinuous at b, then

$$\int_a^b f(x)\,dx = \lim_{t \to b^-} \int_a^t f(x)\,dx$$

if this limit exists (as a finite number).

(b) If f is continuous on $(a, b]$ and is discontinuous at a, then

$$\int_a^b f(x)\,dx = \lim_{t \to a^+} \int_t^b f(x)\,dx$$

if this limit exists (as a finite number).

The improper integral $\int_a^b f(x)\,dx$ is called **convergent** if the corresponding limit exists and **divergent** if the limit does not exist.

(c) If f has a discontinuity at c, where $a < c < b$, and both $\int_a^c f(x)\,dx$ and $\int_c^b f(x)\,dx$ are convergent, then we define

$$\int_a^b f(x)\,dx = \int_a^c f(x)\,dx + \int_c^b f(x)\,dx$$

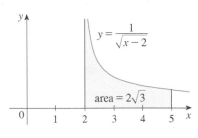

FIGURE 10

EXAMPLE 5   **Integrating a function with a vertical asymptote**   Find $\displaystyle\int_2^5 \frac{1}{\sqrt{x-2}}\,dx$.

SOLUTION   We note first that the given integral is improper because $f(x) = 1/\sqrt{x-2}$ has the vertical asymptote $x = 2$. Since the infinite discontinuity occurs at the left endpoint of $[2, 5]$, we use part (b) of Definition 3:

$$\int_2^5 \frac{dx}{\sqrt{x-2}} = \lim_{t \to 2^+} \int_t^5 \frac{dx}{\sqrt{x-2}}$$

$$= \lim_{t \to 2^+} 2\sqrt{x-2}\,\Big]_t^5$$

$$= \lim_{t \to 2^+} 2\left(\sqrt{3} - \sqrt{t-2}\right)$$

$$= 2\sqrt{3}$$

Thus the given improper integral is convergent and, since the integrand is positive, we can interpret the value of the integral as the area of the shaded region in Figure 10.

V   EXAMPLE 6   Determine whether $\displaystyle\int_0^{\pi/2} \sec x\,dx$ converges or diverges.

SOLUTION   Note that the given integral is improper because $\lim_{x \to (\pi/2)^-} \sec x = \infty$. Using part (a) of Definition 3 and Formula 14 from the Table of Integrals, we have

$$\int_0^{\pi/2} \sec x\,dx = \lim_{t \to (\pi/2)^-} \int_0^t \sec x\,dx = \lim_{t \to (\pi/2)^-} \ln|\sec x + \tan x|\,\Big]_0^t$$

$$= \lim_{t \to (\pi/2)^-} \left[\ln(\sec t + \tan t) - \ln 1\right] = \infty$$

because $\sec t \to \infty$ and $\tan t \to \infty$ as $t \to (\pi/2)^-$. Thus the given improper integral is divergent.

EXAMPLE 7   Evaluate $\int_0^3 \dfrac{dx}{x-1}$ if possible.

SOLUTION   Observe that the line $x = 1$ is a vertical asymptote of the integrand. Since it occurs in the middle of the interval $[0, 3]$, we must use part (c) of Definition 3 with $c = 1$:

$$\int_0^3 \frac{dx}{x-1} = \int_0^1 \frac{dx}{x-1} + \int_1^3 \frac{dx}{x-1}$$

where
$$\int_0^1 \frac{dx}{x-1} = \lim_{t \to 1^-} \int_0^t \frac{dx}{x-1} = \lim_{t \to 1^-} \ln |x-1| \Big]_0^t$$

$$= \lim_{t \to 1^-} \left(\ln |t-1| - \ln |-1| \right)$$

$$= \lim_{t \to 1^-} \ln(1-t) = -\infty$$

because $1 - t \to 0^+$ as $t \to 1^-$. Thus $\int_0^1 dx/(x-1)$ is divergent. This implies that $\int_0^3 dx/(x-1)$ is divergent. [We do not need to evaluate $\int_1^3 dx/(x-1)$.]

⊘   **Warning:** If we had not noticed the asymptote $x = 1$ in Example 7 and had instead confused the integral with an ordinary integral, then we might have made the following erroneous calculation:

$$\int_0^3 \frac{dx}{x-1} = \ln |x-1| \Big]_0^3 = \ln 2 - \ln 1 = \ln 2$$

This is wrong because the integral is improper and must be calculated in terms of limits.

From now on, whenever you meet the symbol $\int_a^b f(x)\, dx$ you must decide, by looking at the function f on $[a, b]$, whether it is an ordinary definite integral or an improper integral.

EXAMPLE 8   **Using l'Hospital's Rule with an improper integral**   Evaluate $\int_0^1 \ln x\, dx$.

SOLUTION   We know that the function $f(x) = \ln x$ has a vertical asymptote at 0 since $\lim_{x \to 0^+} \ln x = -\infty$. Thus the given integral is improper and we have

$$\int_0^1 \ln x\, dx = \lim_{t \to 0^+} \int_t^1 \ln x\, dx$$

Now we integrate by parts with $u = \ln x$, $dv = dx$, $du = dx/x$, and $v = x$:

$$\int_t^1 \ln x\, dx = x \ln x \Big]_t^1 - \int_t^1 dx$$

$$= 1 \ln 1 - t \ln t - (1-t)$$

$$= -t \ln t - 1 + t$$

To find the limit of the first term we use l'Hospital's Rule:

$$\lim_{t \to 0^+} t \ln t = \lim_{t \to 0^+} \frac{\ln t}{1/t} = \lim_{t \to 0^+} \frac{1/t}{-1/t^2} = \lim_{t \to 0^+} (-t) = 0$$

Therefore
$$\int_0^1 \ln x\, dx = \lim_{t \to 0^+} (-t \ln t - 1 + t) = -0 - 1 + 0 = -1$$

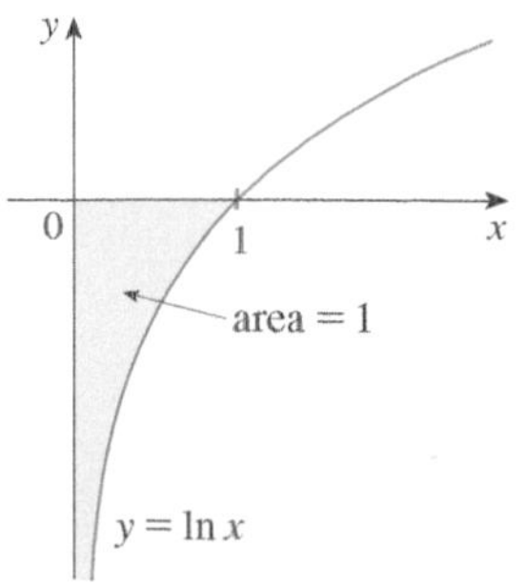

FIGURE 11

Figure 11 shows the geometric interpretation of this result. The area of the shaded region above $y = \ln x$ and below the x-axis is 1.

A Comparison Test for Improper Integrals

Sometimes it is impossible to find the exact value of an improper integral and yet it is important to know whether it is convergent or divergent. In such cases the following theorem is useful. Although we state it for Type 1 integrals, a similar theorem is true for Type 2 integrals.

> **Comparison Theorem** Suppose that f and g are continuous functions with $f(x) \geqslant g(x) \geqslant 0$ for $x \geqslant a$.
>
> (a) If $\int_a^\infty f(x)\,dx$ is convergent, then $\int_a^\infty g(x)\,dx$ is convergent.
>
> (b) If $\int_a^\infty g(x)\,dx$ is divergent, then $\int_a^\infty f(x)\,dx$ is divergent.

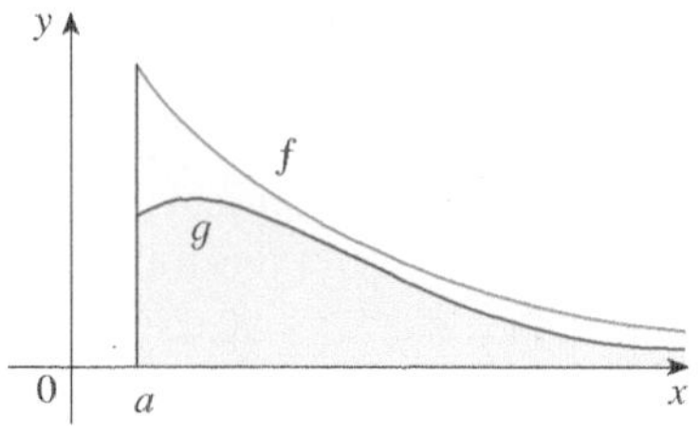

FIGURE 12

We omit the proof of the Comparison Theorem, but Figure 12 makes it seem plausible. If the area under the top curve $y = f(x)$ is finite, then so is the area under the bottom curve $y = g(x)$. And if the area under $y = g(x)$ is infinite, then so is the area under $y = f(x)$. [Note that the reverse is not necessarily true: If $\int_a^\infty g(x)\,dx$ is convergent, $\int_a^\infty f(x)\,dx$ may or may not be convergent, and if $\int_a^\infty f(x)\,dx$ is divergent, $\int_a^\infty g(x)\,dx$ may or may not be divergent.]

V EXAMPLE 9 Show that $\displaystyle\int_0^\infty e^{-x^2}dx$ is convergent.

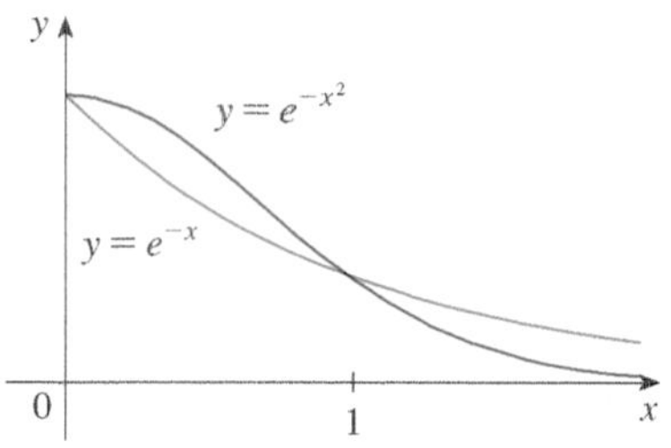

FIGURE 13

SOLUTION We can't evaluate the integral directly because the antiderivative of e^{-x^2} is not an elementary function (as explained in Section 5.8). We write

$$\int_0^\infty e^{-x^2}dx = \int_0^1 e^{-x^2}dx + \int_1^\infty e^{-x^2}dx$$

and observe that the first integral on the right-hand side is just an ordinary definite integral. In the second integral we use the fact that for $x \geqslant 1$ we have $x^2 \geqslant x$, so $-x^2 \leqslant -x$ and therefore $e^{-x^2} \leqslant e^{-x}$. (See Figure 13.) The integral of e^{-x} is easy to evaluate:

$$\int_1^\infty e^{-x}dx = \lim_{t\to\infty}\int_1^t e^{-x}dx = \lim_{t\to\infty}(e^{-1} - e^{-t}) = e^{-1}$$

Thus, taking $f(x) = e^{-x}$ and $g(x) = e^{-x^2}$ in the Comparison Theorem, we see that $\int_1^\infty e^{-x^2}dx$ is convergent. It follows that $\int_0^\infty e^{-x^2}dx$ is convergent.

TABLE 1

t	$\int_0^t e^{-x^2}dx$
1	0.7468241328
2	0.8820813908
3	0.8862073483
4	0.8862269118
5	0.8862269255
6	0.8862269255

In Example 9 we showed that $\int_0^\infty e^{-x^2}dx$ is convergent without computing its value. In Exercise 60 we indicate how to show that its value is approximately 0.8862. In probability theory it is important to know the exact value of this improper integral, as we will see in Section 6.8; using the methods of multivariable calculus it can be shown that the exact value is $\sqrt{\pi}/2$. Table 1 illustrates the definition of an improper integral by showing how the (computer-generated) values of $\int_0^t e^{-x^2}dx$ approach $\sqrt{\pi}/2$ as t becomes large. In fact, these values converge quite quickly because $e^{-x^2} \to 0$ very rapidly as $x \to \infty$.

TABLE 2

t	$\int_1^t [(1 + e^{-x})/x]\,dx$
2	0.8636306042
5	1.8276735512
10	2.5219648704
100	4.8245541204
1000	7.1271392134
10000	9.4297243064

EXAMPLE 10 **Comparing with a simpler function** The integral $\displaystyle\int_1^\infty \frac{1 + e^{-x}}{x}\,dx$ is divergent by the Comparison Theorem because

$$\frac{1 + e^{-x}}{x} > \frac{1}{x}$$

and $\int_1^\infty (1/x)\,dx$ is divergent by Example 1 [or by (2) with $p = 1$].

Table 2 illustrates the divergence of the integral in Example 10. It appears that the values are not approaching any fixed number.

5.10 Exercises

1. Explain why each of the following integrals is improper.

   (a) $\displaystyle\int_1^\infty x^4 e^{-x^4}\,dx$ (b) $\displaystyle\int_0^{\pi/2} \sec x\,dx$

   (c) $\displaystyle\int_0^2 \frac{x}{x^2 - 5x + 6}\,dx$ (d) $\displaystyle\int_{-\infty}^0 \frac{1}{x^2 + 5}\,dx$

2. Which of the following integrals are improper? Why?

   (a) $\displaystyle\int_1^2 \frac{1}{2x - 1}\,dx$ (b) $\displaystyle\int_0^1 \frac{1}{2x - 1}\,dx$

   (c) $\displaystyle\int_{-\infty}^\infty \frac{\sin x}{1 + x^2}\,dx$ (d) $\displaystyle\int_1^2 \ln(x - 1)\,dx$

3. Find the area under the curve $y = 1/x^3$ from $x = 1$ to $x = t$ and evaluate it for $t = 10$, 100, and 1000. Then find the total area under this curve for $x \geq 1$.

4. (a) Graph the functions $f(x) = 1/x^{1.1}$ and $g(x) = 1/x^{0.9}$ in the viewing rectangles $[0, 10]$ by $[0, 1]$ and $[0, 100]$ by $[0, 1]$.
   (b) Find the areas under the graphs of f and g from $x = 1$ to $x = t$ and evaluate for $t = 10$, 100, 10^4, 10^6, 10^{10}, and 10^{20}.
   (c) Find the total area under each curve for $x \geq 1$, if it exists.

5–34 Determine whether each integral is convergent or divergent. Evaluate those that are convergent.

5. $\displaystyle\int_3^\infty \frac{1}{(x - 2)^{3/2}}\,dx$ 6. $\displaystyle\int_0^\infty \frac{1}{\sqrt[4]{1 + x}}\,dx$

7. $\displaystyle\int_{-\infty}^{-1} \frac{1}{\sqrt{2 - w}}\,dw$ 8. $\displaystyle\int_0^\infty \frac{x}{(x^2 + 2)^2}\,dx$

9. $\displaystyle\int_4^\infty e^{-y/2}\,dy$ 10. $\displaystyle\int_{-\infty}^{-1} e^{-2t}\,dt$

11. $\displaystyle\int_{2\pi}^\infty \sin\theta\,d\theta$ 12. $\displaystyle\int_{-\infty}^\infty (y^3 - 3y^2)\,dy$

13. $\displaystyle\int_{-\infty}^\infty x e^{-x^2}\,dx$ 14. $\displaystyle\int_1^\infty \frac{e^{-\sqrt{x}}}{\sqrt{x}}\,dx$

15. $\displaystyle\int_1^\infty \frac{x + 1}{x^2 + 2x}\,dx$ 16. $\displaystyle\int_{-\infty}^\infty \cos \pi t\,dt$

17. $\displaystyle\int_0^\infty s e^{-5s}\,ds$ 18. $\displaystyle\int_{-\infty}^6 r e^{r/3}\,dr$

19. $\displaystyle\int_1^\infty \frac{\ln x}{x}\,dx$ 20. $\displaystyle\int_{-\infty}^\infty x^3 e^{-x^4}\,dx$

21. $\displaystyle\int_{-\infty}^\infty \frac{x^2}{9 + x^6}\,dx$ 22. $\displaystyle\int_1^\infty \frac{\ln x}{x^3}\,dx$

23. $\displaystyle\int_e^\infty \frac{1}{x(\ln x)^3}\,dx$ 24. $\displaystyle\int_0^\infty \frac{e^x}{e^{2x} + 3}\,dx$

25. $\displaystyle\int_0^1 \frac{3}{x^5}\,dx$ 26. $\displaystyle\int_2^3 \frac{1}{\sqrt{3 - x}}\,dx$

27. $\displaystyle\int_{-2}^{14} \frac{dx}{\sqrt[4]{x + 2}}$ 28. $\displaystyle\int_6^8 \frac{4}{(x - 6)^3}\,dx$

29. $\displaystyle\int_0^{33} (x - 1)^{-1/5}\,dx$ 30. $\displaystyle\int_0^1 \frac{1}{4y - 1}\,dy$

31. $\displaystyle\int_{-1}^1 \frac{e^x}{e^x - 1}\,dx$ 32. $\displaystyle\int_{\pi/2}^\pi \csc x\,dx$

33. $\displaystyle\int_0^2 z^2 \ln z\,dz$ 34. $\displaystyle\int_0^1 \frac{\ln x}{\sqrt{x}}\,dx$

35–40 Sketch the region and find its area (if the area is finite).

35. $S = \{(x, y) \mid x \leq 1,\ 0 \leq y \leq e^x\}$

---

36. $S = \{(x, y) \mid x \geq -2,\ 0 \leq y \leq e^{-x/2}\}$

37. $S = \{(x, y) \mid 0 \leq y \leq 2/(x^2 + 9)\}$

38. $S = \{(x, y) \mid x \geq 0,\ 0 \leq y \leq xe^{-x}\}$

39. $S = \{(x, y) \mid 0 \leq x < \pi/2,\ 0 \leq y \leq \sec^2 x\}$

40. $S = \{(x, y) \mid -2 < x \leq 0,\ 0 \leq y \leq 1/\sqrt{x+2}\}$

41. (a) If $g(x) = (\sin^2 x)/x^2$, use your calculator or computer to make a table of approximate values of $\int_1^t g(x)\,dx$ for $t = 2, 5, 10, 100, 1000,$ and $10{,}000$. Does it appear that $\int_1^\infty g(x)\,dx$ is convergent?
(b) Use the Comparison Theorem with $f(x) = 1/x^2$ to show that $\int_1^\infty g(x)\,dx$ is convergent.
(c) Illustrate part (b) by graphing f and g on the same screen for $1 \leq x \leq 10$. Use your graph to explain intuitively why $\int_1^\infty g(x)\,dx$ is convergent.

42. (a) If $g(x) = 1/(\sqrt{x} - 1)$, use your calculator or computer to make a table of approximate values of $\int_2^t g(x)\,dx$ for $t = 5, 10, 100, 1000,$ and $10{,}000$. Does it appear that $\int_2^\infty g(x)\,dx$ is convergent or divergent?
(b) Use the Comparison Theorem with $f(x) = 1/\sqrt{x}$ to show that $\int_2^\infty g(x)\,dx$ is divergent.
(c) Illustrate part (b) by graphing f and g on the same screen for $2 \leq x \leq 20$. Use your graph to explain intuitively why $\int_2^\infty g(x)\,dx$ is divergent.

43–48 Use the Comparison Theorem to determine whether the integral is convergent or divergent.

43. $\int_0^\infty \dfrac{x}{x^3 + 1}\,dx$

44. $\int_1^\infty \dfrac{2 + e^{-x}}{x}\,dx$

45. $\int_1^\infty \dfrac{x+1}{\sqrt{x^4 - x}}\,dx$

46. $\int_0^\infty \dfrac{\arctan x}{2 + e^x}\,dx$

47. $\int_0^1 \dfrac{\sec^2 x}{x\sqrt{x}}\,dx$

48. $\int_0^\pi \dfrac{\sin^2 x}{\sqrt{x}}\,dx$

49. The integral
$$\int_0^\infty \frac{1}{\sqrt{x}\,(1+x)}\,dx$$
is improper for two reasons: The interval $[0, \infty)$ is infinite and the integrand has an infinite discontinuity at 0. Evaluate it by expressing it as a sum of improper integrals of Type 2 and Type 1 as follows:
$$\int_0^\infty \frac{1}{\sqrt{x}\,(1+x)}\,dx = \int_0^1 \frac{1}{\sqrt{x}\,(1+x)}\,dx + \int_1^\infty \frac{1}{\sqrt{x}\,(1+x)}\,dx$$

50–51 Find the values of p for which the integral converges and evaluate the integral for those values of p.

50. $\int_e^\infty \dfrac{1}{x(\ln x)^p}\,dx$

51. $\int_0^1 \dfrac{1}{x^p}\,dx$

52. (a) Evaluate the integral $\int_0^\infty x^n e^{-x}\,dx$ for $n = 0, 1, 2,$ and 3.
(b) Guess the value of $\int_0^\infty x^n e^{-x}\,dx$ when n is an arbitrary positive integer.
(c) Prove your guess using mathematical induction.

53. (a) Show that $\int_{-\infty}^\infty x\,dx$ is divergent.
(b) Show that
$$\lim_{t \to \infty} \int_{-t}^t x\,dx = 0$$
This shows that we can't define
$$\int_{-\infty}^\infty f(x)\,dx = \lim_{t \to \infty} \int_{-t}^t f(x)\,dx$$

54. If $\int_{-\infty}^\infty f(x)\,dx$ is convergent and a and b are real numbers, show that
$$\int_{-\infty}^a f(x)\,dx + \int_a^\infty f(x)\,dx = \int_{-\infty}^b f(x)\,dx + \int_b^\infty f(x)\,dx$$

55. A manufacturer of lightbulbs wants to produce bulbs that last about 700 hours but, of course, some bulbs burn out faster than others. Let $F(t)$ be the fraction of the company's bulbs that burn out before t hours, so $F(t)$ always lies between 0 and 1.
(a) Make a rough sketch of what you think the graph of F might look like.
(b) What is the meaning of the derivative $r(t) = F'(t)$?
(c) What is the value of $\int_0^\infty r(t)\,dt$? Why?

56. The *average speed* of molecules in an ideal gas is
$$\bar{v} = \frac{4}{\sqrt{\pi}} \left(\frac{M}{2RT}\right)^{3/2} \int_0^\infty v^3 e^{-Mv^2/(2RT)}\,dv$$
where M is the molecular weight of the gas, R is the gas constant, T is the gas temperature, and v is the molecular speed. Show that
$$\bar{v} = \sqrt{\frac{8RT}{\pi M}}$$

57. As we will see in Section 7.4, a radioactive substance decays exponentially: The mass at time t is $m(t) = m(0)e^{kt}$, where $m(0)$ is the initial mass and k is a negative constant. The *mean life* M of an atom in the substance is
$$M = -k \int_0^\infty te^{kt}\,dt$$

For the radioactive carbon isotope, ^{14}C, used in radiocarbon dating, the value of k is -0.000121. Find the mean life of a ^{14}C atom.

58. Astronomers use a technique called *stellar stereography* to determine the density of stars in a star cluster from the observed (two-dimensional) density that can be analyzed from a photograph. Suppose that in a spherical cluster of radius R the density of stars depends only on the distance r from the center of the cluster. If the perceived star density is given by $y(s)$, where s is the observed planar distance from the center of the cluster, and $x(r)$ is the actual density, it can be shown that

$$y(s) = \int_s^R \frac{2r}{\sqrt{r^2 - s^2}} x(r)\, dr$$

If the actual density of stars in a cluster is $x(r) = \frac{1}{2}(R - r)^2$, find the perceived density $y(s)$.

59. Determine how large the number a has to be so that

$$\int_a^\infty \frac{1}{x^2 + 1}\, dx < 0.001$$

60. Estimate the numerical value of $\int_0^\infty e^{-x^2}\, dx$ by writing it as the sum of $\int_0^4 e^{-x^2}\, dx$ and $\int_4^\infty e^{-x^2}\, dx$. Approximate the first integral by using Simpson's Rule with $n = 8$ and show that the second integral is smaller than $\int_4^\infty e^{-4x}\, dx$, which is less than 0.0000001.

61. Show that $\int_0^\infty x^2 e^{-x^2}\, dx = \frac{1}{2} \int_0^\infty e^{-x^2}\, dx$.

62. Show that $\int_0^\infty e^{-x^2}\, dx = \int_0^1 \sqrt{-\ln y}\, dy$ by interpreting the integrals as areas.

63. Find the value of the constant C for which the integral

$$\int_0^\infty \left(\frac{1}{\sqrt{x^2 + 4}} - \frac{C}{x + 2} \right) dx$$

converges. Evaluate the integral for this value of C.

64. Find the value of the constant C for which the integral

$$\int_0^\infty \left(\frac{x}{x^2 + 1} - \frac{C}{3x + 1} \right) dx$$

converges. Evaluate the integral for this value of C.

65. Suppose f is continuous on $[0, \infty)$ and $\lim_{x \to \infty} f(x) = 1$. Is it possible that $\int_0^\infty f(x)\, dx$ is convergent?

66. Show that if $a > -1$ and $b > a + 1$, then the following integral is convergent.

$$\int_0^\infty \frac{x^a}{1 + x^b}\, dx$$

5 Review

Concept Check

1. (a) Write an expression for a Riemann sum of a function f. Explain the meaning of the notation that you use.

    (b) If $f(x) \geqslant 0$, what is the geometric interpretation of a Riemann sum? Illustrate with a diagram.

    (c) If $f(x)$ takes on both positive and negative values, what is the geometric interpretation of a Riemann sum? Illustrate with a diagram.

2. (a) Write the definition of the definite integral of a continuous function from a to b.

    (b) What is the geometric interpretation of $\int_a^b f(x)\, dx$ if $f(x) \geqslant 0$?

    (c) What is the geometric interpretation of $\int_a^b f(x)\, dx$ if $f(x)$ takes on both positive and negative values? Illustrate with a diagram.

3. (a) State the Evaluation Theorem.

    (b) State the Net Change Theorem.

4. If $r(t)$ is the rate at which water flows into a reservoir, what does $\int_{t_1}^{t_2} r(t)\, dt$ represent?

5. Suppose a particle moves back and forth along a straight line with velocity $v(t)$, measured in feet per second, and acceleration $a(t)$.

    (a) What is the meaning of $\int_{60}^{120} v(t)\, dt$?

    (b) What is the meaning of $\int_{60}^{120} |v(t)|\, dt$?

    (c) What is the meaning of $\int_{60}^{120} a(t)\, dt$?

6. (a) Explain the meaning of the indefinite integral $\int f(x)\, dx$.

    (b) What is the connection between the definite integral $\int_a^b f(x)\, dx$ and the indefinite integral $\int f(x)\, dx$?

7. State both parts of the Fundamental Theorem of Calculus.

8. (a) State the Substitution Rule. In practice, how do you use it?

(b) State the rule for integration by parts. In practice, how do you use it?

9. State the rules for approximating the definite integral $\int_a^b f(x)\,dx$ with the Midpoint Rule, the Trapezoidal Rule, and Simpson's Rule. Which would you expect to give the best estimate? How do you approximate the error for each rule?

10. Define the following improper integrals.

(a) $\int_a^\infty f(x)\,dx$ (b) $\int_{-\infty}^b f(x)\,dx$ (c) $\int_{-\infty}^\infty f(x)\,dx$

11. Define the improper integral $\int_a^b f(x)\,dx$ for each of the following cases.

(a) f has an infinite discontinuity at a.
(b) f has an infinite discontinuity at b.
(c) f has an infinite discontinuity at c, where $a < c < b$.

12. State the Comparison Theorem for improper integrals.

13. Explain exactly what is meant by the statement that "differentiation and integration are inverse processes."

True-False Quiz

Determine whether the statement is true or false. If it is true, explain why. If it is false, explain why or give an example that disproves the statement.

1. If f and g are continuous on $[a, b]$, then
$$\int_a^b [f(x) + g(x)]\,dx = \int_a^b f(x)\,dx + \int_a^b g(x)\,dx$$

2. If f and g are continuous on $[a, b]$, then
$$\int_a^b [f(x)g(x)]\,dx = \left(\int_a^b f(x)\,dx\right)\left(\int_a^b g(x)\,dx\right)$$

3. If f is continuous on $[a, b]$, then
$$\int_a^b 5f(x)\,dx = 5\int_a^b f(x)\,dx$$

4. If f is continuous on $[a, b]$, then
$$\int_a^b xf(x)\,dx = x\int_a^b f(x)\,dx$$

5. If f is continuous on $[a, b]$ and $f(x) \geq 0$, then
$$\int_a^b \sqrt{f(x)}\,dx = \sqrt{\int_a^b f(x)\,dx}$$

6. If f' is continuous on $[1, 3]$, then $\int_1^3 f'(v)\,dv = f(3) - f(1)$.

7. If f and g are continuous and $f(x) \geq g(x)$ for $a \leq x \leq b$, then
$$\int_a^b f(x)\,dx \geq \int_a^b g(x)\,dx$$

8. If f and g are differentiable and $f(x) \geq g(x)$ for $a < x < b$, then $f'(x) \geq g'(x)$ for $a < x < b$.

9. $\int_{-1}^1 \left(x^5 - 6x^9 + \dfrac{\sin x}{(1 + x^4)^2}\right)dx = 0$

10. $\int_{-5}^5 (ax^2 + bx + c)\,dx = 2\int_0^5 (ax^2 + c)\,dx$

11. $\int_0^4 \dfrac{x}{x^2 - 1}\,dx = \frac{1}{2}\ln 15$

12. $\int_1^\infty \dfrac{1}{x^{\sqrt{2}}}\,dx$ is convergent.

13. $\int_0^2 (x - x^3)\,dx$ represents the area under the curve $y = x - x^3$ from 0 to 2.

14. All continuous functions have antiderivatives.

15. All continuous functions have derivatives.

16. The Midpoint Rule is always more accurate than the Trapezoidal Rule.

17. If f is continuous, then $\int_{-\infty}^\infty f(x)\,dx = \lim_{t\to\infty}\int_{-t}^t f(x)\,dx$.

18. If f is continuous on $[0, \infty)$ and $\int_1^\infty f(x)\,dx$ is convergent, then $\int_0^\infty f(x)\,dx$ is convergent.

19. If f is a continuous, decreasing function on $[1, \infty)$ and $\lim_{x\to\infty} f(x) = 0$, then $\int_1^\infty f(x)\,dx$ is convergent.

20. If $\int_a^\infty f(x)\,dx$ and $\int_a^\infty g(x)\,dx$ are both convergent, then $\int_a^\infty [f(x) + g(x)]\,dx$ is convergent.

21. If $\int_a^\infty f(x)\,dx$ and $\int_a^\infty g(x)\,dx$ are both divergent, then $\int_a^\infty [f(x) + g(x)]\,dx$ is divergent.

22. If $f(x) \leq g(x)$ and $\int_0^\infty g(x)\,dx$ diverges, then $\int_0^\infty f(x)\,dx$ also diverges.

23. If f is continuous on $[a, b]$, then
$$\frac{d}{dx}\left(\int_a^b f(x)\,dx\right) = f(x)$$

Exercises

1. Use the given graph of f to find the Riemann sum with six subintervals. Take the sample points to be (a) left endpoints and (b) midpoints. In each case draw a diagram and explain what the Riemann sum represents.

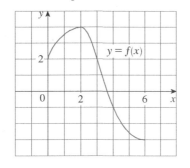

2. (a) Evaluate the Riemann sum for

$$f(x) = x^2 - x \qquad 0 \leqslant x \leqslant 2$$

with four subintervals, taking the sample points to be right endpoints. Explain, with the aid of a diagram, what the Riemann sum represents.

(b) Use the definition of a definite integral (with right endpoints) to calculate the value of the integral

$$\int_0^2 (x^2 - x) \, dx$$

(c) Use the Evaluation Theorem to check your answer to part (b).

(d) Draw a diagram to explain the geometric meaning of the integral in part (b).

3. Evaluate

$$\int_0^1 \left(x + \sqrt{1 - x^2} \right) dx$$

by interpreting it in terms of areas.

4. Express

$$\lim_{n \to \infty} \sum_{i=1}^{n} \sin x_i \, \Delta x$$

as a definite integral on the interval $[0, \pi]$ and then evaluate the integral.

5. If $\int_0^6 f(x) \, dx = 10$ and $\int_0^4 f(x) \, dx = 7$, find $\int_4^6 f(x) \, dx$.

CAS **6.** (a) Write $\int_0^2 e^{3x} \, dx$ as a limit of Riemann sums, taking the sample points to be right endpoints. Use a computer algebra system to evaluate the sum and to compute the limit.

(b) Use the Evaluation Theorem to check your answer to part (a).

7. The following figure shows the graphs of f, f', and $\int_0^x f(t) \, dt$. Identify each graph, and explain your choices.

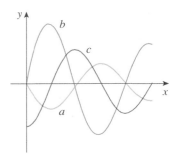

8. Evaluate:

(a) $\displaystyle \int_0^1 \frac{d}{dx} \left(e^{\arctan x} \right) dx$
(b) $\displaystyle \frac{d}{dx} \int_0^1 e^{\arctan x} \, dx$

(c) $\displaystyle \frac{d}{dx} \int_0^x e^{\arctan t} \, dt$

9–34 Evaluate the integral.

9. $\displaystyle \int_1^2 (8x^3 + 3x^2) \, dx$
10. $\displaystyle \int_0^T (x^4 - 8x + 7) \, dx$

11. $\displaystyle \int_0^1 (1 - x^9) \, dx$
12. $\displaystyle \int_0^1 (1 - x)^9 \, dx$

13. $\displaystyle \int \left(\frac{1 - x}{x} \right)^2 dx$
14. $\displaystyle \int_0^1 \left(\sqrt[4]{u} + 1 \right)^2 du$

15. $\displaystyle \int_0^1 \frac{x}{x^2 + 1} \, dx$
16. $\displaystyle \int \frac{\csc^2 x}{1 + \cot x} \, dx$

17. $\displaystyle \int_0^1 v^2 \cos(v^3) \, dv$
18. $\displaystyle \int_0^1 \sin(3\pi t) \, dt$

19. $\displaystyle \int_0^1 e^{\pi t} \, dt$
20. $\displaystyle \int_1^2 \frac{1}{2 - 3x} \, dx$

21. $\displaystyle \int \frac{x + 2}{\sqrt{x^2 + 4x}} \, dx$
22. $\displaystyle \int_1^2 x^3 \ln x \, dx$

23. $\displaystyle \int_0^5 \frac{x}{x + 10} \, dx$
24. $\displaystyle \int_0^5 y e^{-0.6y} \, dy$

25. $\displaystyle \int_{-\pi/4}^{\pi/4} \frac{t^4 \tan t}{2 + \cos t} \, dt$
26. $\displaystyle \int_1^4 \frac{dt}{(2t + 1)^3}$

27. $\displaystyle \int_1^4 x^{3/2} \ln x \, dx$
28. $\displaystyle \int \sin x \cos(\cos x) \, dx$

29. $\displaystyle \int \frac{dt}{t^2 + 6t + 8}$
30. $\displaystyle \int \frac{x}{\sqrt{1 - x^4}} \, dx$

31. $\displaystyle \int e^{\sqrt[3]{x}} \, dx$
32. $\displaystyle \int \tan^{-1} x \, dx$

⟳ Graphing calculator or computer with graphing software required   **CAS** Computer algebra system required

33. $\displaystyle\int \frac{\sec\theta\,\tan\theta}{1+\sec\theta}\,d\theta$

34. $\displaystyle\int_0^1 \frac{e^x}{1+e^{2x}}\,dx$

35–36 Evaluate the indefinite integral. Illustrate and check that your answer is reasonable by graphing both the function and its antiderivative (take $C=0$).

35. $\displaystyle\int \frac{\cos x}{\sqrt{1+\sin x}}\,dx$

36. $\displaystyle\int \frac{x^3}{\sqrt{x^2+1}}\,dx$

37. Use a graph to give a rough estimate of the area of the region that lies under the curve $y=x\sqrt{x}$, $0\le x\le 4$. Then find the exact area.

38. Graph the function $f(x)=\cos^2 x\,\sin^3 x$ and use the graph to guess the value of the integral $\int_0^{2\pi} f(x)\,dx$. Then evaluate the integral to confirm your guess.

39–42 Find the derivative of the function.

39. $\displaystyle F(x)=\int_0^x \frac{t^2}{1+t^3}\,dt$

40. $\displaystyle g(x)=\int_1^{\sin x} \frac{1-t^2}{1+t^4}\,dt$

41. $\displaystyle y=\int_{\sqrt{x}}^x \frac{e^t}{t}\,dt$

42. $\displaystyle y=\int_{2x}^{3x+1} \sin(t^4)\,dt$

43–46 Use the Table of Integrals on the Reference Pages to evaluate the integral.

43. $\displaystyle\int e^x\sqrt{1-e^{2x}}\,dx$

44. $\displaystyle\int \csc^5 t\,dt$

45. $\displaystyle\int \sqrt{x^2+x+1}\,dx$

46. $\displaystyle\int \frac{\cot x}{\sqrt{1+2\sin x}}\,dx$

47–48 Use (a) the Trapezoidal Rule, (b) the Midpoint Rule, and (c) Simpson's Rule with $n=10$ to approximate the given integral. Round your answers to six decimal places. Can you say whether your answers are underestimates or overestimates?

47. $\displaystyle\int_0^1 \sqrt{1+x^4}\,dx$

48. $\displaystyle\int_0^{\pi/2} \sqrt{\sin x}\,dx$

49. Estimate the errors involved in Exercise 47, parts (a) and (b). How large should n be in each case to guarantee an error of less than 0.00001?

50. Use Simpson's Rule with $n=6$ to estimate the area under the curve $y=e^x/x$ from $x=1$ to $x=4$.

CAS **51.** (a) If $f(x)=\sin(\sin x)$, use a graph to find an upper bound for $|f^{(4)}(x)|$.
   (b) Use Simpson's Rule with $n=10$ to approximate $\int_0^\pi f(x)\,dx$ and use part (a) to estimate the error.

(c) How large should n be to guarantee that the size of the error in using S_n is less than 0.00001?

CAS **52.** (a) How would you evaluate $\int x^5 e^{-2x}\,dx$ by hand? (Don't actually carry out the integration.)
   (b) How would you evaluate $\int x^5 e^{-2x}\,dx$ using tables? (Don't actually do it.)
   (c) Use a CAS to evaluate $\int x^5 e^{-2x}\,dx$.
   (d) Graph the integrand and the indefinite integral on the same screen.

53. Use Property 8 of integrals to estimate the value of
$$\int_1^3 \sqrt{x^2+3}\,dx$$

54. Use the properties of integrals to verify that
$$0\le \int_0^1 x^4\cos x\,dx \le 0.2$$

55–60 Evaluate the integral or show that it is divergent.

55. $\displaystyle\int_1^\infty \frac{1}{(2x+1)^3}\,dx$

56. $\displaystyle\int_0^\infty \frac{\ln x}{x^4}\,dx$

57. $\displaystyle\int_{-\infty}^0 e^{-2x}\,dx$

58. $\displaystyle\int_0^1 \frac{1}{2-3x}\,dx$

59. $\displaystyle\int_1^e \frac{dx}{x\sqrt{\ln x}}$

60. $\displaystyle\int_2^6 \frac{y}{\sqrt{y-2}}\,dy$

61. Use the Comparison Theorem to determine whether the integral
$$\int_1^\infty \frac{x^3}{x^5+2}\,dx$$
is convergent or divergent.

62. For what values of a is $\int_0^\infty e^{ax}\cos x\,dx$ convergent? Use the Table of Integrals to evaluate the integral for those values of a.

63. A particle moves along a line with velocity function $v(t)=t^2-t$, where v is measured in meters per second. Find (a) the displacement and (b) the distance traveled by the particle during the time interval $[0,5]$.

64. The speedometer reading (v) on a car was observed at 1-minute intervals and recorded in the chart. Use Simpson's Rule to estimate the distance traveled by the car.

t (min)	v (mi/h)	t (min)	v (mi/h)
0	40	6	56
1	42	7	57
2	45	8	57
3	49	9	55
4	52	10	56
5	54		

65. Let $r(t)$ be the rate at which the world's oil is consumed, where t is measured in years starting at $t = 0$ on January 1, 2000, and $r(t)$ is measured in barrels per year. What does $\int_0^8 r(t)\, dt$ represent?

66. A population of honeybees increased at a rate of $r(t)$ bees per week, where the graph of r is as shown. Use Simpson's Rule with six subintervals to estimate the increase in the bee population during the first 24 weeks.

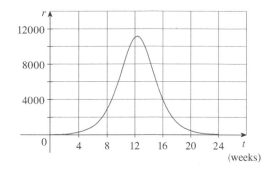

67. Suppose that the temperature in a long, thin rod placed along the x-axis is initially $C/(2a)$ if $|x| \le a$ and 0 if $|x| > a$. It can be shown that if the heat diffusivity of the rod is k, then the temperature of the rod at the point x at time t is

$$T(x, t) = \frac{C}{a\sqrt{4\pi kt}} \int_0^a e^{-(x-u)^2/(4kt)}\, du$$

To find the temperature distribution that results from an initial hot spot concentrated at the origin, we need to compute

$$\lim_{a \to 0} T(x, t)$$

Use l'Hospital's Rule to find this limit.

68. The Fresnel function $S(x) = \int_0^x \sin\left(\frac{1}{2}\pi t^2\right) dt$ was introduced in Section 5.4. Fresnel also used the function

$$C(x) = \int_0^x \cos\left(\frac{1}{2}\pi t^2\right) dt$$

in his theory of the diffraction of light waves.
(a) On what intervals is C increasing?
(b) On what intervals is C concave upward?

[CAS] (c) Use a graph to solve the following equation correct to two decimal places:

$$\int_0^x \cos\left(\frac{1}{2}\pi t^2\right) dt = 0.7$$

[CAS] (d) Plot the graphs of C and S on the same screen. How are these graphs related?

69. If f is a continuous function such that

$$\int_0^x f(t)\, dt = xe^{2x} + \int_0^x e^{-t} f(t)\, dt$$

for all x, find an explicit formula for $f(x)$.

70. Find a function f and a value of the constant a such that

$$2 \int_a^x f(t)\, dt = 2 \sin x - 1$$

71. If f' is continuous on $[a, b]$, show that

$$2 \int_a^b f(x) f'(x)\, dx = [f(b)]^2 - [f(a)]^2$$

72. If n is a positive integer, prove that

$$\int_0^1 (\ln x)^n\, dx = (-1)^n n!$$

73. If f' is continuous on $[0, \infty)$ and $\lim_{x \to \infty} f(x) = 0$, show that

$$\int_0^\infty f'(x)\, dx = -f(0)$$

74. The figure shows two regions in the first quadrant: $A(t)$ is the area under the curve $y = \sin(x^2)$ from 0 to t, and $B(t)$ is the area of the triangle with vertices O, P, and $(t, 0)$. Find $\lim_{t \to 0^+} A(t)/B(t)$.

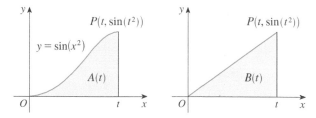

Focus on Problem Solving

Before you look at the solution of the following example, cover it up and first try to solve the problem yourself.

EXAMPLE Evaluate $\displaystyle\lim_{x\to 3}\left(\frac{x}{x-3}\int_3^x \frac{\sin t}{t}\,dt\right)$.

SOLUTION Let's start by having a preliminary look at the ingredients of the function. What happens to the first factor, $x/(x-3)$, when x approaches 3? The numerator approaches 3 and the denominator approaches 0, so we have

$$\frac{x}{x-3}\to\infty \quad \text{as} \quad x\to 3^+ \qquad \text{and} \qquad \frac{x}{x-3}\to-\infty \quad \text{as} \quad x\to 3^-$$

The second factor approaches $\int_3^3 (\sin t)/t\,dt$, which is 0. It's not clear what happens to the function as a whole. (One factor is becoming large while the other is becoming small.) So how do we proceed?

PS The principles of problem solving are discussed on page 83.

One of the principles of problem solving is *recognizing something familiar*. Is there a part of the function that reminds us of something we've seen before? Well, the integral

$$\int_3^x \frac{\sin t}{t}\,dt$$

has x as its upper limit of integration and that type of integral occurs in Part 1 of the Fundamental Theorem of Calculus:

$$\frac{d}{dx}\int_a^x f(t)\,dt = f(x)$$

This suggests that differentiation might be involved.

Once we start thinking about differentiation, the denominator $(x-3)$ reminds us of something else that should be familiar: One of the forms of the definition of the derivative in Chapter 2 is

$$F'(a) = \lim_{x\to a}\frac{F(x)-F(a)}{x-a}$$

and with $a=3$ this becomes

$$F'(3) = \lim_{x\to 3}\frac{F(x)-F(3)}{x-3}$$

So what is the function F in our situation? Notice that if we define

$$F(x) = \int_3^x \frac{\sin t}{t}\,dt$$

then $F(3)=0$. What about the factor x in the numerator? That's just a red herring, so let's factor it out and put together the calculation:

$$\lim_{x\to 3}\left(\frac{x}{x-3}\int_3^x\frac{\sin t}{t}\,dt\right) = \lim_{x\to 3} x \cdot \lim_{x\to 3}\frac{\displaystyle\int_3^x\frac{\sin t}{t}\,dt}{x-3}$$

Another approach is to use l'Hospital's Rule.

$$= 3\lim_{x\to 3}\frac{F(x)-F(3)}{x-3}$$

$$= 3F'(3) = 3\,\frac{\sin 3}{3} \qquad \text{(FTC1)}$$

$$= \sin 3$$

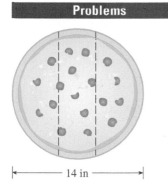

— 14 in —

FIGURE FOR PROBLEM 1

1. Three mathematics students have ordered a 14-inch pizza. Instead of slicing it in the traditional way, they decide to slice it by parallel cuts, as shown in the figure. Being mathematics majors, they are able to determine where to slice so that each gets the same amount of pizza. Where are the cuts made?

2. (a) Graph several members of the family of functions $f(x) = (2cx - x^2)/c^3$ for $c > 0$ and look at the regions enclosed by these curves and the x-axis. Make a conjecture about how the areas of these regions are related.
   (b) Prove your conjecture in part (a).
   (c) Take another look at the graphs in part (a) and use them to sketch the curve traced out by the vertices (highest points) of the family of functions. Can you guess what kind of curve this is?
   (d) Find an equation of the curve you sketched in part (c).

3. If $x \sin \pi x = \int_0^{x^2} f(t)\, dt$, where f is a continuous function, find $f(4)$.

4. If $f(x) = \int_0^x x^2 \sin(t^2)\, dt$, find $f'(x)$.

5. If f is a differentiable function such that $f(x)$ is never 0 and $\int_0^x f(t)\, dt = [f(x)]^2$ for all x, find f.

6. If n is a positive integer, prove that
$$\int_0^1 (\ln x)^n\, dx = (-1)^n n!$$

7. Evaluate $\lim\limits_{x \to 0} \dfrac{1}{x} \int_0^x (1 - \tan 2t)^{1/t}\, dt$.

8. A circular disk of radius r is used in an evaporator and is rotated in a vertical plane. If it is to be partially submerged in the liquid so as to maximize the exposed wetted area of the disk, show that the center of the disk should be positioned at a height $r/\sqrt{1 + \pi^2}$ above the surface of the liquid.

9. If $\int_0^4 e^{(x-2)^4}\, dx = k$, find the value of $\int_0^4 x e^{(x-2)^4}\, dx$.

10. If $f(x) = \int_0^{g(x)} \dfrac{1}{\sqrt{1 + t^3}}\, dt$, where $g(x) = \int_0^{\cos x} [1 + \sin(t^2)]\, dt$, find $f'(\pi/2)$.

11. Find a function f such that $f(1) = -1$, $f(4) = 7$, and $f'(x) > 3$ for all x, or prove that such a function cannot exist.

12. The figure shows a region consisting of all points inside a square that are closer to the center than to the sides of the square. Find the area of the region.

13. Find the interval $[a, b]$ for which the value of the integral $\int_a^b (2 + x - x^2)\, dx$ is a maximum.

14. Suppose f is continuous, $f(0) = 0$, $f(1) = 1$, $f'(x) > 0$, and $\int_0^1 f(x)\, dx = \frac{1}{3}$. Find the value of the integral $\int_0^1 f^{-1}(y)\, dy$.

15. Find $\dfrac{d^2}{dx^2} \int_0^x \left(\int_1^{\sin t} \sqrt{1 + u^4}\, du \right) dt$.

16. Use an integral to estimate the sum $\sum\limits_{i=1}^{10000} \sqrt{i}$.

17. Evaluate $\displaystyle\int_{-1}^{\infty} \left(\dfrac{x^4}{1 + x^6} \right)^2 dx$.

18. Find the minimum value of the area of the region under the curve $y = x + 1/x$ from $x = a$ to $x = a + 1.5$, for all $a > 0$.

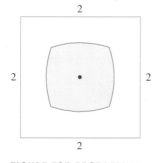

2

2   •   2

2

FIGURE FOR PROBLEM 12

19. Evaluate $\int_0^1 \left(\sqrt[3]{1 - x^7} - \sqrt[7]{1 - x^3} \right) dx$.

20. Evaluate $\displaystyle \lim_{n \to \infty} \left(\frac{1}{\sqrt{n}\,\sqrt{n+1}} + \frac{1}{\sqrt{n}\,\sqrt{n+2}} + \cdots + \frac{1}{\sqrt{n}\,\sqrt{n+n}} \right)$.

21. Show that

$$\int_0^1 (1 - x^2)^n \, dx = \frac{2^{2n}(n!)^2}{(2n+1)!}$$

Hint: Start by showing that if I_n denotes the integral, then

$$I_{k+1} = \frac{2k+2}{2k+3} I_k$$

22. Graph $f(x) = \sin(e^x)$ and use the graph to estimate the value of t such that $\int_t^{t+1} f(x)\,dx$ is a maximum. Then find the exact value of t that maximizes this integral.

23. A man initially standing at the point O walks along a pier pulling a rowboat by a rope of length L. The man keeps the rope straight and taut. The path followed by the boat is a curve called a *tractrix* and it has the property that the rope is always tangent to the curve (see the figure).
(a) Show that if the path followed by the boat is the graph of the function $y = f(x)$, then

$$f'(x) = \frac{dy}{dx} = \frac{-\sqrt{L^2 - x^2}}{x}$$

(b) Determine the function $y = f(x)$.

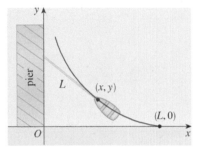

FIGURE FOR PROBLEM 23

24. For any number c, we let $f_c(x)$ be the smaller of the two numbers $(x - c)^2$ and $(x - c - 2)^2$. Then we define

$$g(c) = \int_0^1 f_c(x)\,dx$$

Find the maximum and minimum values of $g(c)$ if $-2 \leqslant c \leqslant 2$.

Applications of Integration

6

In this chapter we explore some of the applications of the definite integral by using it to compute areas between curves, volumes of solids, lengths of curves, the average value of a function, the work done by a varying force, the center of gravity of a plate, the force on a dam, as well as quantities of interest in biology, economics, and statistics. The common theme in most of these applications is the following general method, which is similar to the one we used to find areas under curves: We break up a quantity Q into a large number of small parts. We next approximate each small part by a quantity of the form $f(x_i^*) \, \Delta x$ and thus approximate Q by a Riemann sum. Then we take the limit and express Q as an integral. Finally we evaluate the integral by using the Evaluation Theorem, or Simpson's Rule, or technology.

6.1   More About Areas

In Chapter 5 we defined and calculated areas of regions that lie under the graphs of functions. Here we use integrals to find areas of more general regions. First we consider regions that lie between the graphs of two functions. Then we look at regions enclosed by parametric curves.

Areas Between Curves

Consider the region S that lies between two curves $y = f(x)$ and $y = g(x)$ and between the vertical lines $x = a$ and $x = b$, where f and g are continuous functions and $f(x) \geqslant g(x)$ for all x in $[a, b]$. (See Figure 1.)

Just as we did for areas under curves in Section 5.1, we divide S into n strips of equal width and then we approximate the ith strip by a rectangle with base Δx and height $f(x_i^*) - g(x_i^*)$. (See Figure 2. If we like, we could take all of the sample points to be right endpoints, in which case $x_i^* = x_i$.) The Riemann sum

$$\sum_{i=1}^{n} [f(x_i^*) - g(x_i^*)] \Delta x$$

is therefore an approximation to what we intuitively think of as the area of S.

FIGURE 1
$S = \{(x, y) \mid a \leqslant x \leqslant b, g(x) \leqslant y \leqslant f(x)\}$

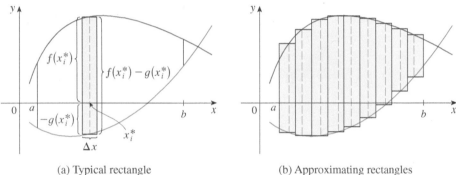

FIGURE 2
(a) Typical rectangle   (b) Approximating rectangles

This approximation appears to become better and better as $n \to \infty$. Therefore we define the **area** A of the region S as the limiting value of the sum of the areas of these approximating rectangles.

$$\boxed{1} \qquad A = \lim_{n \to \infty} \sum_{i=1}^{n} [f(x_i^*) - g(x_i^*)] \Delta x$$

We recognize the limit in (1) as the definite integral of $f - g$. Therefore we have the following formula for area.

2   The area A of the region bounded by the curves $y = f(x)$, $y = g(x)$, and the lines $x = a$, $x = b$, where f and g are continuous and $f(x) \geqslant g(x)$ for all x in $[a, b]$, is

$$A = \int_{a}^{b} [f(x) - g(x)] \, dx$$

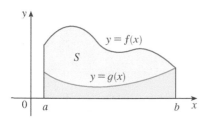
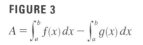

FIGURE 3

$$A = \int_a^b f(x)\,dx - \int_a^b g(x)\,dx$$

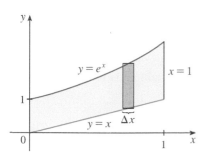

FIGURE 4

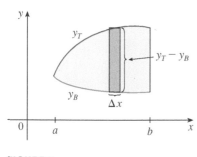

FIGURE 5

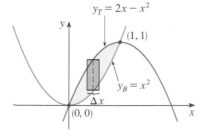

FIGURE 6

Notice that in the special case where $g(x) = 0$, S is the region under the graph of f and our general definition of area (1) reduces to our previous definition (Definition 2 in Section 5.1).

In the case where both f and g are positive, you can see from Figure 3 why (2) is true:

$$A = [\text{area under } y = f(x)] - [\text{area under } y = g(x)]$$

$$= \int_a^b f(x)\,dx - \int_a^b g(x)\,dx = \int_a^b [f(x) - g(x)]\,dx$$

EXAMPLE 1 **Area between two curves** Find the area of the region bounded above by $y = e^x$, bounded below by $y = x$, and bounded on the sides by $x = 0$ and $x = 1$.

SOLUTION The region is shown in Figure 4. The upper boundary curve is $y = e^x$ and the lower boundary curve is $y = x$. So we use the area formula (2) with $f(x) = e^x$, $g(x) = x$, $a = 0$, and $b = 1$:

$$A = \int_0^1 (e^x - x)\,dx = e^x - \tfrac{1}{2}x^2 \Big]_0^1$$

$$= e - \tfrac{1}{2} - 1 = e - 1.5$$

In Figure 4 we drew a typical approximating rectangle with width Δx as a reminder of the procedure by which the area is defined in (1). In general, when we set up an integral for an area, it's helpful to sketch the region to identify the top curve y_T, the bottom curve y_B, and a typical approximating rectangle as in Figure 5. Then the area of a typical rectangle is $(y_T - y_B)\,\Delta x$ and the equation

$$A = \lim_{n \to \infty} \sum_{i=1}^{n} (y_T - y_B)\,\Delta x = \int_a^b (y_T - y_B)\,dx$$

summarizes the procedure of adding (in a limiting sense) the areas of all the typical rectangles.

Notice that in Figure 5 the left-hand boundary reduces to a point, whereas in Figure 3 the right-hand boundary reduces to a point. In the next example both of the side boundaries reduce to a point, so the first step is to find a and b.

V **EXAMPLE 2** Find the area of the region enclosed by the parabolas $y = x^2$ and $y = 2x - x^2$.

SOLUTION We first find the points of intersection of the parabolas by solving their equations simultaneously. This gives $x^2 = 2x - x^2$, or $2x^2 - 2x = 0$. Thus $2x(x - 1) = 0$, so $x = 0$ or 1. The points of intersection are $(0, 0)$ and $(1, 1)$.

We see from Figure 6 that the top and bottom boundaries are

$$y_T = 2x - x^2 \qquad \text{and} \qquad y_B = x^2$$

The area of a typical rectangle is

$$(y_T - y_B)\,\Delta x = (2x - x^2 - x^2)\,\Delta x = (2x - 2x^2)\,\Delta x$$

and the region lies between $x = 0$ and $x = 1$. So the total area is

$$A = \int_0^1 (2x - 2x^2)\,dx = 2\int_0^1 (x - x^2)\,dx$$

$$= 2\left[\frac{x^2}{2} - \frac{x^3}{3}\right]_0^1 = 2\left(\frac{1}{2} - \frac{1}{3}\right) = \frac{1}{3}$$

Sometimes it's difficult, or even impossible, to find the points of intersection of two curves exactly. As shown in the following example, we can use a graphing calculator or computer to find approximate values for the intersection points and then proceed as before.

EXAMPLE 3 Find the approximate area of the region bounded by the curves $y = x/\sqrt{x^2 + 1}$ and $y = x^4 - x$.

SOLUTION If we were to try to find the exact intersection points, we would have to solve the equation

$$\frac{x}{\sqrt{x^2 + 1}} = x^4 - x$$

This looks like a very difficult equation to solve exactly (in fact, it's impossible), so instead we use a graphing device to draw the graphs of the two curves in Figure 7. One intersection point is the origin. We zoom in toward the other point of intersection and find that $x \approx 1.18$. (If greater accuracy is required, we could use Newton's method or a rootfinder, if available on our graphing device.) Thus an approximation to the area between the curves is

$$A \approx \int_0^{1.18} \left[\frac{x}{\sqrt{x^2 + 1}} - (x^4 - x) \right] dx$$

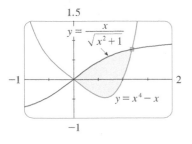

FIGURE 7

To integrate the first term we use the subsitution $u = x^2 + 1$. Then $du = 2x\,dx$, and when $x = 1.18$, we have $u \approx 2.39$. So

$$A \approx \frac{1}{2} \int_1^{2.39} \frac{du}{\sqrt{u}} - \int_0^{1.18} (x^4 - x)\,dx$$

$$= \sqrt{u}\,\Big]_1^{2.39} - \left[\frac{x^5}{5} - \frac{x^2}{2} \right]_0^{1.18}$$

$$= \sqrt{2.39} - 1 - \frac{(1.18)^5}{5} + \frac{(1.18)^2}{2}$$

$$\approx 0.785$$

EXAMPLE 4 Interpreting the area between velocity curves   Figure 8 shows velocity curves for two cars, A and B, that start side by side and move along the same road. What does the area between the curves represent? Use Simpson's Rule to estimate it.

SOLUTION We know from Section 5.3 that the area under the velocity curve A represents the distance traveled by car A during the first 16 seconds. Similarly, the area under curve B is the distance traveled by car B during that time period. So the area between these curves, which is the difference of the areas under the curves, is the distance between the cars after 16 seconds. We read the velocities from the graph and convert them to feet per second (1 mi/h = $\frac{5280}{3600}$ ft/s).

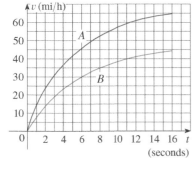

FIGURE 8

t	0	2	4	6	8	10	12	14	16
v_A	0	34	54	67	76	84	89	92	95
v_B	0	21	34	44	51	56	60	63	65
$v_A - v_B$	0	13	20	23	25	28	29	29	30

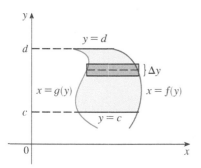

FIGURE 9

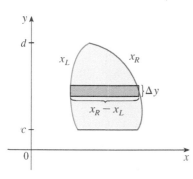

FIGURE 10

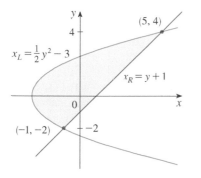

FIGURE 11

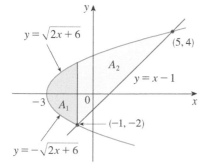

FIGURE 12

Using Simpson's Rule with $n = 8$ intervals, so that $\Delta t = 2$, we estimate the distance between the cars after 16 seconds:

$$\int_0^{16} (v_A - v_B)\, dt$$

$$\approx \tfrac{2}{3}[0 + 4(13) + 2(20) + 4(23) + 2(25) + 4(28) + 2(29) + 4(29) + 30]$$

$$\approx 367 \text{ ft}$$

Some regions are best treated by regarding x as a function of y. If a region is bounded by curves with equations $x = f(y)$, $x = g(y)$, $y = c$, and $y = d$, where f and g are continuous and $f(y) \geqslant g(y)$ for $c \leqslant y \leqslant d$ (see Figure 9), then its area is

$$A = \int_c^d [f(y) - g(y)]\, dy$$

If we write x_R for the right boundary and x_L for the left boundary, then, as Figure 10 illustrates, we have

$$A = \int_c^d (x_R - x_L)\, dy$$

Here a typical approximating rectangle has dimensions $x_R - x_L$ and Δy.

V EXAMPLE 5 **Integrating with respect to y is sometimes easier**
Find the area enclosed by the line $y = x - 1$ and the parabola $y^2 = 2x + 6$.

SOLUTION By solving the two equations we find that the points of intersection are $(-1, -2)$ and $(5, 4)$. We solve the equation of the parabola for x and notice from Figure 11 that the left and right boundary curves are

$$x_L = \tfrac{1}{2}y^2 - 3 \qquad \text{and} \qquad x_R = y + 1$$

We must integrate between the appropriate y-values, $y = -2$ and $y = 4$. Thus

$$A = \int_{-2}^4 (x_R - x_L)\, dy = \int_{-2}^4 \left[(y + 1) - \left(\tfrac{1}{2}y^2 - 3\right)\right] dy$$

$$= \int_{-2}^4 \left(-\tfrac{1}{2}y^2 + y + 4\right) dy$$

$$= -\frac{1}{2}\left(\frac{y^3}{3}\right) + \frac{y^2}{2} + 4y \Bigg]_{-2}^4$$

$$= -\tfrac{1}{6}(64) + 8 + 16 - \left(\tfrac{4}{3} + 2 - 8\right) = 18$$

Note: We could have found the area in Example 5 by integrating with respect to x instead of y, but the calculation is much more involved. It would have meant splitting the region in two and computing the areas labeled A_1 and A_2 in Figure 12. The method we used in Example 5 is *much* easier.

Areas Enclosed by Parametric Curves

We know that the area under a curve $y = F(x)$ from a to b is $A = \int_a^b F(x)\, dx$, where $F(x) \geqslant 0$. If the curve is traced out once by the parametric equations $x = f(t)$ and $y = g(t)$, $\alpha \leqslant t \leqslant \beta$, then we can calculate an area formula by using the Substitution Rule for

The limits of integration for t are found as usual with the Substitution Rule. When $x = a$, t is either α or β. When $x = b$, t is the remaining value.

Definite Integrals as follows:

$$A = \int_a^b y\, dx = \int_\alpha^\beta g(t) f'(t)\, dt \quad \left[\text{or} \quad \int_\beta^\alpha g(t) f'(t)\, dt\right]$$

 EXAMPLE 6   Find the area under one arch of the cycloid

$$x = r(\theta - \sin\theta) \qquad y = r(1 - \cos\theta)$$

(See Figure 13.)

SOLUTION One arch of the cycloid is given by $0 \le \theta \le 2\pi$. Using the Substitution Rule with $y = r(1 - \cos\theta)$ and $dx = r(1 - \cos\theta)\, d\theta$, we have

$$A = \int_0^{2\pi r} y\, dx = \int_0^{2\pi} r(1 - \cos\theta)\, r(1 - \cos\theta)\, d\theta$$

$$= r^2 \int_0^{2\pi} (1 - \cos\theta)^2\, d\theta = r^2 \int_0^{2\pi} (1 - 2\cos\theta + \cos^2\theta)\, d\theta$$

$$= r^2 \int_0^{2\pi} \left[1 - 2\cos\theta + \tfrac{1}{2}(1 + \cos 2\theta)\right] d\theta$$

$$= r^2 \left[\tfrac{3}{2}\theta - 2\sin\theta + \tfrac{1}{4}\sin 2\theta\right]_0^{2\pi}$$

$$= r^2 \left(\tfrac{3}{2} \cdot 2\pi\right) = 3\pi r^2$$

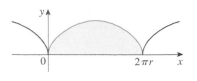

FIGURE 13

The result of Example 6 says that the area under one arch of the cycloid is three times the area of the rolling circle that generates the cycloid (see Example 7 in Section 1.7). Galileo guessed this result but it was first proved by the French mathematician Roberval and the Italian mathematician Torricelli.

6.1 Exercises

1–4 Find the area of the shaded region.

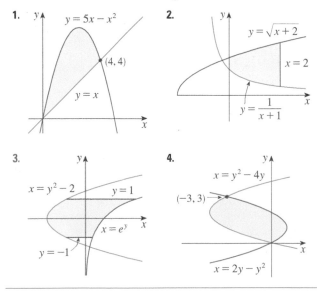

1. $y = 5x - x^2$, $(4, 4)$, $y = x$

2. $y = \sqrt{x + 2}$, $x = 2$, $y = \dfrac{1}{x + 1}$

3. $x = y^2 - 2$, $y = 1$, $x = e^y$, $y = -1$

4. $x = y^2 - 4y$, $(-3, 3)$, $x = 2y - y^2$

5–12 Sketch the region enclosed by the given curves. Decide whether to integrate with respect to x or y. Draw a typical approximating rectangle and label its height and width. Then find the area of the region.

5. $y = e^x$, $y = x^2 - 1$, $x = -1$, $x = 1$

6. $y = \ln x$, $xy = 4$, $x = 1$, $x = 3$

7. $y = x^2$, $y^2 = x$

8. $y = x^2 - 2x$, $y = x + 4$

9. $x = 1 - y^2$, $x = y^2 - 1$

10. $4x + y^2 = 12$, $x = y$

11. $x = 2y^2$, $x = 4 + y^2$

12. $y = \sin x$, $y = 2x/\pi$, $x \ge 0$

13–18 Sketch the region enclosed by the given curves and find its area.

13. $y = 12 - x^2$, $y = x^2 - 6$

---

14. $y = x^2$, $y = 4x - x^2$

15. $y = e^x$, $y = xe^x$, $x = 0$

16. $y = \cos x$, $y = 2 - \cos x$, $0 \le x \le 2\pi$

17. $y = 1/x$, $y = x$, $y = \frac{1}{4}x$, $x > 0$

18. $y = 3x^2$, $y = 8x^2$, $4x + y = 4$, $x \ge 0$

19–22 Use a graph to find approximate x-coordinates of the points of intersection of the given curves. Then find (approximately) the area of the region bounded by the curves.

19. $y = x \sin(x^2)$, $y = x^4$

20. $y = \dfrac{x}{(x^2 + 1)^2}$, $y = x^5 - x$, $x \ge 0$

21. $y = x^2 \ln x$, $y = \sqrt{x - 1}$

22. $y = x \cos x$, $y = x^{10}$

23. Sketch the region that lies between the curves $y = \cos x$ and $y = \sin 2x$ and between $x = 0$ and $x = \pi/2$. Notice that the region consists of two separate parts. Find the area of this region.

24. Sketch the curves $y = \cos x$ and $y = 1 - \cos x$, $0 \le x \le \pi$, and observe that the region between them consists of two separate parts. Find the area of this region.

25. Racing cars driven by Chris and Kelly are side by side at the start of a race. The table shows the velocities of each car (in miles per hour) during the first ten seconds of the race. Use Simpson's Rule to estimate how much farther Kelly travels than Chris does during the first ten seconds.

t	v_C	v_K	t	v_C	v_K
0	0	0	6	69	80
1	20	22	7	75	86
2	32	37	8	81	93
3	46	52	9	86	98
4	54	61	10	90	102
5	62	71			

26. Two cars, A and B, start side by side and accelerate from rest. The figure shows the graphs of their velocity functions.
(a) Which car is ahead after one minute? Explain.
(b) What is the meaning of the area of the shaded region?
(c) Which car is ahead after two minutes? Explain.
(d) Estimate the time at which the cars are again side by side.

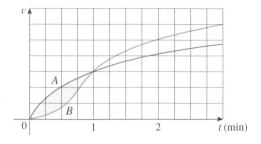

27. The widths (in meters) of a kidney-shaped swimming pool were measured at 2-meter intervals as indicated in the figure. Use Simpson's Rule to estimate the area of the pool.

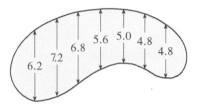

28. A cross-section of an airplane wing is shown. Measurements of the thickness of the wing, in centimeters, at 20-centimeter intervals are 5.8, 20.3, 26.7, 29.0, 27.6, 27.3, 23.8, 20.5, 15.1, 8.7, and 2.8. Use Simpson's Rule to estimate the area of the wing's cross-section.

200 cm

29. If the birth rate of a population is $b(t) = 2200e^{0.024t}$ people per year and the death rate is $d(t) = 1460e^{0.018t}$ people per year, find the area between these curves for $0 \le t \le 10$. What does this area represent?

30. The figure shows graphs of the marginal revenue function R' and the marginal cost function C' for a manufacturer. [Recall from Section 4.6 that $R(x)$ and $C(x)$ represent the revenue and cost when x units are manufactured. Assume that R and C are measured in thousands of dollars.] What is the meaning of the area of the shaded region? Use the Midpoint Rule to estimate the value of this quantity.

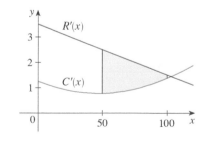

31. Find the area of the crescent-shaped region (called a *lune*) bounded by arcs of circles with radii r and R. (See the figure.)

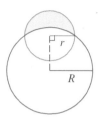

32. Sketch the region in the xy-plane defined by the inequalities $x - 2y^2 \geq 0$, $1 - x - |y| \geq 0$ and find its area.

33. Use the parametric equations of an ellipse, $x = a \cos \theta$, $y = b \sin \theta$, $0 \leq \theta \leq 2\pi$, to find the area that it encloses.

34. Find the area enclosed by the curve $x = t^2 - 2t$, $y = \sqrt{t}$ and the y-axis.

35. Find the area enclosed by the x-axis and the curve $x = 1 + e^t$, $y = t - t^2$.

CAS **36.** Graph the astroid $x = a \cos^3\theta$, $y = a \sin^3\theta$ and set up an integral for the area that it encloses. Then use a computer algebra system to evaluate the integral.

37. Find the area bounded by the loop of the curve with parametric equations $x = t^2$, $y = t^3 - 3t$.

38. Estimate the area of the region enclosed by the loop of the curve $x = t^3 - 12t$, $y = 3t^2 + 2t + 5$.

39. Find the values of c such that the area of the region bounded by the parabolas $y = x^2 - c^2$ and $y = c^2 - x^2$ is 576.

40. Find the area of the region bounded by the parabola $y = x^2$, the tangent line to this parabola at $(1, 1)$, and the x-axis.

41. Find the number b such that the line $y = b$ divides the region bounded by the curves $y = x^2$ and $y = 4$ into two regions with equal area.

42. (a) Find the number a such that the line $x = a$ bisects the area under the curve $y = 1/x^2$, $1 \leq x \leq 4$.
    (b) Find the number b such that the line $y = b$ bisects the area in part (a).

43. Find a positive continuous function f such that the area under the graph of f from 0 to t is $A(t) = t^3$ for all $t > 0$.

44. Suppose that $0 < c < \pi/2$. For what value of c is the area of the region enclosed by the curves $y = \cos x$, $y = \cos(x - c)$, and $x = 0$ equal to the area of the region enclosed by the curves $y = \cos(x - c)$, $x = \pi$, and $y = 0$?

45. For what values of m do the line $y = mx$ and the curve $y = x/(x^2 + 1)$ enclose a region? Find the area of the region.

6.2 Volumes

(a) Cylinder $V = Ah$

(b) Circular cylinder $V = \pi r^2 h$

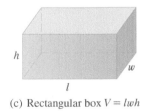

(c) Rectangular box $V = lwh$

FIGURE 1

In trying to find the volume of a solid we face the same type of problem as in finding areas. We have an intuitive idea of what volume means, but we must make this idea precise by using calculus to give an exact definition of volume.

We start with a simple type of solid called a **cylinder** (or, more precisely, a *right cylinder*). As illustrated in Figure 1(a), a cylinder is bounded by a plane region B_1, called the **base**, and a congruent region B_2 in a parallel plane. The cylinder consists of all points on line segments that are perpendicular to the base and join B_1 to B_2. If the area of the base is A and the height of the cylinder (the distance from B_1 to B_2) is h, then the volume V of the cylinder is defined as

$$V = Ah$$

In particular, if the base is a circle with radius r, then the cylinder is a circular cylinder with volume $V = \pi r^2 h$ [see Figure 1(b)], and if the base is a rectangle with length l and width w, then the cylinder is a rectangular box (also called a *rectangular parallelepiped*) with volume $V = lwh$ [see Figure 1(c)].

For a solid S that isn't a cylinder we first "cut" S into pieces and approximate each piece by a cylinder. We estimate the volume of S by adding the volumes of the cylinders. We arrive at the exact volume of S through a limiting process in which the number of pieces becomes large.

We start by intersecting S with a plane and obtaining a plane region that is called a **cross-section** of S. Let $A(x)$ be the area of the cross-section of S in a plane P_x perpendicular to the x-axis and passing through the point x, where $a \leq x \leq b$. (See Figure 2. Think of slicing S with a knife through x and computing the area of this slice.) The cross-sectional area $A(x)$ will vary as x increases from a to b.

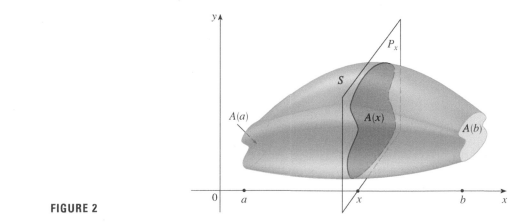

FIGURE 2

Let's divide S into n "slabs" of equal width Δx by using the planes P_{x_1}, P_{x_2}, ... to slice the solid. (Think of slicing a loaf of bread.) If we choose sample points x_i^* in $[x_{i-1}, x_i]$, we can approximate the ith slab S_i (the part of S that lies between the planes $P_{x_{i-1}}$ and P_{x_i}) by a cylinder with base area $A(x_i^*)$ and "height" Δx. (See Figure 3.)

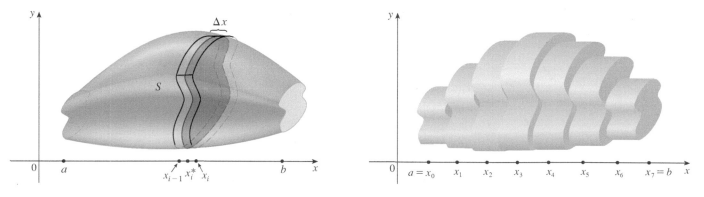

FIGURE 3

The volume of this cylinder is $A(x_i^*)\,\Delta x$, so an approximation to our intuitive conception of the volume of the ith slab S_i is

$$V(S_i) \approx A(x_i^*)\,\Delta x$$

Adding the volumes of these slabs, we get an approximation to the total volume (that is, what we think of intuitively as the volume):

$$V \approx \sum_{i=1}^{n} A(x_i^*)\,\Delta x$$

This approximation appears to become better and better as $n \to \infty$. (Think of the slices as becoming thinner and thinner.) Therefore we *define* the volume as the limit of these sums as $n \to \infty$. But we recognize the limit of Riemann sums as a definite integral and so we have the following definition.

It can be proved that this definition is independent of how S is situated with respect to the x-axis. In other words, no matter how we slice S with parallel planes, we always get the same answer for V.

Definition of Volume   Let S be a solid that lies between $x = a$ and $x = b$. If the cross-sectional area of S in the plane P_x, through x and perpendicular to the x-axis, is $A(x)$, where A is a continuous function, then the **volume** of S is

$$V = \lim_{n \to \infty} \sum_{i=1}^{n} A(x_i^*)\,\Delta x = \int_a^b A(x)\,dx$$

When we use the volume formula $V = \int_a^b A(x)\, dx$, it is important to remember that $A(x)$ is the area of a moving cross-section obtained by slicing through x perpendicular to the x-axis.

Notice that, for a cylinder, the cross-sectional area is constant: $A(x) = A$ for all x. So our definition of volume gives $V = \int_a^b A\, dx = A(b - a)$; this agrees with the formula $V = Ah$.

EXAMPLE 1 Show that the volume of a sphere of radius r is $V = \frac{4}{3}\pi r^3$.

SOLUTION If we place the sphere so that its center is at the origin (see Figure 4), then the plane P_x intersects the sphere in a circle whose radius (from the Pythagorean Theorem) is $y = \sqrt{r^2 - x^2}$. So the cross-sectional area is

$$A(x) = \pi y^2 = \pi(r^2 - x^2)$$

Using the definition of volume with $a = -r$ and $b = r$, we have

$$V = \int_{-r}^{r} A(x)\, dx = \int_{-r}^{r} \pi(r^2 - x^2)\, dx$$

$$= 2\pi \int_{0}^{r} (r^2 - x^2)\, dx \qquad \text{(The integrand is even.)}$$

$$= 2\pi \left[r^2 x - \frac{x^3}{3} \right]_0^r = 2\pi \left(r^3 - \frac{r^3}{3} \right)$$

$$= \tfrac{4}{3}\pi r^3$$

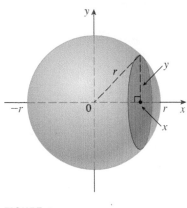

FIGURE 4

Figure 5 illustrates the definition of volume when the solid is a sphere with radius $r = 1$. From the result of Example 1, we know that the volume of the sphere is $\frac{4}{3}\pi$, which is approximately 4.18879. Here the slabs are circular cylinders, or *disks*, and the three parts of Figure 5 show the geometric interpretations of the Riemann sums

$$\sum_{i=1}^{n} A(\bar{x}_i)\, \Delta x = \sum_{i=1}^{n} \pi(1^2 - \bar{x}_i^2)\, \Delta x$$

TEC Visual 6.2A shows an animation of Figure 5.

when $n = 5$, 10, and 20 if we choose the sample points x_i^* to be the midpoints $\bar{x}_i$. Notice that as we increase the number of approximating cylinders, the corresponding Riemann sums become closer to the true volume.

(a) Using 5 disks, $V \approx 4.2726$

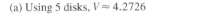

(b) Using 10 disks, $V \approx 4.2097$

(c) Using 20 disks, $V \approx 4.1940$

FIGURE 5 Approximating the volume of a sphere with radius 1

V **EXAMPLE 2 Using the disk method** Find the volume of the solid obtained by rotating about the x-axis the region under the curve $y = \sqrt{x}$ from 0 to 1. Illustrate the definition of volume by sketching a typical approximating cylinder.

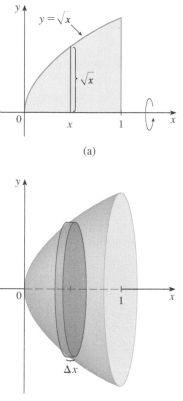

(a)

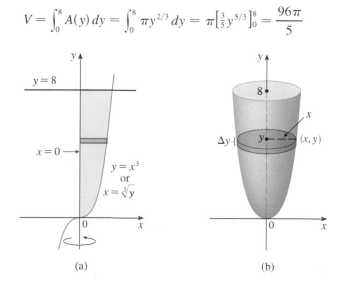

(b)

FIGURE 6

SOLUTION The region is shown in Figure 6(a). If we rotate about the *x*-axis, we get the solid shown in Figure 6(b). When we slice through the point *x*, we get a disk with radius $\sqrt{x}$. The area of this cross-section is

$$A(x) = \pi\left(\sqrt{x}\right)^2 = \pi x$$

and the volume of the approximating cylinder (a disk with thickness Δx) is

$$A(x)\,\Delta x = \pi x\,\Delta x$$

The solid lies between $x = 0$ and $x = 1$, so its volume is

$$V = \int_0^1 A(x)\,dx = \int_0^1 \pi x\,dx = \pi\,\frac{x^2}{2}\bigg]_0^1 = \frac{\pi}{2}$$

Did we get a reasonable answer in Example 2? As a check on our work, let's replace the given region by a square with base $[0, 1]$ and height 1. If we rotate this square, we get a cylinder with radius 1, height 1, and volume $\pi \cdot 1^2 \cdot 1 = \pi$. We computed that the given solid has half this volume. That seems about right.

V EXAMPLE 3 Rotating about the *y*-axis Find the volume of the solid obtained by rotating the region bounded by $y = x^3$, $y = 8$, and $x = 0$ about the *y*-axis.

SOLUTION The region is shown in Figure 7(a) and the resulting solid is shown in Figure 7(b). Because the region is rotated about the *y*-axis, it makes sense to slice the solid perpendicular to the *y*-axis and therefore to integrate with respect to *y*. If we slice at height *y*, we get a circular disk with radius *x*, where $x = \sqrt[3]{y}$. So the area of a cross-section through *y* is

$$A(y) = \pi x^2 = \pi\left(\sqrt[3]{y}\right)^2 = \pi y^{2/3}$$

and the volume of the approximating cylinder pictured in Figure 7(b) is

$$A(y)\,\Delta y = \pi y^{2/3}\,\Delta y$$

Since the solid lies between $y = 0$ and $y = 8$, its volume is

$$V = \int_0^8 A(y)\,dy = \int_0^8 \pi y^{2/3}\,dy = \pi\left[\tfrac{3}{5}y^{5/3}\right]_0^8 = \frac{96\pi}{5}$$

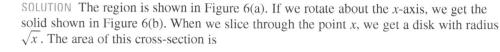

FIGURE 7

(a)

(b)

EXAMPLE 4 **Using the washer method**   The region $\mathcal{R}$ enclosed by the curves $y = x$ and $y = x^2$ is rotated about the x-axis. Find the volume of the resulting solid.

SOLUTION   The curves $y = x$ and $y = x^2$ intersect at the points $(0, 0)$ and $(1, 1)$. The region between them, the solid of rotation, and a cross-section perpendicular to the x-axis are shown in Figure 8. A cross-section in the plane P_x has the shape of a *washer* (an annular ring) with inner radius x^2 and outer radius x, so we find the cross-sectional area by subtracting the area of the inner circle from the area of the outer circle:

$$A(x) = \pi x^2 - \pi(x^2)^2 = \pi(x^2 - x^4)$$

Therefore we have

$$V = \int_0^1 A(x)\, dx = \int_0^1 \pi(x^2 - x^4)\, dx$$

$$= \pi\left[\frac{x^3}{3} - \frac{x^5}{5}\right]_0^1 = \frac{2\pi}{15}$$

TEC Visual 6.2B shows how solids of revolution are formed.

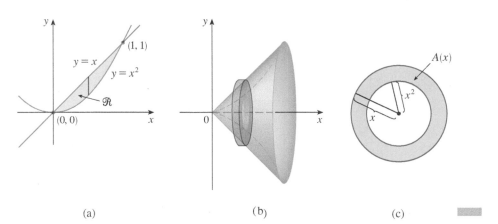

FIGURE 8   (a)   (b)   (c)

EXAMPLE 5 **Rotating about a horizontal line**   Find the volume of the solid obtained by rotating the region in Example 4 about the line $y = 2$.

SOLUTION   The solid and a cross-section are shown in Figure 9. Again the cross-section is a washer, but this time the inner radius is $2 - x$ and the outer radius is $2 - x^2$.

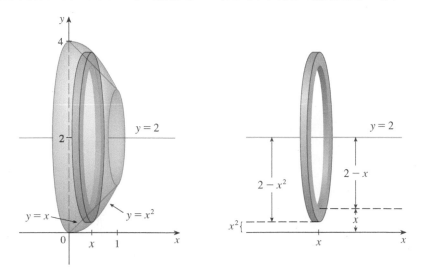

FIGURE 9

The cross-sectional area is

$$A(x) = \pi(2 - x^2)^2 - \pi(2 - x)^2$$

and so the volume of S is

$$V = \int_0^1 A(x)\,dx$$

$$= \pi \int_0^1 \left[(2 - x^2)^2 - (2 - x)^2 \right] dx$$

$$= \pi \int_0^1 (x^4 - 5x^2 + 4x)\,dx$$

$$= \pi \left[\frac{x^5}{5} - 5\frac{x^3}{3} + 4\frac{x^2}{2} \right]_0^1$$

$$= \frac{8\pi}{15}$$

The solids in Examples 1–5 are all called **solids of revolution** because they are obtained by revolving a region about a line. In general, we calculate the volume of a solid of revolution by using the basic defining formula

$$V = \int_a^b A(x)\,dx \qquad \text{or} \qquad V = \int_c^d A(y)\,dy$$

and we find the cross-sectional area $A(x)$ or $A(y)$ in one of the following ways:

- If the cross-section is a disk (as in Examples 1–3), we find the radius of the disk (in terms of x or y) and use

$$A = \pi(\text{radius})^2$$

- If the cross-section is a washer (as in Examples 4 and 5), we find the inner radius r_{in} and outer radius r_{out} from a sketch (as in Figures 8, 9, and 10) and compute the area of the washer by subtracting the area of the inner disk from the area of the outer disk:

$$A = \pi(\text{outer radius})^2 - \pi(\text{inner radius})^2$$

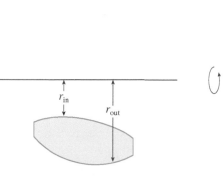
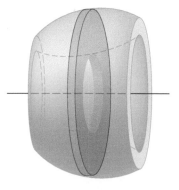

FIGURE 10

The next example gives a further illustration of the procedure.

EXAMPLE 6   **Rotating about a vertical line**   Find the volume of the solid obtained by rotating the region in Example 4 about the line $x = -1$.

SOLUTION   Figure 11 shows a horizontal cross-section. It is a washer with inner radius $1 + y$ and outer radius $1 + \sqrt{y}$, so the cross-sectional area is

$$A(y) = \pi(\text{outer radius})^2 - \pi(\text{inner radius})^2$$
$$= \pi\left(1 + \sqrt{y}\,\right)^2 - \pi(1 + y)^2$$

The volume is

$$V = \int_0^1 A(y)\,dy = \pi \int_0^1 \left[\left(1 + \sqrt{y}\,\right)^2 - (1 + y)^2\right]dy$$

$$= \pi \int_0^1 \left(2\sqrt{y} - y - y^2\right)dy = \pi\left[\frac{4y^{3/2}}{3} - \frac{y^2}{2} - \frac{y^3}{3}\right]_0^1 = \frac{\pi}{2}$$

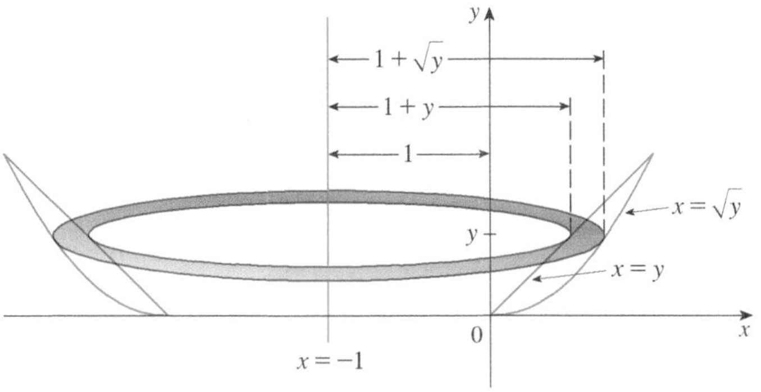

FIGURE 11

We now find the volumes of two solids that are *not* solids of revolution.

EXAMPLE 7   **Triangular cross-sections**   Figure 12 shows a solid with a circular base of radius 1. Parallel cross-sections perpendicular to the base are equilateral triangles. Find the volume of the solid.

TEC Visual 6.2C shows how the solid in Figure 12 is generated.

SOLUTION   Let's take the circle to be $x^2 + y^2 = 1$. The solid, its base, and a typical cross-section at a distance x from the origin are shown in Figure 13.

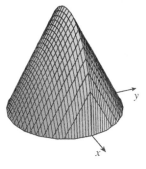

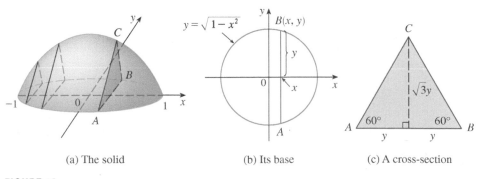

(a) The solid   (b) Its base   (c) A cross-section

FIGURE 12
Computer-generated picture
of the solid in Example 7

FIGURE 13

Since B lies on the circle, we have $y = \sqrt{1 - x^2}$ and so the base of the triangle ABC is $|AB| = 2\sqrt{1 - x^2}$. Since the triangle is equilateral, we see from Figure 13(c) that its height is $\sqrt{3}\,y = \sqrt{3}\,\sqrt{1-x^2}$. The cross-sectional area is therefore

$$A(x) = \tfrac{1}{2} \cdot 2\sqrt{1-x^2} \cdot \sqrt{3}\,\sqrt{1-x^2} = \sqrt{3}\,(1-x^2)$$

and the volume of the solid is

$$V = \int_{-1}^{1} A(x)\,dx = \int_{-1}^{1} \sqrt{3}\,(1-x^2)\,dx$$

$$= 2\int_{0}^{1} \sqrt{3}\,(1-x^2)\,dx = 2\sqrt{3}\left[x - \frac{x^3}{3}\right]_{0}^{1} = \frac{4\sqrt{3}}{3}$$

V **EXAMPLE 8** Find the volume of a pyramid whose base is a square with side L and whose height is h.

SOLUTION We place the origin O at the vertex of the pyramid and the x-axis along its central axis as in Figure 14. Any plane P_x that passes through x and is perpendicular to the x-axis intersects the pyramid in a square with side of length s, say. We can express s in terms of x by observing from the similar triangles in Figure 15 that

$$\frac{x}{h} = \frac{s/2}{L/2} = \frac{s}{L}$$

and so $s = Lx/h$. [Another method is to observe that the line OP has slope $L/(2h)$ and so its equation is $y = Lx/(2h)$.] Thus the cross-sectional area is

$$A(x) = s^2 = \frac{L^2}{h^2}x^2$$

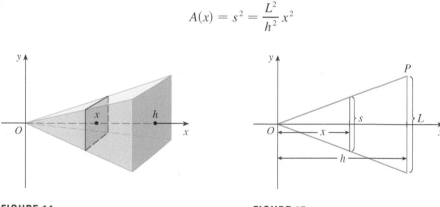

FIGURE 14   **FIGURE 15**

The pyramid lies between $x = 0$ and $x = h$, so its volume is

$$V = \int_{0}^{h} A(x)\,dx = \int_{0}^{h} \frac{L^2}{h^2}x^2\,dx = \frac{L^2}{h^2}\frac{x^3}{3}\bigg]_{0}^{h} = \frac{L^2 h}{3}$$

Note: We didn't need to place the vertex of the pyramid at the origin in Example 8. We did so merely to make the equations simple. If, instead, we had placed the center of the base at the origin and the vertex on the positive y-axis, as in Figure 16, you can verify that we would have obtained the integral

$$V = \int_{0}^{h} \frac{L^2}{h^2}(h-y)^2\,dy = \frac{L^2 h}{3}$$

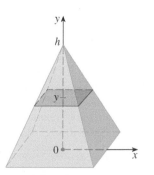

FIGURE 16

6.2 Exercises

1–12 Find the volume of the solid obtained by rotating the region bounded by the given curves about the specified line. Sketch the region, the solid, and a typical disk or washer.

1. $y = 2 - \frac{1}{2}x$, $y = 0$, $x = 1$, $x = 2$; about the x-axis

2. $y = 1 - x^2$, $y = 0$; about the x-axis

3. $x = 2\sqrt{y}$, $x = 0$, $y = 9$; about the y-axis

4. $y = \ln x$, $y = 1$, $y = 2$, $x = 0$; about the y-axis

5. $y = x^3$, $y = x$, $x \geqslant 0$; about the x-axis

6. $y = \frac{1}{4}x^2$, $y = 5 - x^2$; about the x-axis

7. $y^2 = x$, $x = 2y$; about the y-axis

8. $y = \frac{1}{4}x^2$, $x = 2$, $y = 0$; about the y-axis

9. $y = x$, $y = \sqrt{x}$; about $y = 1$

10. $y = e^{-x}$, $y = 1$, $x = 2$; about $y = 2$

11. $y = 1 + \sec x$, $y = 3$; about $y = 1$

12. $y = x$, $y = \sqrt{x}$; about $x = 2$

13–18 The region enclosed by the given curves is rotated about the specified line. Find the volume of the resulting solid.

13. $y = 1/x$, $x = 1$, $x = 2$, $y = 0$; about the x-axis

14. $x = 2y - y^2$, $x = 0$; about the y-axis

15. $x - y = 1$, $y = x^2 - 4x + 3$; about $y = 3$

16. $x = y^2$, $x = 1$; about $x = 1$

17. $y = x^3$, $y = \sqrt{x}$; about $x = 1$

18. $y = x^3$, $y = \sqrt{x}$; about $y = 1$

19–20 Set up, but do not evaluate, an integral for the volume of the solid obtained by rotating the region bounded by the given curves about the specified line.

19. $x^2 - y^2 = 1$, $x = 3$; about $x = -2$

20. $y = \cos x$, $y = 2 - \cos x$, $0 \leqslant x \leqslant 2\pi$; about $y = 4$

21–22 Use a graph to find approximate x-coordinates of the points of intersection of the given curves. Then use your calculator to find (approximately) the volume of the solid obtained by rotating about the x-axis the region bounded by these curves.

21. $y = 2 + x^2 \cos x$, $y = x^4 + x + 1$

22. $y = 3 \sin(x^2)$, $y = e^{x/2} + e^{-2x}$

[CAS] **23–24** Use a computer algebra system to find the exact volume of the solid obtained by rotating the region bounded by the given curves about the specified line.

23. $y = \sin^2 x$, $y = 0$, $0 \leqslant x \leqslant \pi$; about $y = -1$

24. $y = x$, $y = xe^{1-x/2}$; about $y = 3$

25–26 Each integral represents the volume of a solid. Describe the solid.

25. (a) $\pi \displaystyle\int_0^{\pi/2} \cos^2 x \, dx$ (b) $\pi \displaystyle\int_0^1 (y^4 - y^8) \, dy$

26. (a) $\pi \displaystyle\int_2^5 y \, dy$ (b) $\pi \displaystyle\int_0^{\pi/2} [(1 + \cos x)^2 - 1^2] \, dx$

27. A CAT scan produces equally spaced cross-sectional views of a human organ that provide information about the organ otherwise obtained only by surgery. Suppose that a CAT scan of a human liver shows cross-sections spaced 1.5 cm apart. The liver is 15 cm long and the cross-sectional areas, in square centimeters, are 0, 18, 58, 79, 94, 106, 117, 128, 63, 39, and 0. Use the Midpoint Rule to estimate the volume of the liver.

28. A log 10 m long is cut at 1-meter intervals and its cross-sectional areas A (at a distance x from the end of the log) are listed in the table. Use the Midpoint Rule with $n = 5$ to estimate the volume of the log.

x (m)	A (m²)	x (m)	A (m²)
0	0.68	6	0.53
1	0.65	7	0.55
2	0.64	8	0.52
3	0.61	9	0.50
4	0.58	10	0.48
5	0.59		

29. (a) If the region shown in the figure is rotated about the x-axis to form a solid, use Simpson's Rule with $n = 8$ to estimate the volume of the solid.

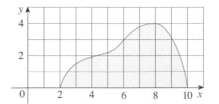

(b) Estimate the volume if the region is rotated about the y-axis. Use Simpson's Rule with $n = 4$.

[CAS] **30.** (a) A model for the shape of a bird's egg is obtained by rotating about the x-axis the region under the graph of

$$f(x) = (ax^3 + bx^2 + cx + d)\sqrt{1 - x^2}$$

Use a CAS to find the volume of such an egg.

(b) For a Red-throated Loon, $a = -0.06$, $b = 0.04$, $c = 0.1$, and $d = 0.54$. Graph f and find the volume of an egg of this species.

31–43 Find the volume of the described solid S.

31. A right circular cone with height h and base radius r

32. A frustum of a right circular cone with height h, lower base radius R, and top radius r

33. A cap of a sphere with radius r and height h

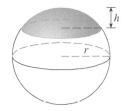

34. A frustum of a pyramid with square base of side b, square top of side a, and height h

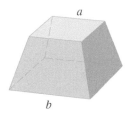

What happens if $a = b$? What happens if $a = 0$?

35. A pyramid with height h and rectangular base with dimensions b and $2b$

36. A pyramid with height h and base an equilateral triangle with side a (a tetrahedron)

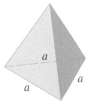

37. A tetrahedron with three mutually perpendicular faces and three mutually perpendicular edges with lengths 3 cm, 4 cm, and 5 cm

38. The base of S is a circular disk with radius r. Parallel cross-sections perpendicular to the base are squares.

39. The base of S is an elliptical region with boundary curve $9x^2 + 4y^2 = 36$. Cross-sections perpendicular to the x-axis are isosceles right triangles with hypotenuse in the base.

40. The base of S is the triangular region with vertices $(0, 0)$, $(1, 0)$, and $(0, 1)$. Cross-sections perpendicular to the y-axis are equilateral triangles.

41. The base of S is the same base as in Exercise 40, but cross-sections perpendicular to the x-axis are squares.

42. The base of S is the region enclosed by the parabola $y = 1 - x^2$ and the x-axis. Cross-sections perpendicular to the y-axis are squares.

43. The base of S is the same base as in Exercise 42, but cross-sections perpendicular to the x-axis are isosceles triangles with height equal to the base.

44. The base of S is a circular disk with radius r. Parallel cross-sections perpendicular to the base are isosceles triangles with height h and unequal side in the base.
 (a) Set up an integral for the volume of S.
 (b) By interpreting the integral as an area, find the volume of S.

45. (a) Set up an integral for the volume of a solid *torus* (the donut-shaped solid shown in the figure) with radii r and R.
 (b) By interpreting the integral as an area, find the volume of the torus.

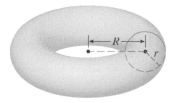

46. A wedge is cut out of a circular cylinder of radius 4 by two planes. One plane is perpendicular to the axis of the cylinder. The other intersects the first at an angle of 30° along a diameter of the cylinder. Find the volume of the wedge.

47. (a) Cavalieri's Principle states that if a family of parallel planes gives equal cross-sectional areas for two solids S_1 and S_2, then the volumes of S_1 and S_2 are equal. Prove this principle.
 (b) Use Cavalieri's Principle to find the volume of the oblique cylinder shown in the figure.

48. Find the volume common to two circular cylinders, each with radius r, if the axes of the cylinders intersect at right angles.

49. Find the volume common to two spheres, each with radius r, if the center of each sphere lies on the surface of the other sphere.

50. A bowl is shaped like a hemisphere with diameter 30 cm. A heavy ball with diameter 10 cm is placed in the bowl and water is poured into the bowl to a depth of h centimeters. Find the volume of water in the bowl.

51. A hole of radius r is bored through the middle of a cylinder of radius $R > r$ at right angles to the axis of the cylinder. Set up, but do not evaluate, an integral for the volume cut out.

52. A hole of radius r is bored through the center of a sphere of radius $R > r$. Find the volume of the remaining portion of the sphere.

53. Some of the pioneers of calculus, such as Kepler and Newton, were inspired by the problem of finding the volumes of wine barrels. (In fact Kepler published a book *Stereometria doliorum* in 1615 devoted to methods for finding the volumes of barrels.) They often approximated the shape of the sides by parabolas.
(a) A barrel with height h and maximum radius R is constructed by rotating about the x-axis the parabola $y = R - cx^2$, $-h/2 \leqslant x \leqslant h/2$, where c is a positive constant. Show that the radius of each end of the barrel is $r = R - d$, where $d = ch^2/4$.
(b) Show that the volume enclosed by the barrel is

$$V = \tfrac{1}{3}\pi h\left(2R^2 + r^2 - \tfrac{2}{5}d^2\right)$$

54. Suppose that a region $\mathcal{R}$ has area A and lies above the x-axis. When $\mathcal{R}$ is rotated about the x-axis, it sweeps out a solid with volume V_1. When $\mathcal{R}$ is rotated about the line $y = -k$ (where k is a positive number), it sweeps out a solid with volume V_2. Express V_2 in terms of V_1, k, and A.

DISCOVERY PROJECT | **Rotating on a Slant**

We know how to find the volume of a solid of revolution obtained by rotating a region about a horizontal or vertical line (see Section 6.2). But what if we rotate about a slanted line, that is, a line that is neither horizontal nor vertical? In this project you are asked to discover a formula for the volume of a solid of revolution when the axis of rotation is a slanted line.

Let C be the arc of the curve $y = f(x)$ between the points $P(p, f(p))$ and $Q(q, f(q))$ and let $\mathcal{R}$ be the region bounded by C, by the line $y = mx + b$ (which lies entirely below C), and by the perpendiculars to the line from P and Q.

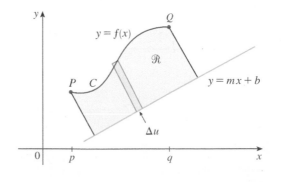

1. Show that the area of $\mathcal{R}$ is

$$\frac{1}{1 + m^2} \int_p^q [f(x) - mx - b][1 + mf'(x)]\, dx$$

[*Hint:* This formula can be verified by subtracting areas, but it will be helpful throughout the project to derive it by first approximating the area using rectangles perpendicular to the line, as shown in the following figure. Use part (a) of the figure to help express Δu in terms of Δx.]

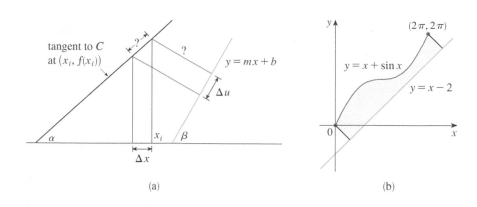

(a) (b)

2. Find the area of the region shown in part (b) of the figure.

3. Find a formula (similar to the one in Problem 1) for the volume of the solid obtained by rotating $\mathcal{R}$ about the line $y = mx + b$.

4. Find the volume of the solid obtained by rotating the region of Problem 2 about the line $y = x - 2$.

6.3 | Volumes by Cylindrical Shells

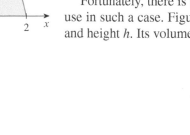

FIGURE 1

Some volume problems are very difficult to handle by the methods of the preceding section. For instance, let's consider the problem of finding the volume of the solid obtained by rotating about the y-axis the region bounded by $y = 2x^2 - x^3$ and $y = 0$. (See Figure 1.) If we slice perpendicular to the y-axis, we get a washer. But to compute the inner radius and the outer radius of the washer, we'd have to solve the cubic equation $y = 2x^2 - x^3$ for x in terms of y; that's not easy.

Fortunately, there is a method, called the **method of cylindrical shells**, that is easier to use in such a case. Figure 2 shows a cylindrical shell with inner radius r_1, outer radius r_2, and height h. Its volume V is calculated by subtracting the volume V_1 of the inner cylinder

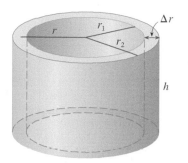

FIGURE 2

from the volume V_2 of the outer cylinder:

$$V = V_2 - V_1$$

$$= \pi r_2^2 h - \pi r_1^2 h = \pi (r_2^2 - r_1^2) h$$

$$= \pi (r_2 + r_1)(r_2 - r_1) h$$

$$= 2\pi \frac{r_2 + r_1}{2} h(r_2 - r_1)$$

If we let $\Delta r = r_2 - r_1$ (the thickness of the shell) and $r = \frac{1}{2}(r_2 + r_1)$ (the average radius of the shell), then this formula for the volume of a cylindrical shell becomes

1

$$V = 2\pi r h \, \Delta r$$

and it can be remembered as

$$V = [\text{circumference}][\text{height}][\text{thickness}]$$

Now let S be the solid obtained by rotating about the y-axis the region bounded by $y = f(x)$ [where $f(x) \geqslant 0$], $y = 0$, $x = a$, and $x = b$, where $b > a \geqslant 0$. (See Figure 3.)

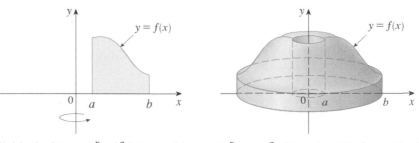

FIGURE 3

We divide the interval $[a, b]$ into n subintervals $[x_{i-1}, x_i]$ of equal width Δx and let $\bar{x}_i$ be the midpoint of the ith subinterval. If the rectangle with base $[x_{i-1}, x_i]$ and height $f(\bar{x}_i)$ is rotated about the y-axis, then the result is a cylindrical shell with average radius $\bar{x}_i$, height $f(\bar{x}_i)$, and thickness Δx (see Figure 4), so by Formula 1 its volume is

$$V_i = (2\pi \bar{x}_i)[f(\bar{x}_i)] \, \Delta x$$

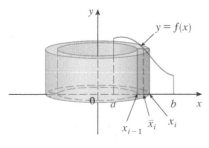

FIGURE 4

Therefore an approximation to the volume V of S is given by the sum of the volumes of these shells:

$$V \approx \sum_{i=1}^{n} V_i = \sum_{i=1}^{n} 2\pi \bar{x}_i f(\bar{x}_i) \, \Delta x$$

This approximation appears to become better as $n \to \infty$. But, from the definition of an integral, we know that

$$\lim_{n \to \infty} \sum_{i=1}^{n} 2\pi \bar{x}_i f(\bar{x}_i) \, \Delta x = \int_a^b 2\pi x f(x) \, dx$$

Thus the following appears plausible:

---

2   The volume of the solid in Figure 3, obtained by rotating about the y-axis the region under the curve $y = f(x)$ from a to b, is

$$V = \int_a^b 2\pi x f(x) \, dx \qquad \text{where } 0 \leqslant a < b$$

The best way to remember Formula 2 is to think of a typical shell, cut and flattened as in Figure 5, with radius x, circumference $2\pi x$, height $f(x)$, and thickness Δx or dx:

$$\int_a^b \underbrace{(2\pi x)}_{\text{circumference}} \underbrace{[f(x)]}_{\text{height}} \underbrace{dx}_{\text{thickness}}$$

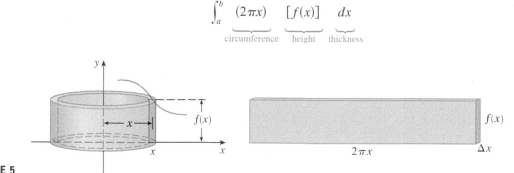

FIGURE 5

This type of reasoning will be helpful in other situations, such as when we rotate about lines other than the y-axis.

EXAMPLE 1   Using the shell method   Find the volume of the solid obtained by rotating about the y-axis the region bounded by $y = 2x^2 - x^3$ and $y = 0$.

SOLUTION   From the sketch in Figure 6 we see that a typical shell has radius x, circumference $2\pi x$, and height $f(x) = 2x^2 - x^3$. So, by the shell method, the volume is

$$V = \int_0^2 (2\pi x)(2x^2 - x^3) \, dx = 2\pi \int_0^2 (2x^3 - x^4) \, dx$$

$$= 2\pi \left[\tfrac{1}{2}x^4 - \tfrac{1}{5}x^5 \right]_0^2 = 2\pi \left(8 - \tfrac{32}{5} \right) = \tfrac{16}{5}\pi$$

It can be verified that the shell method gives the same answer as slicing.

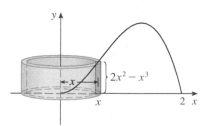

FIGURE 6

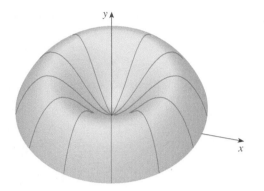

Figure 7 shows a computer-generated picture of the solid whose volume we computed in Example 1.

FIGURE 7

Note: Comparing the solution of Example 1 with the remarks at the beginning of this section, we see that the method of cylindrical shells is much easier than the washer method for this problem. We did not have to find the coordinates of the local maximum and we did not have to solve the equation of the curve for x in terms of y. However, in other examples the methods of the preceding section may be easier.

V   EXAMPLE 2   Find the volume of the solid obtained by rotating about the y-axis the region between $y = x$ and $y = x^2$.

SOLUTION   The region and a typical shell are shown in Figure 8. We see that the shell has radius x, circumference $2\pi x$, and height $x - x^2$. So the volume is

$$V = \int_0^1 (2\pi x)(x - x^2)\, dx = 2\pi \int_0^1 (x^2 - x^3)\, dx$$

$$= 2\pi \left[\frac{x^3}{3} - \frac{x^4}{4} \right]_0^1 = \frac{\pi}{6}$$

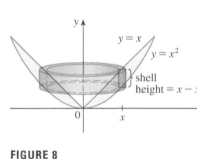

FIGURE 8

As the following example shows, the shell method works just as well if we rotate about the x-axis. We simply have to draw a diagram to identify the radius and height of a shell.

V   EXAMPLE 3   Using shells for rotation about the x-axis   Use cylindrical shells to find the volume of the solid obtained by rotating about the x-axis the region under the curve $y = \sqrt{x}$ from 0 to 1.

SOLUTION   This problem was solved using disks in Example 2 in Section 6.2. To use shells we relabel the curve $y = \sqrt{x}$ (in the figure in that example) as $x = y^2$ in Figure 9. For rotation about the x-axis we see that a typical shell has radius y, circumference $2\pi y$, and height $1 - y^2$. So the volume is

$$V = \int_0^1 (2\pi y)(1 - y^2)\, dy$$

$$= 2\pi \int_0^1 (y - y^3)\, dy$$

$$= 2\pi \left[\frac{y^2}{2} - \frac{y^4}{4} \right]_0^1 = \frac{\pi}{2}$$

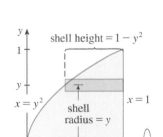

FIGURE 9

In this problem the disk method was simpler.

EXAMPLE 4 **Rotation about a vertical axis** Find the volume of the solid obtained by rotating the region bounded by $y = x - x^2$ and $y = 0$ about the line $x = 2$.

SOLUTION Figure 10 shows the region and a cylindrical shell formed by rotation about the line $x = 2$. It has radius $2 - x$, circumference $2\pi(2 - x)$, and height $x - x^2$.

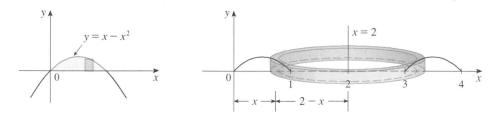

FIGURE 10

The volume of the given solid is

$$V = \int_0^1 2\pi(2 - x)(x - x^2)\, dx$$

$$= 2\pi \int_0^1 (x^3 - 3x^2 + 2x)\, dx$$

$$= 2\pi \left[\frac{x^4}{4} - x^3 + x^2 \right]_0^1 = \frac{\pi}{2}$$

6.3 Exercises

1. Let S be the solid obtained by rotating the region shown in the figure about the y-axis. Explain why it is awkward to use slicing to find the volume V of S. Sketch a typical approximating shell. What are its circumference and height? Use shells to find V.

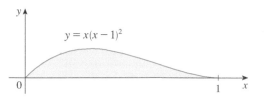

2. Let S be the solid obtained by rotating the region shown in the figure about the y-axis. Sketch a typical cylindrical shell and find its circumference and height. Use shells to find the volume of S. Do you think this method is preferable to slicing? Explain.

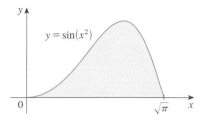

3–7 Use the method of cylindrical shells to find the volume generated by rotating the region bounded by the given curves about the y-axis. Sketch the region and a typical shell.

3. $y = 1/x$, $y = 0$, $x = 1$, $x = 2$

4. $y = x^2$, $y = 0$, $x = 1$

5. $y = e^{-x^2}$, $y = 0$, $x = 0$, $x = 1$

6. $y = 3 + 2x - x^2$, $x + y = 3$

7. $y = 4(x - 2)^2$, $y = x^2 - 4x + 7$

8. Let V be the volume of the solid obtained by rotating about the y-axis the region bounded by $y = \sqrt{x}$ and $y = x^2$. Find V both by slicing and by cylindrical shells. In both cases draw a diagram to explain your method.

9–12 Use the method of cylindrical shells to find the volume of the solid obtained by rotating the region bounded by the given curves about the x-axis.

9. $x = 1 + y^2$, $x = 0$, $y = 1$, $y = 2$

10. $x = \sqrt{y}$, $x = 0$, $y = 1$

---

11. $x = 1 + (y - 2)^2$, $x = 2$

12. $x + y = 3$, $x = 4 - (y - 1)^2$

13–18 Use the method of cylindrical shells to find the volume generated by rotating the region bounded by the given curves about the specified axis. Sketch the region and a typical shell.

13. $y = x^4$, $y = 0$, $x = 1$; about $x = 2$

14. $y = \sqrt{x}$, $y = 0$, $x = 1$; about $x = -1$

15. $y = 4x - x^2$, $y = 3$; about $x = 1$

16. $y = x^2$, $y = 2 - x^2$; about $x = 1$

17. $y = x^3$, $y = 0$, $x = 1$; about $y = 1$

18. $y = x^2$, $x = y^2$; about $y = -1$

19–20 Set up, but do not evaluate, an integral for the volume of the solid obtained by rotating the region bounded by the given curves about the specified axis.

19. $x = \sqrt{\sin y}$, $0 \le y \le \pi$, $x = 0$; about $y = 4$

20. $y = e^{-x^2}$, $y = 0$, $x = 0$, $x = 4$; about $x = 5$

---

21. Use Simpson's Rule with $n = 10$ to estimate the volume obtained by rotating about the y-axis the region under the curve $y = \sqrt{1 + x^3}$, $0 \le x \le 1$.

22. If the region shown in the figure is rotated about the y-axis to form a solid, use Simpson's Rule with $n = 10$ to estimate the volume of the solid.

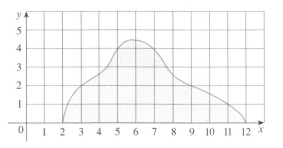

23–24 Each integral represents the volume of a solid. Describe the solid.

23. (a) $\displaystyle\int_0^3 2\pi x^5 \, dx$

(b) $\displaystyle\int_0^1 2\pi (3 - y)(1 - y^2) \, dy$

24. (a) $\displaystyle 2\pi \int_0^2 \frac{y}{1 + y^2} \, dy$

(b) $\displaystyle\int_0^{\pi/4} 2\pi (\pi - x)(\cos x - \sin x) \, dx$

25–26 Use a graph to estimate the x-coordinates of the points of intersection of the given curves. Then use this information and your calculator to estimate the volume of the solid obtained by rotating about the y-axis the region enclosed by these curves.

25. $y = e^x$, $y = \sqrt{x} + 1$

26. $y = x^3 - x + 1$, $y = -x^4 + 4x - 1$

CAS **27–28** Use a computer algebra system to find the exact volume of the solid obtained by rotating the region bounded by the given curves about the specified line.

27. $y = \sin^2 x$, $y = \sin^4 x$, $0 \le x \le \pi$; about $x = \pi/2$

28. $y = x^3 \sin x$, $y = 0$, $0 \le x \le \pi$; about $x = -1$

29–33 The region bounded by the given curves is rotated about the specified axis. Find the volume of the resulting solid by any method.

29. $y = -x^2 + 6x - 8$, $y = 0$; about the y-axis

30. $y = -x^2 + 6x - 8$, $y = 0$; about the x-axis

31. $x^2 + (y - 1)^2 = 1$; about the y-axis

32. $x = (y - 3)^2$, $x = 4$; about $y = 1$

33. $y = 5$, $y = x + (4/x)$; about $x = -1$

---

34. Let T be the triangular region with vertices $(0, 0)$, $(1, 0)$, $(1, 2)$, and let V be the volume of the solid generated when T is rotated about the line $x = a$, where $a > 1$. Express a in terms of V.

35–37 Use cylindrical shells to find the volume of the solid.

35. A sphere of radius r

36. The solid torus of Exercise 45 in Section 6.2

37. A right circular cone with height h and base radius r

---

38. Suppose you make napkin rings by drilling holes with different diameters through two wooden balls (which also have different diameters). You discover that both napkin rings have the same height h, as shown in the figure.
(a) Guess which ring has more wood in it.
(b) Check your guess: Use cylindrical shells to compute the volume of a napkin ring created by drilling a hole with radius r through the center of a sphere of radius R and express the answer in terms of h.

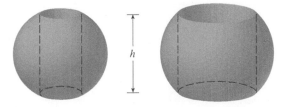

6.4 | Arc Length

FIGURE 1

What do we mean by the length of a curve? We might think of fitting a piece of string to the curve in Figure 1 and then measuring the string against a ruler. But that might be difficult to do with much accuracy if we have a complicated curve. We need a precise definition for the length of an arc of a curve, in the same spirit as the definitions we developed for the concepts of area and volume.

If the curve is a polygon, we can easily find its length; we just add the lengths of the line segments that form the polygon. (We can use the distance formula to find the distance between the endpoints of each segment.) We are going to define the length of a general curve by first approximating it by a polygon and then taking a limit as the number of segments of the polygon is increased. This process is familiar for the case of a circle, where the circumference is the limit of lengths of inscribed polygons (see Figure 2).

 TEC Visual 6.4 shows an animation of Figure 2.

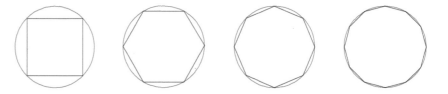

FIGURE 2

Suppose that a curve C is described by the parametric equations

$$x = f(t) \qquad y = g(t) \qquad a \leqslant t \leqslant b$$

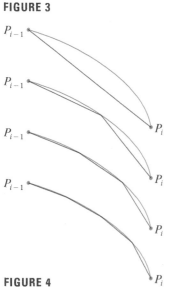

FIGURE 3

FIGURE 4

Let's assume that C is **smooth** in the sense that the derivatives $f'(t)$ and $g'(t)$ are continuous and not simultaneously zero for $a < t < b$. (This ensures that C has no sudden change in direction.) We divide the parameter interval $[a, b]$ into n subintervals of equal width Δt. If $t_0, t_1, t_2, \ldots, t_n$ are the endpoints of these subintervals, then $x_i = f(t_i)$ and $y_i = g(t_i)$ are the coordinates of points $P_i(x_i, y_i)$ that lie on C and the polygon with vertices $P_0, P_1, \ldots, P_n$ approximates C. (See Figure 3.) The length L of C is approximately the length of this polygon and the approximation gets better as we let n increase. (See Figure 4, where the arc of the curve between P_{i-1} and P_i has been magnified and approximations with successively smaller values of Δt are shown.) Therefore we define the **length** of C to be the limit of the lengths of these inscribed polygons:

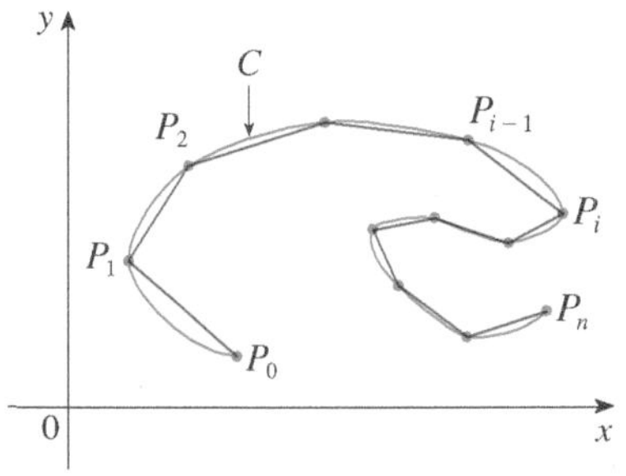

$$L = \lim_{n \to \infty} \sum_{i=1}^{n} |P_{i-1}P_i|$$

Notice that the procedure for defining arc length is very similar to the procedure we used for defining area and volume: We divided the curve into a large number of small parts. We then found the approximate lengths of the small parts and added them. Finally, we took the limit as $n \to \infty$.

For computational purposes we need a more convenient expression for L. If we let $\Delta x_i = x_i - x_{i-1}$ and $\Delta y_i = y_i - y_{i-1}$, then the length of the ith line segment of the polygon is

$$|P_{i-1}P_i| = \sqrt{(\Delta x_i)^2 + (\Delta y_i)^2}$$

But from the definition of a derivative we know that

$$f'(t_i) \approx \frac{\Delta x_i}{\Delta t}$$

if Δt is small. (We could have used any sample point t_i^* in place of t_i.) Therefore

$$\Delta x_i \approx f'(t_i)\,\Delta t \qquad\qquad \Delta y_i \approx g'(t_i)\,\Delta t$$

and so
$$|P_{i-1}P_i| = \sqrt{(\Delta x_i)^2 + (\Delta y_i)^2}$$

$$\approx \sqrt{[f'(t_i)\,\Delta t]^2 + [g'(t_i)\,\Delta t]^2}$$

$$= \sqrt{[f'(t_i)]^2 + [g'(t_i)]^2}\;\Delta t$$

Thus
$$L \approx \sum_{i=1}^{n} \sqrt{[f'(t_i)]^2 + [g'(t_i)]^2}\;\Delta t$$

This is a Riemann sum for the function $\sqrt{[f'(t)]^2 + [g'(t)]^2}$ and so our argument suggests that

$$L = \int_a^b \sqrt{[f'(t)]^2 + [g'(t)]^2}\;dt$$

In fact, our reasoning can be made precise; this formula is correct, provided that we rule out situations where a portion of the curve is traced out more than once.

---

1 **Arc Length Formula** If a smooth curve with parametric equations $x = f(t)$, $y = g(t)$, $a \le t \le b$, is traversed exactly once as t increases from a to b, then its length is

$$L = \int_a^b \sqrt{\left(\frac{dx}{dt}\right)^2 + \left(\frac{dy}{dt}\right)^2}\;dt$$

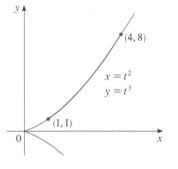

FIGURE 5

As a check on our answer to Example 1, notice from Figure 5 that it ought to be slightly larger than the distance from (1, 1) to (4, 8), which is

$$\sqrt{58} \approx 7.615773$$

According to our calculation in Example 1, we have

$$L = \tfrac{1}{27}\left(80\sqrt{10} - 13\sqrt{13}\right) \approx 7.633705$$

Sure enough, this is a bit greater than the length of the line segment.

EXAMPLE 1 **Length of a parametric curve** Find the length of the arc of the curve $x = t^2$, $y = t^3$ that lies between the points (1, 1) and (4, 8). (See Figure 5.)

SOLUTION First we notice from the equations $x = t^2$ and $y = t^3$ that the portion of the curve between (1, 1) and (4, 8) corresponds to the parameter interval $1 \le t \le 2$. So the arc length formula (1) gives

$$L = \int_1^2 \sqrt{\left(\frac{dx}{dt}\right)^2 + \left(\frac{dy}{dt}\right)^2}\;dt = \int_1^2 \sqrt{(2t)^2 + (3t^2)^2}\;dt$$

$$= \int_1^2 \sqrt{4t^2 + 9t^4}\;dt = \int_1^2 t\sqrt{4 + 9t^2}\;dt$$

If we substitute $u = 4 + 9t^2$, then $du = 18t\,dt$. When $t = 1$, $u = 13$; when $t = 2$, $u = 40$. Therefore

$$L = \tfrac{1}{18}\int_{13}^{40}\sqrt{u}\;du = \tfrac{1}{18}\cdot\tfrac{2}{3}u^{3/2}\Big]_{13}^{40}$$

$$= \tfrac{1}{27}\left[40^{3/2} - 13^{3/2}\right] = \tfrac{1}{27}\left(80\sqrt{10} - 13\sqrt{13}\right)$$

If we are given a curve with equation $y = f(x)$, $a \leqslant x \leqslant b$, then we can regard x as a parameter. Then parametric equations are $x = x$, $y = f(x)$, and Formula 1 becomes

2
$$L = \int_a^b \sqrt{1 + \left(\frac{dy}{dx}\right)^2}\, dx$$

Similarly, if a curve has the equation $x = f(y)$, $a \leqslant y \leqslant b$, we regard y as the parameter and the length is

3
$$L = \int_a^b \sqrt{\left(\frac{dx}{dy}\right)^2 + 1}\, dy$$

Because of the presence of the root sign in Formulas 1, 2, and 3, the calculation of an arc length often leads to an integral that is very difficult or even impossible to evaluate explicitly. Thus we often have to be content with finding an approximation to the length of a curve as in the following example.

V EXAMPLE 2 Approximating a length with Simpson's Rule Estimate the length of the portion of the hyperbola $xy = 1$ from the point $(1, 1)$ to the point $\left(2, \frac{1}{2}\right)$.

SOLUTION We have
$$y = \frac{1}{x} \qquad \frac{dy}{dx} = -\frac{1}{x^2}$$

and so, from Formula 2, the length is
$$L = \int_1^2 \sqrt{1 + \left(\frac{dy}{dx}\right)^2}\, dx = \int_1^2 \sqrt{1 + \frac{1}{x^4}}\, dx$$

It is impossible to evaluate this integral exactly, so let's use Simpson's Rule (see Section 5.9) with $a = 1$, $b = 2$, $n = 10$, $\Delta x = 0.1$, and $f(x) = \sqrt{1 + 1/x^4}$. Thus

$$L = \int_1^2 \sqrt{1 + \frac{1}{x^4}}\, dx$$

$$\approx \frac{\Delta x}{3}[f(1) + 4f(1.1) + 2f(1.2) + 4f(1.3) + \cdots + 2f(1.8) + 4f(1.9) + f(2)]$$

$$\approx 1.1321$$

Checking the value of the definite integral with a more accurate approximation produced by a computer algebra system, we see that the approximation using Simpson's Rule is accurate to four decimal places.

V EXAMPLE 3 Find the length of the arc of the parabola $y^2 = x$ from $(0, 0)$ to $(1, 1)$.

SOLUTION Since $x = y^2$, we have $dx/dy = 2y$, and Formula 3 gives
$$L = \int_0^1 \sqrt{\left(\frac{dx}{dy}\right)^2 + 1}\, dy = \int_0^1 \sqrt{4y^2 + 1}\, dy$$

Using either a computer algebra system or the Table of Integrals (use Formula 21 after substituting $u = 2y$), we find that

$$L = \frac{\sqrt{5}}{2} + \frac{\ln(\sqrt{5} + 2)}{4}$$

Figure 6 shows the arc of the parabola whose length is computed in Example 3, together with polygonal approximations having $n = 1$ and $n = 2$ line segments, respectively. For $n = 1$ the approximate length is $L_1 = \sqrt{2}$, the diagonal of a square. The table shows the approximations L_n that we get by dividing $[0, 1]$ into n equal subintervals. Notice that each time we double the number of sides of the polygon, we get closer to the exact length, which is

$$L = \frac{\sqrt{5}}{2} + \frac{\ln(\sqrt{5} + 2)}{4} \approx 1.478943$$

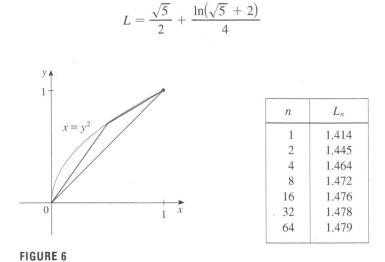

n	L_n
1	1.414
2	1.445
4	1.464
8	1.472
16	1.476
32	1.478
64	1.479

FIGURE 6

V **EXAMPLE 4** Find the length of one arch of the cycloid

$$x = r(\theta - \sin \theta) \qquad y = r(1 - \cos \theta)$$

SOLUTION From Example 7 in Section 1.7 we see that one arch is described by the parameter interval $0 \leqslant \theta \leqslant 2\pi$. Since

$$\frac{dx}{d\theta} = r(1 - \cos \theta) \qquad \text{and} \qquad \frac{dy}{d\theta} = r \sin \theta$$

we have

$$L = \int_0^{2\pi} \sqrt{\left(\frac{dx}{d\theta}\right)^2 + \left(\frac{dy}{d\theta}\right)^2} \, d\theta = \int_0^{2\pi} \sqrt{r^2(1 - \cos \theta)^2 + r^2 \sin^2\theta} \, d\theta$$

$$= \int_0^{2\pi} \sqrt{r^2(1 - 2 \cos \theta + \cos^2\theta + \sin^2\theta)} \, d\theta = r \int_0^{2\pi} \sqrt{2(1 - \cos \theta)} \, d\theta$$

This integral could be evaluated after using further trigonometric identities. Instead we use a computer algebra system:

$$L = r \int_0^{2\pi} \sqrt{2(1 - \cos \theta)} \, d\theta = 8r$$

The result of Example 4 says that the length of one arch of a cycloid is eight times the radius of the generating circle (see Figure 7). This was first proved in 1658 by Sir Christopher Wren, who later became the architect of St. Paul's Cathedral in London.

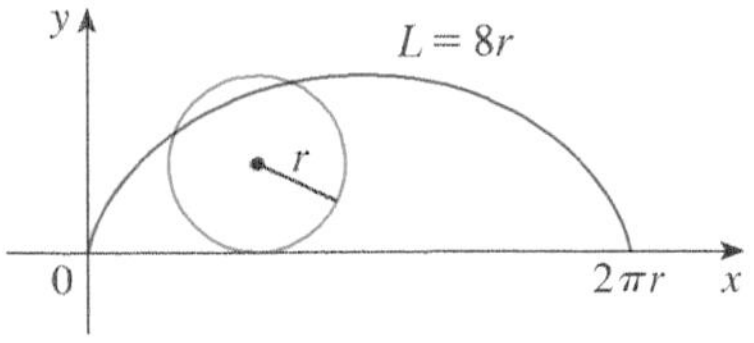

FIGURE 7

6.4 Exercises

1. Use the arc length formula (2) to find the length of the curve $y = 2x - 5$, $-1 \leqslant x \leqslant 3$. Check your answer by noting that the curve is a line segment and calculating its length by the distance formula.

2. (a) In Example 2 in Section 1.7 we showed that the parametric equations $x = \cos t$, $y = \sin t$, $0 \leqslant t \leqslant 2\pi$, represent the unit circle. Use these equations to show that the length of the unit circle has the expected value.

⌂ Graphing calculator or computer with graphing software required   CAS Computer algebra system required   **1.** Homework Hints available in TEC

(b) In Example 3 in Section 1.7 we showed that the equations $x = \sin 2t$, $y = \cos 2t$, $0 \le t \le 2\pi$, also represent the unit circle. What value does the integral in Formula 1 give? How do you explain the discrepancy?

3–6 Set up an integral that represents the length of the curve. Then use your calculator to find the length correct to four decimal places.

3. $y = \sin x$, $0 \le x \le \pi$

4. $x = y^2 - 2y$, $0 \le y \le 2$

5. $x = t + \cos t$, $y = t - \sin t$, $0 \le t \le 2\pi$

6. $x = t \cos t$, $y = t \sin t$, $0 \le t \le 2\pi$

7–12 Find the exact length of the curve.

7. $x = 1 + 3t^2$, $y = 4 + 2t^3$, $0 \le t \le 1$

8. $y^2 = 4(x + 4)^3$, $0 \le x \le 2$, $y > 0$

9. $x = y^{3/2}$, $0 \le y \le 1$

10. $y = \sqrt{x - x^2} + \sin^{-1}(\sqrt{x})$

11. $y = \frac{1}{4}x^2 - \frac{1}{2}\ln x$, $1 \le x \le 2$

12. $x = a(\cos \theta + \theta \sin \theta)$, $y = a(\sin \theta - \theta \cos \theta)$, $0 \le \theta \le \pi$

13–16 Graph the curve and find its exact length.

13. $x = e^t - t$, $y = 4e^{t/2}$, $-8 \le t \le 3$

14. $y = \frac{x^3}{3} + \frac{1}{4x}$, $1 \le x \le 2$

15. $x = e^t \cos t$, $y = e^t \sin t$, $0 \le t \le \pi$

16. $x = e^t + e^{-t}$, $y = 5 - 2t$, $0 \le t \le 3$

17–19 Use Simpson's Rule with $n = 10$ to estimate the arc length of the curve. Compare your answer with the value of the integral produced by your calculator.

17. $y = xe^{-x}$, $0 \le x \le 5$

18. $x = y + \sqrt{y}$, $1 \le y \le 2$

19. $x = \sin t$, $y = t^2$, $0 \le t \le 2\pi$

---

20. Find the length of the loop of the curve $x = 3t - t^3$, $y = 3t^2$.

21. (a) Graph the curve $y = x\sqrt[3]{4 - x}$, $0 \le x \le 4$.
   (b) Compute the lengths of inscribed polygons with $n = 1, 2$, and 4 sides. (Divide the interval into equal subintervals.) Illustrate by sketching these polygons (as in Figure 6).
   (c) Set up an integral for the length of the curve.
   (d) Use your calculator to find the length of the curve to four decimal places. Compare with the approximations in part (b).

22. Repeat Exercise 21 for the curve

$$y = x + \sin x \qquad 0 \le x \le 2\pi$$

23–26 Use either a CAS or a table of integrals to find the exact length of the curve.

23. $x = t^3$, $y = t^4$, $0 \le t \le 1$

24. $y^2 = 4x$, $0 \le y \le 2$

25. $y = \ln(\cos x)$, $0 \le x \le \pi/4$

26. $y = \ln x$, $1 \le x \le \sqrt{3}$

---

27. A hawk flying at 15 m/s at an altitude of 180 m accidentally drops its prey. The parabolic trajectory of the falling prey is described by the equation

$$y = 180 - \frac{x^2}{45}$$

until it hits the ground, where y is its height above the ground and x is the horizontal distance traveled in meters. Calculate the distance traveled by the prey from the time it is dropped until the time it hits the ground. Express your answer correct to the nearest tenth of a meter.

28. A steady wind blows a kite due west. The kite's height above ground from horizontal position $x = 0$ to $x = 80$ ft is given by $y = 150 - \frac{1}{40}(x - 50)^2$. Find the distance traveled by the kite.

29. A manufacturer of corrugated metal roofing wants to produce panels that are 28 in. wide and 2 in. thick by processing flat sheets of metal as shown in the figure. The profile of the roofing takes the shape of a sine wave. Verify that the sine curve has equation $y = \sin(\pi x/7)$ and find the width w of a flat metal sheet that is needed to make a 28-inch panel. (Use your calculator to evaluate the integral correct to four significant digits.)

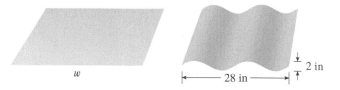

30. Find the total length of the astroid $x = a\cos^3\theta$, $y = a\sin^3\theta$, where $a > 0$.

31. Show that the total length of the ellipse $x = a\sin\theta$, $y = b\cos\theta$, $a > b > 0$, is

$$L = 4a \int_0^{\pi/2} \sqrt{1 - e^2 \sin^2\theta} \; d\theta$$

where e is the eccentricity of the ellipse $\left(e = c/a\right.$, where $c = \sqrt{a^2 - b^2}\left.\right)$.

32. The curves with equations $x^n + y^n = 1$, $n = 4, 6, 8, \ldots$, are called **fat circles**. Graph the curves with $n = 2, 4, 6, 8$, and 10 to see why. Set up an integral for the length L_{2k} of the fat circle with $n = 2k$. Without attempting to evaluate this integral, state the value of $\lim_{k \to \infty} L_{2k}$.

CAS **33.** (a) Graph the **epitrochoid** with equations

$$x = 11 \cos t - 4 \cos(11t/2)$$
$$y = 11 \sin t - 4 \sin(11t/2)$$

What parameter interval gives the complete curve?

(b) Use your CAS to find the approximate length of this curve.

CAS **34.** A curve called **Cornu's spiral** is defined by the parametric equations

$$x = C(t) = \int_0^t \cos(\pi u^2/2) \, du$$

$$y = S(t) = \int_0^t \sin(\pi u^2/2) \, du$$

where C and S are the Fresnel functions that were introduced in Section 5.4.

(a) Graph this curve. What happens as $t \to \infty$ and as $t \to -\infty$?

(b) Find the length of Cornu's spiral from the origin to the point with parameter value t.

DISCOVERY PROJECT | **Arc Length Contest**

The curves shown are all examples of graphs of continuous functions f that have the following properties.

1. $f(0) = 0$ and $f(1) = 0$

2. $f(x) \geqslant 0$ for $0 \leqslant x \leqslant 1$

3. The area under the graph of f from 0 to 1 is equal to 1.

The lengths L of these curves, however, are different.

$L \approx 3.249$ $L \approx 2.919$ $L \approx 3.152$ $L \approx 3.213$

Try to discover formulas for two functions that satisfy the given conditions 1, 2, and 3. (Your graphs might be similar to the ones shown or could look quite different.) Then calculate the arc length of each graph. The winning entry will be the one with the smallest arc length.

6.5 Average Value of a Function

It is easy to calculate the average value of finitely many numbers $y_1, y_2, \ldots, y_n$:

$$y_{\text{ave}} = \frac{y_1 + y_2 + \cdots + y_n}{n}$$

But how do we compute the average temperature during a day if infinitely many tempera-

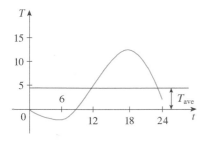

FIGURE 1

ture readings are possible? Figure 1 shows the graph of a temperature function $T(t)$, where t is measured in hours and T in °C, and a guess at the average temperature, T_{ave}.

In general, let's try to compute the average value of a function $y = f(x)$, $a \leqslant x \leqslant b$. We start by dividing the interval $[a, b]$ into n equal subintervals, each with length $\Delta x = (b - a)/n$. Then we choose points $x_1^*, \ldots, x_n^*$ in successive subintervals and calculate the average of the numbers $f(x_1^*), \ldots, f(x_n^*)$:

$$\frac{f(x_1^*) + \cdots + f(x_n^*)}{n}$$

(For example, if f represents a temperature function and $n = 24$, this means that we take temperature readings every hour and then average them.) Since $\Delta x = (b - a)/n$, we can write $n = (b - a)/\Delta x$ and the average value becomes

$$\frac{f(x_1^*) + \cdots + f(x_n^*)}{\dfrac{b - a}{\Delta x}} = \frac{1}{b - a} \left[f(x_1^*) \, \Delta x + \cdots + f(x_n^*) \, \Delta x \right]$$

$$= \frac{1}{b - a} \sum_{i=1}^{n} f(x_i^*) \, \Delta x$$

If we let n increase, we would be computing the average value of a large number of closely spaced values. (For example, we would be averaging temperature readings taken every minute or even every second.) The limiting value is

$$\lim_{n \to \infty} \frac{1}{b - a} \sum_{i=1}^{n} f(x_i^*) \, \Delta x = \frac{1}{b - a} \int_a^b f(x) \, dx$$

by the definition of a definite integral.

Therefore we define the **average value of f** on the interval $[a, b]$ as

$$\boxed{\; f_{ave} = \frac{1}{b - a} \int_a^b f(x) \, dx \;}$$

For a positive function, we can think of this definition as saying

$$\frac{area}{width} = \text{average height}$$

▼ EXAMPLE 1 Find the average value of the function $f(x) = 1 + x^2$ on the interval $[-1, 2]$.

SOLUTION With $a = -1$ and $b = 2$ we have

$$f_{ave} = \frac{1}{b - a} \int_a^b f(x) \, dx = \frac{1}{2 - (-1)} \int_{-1}^{2} (1 + x^2) \, dx$$

$$= \frac{1}{3} \left[x + \frac{x^3}{3} \right]_{-1}^{2} = 2$$

If $T(t)$ is the temperature at time t, we might wonder if there is a specific time when the temperature is the same as the average temperature. For the temperature function graphed in Figure 1, we see that there are two such times—just before noon and just before midnight. In general, is there a number c at which the value of a function f is exactly equal to the average value of the function, that is, $f(c) = f_{ave}$? The following theorem says that this is indeed the case for continuous functions.

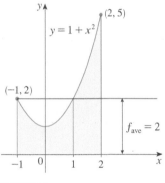

FIGURE 2

You can always chop off the top of a (two-dimensional) mountain at a certain height and use it to fill in the valleys so that the mountain becomes completely flat.

> **The Mean Value Theorem for Integrals**   If f is continuous on $[a, b]$, then there exists a number c in $[a, b]$ such that
>
> $$f(c) = f_{\text{ave}} = \frac{1}{b - a} \int_a^b f(x)\, dx$$
>
> that is,
>
> $$\int_a^b f(x)\, dx = f(c)(b - a)$$

The Mean Value Theorem for Integrals is a consequence of the Mean Value Theorem for derivatives and the Fundamental Theorem of Calculus. The proof is outlined in Exercise 21.

The geometric interpretation of the Mean Value Theorem for Integrals is that, for *positive* functions f, there is a number c such that the rectangle with base $[a, b]$ and height $f(c)$ has the same area as the region under the graph of f from a to b. (See Figure 2 and the more picturesque interpretation in the margin note.)

V   EXAMPLE 2   Finding the value of c in the Mean Value Theorem for Integrals
Since $f(x) = 1 + x^2$ is continuous on the interval $[-1, 2]$, the Mean Value Theorem for Integrals says there is a number c in $[-1, 2]$ such that

$$\int_{-1}^2 (1 + x^2)\, dx = f(c)[2 - (-1)]$$

In this particular case we can find c explicitly. From Example 1 we know that $f_{\text{ave}} = 2$, so the value of c satisfies

$$f(c) = f_{\text{ave}} = 2$$

Therefore $1 + c^2 = 2$ so $c^2 = 1$

So in this case there happen to be two numbers $c = \pm 1$ in the interval $[-1, 2]$ that work in the Mean Value Theorem for Integrals.

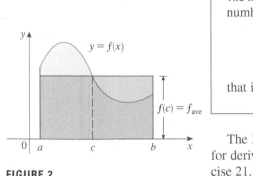

FIGURE 3

Examples 1 and 2 are illustrated by Figure 3.

V   EXAMPLE 3   Show that the average velocity of a car over a time interval $[t_1, t_2]$ is the same as the average of its velocities during the trip.

SOLUTION   If $s(t)$ is the displacement of the car at time t, then, by definition, the average velocity of the car over the interval is

$$\frac{\Delta s}{\Delta t} = \frac{s(t_2) - s(t_1)}{t_2 - t_1}$$

On the other hand, the average value of the velocity function on the interval is

$$v_{\text{ave}} = \frac{1}{t_2 - t_1} \int_{t_1}^{t_2} v(t)\, dt = \frac{1}{t_2 - t_1} \int_{t_1}^{t_2} s'(t)\, dt$$

$$= \frac{1}{t_2 - t_1} [s(t_2) - s(t_1)] \qquad \text{(by the Net Change Theorem)}$$

$$= \frac{s(t_2) - s(t_1)}{t_2 - t_1} = \text{average velocity}$$

6.5 Exercises

1–6 Find the average value of the function on the given interval.

1. $f(x) = 4x - x^2$, $\quad [0, 4]$

2. $f(x) = \sin 4x$, $\quad [-\pi, \pi]$

3. $g(x) = \sqrt[3]{x}$, $\quad [1, 8]$

4. $f(\theta) = \sec^2(\theta/2)$, $\quad [0, \pi/2]$

5. $h(x) = \cos^4 x \sin x$, $\quad [0, \pi]$

6. $h(u) = (3 - 2u)^{-1}$, $\quad [-1, 1]$

7–10
(a) Find the average value of f on the given interval.
(b) Find c such that $f_{\text{ave}} = f(c)$.
(c) Sketch the graph of f and a rectangle whose area is the same as the area under the graph of f.

7. $f(x) = (x - 3)^2$, $\quad [2, 5]$

8. $f(x) = \ln x$, $\quad [1, 3]$

9. $f(x) = 2 \sin x - \sin 2x$, $\quad [0, \pi]$

10. $f(x) = 2x/(1 + x^2)^2$, $\quad [0, 2]$

11. If f is continuous and $\int_1^3 f(x) \, dx = 8$, show that f takes on the value 4 at least once on the interval $[1, 3]$.

12. Find the numbers b such that the average value of $f(x) = 2 + 6x - 3x^2$ on the interval $[0, b]$ is equal to 3.

13. The table gives values of a continuous function. Use Simpson's Rule to estimate the average value of f on $[20, 50]$.

x	20	25	30	35	40	45	50
$f(x)$	42	38	31	29	35	48	60

14. The velocity graph of an accelerating car is shown.

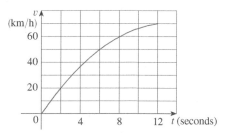

(a) Estimate the average velocity of the car during the first 12 seconds.

(b) At what time was the instantaneous velocity equal to the average velocity?

15. In a certain city the temperature (in °F) t hours after 9 AM was modeled by the function

$$T(t) = 50 + 14 \sin \frac{\pi t}{12}$$

Find the average temperature during the period from 9 AM to 9 PM.

16. If a cup of coffee has temperature 95°C in a room where the temperature is 20°C, then, according to Newton's Law of Cooling, the temperature of the coffee after t minutes is $T(t) = 20 + 75e^{-t/50}$. What is the average temperature of the coffee during the first half hour?

17. The linear density in a rod 8 m long is $12/\sqrt{x + 1}$ kg/m, where x is measured in meters from one end of the rod. Find the average density of the rod.

18. If a freely falling body starts from rest, then its displacement is given by $s = \frac{1}{2}gt^2$. Let the velocity after a time T be v_T. Show that if we compute the average of the velocities with respect to t we get $v_{\text{ave}} = \frac{1}{2}v_T$, but if we compute the average of the velocities with respect to s we get $v_{\text{ave}} = \frac{2}{3}v_T$.

19. Use the result of Exercise 65 in Section 5.5 to compute the average volume of inhaled air in the lungs in one respiratory cycle.

20. The velocity v of blood that flows in a blood vessel with radius R and length l at a distance r from the central axis is

$$v(r) = \frac{P}{4\eta l}(R^2 - r^2)$$

where P is the pressure difference between the ends of the vessel and η is the viscosity of the blood (see Example 7 in Section 3.8). Find the average velocity (with respect to r) over the interval $0 \le r \le R$. Compare the average velocity with the maximum velocity.

21. Prove the Mean Value Theorem for Integrals by applying the Mean Value Theorem for derivatives (see Section 4.3) to the function $F(x) = \int_a^x f(t) \, dt$.

22. If $f_{\text{ave}}[a, b]$ denotes the average value of f on the interval $[a, b]$ and $a < c < b$, show that

$$f_{\text{ave}}[a, b] = \frac{c - a}{b - a} f_{\text{ave}}[a, c] + \frac{b - c}{b - a} f_{\text{ave}}[c, b]$$

[CAS]   **Where To Sit at the Movies**

A movie theater has a screen that is positioned 10 ft off the floor and is 25 ft high. The first row of seats is placed 9 ft from the screen and the rows are set 3 ft apart. The floor of the seating area is inclined at an angle of $\alpha = 20°$ above the horizontal and the distance up the incline that you sit is x. The theater has 21 rows of seats, so $0 \leqslant x \leqslant 60$. Suppose you decide that the best place to sit is in the row where the angle θ subtended by the screen at your eyes is a maximum. Let's also suppose that your eyes are 4 ft above the floor, as shown in the figure. (In Exercise 58 in Section 4.6 we looked at a simpler version of this problem, where the floor is horizontal, but this project involves a more complicated situation and requires technology.)

1. Show that

$$\theta = \arccos\left(\frac{a^2 + b^2 - 625}{2ab}\right)$$

where $a^2 = (9 + x \cos \alpha)^2 + (31 - x \sin \alpha)^2$

and $b^2 = (9 + x \cos \alpha)^2 + (x \sin \alpha - 6)^2$

2. Use a graph of θ as a function of x to estimate the value of x that maximizes θ. In which row should you sit? What is the viewing angle θ in this row?

3. Use your computer algebra system to differentiate θ and find a numerical value for the root of the equation $d\theta/dx = 0$. Does this value confirm your result in Problem 2?

4. Use the graph of θ to estimate the average value of θ on the interval $0 \leqslant x \leqslant 60$. Then use your CAS to compute the average value. Compare with the maximum and minimum values of θ.

[CAS] Computer algebra system required

As a consequence of a calculation of work, you will be able to compute the velocity needed for a rocket to escape the earth's gravitational field. (See Exercise 28.)

Among the many applications of integral calculus to physics and engineering, we consider three: work, force due to water pressure, and centers of mass. As with our previous applications to geometry (areas, volumes, and lengths), our strategy is to break up the physical quantity into a large number of small parts, approximate each small part, add the results, take the limit, and evaluate the resulting integral.

Work

The term *work* is used in everyday language to mean the total amount of effort required to perform a task. In physics it has a technical meaning that depends on the idea of a *force*. Intuitively, you can think of a force as describing a push or pull on an object—for example, a horizontal push of a book across a table or the downward pull of the earth's gravity on a ball. In general, if an object moves along a straight line with position function $s(t)$, then the **force** F on the object (in the same direction) is defined by Newton's Second Law of Motion as the product of its mass m and its acceleration:

$$\boxed{1} \qquad\qquad F = m\,\frac{d^2s}{dt^2}$$

In the SI metric system, the mass is measured in kilograms (kg), the displacement in meters (m), the time in seconds (s), and the force in newtons (N = kg·m/s²). Thus a force of 1 N acting on a mass of 1 kg produces an acceleration of 1 m/s². In the US Customary system the fundamental unit is chosen to be the unit of force, which is the pound.

In the case of constant acceleration, the force F is also constant and the work done is defined to be the product of the force F and the distance d that the object moves:

$$\boxed{2} \qquad\qquad W = Fd \qquad \text{work} = \text{force} \times \text{distance}$$

If F is measured in newtons and d in meters, then the unit for W is a newton-meter, which is called a joule (J). If F is measured in pounds and d in feet, then the unit for W is a foot-pound (ft-lb), which is about 1.36 J.

For instance, suppose you lift a 1.2-kg book off the floor to put it on a desk that is 0.7 m high. The force you exert is equal and opposite to that exerted by gravity, so Equation 1 gives

$$F = mg = (1.2)(9.8) = 11.76 \text{ N}$$

and then Equation 2 gives the work done as

$$W = Fd = (11.76)(0.7) \approx 8.2 \text{ J}$$

But if a 20-lb weight is lifted 6 ft off the ground, then the force is given as $F = 20$ lb, so the work done is

$$W = Fd = 20 \cdot 6 = 120 \text{ ft-lb}$$

Here we didn't multiply by g because we were given the *weight* (a force) and not the mass.

Equation 2 defines work as long as the force is constant, but what happens if the force is variable? Let's suppose that the object moves along the x-axis in the positive direction, from $x = a$ to $x = b$, and at each point x between a and b a force $f(x)$ acts on the object, where f is a continuous function. We divide the interval $[a, b]$ into n subintervals with endpoints $x_0, x_1, \ldots, x_n$ and equal width Δx. We choose a sample point x_i^* in the ith subinterval $[x_{i-1}, x_i]$. Then the force at that point is $f(x_i^*)$. If n is large, then Δx is small, and since f is continuous, the values of f don't change very much over the interval $[x_{i-1}, x_i]$. In other words, f is almost constant on the interval and so the work W_i that is done in moving the particle from x_{i-1} to x_i is approximately given by Equation 2:

$$W_i \approx f(x_i^*)\,\Delta x$$

Thus we can approximate the total work by

$$\boxed{3} \qquad\qquad W \approx \sum_{i=1}^{n} f(x_i^*)\,\Delta x$$

It seems that this approximation becomes better as we make n larger. Therefore we define the **work done in moving the object from a to b** as the limit of this quantity as $n \to \infty$. Since the right side of (3) is a Riemann sum, we recognize its limit as being a definite integral and so

$$\boxed{4} \qquad\qquad W = \lim_{n \to \infty} \sum_{i=1}^{n} f(x_i^*)\,\Delta x = \int_a^b f(x)\,dx$$

EXAMPLE 1 **Work done by a variable force** When a particle is located a distance x feet from the origin, a force of $x^2 + 2x$ pounds acts on it. How much work is done in moving it from $x = 1$ to $x = 3$?

SOLUTION
$$W = \int_1^3 (x^2 + 2x)\, dx = \frac{x^3}{3} + x^2 \Big]_1^3 = \frac{50}{3}$$

The work done is $16\frac{2}{3}$ ft-lb.

In the next example we use a law from physics: **Hooke's Law** states that the force required to maintain a spring stretched x units beyond its natural length is proportional to x:
$$f(x) = kx$$
where k is a positive constant (called the **spring constant**). Hooke's Law holds provided that x is not too large (see Figure 1).

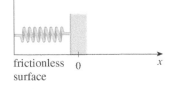

frictionless surface 0 x

(a) Natural position of spring

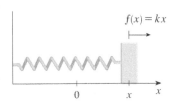

$f(x) = kx$

0   x x

(b) Stretched position of spring

FIGURE 1

Hooke's Law

V **EXAMPLE 2** **Work needed to stretch a spring** A force of 40 N is required to hold a spring that has been stretched from its natural length of 10 cm to a length of 15 cm. How much work is done in stretching the spring from 15 cm to 18 cm?

SOLUTION According to Hooke's Law, the force required to hold the spring stretched x meters beyond its natural length is $f(x) = kx$. When the spring is stretched from 10 cm to 15 cm, the amount stretched is 5 cm $= 0.05$ m. This means that $f(0.05) = 40$, so
$$0.05k = 40 \qquad k = \frac{40}{0.05} = 800$$

Thus $f(x) = 800x$ and the work done in stretching the spring from 15 cm to 18 cm is
$$W = \int_{0.05}^{0.08} 800x\, dx = 800 \frac{x^2}{2} \Big]_{0.05}^{0.08}$$
$$= 400[(0.08)^2 - (0.05)^2] = 1.56 \text{ J}$$

V **EXAMPLE 3** **Work needed to lift a cable** A 200-lb cable is 100 ft long and hangs vertically from the top of a tall building. How much work is required to lift the cable to the top of the building?

SOLUTION Here we don't have a formula for the force function, but we can use an argument similar to the one that led to Definition 4.

Let's place the origin at the top of the building and the x-axis pointing downward as in Figure 2. We divide the cable into small parts with length Δx. If x_i^* is a point in the ith such interval, then all points in the interval are lifted by approximately the same amount, namely x_i^*. The cable weighs 2 pounds per foot, so the weight of the ith part is $2\,\Delta x$. Thus the work done on the ith part, in foot-pounds, is
$$\underbrace{(2\,\Delta x)}_{\text{force}} \cdot \underbrace{x_i^*}_{\text{distance}} = 2x_i^*\, \Delta x$$

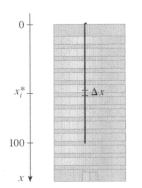

0

x_i^* $\leftrightarrows \Delta x$

100

x ↓

FIGURE 2

If we had placed the origin at the bottom of the cable and the x-axis upward, we would have gotten
$$W = \int_0^{100} 2(100 - x)\, dx$$
which gives the same answer.

We get the total work done by adding all these approximations and letting the number of parts become large (so $\Delta x \to 0$):
$$W = \lim_{n \to \infty} \sum_{i=1}^n 2x_i^*\, \Delta x = \int_0^{100} 2x\, dx$$
$$= x^2 \Big]_0^{100} = 10,000 \text{ ft-lb}$$

EXAMPLE 4 **Work needed to empty a tank** A tank has the shape of an inverted circular cone with height 10 m and base radius 4 m. It is filled with water to a height of 8 m. Find the work required to empty the tank by pumping all of the water to the top of the tank. (The density of water is 1000 kg/m³.)

SOLUTION Let's measure depths from the top of the tank by introducing a vertical coordinate line as in Figure 3. The water extends from a depth of 2 m to a depth of 10 m and so we divide the interval [2, 10] into n subintervals with endpoints $x_0, x_1, \ldots, x_n$ and choose x_i^* in the ith subinterval. This divides the water into n layers. The ith layer is approximated by a circular cylinder with radius r_i and height Δx. We can compute r_i from similar triangles, using Figure 4, as follows:

$$\frac{r_i}{10 - x_i^*} = \frac{4}{10} \qquad r_i = \tfrac{2}{5}(10 - x_i^*)$$

Thus an approximation to the volume of the ith layer of water is

$$V_i \approx \pi r_i^2 \, \Delta x = \frac{4\pi}{25}(10 - x_i^*)^2 \, \Delta x$$

and so its mass is

$$m_i = \text{density} \times \text{volume}$$

$$\approx 1000 \cdot \frac{4\pi}{25}(10 - x_i^*)^2 \, \Delta x = 160\pi(10 - x_i^*)^2 \, \Delta x$$

The force required to raise this layer must overcome the force of gravity and so

$$F_i = m_i g \approx (9.8)160\pi(10 - x_i^*)^2 \, \Delta x$$
$$= 1568\pi(10 - x_i^*)^2 \, \Delta x$$

Each particle in the layer must travel a distance of approximately x_i^*. The work W_i done to raise this layer to the top is approximately the product of the force F_i and the distance x_i^*:

$$W_i \approx F_i x_i^* \approx 1568\pi x_i^*(10 - x_i^*)^2 \, \Delta x$$

To find the total work done in emptying the entire tank, we add the contributions of each of the n layers and then take the limit as $n \to \infty$:

$$W = \lim_{n\to\infty} \sum_{i=1}^{n} 1568\pi x_i^*(10 - x_i^*)^2 \, \Delta x = \int_2^{10} 1568\pi x(10 - x)^2 \, dx$$

$$= 1568\pi \int_2^{10} (100x - 20x^2 + x^3) \, dx = 1568\pi \left[50x^2 - \frac{20x^3}{3} + \frac{x^4}{4} \right]_2^{10}$$

$$= 1568\pi \left(\tfrac{2048}{3} \right) \approx 3.4 \times 10^6 \text{ J}$$

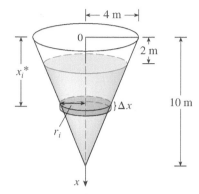

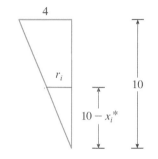

FIGURE 3

FIGURE 4

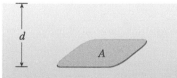

surface of fluid

FIGURE 5

Hydrostatic Pressure and Force

Deep-sea divers realize that water pressure increases as they dive deeper. This is because the weight of the water above them increases.

In general, suppose that a thin horizontal plate with area A square meters is submerged in a fluid of density ρ kilograms per cubic meter at a depth d meters below the surface of the fluid as in Figure 5. The fluid directly above the plate has volume $V = Ad$, so its mass is $m = \rho V = \rho A d$. The force exerted by the fluid on the plate is therefore

$$F = mg = \rho g A d$$

where g is the acceleration due to gravity. The pressure P on the plate is defined to be the force per unit area:

$$P = \frac{F}{A} = \rho g d$$

When using US Customary units, we write $P = \rho g d = \delta d$, where $\delta = \rho g$ is the *weight* density (as opposed to ρ, which is the *mass* density). For instance, the weight density of water is $\delta = 62.5 \text{ lb/ft}^3$.

The SI unit for measuring pressure is newtons per square meter, which is called a pascal (abbreviation: $1 \text{ N/m}^2 = 1 \text{ Pa}$). Since this is a small unit, the kilopascal (kPa) is often used. For instance, because the density of water is $\rho = 1000 \text{ kg/m}^3$, the pressure at the bottom of a swimming pool 2 m deep is

$$P = \rho g d = 1000 \text{ kg/m}^3 \times 9.8 \text{ m/s}^2 \times 2 \text{ m}$$

$$= 19{,}600 \text{ Pa} = 19.6 \text{ kPa}$$

An important principle of fluid pressure is the experimentally verified fact that *at any point in a liquid the pressure is the same in all directions.* (A diver feels the same pressure on nose and both ears.) Thus the pressure in *any* direction at a depth d in a fluid with mass density ρ is given by

$$\boxed{5} \qquad\qquad P = \rho g d = \delta d$$

This helps us determine the hydrostatic force against a *vertical* plate or wall or dam in a fluid. This is not a straightforward problem because the pressure is not constant but increases as the depth increases.

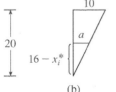

FIGURE 6

V EXAMPLE 5 Hydrostatic force on a dam   A dam has the shape of the trapezoid shown in Figure 6. The height is 20 m and the width is 50 m at the top and 30 m at the bottom. Find the force on the dam due to hydrostatic pressure if the water level is 4 m from the top of the dam.

SOLUTION We choose a vertical x-axis with origin at the surface of the water as in Figure 7(a). The depth of the water is 16 m, so we divide the interval $[0, 16]$ into subintervals of equal length with endpoints x_i and we choose $x_i^* \in [x_{i-1}, x_i]$. The ith horizontal strip of the dam is approximated by a rectangle with height Δx and width w_i, where, from similar triangles in Figure 7(b),

$$\frac{a}{16 - x_i^*} = \frac{10}{20} \qquad \text{or} \qquad a = \frac{16 - x_i^*}{2} = 8 - \frac{x_i^*}{2}$$

and so

$$w_i = 2(15 + a) = 2\left(15 + 8 - \tfrac{1}{2}x_i^*\right) = 46 - x_i^*$$

If A_i is the area of the ith strip, then

$$A_i \approx w_i \, \Delta x = (46 - x_i^*) \, \Delta x$$

If Δx is small, then the pressure P_i on the ith strip is almost constant and we can use Equation 5 to write

$$P_i \approx 1000 g x_i^*$$

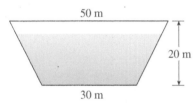

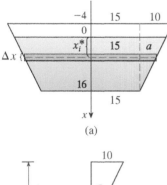

FIGURE 7

The hydrostatic force F_i acting on the ith strip is the product of the pressure and the area:

$$F_i = P_i A_i \approx 1000 g x_i^* (46 - x_i^*) \, \Delta x$$

Adding these forces and taking the limit as $n \to \infty$, we obtain the total hydrostatic force on the dam:

$$F = \lim_{n \to \infty} \sum_{i=1}^{n} 1000 g x_i^* (46 - x_i^*) \, \Delta x = \int_0^{16} 1000 g x (46 - x) \, dx$$

$$= 1000(9.8) \int_0^{16} (46x - x^2) \, dx = 9800 \left[23x^2 - \frac{x^3}{3} \right]_0^{16}$$

$$\approx 4.43 \times 10^7 \text{ N}$$

Moments and Centers of Mass

Our main objective here is to find the point P on which a thin plate of any given shape balances horizontally as in Figure 8. This point is called the **center of mass** (or center of gravity) of the plate.

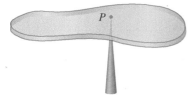

FIGURE 8

We first consider the simpler situation illustrated in Figure 9, where two masses m_1 and m_2 are attached to a rod of negligible mass on opposite sides of a fulcrum and at distances d_1 and d_2 from the fulcrum. The rod will balance if

6	$$m_1 d_1 = m_2 d_2$$

This is an experimental fact discovered by Archimedes and called the Law of the Lever. (Think of a lighter person balancing a heavier one on a seesaw by sitting farther away from the center.)

Now suppose that the rod lies along the x-axis with m_1 at x_1 and m_2 at x_2 and the center of mass at $\bar{x}$. If we compare Figures 9 and 10, we see that $d_1 = \bar{x} - x_1$ and $d_2 = x_2 - \bar{x}$ and so Equation 6 gives

$$m_1(\bar{x} - x_1) = m_2(x_2 - \bar{x})$$

$$m_1 \bar{x} + m_2 \bar{x} = m_1 x_1 + m_2 x_2$$

7	$$\bar{x} = \frac{m_1 x_1 + m_2 x_2}{m_1 + m_2}$$

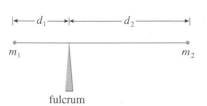

FIGURE 9

The numbers $m_1 x_1$ and $m_2 x_2$ are called the **moments** of the masses m_1 and m_2 (with respect to the origin), and Equation 7 says that the center of mass $\bar{x}$ is obtained by adding the moments of the masses and dividing by the total mass $m = m_1 + m_2$.

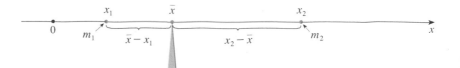

FIGURE 10

In general, if we have a system of n particles with masses $m_1, m_2, \ldots, m_n$ located at the points $x_1, x_2, \ldots, x_n$ on the x-axis, it can be shown similarly that the center of mass of the system is located at

8	$$\bar{x} = \frac{\displaystyle\sum_{i=1}^{n} m_i x_i}{\displaystyle\sum_{i=1}^{n} m_i} = \frac{\displaystyle\sum_{i=1}^{n} m_i x_i}{m}$$

where $m = \Sigma\, m_i$ is the total mass of the system, and the sum of the individual moments

$$M = \sum_{i=1}^{n} m_i x_i$$

is called the **moment of the system about the origin**. Then Equation 8 could be rewritten as $m\bar{x} = M$, which says that if the total mass were considered as being concentrated at the center of mass $\bar{x}$, then its moment would be the same as the moment of the system.

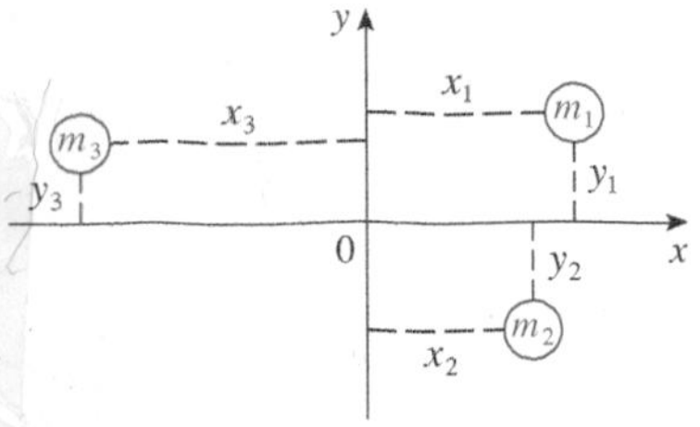

Now we consider a system of n particles with masses $m_1, m_2, \ldots, m_n$ located at the points $(x_1, y_1), (x_2, y_2), \ldots, (x_n, y_n)$ in the xy-plane as shown in Figure 11. By analogy with the one-dimensional case, we define the **moment of the system about the y-axis** to be

$$\boxed{9}\qquad M_y = \sum_{i=1}^{n} m_i x_i$$

and the **moment of the system about the x-axis** as

$$\boxed{10}\qquad M_x = \sum_{i=1}^{n} m_i y_i$$

Then M_y measures the tendency of the system to rotate about the y-axis and M_x measures the tendency to rotate about the x-axis.

As in the one-dimensional case, the coordinates $(\bar{x}, \bar{y})$ of the center of mass are given in terms of the moments by the formulas

$$\boxed{11}\qquad \bar{x} = \frac{M_y}{m}\qquad \bar{y} = \frac{M_x}{m}$$

where $m = \Sigma\, m_i$ is the total mass. Since $m\bar{x} = M_y$ and $m\bar{y} = M_x$, the center of mass $(\bar{x}, \bar{y})$ is the point where a single particle of mass m would have the same moments as the system.

V EXAMPLE 6　Find the moments and center of mass of the system of objects that have masses 3, 4, and 8 at the points $(-1, 1)$, $(2, -1)$, and $(3, 2)$.

SOLUTION　We use Equations 9 and 10 to compute the moments:

$$M_y = 3(-1) + 4(2) + 8(3) = 29$$
$$M_x = 3(1) + 4(-1) + 8(2) = 15$$

Since $m = 3 + 4 + 8 = 15$, we use Equations 11 to obtain

$$\bar{x} = \frac{M_y}{m} = \frac{29}{15}\qquad \bar{y} = \frac{M_x}{m} = \frac{15}{15} = 1$$

Thus the center of mass is $\left(1\tfrac{14}{15}, 1\right)$. (See Figure 12.)

Next we consider a flat plate (called a *lamina*) with uniform density ρ that occupies a region $\mathcal{R}$ of the plane. We wish to locate the center of mass of the plate, which is called the **centroid** of $\mathcal{R}$. In doing so we use the following physical principles: The **symmetry principle** says that if $\mathcal{R}$ is symmetric about a line l, then the centroid of $\mathcal{R}$ lies on l. (If $\mathcal{R}$ is reflected about l, then $\mathcal{R}$ remains the same so its centroid remains fixed. But the only

FIGURE 11

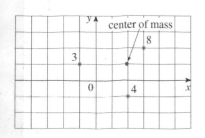

FIGURE 12

fixed points lie on *l*.) Thus the centroid of a rectangle is its center. Moments should be defined so that if the entire mass of a region is concentrated at the center of mass, then its moments remain unchanged. Also, the moment of the union of two nonoverlapping regions should be the sum of the moments of the individual regions.

Suppose that the region $\mathcal{R}$ is of the type shown in Figure 13(a); that is, $\mathcal{R}$ lies between the lines $x = a$ and $x = b$, above the x-axis, and beneath the graph of f, where f is a continuous function. We divide the interval $[a, b]$ into n subintervals with endpoints x_0, $x_1, \ldots, x_n$ and equal width Δx. We choose the sample point x_i^* to be the midpoint $\bar{x}_i$ of the ith subinterval, that is, $\bar{x}_i = (x_{i-1} + x_i)/2$. This determines the polygonal approximation to $\mathcal{R}$ shown in Figure 13(b). The centroid of the ith approximating rectangle R_i is its center $C_i(\bar{x}_i, \frac{1}{2} f(\bar{x}_i))$. Its area is $f(\bar{x}_i)\,\Delta x$, so its mass is

$$\rho f(\bar{x}_i)\,\Delta x$$

The moment of R_i about the y-axis is the product of its mass and the distance from C_i to the y-axis, which is $\bar{x}_i$. Thus

$$M_y(R_i) = [\rho f(\bar{x}_i)\,\Delta x]\,\bar{x}_i = \rho \bar{x}_i f(\bar{x}_i)\,\Delta x$$

Adding these moments, we obtain the moment of the polygonal approximation to $\mathcal{R}$, and then by taking the limit as $n \to \infty$ we obtain the moment of $\mathcal{R}$ itself about the y-axis:

$$M_y = \lim_{n \to \infty} \sum_{i=1}^{n} \rho \bar{x}_i f(\bar{x}_i)\,\Delta x = \rho \int_a^b x f(x)\,dx$$

In a similar fashion we compute the moment of R_i about the x-axis as the product of its mass and the distance from C_i to the x-axis:

$$M_x(R_i) = [\rho f(\bar{x}_i)\,\Delta x]\tfrac{1}{2} f(\bar{x}_i) = \rho \cdot \tfrac{1}{2}[f(\bar{x}_i)]^2\,\Delta x$$

Again we add these moments and take the limit to obtain the moment of $\mathcal{R}$ about the x-axis:

$$M_x = \lim_{n \to \infty} \sum_{i=1}^{n} \rho \cdot \tfrac{1}{2}[f(\bar{x}_i)]^2\,\Delta x = \rho \int_a^b \tfrac{1}{2}[f(x)]^2\,dx$$

Just as for systems of particles, the center of mass of the plate is defined so that $m\bar{x} = M_y$ and $m\bar{y} = M_x$. But the mass of the plate is the product of its density and its area:

$$m = \rho A = \rho \int_a^b f(x)\,dx$$

and so

$$\bar{x} = \frac{M_y}{m} = \frac{\rho \int_a^b x f(x)\,dx}{\rho \int_a^b f(x)\,dx} = \frac{\int_a^b x f(x)\,dx}{\int_a^b f(x)\,dx}$$

$$\bar{y} = \frac{M_x}{m} = \frac{\rho \int_a^b \tfrac{1}{2}[f(x)]^2\,dx}{\rho \int_a^b f(x)\,dx} = \frac{\int_a^b \tfrac{1}{2}[f(x)]^2\,dx}{\int_a^b f(x)\,dx}$$

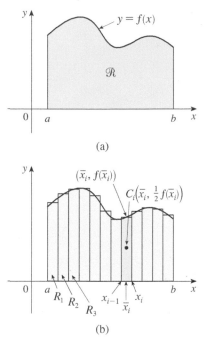

FIGURE 13

Notice the cancellation of the ρ's. The location of the center of mass is independent of the density.

In summary, the center of mass of the plate (or the centroid of $\mathscr{R}$) is located at the point $(\bar{x}, \bar{y})$, where

$$\boxed{12} \qquad \bar{x} = \frac{1}{A} \int_a^b x f(x)\, dx \qquad \bar{y} = \frac{1}{A} \int_a^b \tfrac{1}{2}[f(x)]^2\, dx$$

EXAMPLE 7 Find the center of mass of a semicircular plate of radius r.

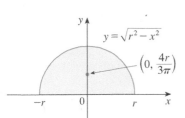

FIGURE 14

SOLUTION In order to use (12) we place the semicircle as in Figure 14 so that $f(x) = \sqrt{r^2 - x^2}$ and $a = -r$, $b = r$. Here there is no need to use the formula to calculate $\bar{x}$ because, by the symmetry principle, the center of mass must lie on the y-axis, so $\bar{x} = 0$. The area of the semicircle is $A = \tfrac{1}{2}\pi r^2$, so

$$\bar{y} = \frac{1}{A} \int_{-r}^r \tfrac{1}{2}[f(x)]^2\, dx$$

$$= \frac{1}{\tfrac{1}{2}\pi r^2} \cdot \tfrac{1}{2} \int_{-r}^r \left(\sqrt{r^2 - x^2}\right)^2 dx$$

$$= \frac{2}{\pi r^2} \int_0^r (r^2 - x^2)\, dx = \frac{2}{\pi r^2}\left[r^2 x - \frac{x^3}{3} \right]_0^r$$

$$= \frac{2}{\pi r^2} \frac{2r^3}{3} = \frac{4r}{3\pi}$$

The center of mass is located at the point $(0, 4r/(3\pi))$.

6.6 Exercises

1. A particle is moved along the x-axis by a force that measures $10/(1 + x)^2$ pounds at a point x feet from the origin. Find the work done in moving the particle from the origin to a distance of 9 ft.

2. When a particle is located a distance x meters from the origin, a force of $\cos(\pi x/3)$ newtons acts on it. How much work is done in moving the particle from $x = 1$ to $x = 2$? Interpret your answer by considering the work done from $x = 1$ to $x = 1.5$ and from $x = 1.5$ to $x = 2$.

3. Shown is the graph of a force function (in newtons) that increases to its maximum value and then remains constant. How much work is done by the force in moving an object a distance of 8 m?

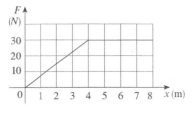

4. The table shows values of a force function $f(x)$, where x is measured in meters and $f(x)$ in newtons. Use Simpson's Rule to estimate the work done by the force in moving an object a distance of 18 m.

x	0	3	6	9	12	15	18
$f(x)$	9.8	9.1	8.5	8.0	7.7	7.5	7.4

5. A force of 10 lb is required to hold a spring stretched 4 in. beyond its natural length. How much work is done in stretching it from its natural length to 6 in. beyond its natural length?

6. A spring has a natural length of 20 cm. If a 25-N force is required to keep it stretched to a length of 30 cm, how much work is required to stretch it from 20 cm to 25 cm?

7. Suppose that 2 J of work is needed to stretch a spring from its natural length of 30 cm to a length of 42 cm.
(a) How much work is needed to stretch the spring from 35 cm to 40 cm?
(b) How far beyond its natural length will a force of 30 N keep the spring stretched?

⊞ Graphing calculator or computer with graphing software required   **1.** Homework Hints available in TEC

8. If the work required to stretch a spring 1 ft beyond its natural length is 12 ft-lb, how much work is needed to stretch it 9 in. beyond its natural length?

9. A spring has natural length 20 cm. Compare the work W_1 done in stretching the spring from 20 cm to 30 cm with the work W_2 done in stretching it from 30 cm to 40 cm. How are W_2 and W_1 related?

10. If 6 J of work is needed to stretch a spring from 10 cm to 12 cm and another 10 J is needed to stretch it from 12 cm to 14 cm, what is the natural length of the spring?

11–18 Show how to approximate the required work by a Riemann sum. Then express the work as an integral and evaluate it.

11. A heavy rope, 50 ft long, weighs 0.5 lb/ft and hangs over the edge of a building 120 ft high.
(a) How much work is done in pulling the rope to the top of the building?
(b) How much work is done in pulling half the rope to the top of the building?

12. A chain lying on the ground is 10 m long and its mass is 80 kg. How much work is required to raise one end of the chain to a height of 6 m?

13. A cable that weighs 2 lb/ft is used to lift 800 lb of coal up a mine shaft 500 ft deep. Find the work done.

14. A bucket that weighs 4 lb and a rope of negligible weight are used to draw water from a well that is 80 ft deep. The bucket is filled with 40 lb of water and is pulled up at a rate of 2 ft/s, but water leaks out of a hole in the bucket at a rate of 0.2 lb/s. Find the work done in pulling the bucket to the top of the well.

15. A leaky 10-kg bucket is lifted from the ground to a height of 12 m at a constant speed with a rope that weighs 0.8 kg/m. Initially the bucket contains 36 kg of water, but the water leaks at a constant rate and finishes draining just as the bucket reaches the 12-m level. How much work is done?

16. A 10-ft chain weighs 25 lb and hangs from a ceiling. Find the work done in lifting the lower end of the chain to the ceiling so that it's level with the upper end.

17. An aquarium 2 m long, 1 m wide, and 1 m deep is full of water. Find the work needed to pump half of the water out of the aquarium. (Use the fact that the density of water is 1000 kg/m³.)

18. A circular swimming pool has a diameter of 24 ft, the sides are 5 ft high, and the depth of the water is 4 ft. How much work is required to pump all of the water out over the side? (Use the fact that water weighs 62.5 lb/ft³.)

19–22 A tank is full of water. Find the work required to pump the water out of the spout. In Exercises 21 and 22 use the fact that water weighs 62.5 lb/ft³.

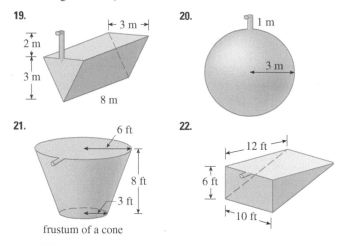

19.

20.

21.

frustum of a cone

22.

23. Suppose that for the tank in Exercise 19 the pump breaks down after 4.7×10^5 J of work has been done. What is the depth of the water remaining in the tank?

24. Solve Exercise 20 if the tank is half full of oil that has a density of 900 kg/m³.

25. When gas expands in a cylinder with radius r, the pressure at any given time is a function of the volume: $P = P(V)$. The force exerted by the gas on the piston (see the figure) is the product of the pressure and the area: $F = \pi r^2 P$. Show that the work done by the gas when the volume expands from volume V_1 to volume V_2 is

$$W = \int_{V_1}^{V_2} P \, dV$$

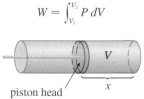

piston head

26. In a steam engine the pressure P and volume V of steam satisfy the equation $PV^{1.4} = k$, where k is a constant. (This is true for adiabatic expansion, that is, expansion in which there is no heat transfer between the cylinder and its surroundings.) Use Exercise 25 to calculate the work done by the engine during a cycle when the steam starts at a pressure of 160 lb/in² and a volume of 100 in³ and expands to a volume of 800 in³.

27. (a) Newton's Law of Gravitation states that two bodies with masses m_1 and m_2 attract each other with a force

$$F = G\frac{m_1 m_2}{r^2}$$

where r is the distance between the bodies and G is the gravitational constant. If one of the bodies is fixed, find the work needed to move the other from $r = a$ to $r = b$.

(b) Compute the work required to launch a 1000-kg satellite vertically to an orbit 1000 km high. You may assume that the earth's mass is 5.98×10^{24} kg and is concentrated at its center. Take the radius of the earth to be 6.37×10^6 m and $G = 6.67 \times 10^{-11}$ N·m²/kg².

28. (a) Use an improper integral and information from Exercise 27 to find the work needed to propel a 1000-kg satellite out of the earth's gravitational field.
(b) Find the *escape velocity* v_0 that is needed to propel a rocket of mass m out of the gravitational field of a planet with mass M and radius R. (Use the fact that the initial kinetic energy of $\frac{1}{2}mv_0^2$ supplies the needed work.)

29. An aquarium 5 ft long, 2 ft wide, and 3 ft deep is full of water. Find (a) the hydrostatic pressure on the bottom of the aquarium, (b) the hydrostatic force on the bottom, and (c) the hydrostatic force on one end of the aquarium.

30. A tank is 8 m long, 4 m wide, 2 m high, and contains kerosene with density 820 kg/m³ to a depth of 1.5 m. Find (a) the hydrostatic pressure on the bottom of the tank, (b) the hydrostatic force on the bottom, and (c) the hydrostatic force on one end of the tank.

31–36 A vertical plate is submerged (or partially submerged) in water and has the indicated shape. Explain how to approximate the hydrostatic force against one side of the plate by a Riemann sum. Then express the force as an integral and evaluate it.

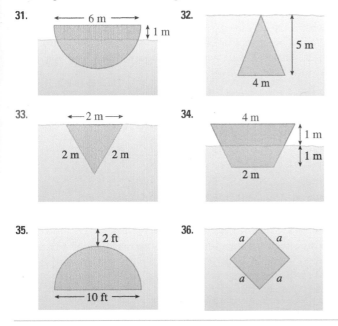

31. 6 m   1 m
32. 5 m   4 m
33. 2 m   2 m   2 m
34. 4 m   1 m   1 m   2 m
35. 2 ft   10 ft
36. a   a   a   a

37. A trough is filled with a liquid of density 840 kg/m³. The ends of the trough are equilateral triangles with sides 8 m long and vertex at the bottom. Find the hydrostatic force on one end of the trough.

38. A large tank is designed with ends in the shape of the region between the curves $y = \frac{1}{2}x^2$ and $y = 12$, measured in feet. Find the hydrostatic force on one end of the tank if it is filled to a depth of 8 ft with gasoline. (Assume the gasoline's density is 42.0 lb/ft³.)

39. A swimming pool is 20 ft wide and 40 ft long and its bottom is an inclined plane, the shallow end having a depth of 3 ft and the deep end, 9 ft. If the pool is full of water, estimate the hydrostatic force on (a) the shallow end, (b) the deep end, (c) one of the sides, and (d) the bottom of the pool.

40. A vertical dam has a semicircular gate as shown in the figure. Find the hydrostatic force against the gate.

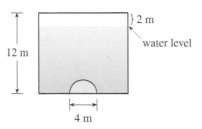

2 m
water level
12 m
4 m

41. A vertical, irregularly shaped plate is submerged in water. The table shows measurements of its width, taken at the indicated depths. Use Simpson's Rule to estimate the force of the water against the plate.

Depth (m)	2.0	2.5	3.0	3.5	4.0	4.5	5.0
Plate width (m)	0	0.8	1.7	2.4	2.9	3.3	3.6

42. Point-masses m_i are located on the x-axis as shown. Find the moment M of the system about the origin and the center of mass $\bar{x}$.

$m_1 = 25$ $m_2 = 20$ $m_3 = 10$
−2   0   3   7 x

43–44 The masses m_i are located at the points P_i. Find the moments M_x and M_y and the center of mass of the system.

43. $m_1 = 6$, $m_2 = 5$, $m_3 = 10$;
$P_1(1, 5)$, $P_2(3, -2)$, $P_3(-2, -1)$

44. $m_1 = 6$, $m_2 = 5$, $m_3 = 1$, $m_4 = 4$;
$P_1(1, -2)$, $P_2(3, 4)$, $P_3(-3, -7)$, $P_4(6, -1)$

45–48 Sketch the region bounded by the curves, and visually estimate the location of the centroid. Then find the exact coordinates of the centroid.

45. $y = 4 - x^2$, $y = 0$

46. $3x + 2y = 6$, $y = 0$, $x = 0$

47. $y = e^x$, $y = 0$, $x = 0$, $x = 1$

48. $y = 1/x$, $y = 0$, $x = 1$, $x = 2$

49–50 Calculate the moments M_x and M_y and the center of mass of a lamina with the given density and shape.

49. $\rho = 10$

50. $\rho = 2$

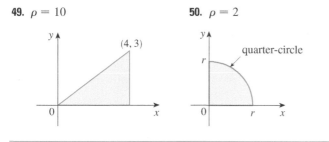

---

51. (a) Let $\mathcal{R}$ be the region that lies between two curves $y = f(x)$ and $y = g(x)$, where $f(x) \geqslant g(x)$ and $a \leqslant x \leqslant b$. By using the same sort of reasoning that led to the formulas in (12), show that the centroid of $\mathcal{R}$ is $(\bar{x}, \bar{y})$, where

$$\bar{x} = \frac{1}{A} \int_a^b x[f(x) - g(x)]\, dx$$

$$\bar{y} = \frac{1}{A} \int_a^b \tfrac{1}{2}\{[f(x)]^2 - [g(x)]^2\}\, dx$$

(b) Find the centroid of the region bounded by the line $y = x$ and the parabola $y = x^2$.

52. Let $\mathcal{R}$ be the region that lies between the curves $y = x^m$ and $y = x^n$, $0 \leqslant x \leqslant 1$, where m and n are integers with $0 \leqslant n < m$.

(a) Sketch the region $\mathcal{R}$.

(b) Find the coordinates of the centroid of $\mathcal{R}$.

(c) Try to find values of m and n such that the centroid lies *outside* $\mathcal{R}$.

DISCOVERY PROJECT | **Complementary Coffee Cups**

Suppose you have a choice of two coffee cups of the type shown, one that bends outward and one inward, and you notice that they have the same height and their shapes fit together snugly. You wonder which cup holds more coffee. Of course you could fill one cup with water and pour it into the other one but, being a calculus student, you decide on a more mathematical approach. Ignoring the handles, you observe that both cups are surfaces of revolution, so you can think of the coffee as a volume of revolution.

Cup A   Cup B

1. Suppose the cups have height h, cup A is formed by rotating the curve $x = f(y)$ about the y-axis, and cup B is formed by rotating the same curve about the line $x = k$. Find the value of k such that the two cups hold the same amount of coffee.

2. What does your result from Problem 1 say about the areas A_1 and A_2 shown in the figure?

3. Based on your own measurements and observations, suggest a value for h and an equation for $x = f(y)$ and calculate the amount of coffee that each cup holds.

6.7   Applications to Economics and Biology

In this section we consider some applications of integration to economics (consumer surplus) and biology (blood flow, cardiac output). Others are described in the exercises.

Consumer Surplus

Recall from Section 4.6 that the demand function $p(x)$ is the price that a company has to charge in order to sell x units of a commodity. Usually, selling larger quantities requires lowering prices, so the demand function is a decreasing function. The graph of a typical demand function, called a **demand curve**, is shown in Figure 1. If X is the amount of the commodity that is currently available, then $P = p(X)$ is the current selling price.

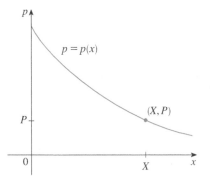

FIGURE 1

A typical demand curve

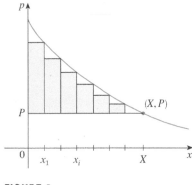

FIGURE 2

We divide the interval $[0, X]$ into n subintervals, each of length $\Delta x = X/n$, and let $x_i^* = x_i$ be the right endpoint of the ith subinterval, as in Figure 2. If, after the first x_{i-1} units were sold, a total of only x_i units had been available and the price per unit had been set at $p(x_i)$ dollars, then the additional Δx units could have been sold (but no more). The consumers who would have paid $p(x_i)$ dollars placed a high value on the product; they would have paid what it was worth to them. So, in paying only P dollars they have saved an amount of

$$(\text{savings per unit})(\text{number of units}) = [p(x_i) - P]\,\Delta x$$

Considering similar groups of willing consumers for each of the subintervals and adding the savings, we get the total savings:

$$\sum_{i=1}^{n} [p(x_i) - P]\,\Delta x$$

(This sum corresponds to the area enclosed by the rectangles in Figure 2.) If we let $n \to \infty$, this Riemann sum approaches the integral

$$\boxed{1} \qquad\qquad \int_0^X [p(x) - P]\,dx$$

which economists call the **consumer surplus** for the commodity.

The consumer surplus represents the amount of money saved by consumers in purchasing the commodity at price P, corresponding to an amount demanded of X. Figure 3 shows the interpretation of the consumer surplus as the area under the demand curve and above the line $p = P$.

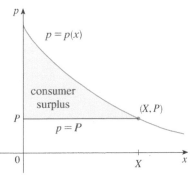

FIGURE 3

V **EXAMPLE 1** **Consumer surplus** The demand for a product, in dollars, is

$$p = 1200 - 0.2x - 0.0001x^2$$

Find the consumer surplus when the sales level is 500.

SOLUTION Since the number of products sold is $X = 500$, the corresponding price is

$$P = 1200 - (0.2)(500) - (0.0001)(500)^2 = 1075$$

Therefore, from Definition 1, the consumer surplus is

$$\int_0^{500} [p(x) - P]\, dx = \int_0^{500} (1200 - 0.2x - 0.0001x^2 - 1075)\, dx$$

$$= \int_0^{500} (125 - 0.2x - 0.0001x^2)\, dx$$

$$= 125x - 0.1x^2 - (0.0001)\left(\frac{x^3}{3}\right)\Bigg]_0^{500}$$

$$= (125)(500) - (0.1)(500)^2 - \frac{(0.0001)(500)^3}{3}$$

$$= \$33{,}333.33$$

Blood Flow

In Example 7 in Section 3.8 we discussed the law of laminar flow:

$$v(r) = \frac{P}{4\eta l}\,(R^2 - r^2)$$

which gives the velocity v of blood that flows along a blood vessel with radius R and length l at a distance r from the central axis, where P is the pressure difference between the ends of the vessel and η is the viscosity of the blood. Now, in order to compute the rate of blood flow, or *flux* (volume per unit time), we consider smaller, equally spaced radii $r_1, r_2, \ldots$. The approximate area of the ring (or washer) with inner radius r_{i-1} and outer radius r_i is

$$2\pi r_i\, \Delta r \qquad \text{where} \quad \Delta r = r_i - r_{i-1}$$

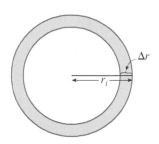

(See Figure 4.) If Δr is small, then the velocity is almost constant throughout this ring and can be approximated by $v(r_i)$. Thus the volume of blood per unit time that flows across the ring is approximately

$$(2\pi r_i\, \Delta r)\, v(r_i) = 2\pi r_i\, v(r_i)\, \Delta r$$

and the total volume of blood that flows across a cross-section per unit time is about

$$\sum_{i=1}^{n} 2\pi r_i\, v(r_i)\, \Delta r$$

FIGURE 4

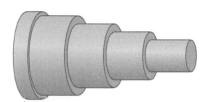

FIGURE 5

This approximation is illustrated in Figure 5. Notice that the velocity (and hence the volume per unit time) increases toward the center of the blood vessel. The approximation gets better as n increases. When we take the limit we get the exact value of the **flux** (or *discharge*), which is the volume of blood that passes a cross-section per unit time:

$$F = \lim_{n \to \infty} \sum_{i=1}^{n} 2\pi r_i \, v(r_i) \, \Delta r = \int_0^R 2\pi r \, v(r) \, dr$$

$$= \int_0^R 2\pi r \frac{P}{4\eta l} (R^2 - r^2) \, dr$$

$$= \frac{\pi P}{2\eta l} \int_0^R (R^2 r - r^3) \, dr = \frac{\pi P}{2\eta l} \left[R^2 \frac{r^2}{2} - \frac{r^4}{4} \right]_{r=0}^{r=R}$$

$$= \frac{\pi P}{2\eta l} \left[\frac{R^4}{2} - \frac{R^4}{4} \right] = \frac{\pi P R^4}{8\eta l}$$

The resulting equation

$$\boxed{2} \qquad\qquad F = \frac{\pi P R^4}{8\eta l}$$

is called **Poiseuille's Law**; it shows that the flux is proportional to the fourth power of the radius of the blood vessel.

Cardiac Output

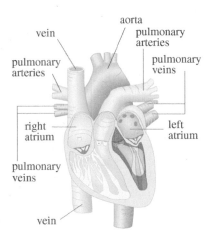

aorta
pulmonary arteries
pulmonary veins
pulmonary arteries
vein
right atrium
left atrium
pulmonary veins
vein

FIGURE 6

Figure 6 shows the human cardiovascular system. Blood returns from the body through the veins, enters the right atrium of the heart, and is pumped to the lungs through the pulmonary arteries for oxygenation. It then flows back into the left atrium through the pulmonary veins and then out to the rest of the body through the aorta. The **cardiac output** of the heart is the volume of blood pumped by the heart per unit time, that is, the rate of flow into the aorta.

The *dye dilution method* is used to measure the cardiac output. Dye is injected into the right atrium and flows through the heart into the aorta. A probe inserted into the aorta measures the concentration of the dye leaving the heart at equally spaced times over a time interval $[0, T]$ until the dye has cleared. Let $c(t)$ be the concentration of the dye at time t. If we divide $[0, T]$ into subintervals of equal length Δt, then the amount of dye that flows past the measuring point during the subinterval from $t = t_{i-1}$ to $t = t_i$ is approximately

$$(\text{concentration})(\text{volume}) = c(t_i)(F \, \Delta t)$$

where F is the rate of flow that we are trying to determine. Thus the total amount of dye is approximately

$$\sum_{i=1}^{n} c(t_i) F \, \Delta t = F \sum_{i=1}^{n} c(t_i) \, \Delta t$$

and, letting $n \to \infty$, we find that the amount of dye is

$$A = F \int_0^T c(t) \, dt$$

Thus the cardiac output is given by

$$\boxed{3} \qquad\qquad F = \frac{A}{\displaystyle\int_0^T c(t) \, dt}$$

where the amount of dye A is known and the integral can be approximated from the concentration readings.

t	$c(t)$	t	$c(t)$
0	0	6	6.1
1	0.4	7	4.0
2	2.8	8	2.3
3	6.5	9	1.1
4	9.8	10	0
5	8.9		

V EXAMPLE 2 Cardiac output A 5-mg bolus of dye is injected into a right atrium. The concentration of the dye (in milligrams per liter) is measured in the aorta at one-second intervals as shown in the chart. Estimate the cardiac output.

SOLUTION Here $A = 5$, $\Delta t = 1$, and $T = 10$. We use Simpson's Rule to approximate the integral of the concentration:

$$\int_0^{10} c(t)\, dt \approx \tfrac{1}{3}[0 + 4(0.4) + 2(2.8) + 4(6.5) + 2(9.8) + 4(8.9)$$

$$+ 2(6.1) + 4(4.0) + 2(2.3) + 4(1.1) + 0]$$

$$\approx 41.87$$

Thus Formula 3 gives the cardiac output to be

$$F = \frac{A}{\displaystyle\int_0^{10} c(t)\, dt} \approx \frac{5}{41.87} \approx 0.12 \text{ L/s} = 7.2 \text{ L/min}$$

6.7 Exercises

1. The marginal cost function $C'(x)$ was defined to be the derivative of the cost function. (See Sections 3.8 and 4.6.) If the marginal cost of maufacturing x meters of a fabric is $C'(x) = 5 - 0.008x + 0.000009x^2$ (measured in dollars per meter) and the fixed start-up cost is $C(0) = \$20{,}000$, use the Net Change Theorem to find the cost of producing the first 2000 units.

2. The marginal revenue from the sale of x units of a product is $12 - 0.0004x$. If the revenue from the sale of the first 1000 units is \$12,400, find the revenue from the sale of the first 5000 units.

3. The marginal cost of producing x units of a certain product is $74 + 1.1x - 0.002x^2 + 0.00004x^3$ (in dollars per unit). Find the increase in cost if the production level is raised from 1200 units to 1600 units.

4. The demand function for a certain commodity is $p = 20 - 0.05x$. Find the consumer surplus when the sales level is 300. Illustrate by drawing the demand curve and identifying the consumer surplus as an area.

5. A demand curve is given by $p = 450/(x + 8)$. Find the consumer surplus when the selling price is \$10.

6. The **supply function** $p_S(x)$ for a commodity gives the relation between the selling price and the number of units that manufacturers will produce at that price. For a higher price, manufacturers will produce more units, so p_S is an increasing function of x. Let X be the amount of the commodity currently produced and let $P = p_S(X)$ be the current price. Some producers would be willing to make and sell the commodity for a lower selling price and are therefore receiving more than their minimal price. The excess is called the **producer surplus**. An argument similar to that for consumer surplus shows that the surplus is given by the integral

$$\int_0^X [P - p_S(x)]\, dx$$

Calculate the producer surplus for the supply function $p_S(x) = 3 + 0.01x^2$ at the sales level $X = 10$. Illustrate by drawing the supply curve and identifying the producer surplus as an area.

7. If a supply curve is modeled by the equation $p = 200 + 0.2x^{3/2}$, find the producer surplus when the selling price is \$400.

8. For a given commodity and pure competition, the number of units produced and the price per unit are determined as the coordinates of the point of intersection of the supply and demand curves. Given the demand curve $p = 50 - \frac{1}{20}x$ and the supply curve $p = 20 + \frac{1}{10}x$, find the consumer surplus and the producer surplus. Illustrate by sketching the supply and demand curves and identifying the surpluses as areas.

9. A company modeled the demand curve for its product (in dollars) by the equation

$$p = \frac{800{,}000e^{-x/5000}}{x + 20{,}000}$$

Use a graph to estimate the sales level when the selling price is \$16. Then find (approximately) the consumer surplus for this sales level.

10. A movie theater has been charging \$7.50 per person and selling about 400 tickets on a typical weeknight. After surveying their

---

Graphing calculator or computer with graphing software required   **1.** Homework Hints available in TEC

customers, the theater estimates that for every 50 cents that they lower the price, the number of moviegoers will increase by 35 per night. Find the demand function and calculate the consumer surplus when the tickets are priced at $6.00.

11. If the amount of capital that a company has at time t is $f(t)$, then the derivative, $f'(t)$, is called the *net investment flow*. Suppose that the net investment flow is $\sqrt{t}$ million dollars per year (where t is measured in years). Find the increase in capital (the *capital formation*) from the fourth year to the eighth year.

12. If revenue flows into a company at a rate of $f(t) = 9000\sqrt{1 + 2t}$, where t is measured in years and $f(t)$ is measured in dollars per year, find the total revenue obtained in the first four years.

13. *Pareto's Law of Income* states that the number of people with incomes between $x = a$ and $x = b$ is $N = \int_a^b Ax^{-k}\, dx$, where A and k are constants with $A > 0$ and $k > 1$. The average income of these people is

$$\bar{x} = \frac{1}{N}\int_a^b Ax^{1-k}\, dx$$

Calculate $\bar{x}$.

14. A hot, wet summer is causing a mosquito population explosion in a lake resort area. The number of mosquitos is increasing at an estimated rate of $2200 + 10e^{0.8t}$ per week (where t is measured in weeks). By how much does the mosquito population increase between the fifth and ninth weeks of summer?

15. Use Poiseuille's Law to calculate the rate of flow in a small human artery where we can take $\eta = 0.027$, $R = 0.008$ cm, $l = 2$ cm, and $P = 4000$ dynes/cm².

16. High blood pressure results from constriction of the arteries. To maintain a normal flow rate (flux), the heart has to pump harder, thus increasing the blood pressure. Use Poiseuille's Law to show that if R_0 and P_0 are normal values of the radius and pressure in an artery and the constricted values are R and P, then for the flux to remain constant, P and R are related by the equation

$$\frac{P}{P_0} = \left(\frac{R_0}{R}\right)^4$$

Deduce that if the radius of an artery is reduced to three-fourths of its former value, then the pressure is more than tripled.

17. The dye dilution method is used to measure cardiac output with 6 mg of dye. The dye concentrations, in mg/L, are modeled by $c(t) = 20te^{-0.6t}$, $0 \le t \le 10$, where t is measured in seconds. Find the cardiac output.

18. After an 8-mg injection of dye, the readings of dye concentration, in mg/L, at two-second intervals are as shown in the table. Use Simpson's Rule to estimate the cardiac output.

t	$c(t)$	t	$c(t)$
0	0	12	3.9
2	2.4	14	2.3
4	5.1	16	1.6
6	7.8	18	0.7
8	7.6	20	0
10	5.4		

19. The graph of the concentration function $c(t)$ is shown after a 7-mg injection of dye into a heart. Use Simpson's Rule to estimate the cardiac output.

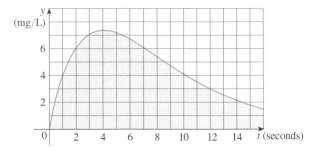

6.8 Probability

Calculus plays a role in the analysis of random behavior. Suppose we consider the cholesterol level of a person chosen at random from a certain age group, or the height of an adult female chosen at random, or the lifetime of a randomly chosen battery of a certain type. Such quantities are called **continuous random variables** because their values actually range over an interval of real numbers, although they might be measured or recorded only to the nearest integer. We might want to know the probability that a blood cholesterol level is greater than 250, or the probability that the height of an adult female is between 60 and 70 inches, or the probability that the battery we are buying lasts between 100 and 200 hours. If X represents the lifetime of that type of battery, we denote this last probability as follows:

$$P(100 \le X \le 200)$$

According to the frequency interpretation of probability, this number is the long-run proportion of all batteries of the specified type whose lifetimes are between 100 and 200 hours. Since it represents a proportion, the probability naturally falls between 0 and 1.

Every continuous random variable X has a **probability density function** f. This means that the probability that X lies between a and b is found by integrating f from a to b:

$$\boxed{1} \qquad\qquad P(a \leqslant X \leqslant b) = \int_a^b f(x)\, dx$$

For example, Figure 1 shows the graph of a model for the probability density function f for a random variable X defined to be the height in inches of an adult female in the United States (according to data from the National Health Survey). The probability that the height of a woman chosen at random from this population is between 60 and 70 inches is equal to the area under the graph of f from 60 to 70.

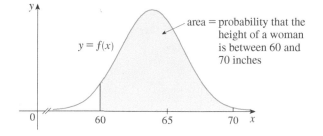

FIGURE 1
Probability density function
for the height of an adult female

In general, the probability density function f of a random variable X satisfies the condition $f(x) \geqslant 0$ for all x. Because probabilities are measured on a scale from 0 to 1, it follows that

$$\boxed{2} \qquad\qquad \int_{-\infty}^{\infty} f(x)\, dx = 1$$

EXAMPLE 1 Let $f(x) = 0.006x(10 - x)$ for $0 \leqslant x \leqslant 10$ and $f(x) = 0$ for all other values of x.
(a) Verify that f is a probability density function.
(b) Find $P(4 \leqslant X \leqslant 8)$.

SOLUTION
(a) For $0 \leqslant x \leqslant 10$ we have $0.006x(10 - x) \geqslant 0$, so $f(x) \geqslant 0$ for all x. We also need to check that Equation 2 is satisfied:

$$\int_{-\infty}^{\infty} f(x)\, dx = \int_0^{10} 0.006x(10 - x)\, dx = 0.006 \int_0^{10} (10x - x^2)\, dx$$

$$= 0.006\left[5x^2 - \tfrac{1}{3}x^3\right]_0^{10} = 0.006\left(500 - \tfrac{1000}{3}\right) = 1$$

Therefore f is a probability density function.
(b) The probability that X lies between 4 and 8 is

$$P(4 \leqslant X \leqslant 8) = \int_4^8 f(x)\, dx = 0.006 \int_4^8 (10x - x^2)\, dx$$

$$= 0.006\left[5x^2 - \tfrac{1}{3}x^3\right]_4^8 = 0.544$$

▼ EXAMPLE 2   **Probability density function for waiting times**   Phenomena such as waiting times and equipment failure times are commonly modeled by exponentially decreasing probability density functions. Find the exact form of such a function.

SOLUTION   Think of the random variable as being the time you wait on hold before an agent of a company you're telephoning answers your call. So instead of x, let's use t to represent time, in minutes. If f is the probability density function and you call at time $t = 0$, then, from Definition 1, $\int_0^2 f(t)\, dt$ represents the probability that an agent answers within the first two minutes and $\int_4^5 f(t)\, dt$ is the probability that your call is answered during the fifth minute.

It's clear that $f(t) = 0$ for $t < 0$ (the agent can't answer before you place the call). For $t > 0$ we are told to use an exponentially decreasing function, that is, a function of the form $f(t) = Ae^{-ct}$, where A and c are positive constants. Thus

$$f(t) = \begin{cases} 0 & \text{if } t < 0 \\ Ae^{-ct} & \text{if } t \geq 0 \end{cases}$$

We use Equation 2 to determine the value of A:

$$1 = \int_{-\infty}^{\infty} f(t)\, dt = \int_{-\infty}^{0} f(t)\, dt + \int_{0}^{\infty} f(t)\, dt$$

$$= \int_{0}^{\infty} Ae^{-ct}\, dt = \lim_{x \to \infty} \int_{0}^{x} Ae^{-ct}\, dt$$

$$= \lim_{x \to \infty} \left[-\frac{A}{c} e^{-ct} \right]_{0}^{x} = \lim_{x \to \infty} \frac{A}{c} (1 - e^{-cx})$$

$$= \frac{A}{c}$$

Therefore $A/c = 1$ and so $A = c$. Thus every exponential density function has the form

$$f(t) = \begin{cases} 0 & \text{if } t < 0 \\ ce^{-ct} & \text{if } t \geq 0 \end{cases}$$

A typical graph is shown in Figure 2.

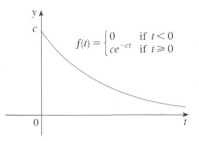

FIGURE 2
An exponential density function

$$f(t) = \begin{cases} 0 & \text{if } t < 0 \\ ce^{-ct} & \text{if } t \geq 0 \end{cases}$$

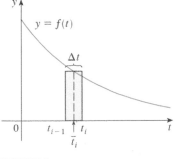

FIGURE 3

Average Values

Suppose you're waiting for a company to answer your phone call and you wonder how long, on average, you can expect to wait. Let $f(t)$ be the corresponding density function, where t is measured in minutes, and think of a sample of N people who have called this company. Most likely, none of them had to wait more than an hour, so let's restrict our attention to the interval $0 \leq t \leq 60$. Let's divide that interval into n intervals of length Δt and endpoints $0, t_1, t_2, \ldots, t_n = 60$. (Think of Δt as lasting a minute, or half a minute, or 10 seconds, or even a second.) The probability that somebody's call gets answered during the time period from t_{i-1} to t_i is the area under the curve $y = f(t)$ from t_{i-1} to t_i, which is approximately equal to $f(\bar{t}_i)\, \Delta t$. (This is the area of the approximating rectangle in Figure 3, where $\bar{t}_i$ is the midpoint of the interval.)

Since the long-run proportion of calls that get answered in the time period from t_{i-1} to t_i is $f(\bar{t}_i)\, \Delta t$, we expect that, out of our sample of N callers, the number whose call was answered in that time period is approximately $Nf(\bar{t}_i)\, \Delta t$ and the time that each waited is about $\bar{t}_i$. Therefore the total time they waited is the product of these numbers: approximately $\bar{t}_i[Nf(\bar{t}_i)\, \Delta t]$. Adding over all such intervals, we get the approximate total of everybody's waiting times:

$$\sum_{i=1}^{n} N\bar{t}_i f(\bar{t}_i)\,\Delta t$$

If we now divide by the number of callers N, we get the approximate *average* waiting time:

$$\sum_{i=1}^{n} \bar{t}_i f(\bar{t}_i)\,\Delta t$$

We recognize this as a Riemann sum for the function $t f(t)$. As the time interval shrinks (that is, $\Delta t \to 0$ and $n \to \infty$), this Riemann sum approaches the integral

$$\int_{0}^{60} t f(t)\,dt$$

This integral is called the *mean waiting time.*

In general, the **mean** of any probability density function f is defined to be

It is traditional to denote the mean by the Greek letter μ (mu).

$$\mu = \int_{-\infty}^{\infty} x f(x)\,dx$$

The mean can be interpreted as the long-run average value of the random variable X. It can also be interpreted as a measure of centrality of the probability density function.

The expression for the mean resembles an integral we have seen before. If $\mathcal{R}$ is the region that lies under the graph of f, we know from Formula 6.6.12 that the x-coordinate of the centroid of $\mathcal{R}$ is

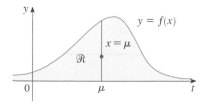

$$\bar{x} = \frac{\displaystyle\int_{-\infty}^{\infty} x f(x)\,dx}{\displaystyle\int_{-\infty}^{\infty} f(x)\,dx} = \int_{-\infty}^{\infty} x f(x)\,dx = \mu$$

FIGURE 4
$\mathcal{R}$ balances at a point on the line $x = \mu$

because of Equation 2. So a thin plate in the shape of $\mathcal{R}$ balances at a point on the vertical line $x = \mu$. (See Figure 4.)

EXAMPLE 3 Find the mean of the exponential distribution of Example 2:

$$f(t) = \begin{cases} 0 & \text{if } t < 0 \\ ce^{-ct} & \text{if } t \geqslant 0 \end{cases}$$

SOLUTION According to the definition of a mean, we have

$$\mu = \int_{-\infty}^{\infty} t f(t)\,dt = \int_{0}^{\infty} tce^{-ct}\,dt$$

To evaluate this integral we use integration by parts, with $u = t$ and $dv = ce^{-ct}\,dt$:

$$\int_{0}^{\infty} tce^{-ct}\,dt = \lim_{x \to \infty} \int_{0}^{x} tce^{-ct}\,dt = \lim_{x \to \infty} \left(-te^{-ct}\Big]_{0}^{x} + \int_{0}^{x} e^{-ct}\,dt \right)$$

The limit of the first term is 0 by l'Hospital's Rule.

$$= \lim_{x \to \infty} \left(-xe^{-cx} + \frac{1}{c} - \frac{e^{-cx}}{c} \right) = \frac{1}{c}$$

The mean is $\mu = 1/c$, so we can rewrite the probability density function as

$$f(t) = \begin{cases} 0 & \text{if } t < 0 \\ \mu^{-1}e^{-t/\mu} & \text{if } t \geqslant 0 \end{cases}$$

V **EXAMPLE 4** Suppose the average waiting time for a customer's call to be answered by a company representative is five minutes.
(a) Find the probability that a call is answered during the first minute.
(b) Find the probability that a customer waits more than five minutes to be answered.

SOLUTION
(a) We are given that the mean of the exponential distribution is $\mu = 5$ min and so, from the result of Example 3, we know that the probability density function is

$$f(t) = \begin{cases} 0 & \text{if } t < 0 \\ 0.2e^{-t/5} & \text{if } t \geqslant 0 \end{cases}$$

Thus the probability that a call is answered during the first minute is

$$P(0 \leqslant T \leqslant 1) = \int_0^1 f(t)\,dt$$

$$= \int_0^1 0.2e^{-t/5}\,dt$$

$$= 0.2(-5)e^{-t/5}\Big]_0^1$$

$$= 1 - e^{-1/5} \approx 0.1813$$

So about 18% of customers' calls are answered during the first minute.

(b) The probability that a customer waits more than five minutes is

$$P(T > 5) = \int_5^\infty f(t)\,dt = \int_5^\infty 0.2e^{-t/5}\,dt$$

$$= \lim_{x \to \infty} \int_5^x 0.2e^{-t/5}\,dt = \lim_{x \to \infty}(e^{-1} - e^{-x/5})$$

$$= \frac{1}{e} \approx 0.368$$

About 37% of customers wait more than five minutes before their calls are answered.

Notice the result of Example 4(b): Even though the mean waiting time is 5 minutes, only 37% of callers wait more than 5 minutes. The reason is that some callers have to wait much longer (maybe 10 or 15 minutes), and this brings up the average.
Another measure of centrality of a probability density function is the *median*. That is a number m such that half the callers have a waiting time less than m and the other callers have a waiting time longer than m. In general, the **median** of a probability density function is the number m such that

$$\int_m^\infty f(x)\,dx = \tfrac{1}{2}$$

This means that half the area under the graph of f lies to the right of m. In Exercise 9 you are asked to show that the median waiting time for the company described in Example 4 is approximately 3.5 minutes.

Normal Distributions

Many important random phenomena—such as test scores on aptitude tests, heights and weights of individuals from a homogeneous population, annual rainfall in a given location—are modeled by a **normal distribution**. This means that the probability density function of the random variable X is a member of the family of functions

$$\boxed{3} \qquad\qquad f(x) = \frac{1}{\sigma\sqrt{2\pi}} \, e^{-(x-\mu)^2/(2\sigma^2)}$$

You can verify that the mean for this function is μ. The positive constant σ is called the **standard deviation**; it measures how spread out the values of X are. From the bell-shaped graphs of members of the family in Figure 5, we see that for small values of σ the values of X are clustered about the mean, whereas for larger values of σ the values of X are more spread out. Statisticians have methods for using sets of data to estimate μ and σ.

The standard deviation is denoted by the lowercase Greek letter σ (sigma).

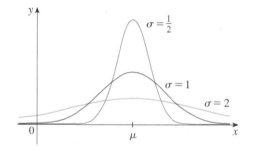

FIGURE 5
Normal distributions

The factor $1/(\sigma\sqrt{2\pi})$ is needed to make f a probability density function. In fact, it can be verified using the methods of multivariable calculus that

$$\int_{-\infty}^{\infty} \frac{1}{\sigma\sqrt{2\pi}} \, e^{-(x-\mu)^2/(2\sigma^2)} \, dx = 1$$

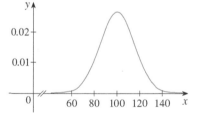

FIGURE 6
Distribution of IQ scores

V **EXAMPLE 5** Intelligence Quotient (IQ) scores are distributed normally with mean 100 and standard deviation 15. (Figure 6 shows the corresponding probability density function.)
(a) What percentage of the population has an IQ score between 85 and 115?
(b) What percentage of the population has an IQ above 140?

SOLUTION
(a) Since IQ scores are normally distributed, we use the probability density function given by Equation 3 with $\mu = 100$ and $\sigma = 15$:

$$P(85 \leqslant X \leqslant 115) = \int_{85}^{115} \frac{1}{15\sqrt{2\pi}} \, e^{-(x-100)^2/(2 \cdot 15^2)} \, dx$$

Recall from Section 5.8 that the function $y = e^{-x^2}$ doesn't have an elementary antiderivative, so we can't evaluate the integral exactly. But we can use the numerical integration capability of a calculator or computer (or the Midpoint Rule or Simpson's

Rule) to estimate the integral. Doing so, we find that

$$P(85 \leqslant X \leqslant 115) \approx 0.68$$

So about 68% of the population has an IQ between 85 and 115, that is, within one standard deviation of the mean.

(b) The probability that the IQ score of a person chosen at random is more than 140 is

$$P(X > 140) = \int_{140}^{\infty} \frac{1}{15\sqrt{2\pi}} e^{-(x-100)^2/450}\, dx$$

To avoid the improper integral we could approximate it by the integral from 140 to 200. (It's quite safe to say that people with an IQ over 200 are extremely rare.) Then

$$P(X > 140) \approx \int_{140}^{200} \frac{1}{15\sqrt{2\pi}} e^{-(x-100)^2/450}\, dx \approx 0.0038$$

Therefore about 0.4% of the population has an IQ over 140.

6.8 Exercises

1. Let $f(x)$ be the probability density function for the lifetime of a manufacturer's highest quality car tire, where x is measured in miles. Explain the meaning of each integral.

(a) $\int_{30,000}^{40,000} f(x)\, dx$

(b) $\int_{25,000}^{\infty} f(x)\, dx$

2. Let $f(t)$ be the probability density function for the time it takes you to drive to school in the morning, where t is measured in minutes. Express the following probabilities as integrals.
   (a) The probability that you drive to school in less than 15 minutes
   (b) The probability that it takes you more than half an hour to get to school

3. Let $f(x) = \frac{3}{64} x\sqrt{16 - x^2}$ for $0 \leqslant x \leqslant 4$ and $f(x) = 0$ for all other values of x.
   (a) Verify that f is a probability density function.
   (b) Find $P(X < 2)$.

4. Let $f(x) = xe^{-x}$ if $x \geqslant 0$ and $f(x) = 0$ if $x < 0$.
   (a) Verify that f is a probability density function.
   (b) Find $P(1 \leqslant X \leqslant 2)$.

5. Let $f(x) = c/(1 + x^2)$.
   (a) For what value of c is f a probability density function?
   (b) For that value of c, find $P(-1 < X < 1)$.

6. Let $f(x) = kx^2(1 - x)$ if $0 \leqslant x \leqslant 1$ and $f(x) = 0$ if $x < 0$ or $x > 1$.
   (a) For what value of k is f a probability density function?
   (b) For that value of k, find $P\left(X \geqslant \frac{1}{2}\right)$.
   (c) Find the mean.

7. A spinner from a board game randomly indicates a real number between 0 and 10. The spinner is fair in the sense that it indicates a number in a given interval with the same probability as it indicates a number in any other interval of the same length.
   (a) Explain why the function

   $$f(x) = \begin{cases} 0.1 & \text{if } 0 \leqslant x \leqslant 10 \\ 0 & \text{if } x < 0 \text{ or } x > 10 \end{cases}$$

   is a probability density function for the spinner's values.
   (b) What does your intuition tell you about the value of the mean? Check your guess by evaluating an integral.

8. (a) Explain why the function whose graph is shown is a probability density function.
   (b) Use the graph to find the following probabilities:
   (i) $P(X < 3)$ (ii) $P(3 \leqslant X \leqslant 8)$
   (c) Calculate the mean.

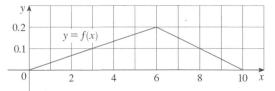

9. Show that the median waiting time for a phone call to the company described in Example 4 is about 3.5 minutes.

10. (a) A type of lightbulb is labeled as having an average lifetime of 1000 hours. It's reasonable to model the probability of failure of these bulbs by an exponential density function

---

1. Homework Hints available in TEC

with mean $\mu = 1000$. Use this model to find the probability that a bulb

(i) fails within the first 200 hours,

(ii) burns for more than 800 hours.

(b) What is the median lifetime of these lightbulbs?

11. The manager of a fast-food restaurant determines that the average time that her customers wait for service is 2.5 minutes.

(a) Find the probability that a customer has to wait more than 4 minutes.

(b) Find the probability that a customer is served within the first 2 minutes.

(c) The manager wants to advertise that anybody who isn't served within a certain number of minutes gets a free hamburger. But she doesn't want to give away free hamburgers to more than 2% of her customers. What should the advertisement say?

12. According to the National Health Survey, the heights of adult males in the United States are normally distributed with mean 69.0 inches and standard deviation 2.8 inches.

(a) What is the probability that an adult male chosen at random is between 65 inches and 73 inches tall?

(b) What percentage of the adult male population is more than 6 feet tall?

13. The "Garbage Project" at the University of Arizona reports that the amount of paper discarded by households per week is normally distributed with mean 9.4 lb and standard deviation 4.2 lb. What percentage of households throw out at least 10 lb of paper a week?

14. Boxes are labeled as containing 500 g of cereal. The machine filling the boxes produces weights that are normally distributed with standard deviation 12 g.

(a) If the target weight is 500 g, what is the probability that the machine produces a box with less than 480 g of cereal?

(b) Suppose a law states that no more than 5% of a manufacturer's cereal boxes can contain less than the stated weight of 500 g. At what target weight should the manufacturer set its filling machine?

15. The speeds of vehicles on a highway with speed limit 100 km/h are normally distributed with mean 112 km/h and standard deviation 8 km/h.

(a) What is the probability that a randomly chosen vehicle is traveling at a legal speed?

(b) If police are instructed to ticket motorists driving 125 km/h or more, what percentage of motorists are targeted?

16. Show that the probability density function for a normally distributed random variable has inflection points at $x = \mu \pm \sigma$.

17. For any normal distribution, find the probability that the random variable lies within two standard deviations of the mean.

18. The standard deviation for a random variable with probability density function f and mean μ is defined by

$$\sigma = \left[\int_{-\infty}^{\infty} (x - \mu)^2 f(x)\, dx \right]^{1/2}$$

Find the standard deviation for an exponential density function with mean μ.

---

6 | Review

Concept Check

1. (a) Draw two typical curves $y = f(x)$ and $y = g(x)$, where $f(x) \geq g(x)$ for $a \leq x \leq b$. Show how to approximate the area between these curves by a Riemann sum and sketch the corresponding approximating rectangles. Then write an expression for the exact area.

(b) Explain how the situation changes if the curves have equations $x = f(y)$ and $x = g(y)$, where $f(y) \geq g(y)$ for $c \leq y \leq d$.

2. Suppose that Sue runs faster than Kathy throughout a 1500-meter race. What is the physical meaning of the area between their velocity curves for the first minute of the race?

3. (a) Suppose S is a solid with known cross-sectional areas. Explain how to approximate the volume of S by a Riemann sum. Then write an expression for the exact volume.

(b) If S is a solid of revolution, how do you find the cross-sectional areas?

4. (a) What is the volume of a cylindrical shell?

(b) Explain how to use cylindrical shells to find the volume of a solid of revolution.

(c) Why might you want to use the shell method instead of slicing?

5. (a) How is the length of a curve defined?

(b) Write an expression for the length of a smooth curve with parametric equations $x = f(t)$, $y = g(t)$, $a \leq t \leq b$.

(c) How does the expression in part (b) simplify if the curve is described by giving y in terms of x, that is, $y = f(x)$, $a \leq x \leq b$? What if x is given as a function of y?

6. (a) What is the average value of a function f on an interval $[a, b]$?

(b) What does the Mean Value Theorem for Integrals say? What is its geometric interpretation?

7. Suppose that you push a book across a 6-meter-long table by exerting a force $f(x)$ at each point from $x = 0$ to $x = 6$. What does $\int_0^6 f(x)\, dx$ represent? If $f(x)$ is measured in newtons, what are the units for the integral?

8. Describe how we can find the hydrostatic force against a vertical wall submersed in a fluid.

9. (a) What is the physical significance of the center of mass of a thin plate?
   (b) If the plate lies between $y = f(x)$ and $y = 0$, where $a \leqslant x \leqslant b$, write expressions for the coordinates of the center of mass.

10. Given a demand function $p(x)$, explain what is meant by the consumer surplus when the amount of a commodity currently available is X and the current selling price is P. Illustrate with a sketch.

11. (a) What is the cardiac output of the heart?
   (b) Explain how the cardiac output can be measured by the dye dilution method.

12. What is a probability density function? What properties does such a function have?

13. Suppose $f(x)$ is the probability density function for the weight of a female college student, where x is measured in pounds.
   (a) What is the meaning of the integral $\int_0^{130} f(x)\, dx$?
   (b) Write an expression for the mean of this density function.
   (c) How can we find the median of this density function?

14. What is a normal distribution? What is the significance of the standard deviation?

Exercises

1–4 Find the area of the region bounded by the given curves.

1. $y = x^2$, $y = 4x - x^2$

2. $y = 1/x$, $y = x^2$, $y = 0$, $x = e$

3. $y = 1 - 2x^2$, $y = |x|$

4. $x + y = 0$, $x = y^2 + 3y$

5. The curve traced out by a point at a distance 1 m from the center of a circle of radius 2 m as the circle rolls along the x-axis is called a *trochoid* and has parametric equations
$$x = 2\theta - \sin\theta \qquad y = 2 - \cos\theta$$
One arch of the trochoid is given by the parameter interval $0 \leqslant \theta \leqslant 2\pi$. Find the area under one arch of this trochoid.

6. Find the volume of the solid obtained by rotating about the x-axis the region bounded by the curves $y = e^{-2x}$, $y = 1 + x$, and $x = 1$.

7. Let $\mathcal{R}$ be the region bounded by the curves $y = \tan(x^2)$, $x = 1$, and $y = 0$. Use the Midpoint Rule with $n = 4$ to estimate the following quantities.
   (a) The area of $\mathcal{R}$
   (b) The volume obtained by rotating $\mathcal{R}$ about the x-axis

8. Let $\mathcal{R}$ be the region in the first quadrant bounded by the curves $y = x^3$ and $y = 2x - x^2$. Calculate the following quantities.
   (a) The area of $\mathcal{R}$
   (b) The volume obtained by rotating $\mathcal{R}$ about the x-axis
   (c) The volume obtained by rotating $\mathcal{R}$ about the y-axis

9. Find the volumes of the solids obtained by rotating the region bounded by the curves $y = x$ and $y = x^2$ about the following lines.
   (a) The x-axis   (b) The y-axis   (c) $y = 2$

10–13 Find the volume of the solid obtained by rotating the region bounded by the given curves about the specified axis.

10. $x = 1 + y^2$, $y = x - 3$;   about the y-axis

11. $x = 0$, $x = 9 - y^2$;   about $x = -1$

12. $y = x^2 + 1$, $y = 9 - x^2$;   about $y = -1$

13. $x^2 - y^2 = a^2$, $x = a + h$ (where $a > 0$, $h > 0$); about the y-axis

14–15 Set up, but do not evaluate, an integral for the volume of the solid obtained by rotating the region bounded by the given curves about the specified axis.

14. $y = \sqrt{x}$, $y = x^2$;   about $y = 2$

15. $y = \cos^2 x$, $|x| \leqslant \pi/2$, $y = \frac{1}{4}$;   about $x = \pi/2$

16. Let $\mathcal{R}$ be the region bounded by the curves $y = 1 - x^2$ and $y = x^6 - x + 1$. Estimate the following quantities.
   (a) The x-coordinates of the points of intersection of the curves
   (b) The area of $\mathcal{R}$
   (c) The volume generated when $\mathcal{R}$ is rotated about the x-axis
   (d) The volume generated when $\mathcal{R}$ is rotated about the y-axis

17. Describe the solid whose volume is given by the integral.
   (a) $\displaystyle\int_0^{\pi/2} 2\pi \cos^2 x\, dx$
   (b) $\displaystyle\int_0^1 \pi\left[(2 - x^2)^2 - (2 - \sqrt{x})^2\right] dx$

18. Suppose you are asked to estimate the volume of a football. You measure and find that a football is 28 cm long. You use a piece of string and measure the circumference at its widest

---

Graphing calculator or computer with graphing software required   **1.** Homework Hints available in TEC

point to be 53 cm. The circumference 7 cm from each end is 45 cm. Use Simpson's Rule to make your estimate.

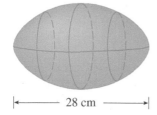

19. The base of a solid is a circular disk with radius 3. Find the volume of the solid if parallel cross-sections perpendicular to the base are isosceles right triangles with hypotenuse lying along the base.

20. The base of a solid is the region bounded by the parabolas $y = x^2$ and $y = 2 - x^2$. Find the volume of the solid if the cross-sections perpendicular to the x-axis are squares with one side lying along the base.

21. The height of a monument is 20 m. A horizontal cross-section at a distance x meters from the top is an equilateral triangle with side $\frac{1}{4}x$ meters. Find the volume of the monument.

22. (a) The base of a solid is a square with vertices located at $(1, 0)$, $(0, 1)$, $(-1, 0)$, and $(0, -1)$. Each cross-section perpendicular to the x-axis is a semicircle. Find the volume of the solid.
    (b) Show that by cutting the solid of part (a), we can rearrange it to form a cone. Thus compute its volume more simply.

23. Find the length of the curve with parametric equations $x = 3t^2$, $y = 2t^3$, $0 \leqslant t \leqslant 2$.

24. Use Simpson's Rule with $n = 10$ to estimate the length of the arc of the curve $y = 1/x^2$ from $(1, 1)$ to $(2, \frac{1}{4})$.

25. Find the length of the curve $y = \frac{1}{6}(x^2 + 4)^{3/2}$, $0 \leqslant x \leqslant 3$.

26. Find the length of the curve

$$y = \int_1^x \sqrt{\sqrt{t} - 1}\, dt \qquad 1 \leqslant x \leqslant 16$$

27. A force of 30 N is required to maintain a spring stretched from its natural length of 12 cm to a length of 15 cm. How much work is done in stretching the spring from 12 cm to 20 cm?

28. A 1600-lb elevator is suspended by a 200-ft cable that weighs 10 lb/ft. How much work is required to raise the elevator from the basement to the third floor, a distance of 30 ft?

29. A tank full of water has the shape of a paraboloid of revolution as shown in the figure; that is, its shape is obtained by rotating a parabola about a vertical axis.
    (a) If its height is 4 ft and the radius at the top is 4 ft, find the work required to pump the water out of the tank.

    (b) After 4000 ft-lb of work has been done, what is the depth of the water remaining in the tank?

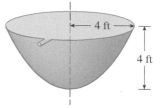

30. A trough is filled with water and its vertical ends have the shape of the parabolic region in the figure. Find the hydrostatic force on one end of the trough.

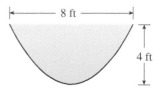

31. A gate in an irrigation canal is constructed in the form of a trapezoid 3 ft wide at the bottom, 5 ft wide at the top, and 2 ft high. It is placed vertically in the canal so that the water just covers the gate. Find the hydrostatic force on one side of the gate.

32. Find the centroid of the region shown.

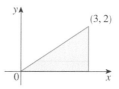

33. The demand function for a commodity is given by

$$p = 2000 - 0.1x - 0.01x^2$$

Find the consumer surplus when the sales level is 100.

34. Find the average value of the function $f(x) = x^2\sqrt{1 + x^3}$ on the interval $[0, 2]$.

35. If f is a continuous function, what is the limit as $h \to 0$ of the average value of f on the interval $[x, x + h]$?

36. After a 6-mg injection of dye into a heart, the readings of dye concentration at two-second intervals are as shown in the table. Use Simpson's Rule to estimate the cardiac output.

t	$c(t)$	t	$c(t)$
0	0	14	4.7
2	1.9	16	3.3
4	3.3	18	2.1
6	5.1	20	1.1
8	7.6	22	0.5
10	7.1	24	0
12	5.8		

37. (a) Explain why the function

$$f(x) = \begin{cases} \dfrac{\pi}{20} \sin\left(\dfrac{\pi x}{10}\right) & \text{if } 0 \leqslant x \leqslant 10 \\ 0 & \text{if } x < 0 \text{ or } x > 10 \end{cases}$$

is a probability density function.
(b) Find $P(X < 4)$.
(c) Calculate the mean. Is the value what you would expect?

38. Lengths of human pregnancies are normally distributed with mean 268 days and standard deviation 15 days. What percentage of pregnancies last between 250 days and 280 days?

39. The length of time spent waiting in line at a certain bank is modeled by an exponential density function with mean 8 minutes.
(a) What is the probability that a customer is served in the first 3 minutes?
(b) What is the probability that a customer has to wait more than 10 minutes?
(c) What is the median waiting time?

Focus on Problem Solving

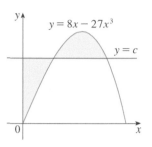

FIGURE FOR PROBLEM 2

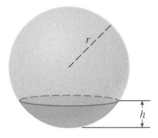

FIGURE FOR PROBLEM 3

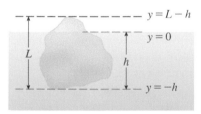

FIGURE FOR PROBLEM 4

1. A solid is generated by rotating about the x-axis the region under the curve $y = f(x)$, where f is a positive function and $x \geq 0$. The volume generated by the part of the curve from $x = 0$ to $x = b$ is b^2 for all $b > 0$. Find the function f.

2. The figure shows a horizontal line $y = c$ intersecting the curve $y = 8x - 27x^3$. Find the number c such that the areas of the shaded regions are equal.

3. (a) Show that the volume of a segment of height h of a sphere of radius r is

$$V = \tfrac{1}{3}\pi h^2(3r - h)$$

   (See the figure.)

   (b) Show that if a sphere of radius 1 is sliced by a plane at a distance x from the center in such a way that the volume of one segment is twice the volume of the other, then x is a solution of the equation $3x^3 - 9x + 2 = 0$, where $0 < x < 1$. Use Newton's method to find x accurate to four decimal places.

   (c) Using the formula for the volume of a segment of a sphere, it can be shown that the depth x to which a floating sphere of radius r sinks in water is a root of the equation $x^3 - 3rx^2 + 4r^3s = 0$, where s is the specific gravity of the sphere. Suppose a wooden sphere of radius 0.5 m has specific gravity 0.75. Calculate, to four-decimal-place accuracy, the depth to which the sphere will sink.

   (d) A hemispherical bowl has radius 5 inches and water is running into the bowl at the rate of 0.2 in³/s.
   (i) How fast is the water level in the bowl rising at the instant the water is 3 inches deep?
   (ii) At a certain instant, the water is 4 inches deep. How long will it take to fill the bowl?

4. Archimedes' Principle states that the buoyant force on an object partially or fully submerged in a fluid is equal to the weight of the fluid that the object displaces. Thus, for an object of density ρ_0 floating partly submerged in a fluid of density ρ_f, the buoyant force is given by $F = \rho_f g \int_{-h}^{0} A(y)\,dy$, where g is the acceleration due to gravity and $A(y)$ is the area of a typical cross-section of the object (see the figure). The weight of the object is given by

$$W = \rho_0 g \int_{-h}^{L-h} A(y)\,dy$$

   (a) Show that the percentage of the volume of the object above the surface of the liquid is

$$100\,\frac{\rho_f - \rho_0}{\rho_f}$$

   (b) The density of ice is 917 kg/m³ and the density of seawater is 1030 kg/m³. What percentage of the volume of an iceberg is above water?

   (c) An ice cube floats in a glass filled to the brim with water. Does the water overflow when the ice melts?

   (d) A sphere of radius 0.4 m and having negligible weight is floating in a large freshwater lake. How much work is required to completely submerge the sphere? The density of the water is 1000 kg/m³.

5. Water in an open bowl evaporates at a rate proportional to the area of the surface of the water. (This means that the rate of decrease of the volume is proportional to the area of the surface.) Show that the depth of the water decreases at a constant rate, regardless of the shape of the bowl.

6. A sphere of radius 1 overlaps a smaller sphere of radius r in such a way that their intersection is a circle of radius r. (In other words, they intersect in a great circle of the small sphere.) Find r so that the volume inside the small sphere and outside the large sphere is as large as possible.

491

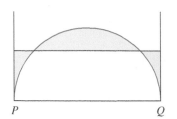

FIGURE FOR PROBLEM 8

FIGURE FOR PROBLEM 10

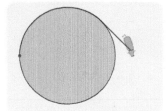

FIGURE FOR PROBLEM 12

7. Let P be a pyramid with a square base of side $2b$ and suppose that S is a sphere with its center on the base of P and S is tangent to all eight edges of P. Find the height of P. Then find the volume of the intersection of S and P.

8. The figure shows a semicircle with radius 1, horizontal diameter PQ, and tangent lines at P and Q. At what height above the diameter should the horizontal line be placed so as to minimize the shaded area?

9. A curve is defined by the parametric equations

$$x = \int_1^t \frac{\cos u}{u}\, du \qquad y = \int_1^t \frac{\sin u}{u}\, du$$

Find the length of the arc of the curve from the origin to the nearest point where there is a vertical tangent line.

10. A paper drinking cup filled with water has the shape of a cone with height h and semivertical angle θ. (See the figure.) A ball is placed carefully in the cup, thereby displacing some of the water and making it overflow. What is the radius of the ball that causes the greatest volume of water to spill out of the cup?

11. A string is wound around a circle and then unwound while being held taut. The curve traced by the point P at the end of the string is called the **involute** of the circle. If the circle has radius r and center O and the initial position of P is $(r, 0)$, and if the parameter θ is chosen as in the figure, show that parametric equations of the involute are

$$x = r(\cos\theta + \theta\sin\theta) \qquad y = r(\sin\theta - \theta\cos\theta)$$

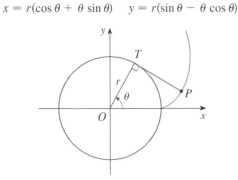

12. A cow is tied to a silo with radius r by a rope just long enough to reach the opposite side of the silo, as shown in the figure. Find the area available for grazing by the cow.

13. A uniform disk with radius 1 m is to be cut by a line so that the center of mass of the smaller piece lies halfway along a radius. How close to the center of the disk should the cut be made? (Express your answer correct to two decimal places.)

14. A triangle with area 30 cm^2 is cut from a corner of a square with side 10 cm, as shown in the figure. If the centroid of the remaining region is 4 cm from the right side of the square, how far is it from the bottom of the square?

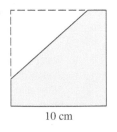

10 cm

15. Suppose the graph of a cubic polynomial intersects the parabola $y = x^2$ when $x = 0$, $x = a$, and $x = b$, where $0 < a < b$. If the two regions between the curves have the same area, how is b related to a?

47. Suppose that $P(x, y)$ is any point on the parabola with focus $(0, p)$ and directrix $y = -p$. (See Figure 14.) Use the definition of a parabola to show that $x^2 = 4py$.

48. Find the focus and directrix of the parabola $y = x^2$. Illustrate with a diagram.

49. Suppose an ellipse has foci $(\pm c, 0)$ and the sum of the distances from any point $P(x, y)$ on the ellipse to the foci is $2a$. Show that the coordinates of P satisfy Equation 1.

50. Find the foci of the ellipse $x^2 + 4y^2 = 4$ and sketch its graph.

51. Use the definition of a hyperbola to derive Equation 2 for a hyperbola with foci $(\pm c, 0)$.

52. (a) Find the foci and asymptotes of the hyperbola $x^2 - y^2 = 1$ and sketch its graph.
   (b) Sketch the graph of $y^2 - x^2 = 1$.

53–54 Sketch the region bounded by the curves.

53. $x + 4y = 8$ and $x = 2y^2 - 8$

54. $y = 4 - x^2$ and $x - 2y = 2$

55. Let $P(x_1, y_1)$ be a point on the ellipse $x^2/a^2 + y^2/b^2 = 1$ with foci F_1 and F_2 and let α and β be the angles between the lines PF_1, PF_2 and the ellipse as shown in the figure. Prove that $\alpha = \beta$. This explains how whispering galleries and lithotripsy work. Sound coming from one focus is reflected and passes through the other focus. [*Hint:* Use the formula in Problem 17 on page 253 to show that $\tan \alpha = \tan \beta$.]

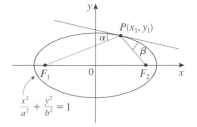

C Trigonometry

Here we review the aspects of trigonometry that are used in calculus: radian measure, trigonometric functions, trigonometric identities, and inverse trigonometric functions.

Angles

Angles can be measured in degrees or in radians (abbreviated as rad). The angle given by a complete revolution contains $360°$, which is the same as 2π rad. Therefore

$$\boxed{1} \qquad \pi \text{ rad} = 180°$$

and

$$\boxed{2} \qquad 1 \text{ rad} = \left(\frac{180}{\pi}\right)^{\circ} \approx 57.3° \qquad 1° = \frac{\pi}{180} \text{ rad} \approx 0.017 \text{ rad}$$

EXAMPLE 1

(a) Find the radian measure of $60°$.   (b) Express $5\pi/4$ rad in degrees.

SOLUTION

(a) From Equation 1 or 2 we see that to convert from degrees to radians we multiply by $\pi/180$. Therefore

$$60° = 60\left(\frac{\pi}{180}\right) = \frac{\pi}{3} \text{ rad}$$

(b) To convert from radians to degrees we multiply by $180/\pi$. Thus

$$\frac{5\pi}{4} \text{ rad} = \frac{5\pi}{4}\left(\frac{180}{\pi}\right) = 225°$$

In calculus we use radians to measure angles except when otherwise indicated. The following table gives the correspondence between degree and radian measures of some common angles.

Degrees	0°	30°	45°	60°	90°	120°	135°	150°	180°	270°	360°
Radians	0	$\dfrac{\pi}{6}$	$\dfrac{\pi}{4}$	$\dfrac{\pi}{3}$	$\dfrac{\pi}{2}$	$\dfrac{2\pi}{3}$	$\dfrac{3\pi}{4}$	$\dfrac{5\pi}{6}$	π	$\dfrac{3\pi}{2}$	2π

Figure 1 shows a sector of a circle with central angle θ and radius r subtending an arc with length a. Since the length of the arc is proportional to the size of the angle, and since the entire circle has circumference $2\pi r$ and central angle 2π, we have

$$\frac{\theta}{2\pi} = \frac{a}{2\pi r}$$

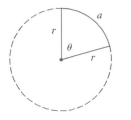

FIGURE 1

Solving this equation for θ and for a, we obtain

3    $$\theta = \frac{a}{r}$$ $$a = r\theta$$

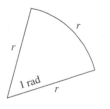

FIGURE 2

Remember that Equations 3 are valid only when θ is measured in radians.

In particular, putting $a = r$ in Equation 3, we see that an angle of 1 rad is the angle subtended at the center of a circle by an arc equal in length to the radius of the circle (see Figure 2).

EXAMPLE 2
(a) If the radius of a circle is 5 cm, what angle is subtended by an arc of 6 cm?
(b) If a circle has radius 3 cm, what is the length of an arc subtended by a central angle of $3\pi/8$ rad?

SOLUTION
(a) Using Equation 3 with $a = 6$ and $r = 5$, we see that the angle is

$$\theta = \tfrac{6}{5} = 1.2 \text{ rad}$$

FIGURE 3 $\theta \geqslant 0$

(b) With $r = 3$ cm and $\theta = 3\pi/8$ rad, the arc length is

$$a = r\theta = 3\left(\frac{3\pi}{8}\right) = \frac{9\pi}{8} \text{ cm}$$

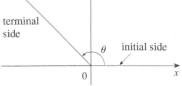

The **standard position** of an angle occurs when we place its vertex at the origin of a coordinate system and its initial side on the positive x-axis as in Figure 3. A **positive** angle is obtained by rotating the initial side counterclockwise until it coincides with the terminal side. Likewise, **negative** angles are obtained by clockwise rotation as in Figure 4.

Figure 5 shows several examples of angles in standard position. Notice that different angles can have the same terminal side. For instance, the angles $3\pi/4$, $-5\pi/4$, and $11\pi/4$

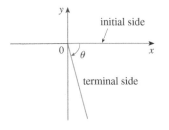

FIGURE 4 $\theta < 0$

have the same initial and terminal sides because

$$\frac{3\pi}{4} - 2\pi = -\frac{5\pi}{4} \qquad \frac{3\pi}{4} + 2\pi = \frac{11\pi}{4}$$

and 2π rad represents a complete revolution.

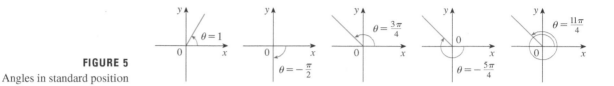

FIGURE 5
Angles in standard position

The Trigonometric Functions

For an acute angle θ the six trigonometric functions are defined as ratios of lengths of sides of a right triangle as follows (see Figure 6).

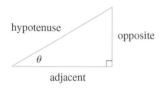

FIGURE 6

$$\sin \theta = \frac{\text{opp}}{\text{hyp}} \qquad \csc \theta = \frac{\text{hyp}}{\text{opp}}$$

$$\cos \theta = \frac{\text{adj}}{\text{hyp}} \qquad \sec \theta = \frac{\text{hyp}}{\text{adj}}$$

$$\tan \theta = \frac{\text{opp}}{\text{adj}} \qquad \cot \theta = \frac{\text{adj}}{\text{opp}}$$

This definition doesn't apply to obtuse or negative angles, so for a general angle θ in standard position we let $P(x, y)$ be any point on the terminal side of θ and we let r be the distance $|OP|$ as in Figure 7. Then we define

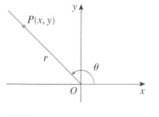

FIGURE 7

$$\sin \theta = \frac{y}{r} \qquad \csc \theta = \frac{r}{y}$$

$$\cos \theta = \frac{x}{r} \qquad \sec \theta = \frac{r}{x}$$

$$\tan \theta = \frac{y}{x} \qquad \cot \theta = \frac{x}{y}$$

Since division by 0 is not defined, $\tan \theta$ and $\sec \theta$ are undefined when $x = 0$ and $\csc \theta$ and $\cot \theta$ are undefined when $y = 0$. Notice that the definitions in (4) and (5) are consistent when θ is an acute angle.

If θ is a number, the convention is that $\sin \theta$ means the sine of the angle whose *radian* measure is θ. For example, the expression $\sin 3$ implies that we are dealing with an angle of 3 rad. When finding a calculator approximation to this number, we must remember to set our calculator in radian mode, and then we obtain

$$\sin 3 \approx 0.14112$$

If we want to know the sine of the angle 3° we would write sin 3° and, with our calculator in degree mode, we find that

$$\sin 3° \approx 0.05234$$

The exact trigonometric ratios for certain angles can be read from the triangles in Figure 8. For instance,

FIGURE 8

$$\sin \frac{\pi}{4} = \frac{1}{\sqrt{2}} \qquad \sin \frac{\pi}{6} = \frac{1}{2} \qquad \sin \frac{\pi}{3} = \frac{\sqrt{3}}{2}$$

$$\cos \frac{\pi}{4} = \frac{1}{\sqrt{2}} \qquad \cos \frac{\pi}{6} = \frac{\sqrt{3}}{2} \qquad \cos \frac{\pi}{3} = \frac{1}{2}$$

$$\tan \frac{\pi}{4} = 1 \qquad \tan \frac{\pi}{6} = \frac{1}{\sqrt{3}} \qquad \tan \frac{\pi}{3} = \sqrt{3}$$

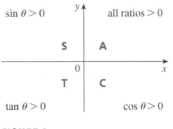

FIGURE 9

The signs of the trigonometric functions for angles in each of the four quadrants can be remembered by means of the rule "All Students Take Calculus" shown in Figure 9.

EXAMPLE 3 Find the exact trigonometric ratios for $\theta = 2\pi/3$.

SOLUTION From Figure 10 we see that a point on the terminal line for $\theta = 2\pi/3$ is $P(-1, \sqrt{3})$. Therefore, taking

$$x = -1 \qquad y = \sqrt{3} \qquad r = 2$$

in the definitions of the trigonometric ratios, we have

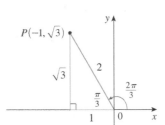

FIGURE 10

$$\sin \frac{2\pi}{3} = \frac{\sqrt{3}}{2} \qquad \cos \frac{2\pi}{3} = -\frac{1}{2} \qquad \tan \frac{2\pi}{3} = -\sqrt{3}$$

$$\csc \frac{2\pi}{3} = \frac{2}{\sqrt{3}} \qquad \sec \frac{2\pi}{3} = -2 \qquad \cot \frac{2\pi}{3} = -\frac{1}{\sqrt{3}}$$

The following table gives some values of $\sin \theta$ and $\cos \theta$ found by the method of Example 3.

θ	0	$\frac{\pi}{6}$	$\frac{\pi}{4}$	$\frac{\pi}{3}$	$\frac{\pi}{2}$	$\frac{2\pi}{3}$	$\frac{3\pi}{4}$	$\frac{5\pi}{6}$	π	$\frac{3\pi}{2}$	2π
$\sin \theta$	0	$\frac{1}{2}$	$\frac{1}{\sqrt{2}}$	$\frac{\sqrt{3}}{2}$	1	$\frac{\sqrt{3}}{2}$	$\frac{1}{\sqrt{2}}$	$\frac{1}{2}$	0	-1	0
$\cos \theta$	1	$\frac{\sqrt{3}}{2}$	$\frac{1}{\sqrt{2}}$	$\frac{1}{2}$	0	$-\frac{1}{2}$	$-\frac{1}{\sqrt{2}}$	$-\frac{\sqrt{3}}{2}$	-1	0	1

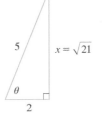

FIGURE 11

EXAMPLE 4 If $\cos \theta = \frac{2}{5}$ and $0 < \theta < \pi/2$, find the other five trigonometric functions of θ.

SOLUTION Since $\cos \theta = \frac{2}{5}$, we can label the hypotenuse as having length 5 and the adjacent side as having length 2 in Figure 11. If the opposite side has length x, then the

Pythagorean Theorem gives $x^2 + 4 = 25$ and so $x^2 = 21$, $x = \sqrt{21}$. We can now use the diagram to write the other five trigonometric functions:

$$\sin\theta = \frac{\sqrt{21}}{5} \qquad \tan\theta = \frac{\sqrt{21}}{2}$$

$$\csc\theta = \frac{5}{\sqrt{21}} \qquad \sec\theta = \frac{5}{2} \qquad \cot\theta = \frac{2}{\sqrt{21}}$$

EXAMPLE 5   Use a calculator to approximate the value of x in Figure 12.

SOLUTION   From the diagram we see that

$$\tan 40° = \frac{16}{x}$$

Therefore
$$x = \frac{16}{\tan 40°} \approx 19.07$$

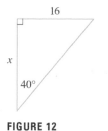

16

x

40°

FIGURE 12

Trigonometric Identities

A trigonometric identity is a relationship among the trigonometric functions. The most elementary are the following, which are immediate consequences of the definitions of the trigonometric functions.

6

$$\csc\theta = \frac{1}{\sin\theta} \qquad \sec\theta = \frac{1}{\cos\theta} \qquad \cot\theta = \frac{1}{\tan\theta}$$

$$\tan\theta = \frac{\sin\theta}{\cos\theta} \qquad \cot\theta = \frac{\cos\theta}{\sin\theta}$$

For the next identity we refer back to Figure 7. The distance formula (or, equivalently, the Pythagorean Theorem) tells us that $x^2 + y^2 = r^2$. Therefore

$$\sin^2\theta + \cos^2\theta = \frac{y^2}{r^2} + \frac{x^2}{r^2} = \frac{x^2 + y^2}{r^2} = \frac{r^2}{r^2} = 1$$

We have therefore proved one of the most useful of all trigonometric identities:

7

$$\sin^2\theta + \cos^2\theta = 1$$

If we now divide both sides of Equation 7 by $\cos^2\theta$ and use Equations 6, we get

8

$$\tan^2\theta + 1 = \sec^2\theta$$

Similarly, if we divide both sides of Equation 7 by $\sin^2\theta$, we get

9

$$1 + \cot^2\theta = \csc^2\theta$$

The identities

10a
$$\sin(-\theta) = -\sin\theta$$

10b
$$\cos(-\theta) = \cos\theta$$

Odd functions and even functions are discussed in Section 1.1.

show that sine is an odd function and cosine is an even function. They are easily proved by drawing a diagram showing θ and $-\theta$ in standard position (see Exercise 19).

Since the angles θ and $\theta + 2\pi$ have the same terminal side, we have

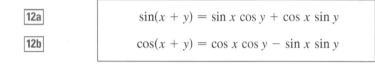

11
$$\sin(\theta + 2\pi) = \sin\theta \qquad \cos(\theta + 2\pi) = \cos\theta$$

These identities show that the sine and cosine functions are periodic with period 2π.

The remaining trigonometric identities are all consequences of two basic identities called the **addition formulas**:

12a
$$\sin(x + y) = \sin x \cos y + \cos x \sin y$$

12b
$$\cos(x + y) = \cos x \cos y - \sin x \sin y$$

The proofs of these addition formulas are outlined in Exercises 43, 44, and 45.

By substituting $-y$ for y in Equations 12a and 12b and using Equations 10a and 10b, we obtain the following **subtraction formulas**:

13a
$$\sin(x - y) = \sin x \cos y - \cos x \sin y$$

13b
$$\cos(x - y) = \cos x \cos y + \sin x \sin y$$

Then, by dividing the formulas in Equations 12 or Equations 13, we obtain the corresponding formulas for $\tan(x \pm y)$:

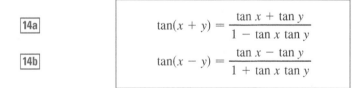

14a
$$\tan(x + y) = \frac{\tan x + \tan y}{1 - \tan x \tan y}$$

14b
$$\tan(x - y) = \frac{\tan x - \tan y}{1 + \tan x \tan y}$$

If we put $y = x$ in the addition formulas (12), we get the **double-angle formulas**:

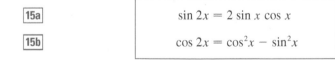

15a
$$\sin 2x = 2 \sin x \cos x$$

15b
$$\cos 2x = \cos^2 x - \sin^2 x$$

Then, by using the identity $\sin^2 x + \cos^2 x = 1$, we obtain the following alternate forms of the double-angle formulas for $\cos 2x$:

16a
$$\cos 2x = 2\cos^2 x - 1$$

16b
$$\cos 2x = 1 - 2\sin^2 x$$

If we now solve these equations for $\cos^2 x$ and $\sin^2 x$, we get the following **half-angle formulas**, which are useful in integral calculus:

17a
$$\cos^2 x = \frac{1 + \cos 2x}{2}$$

17b
$$\sin^2 x = \frac{1 - \cos 2x}{2}$$

There are many other trigonometric identities, but those we have stated are the ones used most often in calculus. If you forget any of them, remember that they can all be deduced from Equations 12a and 12b.

EXAMPLE 6 Find all values of x in the interval $[0, 2\pi]$ such that $\sin x = \sin 2x$.

SOLUTION Using the double-angle formula (15a), we rewrite the given equation as

$$\sin x = 2\sin x \cos x \qquad \text{or} \qquad \sin x (1 - 2\cos x) = 0$$

Therefore there are two possibilities:

$$\sin x = 0 \qquad \text{or} \qquad 1 - 2\cos x = 0$$
$$x = 0, \pi, 2\pi \qquad\qquad\qquad \cos x = \tfrac{1}{2}$$
$$x = \frac{\pi}{3}, \frac{5\pi}{3}$$

The given equation has five solutions: 0, $\pi/3$, π, $5\pi/3$, and 2π.

Graphs of the Trigonometric Functions

The graph of the function $f(x) = \sin x$, shown in Figure 13(a), is obtained by plotting points for $0 \le x \le 2\pi$ and then using the periodic nature of the function (from Equation 11) to complete the graph. Notice that the zeros of the sine function occur at the integer multiples of π, that is,

$$\sin x = 0 \qquad \text{whenever } x = n\pi, \quad n \text{ an integer}$$

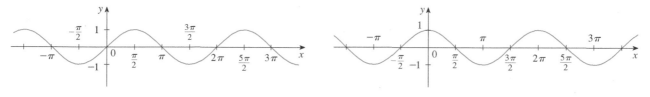

(a) $f(x) = \sin x$ (b) $g(x) = \cos x$

FIGURE 13

Because of the identity

$$\cos x = \sin\left(x + \frac{\pi}{2}\right)$$

(which can be verified using Equation 12a), the graph of cosine is obtained by shifting the graph of sine by an amount $\pi/2$ to the left [see Figure 13(b)]. Note that for both the sine and cosine functions the domain is $(-\infty, \infty)$ and the range is the closed interval $[-1, 1]$. Thus, for all values of x, we have

$$-1 \leqslant \sin x \leqslant 1 \qquad -1 \leqslant \cos x \leqslant 1$$

The graphs of the remaining four trigonometric functions are shown in Figure 14 and their domains are indicated there. Notice that tangent and cotangent have range $(-\infty, \infty)$, whereas cosecant and secant have range $(-\infty, -1] \cup [1, \infty)$. All four functions are periodic: tangent and cotangent have period π, whereas cosecant and secant have period 2π.

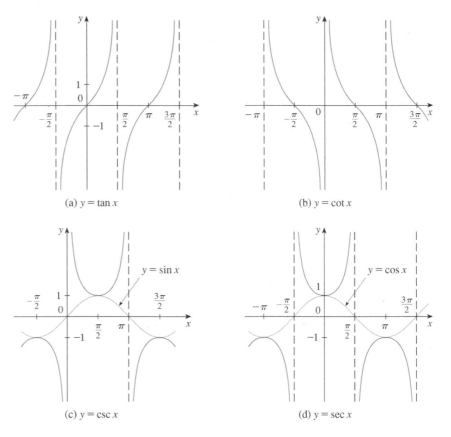

(a) $y = \tan x$

(b) $y = \cot x$

(c) $y = \csc x$

(d) $y = \sec x$

FIGURE 14

C Exercises

1–2 Convert from degrees to radians.

1. (a) $210°$ (b) $9°$

2. (a) $-315°$ (b) $36°$

3–4 Convert from radians to degrees.

3. (a) 4π (b) $-\dfrac{3\pi}{8}$

4. (a) $-\dfrac{7\pi}{2}$ (b) $\dfrac{8\pi}{3}$

5. Find the length of a circular arc subtended by an angle of $\pi/12$ rad if the radius of the circle is 36 cm.

6. If a circle has radius 10 cm, find the length of the arc subtended by a central angle of $72°$.

7. A circle has radius 1.5 m. What angle is subtended at the center of the circle by an arc 1 m long?

8. Find the radius of a circular sector with angle $3\pi/4$ and arc length 6 cm.

9–10 Draw, in standard position, the angle whose measure is given.

9. (a) $315°$ (b) $-\dfrac{3\pi}{4}$ rad

10. (a) $\dfrac{7\pi}{3}$ rad   (b) -3 rad

11–12 Find the exact trigonometric ratios for the angle whose radian measure is given.

11. $\dfrac{3\pi}{4}$ **12.** $\dfrac{4\pi}{3}$

13–14 Find the remaining trigonometric ratios.

13. $\sin\theta = \dfrac{3}{5}$, $0 < \theta < \dfrac{\pi}{2}$

14. $\tan\alpha = 2$, $0 < \alpha < \dfrac{\pi}{2}$

15–18 Find, correct to five decimal places, the length of the side labeled x.

15.   **16.**

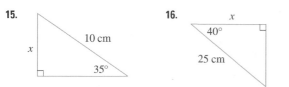

17.   **18.**

19–20 Prove each equation.

19. (a) Equation 10a   (b) Equation 10b

20. (a) Equation 14a   (b) Equation 14b

21–26 Prove the identity.

21. $\sin\left(\dfrac{\pi}{2} + x\right) = \cos x$ **22.** $\sin(\pi - x) = \sin x$

23. $\sin\theta \cot\theta = \cos\theta$ **24.** $(\sin x + \cos x)^2 = 1 + \sin 2x$

25. $\tan 2\theta = \dfrac{2\tan\theta}{1 - \tan^2\theta}$ **26.** $\cos 3\theta = 4\cos^3\theta - 3\cos\theta$

27–28 If $\sin x = \frac{1}{3}$ and $\sec y = \frac{5}{4}$, where x and y lie between 0 and $\pi/2$, evaluate the expression.

27. $\sin(x + y)$ **28.** $\cos 2y$

29–32 Find all values of x in the interval $[0, 2\pi]$ that satisfy the equation.

29. $2\cos x - 1 = 0$ **30.** $2\sin^2 x = 1$

31. $\sin 2x = \cos x$ **32.** $|\tan x| = 1$

33–36 Find all values of x in the interval $[0, 2\pi]$ that satisfy the inequality.

33. $\sin x \leqslant \frac{1}{2}$ **34.** $2\cos x + 1 > 0$

35. $-1 < \tan x < 1$ **36.** $\sin x > \cos x$

37–40 Graph the function by starting with the graphs in Figures 13 and 14 and applying the transformations of Section 1.3 where appropriate.

37. $y = \cos\left(x - \dfrac{\pi}{3}\right)$ **38.** $y = \tan 2x$

39. $y = \dfrac{1}{3}\tan\left(x - \dfrac{\pi}{2}\right)$ **40.** $y = |\sin x|$

41. Prove the **Law of Cosines**: If a triangle has sides with lengths a, b, and c, and θ is the angle between the sides with lengths a and b, then

$$c^2 = a^2 + b^2 - 2ab \cos \theta$$

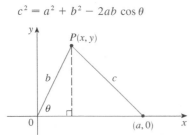

[*Hint:* Introduce a coordinate system so that θ is in standard position, as in the figure. Express x and y in terms of θ and then use the distance formula to compute c.]

42. In order to find the distance $|AB|$ across a small inlet, a point C was located as in the figure and the following measurements were recorded:

$$\angle C = 103° \qquad |AC| = 820 \text{ m} \qquad |BC| = 910 \text{ m}$$

Use the Law of Cosines from Exercise 41 to find the required distance.

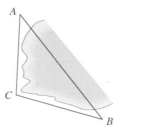

43. Use the figure to prove the subtraction formula

$$\cos(\alpha - \beta) = \cos \alpha \cos \beta + \sin \alpha \sin \beta$$

[*Hint:* Compute c^2 in two ways (using the Law of Cosines from Exercise 41 and also using the distance formula) and compare the two expressions.]

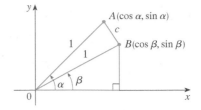

44. Use the formula in Exercise 43 to prove the addition formula for cosine (12b).

45. Use the addition formula for cosine and the identities

$$\cos\left(\frac{\pi}{2} - \theta\right) = \sin \theta \qquad \sin\left(\frac{\pi}{2} - \theta\right) = \cos \theta$$

to prove the subtraction formula (13a) for the sine function.

46. (a) Show that the area of a triangle with sides of lengths a and b and with included angle θ is

$$A = \tfrac{1}{2} ab \sin \theta$$

(b) Find the area of triangle ABC, correct to five decimal places, if

$$|AB| = 10 \text{ cm} \qquad |BC| = 3 \text{ cm} \qquad \angle ABC = 107°$$

D | Precise Definitions of Limits

The definitions of limits that have been given in this book are appropriate for intuitive understanding of the basic concepts of calculus. For the purposes of deeper understanding and rigorous proofs, however, the precise definitions of this appendix are necessary. In particular, the definition of a limit given here is used in Appendix E to prove that the limit of a sum is the sum of the limits.

When we say that $f(x)$ has a limit L as x approaches a, we mean, according to the intuitive definition in Section 2.2, that we can make $f(x)$ arbitrarily close to L by taking x close enough to a (but not equal to a). A more precise definition is based on the idea of specifying just how small we need to make the distance $|x - a|$ in order to make the distance $|f(x) - L|$ less than some given number. The following example illustrates the idea.

It is traditional to use the Greek letter δ (delta) in this situation.

EXAMPLE 1 Use a graph to find a number δ such that

$$\text{if} \quad |x - 1| < \delta \quad \text{then} \quad |(x^3 - 5x + 6) - 2| < 0.2$$

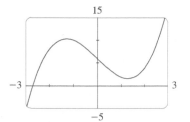

FIGURE 1

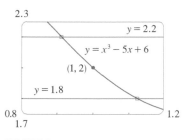

FIGURE 2

SOLUTION   A graph of $f(x) = x^3 - 5x + 6$ is shown in Figure 1; we are interested in the region near the point $(1, 2)$. Notice that we can rewrite the inequality

$$|(x^3 - 5x + 6) - 2| < 0.2$$

as

$$1.8 < x^3 - 5x + 6 < 2.2$$

So we need to determine the values of x for which the curve $y = x^3 - 5x + 6$ lies between the horizontal lines $y = 1.8$ and $y = 2.2$. Therefore we graph the curves $y = x^3 - 5x + 6$, $y = 1.8$, and $y = 2.2$ near the point $(1, 2)$ in Figure 2. Then we use the cursor to estimate that the x-coordinate of the point of intersection of the line $y = 2.2$ and the curve $y = x^3 - 5x + 6$ is about 0.911. Similarly, $y = x^3 - 5x + 6$ intersects the line $y = 1.8$ when $x \approx 1.124$. So, rounding to be safe, we can say that

$$\text{if} \quad 0.92 < x < 1.12 \quad \text{then} \quad 1.8 < x^3 - 5x + 6 < 2.2$$

This interval $(0.92, 1.12)$ is not symmetric about $x = 1$. The distance from $x = 1$ to the left endpoint is $1 - 0.92 = 0.08$ and the distance to the right endpoint is 0.12. We can choose δ to be the smaller of these numbers, that is, $\delta = 0.08$. Then we can rewrite our inequalities in terms of distances as follows:

$$\text{if} \quad |x - 1| < 0.08 \quad \text{then} \quad |(x^3 - 5x + 6) - 2| < 0.2$$

This just says that by keeping x within 0.08 of 1, we are able to keep $f(x)$ within 0.2 of 2.

Although we chose $\delta = 0.08$, any smaller positive value of δ would also have worked.

Using the same graphical procedure as in Example 1, but replacing the number 0.2 by smaller numbers, we find that

$$\text{if} \quad |x - 1| < 0.046 \quad \text{then} \quad |(x^3 - 5x + 6) - 2| < 0.1$$

$$\text{if} \quad |x - 1| < 0.024 \quad \text{then} \quad |(x^3 - 5x + 6) - 2| < 0.05$$

$$\text{if} \quad |x - 1| < 0.004 \quad \text{then} \quad |(x^3 - 5x + 6) - 2| < 0.01$$

In each case we have found a number δ such that the values of the function $f(x) = x^3 - 5x + 6$ lie in successively smaller intervals centered at 2 if the distance from x to 1 is less than δ. It turns out that it is always possible to find such a number δ, no matter how small the interval is. In other words, for *any* positive number ε, no matter how small, there exists a positive number δ such that

$$\text{if} \quad |x - 1| < \delta \quad \text{then} \quad |(x^3 - 5x + 6) - 2| < \varepsilon$$

This indicates that

$$\lim_{x \to 1} (x^3 - 5x + 6) = 2$$

and suggests a more precise way of defining the limit of a general function.

> **1 Definition**   Let f be a function defined on some open interval that contains the number a, except possibly at a itself. Then we say that the **limit of $f(x)$ as x approaches a is L**, and we write
>
> $$\lim_{x \to a} f(x) = L$$
>
> if for every number $\varepsilon > 0$ there is a corresponding number $\delta > 0$ such that
>
> $$\text{if} \quad 0 < |x - a| < \delta \quad \text{then} \quad |f(x) - L| < \varepsilon$$

The condition $0 < |x - a|$ is just another way of saying that $x \neq a$.

Definition 1 is illustrated in Figures 3–5. If a number $\varepsilon > 0$ is given, then we draw the horizontal lines $y = L + \varepsilon$ and $y = L - \varepsilon$ and the graph of f. (See Figure 3.) If $\lim_{x \to a} f(x) = L$, then we can find a number $\delta > 0$ such that if we restrict x to lie in the interval $(a - \delta, a + \delta)$ and take $x \neq a$, then the curve $y = f(x)$ lies between the lines $y = L - \varepsilon$ and $y = L + \varepsilon$. (See Figure 4.) You can see that if such a δ has been found, then any smaller δ will also work.

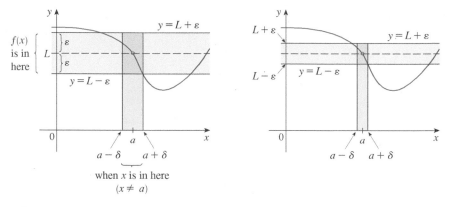

FIGURE 3   **FIGURE 4**   **FIGURE 5**

It's important to realize that the process illustrated in Figures 3 and 4 must work for *every* positive number ε no matter how small it is chosen. Figure 5 shows that if a smaller ε is chosen, then a smaller δ may be required.

EXAMPLE 2   Use the ε, δ definition to prove that $\lim_{x \to 0} x^2 = 0$.

SOLUTION   Let ε be a given positive number. According to Definition 1 with $a = 0$ and $L = 0$, we need to find a number δ such that

$$\text{if} \quad 0 < |x - 0| < \delta \quad \text{then} \quad |x^2 - 0| < \varepsilon$$

that is,

$$\text{if} \quad 0 < |x| < \delta \quad \text{then} \quad x^2 < \varepsilon$$

But, since the square root function is an increasing function, we know that

$$x^2 < \varepsilon \iff \sqrt{x^2} < \sqrt{\varepsilon} \iff |x| < \sqrt{\varepsilon}$$

So if we choose $\delta = \sqrt{\varepsilon}$, then $x^2 < \varepsilon \iff |x| < \delta$. (See Figure 6.) This shows that $\lim_{x \to 0} x^2 = 0$.

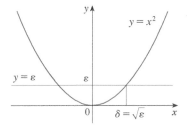

FIGURE 6

In proving limit statements it may be helpful to think of the definition of a limit as a challenge. First it challenges you with a number ε. Then you must be able to produce a suitable δ. You have to be able to do this for *every* $\varepsilon > 0$, not just a particular ε.

Imagine a contest between two people, A and B, and imagine yourself to be B. Person A stipulates that the fixed number L should be approximated by the values of $f(x)$ to within a degree of accuracy ε (say, 0.01). Person B then responds by finding a number δ such that $|f(x) - L| < \varepsilon$ whenever $0 < |x - a| < \delta$. Then A may become more exacting and challenge B with a smaller value of ε (say, 0.0001). Again B has to respond by finding a corresponding δ. Usually the smaller the value of ε, the smaller the corresponding value of δ must be. If B always wins, no matter how small A makes ε, then $\lim_{x \to a} f(x) = L$.

V EXAMPLE 3 Prove that $\lim_{x \to 3} (4x - 5) = 7$.

SOLUTION

1. *Preliminary analysis of the problem* (*guessing a value for* δ). Let ε be a given positive number. We want to find a number δ such that

if $\quad 0 < |x - 3| < \delta \quad$ then $\quad |(4x - 5) - 7| < \varepsilon$

But $|(4x - 5) - 7| = |4x - 12| = |4(x - 3)| = 4|x - 3|$. Therefore we want δ such that

if $\quad 0 < |x - 3| < \delta \quad$ then $\quad 4|x - 3| < \varepsilon$

that is, $\qquad$ if $\quad 0 < |x - 3| < \delta \quad$ then $\quad |x - 3| < \dfrac{\varepsilon}{4}$

This suggests that we should choose $\delta = \varepsilon/4$.

2. *Proof* (*showing that this* δ *works*). Given $\varepsilon > 0$, choose $\delta = \varepsilon/4$. If $0 < |x - 3| < \delta$, then

$$|(4x - 5) - 7| = |4x - 12| = 4|x - 3| < 4\delta = 4\left(\frac{\varepsilon}{4}\right) = \varepsilon$$

Thus

if $\quad 0 < |x - 3| < \delta \quad$ then $\quad |(4x - 5) - 7| < \varepsilon$

Therefore, by the definition of a limit,

$$\lim_{x \to 3} (4x - 5) = 7$$

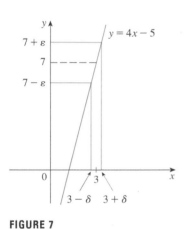

FIGURE 7

This example is illustrated by Figure 7.

Note that in the solution of Example 3 there were two stages—guessing and proving. We made a preliminary analysis that enabled us to guess a value for δ. But then in the second stage we had to go back and prove in a careful, logical fashion that we had made a correct guess. This procedure is typical of much of mathematics. Sometimes it is necessary to first make an intelligent guess about the answer to a problem and then prove that the guess is correct.

It's not always easy to prove that limit statements are true using the ε, δ definition. For a more complicated function such as $f(x) = (6x^2 - 8x + 9)/(2x^2 - 1)$, a proof would require a great deal of ingenuity. Fortunately, this is not necessary because the Limit Laws stated in Section 2.3 can be proved using Definition 1, and then the limits of complicated functions can be found rigorously from the Limit Laws without resorting to the definition directly.

Limits at Infinity

Infinite limits and limits at infinity can also be defined in a precise way. The following is a precise version of Definition 4 in Section 2.5.

---

2 **Definition** Let f be a function defined on some interval (a, ∞). Then

$$\lim_{x \to \infty} f(x) = L$$

means that for every $\varepsilon > 0$ there is a corresponding number N such that

$$\text{if} \quad x > N \quad \text{then} \quad |f(x) - L| < \varepsilon$$

In words, this says that the values of $f(x)$ can be made arbitrarily close to L (within a distance ε, where ε is any positive number) by taking x sufficiently large (larger than N, where N depends on ε). Graphically it says that by choosing x large enough (larger than some number N) we can make the graph of f lie between the given horizontal lines $y = L - \varepsilon$ and $y = L + \varepsilon$ as in Figure 8. This must be true no matter how small we choose ε. If a smaller value of ε is chosen, then a larger value of N may be required.

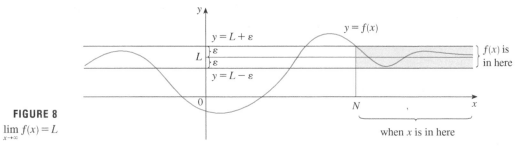

FIGURE 8
$\lim_{x \to \infty} f(x) = L$

In Example 5 in Section 2.5 we calculated that

$$\lim_{x \to \infty} \frac{3x^2 - x - 2}{5x^2 + 4x + 1} = \frac{3}{5}$$

In the next example we use a graphing device to relate this statement to Definition 2 with $L = \frac{3}{5}$ and $\varepsilon = 0.1$.

EXAMPLE 4 Use a graph to find a number N such that

$$\text{if} \quad x > N \quad \text{then} \quad \left| \frac{3x^2 - x - 2}{5x^2 + 4x + 1} - 0.6 \right| < 0.1$$

SOLUTION We rewrite the given inequality as

$$0.5 < \frac{3x^2 - x - 2}{5x^2 + 4x + 1} < 0.7$$

We need to determine the values of x for which the given curve lies between the horizontal lines $y = 0.5$ and $y = 0.7$. So we graph the curve and these lines in Figure 9. Then we use the cursor to estimate that the curve crosses the line $y = 0.5$ when $x \approx 6.7$. To

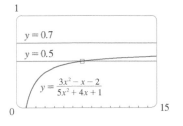

FIGURE 9

the right of this number it seems that the curve stays between the lines $y = 0.5$ and $y = 0.7$. Rounding to be safe, we can say that

$$\text{if} \quad x > 7 \quad \text{then} \quad \left| \frac{3x^2 - x - 2}{5x^2 + 4x + 1} - 0.6 \right| < 0.1$$

In other words, for $\varepsilon = 0.1$ we can choose $N = 7$ (or any larger number) in Definition 2.

EXAMPLE 5 Use Definition 2 to prove that $\lim\limits_{x \to \infty} \dfrac{1}{x} = 0$.

SOLUTION Given $\varepsilon > 0$, we want to find N such that

$$\text{if} \quad x > N \quad \text{then} \quad \left| \frac{1}{x} - 0 \right| < \varepsilon$$

In computing the limit we may assume that $x > 0$. Then $1/x < \varepsilon \iff x > 1/\varepsilon$. Let's choose $N = 1/\varepsilon$. So

$$\text{if} \quad x > N = \frac{1}{\varepsilon} \quad \text{then} \quad \left| \frac{1}{x} - 0 \right| = \frac{1}{x} < \varepsilon$$

Therefore, by Definition 2,

$$\lim_{x \to \infty} \frac{1}{x} = 0$$

Figure 10 illustrates the proof by showing some values of ε and the corresponding values of N.

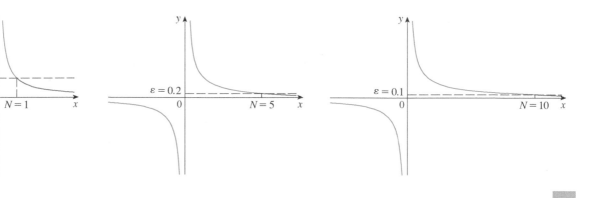

Infinite limits can also be formulated precisely. See Exercise 20.

Definite Integrals

In Section 5.2 we defined the definite integral of a function f on an interval $[a, b]$ as

$$\int_a^b f(x)\,dx = \lim_{n \to \infty} \sum_{i=1}^{n} f(x_i^*)\,\Delta x$$

where, at the nth stage, we have divided $[a, b]$ into n subintervals of equal width,

$\Delta x = (b - a)/n$, and x_i^* is any sample point in the ith subinterval. The precise meaning of this limit that defines the integral is as follows:

For every number $\varepsilon > 0$ there is an integer N such that

$$\left| \int_a^b f(x)\, dx - \sum_{i=1}^{n} f(x_i^*)\, \Delta x \right| < \varepsilon$$

for every integer $n > N$ and for every choice of x_i^* in the ith subinterval.

This means that a definite integral can be approximated to within any desired degree of accuracy by a Riemann sum.

Sequences

In Section 8.1 we used the notation

$$\lim_{n \to \infty} a_n = L$$

to mean that the terms of the sequence $\{a_n\}$ approach L as n becomes large. Notice that the following precise definition of the limit of a sequence is very similar to the definition of a limit of a function at infinity (Definition 2).

---

3 **Definition** A sequence $\{a_n\}$ has the **limit** L and we write

$$\lim_{n \to \infty} a_n = L \qquad \text{or} \qquad a_n \to L \text{ as } n \to \infty$$

if for every $\varepsilon > 0$ there is a corresponding integer N such that

$$\text{if} \quad n > N \quad \text{then} \quad |a_n - L| < \varepsilon$$

Definition 3 is illustrated by Figure 11, in which the terms $a_1, a_2, a_3, \ldots$ are plotted on a number line. No matter how small an interval $(L - \varepsilon, L + \varepsilon)$ is chosen, there exists an N such that all terms of the sequence from a_{N+1} onward must lie in that interval.

FIGURE 11

Another illustration of Definition 3 is given in Figure 12. The points on the graph of $\{a_n\}$ must lie between the horizontal lines $y = L + \varepsilon$ and $y = L - \varepsilon$ if $n > N$. This picture must be valid no matter how small ε is chosen, but usually a smaller ε requires a larger N.

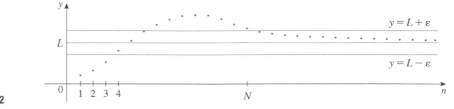

FIGURE 12

If you compare Definition 2 with Definition 3 you will see that the only difference between $\lim_{n \to \infty} a_n = L$ and $\lim_{x \to \infty} f(x) = L$ is that n is required to be an integer. The following definition shows how to make precise the idea that $\{a_n\}$ becomes infinite as n becomes infinite.

> **4** **Definition**   The notation $\lim_{n \to \infty} a_n = \infty$ means that for every positive number M there is an integer N such that
>
> $$\text{if} \quad n > N \quad \text{then} \quad a_n > M$$

EXAMPLE 6   Prove that $\lim_{n \to \infty} \sqrt{n} = \infty$.

SOLUTION   Let M be any positive number. (Think of it as being very large.) Then

$$\sqrt{n} > M \iff n > M^2$$

So if we take $N = M^2$, then Definition 4 shows that $\lim_{n \to \infty} \sqrt{n} = \infty$.

Functions of Two Variables

Here is a precise version of Definition 1 in Section 11.2:

> **5** **Definition**   Let f be a function of two variables whose domain D includes points arbitrarily close to (a, b). Then we say that the **limit of $f(x, y)$ as (x, y) approaches (a, b)** is L and we write
>
> $$\lim_{(x, y) \to (a, b)} f(x, y) = L$$
>
> if for every number $\varepsilon > 0$ there is a corresponding number $\delta > 0$ such that
>
> $$\text{if} \quad (x, y) \in D \quad \text{and} \quad 0 < \sqrt{(x - a)^2 + (y - b)^2} < \delta \quad \text{then} \quad |f(x, y) - L| < \varepsilon$$

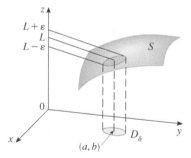

FIGURE 13

Notice that $|f(x, y) - L|$ is the distance between the numbers $f(x, y)$ and L, and $\sqrt{(x - a)^2 + (y - b)^2}$ is the distance between the point (x, y) and the point (a, b). Thus Definition 5 says that the distance between $f(x, y)$ and L can be made arbitrarily small by making the distance from (x, y) to (a, b) sufficiently small (but not 0). An illustration of Definition 5 is given in Figure 13 where the surface S is the graph of f. If $\varepsilon > 0$ is given, we can find $\delta > 0$ such that if (x, y) is restricted to lie in the disk D_δ with center (a, b) and radius δ, and if $(x, y) \neq (a, b)$, then the corresponding part of S lies between the horizontal planes $z = L - \varepsilon$ and $z = L + \varepsilon$.

EXAMPLE 7   Prove that $\lim_{(x, y) \to (0, 0)} \dfrac{3x^2 y}{x^2 + y^2} = 0$.

SOLUTION   Let $\varepsilon > 0$. We want to find $\delta > 0$ such that

$$\text{if} \quad 0 < \sqrt{x^2 + y^2} < \delta \quad \text{then} \quad \left| \frac{3x^2 y}{x^2 + y^2} - 0 \right| < \varepsilon$$

that is,   if $0 < \sqrt{x^2 + y^2} < \delta$ then $\dfrac{3x^2 |y|}{x^2 + y^2} < \varepsilon$

But $x^2 \leqslant x^2 + y^2$ since $y^2 \geqslant 0$, so $x^2/(x^2 + y^2) \leqslant 1$ and therefore

$$\frac{3x^2 |y|}{x^2 + y^2} \leqslant 3|y| = 3\sqrt{y^2} \leqslant 3\sqrt{x^2 + y^2}$$

Thus if we choose $\delta = \varepsilon/3$ and let $0 < \sqrt{x^2 + y^2} < \delta$, then

$$\left| \frac{3x^2 y}{x^2 + y^2} - 0 \right| \leqslant 3\sqrt{x^2 + y^2} < 3\delta = 3\left(\frac{\varepsilon}{3}\right) = \varepsilon$$

Hence, by Definition 5,

$$\lim_{(x,y)\to(0,0)} \frac{3x^2 y}{x^2 + y^2} = 0$$

D   Exercises

1. Use the given graph of $f(x) = 1/x$ to find a number δ such that

if $|x - 2| < \delta$ then $\left| \dfrac{1}{x} - 0.5 \right| < 0.2$

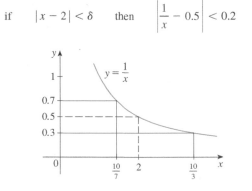

2. Use the given graph of f to find a number δ such that

if $0 < |x - 5| < \delta$ then $|f(x) - 3| < 0.6$

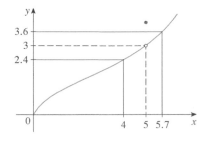

3. Use the given graph of $f(x) = \sqrt{x}$ to find a number δ such that

if $|x - 4| < \delta$ then $|\sqrt{x} - 2| < 0.4$

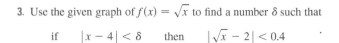

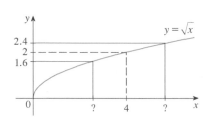

4. Use the given graph of $f(x) = x^2$ to find a number δ such that

if $|x - 1| < \delta$ then $|x^2 - 1| < \frac{1}{2}$

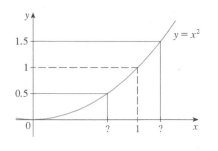

5. Use a graph to find a number δ such that

if $\left| x - \dfrac{\pi}{4} \right| < \delta$ then $|\tan x - 1| < 0.2$

⌂ Graphing calculator or computer with graphing software required   **1.** Homework Hints available in TEC

6. Use a graph to find a number δ such that

$$\text{if} \quad |x - 1| < \delta \quad \text{then} \quad \left| \frac{2x}{x^2 + 4} - 0.4 \right| < 0.1$$

7. For the limit

$$\lim_{x \to 1} (4 + x - 3x^3) = 2$$

illustrate Definition 1 by finding values of δ that correspond to $\varepsilon = 1$ and $\varepsilon = 0.1$.

8. For the limit

$$\lim_{x \to 0} \frac{e^x - 1}{x} = 1$$

illustrate Definition 1 by finding values of δ that correspond to $\varepsilon = 0.5$ and $\varepsilon = 0.1$.

9. Use Definition 1 to prove that $\lim_{x \to 0} x^3 = 0$.

10. (a) How would you formulate an ε, δ definition of the one-sided limit $\lim_{x \to a^+} f(x) = L$?
(b) Use your definition in part (a) to prove that $\lim_{x \to 0^+} \sqrt{x} = 0$.

11. A machinist is required to manufacture a circular metal disk with area 1000 cm^2.
(a) What radius produces such a disk?
(b) If the machinist is allowed an error tolerance of ± 5 cm^2 in the area of the disk, how close to the ideal radius in part (a) must the machinist control the radius?
(c) In terms of the ε, δ definition of $\lim_{x \to a} f(x) = L$, what is x? What is $f(x)$? What is a? What is L? What value of ε is given? What is the corresponding value of δ?

12. A crystal growth furnace is used in research to determine how best to manufacture crystals used in electronic components for the space shuttle. For proper growth of the crystal, the temperature must be controlled accurately by adjusting the input power. Suppose the relationship is given by

$$T(w) = 0.1w^2 + 2.155w + 20$$

where T is the temperature in degrees Celsius and w is the power input in watts.
(a) How much power is needed to maintain the temperature at 200°C ?
(b) If the temperature is allowed to vary from 200°C by up to ± 1°C, what range of wattage is allowed for the input power?
(c) In terms of the ε, δ definition of $\lim_{x \to a} f(x) = L$, what is x? What is $f(x)$? What is a? What is L? What value of ε is given? What is the corresponding value of δ?

13. (a) Find a number δ such that if $|x - 2| < \delta$, then $|4x - 8| < \varepsilon$, where $\varepsilon = 0.1$.
(b) Repeat part (a) with $\varepsilon = 0.01$.

14. Given that $\lim_{x \to 2} (5x - 7) = 3$, illustrate Definition 1 by finding values of δ that correspond to $\varepsilon = 0.1$, $\varepsilon = 0.05$, and $\varepsilon = 0.01$.

15–16 Prove the statement using the ε, δ definition of a limit and illustrate with a diagram like Figure 7.

15. $\lim_{x \to -3} (1 - 4x) = 13$ **16.** $\lim_{x \to -2} \left(\frac{1}{2} x + 3 \right) = 2$

17. Use a graph to find a number N such that

$$\text{if} \quad x > N \quad \text{then} \quad \left| \frac{6x^2 + 5x - 3}{2x^2 - 1} - 3 \right| < 0.2$$

18. For the limit

$$\lim_{x \to \infty} \frac{\sqrt{4x^2 + 1}}{x + 1} = 2$$

illustrate Definition 2 by finding values of N that correspond to $\varepsilon = 0.5$ and $\varepsilon = 0.1$.

19. (a) Determine how large we have to take x so that

$$1/x^2 < 0.0001$$

(b) Use Definition 2 to prove that

$$\lim_{x \to \infty} \frac{1}{x^2} = 0$$

20. (a) For what values of x is it true that

$$\frac{1}{x^2} > 1{,}000{,}000$$

(b) The precise definition of $\lim_{x \to a} f(x) = \infty$ states that for every positive number M (no matter how large) there is a corresponding positive number δ such that if $0 < |x - a| < \delta$, then $f(x) > M$. Use this definition to prove that $\lim_{x \to 0} (1/x^2) = \infty$.

21. (a) Use a graph to guess the value of the limit

$$\lim_{n \to \infty} \frac{n^5}{n!}$$

(b) Use a graph of the sequence in part (a) to find the smallest values of N that correspond to $\varepsilon = 0.1$ and $\varepsilon = 0.001$ in Definition 3.

22. Use Definition 3 to prove that $\lim_{n \to \infty} r^n = 0$ when $|r| < 1$.

23. Use Definition 3 to prove that if $\lim_{n \to \infty} |a_n| = 0$, then $\lim_{n \to \infty} a_n = 0$.

24. Use Definition 4 to prove that $\lim_{n \to \infty} n^3 = \infty$.

25. Use Definition 5 to prove that $\lim_{(x, y) \to (0, 0)} \frac{xy}{\sqrt{x^2 + y^2}} = 0$.

E   A Few Proofs

In this appendix we present proofs of some theorems that were stated in the main body of the text. We start by proving the Triangle Inequality, which is an important property of absolute value.

The Triangle Inequality   If a and b are any real numbers, then

$$|a + b| \leqslant |a| + |b|$$

Observe that if the numbers a and b are both positive or both negative, then the two sides in the Triangle Inequality are actually equal. But if a and b have opposite signs, the left side involves a subtraction and the right side does not. This makes the Triangle Inequality seem reasonable, but we can prove it as follows.

Notice that

$$-|a| \leqslant a \leqslant |a|$$

is always true because a equals either $|a|$ or $-|a|$. The corresponding statement for b is

$$-|b| \leqslant b \leqslant |b|$$

Adding these inequalities, we get

$$-(|a| + |b|) \leqslant a + b \leqslant |a| + |b|$$

When combined, Properties 4 and 5 of absolute value (see Appendix A) say that

$$|x| \leqslant a \iff -a \leqslant x \leqslant a$$

If we now apply Properties 4 and 5 of absolute value from Appendix A (with x replaced by $a + b$ and a by $|a| + |b|$), we obtain

$$|a + b| \leqslant |a| + |b|$$

which is what we wanted to show.   ▭

Next we use the Triangle Inequality to prove the Sum Law for limits.

The Sum Law was first stated in Section 2.3.

Sum Law   If $\lim_{x \to a} f(x) = L$ and $\lim_{x \to a} g(x) = M$ both exist, then

$$\lim_{x \to a} [f(x) + g(x)] = L + M$$

PROOF   Let $\varepsilon > 0$ be given. According to Definition 1 in Appendix D, we must find $\delta > 0$ such that

$$\text{if} \quad 0 < |x - a| < \delta \quad \text{then} \quad |f(x) + g(x) - (L + M)| < \varepsilon$$

Using the Triangle Inequality we can write

$$\boxed{1} \qquad |f(x) + g(x) - (L + M)| = |(f(x) - L) + (g(x) - M)|$$
$$\leqslant |f(x) - L| + |g(x) - M|$$

We will make $|f(x) + g(x) - (L + M)|$ less than ε by making each of the terms $|f(x) - L|$ and $|g(x) - M|$ less than $\varepsilon/2$.

Since $\varepsilon/2 > 0$ and $\lim_{x \to a} f(x) = L$, there exists a number $\delta_1 > 0$ such that

$$\text{if} \quad 0 < |x - a| < \delta_1 \quad \text{then} \quad |f(x) - L| < \frac{\varepsilon}{2}$$

Similarly, since $\lim_{x \to a} g(x) = M$, there exists a number $\delta_2 > 0$ such that

$$\text{if} \quad 0 < |x - a| < \delta_2 \quad \text{then} \quad |g(x) - M| < \frac{\varepsilon}{2}$$

Let $\delta = \min\{\delta_1, \delta_2\}$, the smaller of the numbers δ_1 and δ_2. Notice that

$$\text{if} \quad 0 < |x - a| < \delta \quad \text{then} \quad 0 < |x - a| < \delta_1 \quad \text{and} \quad 0 < |x - a| < \delta_2$$

and so

$$|f(x) - L| < \frac{\varepsilon}{2} \quad \text{and} \quad |g(x) - M| < \frac{\varepsilon}{2}$$

Therefore, by (1),

$$|f(x) + g(x) - (L + M)| \leq |f(x) - L| + |g(x) - M|$$

$$< \frac{\varepsilon}{2} + \frac{\varepsilon}{2} = \varepsilon$$

To summarize,

$$\text{if} \quad 0 < |x - a| < \delta \quad \text{then} \quad |f(x) + g(x) - (L + M)| < \varepsilon$$

Thus, by the definition of a limit,

$$\lim_{x \to a} [f(x) + g(x)] = L + M$$

Fermat's Theorem was discussed in Section 4.2.

> **Fermat's Theorem**   If f has a local maximum or minimum at c, and if $f'(c)$ exists, then $f'(c) = 0$.

PROOF   Suppose, for the sake of definiteness, that f has a local maximum at c. Then, $f(c) \geq f(x)$ if x is sufficiently close to c. This implies that if h is sufficiently close to 0, with h being positive or negative, then

$$f(c) \geq f(c + h)$$

and therefore

$$\boxed{2} \qquad f(c + h) - f(c) \leq 0$$

We can divide both sides of an inequality by a positive number. Thus, if $h > 0$ and h is sufficiently small, we have

$$\frac{f(c + h) - f(c)}{h} \leq 0$$

Taking the right-hand limit of both sides of this inequality (using Theorem 2.3.2), we get

$$\lim_{h \to 0^+} \frac{f(c + h) - f(c)}{h} \leq \lim_{h \to 0^+} 0 = 0$$

But since $f'(c)$ exists, we have

$$f'(c) = \lim_{h \to 0} \frac{f(c + h) - f(c)}{h} = \lim_{h \to 0^+} \frac{f(c + h) - f(c)}{h}$$

and so we have shown that $f'(c) \leq 0$.

If $h < 0$, then the direction of the inequality (2) is reversed when we divide by h:

$$\frac{f(c + h) - f(c)}{h} \geq 0 \qquad h < 0$$

So, taking the left-hand limit, we have

$$f'(c) = \lim_{h \to 0} \frac{f(c + h) - f(c)}{h} = \lim_{h \to 0^-} \frac{f(c + h) - f(c)}{h} \geq 0$$

We have shown that $f'(c) \geq 0$ and also that $f'(c) \leq 0$. Since both of these inequalities must be true, the only possibility is that $f'(c) = 0$.

We have proved Fermat's Theorem for the case of a local maximum. The case of a local minimum can be proved in a similar manner.

This theorem was stated and used in Section 8.1.

> **Theorem** If $\lim\limits_{n \to \infty} a_n = L$ and the function f is continuous at L, then
>
> $$\lim_{n \to \infty} f(a_n) = f(L)$$

PROOF We must show that, given a number $\varepsilon > 0$, there is an integer N such that if $n > N$, then $\left| f(a_n) - f(L) \right| < \varepsilon$.

Suppose $\varepsilon > 0$. Since f is continuous at L, there is a number $\delta > 0$ such that if $\left| x - L \right| < \delta$, then $\left| f(x) - f(L) \right| < \varepsilon$. Because $\lim_{n \to \infty} a_n = L$, there is an integer N such that if $n > N$, then $\left| a_n - L \right| < \delta$. Suppose $n > N$. Then $\left| a_n - L \right| < \delta$ and so $\left| f(a_n) - f(L) \right| < \varepsilon$.

This shows that $\lim_{n \to \infty} f(a_n) = f(L)$.

Clairaut's Theorem was discussed in Section 11.3.

> **Clairaut's Theorem** Suppose f is defined on a disk D that contains the point (a, b). If the functions f_{xy} and f_{yx} are both continuous on D, then $f_{xy}(a, b) = f_{yx}(a, b)$.

PROOF For small values of h, $h \neq 0$, consider the difference

$$\Delta(h) = [f(a + h, b + h) - f(a + h, b)] - [f(a, b + h) - f(a, b)]$$

Notice that if we let $g(x) = f(x, b + h) - f(x, b)$, then

$$\Delta(h) = g(a + h) - g(a)$$

By the Mean Value Theorem, there is a number c between a and $a + h$ such that

$$g(a + h) - g(a) = g'(c)h = h[f_x(c, b + h) - f_x(c, b)]$$

Applying the Mean Value Theorem again, this time to f_x, we get a number d between b and $b + h$ such that

$$f_x(c, b + h) - f_x(c, b) = f_{xy}(c, d)h$$

Combining these equations, we obtain

$$\Delta(h) = h^2 f_{xy}(c, d)$$

If $h \to 0$, then $(c, d) \to (a, b)$, so the continuity of f_{xy} at (a, b) gives

$$\lim_{h \to 0} \frac{\Delta(h)}{h^2} = \lim_{(c, d) \to (a, b)} f_{xy}(c, d) = f_{xy}(a, b)$$

Similarly, by writing

$$\Delta(h) = [f(a + h, b + h) - f(a, b + h)] - [f(a + h, b) - f(a, b)]$$

and using the Mean Value Theorem twice and the continuity of f_{yx} at (a, b), we obtain

$$\lim_{h \to 0} \frac{\Delta(h)}{h^2} = f_{yx}(a, b)$$

It follows that $f_{xy}(a, b) = f_{yx}(a, b)$.

This was stated as Theorem 8 in Section 11.4.

> **Theorem** If the partial derivatives f_x and f_y exist near (a, b) and are continuous at (a, b), then f is differentiable at (a, b).

PROOF Let

$$\Delta z = f(a + \Delta x, b + \Delta y) - f(a, b)$$

According to (11.4.7), to prove that f is differentiable at (a, b) we have to show that we can write Δz in the form

$$\Delta z = f_x(a, b)\,\Delta x + f_y(a, b)\,\Delta y + \varepsilon_1\,\Delta x + \varepsilon_2\,\Delta y$$

where ε_1 and $\varepsilon_2 \to 0$ as $(\Delta x, \Delta y) \to (0, 0)$.
  Referring to Figure 1, we write

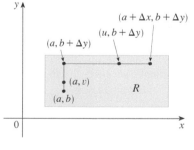

$$\boxed{3} \quad \Delta z = [f(a + \Delta x, b + \Delta y) - f(a, b + \Delta y)] + [f(a, b + \Delta y) - f(a, b)]$$

Observe that the function of a single variable

$$g(x) = f(x, b + \Delta y)$$

is defined on the interval $[a, a + \Delta x]$ and $g'(x) = f_x(x, b + \Delta y)$. If we apply the Mean Value Theorem to g, we get

$$g(a + \Delta x) - g(a) = g'(u)\,\Delta x$$

FIGURE 1

where u is some number between a and $a + \Delta x$. In terms of f, this equation becomes

$$f(a + \Delta x, b + \Delta y) - f(a, b + \Delta y) = f_x(u, b + \Delta y) \, \Delta x$$

This gives us an expression for the first part of the right side of Equation 3. For the second part we let $h(y) = f(a, y)$. Then h is a function of a single variable defined on the interval $[b, b + \Delta y]$ and $h'(y) = f_y(a, y)$. A second application of the Mean Value Theorem then gives

$$h(b + \Delta y) - h(b) = h'(v) \, \Delta y$$

where v is some number between b and $b + \Delta y$. In terms of f, this becomes

$$f(a, b + \Delta y) - f(a, b) = f_y(a, v) \, \Delta y$$

We now substitute these expressions into Equation 3 and obtain

$$\begin{aligned} \Delta z &= f_x(u, b + \Delta y) \, \Delta x + f_y(a, v) \, \Delta y \\ &= f_x(a, b) \, \Delta x + [f_x(u, b + \Delta y) - f_x(a, b)] \, \Delta x + f_y(a, b) \, \Delta y \\ &\quad + [f_y(a, v) - f_y(a, b)] \, \Delta y \\ &= f_x(a, b) \, \Delta x + f_y(a, b) \, \Delta y + \varepsilon_1 \, \Delta x + \varepsilon_2 \, \Delta y \end{aligned}$$

where

$$\varepsilon_1 = f_x(u, b + \Delta y) - f_x(a, b)$$

$$\varepsilon_2 = f_y(a, v) - f_y(a, b)$$

Since $(u, b + \Delta y) \to (a, b)$ and $(a, v) \to (a, b)$ as $(\Delta x, \Delta y) \to (0, 0)$ and since f_x and f_y are continuous at (a, b), we see that $\varepsilon_1 \to 0$ and $\varepsilon_2 \to 0$ as $(\Delta x, \Delta y) \to (0, 0)$.

Therefore f is differentiable at (a, b).

The Second Derivatives Test was discussed in Section 11.7. Parts (b) and (c) have similar proofs.

Second Derivatives Test   Suppose the second partial derivatives of f are continuous on a disk with center (a, b), and suppose that $f_x(a, b) = 0$ and $f_y(a, b) = 0$ [that is, (a, b) is a critical point of f]. Let

$$D = D(a, b) = f_{xx}(a, b) f_{yy}(a, b) - [f_{xy}(a, b)]^2$$

(a) If $D > 0$ and $f_{xx}(a, b) > 0$, then $f(a, b)$ is a local minimum.

(b) If $D > 0$ and $f_{xx}(a, b) < 0$, then $f(a, b)$ is a local maximum.

(c) If $D < 0$, then $f(a, b)$ is not a local maximum or minimum.

PROOF OF PART (A)   We compute the second-order directional derivative of f in the direction of $\mathbf{u} = \langle h, k \rangle$. The first-order derivative is given by Theorem 11.6.3:

$$D_{\mathbf{u}} f = f_x h + f_y k$$

Applying this theorem a second time, we have

$$D_{\mathbf{u}}^2 f = D_{\mathbf{u}}(D_{\mathbf{u}} f) = \frac{\partial}{\partial x}(D_{\mathbf{u}} f)h + \frac{\partial}{\partial y}(D_{\mathbf{u}} f)k$$

$$= (f_{xx}h + f_{yx}k)h + (f_{xy}h + f_{yy}k)k$$

$$= f_{xx}h^2 + 2f_{xy}hk + f_{yy}k^2 \quad \text{(by Clairaut's Theorem)}$$

If we complete the square in this expression, we obtain

$$\boxed{4} \qquad D_{\mathbf{u}}^2 f = f_{xx}\left(h + \frac{f_{xy}}{f_{xx}}k\right)^2 + \frac{k^2}{f_{xx}}(f_{xx}f_{yy} - f_{xy}^2)$$

We are given that $f_{xx}(a, b) > 0$ and $D(a, b) > 0$. But f_{xx} and $D = f_{xx}f_{yy} - f_{xy}^2$ are continuous functions, so there is a disk B with center (a, b) and radius $\delta > 0$ such that $f_{xx}(x, y) > 0$ and $D(x, y) > 0$ whenever (x, y) is in B. Therefore, by looking at Equation 4, we see that $D_{\mathbf{u}}^2 f(x, y) > 0$ whenever (x, y) is in B. This means that if C is the curve obtained by intersecting the graph of f with the vertical plane through $P(a, b, f(a, b))$ in the direction of $\mathbf{u}$, then C is concave upward on an interval of length 2δ. This is true in the direction of every vector $\mathbf{u}$, so if we restrict (x, y) to lie in B, the graph of f lies above its horizontal tangent plane at P. Thus $f(x, y) \geq f(a, b)$ whenever (x, y) is in B. This shows that $f(a, b)$ is a local minimum.

F Sigma Notation

A convenient way of writing sums uses the Greek letter Σ (capital sigma, corresponding to our letter S) and is called **sigma notation**.

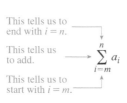

This tells us to end with $i = n$.

This tells us to add.

This tells us to start with $i = m$.

$$\sum_{i=m}^{n} a_i$$

$\boxed{1}$ **Definition** If $a_m, a_{m+1}, \ldots, a_n$ are real numbers and m and n are integers such that $m \leq n$, then

$$\sum_{i=m}^{n} a_i = a_m + a_{m+1} + a_{m+2} + \cdots + a_{n-1} + a_n$$

With function notation, Definition 1 can be written as

$$\sum_{i=m}^{n} f(i) = f(m) + f(m + 1) + f(m + 2) + \cdots + f(n - 1) + f(n)$$

Thus the symbol $\sum_{i=m}^{n}$ indicates a summation in which the letter i (called the **index of summation**) takes on consecutive integer values beginning with m and ending with n, that is, $m, m + 1, \ldots, n$. Other letters can also be used as the index of summation.

EXAMPLE 1

(a) $\sum_{i=1}^{4} i^2 = 1^2 + 2^2 + 3^2 + 4^2 = 30$

(b) $\sum_{i=3}^{n} i = 3 + 4 + 5 + \cdots + (n-1) + n$

(c) $\sum_{j=0}^{5} 2^j = 2^0 + 2^1 + 2^2 + 2^3 + 2^4 + 2^5 = 63$

(d) $\sum_{k=1}^{n} \frac{1}{k} = 1 + \frac{1}{2} + \frac{1}{3} + \cdots + \frac{1}{n}$

(e) $\sum_{i=1}^{3} \frac{i-1}{i^2+3} = \frac{1-1}{1^2+3} + \frac{2-1}{2^2+3} + \frac{3-1}{3^2+3} = 0 + \frac{1}{7} + \frac{1}{6} = \frac{13}{42}$

(f) $\sum_{i=1}^{4} 2 = 2 + 2 + 2 + 2 = 8$

EXAMPLE 2 Write the sum $2^3 + 3^3 + \cdots + n^3$ in sigma notation.

SOLUTION There is no unique way of writing a sum in sigma notation. We could write

$$2^3 + 3^3 + \cdots + n^3 = \sum_{i=2}^{n} i^3$$

or $$2^3 + 3^3 + \cdots + n^3 = \sum_{j=1}^{n-1} (j+1)^3$$

or $$2^3 + 3^3 + \cdots + n^3 = \sum_{k=0}^{n-2} (k+2)^3$$

The following theorem gives three simple rules for working with sigma notation.

2 Theorem If c is any constant (that is, it does not depend on i), then

(a) $\sum_{i=m}^{n} c a_i = c \sum_{i=m}^{n} a_i$ (b) $\sum_{i=m}^{n} (a_i + b_i) = \sum_{i=m}^{n} a_i + \sum_{i=m}^{n} b_i$

(c) $\sum_{i=m}^{n} (a_i - b_i) = \sum_{i=m}^{n} a_i - \sum_{i=m}^{n} b_i$

PROOF To see why these rules are true, all we have to do is write both sides in expanded form. Rule (a) is just the distributive property of real numbers:

$$ca_m + ca_{m+1} + \cdots + ca_n = c(a_m + a_{m+1} + \cdots + a_n)$$

Rule (b) follows from the associative and commutative properties:

$$(a_m + b_m) + (a_{m+1} + b_{m+1}) + \cdots + (a_n + b_n)$$
$$= (a_m + a_{m+1} + \cdots + a_n) + (b_m + b_{m+1} + \cdots + b_n)$$

Rule (c) is proved similarly.

EXAMPLE 3 Find $\displaystyle\sum_{i=1}^{n} 1$.

SOLUTION
$$\sum_{i=1}^{n} 1 = \underbrace{1 + 1 + \cdots + 1}_{n \text{ terms}} = n$$

EXAMPLE 4 Prove the formula for the sum of the first n positive integers:

$$\sum_{i=1}^{n} i = 1 + 2 + 3 + \cdots + n = \frac{n(n+1)}{2}$$

SOLUTION This formula can be proved by mathematical induction (see page 84) or by the following method used by the German mathematician Karl Friedrich Gauss (1777–1855) when he was ten years old.

Write the sum S twice, once in the usual order and once in reverse order:

$$S = 1 + \quad 2 \quad + \quad 3 \quad + \cdots + (n-1) + n$$

$$S = n + (n-1) + (n-2) + \cdots + \quad 2 \quad + 1$$

Adding all columns vertically, we get

$$2S = (n+1) + (n+1) + (n+1) + \cdots + (n+1) + (n+1)$$

On the right side there are n terms, each of which is $n+1$, so

$$2S = n(n+1) \qquad \text{or} \qquad S = \frac{n(n+1)}{2}$$

EXAMPLE 5 Prove the formula for the sum of the squares of the first n positive integers:

$$\sum_{i=1}^{n} i^2 = 1^2 + 2^2 + 3^2 + \cdots + n^2 = \frac{n(n+1)(2n+1)}{6}$$

SOLUTION 1 Let S be the desired sum. We start with the *telescoping sum* (or collapsing sum):

Most terms cancel in pairs.

$$\sum_{i=1}^{n} [(1+i)^3 - i^3] = (2^3 - 1^3) + (3^3 - 2^3) + (4^3 - 3^3) + \cdots + [(n+1)^3 - n^3]$$

$$= (n+1)^3 - 1^3 = n^3 + 3n^2 + 3n$$

On the other hand, using Theorem 2 and Examples 3 and 4, we have

$$\sum_{i=1}^{n} [(1+i)^3 - i^3] = \sum_{i=1}^{n} [3i^2 + 3i + 1] = 3\sum_{i=1}^{n} i^2 + 3\sum_{i=1}^{n} i + \sum_{i=1}^{n} 1$$

$$= 3S + 3\frac{n(n+1)}{2} + n = 3S + \tfrac{3}{2}n^2 + \tfrac{5}{2}n$$

Thus we have

$$n^3 + 3n^2 + 3n = 3S + \tfrac{3}{2}n^2 + \tfrac{5}{2}n$$

Solving this equation for S, we obtain

$$3S = n^3 + \tfrac{3}{2}n^2 + \tfrac{1}{2}n$$

or

$$S = \frac{2n^3 + 3n^2 + n}{6} = \frac{n(n + 1)(2n + 1)}{6}$$

Principle of Mathematical Induction
Let S_n be a statement involving the positive
integer n. Suppose that
1. S_1 is true.
2. If S_k is true, then S_{k+1} is true.
Then S_n is true for all positive integers n.

SOLUTION 2 Let S_n be the given formula.

1. S_1 is true because $1^2 = \dfrac{1(1 + 1)(2 \cdot 1 + 1)}{6}$

2. Assume that S_k is true; that is,

$$1^2 + 2^2 + 3^2 + \cdots + k^2 = \frac{k(k + 1)(2k + 1)}{6}$$

Then

See pages 84 and 87 for a more thorough discussion of mathematical induction.

$$1^2 + 2^2 + 3^2 + \cdots + (k + 1)^2 = (1^2 + 2^2 + 3^2 + \cdots + k^2) + (k + 1)^2$$

$$= \frac{k(k + 1)(2k + 1)}{6} + (k + 1)^2$$

$$= (k + 1)\frac{k(2k + 1) + 6(k + 1)}{6}$$

$$= (k + 1)\frac{2k^2 + 7k + 6}{6}$$

$$= \frac{(k + 1)(k + 2)(2k + 3)}{6}$$

$$= \frac{(k + 1)[(k + 1) + 1][2(k + 1) + 1]}{6}$$

So S_{k+1} is true.

By the Principle of Mathematical Induction, S_n is true for all n.

We list the results of Examples 3, 4, and 5 together with a similar result for cubes (see Exercises 37–40) as Theorem 3. These formulas are needed for finding areas and evaluating integrals in Chapter 5.

---

3 **Theorem** Let c be a constant and n a positive integer. Then

(a) $\displaystyle\sum_{i=1}^{n} 1 = n$ (b) $\displaystyle\sum_{i=1}^{n} c = nc$

(c) $\displaystyle\sum_{i=1}^{n} i = \frac{n(n + 1)}{2}$ (d) $\displaystyle\sum_{i=1}^{n} i^2 = \frac{n(n + 1)(2n + 1)}{6}$

(e) $\displaystyle\sum_{i=1}^{n} i^3 = \left[\frac{n(n + 1)}{2}\right]^2$

EXAMPLE 6   Evaluate $\displaystyle\sum_{i=1}^{n} i(4i^2 - 3)$.

SOLUTION   Using Theorems 2 and 3, we have

$$\sum_{i=1}^{n} i(4i^2 - 3) = \sum_{i=1}^{n} (4i^3 - 3i) = 4\sum_{i=1}^{n} i^3 - 3\sum_{i=1}^{n} i$$

$$= 4\left[\frac{n(n+1)}{2}\right]^2 - 3\,\frac{n(n+1)}{2}$$

$$= \frac{n(n+1)[2n(n+1) - 3]}{2}$$

$$= \frac{n(n+1)(2n^2 + 2n - 3)}{2}$$

The type of calculation in Example 7 arises in Chapter 5 when we compute areas.

EXAMPLE 7   Find $\displaystyle\lim_{n\to\infty} \sum_{i=1}^{n} \frac{3}{n}\left[\left(\frac{i}{n}\right)^2 + 1\right]$.

SOLUTION

$$\lim_{n\to\infty} \sum_{i=1}^{n} \frac{3}{n}\left[\left(\frac{i}{n}\right)^2 + 1\right] = \lim_{n\to\infty} \sum_{i=1}^{n}\left[\frac{3}{n^3}i^2 + \frac{3}{n}\right]$$

$$= \lim_{n\to\infty}\left[\frac{3}{n^3}\sum_{i=1}^{n} i^2 + \frac{3}{n}\sum_{i=1}^{n} 1\right]$$

$$= \lim_{n\to\infty}\left[\frac{3}{n^3}\,\frac{n(n+1)(2n+1)}{6} + \frac{3}{n}\cdot n\right]$$

$$= \lim_{n\to\infty}\left[\frac{1}{2}\cdot\frac{n}{n}\cdot\left(\frac{n+1}{n}\right)\left(\frac{2n+1}{n}\right) + 3\right]$$

$$= \lim_{n\to\infty}\left[\frac{1}{2}\cdot 1\left(1 + \frac{1}{n}\right)\left(2 + \frac{1}{n}\right) + 3\right]$$

$$= \tfrac{1}{2}\cdot 1\cdot 1\cdot 2 + 3 = 4$$

F   Exercises

1–10 Write the sum in expanded form.

1. $\displaystyle\sum_{i=1}^{5} \sqrt{i}$

2. $\displaystyle\sum_{i=1}^{6} \frac{1}{i+1}$

3. $\displaystyle\sum_{i=4}^{6} 3^i$

4. $\displaystyle\sum_{i=4}^{6} i^3$

5. $\displaystyle\sum_{k=0}^{4} \frac{2k-1}{2k+1}$

6. $\displaystyle\sum_{k=5}^{8} x^k$

7. $\displaystyle\sum_{i=1}^{n} i^{10}$

8. $\displaystyle\sum_{j=n}^{n+3} j^2$

9. $\displaystyle\sum_{j=0}^{n-1} (-1)^j$

10. $\displaystyle\sum_{i=1}^{n} f(x_i)\,\Delta x_i$

11–20 Write the sum in sigma notation.

11. $1 + 2 + 3 + 4 + \cdots + 10$

12. $\sqrt{3} + \sqrt{4} + \sqrt{5} + \sqrt{6} + \sqrt{7}$

13. $\frac{1}{2} + \frac{2}{3} + \frac{3}{4} + \frac{4}{5} + \cdots + \frac{19}{20}$

14. $\frac{3}{7} + \frac{4}{8} + \frac{5}{9} + \frac{6}{10} + \cdots + \frac{23}{27}$

15. $2 + 4 + 6 + 8 + \cdots + 2n$

16. $1 + 3 + 5 + 7 + \cdots + (2n - 1)$

17. $1 + 2 + 4 + 8 + 16 + 32$

18. $\frac{1}{1} + \frac{1}{4} + \frac{1}{9} + \frac{1}{16} + \frac{1}{25} + \frac{1}{36}$

19. $x + x^2 + x^3 + \cdots + x^n$

20. $1 - x + x^2 - x^3 + \cdots + (-1)^n x^n$

21–35 Find the value of the sum.

21. $\displaystyle\sum_{i=4}^{8} (3i - 2)$

22. $\displaystyle\sum_{i=3}^{6} i(i + 2)$

23. $\displaystyle\sum_{j=1}^{6} 3^{j+1}$

24. $\displaystyle\sum_{k=0}^{8} \cos k\pi$

25. $\displaystyle\sum_{n=1}^{20} (-1)^n$

26. $\displaystyle\sum_{i=1}^{100} 4$

27. $\displaystyle\sum_{i=0}^{4} (2^i + i^2)$

28. $\displaystyle\sum_{i=-2}^{4} 2^{3-i}$

29. $\displaystyle\sum_{i=1}^{n} 2i$

30. $\displaystyle\sum_{i=1}^{n} (2 - 5i)$

31. $\displaystyle\sum_{i=1}^{n} (i^2 + 3i + 4)$

32. $\displaystyle\sum_{i=1}^{n} (3 + 2i)^2$

33. $\displaystyle\sum_{i=1}^{n} (i + 1)(i + 2)$

34. $\displaystyle\sum_{i=1}^{n} i(i + 1)(i + 2)$

35. $\displaystyle\sum_{i=1}^{n} (i^3 - i - 2)$

---

36. Find the number n such that $\displaystyle\sum_{i=1}^{n} i = 78$.

37. Prove formula (b) of Theorem 3.

38. Prove formula (e) of Theorem 3 using mathematical induction.

39. Prove formula (e) of Theorem 3 using a method similar to that of Example 5, Solution 1 [start with $(1 + i)^4 - i^4$].

40. Prove formula (e) of Theorem 3 using the following method published by Abu Bekr Mohammed ibn Alhusain Alkarchi in about AD 1010. The figure shows a square $ABCD$ in which sides AB and AD have been divided into segments of lengths 1, 2, 3, . . . , n. Thus the side of the square has length $n(n + 1)/2$ so the area is $[n(n + 1)/2]^2$. But the area is also the sum of the

areas of the n "gnomons" $G_1, G_2, \ldots, G_n$ shown in the figure. Show that the area of G_i is i^3 and conclude that formula (e) is true.

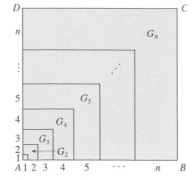

41. Evaluate each telescoping sum.

(a) $\displaystyle\sum_{i=1}^{n} [i^4 - (i - 1)^4]$

(b) $\displaystyle\sum_{i=1}^{100} (5^i - 5^{i-1})$

(c) $\displaystyle\sum_{i=3}^{99} \left(\frac{1}{i} - \frac{1}{i + 1} \right)$

(d) $\displaystyle\sum_{i=1}^{n} (a_i - a_{i-1})$

42. Prove the generalized triangle inequality:

$$\left| \sum_{i=1}^{n} a_i \right| \le \sum_{i=1}^{n} |a_i|$$

43–46 Find the limit.

43. $\displaystyle\lim_{n \to \infty} \sum_{i=1}^{n} \frac{1}{n} \left(\frac{i}{n} \right)^2$

44. $\displaystyle\lim_{n \to \infty} \sum_{i=1}^{n} \frac{1}{n} \left[\left(\frac{i}{n} \right)^3 + 1 \right]$

45. $\displaystyle\lim_{n \to \infty} \sum_{i=1}^{n} \frac{2}{n} \left[\left(\frac{2i}{n} \right)^3 + 5 \left(\frac{2i}{n} \right) \right]$

46. $\displaystyle\lim_{n \to \infty} \sum_{i=1}^{n} \frac{3}{n} \left[\left(1 + \frac{3i}{n} \right)^3 - 2 \left(1 + \frac{3i}{n} \right) \right]$

---

47. Prove the formula for the sum of a finite geometric series with first term a and common ratio $r \ne 1$:

$$\sum_{i=1}^{n} ar^{i-1} = a + ar + ar^2 + \cdots + ar^{n-1} = \frac{a(r^n - 1)}{r - 1}$$

48. Evaluate $\displaystyle\sum_{i=1}^{n} \frac{3}{2^{i-1}}$.

49. Evaluate $\displaystyle\sum_{i=1}^{n} (2i + 2^i)$.

50. Evaluate $\displaystyle\sum_{i=1}^{m} \left[\sum_{j=1}^{n} (i + j) \right]$.

G   Integration of Rational Functions by Partial Fractions

In this appendix we show how to integrate any rational function (a ratio of polynomials) by expressing it as a sum of simpler fractions, called *partial fractions,* that we already know how to integrate. To illustrate the method, observe that by taking the fractions $2/(x-1)$ and $1/(x+2)$ to a common denominator we obtain

$$\frac{2}{x-1} - \frac{1}{x+2} = \frac{2(x+2) - (x-1)}{(x-1)(x+2)} = \frac{x+5}{x^2+x-2}$$

If we now reverse the procedure, we see how to integrate the function on the right side of this equation:

$$\int \frac{x+5}{x^2+x-2}\,dx = \int \left(\frac{2}{x-1} - \frac{1}{x+2} \right) dx$$

$$= 2\ln|x-1| - \ln|x+2| + C$$

To see how the method of partial fractions works in general, let's consider a rational function

$$f(x) = \frac{P(x)}{Q(x)}$$

where P and Q are polynomials. It's possible to express f as a sum of simpler fractions provided that the degree of P is less than the degree of Q. Such a rational function is called *proper.* Recall that if

$$P(x) = a_n x^n + a_{n-1}x^{n-1} + \cdots + a_1 x + a_0$$

where $a_n \neq 0$, then the degree of P is n and we write $\deg(P) = n$.

If f is improper, that is, $\deg(P) \geq \deg(Q)$, then we must take the preliminary step of dividing Q into P (by long division) until a remainder $R(x)$ is obtained such that $\deg(R) < \deg(Q)$. The division statement is

$$\boxed{1} \qquad\qquad f(x) = \frac{P(x)}{Q(x)} = S(x) + \frac{R(x)}{Q(x)}$$

where S and R are also polynomials.

As the following example illustrates, sometimes this preliminary step is all that is required.

V   EXAMPLE 1   Find $\displaystyle\int \frac{x^3+x}{x-1}\,dx$.

SOLUTION   Since the degree of the numerator is greater than the degree of the denominator, we first perform the long division. This enables us to write

$$\int \frac{x^3+x}{x-1}\,dx = \int \left(x^2 + x + 2 + \frac{2}{x-1} \right) dx$$

$$= \frac{x^3}{3} + \frac{x^2}{2} + 2x + 2\ln|x-1| + C$$

The next step is to factor the denominator $Q(x)$ as far as possible. It can be shown that any polynomial Q can be factored as a product of linear factors (of the form $ax + b$) and irreducible quadratic factors (of the form $ax^2 + bx + c$, where $b^2 - 4ac < 0$). For instance, if $Q(x) = x^4 - 16$, we could factor it as

$$Q(x) = (x^2 - 4)(x^2 + 4) = (x - 2)(x + 2)(x^2 + 4)$$

The third step is to express the proper rational function $R(x)/Q(x)$ (from Equation 1) as a sum of **partial fractions** of the form

$$\frac{A}{(ax + b)^i} \quad \text{or} \quad \frac{Ax + B}{(ax^2 + bx + c)^j}$$

A theorem in algebra guarantees that it is always possible to do this. We explain the details for the four cases that occur.

Case I   The denominator $Q(x)$ is a product of distinct linear factors.
This means that we can write

$$Q(x) = (a_1x + b_1)(a_2x + b_2) \cdots (a_kx + b_k)$$

where no factor is repeated (and no factor is a constant multiple of another). In this case the partial fraction theorem states that there exist constants $A_1, A_2, \ldots, A_k$ such that

$$\boxed{2} \qquad \frac{R(x)}{Q(x)} = \frac{A_1}{a_1x + b_1} + \frac{A_2}{a_2x + b_2} + \cdots + \frac{A_k}{a_kx + b_k}$$

These constants can be determined as in the following example.

V EXAMPLE 2 Evaluate $\displaystyle\int \frac{x^2 + 2x - 1}{2x^3 + 3x^2 - 2x} \, dx$.

SOLUTION Since the degree of the numerator is less than the degree of the denominator, we don't need to divide. We factor the denominator as

$$2x^3 + 3x^2 - 2x = x(2x^2 + 3x - 2) = x(2x - 1)(x + 2)$$

Since the denominator has three distinct linear factors, the partial fraction decomposition of the integrand (2) has the form

$$\boxed{3} \qquad \frac{x^2 + 2x - 1}{x(2x - 1)(x + 2)} = \frac{A}{x} + \frac{B}{2x - 1} + \frac{C}{x + 2}$$

Another method for finding A, B, and C is given in the note after this example.

To determine the values of A, B, and C, we multiply both sides of this equation by the product of the denominators, $x(2x - 1)(x + 2)$, obtaining

$$\boxed{4} \qquad x^2 + 2x - 1 = A(2x - 1)(x + 2) + Bx(x + 2) + Cx(2x - 1)$$

Expanding the right side of Equation 4 and writing it in the standard form for polynomials, we get

$$\boxed{5} \qquad x^2 + 2x - 1 = (2A + B + 2C)x^2 + (3A + 2B - C)x - 2A$$

The polynomials in Equation 5 are identical, so their coefficients must be equal. The coefficient of x^2 on the right side, $2A + B + 2C$, must equal the coefficient of x^2 on the left side—namely, 1. Likewise, the coefficients of x are equal and the constant terms are equal. This gives the following system of equations for A, B, and C:

$$2A + \;\; B + 2C = 1$$

$$3A + 2B - \;\; C = 2$$

$$-2A \qquad\qquad = -1$$

Solving, we get $A = \tfrac{1}{2}$, $B = \tfrac{1}{5}$, and $C = -\tfrac{1}{10}$, and so

We could check our work by taking the terms to a common denominator and adding them.

$$\int \frac{x^2 + 2x - 1}{2x^3 + 3x^2 - 2x}\,dx = \int \left[\frac{1}{2}\frac{1}{x} + \frac{1}{5}\frac{1}{2x - 1} - \frac{1}{10}\frac{1}{x + 2} \right] dx$$

$$= \tfrac{1}{2}\ln|x| + \tfrac{1}{10}\ln|2x - 1| - \tfrac{1}{10}\ln|x + 2| + K$$

Figure 1 shows the graphs of the integrand in Example 2 and its indefinite integral (with $K = 0$). Which is which?

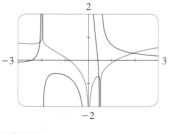

FIGURE 1

In integrating the middle term we have made the mental substitution $u = 2x - 1$, which gives $du = 2\,dx$ and $dx = du/2$.

Note: We can use an alternative method to find the coefficients A, B, and C in Example 2. Equation 4 is an identity; it is true for every value of x. Let's choose values of x that simplify the equation. If we put $x = 0$ in Equation 4, then the second and third terms on the right side vanish and the equation then becomes $-2A = -1$, or $A = \tfrac{1}{2}$. Likewise, $x = \tfrac{1}{2}$ gives $5B/4 = \tfrac{1}{4}$ and $x = -2$ gives $10C = -1$, so $B = \tfrac{1}{5}$ and $C = -\tfrac{1}{10}$. (You may object that Equation 3 is not valid for $x = 0, \tfrac{1}{2}$, or -2, so why should Equation 4 be valid for those values? In fact, Equation 4 is true for all values of x, even $x = 0, \tfrac{1}{2}$, and -2. See Exercise 45 for the reason.)

EXAMPLE 3   Find $\displaystyle\int \frac{dx}{x^2 - a^2}$, where $a \neq 0$.

SOLUTION   The method of partial fractions gives

$$\frac{1}{x^2 - a^2} = \frac{1}{(x - a)(x + a)} = \frac{A}{x - a} + \frac{B}{x + a}$$

and therefore

$$A(x + a) + B(x - a) = 1$$

Using the method of the preceding note, we put $x = a$ in this equation and get $A(2a) = 1$, so $A = 1/(2a)$. If we put $x = -a$, we get $B(-2a) = 1$, so $B = -1/(2a)$. Thus

$$\int \frac{dx}{x^2 - a^2} = \frac{1}{2a} \int \left[\frac{1}{x - a} - \frac{1}{x + a} \right] dx$$

$$= \frac{1}{2a} \big[\ln|x - a| - \ln|x + a| \big] + C$$

Since $\ln x - \ln y = \ln(x/y)$, we can write the integral as

$$\int \frac{dx}{x^2 - a^2} = \frac{1}{2a} \ln \left| \frac{x - a}{x + a} \right| + C$$

Case II $Q(x)$ **is a product of linear factors, some of which are repeated.**

Suppose the first linear factor $(a_1x + b_1)$ is repeated r times; that is, $(a_1x + b_1)^r$ occurs in the factorization of $Q(x)$. Then instead of the single term $A_1/(a_1x + b_1)$ in Equation 2, we would use

$$\boxed{6} \qquad \frac{A_1}{a_1x + b_1} + \frac{A_2}{(a_1x + b_1)^2} + \cdots + \frac{A_r}{(a_1x + b_1)^r}$$

By way of illustration, we could write

$$\frac{x^3 - x + 1}{x^2(x - 1)^3} = \frac{A}{x} + \frac{B}{x^2} + \frac{C}{x - 1} + \frac{D}{(x - 1)^2} + \frac{E}{(x - 1)^3}$$

but we prefer to work out in detail a simpler example.

EXAMPLE 4 Find $\displaystyle\int \frac{x^4 - 2x^2 + 4x + 1}{x^3 - x^2 - x + 1} dx$.

SOLUTION The first step is to divide. The result of long division is

$$\frac{x^4 - 2x^2 + 4x + 1}{x^3 - x^2 - x + 1} = x + 1 + \frac{4x}{x^3 - x^2 - x + 1}$$

The second step is to factor the denominator $Q(x) = x^3 - x^2 - x + 1$. Since $Q(1) = 0$, we know that $x - 1$ is a factor and we obtain

$$x^3 - x^2 - x + 1 = (x - 1)(x^2 - 1) = (x - 1)(x - 1)(x + 1)$$
$$= (x - 1)^2(x + 1)$$

Since the linear factor $x - 1$ occurs twice, the partial fraction decomposition is

$$\frac{4x}{(x - 1)^2(x + 1)} = \frac{A}{x - 1} + \frac{B}{(x - 1)^2} + \frac{C}{x + 1}$$

Multiplying by the least common denominator, $(x - 1)^2(x + 1)$, we get

$$\boxed{7} \qquad 4x = A(x - 1)(x + 1) + B(x + 1) + C(x - 1)^2$$
$$= (A + C)x^2 + (B - 2C)x + (-A + B + C)$$

Another method for finding the coefficients:
Put $x = 1$ in (7): $B = 2$.
Put $x = -1$: $C = -1$.
Put $x = 0$: $A = B + C = 1$.

Now we equate coefficients:

$$A \qquad + \quad C = 0$$
$$B - 2C = 4$$
$$-A + B + \quad C = 0$$

Solving, we obtain $A = 1$, $B = 2$, and $C = -1$, so

$$\int \frac{x^4 - 2x^2 + 4x + 1}{x^3 - x^2 - x + 1} \, dx = \int \left[x + 1 + \frac{1}{x - 1} + \frac{2}{(x - 1)^2} - \frac{1}{x + 1} \right] dx$$

$$= \frac{x^2}{2} + x + \ln|x - 1| - \frac{2}{x - 1} - \ln|x + 1| + K$$

$$= \frac{x^2}{2} + x - \frac{2}{x - 1} + \ln\left|\frac{x - 1}{x + 1}\right| + K$$

Case III $Q(x)$ **contains irreducible quadratic factors, none of which is repeated.**

If $Q(x)$ has the factor $ax^2 + bx + c$, where $b^2 - 4ac < 0$, then, in addition to the partial fractions in Equations 2 and 6, the expression for $R(x)/Q(x)$ will have a term of the form

$$\boxed{8} \qquad \frac{Ax + B}{ax^2 + bx + c}$$

where A and B are constants to be determined. For instance, the function given by $f(x) = x/[(x - 2)(x^2 + 1)(x^2 + 4)]$ has a partial fraction decomposition of the form

$$\frac{x}{(x - 2)(x^2 + 1)(x^2 + 4)} = \frac{A}{x - 2} + \frac{Bx + C}{x^2 + 1} + \frac{Dx + E}{x^2 + 4}$$

When integrating the term given in (8), it will often be necessary to use the formula

$$\boxed{9} \qquad \int \frac{dx}{x^2 + a^2} = \frac{1}{a} \tan^{-1}\left(\frac{x}{a}\right) + C$$

V EXAMPLE 5 Evaluate $\displaystyle\int \frac{2x^2 - x + 4}{x^3 + 4x} \, dx$.

SOLUTION Since $x^3 + 4x = x(x^2 + 4)$ can't be factored further, we write

$$\frac{2x^2 - x + 4}{x(x^2 + 4)} = \frac{A}{x} + \frac{Bx + C}{x^2 + 4}$$

Multiplying by $x(x^2 + 4)$, we have

$$2x^2 - x + 4 = A(x^2 + 4) + (Bx + C)x$$

$$= (A + B)x^2 + Cx + 4A$$

Equating coefficients, we obtain

$$A + B = 2 \qquad C = -1 \qquad 4A = 4$$

Thus $A = 1$, $B = 1$, and $C = -1$ and so

$$\int \frac{2x^2 - x + 4}{x^3 + 4x} \, dx = \int \left(\frac{1}{x} + \frac{x - 1}{x^2 + 4} \right) dx$$

In order to integrate the second term we split it into two parts:

$$\int \frac{x-1}{x^2+4}\,dx = \int \frac{x}{x^2+4}\,dx - \int \frac{1}{x^2+4}\,dx$$

We make the substitution $u = x^2 + 4$ in the first of these integrals so that $du = 2x\,dx$. We evaluate the second integral by means of Formula 9 with $a = 2$:

$$\int \frac{2x^2 - x + 4}{x(x^2+4)}\,dx = \int \frac{1}{x}\,dx + \int \frac{x}{x^2+4}\,dx - \int \frac{1}{x^2+4}\,dx$$

$$= \ln|x| + \tfrac{1}{2}\ln(x^2+4) - \tfrac{1}{2}\tan^{-1}(x/2) + K$$

EXAMPLE 6 Evaluate $\displaystyle\int \frac{4x^2 - 3x + 2}{4x^2 - 4x + 3}\,dx$.

SOLUTION Since the degree of the numerator is *not less than* the degree of the denominator, we first divide and obtain

$$\frac{4x^2 - 3x + 2}{4x^2 - 4x + 3} = 1 + \frac{x-1}{4x^2 - 4x + 3}$$

Notice that the quadratic $4x^2 - 4x + 3$ is irreducible because its discriminant is $b^2 - 4ac = -32 < 0$. This means it can't be factored, so we don't need to use the partial fraction technique.

To integrate the given function we complete the square in the denominator:

$$4x^2 - 4x + 3 = (2x - 1)^2 + 2$$

This suggests that we make the substitution $u = 2x - 1$. Then, $du = 2\,dx$ and $x = \tfrac{1}{2}(u + 1)$, so

$$\int \frac{4x^2 - 3x + 2}{4x^2 - 4x + 3}\,dx = \int \left(1 + \frac{x-1}{4x^2 - 4x + 3}\right) dx$$

$$= x + \tfrac{1}{2}\int \frac{\tfrac{1}{2}(u+1) - 1}{u^2 + 2}\,du = x + \tfrac{1}{4}\int \frac{u - 1}{u^2 + 2}\,du$$

$$= x + \tfrac{1}{4}\int \frac{u}{u^2 + 2}\,du - \tfrac{1}{4}\int \frac{1}{u^2 + 2}\,du$$

$$= x + \tfrac{1}{8}\ln(u^2 + 2) - \frac{1}{4}\cdot\frac{1}{\sqrt{2}}\tan^{-1}\left(\frac{u}{\sqrt{2}}\right) + C$$

$$= x + \tfrac{1}{8}\ln(4x^2 - 4x + 3) - \frac{1}{4\sqrt{2}}\tan^{-1}\left(\frac{2x - 1}{\sqrt{2}}\right) + C$$

Note: Example 6 illustrates the general procedure for integrating a partial fraction of the form

$$\frac{Ax + B}{ax^2 + bx + c} \qquad \text{where } b^2 - 4ac < 0$$

We complete the square in the denominator and then make a substitution that brings the integral into the form

$$\int \frac{Cu + D}{u^2 + a^2} \, du = C \int \frac{u}{u^2 + a^2} \, du + D \int \frac{1}{u^2 + a^2} \, du$$

Then the first integral is a logarithm and the second is expressed in terms of $\tan^{-1}$.

Case IV $Q(x)$ **contains a repeated irreducible quadratic factor.**

If $Q(x)$ has the factor $(ax^2 + bx + c)^r$, where $b^2 - 4ac < 0$, then instead of the single partial fraction (8), the sum

[10] $\qquad \dfrac{A_1 x + B_1}{ax^2 + bx + c} + \dfrac{A_2 x + B_2}{(ax^2 + bx + c)^2} + \cdots + \dfrac{A_r x + B_r}{(ax^2 + bx + c)^r}$

occurs in the partial fraction decomposition of $R(x)/Q(x)$. Each of the terms in (10) can be integrated by using a substitution or by first completing the square.

It would be extremely tedious to work out by hand the numerical values of the coefficients in Example 7. Most computer algebra systems, however, can find the numerical values very quickly. For instance, the Maple command

```
convert(f, parfrac, x)
```

or the Mathematica command

```
Apart[f]
```

gives the following values:

$A = -1$, $\quad B = \frac{1}{8}$, $\quad C = D = -1$,

$E = \frac{15}{8}$, $\quad F = -\frac{1}{8}$, $\quad G = H = \frac{3}{4}$,

$\qquad I = -\frac{1}{2}$, $\quad J = \frac{1}{2}$

EXAMPLE 7 Write out the form of the partial fraction decomposition of the function

$$\frac{x^3 + x^2 + 1}{x(x - 1)(x^2 + x + 1)(x^2 + 1)^3}$$

SOLUTION

$$\frac{x^3 + x^2 + 1}{x(x - 1)(x^2 + x + 1)(x^2 + 1)^3}$$

$$= \frac{A}{x} + \frac{B}{x - 1} + \frac{Cx + D}{x^2 + x + 1} + \frac{Ex + F}{x^2 + 1} + \frac{Gx + H}{(x^2 + 1)^2} + \frac{Ix + J}{(x^2 + 1)^3}$$

EXAMPLE 8 Evaluate $\displaystyle\int \frac{1 - x + 2x^2 - x^3}{x(x^2 + 1)^2} \, dx$.

SOLUTION The form of the partial fraction decomposition is

$$\frac{1 - x + 2x^2 - x^3}{x(x^2 + 1)^2} = \frac{A}{x} + \frac{Bx + C}{x^2 + 1} + \frac{Dx + E}{(x^2 + 1)^2}$$

Multiplying by $x(x^2 + 1)^2$, we have

$$-x^3 + 2x^2 - x + 1 = A(x^2 + 1)^2 + (Bx + C)x(x^2 + 1) + (Dx + E)x$$

$$= A(x^4 + 2x^2 + 1) + B(x^4 + x^2) + C(x^3 + x) + Dx^2 + Ex$$

$$= (A + B)x^4 + Cx^3 + (2A + B + D)x^2 + (C + E)x + A$$

If we equate coefficients, we get the system

$$A + B = 0 \qquad C = -1 \qquad 2A + B + D = 2 \qquad C + E = -1 \qquad A = 1$$

which has the solution $A = 1$, $B = -1$, $C = -1$, $D = 1$, and $E = 0$.

Thus

$$\int \frac{1 - x + 2x^2 - x^3}{x(x^2 + 1)^2}\,dx = \int \left(\frac{1}{x} - \frac{x + 1}{x^2 + 1} + \frac{x}{(x^2 + 1)^2} \right) dx$$

$$= \int \frac{dx}{x} - \int \frac{x}{x^2 + 1}\,dx - \int \frac{dx}{x^2 + 1} + \int \frac{x\,dx}{(x^2 + 1)^2}$$

In the second and fourth terms we made the mental substitution $u = x^2 + 1$.

$$= \ln|x| - \tfrac{1}{2}\ln(x^2 + 1) - \tan^{-1}x - \frac{1}{2(x^2 + 1)} + K$$

G Exercises

1–6 Write out the form of the partial fraction decomposition of the function (as in Example 7). Do not determine the numerical values of the coefficients.

1. (a) $\dfrac{2x}{(x + 3)(3x + 1)}$ (b) $\dfrac{1}{x^3 + 2x^2 + x}$

2. (a) $\dfrac{x}{x^2 + x - 2}$ (b) $\dfrac{x^2}{x^2 + x + 2}$

3. (a) $\dfrac{x^4 + 1}{x^5 + 4x^3}$ (b) $\dfrac{1}{(x^2 - 9)^2}$

4. (a) $\dfrac{x^3}{x^2 + 4x + 3}$ (b) $\dfrac{2x + 1}{(x + 1)^3(x^2 + 4)^2}$

5. (a) $\dfrac{x^4}{x^4 - 1}$ (b) $\dfrac{t^4 + t^2 + 1}{(t^2 + 1)(t^2 + 4)^2}$

6. (a) $\dfrac{x^4}{(x^3 + x)(x^2 - x + 3)}$ (b) $\dfrac{1}{x^6 - x^3}$

7–34 Evaluate the integral.

7. $\displaystyle\int \frac{x}{x - 6}\,dx$ **8.** $\displaystyle\int \frac{r^2}{r + 4}\,dr$

9. $\displaystyle\int \frac{x - 9}{(x + 5)(x - 2)}\,dx$ **10.** $\displaystyle\int \frac{1}{(t + 4)(t - 1)}\,dt$

11. $\displaystyle\int_2^3 \frac{1}{x^2 - 1}\,dx$ **12.** $\displaystyle\int_0^1 \frac{x - 1}{x^2 + 3x + 2}\,dx$

13. $\displaystyle\int \frac{ax}{x^2 - bx}\,dx$ **14.** $\displaystyle\int \frac{1}{(x + a)(x + b)}\,dx$

15. $\displaystyle\int_3^4 \frac{x^3 - 2x^2 - 4}{x^3 - 2x^2}\,dx$ **16.** $\displaystyle\int_0^1 \frac{x^3 - 4x - 10}{x^2 - x - 6}\,dx$

17. $\displaystyle\int_1^2 \frac{4y^2 - 7y - 12}{y(y + 2)(y - 3)}\,dy$ **18.** $\displaystyle\int \frac{x^2 + 2x - 1}{x^3 - x}\,dx$

19. $\displaystyle\int \frac{1}{(x + 5)^2(x - 1)}\,dx$ **20.** $\displaystyle\int \frac{x^2 - 5x + 16}{(2x + 1)(x - 2)^2}\,dx$

21. $\displaystyle\int \frac{5x^2 + 3x - 2}{x^3 + 2x^2}\,dx$ **22.** $\displaystyle\int \frac{x^2 - x + 6}{x^3 + 3x}\,dx$

23. $\displaystyle\int \frac{10}{(x - 1)(x^2 + 9)}\,dx$ **24.** $\displaystyle\int \frac{x^2 - 2x - 1}{(x - 1)^2(x^2 + 1)}\,dx$

25. $\displaystyle\int \frac{x^3 + x^2 + 2x + 1}{(x^2 + 1)(x^2 + 2)}\,dx$ **26.** $\displaystyle\int \frac{x^2 + x + 1}{(x^2 + 1)^2}\,dx$

27. $\displaystyle\int \frac{x + 4}{x^2 + 2x + 5}\,dx$ **28.** $\displaystyle\int_0^1 \frac{x}{x^2 + 4x + 13}\,dx$

29. $\displaystyle\int \frac{1}{x^3 - 1}\,dx$ **30.** $\displaystyle\int \frac{x^3}{x^3 + 1}\,dx$

31. $\displaystyle\int \frac{dx}{x(x^2 + 4)^2}$ **32.** $\displaystyle\int \frac{x^4 + 3x^2 + 1}{x^5 + 5x^3 + 5x}\,dx$

33. $\displaystyle\int \frac{x - 3}{(x^2 + 2x + 4)^2}\,dx$ **34.** $\displaystyle\int \frac{3x^2 + x + 4}{x^4 + 3x^2 + 2}\,dx$

35–38 Make a substitution to express the integrand as a rational function and then evaluate the integral.

35. $\displaystyle\int_9^{16} \frac{\sqrt{x}}{x - 4}\,dx$ **36.** $\displaystyle\int \frac{dx}{2\sqrt{x + 3} + x}$

37. $\displaystyle\int \frac{e^{2x}}{e^{2x} + 3e^x + 2}\,dx$ **38.** $\displaystyle\int \frac{\cos x}{\sin^2 x + \sin x}\,dx$

39. Use a graph of $f(x) = 1/(x^2 - 2x - 3)$ to decide whether $\int_0^2 f(x)\,dx$ is positive or negative. Use the graph to give a rough estimate of the value of the integral and then use partial fractions to find the exact value.

40. Graph both $y = 1/(x^3 - 2x^2)$ and an antiderivative on the same screen.

Graphing calculator or computer with graphing software required   CAS Computer algebra system required   **1.** Homework Hints available in TEC

41. One method of slowing the growth of an insect population without using pesticides is to introduce into the population a number of sterile males that mate with fertile females but produce no offspring. If P represents the number of female insects in a population, S the number of sterile males introduced each generation, and r the population's natural growth rate, then the female population is related to time t by

$$t = \int \frac{P + S}{P[(r-1)P - S]} \, dP$$

Suppose an insect population with 10,000 females grows at a rate of $r = 0.10$ and 900 sterile males are added. Evaluate the integral to give an equation relating the female population to time. (Note that the resulting equation can't be solved explicitly for P.)

42. The region under the curve

$$y = \frac{1}{x^2 + 3x + 2}$$

from $x = 0$ to $x = 1$ is rotated about the x-axis. Find the volume of the resulting solid.

CAS **43.** (a) Use a computer algebra system to find the partial fraction decomposition of the function

$$f(x) = \frac{4x^3 - 27x^2 + 5x - 32}{30x^5 - 13x^4 + 50x^3 - 286x^2 - 299x - 70}$$

(b) Use part (a) to find $\int f(x)\, dx$ (by hand) and compare with the result of using the CAS to integrate f directly. Comment on any discrepancy.

CAS **44.** (a) Find the partial fraction decomposition of the function

$$f(x) = \frac{12x^5 - 7x^3 - 13x^2 + 8}{100x^6 - 80x^5 + 116x^4 - 80x^3 + 41x^2 - 20x + 4}$$

(b) Use part (a) to find $\int f(x)\, dx$ and graph f and its indefinite integral on the same screen.

(c) Use the graph of f to discover the main features of the graph of $\int f(x)\, dx$.

45. Suppose that F, G, and Q are polynomials and

$$\frac{F(x)}{Q(x)} = \frac{G(x)}{Q(x)}$$

for all x except when $Q(x) = 0$. Prove that $F(x) = G(x)$ for all x. [*Hint:* Use continuity.]

46. If f is a quadratic function such that $f(0) = 1$ and

$$\int \frac{f(x)}{x^2(x + 1)^3} \, dx$$

is a rational function, find the value of $f'(0)$.

H | Polar Coordinates

Polar coordinates offer an alternative way of locating points in a plane. They are useful because, for certain types of regions and curves, polar coordinates provide very simple descriptions and equations. The principal applications of this idea occur in multivariable calculus: the evaluation of double integrals and the derivation of Kepler's laws of planetary motion.

H.1 | Curves in Polar Coordinates

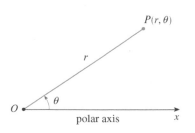

FIGURE 1

A coordinate system represents a point in the plane by an ordered pair of numbers called coordinates. Usually we use Cartesian coordinates, which are directed distances from two perpendicular axes. Here we describe a coordinate system introduced by Newton, called the **polar coordinate system**, which is more convenient for many purposes.

We choose a point in the plane that is called the **pole** (or origin) and is labeled O. Then we draw a ray (half-line) starting at O called the **polar axis**. This axis is usually drawn horizontally to the right and corresponds to the positive x-axis in Cartesian coordinates.

If P is any other point in the plane, let r be the distance from O to P and let θ be the angle (usually measured in radians) between the polar axis and the line OP as in Figure 1. Then the point P is represented by the ordered pair (r, θ) and r, θ are called **polar coordinates** of P. We use the convention that an angle is positive if measured in the counterclock-

J | Answers to Odd-Numbered Exercises

CHAPTER 1

1. (a) 3   (b) -0.2 (c) 0, 3   (d) -0.8
(e) $[-2, 4], [-1, 3]$ (f) $[-2, 1]$
3. $[-85, 115]$ **5.** No
7. Yes, $[-3, 2], [-3, -2) \cup [-1, 3]$
9. Diet, exercise, or illness
11.

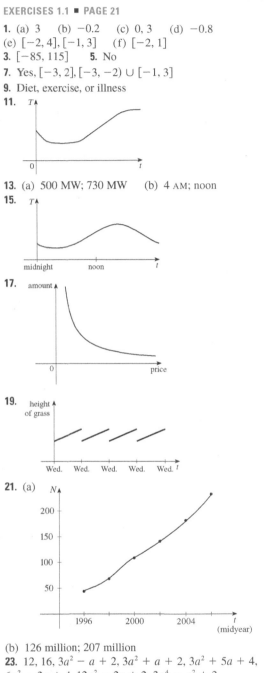

13. (a) 500 MW; 730 MW   (b) 4 AM; noon
15.

17.

19.

21. (a)

(b) 126 million; 207 million
23. $12, 16, 3a^2 - a + 2, 3a^2 + a + 2, 3a^2 + 5a + 4,$
$6a^2 - 2a + 4, 12a^2 - 2a + 2, 3a^4 - a^2 + 2,$
$9a^4 - 6a^3 + 13a^2 - 4a + 4, 3a^2 + 6ah + 3h^2 - a - h + 2$
25. $-3 - h$ **27.** $-1/(ax)$
29. $(-\infty, -3) \cup (-3, 3) \cup (3, \infty)$
31. $(-\infty, \infty)$
33. $(-\infty, 0) \cup (5, \infty)$

35. $(-\infty, \infty)$

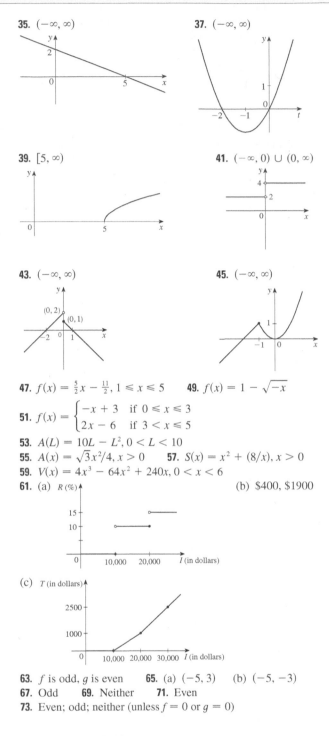

37. $(-\infty, \infty)$

39. $[5, \infty)$

41. $(-\infty, 0) \cup (0, \infty)$

43. $(-\infty, \infty)$

45. $(-\infty, \infty)$

47. $f(x) = \frac{5}{2}x - \frac{11}{2}, 1 \leqslant x \leqslant 5$ **49.** $f(x) = 1 - \sqrt{-x}$
51. $f(x) = \begin{cases} -x + 3 & \text{if } 0 \leqslant x \leqslant 3 \\ 2x - 6 & \text{if } 3 < x \leqslant 5 \end{cases}$
53. $A(L) = 10L - L^2, 0 < L < 10$
55. $A(x) = \sqrt{3}x^2/4, x > 0$ **57.** $S(x) = x^2 + (8/x), x > 0$
59. $V(x) = 4x^3 - 64x^2 + 240x, 0 < x < 6$
61. (a) R (%)   (b) $400, $1900

(c) T (in dollars)

63. f is odd, g is even   **65.** (a) $(-5, 3)$ (b) $(-5, -3)$
67. Odd   **69.** Neither   **71.** Even
73. Even; odd; neither (unless $f = 0$ or $g = 0$)

1. (a) Logarithmic   (b) Root   (c) Rational
(d) Polynomial, degree 2   (e) Exponential   (f) Trigonometric
3. (a) h (b) f (c) g

5. (a) $y = 2x + b$,
where b is the y-intercept.

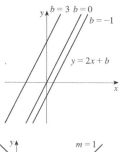

(b) $y = mx + 1 - 2m$,
where m is the slope.
See graph at right.
(c) $y = 2x - 3$

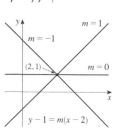

7. Their graphs have slope -1.

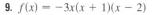

9. $f(x) = -3x(x + 1)(x - 2)$
11. (a) 8.34, change in mg for every 1 year change   (b) 8.34 mg
13. (a)

(b) $\frac{9}{5}$, change in °F for every
1°C change; 32, Fahrenheit
temperature corresponding
to 0°C

15. (a) $T = \frac{1}{6}N + \frac{307}{6}$ (b) $\frac{1}{6}$, change in °F for every chirp per
minute change   (c) 76°F
17. (a) $P = 0.434d + 15$ (b) 196 ft
19. (a) Cosine   (b) Linear
21. (a)

Linear model is
appropriate.

(b) $y = -0.000105x + 14.521$

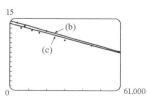

(c) $y = -0.00009979x + 13.951$ [See graph in (b).]
(d) About 11.5 per 100 population   (e) About 6%   (f) No
23. (a)

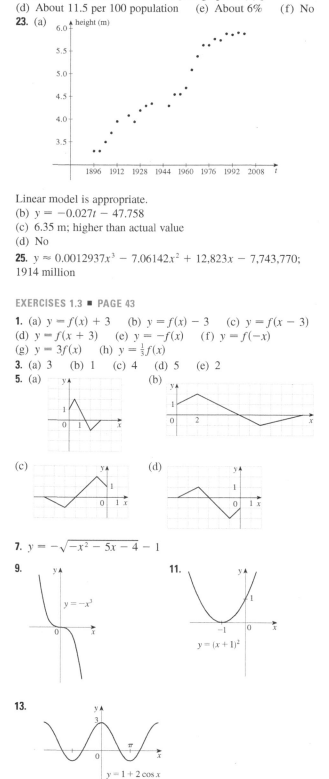

Linear model is appropriate.
(b) $y = -0.027t - 47.758$
(c) 6.35 m; higher than actual value
(d) No
25. $y \approx 0.0012937x^3 - 7.06142x^2 + 12,823x - 7,743,770$;
1914 million

EXERCISES 1.3 ■ PAGE 43

1. (a) $y = f(x) + 3$ (b) $y = f(x) - 3$ (c) $y = f(x - 3)$
(d) $y = f(x + 3)$ (e) $y = -f(x)$ (f) $y = f(-x)$
(g) $y = 3f(x)$ (h) $y = \frac{1}{3}f(x)$
3. (a) 3   (b) 1   (c) 4   (d) 5   (e) 2
5. (a)   (b)

(c)   (d)

7. $y = -\sqrt{-x^2 - 5x - 4} - 1$
9.   **11.**

$y = -x^3$

$y = (x + 1)^2$

13.

$y = 1 + 2\cos x$

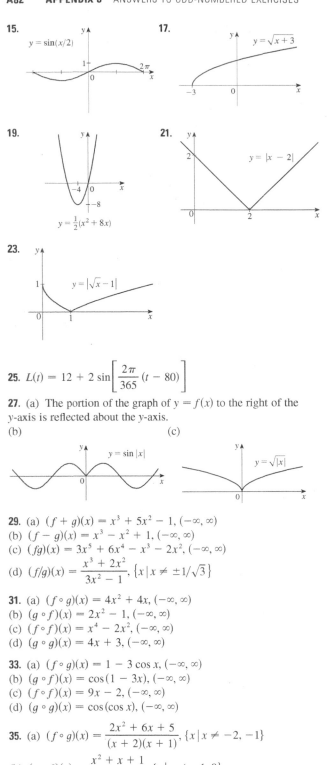

15. $y = \sin(x/2)$

17. $y = \sqrt{x+3}$

19. $y = \frac{1}{2}(x^2 + 8x)$

21. $y = |x - 2|$

23. $y = |\sqrt{x} - 1|$

25. $L(t) = 12 + 2 \sin\left[\dfrac{2\pi}{365}(t - 80)\right]$

27. (a) The portion of the graph of $y = f(x)$ to the right of the y-axis is reflected about the y-axis.

(b) $y = \sin|x|$ (c) $y = \sqrt{|x|}$

29. (a) $(f + g)(x) = x^3 + 5x^2 - 1,\ (-\infty, \infty)$
(b) $(f - g)(x) = x^3 - x^2 + 1,\ (-\infty, \infty)$
(c) $(fg)(x) = 3x^5 + 6x^4 - x^3 - 2x^2,\ (-\infty, \infty)$
(d) $(f/g)(x) = \dfrac{x^3 + 2x^2}{3x^2 - 1},\ \left\{x \mid x \neq \pm 1/\sqrt{3}\right\}$

31. (a) $(f \circ g)(x) = 4x^2 + 4x,\ (-\infty, \infty)$
(b) $(g \circ f)(x) = 2x^2 - 1,\ (-\infty, \infty)$
(c) $(f \circ f)(x) = x^4 - 2x^2,\ (-\infty, \infty)$
(d) $(g \circ g)(x) = 4x + 3,\ (-\infty, \infty)$

33. (a) $(f \circ g)(x) = 1 - 3 \cos x,\ (-\infty, \infty)$
(b) $(g \circ f)(x) = \cos(1 - 3x),\ (-\infty, \infty)$
(c) $(f \circ f)(x) = 9x - 2,\ (-\infty, \infty)$
(d) $(g \circ g)(x) = \cos(\cos x),\ (-\infty, \infty)$

35. (a) $(f \circ g)(x) = \dfrac{2x^2 + 6x + 5}{(x + 2)(x + 1)},\ \{x \mid x \neq -2, -1\}$

(b) $(g \circ f)(x) = \dfrac{x^2 + x + 1}{(x + 1)^2},\ \{x \mid x \neq -1, 0\}$

(c) $(f \circ f)(x) = \dfrac{x^4 + 3x^2 + 1}{x(x^2 + 1)},\ \{x \mid x \neq 0\}$

(d) $(g \circ g)(x) = \dfrac{2x + 3}{3x + 5},\ \left\{x \mid x \neq -2, -\frac{5}{3}\right\}$

37. $(f \circ g \circ h)(x) = 2x - 1$

39. $(f \circ g \circ h)(x) = \sqrt{x^6 + 4x^3 + 1}$

41. $g(x) = 2x + x^2, f(x) = x^4$

43. $g(x) = \sqrt[3]{x},\ f(x) = x/(1 + x)$

45. $g(t) = \cos t,\ f(t) = \sqrt{t}$

47. $h(x) = x^2,\ g(x) = 3^x,\ f(x) = 1 - x$

49. $h(x) = \sqrt{x},\ g(x) = \sec x,\ f(x) = x^4$

51. (a) 4   (b) 3   (c) 0   (d) Does not exist; $f(6) = 6$ is not in the domain of g.   (e) 4   (f) -2

53. (a) $r(t) = 60t$ (b) $(A \circ r)(t) = 3600\pi t^2$; the area of the circle as a function of time

55. (a) $s = \sqrt{d^2 + 36}$ (b) $d = 30t$
(c) $(f \circ g)(t) = \sqrt{900t^2 + 36}$; the distance between the lighthouse and the ship as a function of the time elapsed since noon

57. (a)   (b)

$V(t) = 120H(t)$

(c)

$V(t) = 240H(t - 5)$

59. Yes; $m_1 m_2$

61. (a) $f(x) = x^2 + 6$ (b) $g(x) = x^2 + x - 1$

63. Yes

EXERCISES 1.4 ▪ PAGE 51

1. (c)

3.

5.

7.

9.

11.

13.

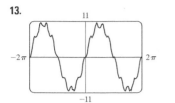

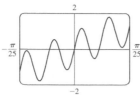

15. (b) Yes; two are needed

17.

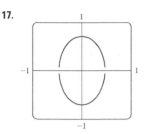

19. No   **21.** $-0.72, 1.22$ **23.** 0.65
25. g **27.** $-0.85 < x < 0.85$
29. (a)

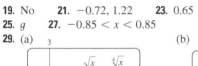

(b)

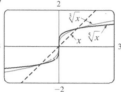

(c)

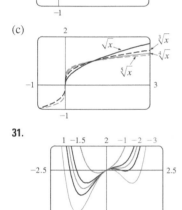

(d) Graphs of even roots are similar to $\sqrt{x}$, graphs of odd roots are similar to $\sqrt[3]{x}$. As n increases, the graph of $y = \sqrt[n]{x}$ becomes steeper near 0 and flatter for $x > 1$.

31.

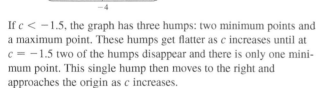

If $c < -1.5$, the graph has three humps: two minimum points and a maximum point. These humps get flatter as c increases until at $c = -1.5$ two of the humps disappear and there is only one minimum point. This single hump then moves to the right and approaches the origin as c increases.
33. The hump gets larger and moves to the right.
35. If $c < 0$, the loop is to the right of the origin; if $c > 0$, the loop is to the left. The closer c is to 0, the larger the loop.

EXERCISES 1.5 ■ PAGE 59

1. (a) 4   (b) $x^{-4/3}$
3. (a) $16b^{12}$ (b) $648y^7$
5. (a) $f(x) = a^x, a > 0$ (b) $\mathbb{R}$ (c) $(0, \infty)$

(d) See Figures 4(c), 4(b), and 4(a), respectively.
7.

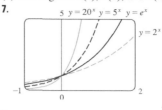

All approach 0 as $x \to -\infty$, all pass through $(0, 1)$, and all are increasing. The larger the base, the faster the rate of increase.

9.

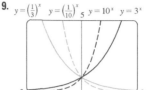

The functions with base greater than 1 are increasing and those with base less than 1 are decreasing. The latter are reflections of the former about the y-axis.

11.

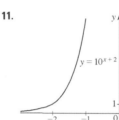

13.

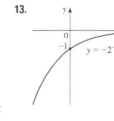

15.

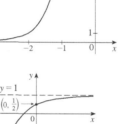

17. (a) $y = e^x - 2$ (b) $y = e^{x-2}$ (c) $y = -e^x$
(d) $y = e^{-x}$ (e) $y = -e^{-x}$
19. (a) $(-\infty, -1) \cup (-1, 1) \cup (1, \infty)$ (b) $(-\infty, \infty)$
21. $f(x) = 3 \cdot 2^x$ **27.** At $x \approx 35.8$
29. (a) 3200   (b) $100 \cdot 2^{1/3}$ (c) 10,159
(d)

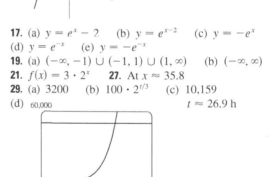

$t \approx 26.9$ h

31. (a) 25 mg   (b) $200 \cdot 2^{-t/5}$ (c) 10.9 mg   (d) 38.2 days
33. $y = ab^t$, where $a \approx 3.154832569 \times 10^{-12}$ and $b \approx 1.017764706$; 5498 million; 7417 million

EXERCISES 1.6 ■ PAGE 69

1. (a) See Definition 1.
(b) It must pass the Horizontal Line Test.
3. No   **5.** No   **7.** Yes   **9.** No
11. Yes   **13.** No   **15.** 2   **17.** 0
19. $F = \frac{9}{5} C + 32$; the Fahrenheit temperature as a function of the Celsius temperature; $[-273.15, \infty)$

21. $y = \frac{1}{3}(x-1)^2 - \frac{2}{3}, x \geq 1$

23. $y = \frac{1}{2}(1 + \ln x)$ **25.** $y = e^x - 3$

27. $f^{-1}(x) = \sqrt[4]{x-1}$ **29.**

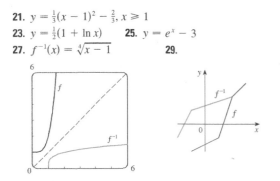

31. (a) $f^{-1}(x) = \sqrt{1-x^2}, 0 \leq x \leq 1; f^{-1}$ and f are the same function.   (b) Quarter-circle in the first quadrant

33. (a) It's defined as the inverse of the exponential function with base a, that is, $\log_a x = y \iff a^y = x$.
(b) $(0, \infty)$ (c) $\mathbb{R}$ (d) See Figure 11.

35. (a) 3   (b) -3 **37.** (a) 3   (b) -2 **39.** $\ln 1215$

41. $\ln \dfrac{(1+x^2)\sqrt{x}}{\sin x}$

43.

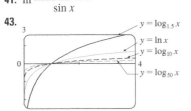

$y = \log_{1.5} x$
$y = \ln x$
$y = \log_{10} x$
$y = \log_{50} x$

All graphs approach $-\infty$ as $x \to 0^+$, all pass through $(1, 0)$, and all are increasing. The larger the base, the slower the rate of increase.

45. About 1,084,588 mi

47. (a)

$y = \log_{10}(x+5)$

(b)
$y = -\ln x$

49. (a) $\frac{1}{4}(7 - \ln 6)$ (b) $\frac{1}{3}(e^2 + 10)$

51. (a) $5 + \log_2 3$ or $5 + (\ln 3)/\ln 2$ (b) $\frac{1}{2}(1 + \sqrt{1 + 4e})$

53. (a) $x < \ln 10$ (b) $x > 1/e$

55. (a) $\left(-\infty, \frac{1}{2}\ln 3\right]$ (b) $f^{-1}(x) = \frac{1}{2}\ln(3 - x^2), [0, \sqrt{3}]$

57.

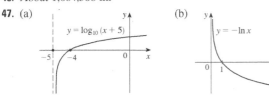

The graph passes the Horizontal Line Test.

$f^{-1}(x) = -\frac{1}{6}\sqrt[3]{4}\left(\sqrt[3]{D - 27x^2 + 20} - \sqrt[3]{D + 27x^2 - 20} + \sqrt[3]{2}\right)$,
where $D = 3\sqrt{3}\sqrt{27x^4 - 40x^2 + 16}$; two of the expressions are complex.

59. (a) $f^{-1}(n) = (3/\ln 2) \ln(n/100)$; the time elapsed when there are n bacteria   (b) After about 26.9 hours

61. (a) $y = \ln x + 3$ (b) $y = \ln(x+3)$ (c) $y = -\ln x$
(d) $y = \ln(-x)$ (e) $y = e^x$ (f) $y = e^{-x}$ (g) $y = -e^x$
(h) $y = e^x - 3$

EXERCISES 1.7 ■ **PAGE 76**

1.

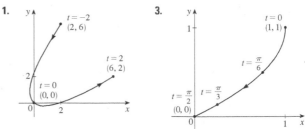

3.

5. (a)

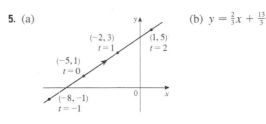

(b) $y = \frac{2}{3}x + \frac{13}{3}$

7. (a)

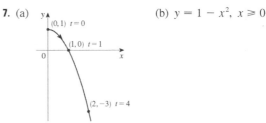

(b) $y = 1 - x^2, x \geq 0$

9. (a) $x^2 + y^2 = 1, y \geq 0$ (b)

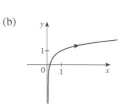

11. (a) $y = 1/x, y > 1$ (b)

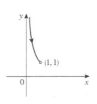

13. (a) $y = \frac{1}{2}\ln x + 1$ (b)

15. (a) $y = 1 - 2x^2, -1 \leqslant x \leqslant 1$ (b)

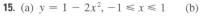

17. Moves counterclockwise along the circle
$(x - 3)^2 + (y - 1)^2 = 4$ from $(3, 3)$ to $(3, -1)$
19. Moves 3 times clockwise around the ellipse
$(x^2/25) + (y^2/4) = 1$, starting and ending at $(0, -2)$
21. It is contained in the rectangle described by $1 \leqslant x \leqslant 4$
and $2 \leqslant y \leqslant 3$.
23.

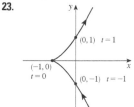

25.

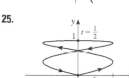

27.

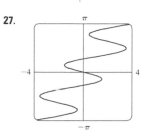

29. (b) $x = -2 + 5t, y = 7 - 8t, 0 \leqslant t \leqslant 1$
31. (a) $x = 2 \cos t, y = 1 - 2 \sin t, 0 \leqslant t \leqslant 2\pi$
(b) $x = 2 \cos t, y = 1 + 2 \sin t, 0 \leqslant t \leqslant 6\pi$
(c) $x = 2 \cos t, y = 1 + 2 \sin t, \pi/2 \leqslant t \leqslant 3\pi/2$
35. The curve $y = x^{2/3}$ is generated in (a). In (b), only the portion
with $x \geqslant 0$ is generated, and in (c) we get only the portion with
$x > 0$.
39. $x = a \cos \theta, y = b \sin \theta; (x^2/a^2) + (y^2/b^2) = 1$, ellipse
41. (a) Two points of intersection

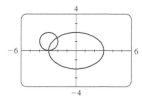

(b) One collision point at $(-3, 0)$ when $t = 3\pi/2$
(c) There are still two intersection points, but no collision point.

43. For $c = 0$, there is a cusp; for $c > 0$, there is a loop whose size
increases as c increases.

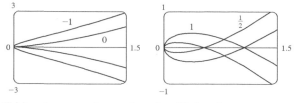

45. As n increases, the number of oscillations increases;
a and b determine the width and height.

CHAPTER 1 REVIEW ■ PAGE 80

True-False Quiz

1 False   **3.** False   **5.** True   **7.** False   **9.** True
11. False

Exercises
1. (a) 2.7   (b) 2.3, 5.6   (c) $[-6, 6]$ (d) $[-4, 4]$
(e) $[-4, 4]$ (f) No; it fails the Horizontal Line Test.
(g) Odd; its graph is symmetric about the origin.
3. $2a + h - 2$ **5.** $\left(-\infty, \frac{1}{3}\right) \cup \left(\frac{1}{3}, \infty\right)$, $(-\infty, 0) \cup (0, \infty)$
7. $(-6, \infty)$, $\mathbb{R}$
9. (a) Shift the graph 8 units upward.
(b) Shift the graph 8 units to the left.
(c) Stretch the graph vertically by a factor of 2, then shift it
1 unit upward.
(d) Shift the graph 2 units to the right and 2 units downward.
(e) Reflect the graph about the x-axis.
(f) Reflect the graph about the line $y = x$ (assuming f is
one-to-one).
11.

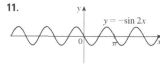

13.

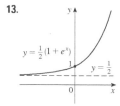

15.

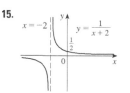

17. (a) Neither   (b) Odd   (c) Even   (d) Neither
19. (a) $(f \circ g)(x) = \ln(x^2 - 9), (-\infty, -3) \cup (3, \infty)$
(b) $(g \circ f)(x) = (\ln x)^2 - 9, (0, \infty)$
(c) $(f \circ f)(x) = \ln \ln x, (1, \infty)$
(d) $(g \circ g)(x) = (x^2 - 9)^2 - 9, (-\infty, \infty)$
21. $y = 0.2493x - 423.4818$; about 77.6 years
23. 1   **25.** (a) 9   (b) 2
27. (a) $\frac{1}{16}$ g   (b) $m(t) = 2^{-t/4}$
(c) $t(m) = -4 \log_2 m$; the time elapsed when there are m grams
of ^{100}Pd   (d) About 26.6 days

29.

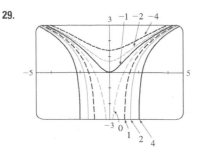

For $c < 0$, f is defined everywhere. As c increases, the dip at $x = 0$ becomes deeper. For $c \geqslant 0$, the graph has asymptotes at $x = \pm\sqrt{c}$.

31. (a)

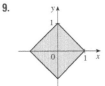

(b) $y = \sqrt{\ln x}$

33.

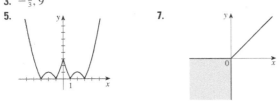

PRINCIPLES OF PROBLEM SOLVING ▪ PAGE 88

1. $a = 4\sqrt{h^2 - 16}/h$, where a is the length of the altitude and h is the length of the hypotenuse

3. $-\frac{7}{3}, 9$

5.

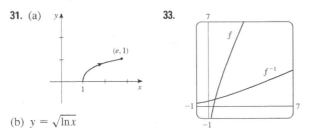

7.

9.

11. 5   **13.** $x \in \left[-1, 1 - \sqrt{3}\right) \cup \left(1 + \sqrt{3}, 3\right]$

15. 40 mi/h   **19.** $f_n(x) = x^{2^{n+1}}$

CHAPTER 2

EXERCISES 2.1 ▪ PAGE 94

1. (a) $-44.4, -38.8, -27.8, -22.2, -16.\overline{6}$
(b) -33.3 (c) $-33\frac{1}{3}$

3. (a) (i) 0.333333   (ii) 0.263158   (iii) 0.251256
(iv) 0.250125   (v) 0.2   (vi) 0.238095   (vii) 0.248756
(viii) 0.249875   (b) $\frac{1}{4}$ (c) $y = \frac{1}{4}x + \frac{1}{4}$

5. (a) (i) -32 ft/s   (ii) -25.6 ft/s   (iii) -24.8 ft/s
(iv) -24.16 ft/s   (b) -24 ft/s

7. (a) (i) 4.65 m/s   (ii) 5.6 m/s   (iii) 7.55 m/s
(iv) 7 m/s   (b) 6.3 m/s

9. (a) 0, 1.7321, -1.0847, -2.7433, 4.3301, -2.8173, 0,
-2.1651, -2.6061, -5, 3.4202; no   (c) -31.4

EXERCISES 2.2 ▪ PAGE 102

1. Yes
3. (a) 2   (b) 3   (c) Does not exist   (d) 4
(e) Does not exist
5. (a) -1 (b) -2 (c) Does not exist   (d) 2   (e) 0
(f) Does not exist   (g) 1   (h) 3
7. $\lim_{x \to a} f(x)$ exists for all a except $a = -1$.
9. (a) 1   (b) 0   (c) Does not exist
11. (a) -2 (b) 2   (c) Does not exist
13.

15.

17. $\frac{2}{3}$ **19.** 5   **21.** $\frac{1}{4}$ **23.** $\frac{3}{5}$ **25.** (a) -1.5
27. (a) 2.71828   (b)

29. (a) 0.998000, 0.638259, 0.358484, 0.158680, 0.038851,
0.008928, 0.001465; 0
(b) 0.000572, -0.000614, -0.000907, -0.000978, -0.000993,
-0.001000; -0.001
31. Within 0.021; within 0.011

EXERCISES 2.3 ▪ PAGE 111

1. (a) -6 (b) -8 (c) 2   (d) -6
(e) Does not exist   (f) 0
3. 59   **5.** 390   **7.** $\frac{3}{2}$ **9.** 4   **11.** Does not exist
13. $\frac{6}{5}$ **15.** 8   **17.** $\frac{1}{12}$
19. $-\frac{1}{16}$ **21.** $\frac{1}{128}$ **23.** $-\frac{1}{2}$ **25.** (a), (b) $\frac{2}{3}$
29. 7   **33.** 6
35. Does not exist
37. (a) (i) 1   (ii) 1   (iii) 3   (iv) -2 (v) -1
(vi) Does not exist
(b)

39. (a) (i) -2 (ii) Does not exist (iii) -3
(b) (i) $n - 1$ (ii) n (c) a is not an integer.
45. 8   **49.** $15; -1$

1. $\lim_{x \to 4} f(x) = f(4)$
3. (a) $f(-4)$ is not defined and $\lim_{x \to a} f(x)$ [for $a = -2, 2,$ and 4]
does not exist
(b) -4, neither; -2, left; 2, right; 4, right

5. 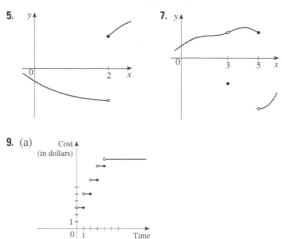   **7.**

9. (a)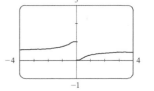

(b) Discontinuous at $t = 1, 2, 3, 4$
11. 6
15. $\lim_{x \to 0} f(x)$ does not exist.   **17.** $\lim_{x \to 0} f(x) \neq f(0)$

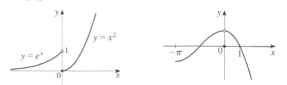

19. $[\frac{1}{2}, \infty)$ **21.** $(-\infty, \infty)$ **23.** $(-\infty, -1) \cup (1, \infty)$
25. $x = 0$

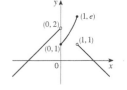

27. $\frac{7}{3}$ **29.** 1
33. 0, right; 1, left

35. $\frac{2}{3}$ **37.** (a) $g(x) = x^3 + x^2 + x + 1$ (b) $g(x) = x^2 + x$
45. (b) $(0.86, 0.87)$ **47.** (b) 70.347
51. Yes

1. (a) As x approaches 2, $f(x)$ becomes large. (b) As x
approaches 1 from the right, $f(x)$ becomes large negative.
(c) As x becomes large, $f(x)$ approaches 5. (d) As x becomes
large negative, $f(x)$ approaches 3.
3. (a) ∞ (b) ∞ (c) $-\infty$ (d) 1 (e) 2
(f) $x = -1, x = 2, y = 1, y = 2$
5.   **7.**

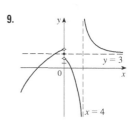

9.

11. 0   **13.** $x \approx -1.62, x \approx 0.62, x = 1; y = 1$
15. ∞ **17.** 0   **19.** $-\infty$ **21.** $-\infty$ **23.** $\frac{1}{2}$ **25.** 2
27. $\frac{1}{6}$ **29.** 0   **31.** Does not exist   **33.** 0   **35.** $-\infty$
37. ∞ **39.** $y = 2; x = -2, x = 1$ **41.** $x = 5$
43. (a), (b) $-\frac{1}{2}$ **45.** $y = 3$ **47.** $f(x) = \dfrac{2 - x}{x^2(x - 3)}$
49. (a) $\frac{5}{4}$ (b) 5   **51.** (a) 0 (b) $\pm\infty$ **53.** 5
55. (b) It approaches the concentration of the brine being pumped
into the tank.
57. (b) $x > 23.03$ (c) Yes, $x > 10 \ln 10$

1. (a) $\dfrac{f(x) - f(3)}{x - 3}$ (b) $\lim_{x \to 3} \dfrac{f(x) - f(3)}{x - 3}$
3. (a) 2   (b) $y = 2x + 1$ (c)

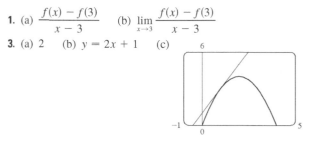

5. $y = -8x + 12$ **7.** $y = \frac{1}{2}x + \frac{1}{2}$
9. (a) $8a - 6a^2$ (b) $y = 2x + 3, y = -8x + 19$
(c)

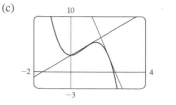

11. (a) Right: $0 < t < 1$ and $4 < t < 6$; left: $2 < t < 3$; standing still: $1 < t < 2$ and $3 < t < 4$

(b)

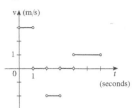

13. -24 ft/s
15. $-2/a^3$ m/s; -2 m/s; $-\frac{1}{4}$ m/s; $-\frac{2}{27}$ m/s
17. $g'(0), 0, g'(4), g'(2), g'(-2)$
19. $f(2) = 3; f'(2) = 4$
21.

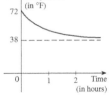

23. $y = 3x - 1$
25. (a) $-\frac{3}{5}; y = -\frac{3}{5}x + \frac{16}{5}$ (b)

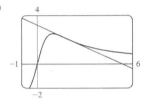

27. $6a - 4$ **29.** $\dfrac{5}{(a+3)^2}$ **31.** $-\dfrac{1}{\sqrt{1-2a}}$

33. $f(x) = x^{10}, a = 1$ or $f(x) = (1+x)^{10}, a = 0$
35. $f(x) = 2^x, a = 5$
37. $f(x) = \cos x, a = \pi$ or $f(x) = \cos(\pi + x), a = 0$
39. 1 m/s; 1 m/s
41.

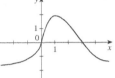

Greater (in magnitude)

43. (a) (i) 23 million/year   (ii) 20.5 million/year
(iii) 16 million/year
(b) 18.25 million/year   (c) 17 million/year
45. (a) (i) \$20.25/unit   (ii) \$20.05/unit   (b) \$20/unit
47. (a) The rate at which the cost is changing per ounce of gold produced; dollars per ounce
(b) When the 800th ounce of gold is produced, the cost of production is \$17/oz.
(c) Decrease in the short term; increase in the long term
49. $5°$F/h

51. (a) The rate at which the oxygen solubility changes with respect to the water temperature; $(\text{mg/L})/°C$
(b) $S'(16) \approx -0.25$; as the temperature increases past $16°C$, the oxygen solubility is decreasing at a rate of 0.25 $(\text{mg/L})/°C$.
53. Does not exist

EXERCISES 2.7 ■ PAGE 155
1. (a) -0.2 (b) 0   (c) 1   (d) 2
(e) 1   (f) 0   (g) -0.2

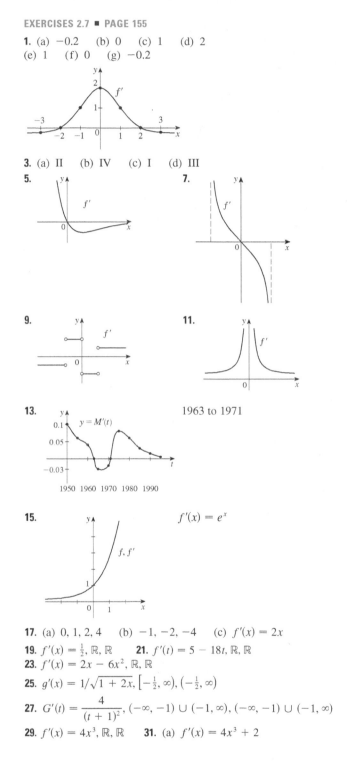

3. (a) II   (b) IV   (c) I   (d) III
5.   **7.**

9.   **11.**

13.   1963 to 1971

15. $f'(x) = e^x$

17. (a) 0, 1, 2, 4   (b) $-1, -2, -4$ (c) $f'(x) = 2x$
19. $f'(x) = \frac{1}{2}, \mathbb{R}, \mathbb{R}$ **21.** $f'(t) = 5 - 18t, \mathbb{R}, \mathbb{R}$
23. $f'(x) = 2x - 6x^2, \mathbb{R}, \mathbb{R}$
25. $g'(x) = 1/\sqrt{1 + 2x}, \left[-\frac{1}{2}, \infty\right), \left(-\frac{1}{2}, \infty\right)$
27. $G'(t) = \dfrac{4}{(t+1)^2}, (-\infty, -1) \cup (-1, \infty), (-\infty, -1) \cup (-1, \infty)$
29. $f'(x) = 4x^3, \mathbb{R}, \mathbb{R}$ **31.** (a) $f'(x) = 4x^3 + 2$

33. (a) The rate at which the unemployment rate is changing, in percent unemployed per year

(b)

t	$U'(t)$	t	$U'(t)$
1998	−0.30	2003	−0.15
1999	−0.25	2004	−0.45
2000	0.25	2005	−0.45
2001	0.90	2006	−0.25
2002	0.65	2007	0.00

35. −4 (corner); 0 (discontinuity)
37. −1 (vertical tangent); 4 (corner)
39.

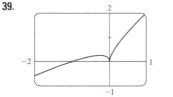

Differentiable at −1; not differentiable at 0

41. $a = f, b = f', c = f''$
43. a = acceleration, b = velocity, c = position
45. $6x + 2$; 6

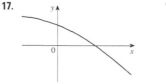

47.

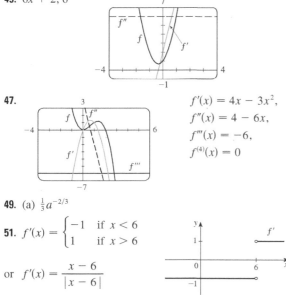

$f'(x) = 4x - 3x^2$,
$f''(x) = 4 - 6x$,
$f'''(x) = -6$,
$f^{(4)}(x) = 0$

49. (a) $\frac{1}{3}a^{-2/3}$

51. $f'(x) = \begin{cases} -1 & \text{if } x < 6 \\ 1 & \text{if } x > 6 \end{cases}$

or $f'(x) = \dfrac{x - 6}{|x - 6|}$

55. 63°

EXERCISES 2.8 ■ PAGE 162

Abbreviations: inc, increasing; dec, decreasing; loc, local; max, maximum; min, minimum

1. (a) Inc on (0, 1), (4, 5); dec on (1, 4)
(b) Loc max at $x = 1$; loc min at $x = 4$
(c)

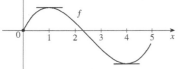

3. (a) Inc on (−2, −1), (0, 1), (2, 3); dec on (−1, 0), (1, 2)
(b) Loc max at $x = -1, 1$; loc min at $x = 0, 2$
(c)

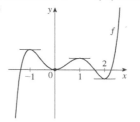

5. Inc on (2, 5); dec on (−∞, 2) and (5, ∞)   **7.** $f''(1)$
9. If $D(t)$ is the size of the deficit as a function of time, then at the time of the speech $D'(t) > 0$, but $D''(t) < 0$.
11. (a) The rate starts small, grows rapidly, levels off, then decreases and becomes negative.
(b) (1932, 2.5) and (1937, 4.3); the rate of change of population density starts to decrease in 1932 and starts to increase in 1937.
13. $K(3) - K(2)$; CD
15. (a) Inc on (0, 2), (4, 6), (8, ∞); dec on (2, 4), (6, 8)
(b) Loc max at $x = 2, 6$; loc min at $x = 4, 8$
(c) CU on (3, 6), (6, ∞); CD on (0, 3)
(d) 3
(e) See graph at right.

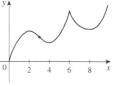

17.

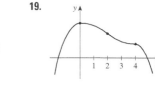

19.

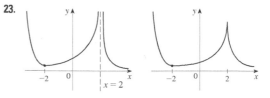

21.

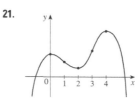

23.

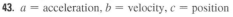

25. (a) Inc on (0, ∞); dec on (−∞, 0)
(b) Min at $x = 0$
27. (a) Inc on $\left(-\infty, -\sqrt{\frac{1}{3}}\right), \left(\sqrt{\frac{1}{3}}, \infty\right)$; dec on $\left(-\sqrt{\frac{1}{3}}, \sqrt{\frac{1}{3}}\right)$
(b) CU on (0, ∞); CD on (−∞, 0)
(c) IP at (0, 0)
29. b

31.

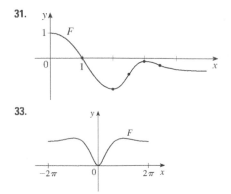

33.

CHAPTER 2 REVIEW ■ **PAGE 165**

True-False Quiz

1. False   **3.** True   **5.** False   **7.** True   **9.** True
11. False   **13.** True   **15.** False   **17.** False

Exercises

1. (a) (i) 3   (ii) 0   (iii) Does not exist   (iv) 2
(v) ∞ (vi) $-\infty$ (vii) 4   (viii) -1
(b) $y = 4$, $y = -1$ (c) $x = 0$, $x = 2$ (d) $-3, 0, 2, 4$
3. 1   **5.** $\frac{3}{2}$ **7.** 3   **9.** ∞ **11.** $\frac{4}{7}$ **13.** $-\infty$ **15.** $\frac{1}{2}$
17. 2   **19.** $x = 0$, $y = 0$ **21.** 1
23. (a) (i) 3   (ii) 0   (iii) Does not exist   (iv) 0   (v) 0   (vi) 0
(b) At 0 and 3   (c)

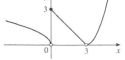

27. (a) (i) 3 m/s   (ii) 2.75 m/s   (iii) 2.625 m/s
(iv) 2.525 m/s   (b) 2.5 m/s
29. $f''(5), 0, f'(5), f'(2), 1, f'(3)$
31. (a) -0.736 (b) $y \approx -0.736x + 1.104$
(c)

33. (a) The rate at which the cost changes with respect to the
interest rate; dollars/(percent per year)
(b) As the interest rate increases past 10%, the cost is increasing
at a rate of $1200/(percent per year).
(c) Always positive
35.

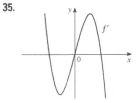

37. (a) $f'(x) = -\frac{5}{2}(3 - 5x)^{-1/2}$ (b) $\left(-\infty, \frac{3}{5}\right], \left(-\infty, \frac{3}{5}\right)$
(c)

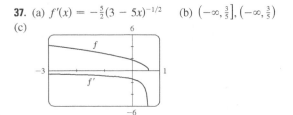

39. -4 (discontinuity), -1 (corner), 2 (discontinuity),
5 (vertical tangent)
41. The rate at which the total value of US currency in circulation
is changing in billions of dollars per year; $22.2 billion/year
43. (a) Inc on $(-2, 0)$ and $(2, \infty)$; dec on $(-\infty, -2)$ and $(0, 2)$
(b) Max at 0; min at -2 and 2
(c) CU on $(-\infty, -1)$ and $(1, \infty)$; CD on $(-1, 1)$
(d)

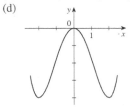

45.

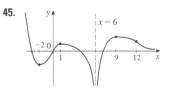

47. (a) About 35 ft/s   (b) About (8, 180)
(c) The point at which the car's velocity is maximized

FOCUS ON PROBLEM SOLVING ■ **PAGE 170**

1. $\frac{2}{3}$ **3.** -4 **5.** 1   **7.** $a = \frac{1}{2} \pm \frac{1}{2}\sqrt{5}$
9. (b) Yes   (c) Yes; no   **11.** $\left(\pm\sqrt{3}/2, \frac{1}{4}\right)$
13. (a) 0   (b) 1   (c) $f'(x) = x^2 + 1$ **15.** $\frac{3}{4}$

CHAPTER 3

EXERCISES 3.1 ■ **PAGE 181**

1. (a) See Definition of the Number e (page 180).
(b) 0.99, 1.03; $2.7 < e < 2.8$
3. $f'(x) = 0$ **5.** $f'(t) = -\frac{2}{3}$ **7.** $f'(x) = 3x^2 - 4$
9. $f'(t) = t^3$ **11.** $A'(s) = 60/s^6$ **13.** $g'(t) = -\frac{3}{2}t^{-7/4}$
15. $y' = 3e^x - \frac{4}{3}x^{-4/3}$ **17.** $F'(x) = \frac{5}{32}x^4$
19. $y' = \frac{3}{2}\sqrt{x} + \dfrac{2}{\sqrt{x}} - \dfrac{3}{2x\sqrt{x}}$
21. $y' = 0$ **23.** $u' = \frac{1}{5}t^{-4/5} + 10t^{3/2}$
25. $z' = -10A/y^{11} + Be^y$ **27.** $y = \frac{1}{4}x + \frac{3}{4}$
29. Tangent: $y = 2x + 2$; normal: $y = -\frac{1}{2}x + 2$
31. $y = 3x - 1$ **33.** $e^x - 5$ **35.** $45x^{14} - 15x^2$ **37.** 3

39. (a)   (c) $4x^3 - 9x^2 - 12x + 7$

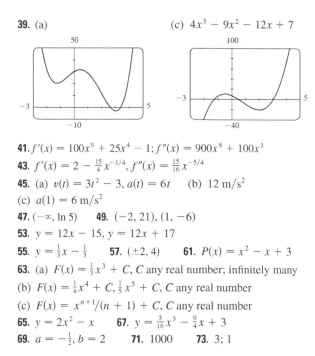

41. $f'(x) = 100x^9 + 25x^4 - 1; f''(x) = 900x^8 + 100x^3$

43. $f'(x) = 2 - \frac{15}{4}x^{-1/4}, f''(x) = \frac{15}{16}x^{-5/4}$

45. (a) $v(t) = 3t^2 - 3, a(t) = 6t$ (b) 12 m/s^2
(c) $a(1) = 6$ m/s^2

47. $(-\infty, \ln 5)$ **49.** $(-2, 21), (1, -6)$

53. $y = 12x - 15, y = 12x + 17$

55. $y = \frac{1}{3}x - \frac{1}{3}$ **57.** $(\pm 2, 4)$ **61.** $P(x) = x^2 - x + 3$

63. (a) $F(x) = \frac{1}{3}x^3 + C, C$ any real number; infinitely many
(b) $F(x) = \frac{1}{4}x^4 + C, \frac{1}{5}x^5 + C, C$ any real number
(c) $F(x) = x^{n+1}/(n+1) + C, C$ any real number

65. $y = 2x^2 - x$ **67.** $y = \frac{3}{16}x^3 - \frac{9}{4}x + 3$

69. $a = -\frac{1}{2}, b = 2$ **71.** 1000 **73.** $3; 1$

EXERCISES 3.2 ■ **PAGE 188**

1. $1 - 2x + 6x^2 - 8x^3$ **3.** $f'(x) = e^x(x^3 + 3x^2 + 2x + 2)$

5. $y' = (x - 2)e^x/x^3$ **7.** $g'(x) = 5/(2x + 1)^2$

9. $F'(y) = 5 + 14/y^2 + 9/y^4$

11. $y' = \dfrac{x^2(3 - x^2)}{(1 - x^2)^2}$ **13.** $y' = \dfrac{2t(-t^4 - 4t^2 + 7)}{(t^4 - 3t^2 + 1)^2}$

15. $y' = (r^2 - 2)e^r$ **17.** $y' = 2v - 1/\sqrt{v}$

19. $f'(t) = \dfrac{4 + t^{1/2}}{(2 + \sqrt{t})^2}$ **21.** $f'(x) = -ACe^x/(B + Ce^x)^2$

23. $f'(x) = 2cx/(x^2 + c)^2$

25. $(x^4 + 4x^3)e^x; (x^4 + 8x^3 + 12x^2)e^x$

27. $\dfrac{2x^2 + 2x}{(1 + 2x)^2}; \dfrac{2}{(1 + 2x)^3}$

29. $y = \frac{1}{2}x + \frac{1}{2}$ **31.** $y = 2x; y = -\frac{1}{2}x$

33. (a) $y = \frac{1}{2}x + 1$ (b)

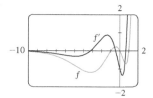

35. (a) $e^x(x^3 + 3x^2 - x - 1)$ (b)

37. (a) $f'(x) = \dfrac{4x}{(x^2 + 1)^2}; f''(x) = \dfrac{4(1 - 3x^2)}{(x^2 + 1)^3}$
(b)

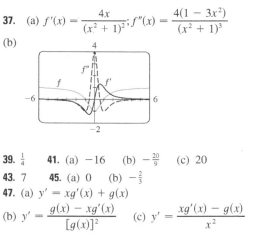

39. $\frac{1}{4}$ **41.** (a) -16 (b) $-\frac{20}{9}$ (c) 20

43. 7 **45.** (a) 0 (b) $-\frac{2}{3}$

47. (a) $y' = xg'(x) + g(x)$
(b) $y' = \dfrac{g(x) - xg'(x)}{[g(x)]^2}$ (c) $y' = \dfrac{xg'(x) - g(x)}{x^2}$

49. $\$1.627$ billion/year   **51.** $(-3, \infty)$

53. Two, $\left(-2 \pm \sqrt{3}, \frac{1}{2}(1 \mp \sqrt{3})\right)$ **55.** 1 **57.** (c) $3e^{3x}$

59. $f'(x) = (x^2 + 2x)e^x, f''(x) = (x^2 + 4x + 2)e^x,$
$f'''(x) = (x^2 + 6x + 6)e^x, f^{(4)}(x) = (x^2 + 8x + 12)e^x,$
$f^{(5)}(x) = (x^2 + 10x + 20)e^x; f^{(n)}(x) = [x^2 + 2nx + n(n - 1)]e^x$

EXERCISES 3.3 ■ **PAGE 195**

1. $f'(x) = 6x + 2 \sin x$ **3.** $f'(x) = \cos x - \frac{1}{2}\csc^2 x$

5. $y' = \sec \theta (\sec^2\theta + \tan^2\theta)$

7. $y' = -c \sin t + t(t \cos t + 2 \sin t)$

9. $y' = \dfrac{2 - \tan x + x \sec^2 x}{(2 - \tan x)^2}$ **11.** $f'(\theta) = \dfrac{\sec \theta \tan \theta}{(1 + \sec \theta)^2}$

13. $f'(x) = e^x \csc x (-x \cot x + x + 1)$

19. $y = 2\sqrt{3}x - \frac{2}{3}\sqrt{3}\pi + 2$ **21.** $y = x + 1$

23. (a) $y = 2x$ (b) $\dfrac{3\pi}{2}$

25. (a) $\sec x \tan x - 1$

27. $\theta \cos \theta + \sin \theta; 2 \cos \theta - \theta \sin \theta$

29. (a) $f'(x) = (1 + \tan x)/\sec x$ (b) $f'(x) = \cos x + \sin x$

31. $(2n + 1)\pi \pm \frac{1}{3}\pi, n$ an integer   **33.** $(\pi/3, 5\pi/3)$

35. (a) $v(t) = 8 \cos t, a(t) = -8 \sin t$
(b) $4\sqrt{3}, -4, -4\sqrt{3}$; to the left

37. 5 ft/rad   **39.** $-\cos x$

41. $A = -\frac{3}{10}, B = -\frac{1}{10}$

43. 3 **45.** $\frac{1}{2}$

47. (a) $\sec^2 x = \dfrac{1}{\cos^2 x}$ (b) $\sec x \tan x = \dfrac{\sin x}{\cos^2 x}$
(c) $\cos x - \sin x = \dfrac{\cot x - 1}{\csc x}$

49. 1

EXERCISES 3.4 ■ PAGE 205

1. $\dfrac{4}{3\sqrt[3]{(1 + 4x)^2}}$ **3.** $\pi \sec^2 \pi x$ **5.** $e^{\sqrt{x}}/(2\sqrt{x})$

7. $F'(x) = 10x(x^4 + 3x^2 - 2)^4(2x^2 + 3)$

9. $F'(x) = -\dfrac{1}{\sqrt{1 - 2x}}$ **11.** $f'(z) = -\dfrac{2z}{(z^2 + 1)^2}$

13. $y' = -3x^2 \sin(a^3 + x^3)$ **15.** $h'(t) = 3t^2 - 3^t \ln 3$

17. $y' = e^{-kx}(-kx + 1)$

19. $y' = 8(2x - 5)^3(8x^2 - 5)^{-4}(-4x^2 + 30x - 5)$

21. $y' = (\cos x - x \sin x)e^{x \cos x}$ **23.** $y' = \dfrac{-12x(x^2 + 1)^2}{(x^2 - 1)^4}$

25. $y' = 4 \sec^2 x \tan x$ **27.** $y' = (r^2 + 1)^{-3/2}$

29. $y' = 2 \cos(\tan 2x) \sec^2(2x)$ **31.** $y' = 2^{\sin \pi x}(\pi \ln 2) \cos \pi x$

33. $y' = -2 \cos \theta \cot(\sin \theta) \csc^2(\sin \theta)$

35. $y' = \dfrac{-\pi \cos(\tan \pi x) \sec^2(\pi x) \sin\sqrt{\sin(\tan \pi x)}}{2\sqrt{\sin(\tan \pi x)}}$

37. $y' = -2x \sin(x^2); \; y'' = -4x^2\cos(x^2) - 2 \sin(x^2)$

39. $e^{\alpha x}(\beta \cos \beta x + \alpha \sin \beta x);$
$e^{\alpha x}[(\alpha^2 - \beta^2) \sin \beta x + 2\alpha\beta \cos \beta x]$

41. $y = 20x + 1$ **43.** $y = -x + \pi$

45. (a) $y = \frac{1}{2}x + 1$ (b)

47. (a) $f'(x) = \dfrac{2 - 2x^2}{\sqrt{2 - x^2}}$

49. $((\pi/2) + 2n\pi, 3), ((3\pi/2) + 2n\pi, -1),$ n an integer

51. 24   **53.** (a) 30   (b) 36

55. (a) $\frac{3}{4}$ (b) Does not exist   (c) -2 **57.** -17.4

59. (a) $F'(x) = e^x f'(e^x)$ (b) $G'(x) = e^{f(x)}f'(x)$

61. 120   **63.** 96

67. $-2^{50} \cos 2x$ **69.** $v(t) = \frac{5}{2}\pi \cos(10\pi t)$ cm/s

71. (a) $\dfrac{dB}{dt} = \dfrac{7\pi}{54} \cos \dfrac{2\pi t}{5.4}$ (b) 0.16

73. $v(t) = 2e^{-1.5t}(2\pi \cos 2\pi t - 1.5 \sin 2\pi t)$

75. dv/dt is the rate of change of velocity with respect to time; dv/ds is the rate of change of velocity with respect to displacement

77. (a) $Q = ab^t$, where $a \approx 100.012437, b \approx 0.0000451459$
(b) -670.63 μA

79. $y = -x$ **81.** $y = -(2/e)x + 3$

83. Horizontal at $(6, \pm16)$, vertical at $(10, 0)$

85. (a) $y = \sqrt{3}x - 3\sqrt{3}, \; y = -\sqrt{3}x + 3\sqrt{3}$
(b) Horizontal at $(1, \pm2)$; vertical at $(0, 0)$
(c)

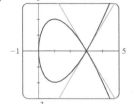

87. (b) The factored form   **89.** (b) $-n \cos^{n-1}x \sin[(n + 1)x]$

EXERCISES 3.5 ■ PAGE 214

1. (a) $y' = -(y + 2 + 6x)/x$
(b) $y = (4/x) - 2 - 3x, \; y' = -(4/x^2) - 3$

3. $y' = -x^2/y^2$ **5.** $y' = \dfrac{2x + y}{2y - x}$

7. $y' = \dfrac{3y^2 - 5x^4 - 4x^3y}{x^4 + 3y^2 - 6xy}$ **9.** $y' = \dfrac{-2xy^2 - \sin y}{2x^2y + x \cos y}$

11. $y' = \tan x \tan y$ **13.** $y' = \dfrac{y(y - e^{x/y})}{y^2 - xe^{x/y}}$

15. $y' = \dfrac{e^y \sin x + y \cos(xy)}{e^y \cos x - x \cos(xy)}$ **17.** $-\frac{16}{13}$

19. $x' = \dfrac{-2x^4y + x^3 - 6xy^2}{4x^3y^2 - 3x^2y + 2y^3}$ **21.** $y = \frac{1}{2}x$

23. $y = -x + 2$ **25.** $y = x + \frac{1}{2}$ **27.** $y = -\frac{9}{13}x + \frac{40}{13}$

29. (a) $y = \frac{9}{2}x - \frac{5}{2}$ (b)

31. $-81/y^3$ **33.** $-2x/y^5$ **35.** $1/e^2$

37. (a)

Eight; $x \approx 0.42, 1.58$

(b) $y = -x + 1, \; y = \frac{1}{3}x + 2$ (c) $1 \mp \frac{1}{3}\sqrt{3}$

39. $\left(\pm\frac{5}{4}\sqrt{3}, \pm\frac{5}{4}\right)$

41.   **43.**

47. (a) $\dfrac{V^3(nb - V)}{PV^3 - n^2aV + 2n^3ab}$ (b) -4.04 L/atm

51. $(\pm\sqrt{3}, 0)$ **53.** $(-1, -1), (1, 1)$ **55.** (a) 0   (b) $-\frac{1}{2}$

EXERCISES 3.6 ▪ PAGE 220

1. (a) $\pi/3$ (b) π **3.** (a) $\pi/4$ (b) $\pi/4$

5. $2/\sqrt{5}$ **7.** $\frac{2}{3}\sqrt{2}$ **11.** $x/\sqrt{1 + x^2}$

13.

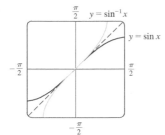

The second graph is the reflection of the first graph about the line $y = x$.

17. $y' = \dfrac{2\tan^{-1}x}{1 + x^2}$ **19.** $y' = \dfrac{1}{\sqrt{-x^2 - x}}$

21. $G'(x) = -1 - \dfrac{x \arccos x}{\sqrt{1 - x^2}}$

23. $y' = -\dfrac{2e^{2x}}{\sqrt{1 - e^{4x}}}$ **25.** $y' = -\dfrac{\sin\theta}{1 + \cos^2\theta}$

27. $y' = \sin^{-1}x$ **29.** $y' = \dfrac{\sqrt{a^2 - b^2}}{a + b\cos x}$

31. $g'(x) = \dfrac{2}{\sqrt{1 - (3 - 2x)^2}}$; $[1, 2], (1, 2)$ **33.** $\pi/6$

35. $1 - \dfrac{x \arcsin x}{\sqrt{1 - x^2}}$ **37.** $-\pi/2$ **39.** $\pi/2$ **41.** (b) $\frac{3}{2}$

EXERCISES 3.7 ▪ PAGE 226

1. The differentiation formula is simplest.

3. $f'(x) = \dfrac{\cos(\ln x)}{x}$ **5.** $f'(x) = \dfrac{3}{(3x - 1)\ln 2}$

7. $f'(x) = \dfrac{1}{5x\sqrt[5]{(\ln x)^4}}$ **9.** $f'(x) = \dfrac{\sin x}{x} + \cos x \ln(5x)$

11. $F'(t) = \dfrac{6}{2t + 1} - \dfrac{12}{3t - 1}$ **13.** $g'(x) = \dfrac{2x^2 - 1}{x(x^2 - 1)}$

15. $y' = \dfrac{10x + 1}{5x^2 + x - 2}$ **17.** $y' = \dfrac{-x}{1 + x}$

19. $y' = \dfrac{1}{\ln 10} + \log_{10} x$

21. $y' = x + 2x\ln(2x); y'' = 3 + 2\ln(2x)$

23. $f'(x) = \dfrac{2x - 1 - (x - 1)\ln(x - 1)}{(x - 1)[1 - \ln(x - 1)]^2}$;
$(1, 1 + e) \cup (1 + e, \infty)$

25. $y = 3x - 9$ **27.** $y = 3x - 2$

29. (a) $(0, 1/e)$ (b) $(0, \infty)$ **31.** 7

33. $y' = (2x + 1)^5(x^4 - 3)^6\left(\dfrac{10}{2x + 1} + \dfrac{24x^3}{x^4 - 3}\right)$

35. $y' = \dfrac{\sin^2 x \tan^4 x}{(x^2 + 1)^2}\left(2\cot x + \dfrac{4\sec^2 x}{\tan x} - \dfrac{4x}{x^2 + 1}\right)$

37. $y' = x^x(1 + \ln x)$

39. $y' = (\cos x)^x(-x\tan x + \ln\cos x)$

41. $y' = (\tan x)^{1/x}\left(\dfrac{\sec^2 x}{x\tan x} - \dfrac{\ln\tan x}{x^2}\right)$

43. $y' = \dfrac{2x}{x^2 + y^2 - 2y}$ **45.** $f^{(n)}(x) = \dfrac{(-1)^{n-1}(n - 1)!}{(x - 1)^n}$

EXERCISES 3.8 ▪ PAGE 237

1. (a) $3t^2 - 24t + 36$ (b) -9 ft/s   (c) $t = 2, 6$
(d) $0 \leqslant t < 2, t > 6$ (e) 96 ft
(f)

(g) $6t - 24; -6$ ft/s^2

(h)

(i) Speeding up when $2 < t < 4$ or $t > 6$; slowing down when $0 \leqslant t < 2$ or $4 < t < 6$

3. (a) $-\dfrac{\pi}{4}\sin\left(\dfrac{\pi t}{4}\right)$ (b) $-\frac{1}{8}\pi\sqrt{2}$ ft/s   (c) $t = 0, 4, 8$
(d) $4 < t < 8$ (e) 4 ft
(f)

(g) $-\frac{1}{16}\pi^2\cos(\pi t/4); \frac{1}{32}\pi^2\sqrt{2}$ ft/s^2
(h)

(i) Speeding up when $0 < t < 2, 4 < t < 6, 8 < t < 10$; slowing down when $2 < t < 4, 6 < t < 8$
5. (a) Speeding up when $0 < t < 1$ or $2 < t < 3$; slowing down when $1 < t < 2$
(b) Speeding up when $1 < t < 2$ or $3 < t < 4$; slowing down when $0 < t < 1$ or $2 < t < 3$
7. (a) $t \approx 4$ s
(b) $t = 1.5$ s; the velocity has an absolute minimum.
9. (a) 5.02 m/s   (b) $\sqrt{17}$ m/s
11. (a) 30 mm^2/mm; the rate at which the area is increasing with respect to side length as x reaches 15 mm
(b) $\Delta A \approx 2x\,\Delta x$

13. (a) (i) 5π (ii) 4.5π (iii) 4.1π
(b) 4π (c) $\Delta A \approx 2\pi r \, \Delta r$
15. (a) 8π ft²/ft   (b) 16π ft²/ft   (c) 24π ft²/ft
The rate increases as the radius increases.
17. (a) 6 kg/m   (b) 12 kg/m   (c) 18 kg/m
At the right end; at the left end
19. (a) 4.75 A   (b) 5 A; $t = \frac{2}{3}$ s
21. (a) $dV/dP = -C/P^2$ (b) At the beginning
23. $400(3^t) \ln 3;$ ≈ 6850 bacteria/h
25. (a) 16 million/year; 78.5 million/year
(b) $P(t) = at^3 + bt^2 + ct + d$, where $a \approx 0.00129371$,
$b \approx -7.061422$, $c \approx 12{,}822.979$, $d \approx -7{,}743{,}770$
(c) $P'(t) = 3at^2 + 2bt + c$
(d) 14.48 million/year; 75.29 million/year (smaller)
(e) 81.62 million/year
27. (a) 0.926 cm/s; 0.694 cm/s; 0
(b) 0; -92.6 (cm/s)/cm; -185.2 (cm/s)/cm
(c) At the center; at the edge
29. (a) $C'(x) = 12 - 0.2x + 0.0015x^2$
(b) \$32/yard; the cost of producing the 201st yard
(c) \$32.20
31. (a) $[xp'(x) - p(x)]/x^2$; the average productivity increases as new workers are added.
33. -0.2436 K/min
35. (a) 0 and 0   (b) $C = 0$
(c) $(0, 0)$, $(500, 50)$; it is possible for the species to coexist.

EXERCISES 3.9 ■ PAGE 245

1. $148°$F; underestimate
3. 22.6%, 24.2%; too high; tangent lines lie above the curve
5. $L(x) = -10x - 6$ **7.** $L(x) = -x + \pi/2$
9. $\sqrt{1 - x} \approx 1 - \frac{1}{2}x;$
$\sqrt{0.9} \approx 0.95,$
$\sqrt{0.99} \approx 0.995$

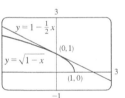

11. $-1.204 < x < 0.706$ **13.** $-0.045 < x < 0.055$
15. 32.08   **17.** 4.02
23. (a) $dy = -\dfrac{2}{(u - 1)^2}\, du$ (b) $dy = -\dfrac{6r^2}{(1 + r^3)^3}\, dr$
25. (a) $dy = \frac{1}{10} e^{x/10}\, dx$ (b) 0.01; 0.0101
27. (a) 270 cm³, 0.01, 1%   (b) 36 cm², 0.006, 0.6%
29. (a) $84/\pi \approx 27$ cm²; $\frac{1}{84} \approx 0.012 = 1.2\%$
(b) $1764/\pi^2 \approx 179$ cm³; $\frac{1}{56} \approx 0.018 = 1.8\%$
31. (a) $2\pi rh \, \Delta r$ (b) $\pi(\Delta r)^2 h$
33. A 5% increase in the radius corresponds to a 20% increase in blood flow.
35. (a) 4.8, 5.2   (b) Too large

True-False Quiz
1. True   **3.** True   **5.** False   **7.** False   **9.** True
11. True

Exercises
1. $6x(x^4 - 3x^2 + 5)^2(2x^2 - 3)$ **3.** $\dfrac{1}{2\sqrt{x}} - \dfrac{4}{3\sqrt[3]{x^7}}$
5. $\dfrac{2(2x^2 + 1)}{\sqrt{x^2 + 1}}$ **7.** $2 \cos 2\theta \, e^{\sin 2\theta}$
9. $\dfrac{t^2 + 1}{(1 - t^2)^2}$ **11.** $-\dfrac{e^{1/x}(1 + 2x)}{x^4}$ **13.** $\dfrac{1 - y^4 - 2xy}{4xy^3 + x^2 - 3}$
15. $\dfrac{2 \sec 2\theta \, (\tan 2\theta - 1)}{(1 + \tan 2\theta)^2}$ **17.** $(1 + c^2)e^{cx} \sin x$
19. $\dfrac{2}{(1 + 2x) \ln 5}$ **21.** $\dfrac{2x - y \cos(xy)}{x \cos(xy) + 1}$
23. $3^{x \ln x}(\ln 3)(1 + \ln x)$ **25.** $\cot x - \sin x \cos x$
27. $\dfrac{4x}{1 + 16x^2} + \tan^{-1}(4x)$ **29.** $5 \sec 5x$
31. $2 \cos \theta \tan(\sin \theta) \sec^2(\sin \theta)$
33. $\cos(\tan \sqrt{1 + x^3})\left(\sec^2 \sqrt{1 + x^3}\right) \dfrac{3x^2}{2\sqrt{1 + x^3}}$
35. $\dfrac{-3 \sin(e^{\sqrt{\tan 3x}})e^{\sqrt{\tan 3x}} \sec^2(3x)}{2\sqrt{\tan 3x}}$ **37.** $-\frac{4}{27}$
39. $2^x(\ln 2)^n$ **41.** $y = 2\sqrt{3}x + 1 - \pi\sqrt{3}/3$
43. $y = 2x + 2$ **45.** $y = -x + 2$; $y = x + 2$
47. (a) $\dfrac{10 - 3x}{2\sqrt{5 - x}}$ (b) $y = \frac{7}{4}x + \frac{1}{4}$, $y = -x + 8$
(c)

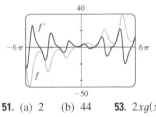

49. $e^{\sin x}(x \cos x + 1)$

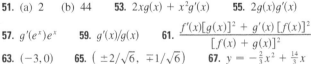

The sizes of the oscillations of f and f' are linked.

51. (a) 2   (b) 44   **53.** $2xg(x) + x^2 g'(x)$ **55.** $2g(x)g'(x)$
57. $g'(e^x)e^x$ **59.** $g'(x)/g(x)$ **61.** $\dfrac{f'(x)[g(x)]^2 + g'(x)\,[f(x)]^2}{[f(x) + g(x)]^2}$
63. $(-3, 0)$ **65.** $\left(\pm 2/\sqrt{6}, \mp 1/\sqrt{6}\right)$ **67.** $y = -\frac{2}{3}x^2 + \frac{14}{3}x$
69. $v(t) = -Ae^{-ct}[c \cos(\omega t + \delta) + \omega \sin(\omega t + \delta)]$,
$a(t) = Ae^{-ct}[(c^2 - \omega^2) \cos(\omega t + \delta) + 2c\omega \sin(\omega t + \delta)]$
71. 4 kg/m
73. (a) $C'(x) = 2 - 0.04x + 0.00021x^2$
(b) \$0.10/unit; the approximate cost of producing the 101st unit
(c) $C(101) - C(100) = 0.10107$
(d) About 95.24; at this value of x the marginal cost is minimized.

75. (a) $L(x) = 1 + x$; $\sqrt[3]{1 + 3x} \approx 1 + x$; $\sqrt[3]{1.03} \approx 1.01$
(b) $-0.23 < x < 0.40$
77. $(\cos \theta)'|_{\theta = \pi/3} = -\sqrt{3}/2$ **79.** $\frac{1}{4}$

FOCUS ON PROBLEM SOLVING ■ PAGE 252

1. $\left(0, \frac{5}{4}\right)$ **5.** $3\sqrt{2}$
7. (a) $4\pi\sqrt{3}/\sqrt{11}$ rad/s   (b) $40\left(\cos \theta + \sqrt{8 + \cos^2\theta}\right)$ cm
(c) $-480\pi \sin \theta \left(1 + \cos \theta/\sqrt{8 + \cos^2\theta}\right)$ cm/s
11. $x_T \in (3, \infty), y_T \in (2, \infty), x_N \in \left(0, \frac{5}{3}\right), y_N \in \left(-\frac{5}{2}, 0\right)$
15. $2\sqrt{e}$ **17.** (b) (i) $53°$ (or $127°$)   (ii) $63°$ (or $117°$)
19. R approaches the midpoint of the radius AO.
21. $(1, -2), (-1, 0)$ **23.** $\sqrt{29}/58$

CHAPTER 4

EXERCISES 4.1 ■ PAGE 260

1. $dV/dt = 3x^2\, dx/dt$ **3.** 48 cm²/s   **5.** $3/(25\pi)$ m/min
7. (a) 1 (b) 25 **9.** $\pm\frac{46}{13}$
11. (a) The rate of decrease of the surface area is 1 cm²/min.
(b) The rate of decrease of the diameter when the diameter is 10 cm
(c)   (d) $S = \pi x^2$
(e) $1/(20\pi)$ cm/min

13. (a) The plane's altitude is 1 mi and its speed is 500 mi/h.
(b) The rate at which the distance from the plane to the station is increasing when the plane is 2 mi from the station
(c)   (d) $y^2 = x^2 + 1$
(e) $250\sqrt{3}$ mi/h

15. 65 mi/h   **17.** $837/\sqrt{8674} \approx 8.99$ ft/s
19. -1.6 cm/min   **21.** $\frac{720}{13} \approx 55.4$ km/h
23. 5 m   **25.** $10/\sqrt{133} \approx 0.87$ ft/s   **27.** $\frac{4}{5}$ ft/min
29. $6/(5\pi) \approx 0.38$ ft/min   **31.** 0.3 m²/s   **33.** 80 cm³/min
35. $\frac{107}{810} \approx 0.132$ Ω/s   **37.** (a) 360 ft/s   (b) 0.096 rad/s
39. $\frac{10}{9}\pi$ km/min   **41.** $1650/\sqrt{31} \approx 296$ km/h
43. $\frac{7}{4}\sqrt{15} \approx 6.78$ m/s

EXERCISES 4.2 ■ PAGE 268

Abbreviations: abs, absolute; loc, local; max, maximum; min, minimum

1. Abs min: smallest function value on the entire domain of the function; loc min at c: smallest function value when x is near c
3. Abs max at s, abs min at r, loc max at c, loc min at b and r
5. Abs max $f(4) = 5$, loc max $f(4) = 5$ and $f(6) = 4$,
loc min $f(2) = 2$ and $f(1) = f(5) = 3$

7.   **9.**

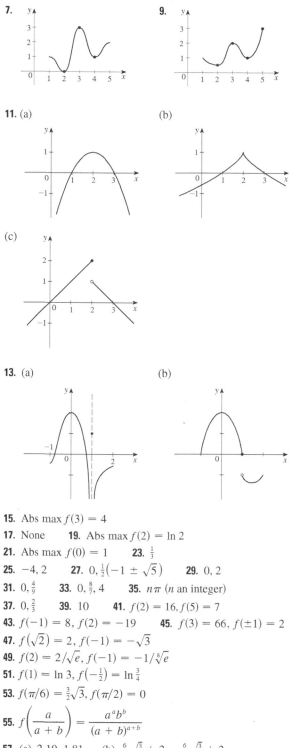

11. (a)   (b)

(c)

13. (a)   (b)

15. Abs max $f(3) = 4$
17. None   **19.** Abs max $f(2) = \ln 2$
21. Abs max $f(0) = 1$ **23.** $\frac{1}{3}$
25. $-4, 2$ **27.** $0, \frac{1}{2}\left(-1 \pm \sqrt{5}\right)$ **29.** $0, 2$
31. $0, \frac{4}{9}$ **33.** $0, \frac{8}{7}, 4$ **35.** $n\pi$ (n an integer)
37. $0, \frac{2}{3}$ **39.** 10 **41.** $f(2) = 16, f(5) = 7$
43. $f(-1) = 8, f(2) = -19$ **45.** $f(3) = 66, f(\pm 1) = 2$
47. $f(\sqrt{2}) = 2, f(-1) = -\sqrt{3}$
49. $f(2) = 2/\sqrt{e}, f(-1) = -1/\sqrt[8]{e}$
51. $f(1) = \ln 3, f\left(-\frac{1}{2}\right) = \ln \frac{3}{4}$
53. $f(\pi/6) = \frac{3}{2}\sqrt{3}, f(\pi/2) = 0$
55. $f\left(\dfrac{a}{a + b}\right) = \dfrac{a^a b^b}{(a + b)^{a+b}}$
57. (a) $2.19, 1.81$ (b) $\frac{6}{25}\sqrt{\frac{3}{5}} + 2, -\frac{6}{25}\sqrt{\frac{3}{5}} + 2$
59. (a) $0.32, 0.00$ (b) $\frac{3}{16}\sqrt{3}, 0$ **61.** $\approx 3.9665°$C
63. Cheapest, $t \approx 0.855$ (June 1994);
most expensive, $t \approx 4.618$ (March 1998)

65. (a) $r = \frac{2}{3}r_0$ (b) $v = \frac{4}{27}kr_0^3$

(c)

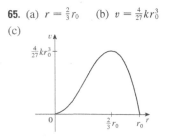

EXERCISES 4.3 ■ PAGE 279

Abbreviations: inc, increasing; dec, decreasing; CD, concave downward; CU, concave upward; HA, horizontal asymptote; VA, vertical asymptote; IP, inflection point(s)

1. 0.8, 3.2, 4.4, 6.1

3. (a) I/D Test   (b) Concavity Test
(c) Find points at which the concavity changes.

5. (a) 3, 5   (b) 2, 4, 6   (c) 1, 7

7. (a) Inc on $(-\infty, -3)$, $(2, \infty)$; dec on $(-3, 2)$
(b) Loc max $f(-3) = 81$; loc min $f(2) = -44$
(c) CU on $\left(-\frac{1}{2}, \infty\right)$; CD on $\left(-\infty, -\frac{1}{2}\right)$; IP $\left(-\frac{1}{2}, \frac{37}{2}\right)$

9. (a) Inc on $(-1, 0)$, $(1, \infty)$; dec on $(-\infty, -1)$, $(0, 1)$
(b) Loc max $f(0) = 3$; loc min $f(\pm 1) = 2$
(c) CU on $\left(-\infty, -\sqrt{3}/3\right)$, $\left(\sqrt{3}/3, \infty\right)$;
CD on $\left(-\sqrt{3}/3, \sqrt{3}/3\right)$; IP $\left(\pm\sqrt{3}/3, \frac{22}{9}\right)$

11. (a) Inc on $(0, \pi/4)$, $(5\pi/4, 2\pi)$; dec on $(\pi/4, 5\pi/4)$
(b) Loc max $f(\pi/4) = \sqrt{2}$; loc min $f(5\pi/4) = -\sqrt{2}$
(c) CU on $(3\pi/4, 7\pi/4)$; CD on $(0, 3\pi/4)$, $(7\pi/4, 2\pi)$;
IP $(3\pi/4, 0)$, $(7\pi/4, 0)$

13. (a) Inc on $\left(-\frac{1}{3}\ln 2, \infty\right)$; dec on $\left(-\infty, -\frac{1}{3}\ln 2\right)$
(b) Loc min $f\left(-\frac{1}{3}\ln 2\right) = 2^{-2/3} + 2^{1/3}$ (c) CU on $(-\infty, \infty)$

15. (a) Inc on $(0, e^2)$; dec on (e^2, ∞)
(b) Loc max $f(e^2) = 2/e$
(c) CU on $(e^{8/3}, \infty)$; CD on $(0, e^{8/3})$; IP $\left(e^{8/3}, \frac{8}{3}e^{-4/3}\right)$

17. Loc max $f\left(\frac{3}{4}\right) = \frac{5}{4}$

19. (a) f has a local maximum at 2.
(b) f has a horizontal tangent at 6.

21. (a) Inc on $(-\infty, -1)$, $(2, \infty)$;
dec on $(-1, 2)$
(b) Loc max $f(-1) = 7$;
loc min $f(2) = -20$
(c) CU on $\left(\frac{1}{2}, \infty\right)$; CD on $\left(-\infty, \frac{1}{2}\right)$;
IP $\left(\frac{1}{2}, -\frac{13}{2}\right)$
(d) See graph at right.

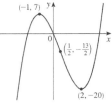

23. (a) Inc on $(-\infty, -1)$, $(0, 1)$;
dec on $(-1, 0)$, $(1, \infty)$
(b) Loc max $f(-1) = 3$, $f(1) = 3$;
loc min $f(0) = 2$
(c) CU on $\left(-1/\sqrt{3}, 1/\sqrt{3}\right)$;
CD on $\left(-\infty, -1/\sqrt{3}\right)$, $\left(1/\sqrt{3}, \infty\right)$;
IP $\left(\pm 1/\sqrt{3}, \frac{23}{9}\right)$
(d) See graph at right.

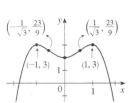

25. (a) Inc on $(-\infty, -2)$, $(0, \infty)$;
dec on $(-2, 0)$
(b) Loc max $h(-2) = 7$;
loc min $h(0) = -1$
(c) CU on $(-1, \infty)$;
CD on $(-\infty, -1)$; IP $(-1, 3)$
(d) See graph at right.

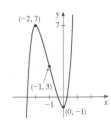

27. (a) Inc on $(-2, \infty)$;
dec on $(-3, -2)$
(b) Loc min $A(-2) = -2$
(c) CU on $(-3, \infty)$
(d) See graph at right.

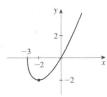

29. (a) Inc on $(-1, \infty)$;
dec on $(-\infty, -1)$
(b) Loc min $C(-1) = -3$
(c) CU on $(-\infty, 0)$, $(2, \infty)$;
CD on $(0, 2)$;
IP $(0, 0)$, $\left(2, 6\sqrt[3]{2}\right)$
(d) See graph at right

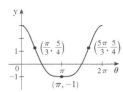

31. (a) Inc on $(\pi, 2\pi)$;
dec on $(0, \pi)$
(b) Loc min $f(\pi) = -1$
(c) CU on $(\pi/3, 5\pi/3)$;
CD on $(0, \pi/3)$, $(5\pi/3, 2\pi)$;
IP $\left(\pi/3, \frac{5}{4}\right)$, $\left(5\pi/3, \frac{5}{4}\right)$
(d) See graph at right.

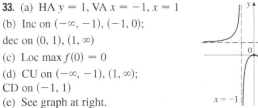

33. (a) HA $y = 1$, VA $x = -1$, $x = 1$
(b) Inc on $(-\infty, -1)$, $(-1, 0)$;
dec on $(0, 1)$, $(1, \infty)$
(c) Loc max $f(0) = 0$
(d) CU on $(-\infty, -1)$, $(1, \infty)$;
CD on $(-1, 1)$
(e) See graph at right.

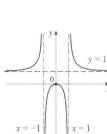

35. (a) HA $y = 0$
(b) Dec on $(-\infty, \infty)$
(c) None
(d) CU on $(-\infty, \infty)$
(e) See graph at right.

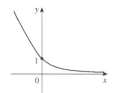

37. (a) VA $x = 0$, $x = e$
(b) Dec on $(0, e)$
(c) None
(d) CU on $(0, 1)$; CD on $(1, e)$;
IP $(1, 0)$
(e) See graph at right.

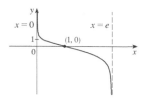

39. (a) HA $y = 1$, VA $x = -1$
(b) Inc on $(-\infty, -1)$, $(-1, \infty)$
(c) None
(d) CU on $(-\infty, -1)$, $\left(-1, -\frac{1}{2}\right)$;
CD on $\left(-\frac{1}{2}, \infty\right)$; IP $\left(-\frac{1}{2}, 1/e^2\right)$
(e) See graph at right.

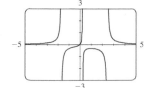

41. $(3, \infty)$
43. (a) Loc and abs max $f(1) = \sqrt{2}$, no min
(b) $\frac{1}{4}\left(3 - \sqrt{17}\right)$
45. (b) CU on $(0.94, 2.57)$, $(3.71, 5.35)$;
CD on $(0, 0.94)$, $(2.57, 3.71)$, $(5.35, 2\pi)$;
IP $(0.94, 0.44)$, $(2.57, -0.63)$, $(3.71, -0.63)$, $(5.35, 0.44)$
47. CU on $(-\infty, -0.6)$, $(0.0, \infty)$; CD on $(-0.6, 0.0)$
49. (a) Very unhappy   (b) Unhappy   (c) Happy
(d) Very happy
51. $\dfrac{2t}{3t^2 - 12}$, $\dfrac{-2(t^2 + 4)}{9(t^2 - 4)^3}$, $-2 < t < 2$

53.   **55.**

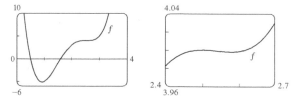

57. 28.57 min, when the rate of increase of drug level in the blood-stream is greatest; 85.71 min, when rate of decrease is greatest
59. $f(x) = \frac{1}{9}(2x^3 + 3x^2 - 12x + 7)$ **63.** 17
71. (a) $a = 0$, $b = -1$ (b) $y = -x$ at $(0, 0)$

EXERCISES 4.4 ■ PAGE 288

1. Inc on $(0.92, 2.5)$, $(2.58, \infty)$; dec on $(-\infty, 0.92)$, $(2.5, 2.58)$;
loc max $f(2.5) = 4$; loc min $f(0.92) \approx -5.12$, $f(2.58) \approx 3.998$;
CU on $(-\infty, 1.46)$, $(2.54, \infty)$;
CD on $(1.46, 2.54)$; IP $(1.46, -1.40)$, $(2.54, 3.999)$

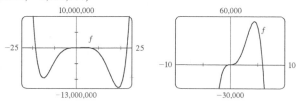

3. Inc on $(-15, 4.40)$, $(18.93, \infty)$;
dec on $(-\infty, -15)$, $(4.40, 18.93)$;
loc max $f(4.40) \approx 53,800$; loc min $f(-15) \approx -9,700,000$,
$f(18.93) \approx -12,700,000$; CU on $(-\infty, -11.34)$, $(0, 2.92)$,
$(15.08, \infty)$; CD on $(-11.34, 0)$, $(2.92, 15.08)$;
IP $(0, 0)$, $\approx (-11.34, -6,250,000)$, $(2.92, 31,800)$,
$(15.08, -8,150,000)$

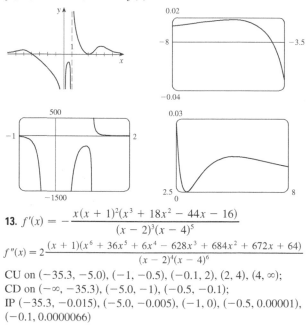

5. Inc on $(-\infty, -1.7)$, $(-1.7, 0.24)$, $(0.24, 1)$;
dec on $(1, 2.46)$, $(2.46, \infty)$; loc max $f(1) = -\frac{1}{3}$;
CU on $(-\infty, -1.7)$, $(-0.506, 0.24)$, $(2.46, \infty)$;
CD on $(-1.7, -0.506)$, $(0.24, 2.46)$; IP $(-0.506, -0.192)$

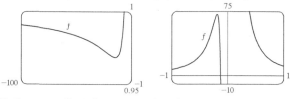

7. Inc on $(-1.49, -1.07)$, $(2.89, 4)$; dec on $(-4, -1.49)$,
$(-1.07, 2.89)$; loc max $f(-1.07) \approx 8.79$;
loc min $f(-1.49) \approx 8.75$, $f(2.89) \approx -9.99$; CU on $(-4, -1.28)$,
$(1.28, 4)$; CD on $(-1.28, 1.28)$; IP $(-1.28, 8.77)$, $(1.28, -1.48)$

9. Inc on $\left(-8 - \sqrt{61}, -8 + \sqrt{61}\right)$; dec on $\left(-\infty, -8 - \sqrt{61}\right)$,
$\left(-8 + \sqrt{61}, 0\right)$, $(0, \infty)$; CU on $\left(-12 - \sqrt{138}, -12 + \sqrt{138}\right)$,
$(0, \infty)$; CD on $\left(-\infty, -12 - \sqrt{138}\right)$, $\left(-12 + \sqrt{138}, 0\right)$

11. Loc max $f(-5.6) \approx 0.018$, $f(0.82) \approx -281.5$,
$f(5.2) \approx 0.0145$; loc min $f(3) = 0$

13. $f'(x) = -\dfrac{x(x + 1)^2(x^3 + 18x^2 - 44x - 16)}{(x - 2)^3(x - 4)^5}$

$f''(x) = 2\dfrac{(x + 1)(x^6 + 36x^5 + 6x^4 - 628x^3 + 684x^2 + 672x + 64)}{(x - 2)^4(x - 4)^6}$

CU on $(-35.3, -5.0)$, $(-1, -0.5)$, $(-0.1, 2)$, $(2, 4)$, $(4, \infty)$;
CD on $(-\infty, -35.3)$, $(-5.0, -1)$, $(-0.5, -0.1)$;
IP $(-35.3, -0.015)$, $(-5.0, -0.005)$, $(-1, 0)$, $(-0.5, 0.00001)$,
$(-0.1, 0.0000066)$

15. Inc on $(0, 0.43)$; dec on $(0.43, \infty)$; loc max $f(0.43) \approx 0.41$;
CU on $(0.94, \infty)$; CD on $(0, 0.94)$; IP $(0.94, 0.34)$

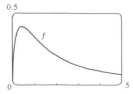

17. Inc on $(-4.91, -4.51)$, $(0, 1.77)$, $(4.91, 8.06)$, $(10.79, 14.34)$,
$(17.08, 20)$;
dec on $(-4.51, -4.10)$, $(1.77, 4.10)$, $(8.06, 10.79)$, $(14.34, 17.08)$;
loc max $f(-4.51) \approx 0.62$, $f(1.77) \approx 2.58$, $f(8.06) \approx 3.60$,
$f(14.34) \approx 4.39$;
loc min $f(10.79) \approx 2.43$, $f(17.08) \approx 3.49$;
CU on $(9.60, 12.25)$, $(15.81, 18.65)$;
CD on $(-4.91, -4.10)$, $(0, 4.10)$, $(4.91, 9.60)$, $(12.25, 15.81)$,
$(18.65, 20)$;
IP at $(9.60, 2.95)$, $(12.25, 3.27)$, $(15.81, 3.91)$, $(18.65, 4.20)$

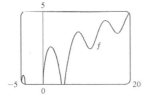

19. Inc on $(-\infty, 0)$, $(0, \infty)$;
CU on $(-\infty, -0.42)$, $(0, 0.42)$;
CD on $(-0.42, 0)$, $(0.42, \infty)$;
IP $(\mp 0.42, \pm 0.83)$

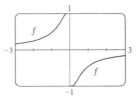

21. Max $f(0.59) \approx 1$, $f(0.68) \approx 1$, $f(1.96) \approx 1$;
min $f(0.64) \approx 0.99996$, $f(1.46) \approx 0.49$, $f(2.73) \approx -0.51$;
IP $(0.61, 0.99998)$, $(0.66, 0.99998)$, $(1.17, 0.72)$,
$(1.75, 0.77)$, $(2.28, 0.34)$

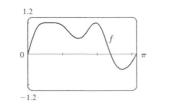

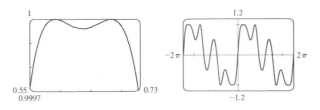

23.

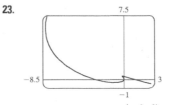

Vertical tangents at $(0, 0)$, $\left(-\frac{3}{16}, \frac{3}{8}\right)$, $(-8, 6)$; horizontal tangents at
$\left(-(2\sqrt{3} + 5)/9, -2\sqrt{3}/9\right)$, $\left((2\sqrt{3} - 5)/9, 2\sqrt{3}/9\right)$

25. For $c = 0$, there is a cusp; for $c > 0$, there is a loop whose size
increases as c increases and the curve intersects itself at $(0, c)$; leftmost point $\left(-2c\sqrt{3c}/9, c/3\right)$, rightmost point $\left(2c\sqrt{3c}/9, c/3\right)$

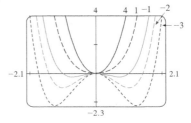

27. For $c \geq 0$, there is no IP and only one extreme point, the
origin. For $c < 0$, there is a maximum point at the origin, two
minimum points, and two IPs, which move downward and away
from the origin as $c \to -\infty$.

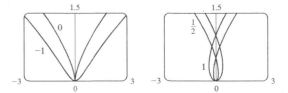

29. For $c < 0$, there is no extreme point and one IP, which
decreases along the x-axis. For $c > 0$, there is no IP, and one
minimum point.

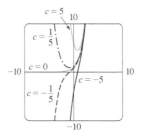

31. For $c > 0$, the maximum and minimum values are always
$\pm\frac{1}{2}$, but the extreme points and IPs move closer to the y-axis as c
increases. $c = 0$ is a transitional value: when c is replaced by $-c$,
the curve is reflected in the x-axis.

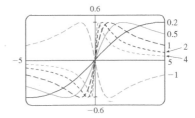

33. For $|c| < 1$, the graph has loc max and min values; for $|c| \geq 1$ it does not. The function increases for $c \geq 1$ and decreases for $c \leq -1$. As c changes, the IPs move vertically but not horizontally.

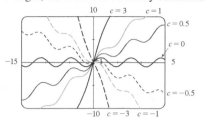

35. (a) Positive (b)

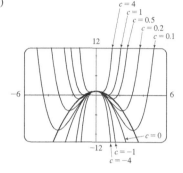

EXERCISES 4.5 ▪ PAGE 296

1. (a) Indeterminate (b) 0 (c) 0
(d) ∞, $-\infty$, or does not exist (e) Indeterminate
3. (a) $-\infty$ (b) Indeterminate (c) ∞
5. 2 **7.** $-\infty$ **9.** ∞ **11.** 0 **13.** $-\infty$
15. 3 **17.** $\ln\frac{5}{3}$ **19.** $\frac{1}{2}$ **21.** $-1/\pi^2$ **23.** $\frac{1}{2}a(a-1)$
25. $\frac{1}{24}$ **27.** π **29.** 3 **31.** 0 **33.** $\frac{1}{2}$ **35.** $\frac{1}{2}$ **37.** ∞
39. 1 **41.** e^{-2} **43.** 1 **45.** e^4 **47.** e^2 **49.** $\frac{1}{4}$
51. HA $y = 0$

53. HA $y = 0$, VA $x = 0$

55. (a)

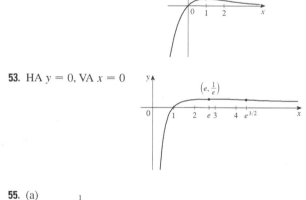

(b) $\lim_{x \to 0^+} f(x) = 0$
(c) Loc min $f(1/\sqrt{e}) = -1/(2e)$; CD on $(0, e^{-3/2})$; CU on $(e^{-3/2}, \infty)$
57. (a)

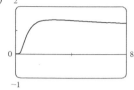

(b) $\lim_{x \to 0^+} x^{1/x} = 0$, $\lim_{x \to \infty} x^{1/x} = 1$
(c) Loc max $f(e) = e^{1/e}$ (d) IP at $x \approx 0.58, 4.37$
59.

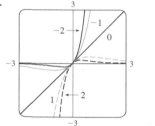

For $c > 0$, $\lim_{x \to \infty} f(x) = 0$ and $\lim_{x \to -\infty} f(x) = -\infty$.
For $c < 0$, $\lim_{x \to \infty} f(x) = \infty$ and $\lim_{x \to -\infty} f(x) = 0$.
As $|c|$ increases, the max and min points and the IPs get closer to the origin.
61. 1 **69.** $\frac{16}{9}a$ **71.** $\frac{1}{2}$ **73.** 56

EXERCISES 4.6 ▪ PAGE 305

1. (a) 11, 12 (b) 11.5, 11.5 **3.** 10, 10
5. 25 m by 25 m **7.** $N = 1$
9. (a)

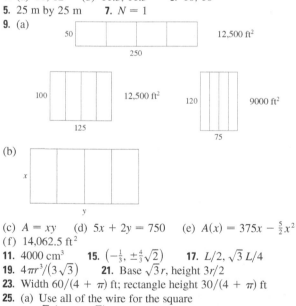

(b)

(c) $A = xy$ (d) $5x + 2y = 750$ (e) $A(x) = 375x - \frac{5}{2}x^2$
(f) 14,062.5 ft^2
11. 4000 cm^3 **15.** $\left(-\frac{1}{3}, \pm\frac{4}{3}\sqrt{2}\right)$ **17.** $L/2, \sqrt{3}L/4$
19. $4\pi r^3/(3\sqrt{3})$ **21.** Base $\sqrt{3}r$, height $3r/2$
23. Width $60/(4 + \pi)$ ft; rectangle height $30/(4 + \pi)$ ft
25. (a) Use all of the wire for the square
(b) $40\sqrt{3}/(9 + 4\sqrt{3})$ m for the square
27. $V = 2\pi R^3/(9\sqrt{3})$ **31.** $E^2/(4r)$
33. (a) $\frac{3}{2}s^2\csc\theta\,(\csc\theta - \sqrt{3}\cot\theta)$ (b) $\cos^{-1}(1/\sqrt{3}) \approx 55°$
(c) $6s[h + s/(2\sqrt{2})]$

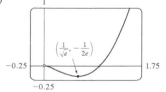

35. ≈ 4.85 km east of the refinery

37. $10\sqrt[3]{3}/(1 + \sqrt[3]{3})$ ft from the stronger source

39. $y = -\frac{5}{3}x + 10$ **41.** $2\sqrt{6}$

43. (b) (i) \$342,491; \$342/unit; \$390/unit   (ii) 400
(iii) \$320/unit

45. (a) $p(x) = 19 - \frac{1}{3000}x$ (b) \$9.50

47. (a) $p(x) = 550 - \frac{1}{10}x$ (b) \$175   (c) \$100

49. $(a^{2/3} + b^{2/3})^{3/2}$ **53.** $x = 6$ in.   **55.** $\frac{1}{2}(L + W)^2$

57. At a distance $5 - 2\sqrt{5}$ from A

59. (a) About 5.1 km from B (b) C is close to B; C is close to
D; $W/L = \sqrt{25 + x^2}/x$, where $x = |BC|$ (c) ≈ 1.07; no such
value   (d) $\sqrt{41}/4 \approx 1.6$

61. (a) $T_1 = D/c_1$, $T_2 = (2h \sec \theta)/c_1 + (D - 2h \tan \theta)/c_2$,
$T_3 = \sqrt{4h^2 + D^2}/c_1$
(c) $c_1 \approx 3.85$ km/s, $c_2 \approx 7.66$ km/s, $h \approx 0.42$ km

EXERCISES 4.7 ▪ PAGE 315

1. (a) $x_2 \approx 2.3$, $x_3 \approx 3$ (b) No   **3.** $\frac{4}{5}$ **5.** 1.1797

7. 1.1785   **9.** -1.25 **11.** 1.82056420

13. -0.724492, 1.220744   **15.** 1.412391, 3.057104

17. -1.93822883, -1.21997997, 1.13929375, 2.98984102

19. -1.97806681, -0.82646233

21. 0.21916368, 1.08422462   **23.** (b) 31.622777

29. (0.904557, 1.855277)   **31.** (0.410245, 0.347810)

33. 0.76286%

EXERCISES 4.8 ▪ PAGE 321

1. $F(x) = \frac{1}{2}x + \frac{1}{4}x^3 - \frac{1}{5}x^4 + C$

3. $F(x) = \frac{2}{3}x^3 + \frac{1}{2}x^2 - x + C$ **5.** $F(x) = 4x^{5/4} - 4x^{7/4} + C$

7. $F(x) = 4x^{3/2} - \frac{6}{7}x^{7/6} + C$

9. $F(x) = \begin{cases} -5/(4x^8) + C_1 & \text{if } x < 0 \\ -5/(4x^8) + C_2 & \text{if } x > 0 \end{cases}$

11. $F(u) = \frac{1}{3}u^3 - 6u^{-1/2} + C$

13. $G(\theta) = \sin \theta + 5 \cos \theta + C$

15. $F(x) = \frac{1}{2}x^2 - \ln|x| - 1/x^2 + C$

17. $F(x) = x^5 - \frac{1}{3}x^6 + 4$ **19.** $x^3 + x^4 + Cx + D$

21. $\frac{3}{20}x^{8/3} + Cx + D$ **23.** $x - 3x^2 + 8$

25. $4x^{3/2} + 2x^{5/2} + 4$ **27.** $2 \sin t + \tan t + 4 - 2\sqrt{3}$

29. $-x^2 + 2x^3 - x^4 + 12x + 4$

31. $-\sin \theta - \cos \theta + 5\theta + 4$ **33.** $x^2 - 2x^3 + 9x + 9$

35. $x^2 - \cos x - \frac{1}{2}\pi x$ **37.** 10

39.

(graph showing piecewise linear function with points (1,1), (2,2), (3,1))

41. $s(t) = 1 - \cos t - \sin t$

43. (a) $s(t) = 450 - 4.9t^2$ (b) $\sqrt{450/4.9} \approx 9.58$ s
(c) $-9.8\sqrt{450/4.9} \approx -93.9$ m/s   (d) About 9.09 s

47. \$742.08   **49.** 225 ft   **51.** $\frac{88}{15} \approx 5.87$ ft/s^2

53. 62,500 km/h$^2 \approx 4.82$ m/s^2

57. (a) 22.9125 mi   (b) 21.675 mi   (c) 30 min 33 s
(d) 55.425 mi

CHAPTER 4 REVIEW ▪ PAGE 323

True-False Quiz

1. False   **3.** False   **5.** True   **7.** False   **9.** True
11. True   **13.** False   **15.** True   **17.** True   **19.** True

Exercises

1. Abs max $f(4) = 5$, abs and loc min $f(3) = 1$

3. Abs max $f(2) = \frac{2}{5}$, abs and loc min $f\left(-\frac{1}{3}\right) = -\frac{9}{2}$

5. Abs max $f(\pi) = \pi$; abs min $f(0) = 0$;
loc max $f(\pi/3) = (\pi/3) + \frac{1}{2}\sqrt{3}$;
loc min $f(2\pi/3) = (2\pi/3) - \frac{1}{2}\sqrt{3}$

7. (a) None
(b) Dec on $(-\infty, \infty)$
(c) None
(d) CU on $(-\infty, 0)$; CD on $(0, \infty)$;
IP $(0, 2)$
(e) See graph at right.

(graph at right)

9. (a) None
(b) Inc on $\left(-\infty, \frac{3}{4}\right)$, dec on $\left(\frac{3}{4}, 1\right)$
(c) Loc max $f\left(\frac{3}{4}\right) = \frac{5}{4}$
(d) CD on $(-\infty, 1)$
(e) See graph at right.

(graph at right)

11. (a) None
(b) Inc on $(2n\pi, (2n + 1)\pi)$, n an integer;
dec on $((2n + 1)\pi, (2n + 2)\pi)$
(c) Loc max $f((2n + 1)\pi) = 2$; loc min $f(2n\pi) = -2$
(d) CU on $(2n\pi - (\pi/3), 2n\pi + (\pi/3))$;
CD on $(2n\pi + (\pi/3), 2n\pi + (5\pi/3))$; IPs $\left(2n\pi \pm (\pi/3), -\frac{1}{4}\right)$
(e)

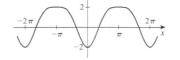

13. (a) None
(b) Inc on $\left(\frac{1}{4}\ln 3, \infty\right)$,
dec on $\left(-\infty, \frac{1}{4}\ln 3\right)$
(c) Loc min
$f\left(\frac{1}{4}\ln 3\right) = 3^{1/4} + 3^{-3/4}$
(d) CU on $(-\infty, \infty)$
(e) See graph at right.

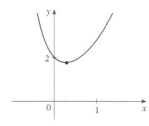

15. Inc on $\left(-\sqrt{3}, 0\right)$, $\left(0, \sqrt{3}\right)$;
dec on $\left(-\infty, -\sqrt{3}\right)$, $\left(\sqrt{3}, \infty\right)$;
loc max $f\left(\sqrt{3}\right) = \frac{2}{9}\sqrt{3}$,
loc min $f\left(-\sqrt{3}\right) = -\frac{2}{9}\sqrt{3}$;
CU on $\left(-\sqrt{6}, 0\right)$, $\left(\sqrt{6}, \infty\right)$;
CD on $\left(-\infty, -\sqrt{6}\right)$, $\left(0, \sqrt{6}\right)$;
IP $\left(\sqrt{6}, \frac{5}{36}\sqrt{6}\right)$, $\left(-\sqrt{6}, -\frac{5}{36}\sqrt{6}\right)$

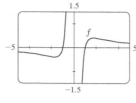

17. Inc on $(-0.23, 0)$, $(1.62, \infty)$; dec on $(-\infty, -0.23)$, $(0, 1.62)$;
loc max $f(0) = 2$; loc min $f(-0.23) \approx 1.96$, $f(1.62) \approx -19.2$;
CU on $(-\infty, -0.12)$, $(1.24, \infty)$;
CD on $(-0.12, 1.24)$; IP $(-0.12, 1.98)$, $(1.24, -12.1)$

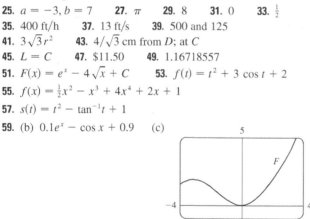

19.

21. $-2.96, -0.18, 3.01; -1.57, 1.57; -2.16, -0.75, 0.46, 2.21$

23. For $C > -1$, f is periodic with period 2π and has local maxima at $2n\pi + \pi/2$, n an integer. For $C \leq -1$, f has no graph. For $-1 < C \leq 1$, f has vertical asymptotes. For $C > 1$, f is continuous on $\mathbb{R}$. As C increases, f moves upward and its oscillations become less pronounced.

25. $a = -3, b = 7$ **27.** π **29.** 8   **31.** 0   **33.** $\frac{1}{2}$

35. 400 ft/h   **37.** 13 ft/s   **39.** 500 and 125

41. $3\sqrt{3}\,r^2$ **43.** $4/\sqrt{3}$ cm from D; at C

45. $L = C$ **47.** \$11.50   **49.** 1.16718557

51. $F(x) = e^x - 4\sqrt{x} + C$ **53.** $f(t) = t^2 + 3\cos t + 2$

55. $f(x) = \frac{1}{2}x^2 - x^3 + 4x^4 + 2x + 1$

57. $s(t) = t^2 - \tan^{-1}t + 1$

59. (b) $0.1e^x - \cos x + 0.9$ (c)

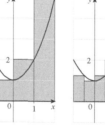

61. No

63. (b) About 8.5 in. by 2 in.   (c) $20/\sqrt{3}$ in., $20\sqrt{2/3}$ in.

65. (a) $20\sqrt{2} \approx 28$ ft

(b) $\dfrac{dI}{dt} = \dfrac{-480k(h-4)}{[(h-4)^2 + 1600]^{5/2}}$, where k is the constant of proportionality

FOCUS ON PROBLEM SOLVING ■ **PAGE 328**

5. Abs max $f(-5) = e^{45}$, no abs min

7. $(-2, 4), (2, -4)$ **9.** 24   **11.** $-3.5 < a < -2.5$

13. $c > 0$ (one IP) and $c < -e/6$ (two IP)   **17.** $(m/2, m^2/4)$

23. $2 + \frac{375}{128}\pi \approx 11.204$ cm³/min

CHAPTER 5

EXERCISES 5.1 ■ **PAGE 341**

1. (a) $L_4 = 33, R_4 = 41$

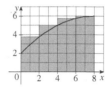

(b) $L_8 \approx 35.1, R_8 \approx 39.1$

3. (a) 0.7908, underestimate   (b) 1.1835, overestimate

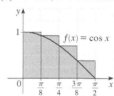

5. (a) 8, 6.875   (b) 5, 5.375

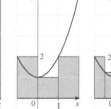

(c) 5.75, 5.9375

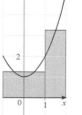
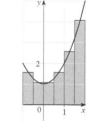

(d) M_6

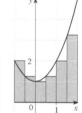
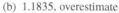

7. 0.2533, 0.2170, 0.2101, 0.2050; 0.2

9. (a) Left: 0.8100, 0.7937, 0.7904;

right: 0.7600, 0.7770, 0.7804

11. 34.7 ft, 44.8 ft   **13.** 63.2 L, 70 L   **15.** 155 ft

17. $\displaystyle\lim_{n\to\infty}\sum_{i=1}^{n}\frac{2(1+2i/n)}{(1+2i/n)^2+1}\cdot\frac{2}{n}$ **19.** $\displaystyle\lim_{n\to\infty}\sum_{i=1}^{n}\left(\frac{i\pi}{2n}\cos\frac{i\pi}{2n}\right)\frac{\pi}{2n}$

21. The region under the graph of $y=\tan x$ from 0 to $\pi/4$

23. (a) $L_n < A < R_n$

25. (a) $\displaystyle\lim_{n\to\infty}\frac{64}{n^6}\sum_{i=1}^{n}i^5$ (b) $\dfrac{n^2(n+1)^2(2n^2+2n-1)}{12}$ (c) $\frac{32}{3}$

27. $\sin b$, 1

EXERCISES 5.2 ■ PAGE 353

1. −6

The Riemann sum represents
the sum of the areas of the two
rectangles above the x-axis
minus the sum of the areas of
the three rectangles below the
x-axis; that is, the net area of the
rectangles with respect to the
x-axis.

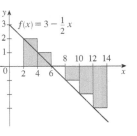

3. 2.322986

The Riemann sum represents the sum
of the areas of the three rectangles
above the x-axis minus the area of the
rectangle below the x-axis.

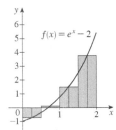

5. (a) 4   (b) 6   (c) 10

7. Lower, $L_5 = -64$; upper, $R_5 = 16$

9. 124.1644   **11.** 0.3084

13. 0.30843908, 0.30981629, 0.31015563

15.

n	R_n
5	1.933766
10	1.983524
50	1.999342
100	1.999836

The values of R_n appear to be
approaching 2.

17. $\int_2^6 x\ln(1+x^2)\,dx$ **19.** $\int_1^8 \sqrt{2x+x^2}\,dx$ **21.** 42

23. $\frac{4}{3}$ **25.** 3.75   **27.** $\displaystyle\lim_{n\to\infty}\sum_{i=1}^{n}\frac{2+4i/n}{1+(2+4i/n)^5}\cdot\frac{4}{n}$

29. $\displaystyle\lim_{n\to\infty}\sum_{i=1}^{n}\left(\sin\frac{5\pi i}{n}\right)\frac{\pi}{n}=\frac{2}{5}$

31. (a) 4   (b) 10   (c) −3   (d) 2   **33.** $-\frac{3}{4}$

35. $3+\frac{9}{4}\pi$ **37.** 2.5   **39.** 0

41. $\int_{-1}^5 f(x)\,dx$ **43.** 122   **45.** $e^5 - e^3$

47. $B < E < A < D < C$ **49.** 15   **53.** $\int_0^1 x^4\,dx$

EXERCISES 5.3 ■ PAGE 363

1. $-\frac{10}{3}$ **3.** $\frac{56}{15}$ **5.** $\frac{5}{9}$ **7.** $-2 + 1/e$ **9.** $\frac{49}{3}$ **11.** $\frac{40}{3}$

13. $\frac{55}{63}$ **15.** 1   **17.** $\ln 3$ **19.** π **21.** $e^2 - 1$

23. $\ln 2 + 7$ **25.** $1 + \pi/4$ **27.** $\pi/6$ **29.** −3.5

31. The function $f(x) = 1/x^2$ is not continuous on the interval
$[-1, 3]$, so the Evaluation Theorem cannot be applied.

33. 2   **35.** ≈1.36

37. 3.75   **41.** $\sin x + \frac{1}{4}x^2 + C$

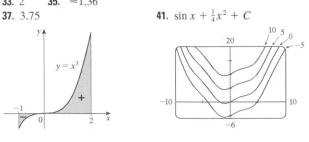

43. $2t - t^2 + \frac{1}{3}t^3 - \frac{1}{4}t^4 + C$ **45.** $\tan\alpha + C$

47. $\sec x + C$ **49.** $\frac{4}{3}$

51. The increase in the child's weight (in pounds) between the
ages of 5 and 10

53. Number of gallons of oil leaked in the first 2 hours

55. Increase in revenue when production is increased from
1000 to 5000 units

57. Newton-meters   **59.** (a) $-\frac{3}{2}$ m   (b) $\frac{41}{6}$ m

61. (a) $v(t) = \frac{1}{2}t^2 + 4t + 5$ m/s   (b) $416\frac{2}{3}$ m

63. $46\frac{2}{3}$ kg   **65.** 1.4 mi   **67.** $58,000

69. (b) At most 40%; $\frac{5}{36}$ **73.** 3   **75.** $\frac{1}{4}$

EXERCISES 5.4 ■ PAGE 372

1. One process undoes what the other one does. See the
Fundamental Theorem of Calculus, page 371.

3. (a) 0, 2, 5, 7, 3   (d)

(b) (0, 3)

(c) $x = 3$

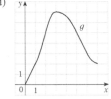

5. $g'(x) = 1 + x^2$

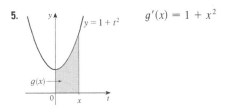

7. $g'(x) = 1/(x^3 + 1)$

9. $g'(y) = y^2\sin y$ **11.** $F'(x) = -\sqrt{1+\sec x}$

13. $h'(x) = -\dfrac{\arctan(1/x)}{x^2}$ **15.** $y' = \sqrt{\tan x + \sqrt{\tan x}}\,\sec^2 x$

17. $g'(x) = \dfrac{-2(4x^2-1)}{4x^2+1} + \dfrac{3(9x^2-1)}{9x^2+1}$

19. (a) Loc max at 1 and 5;
loc min at 3 and 7
(b) $x = 9$
(c) $\left(\frac{1}{2}, 2\right), (4, 6), (8, 9)$
(d) See graph at right.

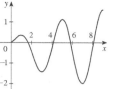

21. $(-1, 1)$ **23.** $(-4, 0)$ **25.** 29
27. (a) $-2\sqrt{n}, \sqrt{4n - 2}$, n an integer > 0
(b) $(0, 1), (-\sqrt{4n - 1}, -\sqrt{4n - 3})$, and $(\sqrt{4n - 1}, \sqrt{4n + 1})$,
n an integer > 0 (c) 0.74
29. $f(x) = \int_1^x (2^t/t)\,dt$ **31.** $f(x) = x^{3/2}, a = 9$
33. (b) Average expenditure over $[0, t]$; minimize average
expenditure

EXERCISES 5.5 ▪ PAGE 381

1. $-e^{-x} + C$ **3.** $\frac{2}{9}(x^3 + 1)^{3/2} + C$ **5.** $-\frac{1}{4}\cos^4\theta + C$
7. $-\frac{1}{2}\cos(x^2) + C$ **9.** $\frac{1}{63}(3x - 2)^{21} + C$
11. $-(1/\pi)\cos \pi t + C$ **13.** $\frac{1}{3}(\ln x)^3 + C$
15. $-\frac{1}{3}\ln|5 - 3x| + C$ **17.** $\frac{2}{3}\sqrt{3ax + bx^3} + C$
19. $\frac{2}{3}(1 + e^x)^{3/2} + C$ **21.** $-1/(\sin x) + C$
23. $\frac{1}{15}(x^3 + 3x)^5 + C$ **25.** $-\frac{2}{3}(\cot x)^{3/2} + C$
27. $\ln|\sin^{-1}x| + C$ **29.** $\frac{1}{3}\sec^3 x + C$
31. $\frac{1}{40}(2x + 5)^{10} - \frac{5}{36}(2x + 5)^9 + C$
33. $-\ln(1 + \cos^2 x) + C$ **35.** $\tan^{-1}x + \frac{1}{2}\ln(1 + x^2) + C$
37. $\frac{1}{8}(x^2 - 1)^4 + C$ **39.** $-e^{\cos x} + C$

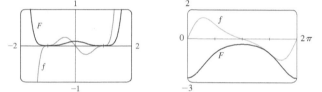

41. $2/\pi$ **43.** $\frac{45}{28}$ **45.** $\frac{182}{9}$ **47.** $2(e^2 - e)$
49. 0   **51.** $\frac{16}{15}$ **53.** $\ln(e + 1)$ **55.** 2   **57.** $\frac{1}{6}$
59. 6π **61.** All three areas are equal.   **63.** ≈ 4512 L

65. $\dfrac{5}{4\pi}\left(1 - \cos\dfrac{2\pi t}{5}\right)$ L   **67.** 5

EXERCISES 5.6 ▪ PAGE 387

1. $\frac{1}{3}x^3 \ln x - \frac{1}{9}x^3 + C$ **3.** $\frac{1}{5}x \sin 5x + \frac{1}{25}\cos 5x + C$
5. $2(r - 2)e^{r/2} + C$

7. $-\dfrac{1}{\pi}x^2 \cos \pi x + \dfrac{2}{\pi^2}x \sin \pi x + \dfrac{2}{\pi^3}\cos \pi x + C$

9. $x \ln \sqrt[3]{x} - \frac{1}{3}x + C$ **11.** $t \arctan 4t - \frac{1}{8}\ln(1 + 16t^2) + C$
13. $\frac{1}{13}e^{2\theta}(2 \sin 3\theta - 3 \cos 3\theta) + C$ **15.** $\pi/3$ **17.** $\frac{1}{2} - \frac{1}{4}\ln 2$
19. $\frac{1}{4} - \frac{3}{4}e^{-2}$ **21.** $\frac{1}{6}(\pi + 6 - 3\sqrt{3})$
23. $2(\ln 2)^2 - 4 \ln 2 + 2$
25. $2\sqrt{x} \sin \sqrt{x} + 2 \cos \sqrt{x} + C$ **27.** $-\frac{1}{2} - \pi/4$
29. $\frac{1}{2}(x^2 - 1)\ln(1 + x) - \frac{1}{4}x^2 + \frac{1}{2}x + \frac{3}{4} + C$

31. $-\frac{1}{2}xe^{-2x} - \frac{1}{4}e^{-2x} + C$

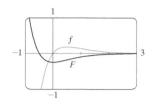

33. $\frac{1}{3}x^2(1 + x^2)^{3/2} - \frac{2}{15}(1 + x^2)^{5/2} + C$

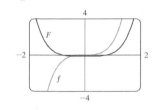

35. (b) $-\frac{1}{4}\cos x \sin^3 x + \frac{3}{8}x - \frac{3}{16}\sin 2x + C$
37. (b) $\frac{2}{3}, \frac{8}{15}$
41. $x[(\ln x)^3 - 3(\ln x)^2 + 6 \ln x - 6] + C$
43. $2 - e^{-t}(t^2 + 2t + 2)$ m   **45.** 2

EXERCISES 5.7 ▪ PAGE 393

1. $\frac{1}{5}\cos^5 x - \frac{1}{3}\cos^3 x + C$ **3.** $-\frac{11}{384}$ **5.** π
7. $\frac{1}{3}\sec^3 x - \sec x + C$ **9.** $\frac{8}{15}$
11. $-\dfrac{\sqrt{9 - x^2}}{x} - \sin^{-1}\left(\dfrac{x}{3}\right) + C$
13. $-\dfrac{\sqrt{x^2 + 4}}{4x} + C$ **15.** $\dfrac{\pi}{24} + \dfrac{\sqrt{3}}{8} - \dfrac{1}{4}$
17. $-\dfrac{\sqrt{4 - x^2}}{4x} + C$
19. (a) $\dfrac{A}{x + 3} + \dfrac{B}{3x + 1}$ (b) $\dfrac{A}{x} + \dfrac{B}{x + 1} + \dfrac{C}{(x + 1)^2}$
21. $\frac{1}{2}\ln|2x + 1| + 2 \ln|x - 1| + C$
23. $\frac{1}{2}\ln\frac{3}{2}$ **25.** $\ln|x - 1| - \frac{1}{2}\ln(x^2 + 9) - \frac{1}{3}\tan^{-1}(x/3) + C$
27. $\frac{1}{2}\ln(x^2 + 1) + (1/\sqrt{2})\tan^{-1}(x/\sqrt{2}) + C$
29. $x + 6 \ln|x - 6| + C$
31. $\frac{1}{2}x^2 - 2 \ln(x^2 + 4) + 2 \tan^{-1}(x/2) + C$
33. $2 + \ln\frac{25}{9}$ **35.** $\dfrac{2}{\sqrt{3}}\tan^{-1}\left(\dfrac{2x + 1}{\sqrt{3}}\right) + C$

EXERCISES 5.8 ▪ PAGE 399

1. $\dfrac{1}{2\pi}\tan^2(\pi x) + \dfrac{1}{\pi}\ln|\cos(\pi x)| + C$
3. $-\sqrt{4x^2 + 9}/(9x) + C$ **5.** $\frac{1}{2}(e^{2x} + 1)\arctan(e^x) - \frac{1}{2}e^x + C$
7. $\pi^3 - 6\pi$ **9.** $-\frac{1}{2}\tan^2(1/z) - \ln|\cos(1/z)| + C$
11. $\dfrac{2y - 1}{8}\sqrt{6 + 4y - 4y^2} + \dfrac{7}{8}\sin^{-1}\left(\dfrac{2y - 1}{\sqrt{7}}\right)$
$- \frac{1}{12}(6 + 4y - 4y^2)^{3/2} + C$

13. $\frac{1}{9}\sin^3 x\,[3\ln(\sin x) - 1] + C$ **15.** $\frac{1}{2\sqrt{3}}\ln\left|\dfrac{e^x + \sqrt{3}}{e^x - \sqrt{3}}\right| + C$

17. $\frac{1}{5}\ln|x^5 + \sqrt{x^{10} - 2}| + C$

19. $\frac{1}{2}(\ln x)\sqrt{4 + (\ln x)^2} + 2\ln\left[\ln x + \sqrt{4 + (\ln x)^2}\right] + C$

21. $\sqrt{e^{2x} - 1} - \cos^{-1}(e^{-x}) + C$

25. $\frac{1}{3}\tan x\,\sec^2 x + \frac{2}{3}\tan x + C$

27. $\frac{1}{4}x(x^2 + 2)\sqrt{x^2 + 4} - 2\ln(\sqrt{x^2 + 4} + x) + C$

29. $\frac{1}{10}(1 + 2x)^{5/2} - \frac{1}{6}(1 + 2x)^{3/2} + C$

31. $-\ln|\cos x| - \frac{1}{2}\tan^2 x + \frac{1}{4}\tan^4 x + C$

33. (a) $-\ln\left|\dfrac{1 + \sqrt{1 - x^2}}{x}\right| + C$;

both have domain $(-1, 0) \cup (0, 1)$

EXERCISES 5.9 ■ **PAGE 411**

1. (a) $L_2 = 6, R_2 = 12, M_2 \approx 9.6$

(b) L_2 is an underestimate, R_2 and M_2 are overestimates.

(c) $T_2 = 9 < I$ (d) $L_n < T_n < I < M_n < R_n$

3. (a) $T_4 \approx 0.895759$ (underestimate)

(b) $M_4 \approx 0.908907$ (overestimate)

$T_4 < I < M_4$

5. (a) $M_{10} \approx 0.806598, E_M \approx -0.001879$

(b) $S_{10} \approx 0.804779, E_S \approx -0.000060$

7. (a) 2.413790   (b) 2.411453   (c) 2.412232

9. (a) 0.146879   (b) 0.147391   (c) 0.147219

11. (a) 0.451948   (b) 0.451991   (c) 0.451976

13. (a) 4.513618   (b) 4.748256   (c) 4.675111

15. (a) -0.495333 (b) -0.543321 (c) -0.526123

17. (a) $T_8 \approx 0.902333, M_8 \approx 0.905620$

(b) $|E_T| \leq 0.0078, |E_M| \leq 0.0039$

(c) $n = 71$ for T_n, $n = 50$ for M_n

19. (a) $T_{10} \approx 1.983524, E_T \approx 0.016476$;

$M_{10} \approx 2.008248, E_M \approx -0.008248$;

$S_{10} \approx 2.000110, E_S \approx -0.000110$

(b) $|E_T| \leq 0.025839, |E_M| \leq 0.012919, |E_S| \leq 0.000170$

(c) $n = 509$ for T_n, $n = 360$ for M_n, $n = 22$ for S_n

21. (a) 2.8   (b) 7.954926518   (c) 0.2894

(d) 7.954926521   (e) The actual error is much smaller.

(f) 10.9   (g) 7.953789422   (h) 0.0593

(i) The actual error is smaller.   (j) $n \geq 50$

23.

n	L_n	R_n	T_n	M_n
5	0.742943	1.286599	1.014771	0.992621
10	0.867782	1.139610	1.003696	0.998152
20	0.932967	1.068881	1.000924	0.999538

n	E_L	E_R	E_T	E_M
5	0.257057	-0.286599	-0.014771	0.007379
10	0.132218	-0.139610	-0.003696	0.001848
20	0.067033	-0.068881	-0.000924	0.000462

Observations are the same as after Example 1.

25.

n	T_n	M_n	S_n
6	6.695473	6.252572	6.403292
12	6.474023	6.363008	6.400206

n	E_T	E_M	E_S
6	-0.295473	0.147428	-0.003292
12	-0.074023	0.036992	-0.000206

Observations are the same as after Example 1.

27. (a) $19.\overline{8}$ (b) 20.6   (c) $20.5\overline{3}$

29. $37.7\overline{3}$ ft/s   **31.** 10,177 megawatt-hours

33. (a) 23.44   (b) $0.341\overline{3}$ **35.** 59.4

37.

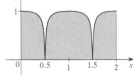

EXERCISES 5.10 ■ **PAGE 421**

Abbreviations: C, convergent; D, divergent

1. (a) Infinite interval   (b) Infinite discontinuity

(c) Infinite discontinuity   (d) Infinite interval

3. $\frac{1}{2} - 1/(2t^2)$; 0.495, 0.49995, 0.4999995; 0.5

5. 2   **7.** D   **9.** $2e^{-2}$ **11.** D   **13.** 0   **15.** D

17. $\frac{1}{25}$ **19.** D   **21.** $\pi/9$ **23.** $\frac{1}{2}$ **25.** D

27. $\frac{32}{3}$ **29.** $\frac{75}{4}$ **31.** D   **33.** $\frac{8}{3}\ln 2 - \frac{8}{9}$

35. e **37.** $2\pi/3$

39. Infinite area

41. (a)

t	$\displaystyle\int_1^t [(\sin^2 x)/x^2]\,dx$
2	0.447453
5	0.577101
10	0.621306
100	0.668479
1,000	0.672957
10,000	0.673407

It appears that the integral is convergent.

(c)

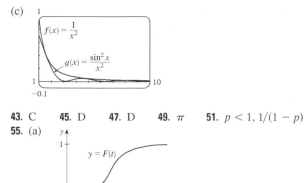

43. C   **45.** D   **47.** D   **49.** π **51.** $p < 1, 1/(1-p)$
55. (a)

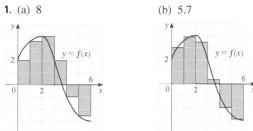

(b) The rate at which the fraction $F(t)$ increases as t increases
(c) 1; all bulbs burn out eventually
57. 8264.5 years   **59.** 1000   **63.** $C = 1$; ln 2   **65.** No

CHAPTER 5 REVIEW ■ PAGE 424

True-False Quiz

1. True   **3.** True   **5.** False   **7.** True   **9.** True
11. False   **13.** False   **15.** False   **17.** False   **19.** False
21. False   **23.** False

Exercises

1. (a) 8   (b) 5.7

3. $\frac{1}{2} + \pi/4$ **5.** 3   **7.** f is c, f' is b, $\int_0^x f(t)\,dt$ is a
9. 37   **11.** $\frac{9}{10}$ **13.** $-(1/x) - 2\ln|x| + x + C$
15. $\frac{1}{2}\ln 2$ **17.** $\frac{1}{3}\sin 1$ **19.** $(1/\pi)(e^{\pi} - 1)$
21. $\sqrt{x^2 + 4x} + C$ **23.** $5 + 10\ln\frac{2}{3}$ **25.** 0
27. $\frac{64}{5}\ln 4 - \frac{124}{25}$ **29.** $\frac{1}{2}\ln\left|\frac{t+2}{t+4}\right| + C$
31. $3e^{\sqrt[3]{x}}(x^{2/3} - 2x^{1/3} + 2) + C$ **33.** $\ln|1 + \sec\theta| + C$
35. $2\sqrt{1 + \sin x} + C$ **37.** $\frac{64}{5}$ **39.** $F'(x) = x^2/(1 + x^3)$
41. $y' = (2e^x - e^{\sqrt{x}})/(2x)$ **43.** $\frac{1}{2}[e^x\sqrt{1 - e^{2x}} + \sin^{-1}(e^x)] + C$
45. $\frac{1}{4}(2x + 1)\sqrt{x^2 + x + 1} + \frac{3}{8}\ln(x + \frac{1}{2} + \sqrt{x^2 + x + 1}) + C$
47. (a) 1.090608 (overestimate)
(b) 1.088840 (underestimate)   (c) 1.089429 (unknown)
49. (a) $0.00\overline{6}$, $n \geq 259$ (b) $0.00\overline{3}$, $n \geq 183$
51. (a) 3.8   (b) 1.7867, 0.000646   (c) $n \geq 30$
53. $4 \leq \int_1^3 \sqrt{x^2 + 3}\,dx \leq 4\sqrt{3}$ **55.** $\frac{1}{36}$ **57.** D   **59.** 2
61. C   **63.** (a) $29.1\overline{6}$ m   (b) 29.5 m

65. Number of barrels of oil consumed from Jan. 1, 2000, through Jan. 1, 2008
67. $Ce^{-x^2/(4kt)}/\sqrt{4\pi kt}$ **69.** $e^{2x}(1 + 2x)/(1 - e^{-x})$

FOCUS ON PROBLEM SOLVING ■ PAGE 429

1. About 1.85 inches from the center   **3.** $\pi/2$ **5.** $f(x) = \frac{1}{2}x$
7. e^{-2} **9.** $2k$ **11.** Does not exist   **13.** $[-1, 2]$
15. $\sqrt{1 + \sin^4 x}\cos x$ **17.** $\frac{1}{8}\pi - \frac{1}{12}$ **19.** 0
23. (b) $y = -\sqrt{L^2 - x^2} - L\ln\left(\dfrac{L - \sqrt{L^2 - x^2}}{x}\right)$

CHAPTER 6

EXERCISES 6.1 ■ PAGE 436

1. $\frac{32}{3}$ **3.** $e - (1/e) + \frac{10}{3}$ **5.** $e - (1/e) + \frac{4}{3}$ **7.** $\frac{1}{3}$
9. $\frac{8}{3}$ **11.** $\frac{32}{3}$ **13.** 72   **15.** $e - 2$ **17.** ln 2
19. 0, 0.90; 0.04   **21.** 1, 1.38; 0.05
23. $\frac{1}{2}$

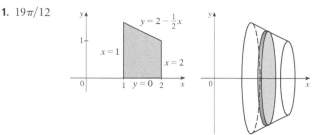

25. 118 ft   **27.** 84 m^2 **29.** 8868; increase in population over a 10-year period   **31.** $r\sqrt{R^2 - r^2} + \pi r^2/2 - R^2\arcsin(r/R)$
33. πab **35.** $3 - e$ **37.** $24\sqrt{3}/5$ **39.** ± 6
41. $4^{2/3}$ **43.** $f(t) = 3t^2$ **45.** $0 < m < 1$; $m - \ln m - 1$

EXERCISES 6.2 ■ PAGE 446

1. $19\pi/12$

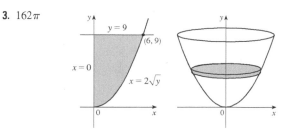

3. 162π

5. $4\pi/21$

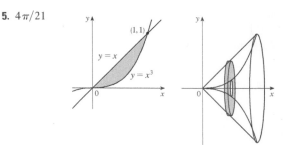

7. $64\pi/15$

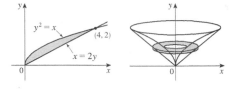

9. $\pi/6$

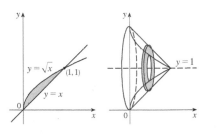

11. $2\pi\left(\frac{4}{3}\pi - \sqrt{3}\right)$

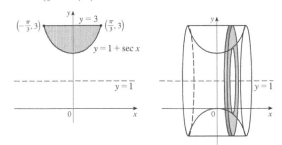

13. $\pi/2$ **15.** $108\pi/5$ **17.** $13\pi/30$

19. $\pi \int_{-2\sqrt{2}}^{2\sqrt{2}} \left[5^2 - \left(\sqrt{1 + y^2} + 2\right)^2\right] dy$

21. $-1.288, 0.884; 23.780$ **23.** $\frac{11}{8}\pi^2$

25. (a) Solid obtained by rotating the region $0 \le y \le \cos x$,
$0 \le x \le \pi/2$ about the x-axis
(b) Solid obtained by rotating the region above the x-axis bounded
by $x = y^2$ and $x = y^4$ about the y-axis

27. 1110 cm^3 **29.** (a) 190 (b) 823

31. $\frac{1}{3}\pi r^2 h$ **33.** $\pi h^2\left(r - \frac{1}{3}h\right)$ **35.** $\frac{2}{3}b^2 h$ **37.** 10 cm^3

39. 24 **41.** $\frac{1}{3}$ **43.** $\frac{8}{15}$ **45.** (a) $8\pi R \int_0^r \sqrt{r^2 - y^2} \, dy$

(b) $2\pi^2 r^2 R$ **47.** (b) $\pi r^2 h$ **49.** $\frac{5}{12}\pi r^3$

51. $8\int_0^r \sqrt{R^2 - y^2}\sqrt{r^2 - y^2} \, dy$

1. Circumference $= 2\pi x$, height $= x(x - 1)^2$; $\pi/15$

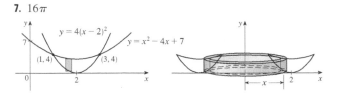

3. 2π

5. $\pi(1 - 1/e)$

7. 16π

9. $21\pi/2$ **11.** $16\pi/3$ **13.** $7\pi/15$ **15.** $8\pi/3$

17. $5\pi/14$ **19.** $\int_0^\pi 2\pi(4 - y)\sqrt{\sin y} \, dy$ **21.** 3.70

23. (a) Solid obtained by rotating the region $0 \le y \le x^4$,
$0 \le x \le 3$ about the y-axis
(b) Solid obtained by rotating the region bounded by
(i) $x = 1 - y^2$, $x = 0$, and $y = 0$, or (ii) $x = y^2$, $x = 1$, and $y = 0$
about the line $y = 3$

25. 0.13 **27.** $\frac{1}{32}\pi^3$ **29.** 8π **31.** $\frac{4}{3}\pi$

33. $2\pi(12 - 4\ln 4)$ **35.** $\frac{4}{3}\pi r^3$ **37.** $\frac{1}{3}\pi r^2 h$

1. $4\sqrt{5}$ **3.** 3.8202

5. $\int_0^{2\pi} \sqrt{3 - 2\sin t - 2\cos t} \, dt \approx 10.0367$ **7.** $4\sqrt{2} - 2$

9. $\left(13\sqrt{13} - 8\right)/27$ **11.** $\frac{3}{4} + \frac{1}{2}\ln 2$

13. $e^3 + 11 - e^{-8}$

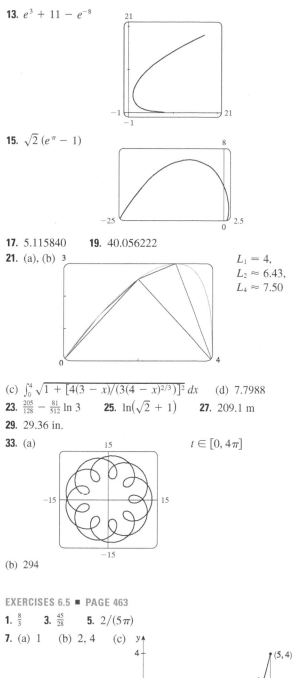

15. $\sqrt{2}\,(e^\pi - 1)$

17. 5.115840   **19.** 40.056222

21. (a), (b)

$L_1 = 4$,
$L_2 \approx 6.43$,
$L_4 \approx 7.50$

(c) $\int_0^4 \sqrt{1 + [4(3-x)/(3(4-x)^{2/3})]^2}\, dx$ (d) 7.7988

23. $\frac{205}{128} - \frac{81}{512}\ln 3$ **25.** $\ln(\sqrt{2}+1)$ **27.** 209.1 m

29. 29.36 in.

33. (a) $t \in [0, 4\pi]$

(b) 294

EXERCISES 6.5 ▪ PAGE 463

1. $\frac{8}{3}$ **3.** $\frac{45}{28}$ **5.** $2/(5\pi)$

7. (a) 1   (b) 2, 4   (c)

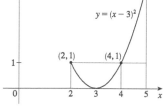

9. (a) $4/\pi$ (b) $\approx 1.24, 2.81$
(c)

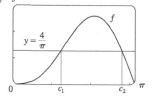

13. 38.6   **15.** $(50 + 28/\pi)°\text{F} \approx 59°\text{F}$
17. 6 kg/m   **19.** $5/(4\pi) \approx 0.4$ L

EXERCISES 6.6 ▪ PAGE 472

1. 9 ft-lb   **3.** 180 J   **5.** $\frac{15}{4}$ ft-lb
7. (a) $\frac{25}{24} \approx 1.04$ J   (b) 10.8 cm   **9.** $W_2 = 3W_1$
11. (a) 625 ft-lb   (b) $\frac{1875}{4}$ ft-lb   **13.** 650,000 ft-lb
15. 3857 J   **17.** 2450 J   **19.** $\approx 1.06 \times 10^6$ J
21. $\approx 1.04 \times 10^5$ ft-lb   **23.** 2.0 m
27. (a) $Gm_1m_2\left(\dfrac{1}{a} - \dfrac{1}{b}\right)$ (b) $\approx 8.50 \times 10^9$ J
29. (a) 187.5 lb/ft^2 (b) 1875 lb   (c) 562.5 lb
31. 6.7×10^4 N   **33.** 9.8×10^3 N   **35.** 1.2×10^4 lb
37. 5.27×10^5 N
39. (a) 5.63×10^3 lb   (b) 5.06×10^4 lb
(c) 4.88×10^4 lb   (d) 3.03×10^5 lb
41. 2.5×10^5 N   **43.** $10; 1; \left(\frac{1}{21}, \frac{10}{21}\right)$
45. $(0, 1.6)$ **47.** $\left(\dfrac{1}{e-1}, \dfrac{e+1}{4}\right)$ **49.** $60; 160; \left(\frac{8}{3}, 1\right)$
51. (b) $\left(\frac{1}{2}, \frac{2}{5}\right)$

EXERCISES 6.7 ▪ PAGE 479

1. \$38,000   **3.** \$43,866,933.33   **5.** \$407.25
7. \$12,000   **9.** 3727; \$37,753
11. $\frac{2}{3}(16\sqrt{2} - 8) \approx \$9.75$ million   **13.** $\dfrac{(1-k)(b^{2-k} - a^{2-k})}{(2-k)(b^{1-k} - a^{1-k})}$
15. 1.19×10^{-4} cm^3/s   **17.** 6.60 L/min   **19.** 5.77 L/min

EXERCISES 6.8 ▪ PAGE 486

1. (a) The probability that a randomly chosen tire will have a lifetime between 30,000 and 40,000 miles
(b) The probability that a randomly chosen tire will have a lifetime of at least 25,000 miles
3. (b) $1 - \frac{3}{8}\sqrt{3} \approx 0.35$
5. (a) $1/\pi$ (b) $\frac{1}{2}$
7. (a) $f(x) \geq 0$ for all x and $\int_{-\infty}^{\infty} f(x)\, dx = 1$ (b) 5
11. (a) $e^{-4/2.5} \approx 0.20$ (b) $1 - e^{-2/2.5} \approx 0.55$ (c) If you aren't served within 10 minutes, you get a free hamburger.
13. $\approx 44\%$
15. (a) 0.0668   (b) $\approx 5.21\%$
17. ≈ 0.9545

CHAPTER 6 REVIEW ▪ PAGE 488

1. $\frac{8}{3}$ **3.** $\frac{7}{12}$ **5.** 9π **7.** (a) 0.38   (b) 0.87

9. (a) $2\pi/15$ (b) $\pi/6$ (c) $8\pi/15$ **11.** $1656\pi/5$

13. $\frac{4}{3}\pi(2ah + h^2)^{3/2}$ **15.** $\int_{-\pi/3}^{\pi/3} 2\pi(\pi/2 - x)(\cos^2 x - \frac{1}{4})\, dx$

17. (a) Solid obtained by rotating the region $0 \le y \le \sqrt{2}\,\cos x$,
$0 \le x \le \pi/2$ about the x-axis

(b) Solid obtained by rotating the region $2 - \sqrt{x} \le y \le 2 - x^2$,
$0 \le x \le 1$ about the x-axis

19. 36   **21.** $\frac{125}{3}\sqrt{3}\ \mathrm{m}^3$ **23.** $2(5\sqrt{5} - 1)$ **25.** $\frac{15}{2}$

27. 3.2 J   **29.** (a) $8000\pi/3 \approx 8378$ ft-lb   (b) 2.1 ft

31. ≈ 458 lb   **33.** $7166.67   **35.** $f(x)$

37. (a) $f(x) \ge 0$ for all x and $\int_{-\infty}^{\infty} f(x)\, dx = 1$
(b) ≈ 0.3455 (c) 5, yes

39. (a) $1 - e^{-3/8} \approx 0.31$ (b) $e^{-5/4} \approx 0.29$
(c) $8 \ln 2 \approx 5.55$ min

FOCUS ON PROBLEM SOLVING ▪ PAGE 491

1. $f(x) = \sqrt{2x/\pi}$ **3.** (b) 0.2261   (c) 0.6736 m
(d) (i) $1/(105\pi) \approx 0.003$ in/s   (ii) $370\pi/3$ s ≈ 6.5 min
7. Height $\sqrt{2}\, b$, volume $\left(\frac{28}{27}\sqrt{6} - 2\right)\pi b^3$ **9.** $\ln(\pi/2)$
13. 0.14 m   **15.** $b = 2a$

CHAPTER 7

EXERCISES 7.1 ▪ PAGE 498

3. (a) $\frac{1}{2}, -1$ **5.** (d)

7. (a) It must be either 0 or decreasing
(c) $y = 0$ (d) $y = 1/(x + 2)$

9. (a) $0 < P < 4200$ (b) $P > 4200$
(c) $P = 0, P = 4200$

13. (a) III   (b) I   (c) IV   (d) II

15. (a) At the beginning; stays positive, but decreases

(c)

EXERCISES 7.2 ▪ PAGE 506

1. (a)
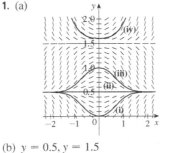

(b) $y = 0.5, y = 1.5$

3. III   **5.** IV

7.
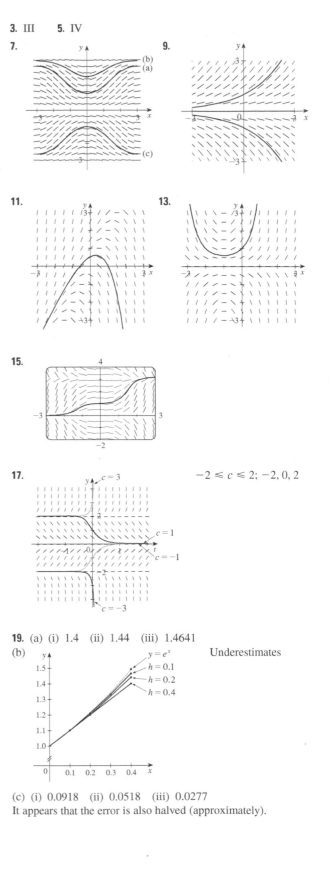

9.

11.

13.

15.

17. $-2 \le c \le 2; -2, 0, 2$

19. (a) (i) 1.4   (ii) 1.44   (iii) 1.4641

(b) $y = e^x$ Underestimates
$h = 0.1$
$h = 0.2$
$h = 0.4$

(c) (i) 0.0918   (ii) 0.0518   (iii) 0.0277
It appears that the error is also halved (approximately).

21. $-1, -3, -6.5, -12.25$ **23.** 1.7616
25. (a) (i) 3   (ii) 2.3928   (iii) 2.3701   (iv) 2.3681
(c) (i) -0.6321 (ii) -0.0249 (iii) -0.0022 (iv) -0.0002
It appears that the error is also divided by 10 (approximately).
27. (a), (d)   (b) 3
(c) Yes; $Q = 3$
(e) 2.77 C

EXERCISES 7.3 ■ PAGE 514

1. $y = \dfrac{2}{K - x^2}, y = 0$ **3.** $y = K\sqrt{x^2 + 1}$
5. $\frac{1}{2}y^2 - \cos y = \frac{1}{2}x^2 + \frac{1}{4}x^4 + C$
7. $y = \pm\sqrt{[3(te^t - e^t + C)]^{2/3} - 1}$ **9.** $u = Ae^{2t+t^2/2} - 1$
11. $y = -\sqrt{x^2 + 9}$ **13.** $u = -\sqrt{t^2 + \tan t + 25}$
15. $\frac{1}{2}y^2 + \frac{1}{3}(3 + y^2)^{3/2} = \frac{1}{2}x^2 \ln x - \frac{1}{4}x^2 + \frac{41}{12}$
17. $y = \dfrac{4a}{\sqrt{3}} \sin x - a$
19. $y = e^{x^2/2}$ **21.** $y = Ke^x - x - 1$
23. (a) $\sin^{-1}y = x^2 + C$
(b) $y = \sin(x^2), -\sqrt{\pi/2} \le x \le \sqrt{\pi/2}$ (c) No

25. $\cos y = \cos x - 1$

27. (a)   (b) $y = \dfrac{1}{K - x}$

29. $y = Cx^2$

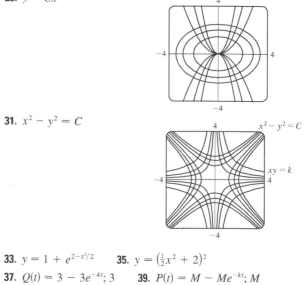

31. $x^2 - y^2 = C$

33. $y = 1 + e^{2-x^2/2}$ **35.** $y = \left(\frac{1}{2}x^2 + 2\right)^2$
37. $Q(t) = 3 - 3e^{-4t}; 3$ **39.** $P(t) = M - Me^{-kt}; M$
41. (a) $x = a - \dfrac{4}{(kt + 2/\sqrt{a})^2}$
(b) $t = \dfrac{2}{k\sqrt{a - b}}\left(\tan^{-1}\sqrt{\dfrac{b}{a - b}} - \tan^{-1}\sqrt{\dfrac{b - x}{a - b}}\right)$
43. (a) $C(t) = (C_0 - r/k)e^{-kt} + r/k$
(b) r/k; the concentration approaches r/k regardless of the value of C_0
45. (a) $15e^{-t/100}$ kg   (b) $15e^{-0.2} \approx 12.3$ kg
47. About 4.9%   **49.** g/k
51. (a) $L_1 = KL_2^k$ (b) $B = KV^{0.0794}$

53. (a) $dA/dt = k\sqrt{A}(M - A)$ (b) $A(t) = M\left(\dfrac{Ce^{\sqrt{M}kt} - 1}{Ce^{\sqrt{M}kt} + 1}\right)^2$,
where $C = \dfrac{\sqrt{M} + \sqrt{A_0}}{\sqrt{M} - \sqrt{A_0}}$ and $A_0 = A(0)$

EXERCISES 7.4 ■ PAGE 527

1. About 235
3. (a) $100(4.2)^t$ (b) ≈ 7409 (c) $\approx 10{,}632$ bacteria/h
(d) $(\ln 100)/(\ln 4.2) \approx 3.2$ h
5. (a) 1508 million, 1871 million   (b) 2161 million
(c) 3972 million; wars in the first half of century, increased life expectancy in second half
7. (a) $Ce^{-0.0005t}$ (b) $-2000 \ln 0.9 \approx 211$ s
9. (a) $100 \times 2^{-t/30}$ mg   (b) ≈ 9.92 mg   (c) ≈ 199.3 years
11. ≈ 2500 years   **13.** (a) $\approx 137°F$ (b) ≈ 116 min
15. (a) $13.3°C$ (b) ≈ 67.74 min
17. (a) ≈ 64.5 kPa   (b) ≈ 39.9 kPa
19. (a) (i) $3828.84   (ii) $3840.25   (iii) $3850.08
(iv) $3851.61   (v) $3852.01   (vi) $3852.08
(b) $dA/dt = 0.05A, A(0) = 3000$

21. (a) $P(t) = \dfrac{m}{k} + \left(P_0 - \dfrac{m}{k}\right)e^{kt}$ (b) $m < kP_0$
(c) $m = kP_0, m > kP_0$ (d) Declining

1. (a) 100; 0.05 (b) Where P is close to 0 or 100; on the line $P = 50$; $0 < P_0 < 100$; $P_0 > 100$

(c)

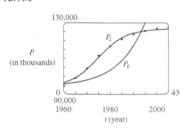

Solutions approach 100; some increase and some decrease, some have an inflection point but others don't; solutions with $P_0 = 20$ and $P_0 = 40$ have inflection points at $P = 50$

(d) $P = 0$, $P = 100$; other solutions move away from $P = 0$ and toward $P = 100$

3. (a) 3.23×10^7 kg (b) ≈ 1.55 years

5. 9000

7. (a) $dP/dt = \frac{1}{265}P(1 - P/100)$, P in billions

(b) 5.49 billion (c) In billions: 7.81, 27.72

(d) In billions: 5.48, 7.61, 22.41

9. (a) $dy/dt = ky(1 - y)$ (b) $y = \dfrac{y_0}{y_0 + (1 - y_0)e^{-kt}}$

(c) 3:36 PM

13. $P_E(t) = 1578.3(1.0933)^t + 94{,}000$;

$$P_L(t) = \frac{32{,}658.5}{1 + 12.75e^{-0.1706t}} + 94{,}000$$

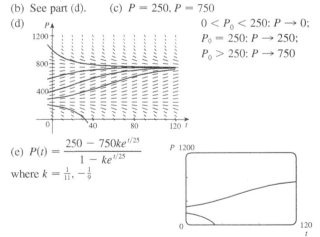

15. (a) Fish are caught at a rate of 15 per week.

(b) See part (d). (c) $P = 250$, $P = 750$

(d)

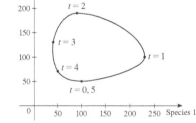

$0 < P_0 < 250$: $P \to 0$;
$P_0 = 250$: $P \to 250$;
$P_0 > 250$: $P \to 750$

(e) $P(t) = \dfrac{250 - 750ke^{t/25}}{1 - ke^{t/25}}$

where $k = \frac{1}{11}, -\frac{1}{9}$

17. (b)

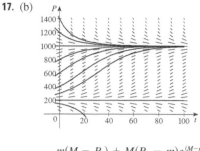

$0 < P_0 < 200$: $P \to 0$;
$P_0 = 200$: $P \to 200$;
$P_0 > 200$: $P \to 1000$

(c) $P(t) = \dfrac{m(M - P_0) + M(P_0 - m)e^{(M-m)(k/M)t}}{M - P_0 + (P_0 - m)e^{(M-m)(k/M)t}}$

19. (a) $P(t) = P_0 e^{(k/r)[\sin(rt - \phi) + \sin\phi]}$ (b) Does not exist

1. (a) $x = $ predators, $y = $ prey; growth is restricted only by predators, which feed only on prey.

(b) $x = $ prey, $y = $ predators; growth is restricted by carrying capacity and by predators, which feed only on prey.

3. (a) Competition

(b) (i) $x = 0$, $y = 0$: zero populations

(ii) $x = 0$, $y = 400$: In the absence of an x-population, the y-population stabilizes at 400.

(iii) $x = 125$, $y = 0$: In the absence of a y-population, the x-population stabilizes at 125.

(iv) $x = 50$, $y = 300$: Both populations are stable.

5. (a) The rabbit population starts at about 300, increases to 2400, then decreases back to 300. The fox population starts at 100, decreases to about 20, increases to about 315, decreases to 100, and the cycle starts again.

(b)

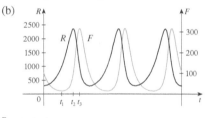

7.

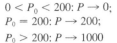

11. (a) Population stabilizes at 5000.

(b) (i) $W = 0$, $R = 0$: Zero populations

(ii) $W = 0$, $R = 5000$: In the absence of wolves, the rabbit population is always 5000.

(iii) $W = 64$, $R = 1000$: Both populations are stable.

(c) The populations stabilize at 1000 rabbits and 64 wolves.

(d)
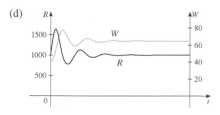

(d)
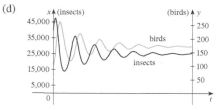

CHAPTER 7 REVIEW ■ PAGE 547

True-False Quiz

1. True **3.** False **5.** True

Exercises

1. (a)
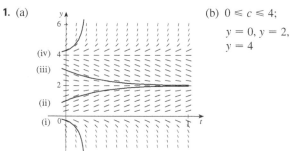
(b) $0 \leqslant c \leqslant 4$;
$y = 0$, $y = 2$,
$y = 4$

3. (a)
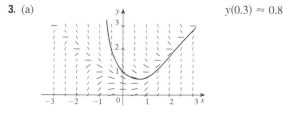
$y(0.3) \approx 0.8$

(b) 0.75676
(c) $y = x$ and $y = -x$; there is a loc max or loc min
5. $y = \pm\sqrt{\ln(x^2 + 2x^{3/2} + C)}$ **7.** $r(t) = 5e^{t-t^2}$
9. $x = C - \frac{1}{2}y^2$
11. (a) $200(3.24)^t$ (b) $\approx 22{,}040$
(c) $\approx 25{,}910$ bacteria/h (d) $(\ln 50)/(\ln 3.24) \approx 3.33$ h
13. (a) $C_0 e^{-kt}$ (b) ≈ 100 h
15. (a) $P(t) = \dfrac{2000}{1 + 19e^{-0.1t}}$; ≈ 560 (b) $t = -10 \ln \frac{2}{57} \approx 33.5$
17. (a) $L(t) = L_\infty - [L_\infty - L(0)]e^{-kt}$ (b) $L(t) = 53 - 43e^{-0.2t}$
19. 15 days **21.** $k \ln h + h = (-R/V)t + C$
23. (a) Stabilizes at 200,000
(b) (i) $x = 0$, $y = 0$: Zero populations
(ii) $x = 200{,}000$, $y = 0$: In the absence of birds, the insect population is always 200,000.
(iii) $x = 25{,}000$, $y = 175$: Both populations are stable.
(c) The populations stabilize at 25,000 insects and 175 birds.

FOCUS ON PROBLEM SOLVING ■ PAGE 551

1. $f(x) = \pm 10e^x$ **5.** $y = x^{1/n}$ **7.** 20°C
9. (b) $f(x) = \dfrac{x^2 - L^2}{4L} - \frac{1}{2}L \ln\left(\dfrac{x}{L}\right)$ (c) No
11. (a) 9.8 h (b) $31{,}900\pi$ ft²; 2000π ft²/h
(c) 5.1 h
13. $x^2 + (y - 6)^2 = 25$

CHAPTER 8

EXERCISES 8.1 ■ PAGE 562

Abbreviations: C, convergent; D, divergent

1. (a) A sequence is an ordered list of numbers. It can also be defined as a function whose domain is the set of positive integers.
(b) The terms a_n approach 8 as n becomes large.
(c) The terms a_n become large as n becomes large.

3. $\frac{1}{3}, \frac{2}{5}, \frac{3}{7}, \frac{4}{9}, \frac{5}{11}, \frac{6}{13}$; yes; $\frac{1}{2}$ **5.** $a_n = 1/(2n - 1)$
7. $a_n = 5n - 3$ **9.** $a_n = \left(-\frac{2}{3}\right)^{n-1}$ **11.** 5
13. 1 **15.** 1 **17.** 1 **19.** 0 **21.** 0 **23.** 0
25. 0 **27.** e^2 **29.** 0 **31.** D **33.** $\ln 2$ **35.** 1
37. $\frac{1}{2}$ **39.** D
41. (a) 1060, 1123.60, 1191.02, 1262.48, 1338.23 (b) D
43. (a) $P_n = 1.08P_{n-1} - 300$ (b) 5734
45. (a) D (b) C **47.** (b) $\frac{1}{2}(1 + \sqrt{5})$
49. Decreasing; yes **51.** Not monotonic; no
53. Convergent by the Monotonic Sequence Theorem; $5 \leqslant L < 8$
55. $\frac{1}{2}(3 + \sqrt{5})$ **57.** 62

EXERCISES 8.2 ■ PAGE 572

1. (a) A sequence is an ordered list of numbers whereas a series is the *sum* of a list of numbers.
(b) A series is convergent if the sequence of partial sums is a convergent sequence. A series is divergent if it is not convergent.

3. -2.40000, -1.92000,
-2.01600, -1.99680,
-2.00064, -1.99987,
-2.00003, -1.99999,
-2.00000, -2.00000;
convergent, sum $= -2$

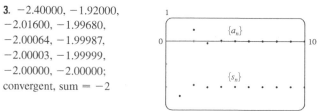

5. 0.44721, 1.15432, 1.98637, 2.88080, 3.80927, 4.75796, 5.71948, 6.68962, 7.66581, 8.64639; divergent

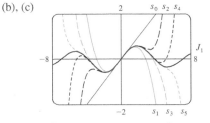

7. 0.29289, 0.42265, 0.50000, 0.55279, 0.59175, 0.62204, 0.64645, 0.66667, 0.68377, 0.69849; convergent, sum = 1

9. (a) C   (b) D   **11.** D   **13.** $\frac{25}{3}$ **15.** 60   **17.** D
19. D   **21.** D   **23.** $\frac{5}{2}$ **25.** D   **27.** D   **29.** $e/(e-1)$
31. $\frac{3}{2}$ **33.** $\frac{11}{6}$
35. (b) 1   (c) 2   (d) All rational numbers with a terminating decimal representation, except 0.
37. $\frac{2}{9}$ **39.** 5063/3300   **41.** $-3 < x < 3; \dfrac{x}{3-x}$
43. All x; $\dfrac{2}{2 - \cos x}$ **45.** 1
47. $a_1 = 0, a_n = \dfrac{2}{n(n+1)}$ for $n > 1$, sum = 1
49. (a) 105.25 mg   (b) $\dfrac{100(1 - 0.05^n)}{1 - 0.05}$ mg
(c) The quantity of the drug approaches $\dfrac{100}{0.95} \approx 105.26$ mg
51. (a) $S_n = \dfrac{D(1 - c^n)}{1 - c}$ (b) 5   **53.** $\frac{1}{2}(\sqrt{3} - 1)$
57. $\dfrac{1}{n(n+1)}$ **59.** The series is divergent.
63. $\{s_n\}$ is bounded and increasing.
65. (a) $0, \frac{1}{9}, \frac{2}{9}, \frac{1}{3}, \frac{2}{3}, \frac{7}{9}, \frac{8}{9}, 1$
67. (a) $\frac{1}{2}, \frac{5}{6}, \frac{23}{24}, \frac{119}{120}; \dfrac{(n+1)! - 1}{(n+1)!}$ (c) 1

EXERCISES 8.3 ■ PAGE 583

1. C

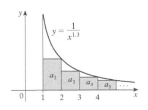

3. (a) Nothing   (b) C
5. p-series; geometric series; $b < -1$; $-1 < b < 1$ **7.** D

9. C   **11.** D   **13.** C   **15.** C   **17.** D   **19.** C
21. C   **23.** D   **25.** D   **27.** C   **29.** D   **31.** $p > 1$
33. (a) 1.54977, error ≤ 0.1 (b) 1.64522, error ≤ 0.005
(c) $n > 1000$
35. 0.00145   **37.** 1.249, error < 0.1 **43.** Yes

EXERCISES 8.4 ■ PAGE 591

1. (a) A series whose terms are alternately positive and negative   (b) $0 < b_{n+1} \leq b_n$ and $\lim_{n \to \infty} b_n = 0$, where $b_n = |a_n|$ (c) $|R_n| \leq b_{n+1}$
3. C   **5.** C   **7.** D   **9.** C
11. An underestimate   **13.** $p > 0$ **15.** 5   **17.** -0.5507
19. 0.0676   **21.** No   **23.** Yes   **25.** Yes   **27.** No
29. Yes   **31.** Yes   **33.** Yes   **35.** D   **37.** (a) and (d)
39. AC

EXERCISES 8.5 ■ PAGE 597

1. A series of the form $\sum_{n=0}^{\infty} c_n(x - a)^n$, where x is a variable and a and the c_n's are constants
3. $1, [-1, 1)$ **5.** $1, [-1, 1]$ **7.** $\infty, (-\infty, \infty)$
9. $2, (-2, 2)$ **11.** $\frac{1}{2}, (-\frac{1}{2}, \frac{1}{2}]$ **13.** $1, [1, 3]$
15. $\frac{1}{3}, [-\frac{13}{3}, -\frac{11}{3})$ **17.** $\frac{1}{4}, [-\frac{1}{2}, 0]$ **19.** $0, \{\frac{1}{2}\}$
21. $b, (a - b, a + b)$ **23.** $\infty, (-\infty, \infty)$
25. (a) Yes   (b) No   **27.** k^k
29. (a) $(-\infty, \infty)$
(b), (c)

31. $(-1, 1), f(x) = (1 + 2x)/(1 - x^2)$ **33.** 2   **35.** No

EXERCISES 8.6 ■ PAGE 603

1. 10   **3.** $\displaystyle\sum_{n=0}^{\infty} (-1)^n x^n, (-1, 1)$ **5.** $2\displaystyle\sum_{n=0}^{\infty} \dfrac{1}{3^{n+1}} x^n, (-3, 3)$
7. $\displaystyle\sum_{n=0}^{\infty} (-1)^n \dfrac{1}{9^{n+1}} x^{2n+1}, (-3, 3)$ **9.** $1 + 2\displaystyle\sum_{n=1}^{\infty} x^n, (-1, 1)$
11. (a) $\displaystyle\sum_{n=0}^{\infty} (-1)^n(n+1)x^n, R = 1$
(b) $\dfrac{1}{2}\displaystyle\sum_{n=0}^{\infty} (-1)^n(n+2)(n+1)x^n, R = 1$
(c) $\dfrac{1}{2}\displaystyle\sum_{n=2}^{\infty} (-1)^n n(n-1)x^n, R = 1$
13. $\ln 5 - \displaystyle\sum_{n=1}^{\infty} \dfrac{x^n}{n5^n}, R = 5$

15. $\displaystyle\sum_{n=0}^{\infty}(-1)^n 4^n(n+1)x^{n+1}$, $R = \frac{1}{4}$

17. $\displaystyle\sum_{n=0}^{\infty}(2n+1)x^n$, $R = 1$

19. $\displaystyle\sum_{n=0}^{\infty}(-1)^n\frac{1}{16^{n+1}}x^{2n+1}$, $R = 4$

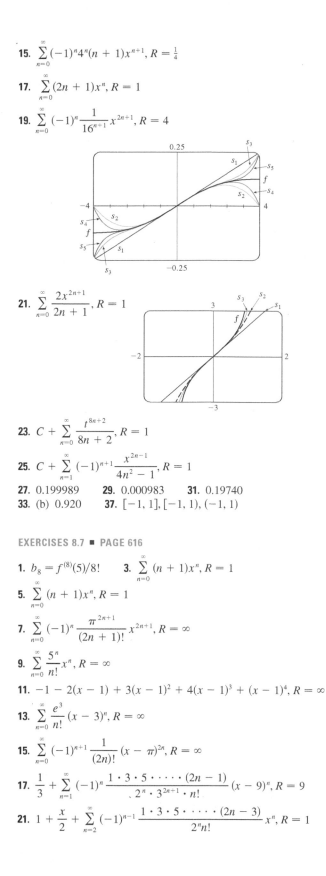

21. $\displaystyle\sum_{n=0}^{\infty}\frac{2x^{2n+1}}{2n+1}$, $R = 1$

23. $\displaystyle C + \sum_{n=0}^{\infty}\frac{t^{8n+2}}{8n+2}$, $R = 1$

25. $\displaystyle C + \sum_{n=1}^{\infty}(-1)^{n+1}\frac{x^{2n-1}}{4n^2-1}$, $R = 1$

27. 0.199989 **29.** 0.000983 **31.** 0.19740
33. (b) 0.920 **37.** $[-1, 1], [-1, 1), (-1, 1)$

EXERCISES 8.7 ■ PAGE 616

1. $b_8 = f^{(8)}(5)/8!$ **3.** $\displaystyle\sum_{n=0}^{\infty}(n+1)x^n$, $R = 1$

5. $\displaystyle\sum_{n=0}^{\infty}(n+1)x^n$, $R = 1$

7. $\displaystyle\sum_{n=0}^{\infty}(-1)^n\frac{\pi^{2n+1}}{(2n+1)!}x^{2n+1}$, $R = \infty$

9. $\displaystyle\sum_{n=0}^{\infty}\frac{5^n}{n!}x^n$, $R = \infty$

11. $-1 - 2(x-1) + 3(x-1)^2 + 4(x-1)^3 + (x-1)^4$, $R = \infty$

13. $\displaystyle\sum_{n=0}^{\infty}\frac{e^3}{n!}(x-3)^n$, $R = \infty$

15. $\displaystyle\sum_{n=0}^{\infty}(-1)^{n+1}\frac{1}{(2n)!}(x-\pi)^{2n}$, $R = \infty$

17. $\displaystyle\frac{1}{3} + \sum_{n=1}^{\infty}(-1)^n\frac{1\cdot 3\cdot 5\cdot\,\cdots\,\cdot(2n-1)}{2^n\cdot 3^{2n+1}\cdot n!}(x-9)^n$, $R = 9$

21. $\displaystyle 1 + \frac{x}{2} + \sum_{n=2}^{\infty}(-1)^{n-1}\frac{1\cdot 3\cdot 5\cdot\,\cdots\,\cdot(2n-3)}{2^n n!}x^n$, $R = 1$

23. $\displaystyle\sum_{n=0}^{\infty}(-1)^n\frac{(n+1)(n+2)}{2^{n+4}}x^n$, $R = 2$

25. $\displaystyle\sum_{n=0}^{\infty}(-1)^n\frac{\pi^{2n+1}}{(2n+1)!}x^{2n+1}$, $R = \infty$

27. $\displaystyle\sum_{n=0}^{\infty}\frac{2^n+1}{n!}x^n$, $R = \infty$

29. $\displaystyle\sum_{n=0}^{\infty}(-1)^n\frac{1}{2^{2n}(2n)!}x^{4n+1}$, $R = \infty$

31. $\displaystyle\frac{1}{2}x + \sum_{n=1}^{\infty}(-1)^n\frac{1\cdot 3\cdot 5\cdot\,\cdots\,\cdot(2n-1)}{n!\,2^{3n+1}}x^{2n+1}$, $R = 2$

33. $\displaystyle\sum_{n=1}^{\infty}(-1)^{n+1}\frac{2^{2n-1}}{(2n)!}x^{2n}$, $R = \infty$

35. $\displaystyle\sum_{n=0}^{\infty}(-1)^n\frac{1}{(2n)!}x^{4n}$, $R = \infty$

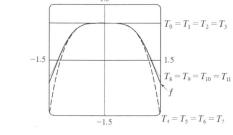

37. $\displaystyle\sum_{n=1}^{\infty}\frac{(-1)^{n-1}}{(n-1)!}x^n$, $R = \infty$

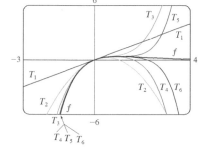

39. 0.81873

41. (a) $\displaystyle 1 + \sum_{n=1}^{\infty}\frac{1\cdot 3\cdot 5\cdot\,\cdots\,\cdot(2n-1)}{2^n n!}x^{2n}$

(b) $\displaystyle x + \sum_{n=1}^{\infty}\frac{1\cdot 3\cdot 5\cdot\,\cdots\,\cdot(2n-1)}{(2n+1)2^n n!}x^{2n+1}$

43. $\displaystyle C + \sum_{n=0}^{\infty}(-1)^n\frac{x^{6n+2}}{(6n+2)(2n)!}$, $R = \infty$

45. $\displaystyle C + \sum_{n=1}^{\infty}(-1)^n\frac{1}{2n\,(2n)!}x^{2n}$, $R = \infty$

47. 0.440 **49.** 0.40102 **51.** $\frac{1}{2}$ **53.** $\frac{1}{120}$

55. $1 - \frac{3}{2}x^2 + \frac{25}{24}x^4$ **57.** $1 + \frac{1}{6}x^2 + \frac{7}{360}x^4$ **59.** e^{-x^4}

61. $\ln\frac{8}{5}$ **63.** $1/\sqrt{2}$ **65.** $e^3 - 1$

EXERCISES 8.8 ■ PAGE 625

1. (a) $T_0(x) = 1 = T_1(x)$, $T_2(x) = 1 - \frac{1}{2}x^2 = T_3(x)$,
$T_4(x) = 1 - \frac{1}{2}x^2 + \frac{1}{24}x^4 = T_5(x)$,
$T_6(x) = 1 - \frac{1}{2}x^2 + \frac{1}{24}x^4 - \frac{1}{720}x^6$

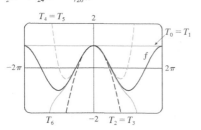

(b)

x	f	$T_0 = T_1$	$T_2 = T_3$	$T_4 = T_5$	T_6
$\frac{\pi}{4}$	0.7071	1	0.6916	0.7074	0.7071
$\frac{\pi}{2}$	0	1	−0.2337	0.0200	−0.0009
π	−1	1	−3.9348	0.1239	−1.2114

(c) As n increases, $T_n(x)$ is a good approximation to $f(x)$ on a larger and larger interval.

3. $\frac{1}{2} - \frac{1}{4}(x - 2) + \frac{1}{8}(x - 2)^2 - \frac{1}{16}(x - 2)^3$

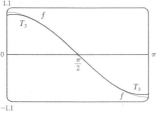

5. $-\left(x - \frac{\pi}{2}\right) + \frac{1}{6}\left(x - \frac{\pi}{2}\right)^3$

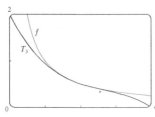

7. $x - 2x^2 + 2x^3$

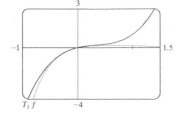

9. $T_5(x) = 1 - 2\left(x - \frac{\pi}{4}\right) + 2\left(x - \frac{\pi}{4}\right)^2 - \frac{8}{3}\left(x - \frac{\pi}{4}\right)^3$
$+ \frac{10}{3}\left(x - \frac{\pi}{4}\right)^4 - \frac{64}{15}\left(x - \frac{\pi}{4}\right)^5$

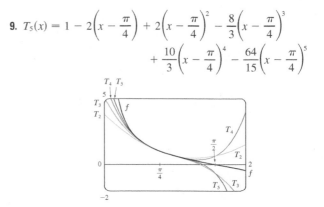

11. (a) $2 + \frac{1}{4}(x - 4) - \frac{1}{64}(x - 4)^2$ (b) 1.5625×10^{-5}
13. (a) $1 + \frac{2}{3}(x - 1) - \frac{1}{9}(x - 1)^2 + \frac{4}{81}(x - 1)^3$ (b) 0.000097
15. (a) $1 + x^2$ (b) 0.00006 **17.** (a) $x^2 - \frac{1}{6}x^4$ (b) 0.042
19. 0.17365 **21.** Four   **23.** $-1.037 < x < 1.037$
25. $-0.86 < x < 0.86$ **27.** 21 m, no
31. (c) They differ by about 8×10^{-9} km.

CHAPTER 8 REVIEW ■ PAGE 629

True-False Quiz

1. False   **3.** True   **5.** False   **7.** False   **9.** False
11. True   **13.** True   **15.** False   **17.** True   **19.** True

Exercises

1. $\frac{1}{2}$ **3.** D   **5.** 0   **7.** e^{12} **9.** C   **11.** C   **13.** D
15. C   **17.** C   **19.** $\frac{1}{11}$ **21.** $\pi/4$ **23.** $\frac{4111}{3330}$
25. 0.9721 **27.** 0.18976224, error $< 6.4 \times 10^{-7}$
31. $4, [-6, 2)$ **33.** $0.5, [2.5, 3.5)$

35. $\frac{1}{2} \sum_{n=0}^{\infty} (-1)^n \left[\frac{1}{(2n)!} \left(x - \frac{\pi}{6}\right)^{2n} + \frac{\sqrt{3}}{(2n + 1)!} \left(x - \frac{\pi}{6}\right)^{2n+1} \right]$

37. $\sum_{n=0}^{\infty} (-1)^n x^{n+2}, R = 1$ **39.** $\ln 4 - \sum_{n=1}^{\infty} \frac{x^n}{n4^n}, R = 4$

41. $\sum_{n=0}^{\infty} (-1)^n \frac{x^{8n+4}}{(2n + 1)!}, R = \infty$

43. $\frac{1}{2} + \sum_{n=1}^{\infty} \frac{1 \cdot 5 \cdot 9 \cdot \cdots \cdot (4n - 3)}{n! 2^{6n+1}} x^n, R = 16$

45. $C + \ln|x| + \sum_{n=1}^{\infty} \frac{x^n}{n \cdot n!}$

47. (a) $1 + \frac{1}{2}(x - 1) - \frac{1}{8}(x - 1)^2 + \frac{1}{16}(x - 1)^3$

(b)   (c) 0.000006

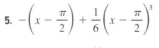

49. $-\frac{1}{6}$

PRINCIPLES OF PROBLEM SOLVING ▪ PAGE 631

1. $15!/5! = 10,897,286,400$

3. (a) $s_n = 3 \cdot 4^n$, $l_n = 1/3^n$, $p_n = 4^n/3^{n-1}$ (c) $\frac{2}{5}\sqrt{3}$

5. $\ln \frac{1}{2}$ **11.** $\dfrac{\pi}{2\sqrt{3}} - 1$

13. $-\left(\dfrac{\pi}{2} - \pi k\right)^2$ where k is a positive integer

CHAPTER 9

EXERCISES 9.1 ▪ PAGE 638

1. $(4, 0, -3)$ **3.** Q; R

5. A vertical plane that intersects the xy-plane in the line $y = 2 - x$, $z = 0$ (see graph at right)

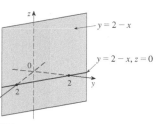

7. (a) $|PQ| = 6$, $|QR| = 2\sqrt{10}$, $|RP| = 6$; isosceles triangle
(b) $|PQ| = 3$, $|QR| = 3\sqrt{5}$, $|RP| = 6$; right triangle
9. (a) No   (b) Yes
11. $(x - 3)^2 + (y - 8)^2 + (z - 1)^2 = 30$
13. $(3, -2, 1)$, 5 **15.** $(2, 0, -6)$, $9/\sqrt{2}$
17. (b) $\frac{5}{2}$, $\frac{1}{2}\sqrt{94}$, $\frac{1}{2}\sqrt{85}$
19. (a) $(x - 2)^2 + (y + 3)^2 + (z - 6)^2 = 36$
(b) $(x - 2)^2 + (y + 3)^2 + (z - 6)^2 = 4$
(c) $(x - 2)^2 + (y + 3)^2 + (z - 6)^2 = 9$
21. A plane parallel to the yz-plane and 5 units in front of it
23. A half-space consisting of all points to the left of the plane $y = 8$
25. All points on or between the horizontal planes $z = 0$ and $z = 6$
27. All points on a circle with radius 2 and center on the z-axis that is contained in the plane $z = -1$
29. All points on or inside a sphere with radius $\sqrt{3}$ and center O
31. All points on or inside a circular cylinder of radius 3 with axis the y-axis
33. $0 < x < 5$ **35.** $r^2 < x^2 + y^2 + z^2 < R^2$
37. (a) $(2, 1, 4)$ (b)

39. $14x - 6y - 10z = 9$, a plane perpendicular to AB
41. $2\sqrt{3} - 3$

EXERCISES 9.2 ▪ PAGE 646

1. (a) Scalar   (b) Vector   (c) Vector   (d) Scalar
3. $\overrightarrow{AB} = \overrightarrow{DC}$, $\overrightarrow{DA} = \overrightarrow{CB}$, $\overrightarrow{DE} = \overrightarrow{EB}$, $\overrightarrow{EA} = \overrightarrow{CE}$

5. (a)   (b)
(c)   (d)

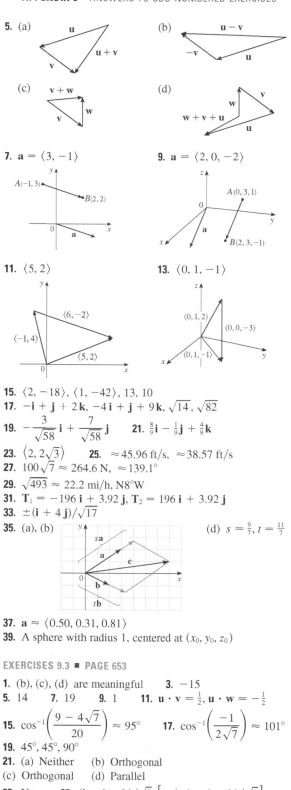

7. $\mathbf{a} = \langle 3, -1 \rangle$ **9.** $\mathbf{a} = \langle 2, 0, -2 \rangle$

11. $\langle 5, 2 \rangle$ **13.** $\langle 0, 1, -1 \rangle$

15. $\langle 2, -18 \rangle$, $\langle 1, -42 \rangle$, 13, 10
17. $-\mathbf{i} + \mathbf{j} + 2\mathbf{k}$, $-4\mathbf{i} + \mathbf{j} + 9\mathbf{k}$, $\sqrt{14}$, $\sqrt{82}$
19. $-\dfrac{3}{\sqrt{58}}\mathbf{i} + \dfrac{7}{\sqrt{58}}\mathbf{j}$ **21.** $\frac{8}{9}\mathbf{i} - \frac{1}{9}\mathbf{j} + \frac{4}{9}\mathbf{k}$
23. $\langle 2, 2\sqrt{3} \rangle$ **25.** ≈ 45.96 ft/s, ≈ 38.57 ft/s
27. $100\sqrt{7} \approx 264.6$ N, $\approx 139.1°$
29. $\sqrt{493} \approx 22.2$ mi/h, N8°W
31. $\mathbf{T_1} = -196\mathbf{i} + 3.92\mathbf{j}$, $\mathbf{T_2} = 196\mathbf{i} + 3.92\mathbf{j}$
33. $\pm(\mathbf{i} + 4\mathbf{j})/\sqrt{17}$
35. (a), (b)   (d) $s = \frac{9}{7}$, $t = \frac{11}{7}$

37. $\mathbf{a} \approx \langle 0.50, 0.31, 0.81 \rangle$
39. A sphere with radius 1, centered at (x_0, y_0, z_0)

EXERCISES 9.3 ▪ PAGE 653

1. (b), (c), (d) are meaningful   **3.** -15
5. 14 **7.** 19 **9.** 1 **11.** $\mathbf{u} \cdot \mathbf{v} = \frac{1}{2}$, $\mathbf{u} \cdot \mathbf{w} = -\frac{1}{2}$
15. $\cos^{-1}\left(\dfrac{9 - 4\sqrt{7}}{20}\right) \approx 95°$ **17.** $\cos^{-1}\left(\dfrac{-1}{2\sqrt{7}}\right) \approx 101°$
19. $45°$, $45°$, $90°$
21. (a) Neither   (b) Orthogonal
(c) Orthogonal   (d) Parallel
23. Yes   **25.** $(\mathbf{i} - \mathbf{j} - \mathbf{k})/\sqrt{3}$ $\left[\text{or } (-\mathbf{i} + \mathbf{j} + \mathbf{k})/\sqrt{3}\right]$
27. $45°$ **29.** 3, $\langle \frac{9}{5}, -\frac{12}{5} \rangle$ **31.** $1/\sqrt{21}$, $\frac{2}{21}\mathbf{i} - \frac{1}{21}\mathbf{j} + \frac{4}{21}\mathbf{k}$

35. $\langle 0, 0, -2\sqrt{10}\rangle$ or any vector of the form
$\langle s, t, 3s - 2\sqrt{10}\rangle$, $s, t \in \mathbb{R}$
37. 144 J   **39.** $2400 \cos(40°) \approx 1839$ ft-lb
41. $\frac{13}{5}$ **43.** $\cos^{-1}(1/\sqrt{3}) \approx 55°$

EXERCISES 9.4 ■ PAGE 661

1. (a) Scalar (b) Meaningless   (c) Vector
(d) Meaningless   (e) Meaningless   (f) Scalar
3. $96\sqrt{3}$; into the page   **5.** $10.8 \sin 80° \approx 10.6$ N·m
7. $16\,\mathbf{i} + 48\,\mathbf{k}$ **9.** $15\,\mathbf{i} - 3\,\mathbf{j} + 3\,\mathbf{k}$ **11.** $\frac{1}{2}\mathbf{i} - \mathbf{j} + \frac{3}{2}\mathbf{k}$
13. $t^4\mathbf{i} - 2t^3\mathbf{j} + t^2\mathbf{k}$ **15.** $\mathbf{0}$ **17.** $\mathbf{i} + \mathbf{j} + \mathbf{k}$
19. $\langle -2/\sqrt{6}, -1/\sqrt{6}, 1/\sqrt{6}\rangle$, $\langle 2/\sqrt{6}, 1/\sqrt{6}, -1/\sqrt{6}\rangle$
21. 16   **23.** (a) $\langle 13, -14, 5\rangle$ (b) $\frac{1}{2}\sqrt{390}$
25. ≈ 417 N   **27.** 82   **29.** 3
33. (b) $\sqrt{97/3}$ **39.** (a) No   (b) No   (c) Yes

EXERCISES 9.5 ■ PAGE 670

1. (a) True   (b) False   (c) True   (d) False   (e) False
(f) True   (g) False   (h) True   (i) True   (j) False
(k) True
3. $\mathbf{r} = (2\,\mathbf{i} + 2.4\,\mathbf{j} + 3.5\,\mathbf{k}) + t(3\,\mathbf{i} + 2\,\mathbf{j} - \mathbf{k})$;
$x = 2 + 3t$, $y = 2.4 + 2t$, $z = 3.5 - t$
5. $\mathbf{r} = (\mathbf{i} + 6\mathbf{k}) + t(\mathbf{i} + 3\mathbf{j} + \mathbf{k})$;
$x = 1 + t$, $y = 3t$, $z = 6 + t$
7. $x = 2 + 2t$, $y = 1 + \frac{1}{2}t$,
$z = -3 - 4t$;
$(x - 2)/2 = 2y - 2 = (z + 3)/(-4)$
9. $x = 1 + t$, $y = -1 + 2t$, $z = 1 + t$;
$x - 1 = (y + 1)/2 = z - 1$
11. Yes
13. (a) $(x - 1)/(-1) = (y + 5)/2 = (z - 6)/(-3)$
(b) $(-1, -1, 0)$, $\left(-\frac{3}{2}, 0, -\frac{3}{2}\right)$, $(0, -3, 3)$
15. $\mathbf{r}(t) = (2\mathbf{i} - \mathbf{j} + 4\mathbf{k}) + t(2\mathbf{i} + 7\mathbf{j} - 3\mathbf{k})$, $0 \le t \le 1$
17. Parallel   **19.** Skew   **21.** $-2x + y + 5z = 1$
23. $3x - 7z = -9$ **25.** $x + y + z = 2$
27. $33x + 10y + 4z = 190$ **29.** $x - 2y + 4z = -1$
31. $3x - 8y - z = -38$

33.   **35.**

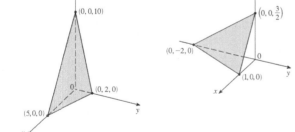

37. $(2, 3, 5)$ **39.** Perpendicular
41. Neither, $\cos^{-1}\left(\frac{1}{3}\right) \approx 70.5°$

43. (a) $x = 1$, $y = -t$, $z = t$ (b) $\cos^{-1}\left(\dfrac{5}{3\sqrt{3}}\right) \approx 15.8°$

45. $x = 1$, $y - 2 = -z$ **47.** $(x/a) + (y/b) + (z/c) = 1$
49. $x = 3t$, $y = 1 - t$, $z = 2 - 2t$
51. P_2 and P_3 are parallel, P_1 and P_4 are identical
53. $\sqrt{61/14}$ **55.** $\frac{18}{7}$ **57.** $5/(2\sqrt{14})$ **61.** $1/\sqrt{6}$

EXERCISES 9.6 ■ PAGE 680

1. (a) 25; a 40-knot wind blowing in the open sea for 15 h will create waves about 25 ft high.
(b) $f(30, t)$ is a function of t giving the wave heights produced by
30-knot winds blowing for t hours.
(c) $f(v, 30)$ is a function of v giving the wave heights produced by
winds of speed v blowing for 30 hours.
3. (a) 1   (b) $\mathbb{R}^2$ (c) $[-1, 1]$
5. $\{(x, y) \mid y \ge x^2, x \ne \pm 1\}$

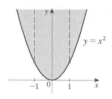

7. $\{(x, y) \mid -1 \le x \le 1, -1 \le y \le 1\}$

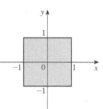

9. $z = 3$, horizontal plane

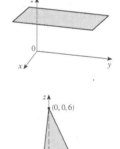

11. $3x + 2y + z = 6$, plane

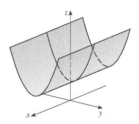

13. $z = y^2 + 1$, parabolic cylinder

15. (a) VI   (b) V   (c) I   (d) IV   (e) II   (f) III

17. $z = \sqrt{4x^2 + y^2}$

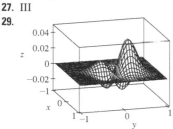

19.

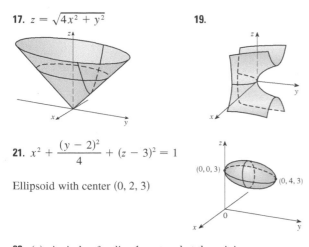

21. $x^2 + \dfrac{(y-2)^2}{4} + (z-3)^2 = 1$

Ellipsoid with center $(0, 2, 3)$

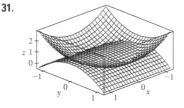

23. (a) A circle of radius 1 centered at the origin
(b) A circular cylinder of radius 1 with axis the z-axis
(c) A circular cylinder of radius 1 with axis the y-axis
25. (a) $x = k$, $y^2 - z^2 = 1 - k^2$, hyperbola $(k \neq \pm1)$;
$y = k$, $x^2 - z^2 = 1 - k^2$, hyperbola $(k \neq \pm1)$;
$z = k$, $x^2 + y^2 = 1 + k^2$, circle
(b) The hyperboloid is rotated so that it has axis the y-axis
(c) The hyperboloid is shifted one unit in the negative y-direction
27. III
29.

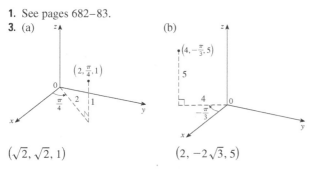

f appears to have a maximum value of about 0.044. There are two local maximum points and two local minimum points.
31.

EXERCISES 9.7 ■ PAGE 686

1. See pages 682–83.
3. (a)

(b)

$(\sqrt{2}, \sqrt{2}, 1)$ $(2, -2\sqrt{3}, 5)$

5. (a) $(\sqrt{2}, 7\pi/4, 4)$ (b) $(2, 4\pi/3, 2)$
7. (a)

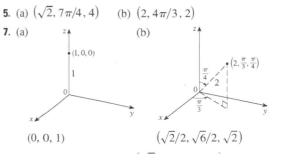

(0, 0, 1) $(\sqrt{2}/2, \sqrt{6}/2, \sqrt{2})$

9. (a) $(4, \pi/3, \pi/6)$ (b) $(\sqrt{2}, 3\pi/2, 3\pi/4)$
11. Vertical half-plane through the z-axis   **13.** Half-cone
15. Circular paraboloid
17. Circular cylinder, radius 1, axis parallel to the z-axis
19. Sphere, radius $\frac{1}{2}$, center $\left(0, \frac{1}{2}, 0\right)$
21. (a) $r = 2\sin\theta$ (b) $\rho\sin\phi = 2\sin\theta$
23. (a) $z = 6 - r(3\cos\theta + 2\sin\theta)$
(b) $\rho(3\sin\phi\cos\theta + 2\sin\phi\sin\theta + \cos\phi) = 6$
25.

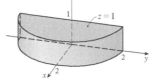

27.   **29.**

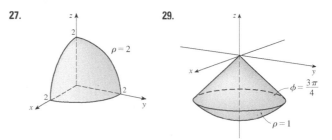

31. Cylindrical coordinates: $6 \le r \le 7$, $0 \le \theta \le 2\pi$, $0 \le z \le 20$
33. $0 \le \phi \le \pi/4$, $0 \le \rho \le \cos\phi$
35.

CHAPTER 9 REVIEW ■ PAGE 688

True-False Quiz

1. True   **3.** True   **5.** True   **7.** True   **9.** True
11. False   **13.** False   **15.** False   **17.** True

Exercises
1. (a) $(x+1)^2 + (y-2)^2 + (z-1)^2 = 69$
(b) $(y-2)^2 + (z-1)^2 = 68$, $x = 0$
(c) Center $(4, -1, -3)$, radius 5

3. $\mathbf{u} \cdot \mathbf{v} = 3\sqrt{2}; |\mathbf{u} \times \mathbf{v}| = 3\sqrt{2}$; out of the page
5. $-2, -4$ **7.** (a) 2 (b) -2 (c) -2 (d) 0
9. $\cos^{-1}(\tfrac{1}{3}) \approx 71°$ **11.** (a) $\langle 4, -3, 4 \rangle$ (b) $\sqrt{41}/2$
13. 166 N, 114 N
15. $x = 4 - 3t, y = -1 + 2t, z = 2 + 3t$
17. $x = -2 + 2t, y = 2 - t, z = 4 + 5t$
19. $-4x + 3y + z = -14$ **21.** $x + y + z = 4$
23. Skew   **25.** (a) $22/\sqrt{26}$ (b) $3/\sqrt{2}$
27. $\{(x, y) \mid x > y^2\}$

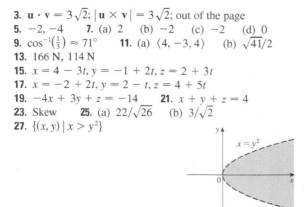

29. 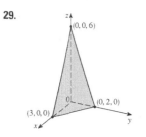   **31.**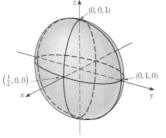

33. Ellipsoid

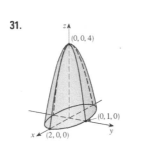

35. Circular cylinder

37. $(\sqrt{3}, 3, 2), (4, \pi/3, \pi/3)$
39. $(2\sqrt{2}, 2\sqrt{2}, 4\sqrt{3}), (4, \pi/4, 4\sqrt{3})$
41. $r^2 + z^2 = 4, \rho = 2$ **43.** $z = 4r^2$

FOCUS ON PROBLEM SOLVING ■ PAGE 691

1. $(\sqrt{3} - \tfrac{3}{2})$ m
3. (a) $(x + 1)/(-2c) = (y - c)/(c^2 - 1) = (z - c)/(c^2 + 1)$
(b) $x^2 + y^2 = t^2 + 1, z = t$ (c) $4\pi/3$
5. 20

CHAPTER 10

EXERCISES 10.1 ■ PAGE 699

1. $(-1, 2]$ **3.** $\langle -1, \pi/2, 0 \rangle$

5.   **7.**

9.   **11.**

13.

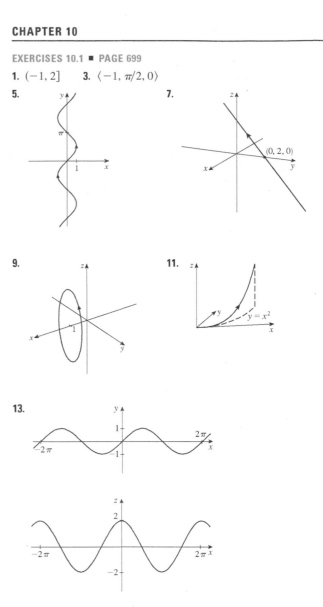
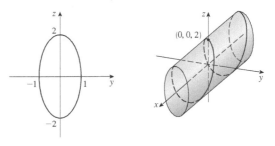

15. $\mathbf{r}(t) = \langle t, 2t, 3t \rangle, 0 \le t \le 1$;
$x = t, y = 2t, z = 3t, 0 \le t \le 1$
17. $\mathbf{r}(t) = \langle 3t + 1, 2t - 1, 5t + 2 \rangle, 0 \le t \le 1$;
$x = 3t + 1, y = 2t - 1, z = 5t + 2, 0 \le t \le 1$
19. II   **21.** V   **23.** IV

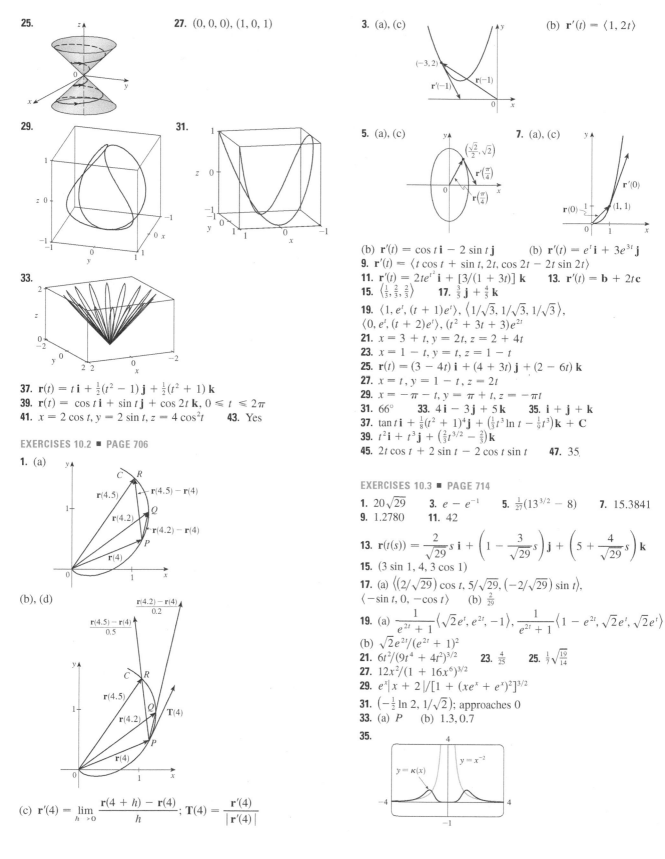

25.

27. $(0, 0, 0), (1, 0, 1)$

29.

31.

33.

37. $\mathbf{r}(t) = t\,\mathbf{i} + \frac{1}{2}(t^2 - 1)\,\mathbf{j} + \frac{1}{2}(t^2 + 1)\,\mathbf{k}$

39. $\mathbf{r}(t) = \cos t\,\mathbf{i} + \sin t\,\mathbf{j} + \cos 2t\,\mathbf{k}, \; 0 \le t \le 2\pi$

41. $x = 2\cos t, \; y = 2\sin t, \; z = 4\cos^2 t$ **43.** Yes

EXERCISES 10.2 ■ PAGE 706

1. (a)

(b), (d)

(c) $\mathbf{r}'(4) = \displaystyle\lim_{h \to 0} \frac{\mathbf{r}(4 + h) - \mathbf{r}(4)}{h}$; $\mathbf{T}(4) = \dfrac{\mathbf{r}'(4)}{|\mathbf{r}'(4)|}$

3. (a), (c)   (b) $\mathbf{r}'(t) = \langle 1, 2t \rangle$

5. (a), (c)   **7.** (a), (c)

(b) $\mathbf{r}'(t) = \cos t\,\mathbf{i} - 2\sin t\,\mathbf{j}$ (b) $\mathbf{r}'(t) = e^t\,\mathbf{i} + 3e^{3t}\,\mathbf{j}$

9. $\mathbf{r}'(t) = \langle t\cos t + \sin t, 2t, \cos 2t - 2t\sin 2t \rangle$

11. $\mathbf{r}'(t) = 2te^{t^2}\,\mathbf{i} + [3/(1 + 3t)]\,\mathbf{k}$ **13.** $\mathbf{r}'(t) = \mathbf{b} + 2t\mathbf{c}$

15. $\langle \frac{1}{3}, \frac{2}{3}, \frac{2}{3} \rangle$ **17.** $\frac{3}{5}\,\mathbf{j} + \frac{4}{5}\,\mathbf{k}$

19. $\langle 1, e^t, (t + 1)e^t \rangle, \; \langle 1/\sqrt{3}, 1/\sqrt{3}, 1/\sqrt{3} \rangle,$

     $\langle 0, e^t, (t + 2)e^t \rangle, \; (t^2 + 3t + 3)e^{2t}$

21. $x = 3 + t, \; y = 2t, \; z = 2 + 4t$

23. $x = 1 - t, \; y = t, \; z = 1 - t$

25. $\mathbf{r}(t) = (3 - 4t)\,\mathbf{i} + (4 + 3t)\,\mathbf{j} + (2 - 6t)\,\mathbf{k}$

27. $x = t, \; y = 1 - t, \; z = 2t$

29. $x = -\pi - t, \; y = \pi + t, \; z = -\pi t$

31. $66°$ **33.** $4\,\mathbf{i} - 3\,\mathbf{j} + 5\,\mathbf{k}$ **35.** $\mathbf{i} + \mathbf{j} + \mathbf{k}$

37. $\tan t\,\mathbf{i} + \frac{1}{8}(t^2 + 1)^4\,\mathbf{j} + \left(\frac{1}{3}t^3 \ln t - \frac{1}{9}t^3\right)\mathbf{k} + \mathbf{C}$

39. $t^2\,\mathbf{i} + t^3\,\mathbf{j} + \left(\frac{2}{3}t^{3/2} - \frac{2}{3}\right)\mathbf{k}$

45. $2t\cos t + 2\sin t - 2\cos t\sin t$ **47.** 35

EXERCISES 10.3 ■ PAGE 714

1. $20\sqrt{29}$ **3.** $e - e^{-1}$ **5.** $\frac{1}{27}(13^{3/2} - 8)$ **7.** 15.3841

9. 1.2780 **11.** 42

13. $\mathbf{r}(t(s)) = \dfrac{2}{\sqrt{29}}s\,\mathbf{i} + \left(1 - \dfrac{3}{\sqrt{29}}s\right)\mathbf{j} + \left(5 + \dfrac{4}{\sqrt{29}}s\right)\mathbf{k}$

15. $(3\sin 1, 4, 3\cos 1)$

17. (a) $\langle (2/\sqrt{29})\cos t, 5/\sqrt{29}, (-2/\sqrt{29})\sin t \rangle,$

     $\langle -\sin t, 0, -\cos t \rangle$ (b) $\frac{2}{29}$

19. (a) $\dfrac{1}{e^{2t} + 1}\langle \sqrt{2}e^t, e^{2t}, -1 \rangle, \; \dfrac{1}{e^{2t} + 1}\langle 1 - e^{2t}, \sqrt{2}e^t, \sqrt{2}e^t \rangle$

(b) $\sqrt{2}e^{2t}/(e^{2t} + 1)^2$

21. $6t^2/(9t^4 + 4t^2)^{3/2}$ **23.** $\frac{4}{25}$ **25.** $\frac{1}{7}\sqrt{\frac{19}{14}}$

27. $12x^2/(1 + 16x^6)^{3/2}$

29. $e^x|x + 2|/[1 + (xe^x + e^x)^2]^{3/2}$

31. $\left(-\frac{1}{2}\ln 2, 1/\sqrt{2}\right)$; approaches 0

33. (a) P (b) $1.3, 0.7$

35.

37. a is $y = f(x)$, b is $y = \kappa(x)$

39. $\kappa(t) = \dfrac{6\sqrt{4\cos^2 t - 12\cos t + 13}}{(17 - 12\cos t)^{3/2}}$

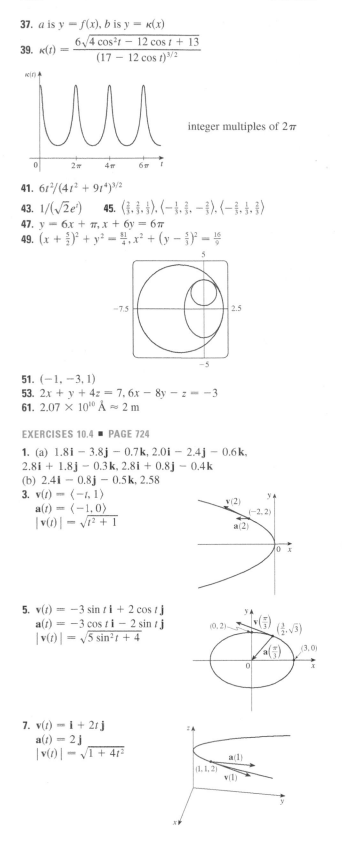

integer multiples of 2π

41. $6t^2/(4t^2 + 9t^4)^{3/2}$

43. $1/(\sqrt{2}\,e^t)$ **45.** $\left\langle \frac{2}{3}, \frac{2}{3}, \frac{1}{3} \right\rangle, \left\langle -\frac{1}{3}, \frac{2}{3}, -\frac{2}{3} \right\rangle, \left\langle -\frac{2}{3}, \frac{1}{3}, \frac{2}{3} \right\rangle$

47. $y = 6x + \pi,\ x + 6y = 6\pi$

49. $\left(x + \frac{5}{2}\right)^2 + y^2 = \frac{81}{4},\ x^2 + \left(y - \frac{5}{3}\right)^2 = \frac{16}{9}$

51. $(-1, -3, 1)$

53. $2x + y + 4z = 7,\ 6x - 8y - z = -3$

61. 2.07×10^{10} Å ≈ 2 m

EXERCISES 10.4 ■ PAGE 724

1. (a) $1.8\mathbf{i} - 3.8\mathbf{j} - 0.7\mathbf{k}, 2.0\mathbf{i} - 2.4\mathbf{j} - 0.6\mathbf{k},$
$2.8\mathbf{i} + 1.8\mathbf{j} - 0.3\mathbf{k}, 2.8\mathbf{i} + 0.8\mathbf{j} - 0.4\mathbf{k}$
(b) $2.4\mathbf{i} - 0.8\mathbf{j} - 0.5\mathbf{k}, 2.58$

3. $\mathbf{v}(t) = \langle -t, 1 \rangle$
$\mathbf{a}(t) = \langle -1, 0 \rangle$
$|\mathbf{v}(t)| = \sqrt{t^2 + 1}$

5. $\mathbf{v}(t) = -3\sin t\,\mathbf{i} + 2\cos t\,\mathbf{j}$
$\mathbf{a}(t) = -3\cos t\,\mathbf{i} - 2\sin t\,\mathbf{j}$
$|\mathbf{v}(t)| = \sqrt{5\sin^2 t + 4}$

7. $\mathbf{v}(t) = \mathbf{i} + 2t\,\mathbf{j}$
$\mathbf{a}(t) = 2\,\mathbf{j}$
$|\mathbf{v}(t)| = \sqrt{1 + 4t^2}$

9. $\sqrt{2}\,\mathbf{i} + e^t\mathbf{j} - e^{-t}\mathbf{k}, e^t\mathbf{j} + e^{-t}\mathbf{k}, e^t + e^{-t}$

11. $e^t[(\cos t - \sin t)\mathbf{i} + (\sin t + \cos t)\mathbf{j} + (t + 1)\mathbf{k}],$
$e^t[-2\sin t\,\mathbf{i} + 2\cos t\,\mathbf{j} + (t + 2)\mathbf{k}], e^t\sqrt{t^2 + 2t + 3}$

13. $\mathbf{v}(t) = t\,\mathbf{i} + 2t\,\mathbf{j} + \mathbf{k}, \mathbf{r}(t) = \left(\frac{1}{2}t^2 + 1\right)\mathbf{i} + t^2\mathbf{j} + t\,\mathbf{k}$

15. (a) $\mathbf{r}(t) = \left(\frac{1}{3}t^3 + t\right)\mathbf{i} + (t - \sin t + 1)\mathbf{j} + \left(\frac{1}{4} - \frac{1}{4}\cos 2t\right)\mathbf{k}$
(b)

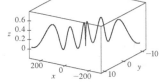

17. $t = 4$

19. $\mathbf{r}(t) = t\,\mathbf{i} - t\,\mathbf{j} + \frac{5}{2}t^2\,\mathbf{k}, |\mathbf{v}(t)| = \sqrt{25t^2 + 2}$

21. (a) ≈ 3535 m   (b) ≈ 1531 m   (c) 200 m/s

23. 30 m/s   **25.** $\approx 10.2°, \approx 79.8°$

27. $13.0° < \theta < 36.0°, 55.4° < \theta < 85.5°$

29. (a) 16 m   (b) $\approx 23.6°$ upstream

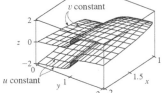

31. The path is contained in a circle that lies in a plane perpendicular to $\mathbf{c}$ with center on a line through the origin in the direction of $\mathbf{c}$.

33. $(18t^3 + 4t)/\sqrt{9t^4 + 4t^2}, 6t^2/\sqrt{9t^4 + 4t^2}$

35. $0, 1$ **37.** 4.5 cm/s^2, 9.0 cm/s^2 **39.** $t = 1$

EXERCISES 10.5 ■ PAGE 731

1. P: no; Q: yes

3. Plane through $(0, 3, 1)$ containing vectors $\langle 1, 0, 4 \rangle, \langle 1, -1, 5 \rangle$

5. Hyperbolic paraboloid

7.

9.

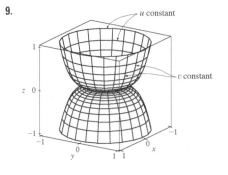

11.

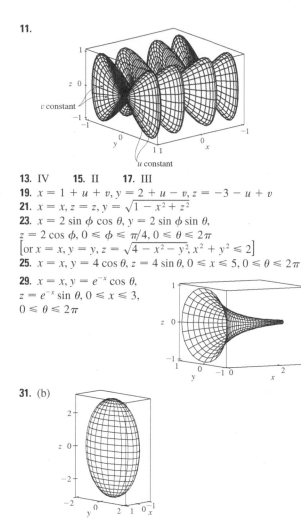

13. IV   **15.** II   **17.** III
19. $x = 1 + u + v, y = 2 + u - v, z = -3 - u + v$
21. $x = x, z = z, y = \sqrt{1 - x^2 + z^2}$
23. $x = 2 \sin \phi \cos \theta, y = 2 \sin \phi \sin \theta,$
$z = 2 \cos \phi, 0 \leq \phi \leq \pi/4, 0 \leq \theta \leq 2\pi$
$\left[\text{or } x = x, y = y, z = \sqrt{4 - x^2 - y^2}, x^2 + y^2 \leq 2 \right]$
25. $x = x, y = 4 \cos \theta, z = 4 \sin \theta, 0 \leq x \leq 5, 0 \leq \theta \leq 2\pi$

29. $x = x, y = e^{-x} \cos \theta,$
$z = e^{-x} \sin \theta, 0 \leq x \leq 3,$
$0 \leq \theta \leq 2\pi$

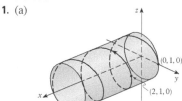

31. (b)

33. (a) Direction reverses   (b) Number of coils doubles

CHAPTER 10 REVIEW ■ PAGE 733

True-False Quiz

1. True   **3.** False   **5.** False   **7.** True   **9.** False
11. True

Exercises

1. (a)

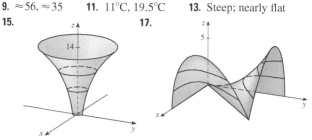

(b) $\mathbf{r}'(t) = \mathbf{i} - \pi \sin \pi t \, \mathbf{j} + \pi \cos \pi t \, \mathbf{k},$
$\mathbf{r}''(t) = -\pi^2 \cos \pi t \, \mathbf{j} - \pi^2 \sin \pi t \, \mathbf{k}$
3. $\mathbf{r}(t) = 4 \cos t \, \mathbf{i} + 4 \sin t \, \mathbf{j} + (5 - 4 \cos t) \mathbf{k}, 0 \leq t \leq 2\pi$
5. $\frac{1}{3} \mathbf{1} - (2/\pi^2) \mathbf{j} + (2/\pi) \mathbf{k}$ **7.** 86.631   **9.** $\pi/2$

11. (a) $\langle t^2, t, 1 \rangle / \sqrt{t^4 + t^2 + 1}$
(b) $\langle 2t, 1 - t^4, -2t^3 - t \rangle / \sqrt{t^8 + 4t^6 + 2t^4 + 5t^2}$
(c) $\sqrt{t^8 + 4t^6 + 2t^4 + 5t^2} / (t^4 + t^2 + 1)^2$
13. $12/17^{3/2}$ **15.** $x - 2y + 2\pi = 0$
17. $\mathbf{v}(t) = (1 + \ln t) \mathbf{i} + \mathbf{j} - e^{-t} \mathbf{k},$
$|\mathbf{v}(t)| = \sqrt{2 + 2 \ln t + (\ln t)^2 + e^{-2t}}, \mathbf{a}(t) = (1/t) \mathbf{i} + e^{-t} \mathbf{k}$
19. (a) About 3.8 ft above the ground, 60.8 ft from the athlete
(b) ≈ 21.4 ft   (c) ≈ 64.2 ft from the athlete
21. $x = 2 \sin \phi \cos \theta, y = 2 \sin \phi \sin \theta, z = 2 \cos \phi,$
$0 \leq \theta \leq 2\pi, \pi/3 \leq \phi \leq 2\pi/3$
23. $\pi |t|$

FOCUS ON PROBLEM SOLVING ■ PAGE 735

1. (a) $\mathbf{v} = \omega R(-\sin \omega t \, \mathbf{i} + \cos \omega t \, \mathbf{j})$ (c) $\mathbf{a} = -\omega^2 \mathbf{r}$
3. (a) $90°, v_0^2/(2g)$
5. (a) ≈ 0.94 ft to the right of the table's edge, ≈ 15 ft/s
(b) $\approx 7.6°$ (c) ≈ 2.13 ft to the right of the table's edge
7. $56°$
9. $\mathbf{r}(u, v) = \mathbf{c} + u\mathbf{a} + v\mathbf{b}$ where $\mathbf{a} = \langle a_1, a_2, a_3 \rangle,$
$\mathbf{b} = \langle b_1, b_2, b_3 \rangle, \mathbf{c} = \langle c_1, c_2, c_3 \rangle$

CHAPTER 11

EXERCISES 11.1 ■ PAGE 745

1. (a) -27; a temperature of $-15°C$ with wind blowing at
40 km/h feels equivalent to about $-27°C$ without wind.
(b) When the temperature is $-20°C$, what wind speed gives a wind
chill of $-30°C$?   20 km/h
(c) With a wind speed of 20 km/h, what temperature gives a wind
chill of $-49°C$? $-35°C$
(d) A function of wind speed that gives wind-chill values when the
temperature is $-5°C$
(e) A function of temperature that gives wind-chill values when
the wind speed is 50 km/h
3. Yes
5. $\{(x, y) \mid \frac{1}{9}x^2 + y^2 < 1\}, (-\infty, \ln 9]$

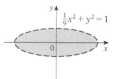

7. (a) 3   (b) $\{(x, y, z) \mid x^2 + y^2 + z^2 < 4, x \geq 0, y \geq 0, z \geq 0\}$,
interior of a sphere of radius 2, center the origin, in the first octant
9. $\approx 56, \approx 35$ **11.** $11°C, 19.5°C$ **13.** Steep; nearly flat
15.   **17.**

19. $(y - 2x)^2 = k$

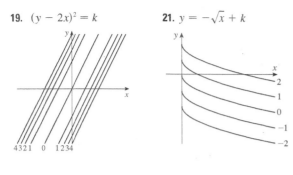

21. $y = -\sqrt{x} + k$

23. $y = ke^{-x}$

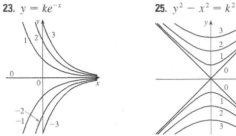

25. $y^2 - x^2 = k^2$

27. $x^2 + 9y^2 = k$

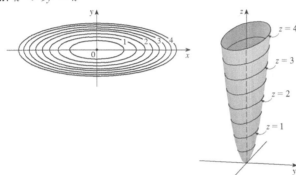

29.

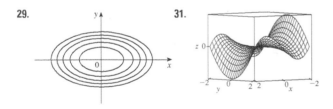

31.

33.

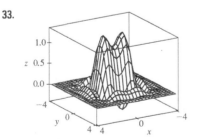

35. (a) C   (b) II   **37.** (a) F   (b) I
39. (a) B   (b) VI   **41.** Family of parallel planes
43. Family of circular cylinders with axis the x-axis ($k > 0$)
45. (a) Shift the graph of f upward 2 units
(b) Stretch the graph of f vertically by a factor of 2
(c) Reflect the graph of f about the xy-plane
(d) Reflect the graph of f about the xy-plane and then shift it
upward 2 units
47. If $c = 0$, the graph is a cylindrical surface. For $c > 0$, the level
curves are ellipses. The graph curves upward as we leave the origin, and the steepness increases as c increases. For $c < 0$, the level
curves are hyperbolas. The graph curves upward in the y-direction
and downward, approaching the xy-plane, in the x-direction giving
a saddle-shaped appearance near $(0, 0, 1)$.
49. (b) $y = 0.75x + 0.01$

EXERCISES 11.2 ■ PAGE 755

1. Nothing; if f is continuous, $f(3, 1) = 6$ **3.** $-\frac{5}{2}$
5. 1   **7.** Does not exist   **9.** Does not exist   **11.** 0
13. Does not exist   **15.** 2   **17.** 1   **19.** Does not exist
21. The graph shows that the function approaches different numbers along different lines.
23. $h(x, y) = (2x + 3y - 6)^2 + \sqrt{2x + 3y - 6}$;
$\{(x, y) \mid 2x + 3y \geqslant 6\}$
25. Along the line $y = x$ **27.** $\{(x, y) \mid y \geqslant 0\}$
29. $\{(x, y) \mid x^2 + y^2 > 4\}$ **31.** $\{(x, y, z) \mid y \geqslant 0, y \neq \sqrt{x^2 + z^2}\}$
33. $\{(x, y) \mid (x, y) \neq (0, 0)\}$ **35.** 0
37. 0
39.

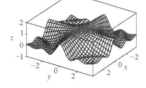

f is continuous on $\mathbb{R}^2$

EXERCISES 11.3 ■ PAGE 766

1. (a) The rate of change of temperature as longitude varies, with
latitude and time fixed; the rate of change as only latitude varies;
the rate of change as only time varies.
(b) Positive, negative, positive
3. (a) $f_T(-15, 30) \approx 1.3$; for a temperature of $-15°C$ and wind
speed of 30 km/h, the wind-chill index rises by $1.3°C$ for each
degree the temperature increases. $f_v(-15, 30) \approx -0.15$; for a
temperature of $-15°C$ and wind speed of 30 km/h, the wind-chill
index decreases by $0.15°C$ for each km/h the wind speed
increases.
(b) Positive, negative   (c) 0
5. (a) Positive   (b) Negative
7. (a) Positive   (b) Negative
9. $c = f, b = f_x, a = f_y$

11. $f_x(1, 2) = -8 =$ slope of C_1, $f_y(1, 2) = -4 =$ slope of C_2

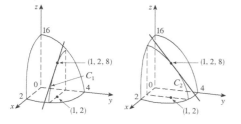

13. $f_x = 2x + 2xy$, $f_y = 2y + x^2$

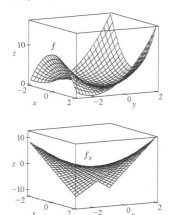

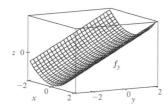

15. $f_x(x, y) = -3y$, $f_y(x, y) = 5y^4 - 3x$
17. $f_x(x, t) = -\pi e^{-t} \sin \pi x$, $f_t(x, t) = -e^{-t} \cos \pi x$
19. $\partial z / \partial x = 20(2x + 3y)^9$, $\partial z / \partial y = 30(2x + 3y)^9$
21. $f_x(x, y) = 2y/(x + y)^2$, $f_y(x, y) = -2x/(x + y)^2$
23. $\partial w / \partial \alpha = \cos \alpha \cos \beta$, $\partial w / \partial \beta = -\sin \alpha \sin \beta$
25. $f_r(r, s) = \dfrac{2r^2}{r^2 + s^2} + \ln(r^2 + s^2)$, $f_s(r, s) = \dfrac{2rs}{r^2 + s^2}$
27. $\partial u / \partial t = e^{w/t}(1 - w/t)$, $\partial u / \partial w = e^{w/t}$
29. $f_x = z - 10xy^3z^4$, $f_y = -15x^2y^2z^4$, $f_z = x - 20x^2y^3z^3$
31. $\partial w / \partial x = 1/(x + 2y + 3z)$, $\partial w / \partial y = 2/(x + 2y + 3z)$, $\partial w / \partial z = 3/(x + 2y + 3z)$
33. $\partial u / \partial x = y \sin^{-1}(yz)$, $\partial u / \partial y = x \sin^{-1}(yz) + xyz/\sqrt{1 - y^2z^2}$, $\partial u / \partial z = xy^2/\sqrt{1 - y^2z^2}$
35. $f_x = yz^2 \tan(yt)$, $f_y = xyz^2t \sec^2(yt) + xz^2 \tan(yt)$, $f_z = 2xyz \tan(yt)$, $f_t = xy^2z^2 \sec^2(yt)$
37. $\partial u / \partial x_i = x_i/\sqrt{x_1^2 + x_2^2 + \cdots + x_n^2}$
39. $\frac{1}{5}$ **41.** $\frac{1}{4}$
43. $f_x(x, y) = y^2 - 3x^2y$, $f_y(x, y) = 2xy - x^3$

45. $\dfrac{\partial z}{\partial x} = \dfrac{3yz - 2x}{2z - 3xy}$, $\dfrac{\partial z}{\partial y} = \dfrac{3xz - 2y}{2z - 3xy}$
47. $\dfrac{\partial z}{\partial x} = \dfrac{1 + y^2z^2}{1 + y + y^2z^2}$, $\dfrac{\partial z}{\partial y} = \dfrac{-z}{1 + y + y^2z^2}$
49. (a) $f'(x), g'(y)$ (b) $f'(x + y), f'(x + y)$
51. $f_{xx} = 6xy^5 + 24x^2y$, $f_{xy} = 15x^2y^4 + 8x^3 = f_{yx}$, $f_{yy} = 20x^3y^3$
53. $w_{uu} = v^2/(u^2 + v^2)^{3/2}$, $w_{uv} = -uv/(u^2 + v^2)^{3/2} = w_{vu}$, $w_{vv} = u^2/(u^2 + v^2)^{3/2}$
55. $z_{xx} = -2x/(1 + x^2)^2$, $z_{xy} = 0 = z_{yx}$, $z_{yy} = -2y/(1 + y^2)^2$
59. $12xy, 72xy$
61. $24 \sin(4x + 3y + 2z)$, $12 \sin(4x + 3y + 2z)$
63. $\theta e^{r\theta}(2 \sin \theta + \theta \cos \theta + r\theta \sin \theta)$ **65.** $6yz^2$
67. $\approx 12.2, \approx 16.8, \approx 23.25$ **79.** R^2/R_1^2
85. No   **87.** $x = 1 + t, y = 2, z = 2 - 2t$ **89.** -2
91. (a)

(b) $f_x(x, y) = \dfrac{x^4y + 4x^2y^3 - y^5}{(x^2 + y^2)^2}$, $f_y(x, y) = \dfrac{x^5 - 4x^3y^2 - xy^4}{(x^2 + y^2)^2}$
(c) $0, 0$ (e) No, since f_{xy} and f_{yx} are not continuous.

EXERCISES 11.4 ■ PAGE 778

1. $z = -7x - 6y + 5$ **3.** $x + y - 2z = 0$ **5.** $z = y$
7.   **9.**

11. $2x + \frac{1}{4}y - 1$ **13.** $\frac{1}{9}x - \frac{2}{9}y + \frac{2}{3}$ **17.** 6.3
19. $\frac{3}{7}x + \frac{2}{7}y + \frac{6}{7}z; 6.9914$ **21.** $4T + H - 329; 129°F$
23. $dz = 3x^2 \ln(y^2) \, dx + (2x^3/y) \, dy$
25. $dm = 5p^4q^3 \, dp + 3p^5q^2 \, dq$
27. $dR = \beta^2 \cos \gamma \, d\alpha + 2\alpha\beta \cos \gamma \, d\beta - \alpha\beta^2 \sin \gamma \, d\gamma$
29. $\Delta z = 0.9225, dz = 0.9$ **31.** 5.4 cm^2 **33.** 16 cm^3
35. 2.3% **37.** $\frac{1}{17} \approx 0.059 \, \Omega$ **39.** $3x - y + 3z = 3$
41. $-x + 2z = 1$ **43.** $x - y + z = 2$
45. $\varepsilon_1 = \Delta x, \varepsilon_2 = \Delta y$

EXERCISES 11.5 ■ PAGE 786

1. $(2x + y) \cos t + (2y + x)e^t$
3. $[(x/t) - y \sin t]/\sqrt{1 + x^2 + y^2}$
5. $e^{y/z}[2t - (x/z) - (2xy/z^2)]$
7. $\partial z / \partial s = 2xy^3 \cos t + 3x^2y^2 \sin t$, $\partial z / \partial t = -2sxy^3 \sin t + 3sx^2y^2 \cos t$
9. $\partial z / \partial s = t^2 \cos \theta \cos \phi - 2st \sin \theta \sin \phi$, $\partial z / \partial t = 2st \cos \theta \cos \phi - s^2 \sin \theta \sin \phi$

11. $\dfrac{\partial z}{\partial s} = e^r\left(t\cos\theta - \dfrac{s}{\sqrt{s^2 + t^2}}\sin\theta\right),$

$\dfrac{\partial z}{\partial t} = e^r\left(s\cos\theta - \dfrac{t}{\sqrt{s^2 + t^2}}\sin\theta\right)$

13. 62   **15.** 7, 2

17. $\dfrac{\partial u}{\partial r} = \dfrac{\partial u}{\partial x}\dfrac{\partial x}{\partial r} + \dfrac{\partial u}{\partial y}\dfrac{\partial y}{\partial r},\ \dfrac{\partial u}{\partial s} = \dfrac{\partial u}{\partial x}\dfrac{\partial x}{\partial s} + \dfrac{\partial u}{\partial y}\dfrac{\partial y}{\partial s},$

$\dfrac{\partial u}{\partial t} = \dfrac{\partial u}{\partial x}\dfrac{\partial x}{\partial t} + \dfrac{\partial u}{\partial y}\dfrac{\partial y}{\partial t}$

19. $\dfrac{\partial w}{\partial x} = \dfrac{\partial w}{\partial r}\dfrac{\partial r}{\partial x} + \dfrac{\partial w}{\partial s}\dfrac{\partial s}{\partial x} + \dfrac{\partial w}{\partial t}\dfrac{\partial t}{\partial x},$

$\dfrac{\partial w}{\partial y} = \dfrac{\partial w}{\partial r}\dfrac{\partial r}{\partial y} + \dfrac{\partial w}{\partial s}\dfrac{\partial s}{\partial y} + \dfrac{\partial w}{\partial t}\dfrac{\partial t}{\partial y}$

21. 85, 178, 54   **23.** $\frac{9}{7}, \frac{9}{7}$ **25.** 36, 24, 30

27. $\dfrac{\sin(x - y) + e^y}{\sin(x - y) - xe^y}$ **29.** $\dfrac{3yz - 2x}{2z - 3xy}, \dfrac{3xz - 2y}{2z - 3xy}$

31. $\dfrac{1 + y^2z^2}{1 + y + y^2z^2}, -\dfrac{z}{1 + y + y^2z^2}$

33. 2°C/s   **35.** ≈ -0.33 m/s per minute

37. (a) 6 m³/s   (b) 10 m²/s   (c) 0 m/s

39. ≈ -0.27 L/s   **41.** $-1/(12\sqrt{3})$ rad/s

43. (a) $\partial z/\partial r = (\partial z/\partial x)\cos\theta + (\partial z/\partial y)\sin\theta,$

$\partial z/\partial\theta = -(\partial z/\partial x)r\sin\theta + (\partial z/\partial y)r\cos\theta$

49. $4rs\,\partial^2z/\partial x^2 + (4r^2 + 4s^2)\partial^2z/\partial x\,\partial y + 4rs\,\partial^2z/\partial y^2 + 2\,\partial z/\partial y$

EXERCISES 11.6 ■ PAGE 799

1. ≈ -0.08 mb/km   **3.** ≈ 0.778 **5.** $2 + \sqrt{3}/2$

7. (a) $\nabla f(x, y) = \langle 2\cos(2x + 3y), 3\cos(2x + 3y)\rangle$

(b) $\langle 2, 3\rangle$ (c) $\sqrt{3} - \frac{3}{2}$

9. (a) $\langle e^{2yz}, 2xze^{2yz}, 2xye^{2yz}\rangle$ (b) $\langle 1, 12, 0\rangle$ (c) $-\frac{22}{3}$

11. 23/10   **13.** $-8/\sqrt{10}$ **15.** $4/\sqrt{30}$ **17.** $9/(2\sqrt{5})$

19. 2/5   **21.** 1, $\langle 0, 1\rangle$ **23.** 1, $\langle 3, 6, -2\rangle$

25. (b) $\langle -12, 92\rangle$

27. All points on the line $y = x + 1$

29. (a) $-40/(3\sqrt{3})$

31. (a) $32/\sqrt{3}$ (b) $\langle 38, 6, 12\rangle$ (c) $2\sqrt{406}$

33. $\frac{327}{13}$ **37.** $\frac{774}{25}$

39. (a) $x + y + z = 11$ (b) $x - 3 = y - 3 = z - 5$

41. (a) $4x - 5y - z = 4$ (b) $\dfrac{x - 2}{4} = \dfrac{y - 1}{-5} = \dfrac{z + 1}{-1}$

43. (a) $x + y - z = 1$ (b) $x - 1 = y = -z$

45.

47. $\langle 2, 3\rangle$, $2x + 3y = 12$

51. No   **57.** $x = -1 - 10t, y = 1 - 16t, z = 2 - 12t$

61. If $\mathbf{u} = \langle a, b\rangle$ and $\mathbf{v} = \langle c, d\rangle$, then $af_x + bf_y$ and $cf_x + df_y$ are known, so we solve linear equations for f_x and f_y.

EXERCISES 11.7 ■ PAGE 809

1. (a) f has a local minimum at $(1, 1)$.

(b) f has a saddle point at $(1, 1)$.

3. Local minimum at $(1, 1)$, saddle point at $(0, 0)$

5. Minimum $f\left(\frac{1}{3}, -\frac{2}{3}\right) = -\frac{1}{3}$

7. Minima $f(1, 1) = 0, f(-1, -1) = 0$, saddle point at $(0, 0)$

9. Minimum $f(2, 1) = -8$, saddle point at $(0, 0)$

11. None   **13.** Minimum $f(0, 0) = 0$, saddle points at $(\pm 1, 0)$

15. Minima $f(0, 1) = f(\pi, -1) = f(2\pi, 1) = -1$, saddle points at $(\pi/2, 0), (3\pi/2, 0)$

19. Minima $f(1, \pm 1) = 3, f(-1, \pm 1) = 3$

21. Maximum $f(\pi/3, \pi/3) = 3\sqrt{3}/2$, minimum $f(5\pi/3, 5\pi/3) = -3\sqrt{3}/2$, saddle point at (π, π)

23. Minima $f(-1.714, 0) \approx -9.200, f(1.402, 0) \approx 0.242$, saddle point $(0.312, 0)$, lowest point $(-1.714, 0, -9.200)$

25. Maxima $f(-1.267, 0) \approx 1.310, f(1.629, \pm 1.063) \approx 8.105$, saddle points $(-0.259, 0), (1.526, 0)$, highest points $(1.629, \pm 1.063, 8.105)$

27. Maximum $f(2, 0) = 9$, minimum $f(0, 3) = -14$

29. Maximum $f(\pm 1, 1) = 7$, minimum $f(0, 0) = 4$

31. Maximum $f(1, 0) = 2$, minimum $f(-1, 0) = -2$

33.

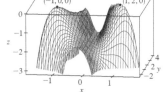

35. $\sqrt{3}$ **37.** $(2, 1, \sqrt{5}), (2, 1, -\sqrt{5})$ **39.** $\frac{100}{3}, \frac{100}{3}, \frac{100}{3}$

41. $8r^3/(3\sqrt{3})$ **43.** $\frac{4}{3}$ **45.** Cube, edge length $c/12$

47. Square base of side 40 cm, height 20 cm   **49.** $L^3/(3\sqrt{3})$

EXERCISES 11.8 ■ PAGE 818

1. $\approx 59, 30$

3. No maximum, minimum $f(1, 1) = f(-1, -1) = 2$

5. Maximum $f(\pm 2, 1) = 4$, minimum $f(\pm 2, -1) = -4$

7. Maximum $f(1, 3, 5) = 70$, minimum $f(-1, -3, -5) = -70$

9. Maximum $2/\sqrt{3}$, minimum $-2/\sqrt{3}$

11. Maximum $\sqrt{3}$, minimum 1

13. Maximum $f\left(\frac{1}{2}, \frac{1}{2}, \frac{1}{2}, \frac{1}{2}\right) = 2$, minimum $f\left(-\frac{1}{2}, -\frac{1}{2}, -\frac{1}{2}, -\frac{1}{2}\right) = -2$

15. Maximum $f(1, \sqrt{2}, -\sqrt{2}) = 1 + 2\sqrt{2}$, minimum $f(1, -\sqrt{2}, \sqrt{2}) = 1 - 2\sqrt{2}$

17. Maximum $\frac{3}{2}$, minimum $\frac{1}{2}$

19. Maximum $f\left(\pm 1/\sqrt{2}, \mp 1/(2\sqrt{2})\right) = e^{1/4}$, minimum $f\left(\pm 1/\sqrt{2}, \pm 1/(2\sqrt{2})\right) = e^{-1/4}$

27–37. See Exercises 35–45 in Section 11.7.

39. $L^3/(3\sqrt{3})$

41. Nearest $\left(\frac{1}{2}, \frac{1}{2}, \frac{1}{2}\right)$, farthest $(-1, -1, 2)$
43. Maximum ≈ 9.7938, minimum ≈ -5.3506
45. (a) c/n (b) When $x_1 = x_2 = \cdots = x_n$

CHAPTER 11 REVIEW ■ PAGE 823

True-False Quiz

1. True   **3.** False   **5.** False   **7.** True   **9.** False
11. True

Exercises

1. $\{(x, y) \mid y > -x - 1\}$ **3.**

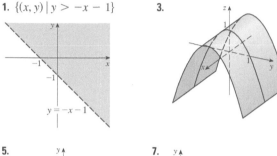

5.

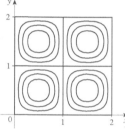

7.

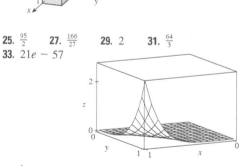

9. $\frac{2}{3}$
11. (a) $\approx 3.5°C/m$, $-3.0°C/m$ (b) $\approx 0.35°C/m$ by
Equation 11.6.9 (Definition 11.6.2 gives $\approx 1.1°C/m$.)
(c) -0.25
13. $f_x = 1/\sqrt{2x + y^2}$, $f_y = y/\sqrt{2x + y^2}$
15. $g_u = \tan^{-1}v$, $g_v = u/(1 + v^2)$
17. $T_p = \ln(q + e^r)$, $T_q = p/(q + e^r)$, $T_r = pe^r/(q + e^r)$
19. $f_{xx} = 24x$, $f_{xy} = -2y = f_{yx}$, $f_{yy} = -2x$
21. $f_{xx} = k(k - 1)x^{k-2}y^l z^m$, $f_{xy} = klx^{k-1}y^{l-1}z^m = f_{yx}$,
$f_{xz} = kmx^{k-1}y^l z^{m-1} = f_{zx}$, $f_{yy} = l(l - 1)x^k y^{l-2}z^m$,
$f_{yz} = lmx^k y^{l-1}z^{m-1} = f_{zy}$, $f_{zz} = m(m - 1)x^k y^l z^{m-2}$
25. (a) $z = 8x + 4y + 1$ (b) $\dfrac{x - 1}{8} = \dfrac{y + 2}{4} = \dfrac{z - 1}{-1}$
27. (a) $2x - 2y - 3z = 3$ (b) $\dfrac{x - 2}{4} = \dfrac{y + 1}{-4} = \dfrac{z - 1}{-6}$
29. (a) $4x - y - 2z = 6$
(b) $x = 3 + 8t, y = 4 - 2t, z = 1 - 4t$
31. $\left(2, \frac{1}{2}, -1\right), \left(-2, -\frac{1}{2}, 1\right)$
33. $60x + \frac{24}{5}y + \frac{32}{5}z - 120$; 38.656
35. $2xy^3(1 + 6p) + 3x^2 y^2(pe^p + e^p) + 4z^3(p \cos p + \sin p)$
37. $-47, 108$
43. $\langle 2xe^{yz^2}, x^2 z^2 e^{yz^2}, 2x^2 yze^{yz^2} \rangle$ **45.** $-\frac{4}{5}$
47. $\sqrt{145}/2, \left\langle 4, \frac{9}{2} \right\rangle$ **49.** $\approx \frac{5}{8}$ knot/mi

51. Minimum $f(-4, 1) = -11$
53. Maximum $f(1, 1) = 1$; saddle points $(0, 0), (0, 3), (3, 0)$
55. Maximum $f(1, 2) = 4$, minimum $f(2, 4) = -64$
57. Maximum $f(-1, 0) = 2$, minima $f(1, \pm 1) = -3$,
saddle points $(-1, \pm 1), (1, 0)$
59. Maximum $f\left(\pm\sqrt{2/3}, 1/\sqrt{3}\right) = 2/\left(3\sqrt{3}\right)$,
minimum $f\left(\pm\sqrt{2/3}, -1/\sqrt{3}\right) = -2/\left(3\sqrt{3}\right)$
61. Maximum 1, minimum -1
63. $\left(\pm 3^{-1/4}, 3^{-1/4}\sqrt{2}, \pm 3^{1/4}\right), \left(\pm 3^{-1/4}, -3^{-1/4}\sqrt{2}, \pm 3^{1/4}\right)$
65. $P\left(2 - \sqrt{3}\right), P\left(3 - \sqrt{3}\right)/6, P\left(2\sqrt{3} - 3\right)/3$

FOCUS ON PROBLEM SOLVING ■ PAGE 827

1. $L^2 W^2, \frac{1}{4}L^2 W^2$ **3.** (a) $x = w/3$, base $= w/3$ (b) Yes
9. $\sqrt{3/2}, 3/\sqrt{2}$

CHAPTER 12

EXERCISES 12.1 ■ PAGE 837

1. (a) 288   (b) 144   **3.** (a) $\pi^2/2 \approx 4.935$ (b) 0
5. (a) 4   (b) -8 **7.** $U < V < L$
9. (a) ≈ 248 (b) ≈ 15.5 **11.** 60   **13.** 3
15. 1.141606, 1.143191, 1.143535, 1.143617, 1.143637, 1.143642

EXERCISES 12.2 ■ PAGE 843

1. $500y^3, 3x^2$ **3.** 10   **5.** 2   **7.** $261,632/45$ **9.** $\frac{21}{2}\ln 2$
11. 0   **13.** π **15.** $\frac{21}{2}$ **17.** $9 \ln 2$
19. $\frac{1}{2}\left(\sqrt{3} - 1\right) - \frac{1}{12}\pi$ **21.** $\frac{1}{2}(e^2 - 3)$
23.

25. $\frac{95}{2}$ **27.** $\frac{166}{27}$ **29.** 2   **31.** $\frac{64}{3}$
33. $21e - 57$

35. $\frac{5}{6}$ **37.** 0
39. Fubini's Theorem does not apply. The integrand has an infinite
discontinuity at the origin.

EXERCISES 12.3 ■ PAGE 850

1. 32   **3.** $\frac{3}{10}$ **5.** $e - 1$ **7.** $\frac{4}{3}$ **9.** π

11. (a) 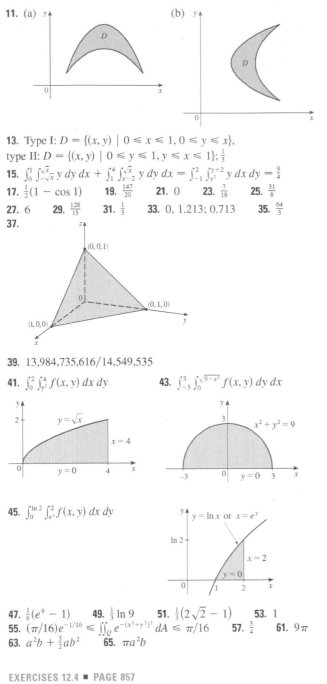 (b)

13. Type I: $D = \{(x, y) \mid 0 \le x \le 1, 0 \le y \le x\}$,
type II: $D = \{(x, y) \mid 0 \le y \le 1, y \le x \le 1\}$; $\frac{1}{3}$

15. $\int_0^1 \int_{-\sqrt{x}}^{\sqrt{x}} y \, dy \, dx + \int_1^4 \int_{x-2}^{\sqrt{x}} y \, dy \, dx = \int_{-1}^2 \int_{y^2}^{y+2} y \, dx \, dy = \frac{9}{4}$

17. $\frac{1}{2}(1 - \cos 1)$ **19.** $\frac{147}{20}$ **21.** 0 **23.** $\frac{7}{18}$ **25.** $\frac{31}{8}$

27. 6 **29.** $\frac{128}{15}$ **31.** $\frac{1}{3}$ **33.** 0, 1.213; 0.713 **35.** $\frac{64}{3}$

37.

39. 13,984,735,616/14,549,535

41. $\int_0^2 \int_{y^2}^4 f(x, y) \, dx \, dy$ **43.** $\int_{-3}^3 \int_0^{\sqrt{9-x^2}} f(x, y) \, dy \, dx$

45. $\int_0^{\ln 2} \int_{e^y}^2 f(x, y) \, dx \, dy$

47. $\frac{1}{6}(e^9 - 1)$ **49.** $\frac{1}{3} \ln 9$ **51.** $\frac{1}{3}(2\sqrt{2} - 1)$ **53.** 1
55. $(\pi/16)e^{-1/16} \le \iint_Q e^{-(x^2+y^2)^2} dA \le \pi/16$ **57.** $\frac{3}{4}$ **61.** 9π
63. $a^2 b + \frac{3}{2} ab^2$ **65.** $\pi a^2 b$

EXERCISES 12.4 ■ PAGE 857

1. $\int_0^{3\pi/2} \int_0^4 f(r \cos\theta, r \sin\theta) r \, dr \, d\theta$ **3.** $\int_{-1}^1 \int_0^{(x+1)/2} f(x, y) \, dy \, dx$

5. 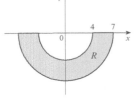 $33\pi/2$

7. 0 **9.** $\frac{1}{2}\pi \sin 9$ **11.** $(\pi/2)(1 - e^{-4})$ **13.** $\frac{3}{64}\pi^2$

15. $\frac{16}{3}\pi$ **17.** $\frac{4}{3}\pi$ **19.** $\frac{4}{3}\pi a^3$ **21.** $(2\pi/3)\left[1 - (1/\sqrt{2})\right]$

23. $(8\pi/3)(64 - 24\sqrt{3})$ **25.** $\pi/12$ **27.** $\frac{1}{2}\pi(1 - \cos 9)$

29. $2\sqrt{2}/3$ **31.** 1800π ft^3 **33.** $2/(a + b)$

35. $\frac{15}{16}$ **37.** (a) $\sqrt{\pi}/4$ (b) $\sqrt{\pi}/2$

EXERCISES 12.5 ■ PAGE 866

1. $\frac{64}{3}$ C **3.** $\frac{4}{3}$, $\left(\frac{4}{3}, 0\right)$ **5.** 6, $\left(\frac{3}{4}, \frac{3}{2}\right)$

7. $\frac{1}{4}(e^2 - 1)$, $\left(\dfrac{e^2 + 1}{2(e^2 - 1)}, \dfrac{4(e^3 - 1)}{9(e^2 - 1)}\right)$

9. $L/4$, $(L/2, 16/(9\pi))$ **11.** $\left(\frac{3}{8}, 3\pi/16\right)$ **13.** $(0, 45/(14\pi))$

15. $(2a/5, 2a/5)$ if vertex is $(0, 0)$ and sides are along positive axes

17. $\frac{1}{16}(e^4 - 1)$, $\frac{1}{8}(e^2 - 1)$, $\frac{1}{16}(e^4 + 2e^2 - 3)$

19. $7ka^6/180$, $7ka^6/180$, $7ka^6/90$ if vertex is $(0, 0)$ and sides are along positive axes

21. $m = \pi^2/8$, $(\bar{x}, \bar{y}) = \left(\dfrac{2\pi}{3} - \dfrac{1}{\pi}, \dfrac{16}{9\pi}\right)$, $I_x = 3\pi^2/64$,
$I_y = \frac{1}{16}(\pi^4 - 3\pi^2)$, $I_0 = \pi^4/16 - 9\pi^2/64$

23. (a) $\frac{1}{2}$ (b) 0.375 (c) $\frac{5}{48} \approx 0.1042$

25. (b) (i) $e^{-0.2} \approx 0.8187$
(ii) $1 + e^{-1.8} - e^{-0.8} - e^{-1} \approx 0.3481$ (c) 2, 5

27. (a) ≈ 0.500 (b) ≈ 0.632

29. (a) $\iint_D k\left[1 - \frac{1}{20}\sqrt{(x - x_0)^2 + (y - y_0)^2}\right] dA$, where D is the disk with radius 10 mi centered at the center of the city
(b) $200\pi k/3 \approx 209k$, $200\left(\pi/2 - \frac{8}{9}\right)k \approx 136k$, on the edge

EXERCISES 12.6 ■ PAGE 871

1. $\sqrt{14}\,\pi$ **3.** $3\sqrt{14}$ **5.** $\sqrt{2}/6$ **7.** 4

9. $(2\pi/3)(2\sqrt{2} - 1)$ **11.** $4\pi b\left(b - \sqrt{b^2 - a^2}\right)$ **13.** 13.9783

15. (a) 24.2055 (b) 24.2476 **17.** 4.4506

19. $\frac{45}{8}\sqrt{14} + \frac{15}{16}\ln\left[(11\sqrt{5} + 3\sqrt{70})/(3\sqrt{5} + \sqrt{70})\right]$

21. (b)

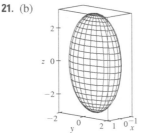

(c) $\int_0^{2\pi} \int_0^\pi \sqrt{36 \sin^4 u \cos^2 v + 9 \sin^4 u \sin^2 v + 4 \cos^2 u \sin^2 u} \, du \, dv$

25. $\frac{98}{3}\pi$ **27.** 4π.

EXERCISES 12.7 ■ PAGE 880

1. $\frac{27}{4}$ **3.** 1 **5.** $\frac{1}{3}(e^3 - 1)$ **7.** $-\frac{1}{3}$ **9.** 4 **11.** $\frac{65}{28}$

13. $8/(3e)$ **15.** $\frac{1}{60}$ **17.** $16\pi/3$ **19.** $\frac{16}{3}$ **21.** 36π

23. (a) $\int_0^1 \int_0^x \int_0^{\sqrt{1-y^2}} dz \, dy \, dx$ (b) $\frac{1}{4}\pi - \frac{1}{3}$ **25.** 60.533

27.

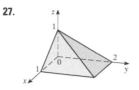

29. $\int_{-2}^{2}\int_{0}^{4-x^2}\int_{-\sqrt{4-x^2-y}/2}^{\sqrt{4-x^2-y}/2} f(x, y, z)\, dz\, dy\, dx$

$= \int_{0}^{4}\int_{-\sqrt{4-y}}^{\sqrt{4-y}}\int_{-\sqrt{4-x^2-y}/2}^{\sqrt{4-x^2-y}/2} f(x, y, z)\, dz\, dx\, dy$

$= \int_{-1}^{1}\int_{0}^{4-4z^2}\int_{-\sqrt{4-y-4z^2}}^{\sqrt{4-y-4z^2}} f(x, y, z)\, dx\, dy\, dz$

$= \int_{0}^{4}\int_{-\sqrt{4-y}/2}^{\sqrt{4-y}/2}\int_{-\sqrt{4-y-4z^2}}^{\sqrt{4-y-4z^2}} f(x, y, z)\, dx\, dz\, dy$

$= \int_{-2}^{2}\int_{-\sqrt{4-x^2}/2}^{\sqrt{4-x^2}/2}\int_{0}^{4-x^2-4z^2} f(x, y, z)\, dy\, dz\, dx$

$= \int_{-1}^{1}\int_{-\sqrt{4-4z^2}}^{\sqrt{4-4z^2}}\int_{0}^{4-x^2-4z^2} f(x, y, z)\, dy\, dx\, dz$

31. $\int_{-2}^{2}\int_{x^2}^{4}\int_{0}^{2-y/2} f(x, y, z)\, dz\, dy\, dx$

$= \int_{0}^{4}\int_{-\sqrt{y}}^{\sqrt{y}}\int_{0}^{2-y/2} f(x, y, z)\, dz\, dx\, dy$

$= \int_{0}^{2}\int_{0}^{4-2z}\int_{-\sqrt{y}}^{\sqrt{y}} f(x, y, z)\, dx\, dy\, dz$

$= \int_{0}^{4}\int_{0}^{2-y/2}\int_{-\sqrt{y}}^{\sqrt{y}} f(x, y, z)\, dx\, dz\, dy$

$= \int_{-2}^{2}\int_{0}^{2-x^2/2}\int_{x^2}^{4-2z} f(x, y, z)\, dy\, dz\, dx$

$= \int_{0}^{2}\int_{-\sqrt{4-2z}}^{\sqrt{4-2z}}\int_{x^2}^{4-2z} f(x, y, z)\, dy\, dx\, dz$

33. $\int_{0}^{1}\int_{\sqrt{x}}^{1}\int_{0}^{1-y} f(x, y, z)\, dz\, dy\, dx$

$= \int_{0}^{1}\int_{0}^{y^2}\int_{0}^{1-y} f(x, y, z)\, dz\, dx\, dy$

$= \int_{0}^{1}\int_{0}^{1-z}\int_{0}^{y^2} f(x, y, z)\, dx\, dy\, dz$

$= \int_{0}^{1}\int_{0}^{1-y}\int_{0}^{y^2} f(x, y, z)\, dx\, dz\, dy$

$= \int_{0}^{1}\int_{0}^{1-\sqrt{x}}\int_{\sqrt{x}}^{1-z} f(x, y, z)\, dy\, dz\, dx$

$= \int_{0}^{1}\int_{0}^{(1-z)^2}\int_{\sqrt{x}}^{1-z} f(x, y, z)\, dy\, dx\, dz$

35. $\int_{0}^{1}\int_{y}^{1}\int_{0}^{y} f(x, y, z)\, dz\, dx\, dy = \int_{0}^{1}\int_{0}^{x}\int_{0}^{y} f(x, y, z)\, dz\, dy\, dx$

$= \int_{0}^{1}\int_{z}^{1}\int_{y}^{1} f(x, y, z)\, dx\, dy\, dz = \int_{0}^{1}\int_{0}^{y}\int_{y}^{1} f(x, y, z)\, dx\, dz\, dy$

$= \int_{0}^{1}\int_{0}^{x}\int_{z}^{x} f(x, y, z)\, dy\, dz\, dx = \int_{0}^{1}\int_{z}^{1}\int_{z}^{x} f(x, y, z)\, dy\, dx\, dz$

37. $\frac{79}{30}, \left(\frac{358}{553}, \frac{33}{79}, \frac{571}{553}\right)$ **39.** $a^5, (7a/12, 7a/12, 7a/12)$

41. $I_x = I_y = I_z = \frac{2}{3}kL^5$ **43.** $\frac{1}{2}\pi kha^4$

45. (a) $m = \int_{-3}^{3}\int_{-\sqrt{9-x^2}}^{\sqrt{9-x^2}}\int_{1}^{5-y} \sqrt{x^2+y^2}\, dz\, dy\, dx$

(b) $(\bar{x}, \bar{y}, \bar{z})$, where

$\bar{x} = (1/m)\int_{-3}^{3}\int_{-\sqrt{9-x^2}}^{\sqrt{9-x^2}}\int_{1}^{5-y} x\sqrt{x^2+y^2}\, dz\, dy\, dx$

$\bar{y} = (1/m)\int_{-3}^{3}\int_{-\sqrt{9-x^2}}^{\sqrt{9-x^2}}\int_{1}^{5-y} y\sqrt{x^2+y^2}\, dz\, dy\, dx$

$\bar{z} = (1/m)\int_{-3}^{3}\int_{-\sqrt{9-x^2}}^{\sqrt{9-x^2}}\int_{1}^{5-y} z\sqrt{x^2+y^2}\, dz\, dy\, dx$

(c) $\int_{-3}^{3}\int_{-\sqrt{9-x^2}}^{\sqrt{9-x^2}}\int_{1}^{5-y} (x^2+y^2)^{3/2}\, dz\, dy\, dx$

47. (a) $\frac{3}{32}\pi + \frac{11}{24}$

(b) $\left(\dfrac{28}{9\pi+44}, \dfrac{30\pi+128}{45\pi+220}, \dfrac{45\pi+208}{135\pi+660}\right)$

(c) $\frac{1}{240}(68+15\pi)$

49. (a) $\frac{1}{8}$ (b) $\frac{1}{64}$ (c) $\frac{1}{5760}$ **51.** $L^3/8$

53. (a) The region bounded by the ellipsoid $x^2 + 2y^2 + 3z^2 = 1$

(b) $4\sqrt{6}\pi/45$

1.   **3.**

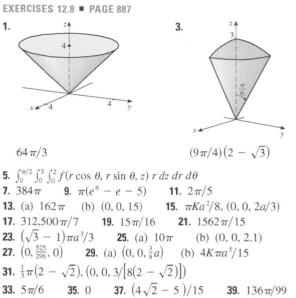

$64\pi/3$ $(9\pi/4)(2-\sqrt{3})$

5. $\int_{0}^{\pi/2}\int_{0}^{3}\int_{0}^{2} f(r\cos\theta, r\sin\theta, z)\, r\, dz\, dr\, d\theta$

7. 384π **9.** $\pi(e^6 - e - 5)$ **11.** $2\pi/5$

13. (a) 162π (b) $(0, 0, 15)$ **15.** $\pi Ka^2/8, (0, 0, 2a/3)$

17. $312{,}500\,\pi/7$ **19.** $15\pi/16$ **21.** $1562\pi/15$

23. $(\sqrt{3}-1)\pi a^3/3$ **25.** (a) 10π (b) $(0, 0, 2.1)$

27. $(0, \frac{525}{296}, 0)$ **29.** (a) $(0, 0, \frac{3}{8}a)$ (b) $4K\pi a^5/15$

31. $\frac{1}{3}\pi(2-\sqrt{2}), (0, 0, 3/[8(2-\sqrt{2})])$

33. $5\pi/6$ **35.** 0 **37.** $(4\sqrt{2}-5)/15$ **39.** $136\pi/99$

41. (a) $\iiint_{C} h(P)g(P)\, dV$, where C is the cone

(b) $\approx 3.1 \times 10^{19}$ ft-lb

1. 16 **3.** $\sin^2\theta - \cos^2\theta$ **5.** 0

7. The parallelogram with vertices $(0, 0)$, $(6, 3)$, $(12, 1)$, $(6, -2)$

9. The region bounded by the line $y = 1$, the y-axis, and $y = \sqrt{x}$

11. $x = \frac{1}{3}(v-u), y = \frac{1}{3}(u+2v)$ is one possible transformation, where $S = \{(u, v) \mid -1 \leq u \leq 1, 1 \leq v \leq 3\}$

13. $x = u\cos v, y = u\sin v$ is one possible transformation, where $S = \{(u, v) \mid 1 \leq u \leq \sqrt{2}, 0 \leq v \leq \pi/2\}$

15. -3 **17.** 6π **19.** $2\ln 3$

21. (a) $\frac{4}{3}\pi abc$ (b) 1.083×10^{12} km^3

23. $\frac{8}{5}\ln 8$ **25.** $\frac{3}{2}\sin 1$ **27.** $e - e^{-1}$

True-False Quiz

1. True   **3.** True   **5.** True   **7.** True   **9.** False

Exercises

1. ≈ 64.0 **3.** $4e^2 - 4e + 3$ **5.** $\frac{1}{2}\sin 1$ **7.** $\frac{2}{3}$

9. $\int_{0}^{\pi}\int_{2}^{4} f(r\cos\theta, r\sin\theta)\, r\, dr\, d\theta$

11. The region inside the loop of the four-leaved rose $r = \sin 2\theta$ in the first quadrant

13. $\frac{1}{2}\sin 1$ **15.** $\frac{1}{2}e^6 - \frac{7}{2}$ **17.** $\frac{1}{4}\ln 2$ **19.** 8

21. $81\pi/5$ **23.** $\frac{81}{2}$ **25.** $\pi/96$ **27.** $\frac{64}{15}$

29. 176 **31.** $\frac{2}{3}$ **33.** $2ma^3/9$

35. (a) $\frac{1}{4}$ (b) $(\frac{1}{3}, \frac{8}{15})$ (c) $I_0 = \frac{1}{8}, I_x = \frac{1}{12}, I_y = \frac{1}{24}$

37. (a) $(0, 0, h/4)$ (b) $\pi a^4 h/10$

39. $\ln(\sqrt{2}+\sqrt{3}) + \sqrt{2}/3$ **41.** $\frac{486}{5}$ **43.** 0.0512

45. (a) $\frac{1}{15}$ (b) $\frac{1}{3}$ (c) $\frac{1}{45}$

47. $\int_{0}^{1}\int_{0}^{1-z}\int_{-\sqrt{y}}^{\sqrt{y}} f(x, y, z)\, dx\, dy\, dz$ **49.** $\ln 2$ **51.** 0

FOCUS ON PROBLEM SOLVING ▪ PAGE 903

1. 30 **3.** $\frac{1}{2}\sin 1$ **7.** (b) 0.90

11. $abc\pi\left(\dfrac{2}{3} - \dfrac{8}{9\sqrt{3}}\right)$

CHAPTER 13

EXERCISES 13.1 ▪ PAGE 911

1.

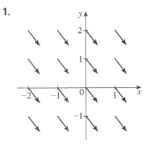

3.

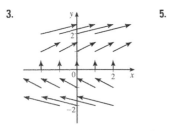

5.

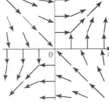

7.

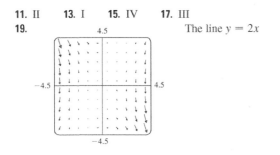

9.

11. II **13.** I **15.** IV **17.** III
19. The line $y = 2x$

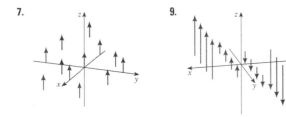

21. $\nabla f(x, y) = (xy + 1)e^{xy}\,\mathbf{i} + x^2 e^{xy}\,\mathbf{j}$

23. $\nabla f(x, y, z) = \dfrac{x}{\sqrt{x^2 + y^2 + z^2}}\,\mathbf{i}$
$\quad + \dfrac{y}{\sqrt{x^2 + y^2 + z^2}}\,\mathbf{j} + \dfrac{z}{\sqrt{x^2 + y^2 + z^2}}\,\mathbf{k}$

25. $\nabla f(x, y) = 2x\,\mathbf{i} - \mathbf{j}$

27.

29. III **31.** II **33.** (2.04, 1.03)
35. (a) (b) $y = 1/x,\ x > 0$

$y = C/x$

EXERCISES 13.2 ▪ PAGE 922

1. $\frac{1}{54}(145^{3/2} - 1)$ **3.** 1638.4 **5.** $\frac{243}{8}$ **7.** $\frac{17}{3}$ **9.** $\sqrt{5}\,\pi$
11. $\frac{1}{12}\sqrt{14}(e^6 - 1)$ **13.** $\frac{1}{5}$ **15.** $\frac{97}{3}$
17. (a) Positive (b) Negative
19. 45 **21.** $\frac{6}{5} - \cos 1 - \sin 1$ **23.** 1.9633 **25.** 15.0074
27. $3\pi + \frac{2}{3}$

29. (a) $\frac{11}{8} - 1/e$ (b) 2.1

31. $\frac{172,704}{5,632,705}\sqrt{2}(1 - e^{-14\pi})$ **33.** $2\pi k,\ (4/\pi, 0)$

35. (a) $\bar{x} = (1/m) \int_C x\rho(x, y, z) \, ds$,
$\bar{y} = (1/m) \int_C y\rho(x, y, z) \, ds$,
$\bar{z} = (1/m) \int_C z\rho(x, y, z) \, ds$, where $m = \int_C \rho(x, y, z) \, ds$
(b) $(0, 0, 3\pi)$
37. $I_x = k\left(\frac{1}{2}\pi - \frac{4}{3}\right)$, $I_y = k\left(\frac{1}{2}\pi - \frac{2}{3}\right)$
39. $2\pi^2$ **41.** 26   **43.** $\approx 1.67 \times 10^4$ ft-lb   **45.** (b) Yes
47. ≈ 22 J

EXERCISES 13.3 ▪ PAGE 932

1. 40   **3.** $f(x, y) = x^2 - 3xy + 2y^2 - 8y + K$
5. Not conservative   **7.** $f(x, y) = ye^x + x \sin y + K$
9. $f(x, y) = x \ln y + x^2 y^3 + K$
11. (b) 16   **13.** (a) $f(x, y) = \frac{1}{2}x^2 y^2$ (b) 2
15. (a) $f(x, y, z) = xyz + z^2$ (b) 77
17. (a) $f(x, y, z) = xy^2 \cos z$ (b) 0   **19.** 2
21. It doesn't matter which curve is chosen.
23. 30   **25.** No   **27.** Conservative
31. (a) Yes   (b) Yes   (c) Yes
33. (a) No   (b) Yes   (c) Yes

EXERCISES 13.4 ▪ PAGE 939

1. 8π **3.** $\frac{2}{3}$ **5.** 12   **7.** $\frac{1}{3}$ **9.** -24π **11.** $\frac{4}{3} - 2\pi$
13. $\frac{625}{2}\pi$ **17.** $-\frac{1}{12}$ **19.** 3π **21.** (c) $\frac{9}{2}$
23. $(4a/3\pi, 4a/3\pi)$ if the region is the portion of the disk
$x^2 + y^2 = a^2$ in the first quadrant
27. 0

EXERCISES 13.5 ▪ PAGE 947

1. (a) $-x^2 \mathbf{i} + 3xy \mathbf{j} - xz \mathbf{k}$ (b) yz
3. (a) $ze^x \mathbf{i} + (xye^z - yze^x) \mathbf{j} - xe^z \mathbf{k}$ (b) $y(e^z + e^x)$
5. (a) $\mathbf{0}$ (b) $2/\sqrt{x^2 + y^2 + z^2}$
7. (a) $\langle 1/y, -1/x, 1/x \rangle$ (b) $1/x + 1/y + 1/z$
9. (a) Negative   (b) curl $\mathbf{F} = \mathbf{0}$
11. (a) Zero   (b) curl $\mathbf{F}$ points in the negative z-direction
13. $f(x, y, z) = xy^2 z^3 + K$ **15.** $f(x, y, z) = x^2 y + y^2 z + K$
17. Not conservative   **19.** No

EXERCISES 13.6 ▪ PAGE 959

1. 49.09   **3.** 900π **5.** $11\sqrt{14}$ **7.** $\frac{2}{3}(2\sqrt{2} - 1)$
9. $171\sqrt{14}$ **11.** $\sqrt{3}/24$ **13.** $364\sqrt{2}\pi/3$
15. $(\pi/60)(391\sqrt{17} + 1)$ **17.** 16π **19.** 12   **21.** $\frac{713}{180}$
23. $-\frac{1}{6}$ **25.** $-\frac{4}{3}\pi$ **27.** 0   **29.** 48   **31.** $2\pi + \frac{8}{3}$
33. 3.4895
35. $\iint_S \mathbf{F} \cdot d\mathbf{S} = \iint_D [P(\partial h/\partial x) - Q + R(\partial h/\partial z)] \, dA$,
where D = projection of S on xz-plane
37. $(0, 0, a/2)$
39. (a) $I_z = \iint_S (x^2 + y^2)\rho(x, y, z) \, dS$ (b) $4329\sqrt{2}\,\pi/5$
41. 0 kg/s   **43.** $\frac{8}{3}\pi a^3 \varepsilon_0$ **45.** 1248π

EXERCISES 13.7 ▪ PAGE 965

3. 0   **5.** 0   **7.** -1 **9.** 80π

11. (a) $81\pi/2$ (b)

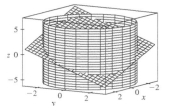

(c) $x = 3 \cos t, y = 3 \sin t$,
$z = 1 - 3(\cos t + \sin t)$,
$0 \le t \le 2\pi$

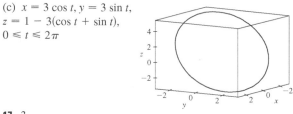

17. 3

EXERCISES 13.8 ▪ PAGE 971

5. $\frac{9}{2}$ **7.** $9\pi/2$ **9.** 0   **11.** $32\pi/3$ **13.** 0
15. $341\sqrt{2}/60 + \frac{81}{20}\arcsin(\sqrt{3}/3)$
17. $13\pi/20$ **19.** Negative at P_1, positive at P_2
21. div $\mathbf{F} > 0$ in quadrants I, II; div $\mathbf{F} < 0$ in quadrants III, IV

CHAPTER 13 REVIEW ▪ PAGE 974

True-False Quiz

1. False   **3.** True   **5.** False   **7.** True

Exercises

1. (a) Negative   (b) Positive   **3.** $6\sqrt{10}$ **5.** $\frac{4}{15}$
7. $\frac{110}{3}$ **9.** $\frac{11}{12} - 4/e$ **11.** $f(x, y) = e^y + xe^{xy}$ **13.** 0
17. -8π **25.** $(\pi/60)(391\sqrt{17} + 1)$ **27.** $-64\pi/3$
31. $-\frac{1}{2}$ **35.** -4 **37.** 21

APPENDIXES

EXERCISES A ▪ PAGE A6

1. 18   **3.** $5 - \sqrt{5}$ **5.** $2 - x$
7. $|x + 1| = \begin{cases} x + 1 & \text{for } x \ge -1 \\ -x - 1 & \text{for } x < -1 \end{cases}$ **9.** $x^2 + 1$
11. $(-2, \infty)$ **13.** $[-1, \infty)$
15. $(0, 1]$ **17.** $(-\infty, 1) \cup (2, \infty)$
19. $(-\sqrt{3}, \sqrt{3})$ **21.** $(-\infty, 1]$

23. $(-1, 0) \cup (1, \infty)$ **25.** $(-\infty, 0) \cup \left(\frac{1}{4}, \infty\right)$

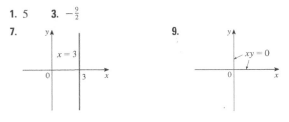

27. $10 \le C \le 35$ **29.** (a) $T = 20 - 10h, 0 \le h \le 12$
(b) $-30°C \le T \le 20°C$ **31.** $2, -\frac{4}{3}$ **33.** $(-3, 3)$
35. $(3, 5)$ **37.** $(-\infty, -7] \cup [-3, \infty)$
39. $[1.3, 1.7]$ **41.** $x \ge (a + b)c/(ab)$

EXERCISES B ■ **PAGE A16**

1. 5   **3.** $-\frac{9}{2}$

7.

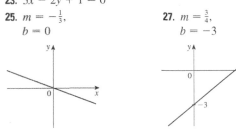

9.

11. $y = 6x - 15$ **13.** $5x + y = 11$ **15.** $y = 3x - 2$
17. $y = 3x - 3$ **19.** $y = 5$ **21.** $x + 2y + 11 = 0$
23. $5x - 2y + 1 = 0$
25. $m = -\frac{1}{3},$ **27.** $m = \frac{3}{4},$
      $b = 0$ $b = -3$

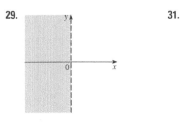

29.   **31.**

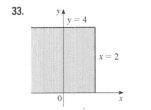

33.   **35.**

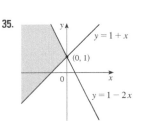

37. $(x - 3)^2 + (y + 1)^2 = 25$ **39.** $(2, -5), 4$ **41.** $(1, -2)$
45. $y = x - 3$

53.

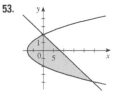

EXERCISES C ■ **PAGE A25**

1. (a) $7\pi/6$ (b) $\pi/20$ **3.** (a) $720°$ (b) $-67.5°$
5. 3π cm   **7.** $\frac{2}{3}$ rad $= (120/\pi)°$
9. (a)   (b)

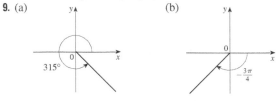

11. $\sin(3\pi/4) = 1/\sqrt{2}, \cos(3\pi/4) = -1/\sqrt{2}, \tan(3\pi/4) = -1,$
$\csc(3\pi/4) = \sqrt{2}, \sec(3\pi/4) = -\sqrt{2}, \cot(3\pi/4) = -1$
13. $\cos\theta = \frac{4}{5}, \tan\theta = \frac{3}{4}, \csc\theta = \frac{5}{3}, \sec\theta = \frac{5}{4}, \cot\theta = \frac{4}{3}$
15. 5.73576 cm   **17.** 24.62147 cm   **27.** $\frac{1}{15}\left(4 + 6\sqrt{2}\right)$
29. $\pi/3, 5\pi/3$ **31.** $\pi/6, \pi/2, 5\pi/6, 3\pi/2$
33. $0 \le x \le \pi/6$ and $5\pi/6 \le x \le 2\pi$
35. $0 \le x < \pi/4, 3\pi/4 < x < 5\pi/4, 7\pi/4 < x \le 2\pi$

37.

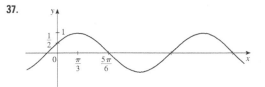

39.

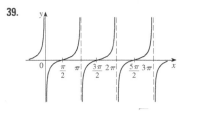

EXERCISES D ■ **PAGE A34**

1. $\frac{4}{7}$ (or any smaller positive number)
3. 1.44 (or any smaller positive number)
5. 0.0906 (or any smaller positive number)
7. 0.11, 0.012 (or smaller positive numbers)
11. (a) $\sqrt{1000/\pi}$ cm   (b) Within approximately 0.0445 cm
(c) Radius; area; $\sqrt{1000/\pi}$; 1000; 5; $\approx$0.0445

13. (a) 0.025   (b) 0.0025   **17.**
19. (a) $x > 100$ **21.** (a) 0   (b) 9, 11

EXERCISES F ▪ PAGE A45

1. $\sqrt{1} + \sqrt{2} + \sqrt{3} + \sqrt{4} + \sqrt{5}$ **3.** $3^4 + 3^5 + 3^6$
5. $-1 + \frac{1}{3} + \frac{3}{5} + \frac{5}{7} + \frac{7}{9}$ **7.** $1^{10} + 2^{10} + 3^{10} + \cdots + n^{10}$

9. $1 - 1 + 1 - 1 + \cdots + (-1)^{n-1}$ **11.** $\sum_{i=1}^{10} i$

13. $\sum_{i=1}^{19} \frac{i}{i+1}$ **15.** $\sum_{i=1}^{n} 2i$ **17.** $\sum_{i=0}^{5} 2^i$ **19.** $\sum_{i=1}^{n} x^i$

21. 80   **23.** 3276   **25.** 0   **27.** 61   **29.** $n(n+1)$
31. $n(n^2 + 6n + 17)/3$ **33.** $n(n^2 + 6n + 11)/3$
35. $n(n^3 + 2n^2 - n - 10)/4$
41. (a) n^4 (b) $5^{100} - 1$ (c) $\frac{97}{300}$ (d) $a_n - a_0$
43. $\frac{1}{3}$ **45.** 14   **49.** $2^{n+1} + n^2 + n - 2$

EXERCISES G ▪ PAGE A54

1. (a) $\dfrac{A}{x+3} + \dfrac{B}{3x+1}$ (b) $\dfrac{A}{x} + \dfrac{B}{x+1} + \dfrac{C}{(x+1)^2}$

3. (a) $\dfrac{A}{x} + \dfrac{B}{x^2} + \dfrac{C}{x^3} + \dfrac{Dx+E}{x^2+4}$

(b) $\dfrac{A}{x+3} + \dfrac{B}{(x+3)^2} + \dfrac{C}{x-3} + \dfrac{D}{(x-3)^2}$

5. (a) $1 + \dfrac{A}{x-1} + \dfrac{B}{x+1} + \dfrac{Cx+D}{x^2+1}$

(b) $\dfrac{At+B}{t^2+1} + \dfrac{Ct+D}{t^2+4} + \dfrac{Et+F}{(t^2+4)^2}$

7. $x + 6\ln|x-6| + C$

9. $2\ln|x+5| - \ln|x-2| + C$ **11.** $\frac{1}{2}\ln\frac{3}{2}$

13. $a\ln|x-b| + C$ **15.** $\frac{7}{6} + \ln\frac{2}{3}$

17. $\frac{27}{5}\ln 2 - \frac{9}{5}\ln 3 \left(\text{or } \frac{9}{5}\ln\frac{8}{3}\right)$

19. $-\dfrac{1}{36}\ln|x+5| + \dfrac{1}{6}\dfrac{1}{x+5} + \dfrac{1}{36}\ln|x-1| + C$

21. $2\ln|x| + (1/x) + 3\ln|x+2| + C$

23. $\ln|x-1| - \frac{1}{2}\ln(x^2+9) - \frac{1}{3}\tan^{-1}(x/3) + C$

25. $\frac{1}{2}\ln(x^2+1) + \left(1/\sqrt{2}\right)\tan^{-1}\left(x/\sqrt{2}\right) + C$

27. $\frac{1}{2}\ln(x^2+2x+5) + \frac{3}{2}\tan^{-1}\left(\dfrac{x+1}{2}\right) + C$

29. $\frac{1}{3}\ln|x-1| - \frac{1}{6}\ln(x^2+x+1) - \dfrac{1}{\sqrt{3}}\tan^{-1}\dfrac{2x+1}{\sqrt{3}} + C$

31. $\frac{1}{16}\ln|x| - \frac{1}{32}\ln(x^2+4) + \dfrac{1}{8(x^2+4)} + C$

33. $\dfrac{-1}{2(x^2+2x+4)} - \dfrac{2\sqrt{3}}{9}\tan^{-1}\left(\dfrac{x+1}{\sqrt{3}}\right) - \dfrac{2(x+1)}{3(x^2+2x+4)} + C$

35. $2 + \ln\frac{25}{9}$ **37.** $\ln\left[\dfrac{(e^x+2)^2}{e^x+1}\right] + C$

39. $-\frac{1}{2}\ln 3 \approx -0.55$

41. $t = -\ln P - \frac{1}{9}\ln(0.9P + 900) + C$, where $C \approx 10.23$

43. (a) $\dfrac{24{,}110}{4879}\dfrac{1}{5x+2} - \dfrac{668}{323}\dfrac{1}{2x+1} - \dfrac{9438}{80{,}155}\dfrac{1}{3x-7} +$

$\dfrac{1}{260{,}015}\dfrac{22{,}098x + 48{,}935}{x^2+x+5}$

(b) $\dfrac{4822}{4879}\ln|5x+2| - \dfrac{334}{323}\ln|2x+1| - \dfrac{3146}{80{,}155}\ln|3x-7| +$

$\dfrac{11{,}049}{260{,}015}\ln(x^2+x+5) + \dfrac{75{,}772}{260{,}015\sqrt{19}}\tan^{-1}\dfrac{2x+1}{\sqrt{19}} + C$

The CAS omits the absolute value signs and the constant of integration.

EXERCISES H.1 ▪ PAGE A63

1. (a)   (b)

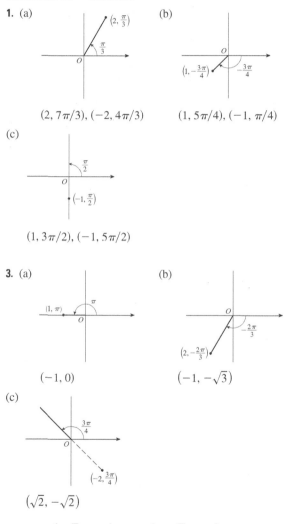

$(2, 7\pi/3), (-2, 4\pi/3)$ $(1, 5\pi/4), (-1, \pi/4)$

(c)

$(1, 3\pi/2), (-1, 5\pi/2)$

3. (a)   (b)

$(-1, 0)$ $(-1, -\sqrt{3})$

(c)

$\left(\sqrt{2}, -\sqrt{2}\right)$

5. (a) (i) $\left(2\sqrt{2}, 7\pi/4\right)$ (ii) $\left(-2\sqrt{2}, 3\pi/4\right)$
(b) (i) $(2, 2\pi/3)$ (ii) $(-2, 5\pi/3)$

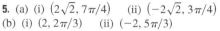

7.

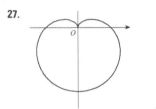

9.

11.

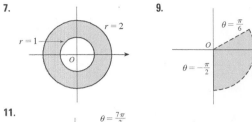

13. Circle, center $\left(0, \frac{3}{2}\right)$, radius $\frac{3}{2}$
15. Horizontal line, 1 unit above the x-axis
17. $r = -\cot\theta\,\csc\theta$ **19.** $r = 2c\cos\theta$
21. (a) $\theta = \pi/6$ (b) $x = 3$
23.

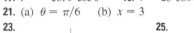

25.

27.

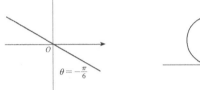

29.

31.

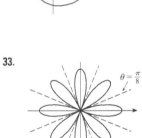

33.

35.

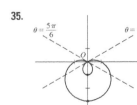

37.

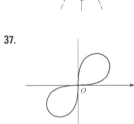

39.

41.

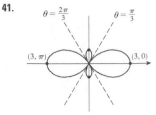

43.

45.

47. (a) For $c < -1$, the inner loop begins at $\theta = \sin^{-1}(-1/c)$ and ends at $\theta = \pi - \sin^{-1}(-1/c)$; for $c > 1$, it begins at $\theta = \pi + \sin^{-1}(1/c)$ and ends at $\theta = 2\pi - \sin^{-1}(1/c)$.
49. $-\pi$ **51.** 1
53. Horizontal at $\left(3/\sqrt{2}, \pi/4\right)$, $\left(-3/\sqrt{2}, 3\pi/4\right)$; vertical at $(3, 0)$, $(0, \pi/2)$
55. Horizontal at $\left(\frac{3}{2}, \pi/3\right)$, $(0, \pi)$ [the pole], and $\left(\frac{3}{2}, 5\pi/3\right)$; vertical at $(2, 0)$, $\left(\frac{1}{2}, 2\pi/3\right)$, $\left(\frac{1}{2}, 4\pi/3\right)$
57. Center $(b/2, a/2)$, radius $\sqrt{a^2 + b^2}/2$
59.   **61.**

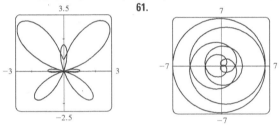

63. By counterclockwise rotation through angle $\pi/6$, $\pi/3$, or α about the origin
65. (a) A rose with n loops if n is odd and $2n$ loops if n is even
(b) Number of loops is always $2n$
67. For $0 < a < 1$, the curve is an oval, which develops a dimple as $a \to 1^-$. When $a > 1$, the curve splits into two parts, one of which has a loop.

EXERCISES H.2 ■ PAGE A69

1. $\pi^5/10{,}240$ **3.** $\pi/12 + \frac{1}{8}\sqrt{3}$ ·   **5.** π^2 **7.** $\frac{41}{4}\pi$
9. 4

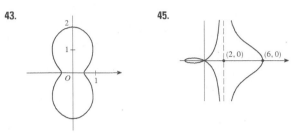

11. π **13.** 3π

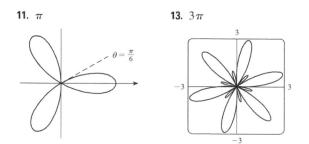

15. $\frac{1}{8}\pi$ **17.** $\pi - \frac{3}{2}\sqrt{3}$ **19.** $\frac{1}{3}\pi + \frac{1}{2}\sqrt{3}$ **21.** π

23. $\frac{5}{24}\pi - \frac{1}{4}\sqrt{3}$ **25.** $\frac{1}{2}\pi - 1$ **27.** $\frac{1}{4}(\pi + 3\sqrt{3})$

29. $(1, \theta)$ where $\theta = \pi/12, 5\pi/12, 13\pi/12, 17\pi/12$
and $(-1, \theta)$ where $\theta = 7\pi/12, 11\pi/12, 19\pi/12, 23\pi/12$

31. $\left(\frac{1}{2}\sqrt{3}, \pi/3\right), \left(\frac{1}{2}\sqrt{3}, 2\pi/3\right)$, and the pole

33. Intersection at $\theta \approx 0.89, 2.25$; area ≈ 3.46 **35.** π

37. $\frac{8}{3}\left[(\pi^2 + 1)^{3/2} - 1\right]$ **39.** 29.0653

EXERCISES I ■ PAGE A78

1. $8 - 4i$ **3.** $13 + 18i$ **5.** $12 - 7i$ **7.** $\frac{11}{13} + \frac{10}{13}i$

9. $\frac{1}{2} - \frac{1}{2}i$ **11.** $-i$ **13.** $5i$ **15.** $12 + 5i, 13$

17. $4i, 4$ **19.** $\pm \frac{3}{2}i$ **21.** $-1 \pm 2i$

23. $-\frac{1}{2} \pm (\sqrt{7}/2)i$ **25.** $3\sqrt{2}\left[\cos(3\pi/4) + i\sin(3\pi/4)\right]$

27. $5\left\{\cos\left[\tan^{-1}\left(\frac{4}{3}\right)\right] + i\sin\left[\tan^{-1}\left(\frac{4}{3}\right)\right]\right\}$

29. $4[\cos(\pi/2) + i\sin(\pi/2)], \cos(-\pi/6) + i\sin(-\pi/6),$
$\frac{1}{2}[\cos(-\pi/6) + i\sin(-\pi/6)]$

31. $4\sqrt{2}\left[\cos(7\pi/12) + i\sin(7\pi/12)\right],$
$(2\sqrt{2})[\cos(13\pi/12) + i\sin(13\pi/12)], \frac{1}{4}[\cos(\pi/6) + i\sin(\pi/6)]$

33. -1024 **35.** $-512\sqrt{3} + 512i$

37. $\pm 1, \pm i, (1/\sqrt{2})(\pm 1 \pm i)$ **39.** $\pm(\sqrt{3}/2) + \frac{1}{2}i, -i$

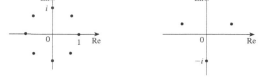

41. i **43.** $\frac{1}{2} + (\sqrt{3}/2)i$ **45.** $-e^2$

47. $\cos 3\theta = \cos^3\theta - 3\cos\theta\sin^2\theta,$
$\sin 3\theta = 3\cos^2\theta\sin\theta - \sin^3\theta$

Index

Cut here and keep for reference

ALGEBRA

Arithmetic Operations

$$a(b + c) = ab + ac$$

$$\frac{a}{b} + \frac{c}{d} = \frac{ad + bc}{bd}$$

$$\frac{a + c}{b} = \frac{a}{b} + \frac{c}{b}$$

$$\frac{\dfrac{a}{b}}{\dfrac{c}{d}} = \frac{a}{b} \times \frac{d}{c} = \frac{ad}{bc}$$

Exponents and Radicals

$$x^m x^n = x^{m+n}$$

$$\frac{x^m}{x^n} = x^{m-n}$$

$$(x^m)^n = x^{mn}$$

$$x^{-n} = \frac{1}{x^n}$$

$$(xy)^n = x^n y^n$$

$$\left(\frac{x}{y}\right)^n = \frac{x^n}{y^n}$$

$$x^{1/n} = \sqrt[n]{x}$$

$$x^{m/n} = \sqrt[n]{x^m} = \left(\sqrt[n]{x}\right)^m$$

$$\sqrt[n]{xy} = \sqrt[n]{x}\sqrt[n]{y}$$

$$\sqrt[n]{\frac{x}{y}} = \frac{\sqrt[n]{x}}{\sqrt[n]{y}}$$

Factoring Special Polynomials

$$x^2 - y^2 = (x + y)(x - y)$$

$$x^3 + y^3 = (x + y)(x^2 - xy + y^2)$$

$$x^3 - y^3 = (x - y)(x^2 + xy + y^2)$$

Binomial Theorem

$$(x + y)^2 = x^2 + 2xy + y^2 \qquad (x - y)^2 = x^2 - 2xy + y^2$$

$$(x + y)^3 = x^3 + 3x^2y + 3xy^2 + y^3$$

$$(x - y)^3 = x^3 - 3x^2y + 3xy^2 - y^3$$

$$(x + y)^n = x^n + nx^{n-1}y + \frac{n(n-1)}{2}x^{n-2}y^2$$

$$+ \cdots + \binom{n}{k}x^{n-k}y^k + \cdots + nxy^{n-1} + y^n$$

where $\binom{n}{k} = \dfrac{n(n-1)\cdots(n-k+1)}{1 \cdot 2 \cdot 3 \cdot \cdots \cdot k}$

Quadratic Formula

If $ax^2 + bx + c = 0$, then $x = \dfrac{-b \pm \sqrt{b^2 - 4ac}}{2a}$.

Inequalities and Absolute Value

If $a < b$ and $b < c$, then $a < c$.

If $a < b$, then $a + c < b + c$.

If $a < b$ and $c > 0$, then $ca < cb$.

If $a < b$ and $c < 0$, then $ca > cb$.

If $a > 0$, then

$$|x| = a \quad \text{means} \quad x = a \quad \text{or} \quad x = -a$$

$$|x| < a \quad \text{means} \quad -a < x < a$$

$$|x| > a \quad \text{means} \quad x > a \quad \text{or} \quad x < -a$$

GEOMETRY

Geometric Formulas

Formulas for area A, circumference C, and volume V:

Triangle
$$A = \tfrac{1}{2}bh$$
$$= \tfrac{1}{2}ab \sin \theta$$

Circle
$$A = \pi r^2$$
$$C = 2\pi r$$

Sector of Circle
$$A = \tfrac{1}{2}r^2\theta$$
$$s = r\theta \quad (\theta \text{ in radians})$$

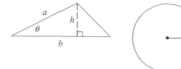

Sphere
$$V = \tfrac{4}{3}\pi r^3$$
$$A = 4\pi r^2$$

Cylinder
$$V = \pi r^2 h$$

Cone
$$V = \tfrac{1}{3}\pi r^2 h$$
$$A = \pi r\sqrt{r^2 + h^2}$$

Distance and Midpoint Formulas

Distance between $P_1(x_1, y_1)$ and $P_2(x_2, y_2)$:

$$d = \sqrt{(x_2 - x_1)^2 + (y_2 - y_1)^2}$$

Midpoint of $\overline{P_1 P_2}$: $\left(\dfrac{x_1 + x_2}{2}, \dfrac{y_1 + y_2}{2}\right)$

Lines

Slope of line through $P_1(x_1, y_1)$ and $P_2(x_2, y_2)$:

$$m = \frac{y_2 - y_1}{x_2 - x_1}$$

Point-slope equation of line through $P_1(x_1, y_1)$ with slope m:

$$y - y_1 = m(x - x_1)$$

Slope-intercept equation of line with slope m and y-intercept b:

$$y = mx + b$$

Circles

Equation of the circle with center (h, k) and radius r:

$$(x - h)^2 + (y - k)^2 = r^2$$

TRIGONOMETRY

Angle Measurement

π radians $= 180°$

$$1° = \frac{\pi}{180} \text{ rad} \qquad 1 \text{ rad} = \frac{180°}{\pi}$$

$s = r\theta$

(θ in radians)

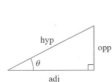

Right Angle Trigonometry

$$\sin \theta = \frac{\text{opp}}{\text{hyp}} \qquad \csc \theta = \frac{\text{hyp}}{\text{opp}}$$

$$\cos \theta = \frac{\text{adj}}{\text{hyp}} \qquad \sec \theta = \frac{\text{hyp}}{\text{adj}}$$

$$\tan \theta = \frac{\text{opp}}{\text{adj}} \qquad \cot \theta = \frac{\text{adj}}{\text{opp}}$$

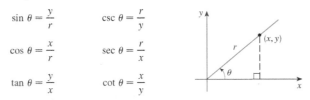

Trigonometric Functions

$$\sin \theta = \frac{y}{r} \qquad \csc \theta = \frac{r}{y}$$

$$\cos \theta = \frac{x}{r} \qquad \sec \theta = \frac{r}{x}$$

$$\tan \theta = \frac{y}{x} \qquad \cot \theta = \frac{x}{y}$$

Graphs of Trigonometric Functions

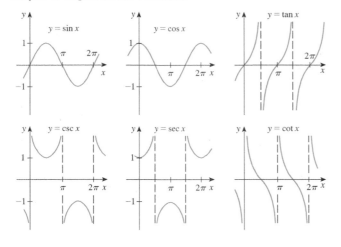

Trigonometric Functions of Important Angles

θ	radians	$\sin \theta$	$\cos \theta$	$\tan \theta$
0°	0	0	1	0
30°	$\pi/6$	1/2	$\sqrt{3}/2$	$\sqrt{3}/3$
45°	$\pi/4$	$\sqrt{2}/2$	$\sqrt{2}/2$	1
60°	$\pi/3$	$\sqrt{3}/2$	1/2	$\sqrt{3}$
90°	$\pi/2$	1	0	—

Fundamental Identities

$$\csc \theta = \frac{1}{\sin \theta} \qquad\qquad \sec \theta = \frac{1}{\cos \theta}$$

$$\tan \theta = \frac{\sin \theta}{\cos \theta} \qquad\qquad \cot \theta = \frac{\cos \theta}{\sin \theta}$$

$$\cot \theta = \frac{1}{\tan \theta} \qquad\qquad \sin^2\theta + \cos^2\theta = 1$$

$$1 + \tan^2\theta = \sec^2\theta \qquad 1 + \cot^2\theta = \csc^2\theta$$

$$\sin(-\theta) = -\sin \theta \qquad \cos(-\theta) = \cos \theta$$

$$\tan(-\theta) = -\tan \theta \qquad \sin\left(\frac{\pi}{2} - \theta\right) = \cos \theta$$

$$\cos\left(\frac{\pi}{2} - \theta\right) = \sin \theta \qquad \tan\left(\frac{\pi}{2} - \theta\right) = \cot \theta$$

The Law of Sines

$$\frac{\sin A}{a} = \frac{\sin B}{b} = \frac{\sin C}{c}$$

The Law of Cosines

$$a^2 = b^2 + c^2 - 2bc \cos A$$

$$b^2 = a^2 + c^2 - 2ac \cos B$$

$$c^2 = a^2 + b^2 - 2ab \cos C$$

Addition and Subtraction Formulas

$$\sin(x + y) = \sin x \cos y + \cos x \sin y$$

$$\sin(x - y) = \sin x \cos y - \cos x \sin y$$

$$\cos(x + y) = \cos x \cos y - \sin x \sin y$$

$$\cos(x - y) = \cos x \cos y + \sin x \sin y$$

$$\tan(x + y) = \frac{\tan x + \tan y}{1 - \tan x \tan y}$$

$$\tan(x - y) = \frac{\tan x - \tan y}{1 + \tan x \tan y}$$

Double-Angle Formulas

$$\sin 2x = 2 \sin x \cos x$$

$$\cos 2x = \cos^2 x - \sin^2 x = 2 \cos^2 x - 1 = 1 - 2 \sin^2 x$$

$$\tan 2x = \frac{2 \tan x}{1 - \tan^2 x}$$

Half-Angle Formulas

$$\sin^2 x = \frac{1 - \cos 2x}{2} \qquad \cos^2 x = \frac{1 + \cos 2x}{2}$$

SPECIAL FUNCTIONS

Power Functions $f(x) = x^a$

(i) $f(x) = x^n, n$ a positive integer

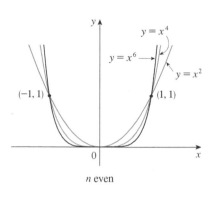

n even

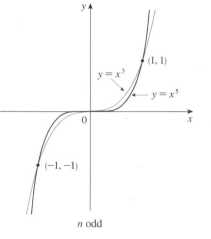

n odd

(ii) $f(x) = x^{1/n} = \sqrt[n]{x}, n$ a positive integer

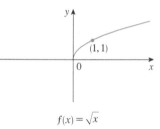

$f(x) = \sqrt{x}$

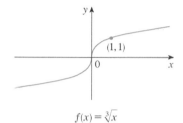

$f(x) = \sqrt[3]{x}$

(iii) $f(x) = x^{-1} = \dfrac{1}{x}$

$y = \dfrac{1}{x}$

Inverse Trigonometric Functions

$\arcsin x = \sin^{-1}x = y \iff \sin y = x \quad \text{and} \quad -\dfrac{\pi}{2} \le y \le \dfrac{\pi}{2}$

$\arccos x = \cos^{-1}x = y \iff \cos y = x \quad \text{and} \quad 0 \le y \le \pi$

$\arctan x = \tan^{-1}x = y \iff \tan y = x \quad \text{and} \quad -\dfrac{\pi}{2} < y < \dfrac{\pi}{2}$

$\displaystyle\lim_{x \to -\infty} \tan^{-1}x = -\dfrac{\pi}{2}$

$\displaystyle\lim_{x \to \infty} \tan^{-1}x = \dfrac{\pi}{2}$

$y = \tan^{-1}x = \arctan x$

SPECIAL FUNCTIONS

Exponential and Logarithmic Functions

$$\log_a x = y \iff a^y = x$$

$$\ln x = \log_e x, \quad \text{where} \quad \ln e = 1$$

$$\ln x = y \iff e^y = x$$

Cancellation Equations

$$\log_a(a^x) = x \qquad a^{\log_a x} = x$$

$$\ln(e^x) = x \qquad e^{\ln x} = x$$

Laws of Logarithms

1. $\log_a(xy) = \log_a x + \log_a y$

2. $\log_a\left(\dfrac{x}{y}\right) = \log_a x - \log_a y$

3. $\log_a(x^r) = r \log_a x$

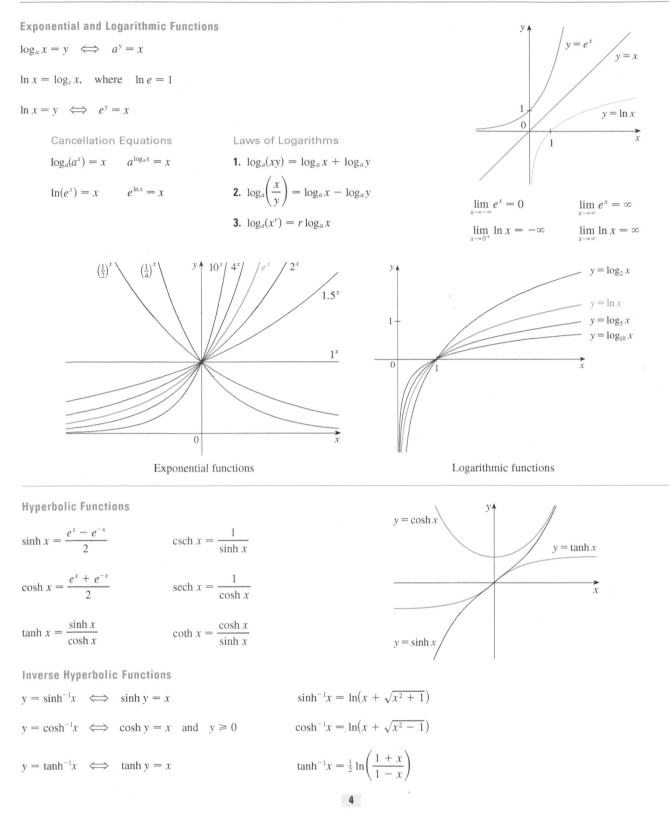

$$\lim_{x \to -\infty} e^x = 0 \qquad \lim_{x \to \infty} e^x = \infty$$

$$\lim_{x \to 0^+} \ln x = -\infty \qquad \lim_{x \to \infty} \ln x = \infty$$

Exponential functions

Logarithmic functions

Hyperbolic Functions

$$\sinh x = \frac{e^x - e^{-x}}{2} \qquad\qquad \operatorname{csch} x = \frac{1}{\sinh x}$$

$$\cosh x = \frac{e^x + e^{-x}}{2} \qquad\qquad \operatorname{sech} x = \frac{1}{\cosh x}$$

$$\tanh x = \frac{\sinh x}{\cosh x} \qquad\qquad \coth x = \frac{\cosh x}{\sinh x}$$

Inverse Hyperbolic Functions

$$y = \sinh^{-1}x \iff \sinh y = x \qquad\qquad \sinh^{-1}x = \ln\left(x + \sqrt{x^2 + 1}\right)$$

$$y = \cosh^{-1}x \iff \cosh y = x \quad \text{and} \quad y \geq 0 \qquad\qquad \cosh^{-1}x = \ln\left(x + \sqrt{x^2 - 1}\right)$$

$$y = \tanh^{-1}x \iff \tanh y = x \qquad\qquad \tanh^{-1}x = \tfrac{1}{2}\ln\left(\frac{1 + x}{1 - x}\right)$$

Cut here and keep for reference

DIFFERENTIATION RULES

General Formulas

1. $\dfrac{d}{dx}(c) = 0$

2. $\dfrac{d}{dx}[cf(x)] = cf'(x)$

3. $\dfrac{d}{dx}[f(x) + g(x)] = f'(x) + g'(x)$

4. $\dfrac{d}{dx}[f(x) - g(x)] = f'(x) - g'(x)$

5. $\dfrac{d}{dx}[f(x)g(x)] = f(x)g'(x) + g(x)f'(x)$ (Product Rule)

6. $\dfrac{d}{dx}\left[\dfrac{f(x)}{g(x)}\right] = \dfrac{g(x)f'(x) - f(x)g'(x)}{[g(x)]^2}$ (Quotient Rule)

7. $\dfrac{d}{dx}f(g(x)) = f'(g(x))g'(x)$ (Chain Rule)

8. $\dfrac{d}{dx}(x^n) = nx^{n-1}$ (Power Rule)

Exponential and Logarithmic Functions

9. $\dfrac{d}{dx}(e^x) = e^x$

10. $\dfrac{d}{dx}(a^x) = a^x \ln a$

11. $\dfrac{d}{dx}\ln|x| = \dfrac{1}{x}$

12. $\dfrac{d}{dx}(\log_a x) = \dfrac{1}{x \ln a}$

Trigonometric Functions

13. $\dfrac{d}{dx}(\sin x) = \cos x$

14. $\dfrac{d}{dx}(\cos x) = -\sin x$

15. $\dfrac{d}{dx}(\tan x) = \sec^2 x$

16. $\dfrac{d}{dx}(\csc x) = -\csc x \cot x$

17. $\dfrac{d}{dx}(\sec x) = \sec x \tan x$

18. $\dfrac{d}{dx}(\cot x) = -\csc^2 x$

Inverse Trigonometric Functions

19. $\dfrac{d}{dx}(\sin^{-1}x) = \dfrac{1}{\sqrt{1-x^2}}$

20. $\dfrac{d}{dx}(\cos^{-1}x) = -\dfrac{1}{\sqrt{1-x^2}}$

21. $\dfrac{d}{dx}(\tan^{-1}x) = \dfrac{1}{1+x^2}$

22. $\dfrac{d}{dx}(\csc^{-1}x) = -\dfrac{1}{x\sqrt{x^2-1}}$

23. $\dfrac{d}{dx}(\sec^{-1}x) = \dfrac{1}{x\sqrt{x^2-1}}$

24. $\dfrac{d}{dx}(\cot^{-1}x) = -\dfrac{1}{1+x^2}$

Hyperbolic Functions

25. $\dfrac{d}{dx}(\sinh x) = \cosh x$

26. $\dfrac{d}{dx}(\cosh x) = \sinh x$

27. $\dfrac{d}{dx}(\tanh x) = \operatorname{sech}^2 x$

28. $\dfrac{d}{dx}(\operatorname{csch} x) = -\operatorname{csch} x \coth x$

29. $\dfrac{d}{dx}(\operatorname{sech} x) = -\operatorname{sech} x \tanh x$

30. $\dfrac{d}{dx}(\coth x) = -\operatorname{csch}^2 x$

Inverse Hyperbolic Functions

31. $\dfrac{d}{dx}(\sinh^{-1}x) = \dfrac{1}{\sqrt{1+x^2}}$

32. $\dfrac{d}{dx}(\cosh^{-1}x) = \dfrac{1}{\sqrt{x^2-1}}$

33. $\dfrac{d}{dx}(\tanh^{-1}x) = \dfrac{1}{1-x^2}$

34. $\dfrac{d}{dx}(\operatorname{csch}^{-1}x) = -\dfrac{1}{|x|\sqrt{x^2+1}}$

35. $\dfrac{d}{dx}(\operatorname{sech}^{-1}x) = -\dfrac{1}{x\sqrt{1-x^2}}$

36. $\dfrac{d}{dx}(\coth^{-1}x) = \dfrac{1}{1-x^2}$

TABLE OF INTEGRALS

Basic Forms

1. $\int u\,dv = uv - \int v\,du$

2. $\int u^n\,du = \dfrac{u^{n+1}}{n+1} + C, \quad n \neq -1$

3. $\int \dfrac{du}{u} = \ln|u| + C$

4. $\int e^u\,du = e^u + C$

5. $\int a^u\,du = \dfrac{a^u}{\ln a} + C$

6. $\int \sin u\,du = -\cos u + C$

7. $\int \cos u\,du = \sin u + C$

8. $\int \sec^2 u\,du = \tan u + C$

9. $\int \csc^2 u\,du = -\cot u + C$

10. $\int \sec u \tan u\,du = \sec u + C$

11. $\int \csc u \cot u\,du = -\csc u + C$

12. $\int \tan u\,du = \ln|\sec u| + C$

13. $\int \cot u\,du = \ln|\sin u| + C$

14. $\int \sec u\,du = \ln|\sec u + \tan u| + C$

15. $\int \csc u\,du = \ln|\csc u - \cot u| + C$

16. $\int \dfrac{du}{\sqrt{a^2 - u^2}} = \sin^{-1}\dfrac{u}{a} + C, \quad a > 0$

17. $\int \dfrac{du}{a^2 + u^2} = \dfrac{1}{a}\tan^{-1}\dfrac{u}{a} + C$

18. $\int \dfrac{du}{u\sqrt{u^2 - a^2}} = \dfrac{1}{a}\sec^{-1}\dfrac{u}{a} + C$

19. $\int \dfrac{du}{a^2 - u^2} = \dfrac{1}{2a}\ln\left|\dfrac{u+a}{u-a}\right| + C$

20. $\int \dfrac{du}{u^2 - a^2} = \dfrac{1}{2a}\ln\left|\dfrac{u-a}{u+a}\right| + C$

Forms Involving $\sqrt{a^2 + u^2}$, $a > 0$

21. $\int \sqrt{a^2 + u^2}\,du = \dfrac{u}{2}\sqrt{a^2 + u^2} + \dfrac{a^2}{2}\ln\left(u + \sqrt{a^2 + u^2}\right) + C$

22. $\int u^2\sqrt{a^2 + u^2}\,du = \dfrac{u}{8}(a^2 + 2u^2)\sqrt{a^2 + u^2} - \dfrac{a^4}{8}\ln\left(u + \sqrt{a^2 + u^2}\right) + C$

23. $\int \dfrac{\sqrt{a^2 + u^2}}{u}\,du = \sqrt{a^2 + u^2} - a\ln\left|\dfrac{a + \sqrt{a^2 + u^2}}{u}\right| + C$

24. $\int \dfrac{\sqrt{a^2 + u^2}}{u^2}\,du = -\dfrac{\sqrt{a^2 + u^2}}{u} + \ln\left(u + \sqrt{a^2 + u^2}\right) + C$

25. $\int \dfrac{du}{\sqrt{a^2 + u^2}} = \ln\left(u + \sqrt{a^2 + u^2}\right) + C$

26. $\int \dfrac{u^2\,du}{\sqrt{a^2 + u^2}} = \dfrac{u}{2}\sqrt{a^2 + u^2} - \dfrac{a^2}{2}\ln\left(u + \sqrt{a^2 + u^2}\right) + C$

27. $\int \dfrac{du}{u\sqrt{a^2 + u^2}} = -\dfrac{1}{a}\ln\left|\dfrac{\sqrt{a^2 + u^2} + a}{u}\right| + C$

28. $\int \dfrac{du}{u^2\sqrt{a^2 + u^2}} = -\dfrac{\sqrt{a^2 + u^2}}{a^2 u} + C$

29. $\int \dfrac{du}{(a^2 + u^2)^{3/2}} = \dfrac{u}{a^2\sqrt{a^2 + u^2}} + C$

TABLE OF INTEGRALS

Cut here and keep for reference

Forms Involving $\sqrt{a^2 - u^2}$, $a > 0$

30. $\displaystyle\int \sqrt{a^2 - u^2}\, du = \frac{u}{2}\sqrt{a^2 - u^2} + \frac{a^2}{2}\sin^{-1}\frac{u}{a} + C$

31. $\displaystyle\int u^2\sqrt{a^2 - u^2}\, du = \frac{u}{8}(2u^2 - a^2)\sqrt{a^2 - u^2} + \frac{a^4}{8}\sin^{-1}\frac{u}{a} + C$

32. $\displaystyle\int \frac{\sqrt{a^2 - u^2}}{u}\, du = \sqrt{a^2 - u^2} - a\ln\left|\frac{a + \sqrt{a^2 - u^2}}{u}\right| + C$

33. $\displaystyle\int \frac{\sqrt{a^2 - u^2}}{u^2}\, du = -\frac{1}{u}\sqrt{a^2 - u^2} - \sin^{-1}\frac{u}{a} + C$

34. $\displaystyle\int \frac{u^2\, du}{\sqrt{a^2 - u^2}} = -\frac{u}{2}\sqrt{a^2 - u^2} + \frac{a^2}{2}\sin^{-1}\frac{u}{a} + C$

35. $\displaystyle\int \frac{du}{u\sqrt{a^2 - u^2}} = -\frac{1}{a}\ln\left|\frac{a + \sqrt{a^2 - u^2}}{u}\right| + C$

36. $\displaystyle\int \frac{du}{u^2\sqrt{a^2 - u^2}} = -\frac{1}{a^2 u}\sqrt{a^2 - u^2} + C$

37. $\displaystyle\int (a^2 - u^2)^{3/2}\, du = -\frac{u}{8}(2u^2 - 5a^2)\sqrt{a^2 - u^2} + \frac{3a^4}{8}\sin^{-1}\frac{u}{a} + C$

38. $\displaystyle\int \frac{du}{(a^2 - u^2)^{3/2}} = \frac{u}{a^2\sqrt{a^2 - u^2}} + C$

Forms Involving $\sqrt{u^2 - a^2}$, $a > 0$

39. $\displaystyle\int \sqrt{u^2 - a^2}\, du = \frac{u}{2}\sqrt{u^2 - a^2} - \frac{a^2}{2}\ln\left|u + \sqrt{u^2 - a^2}\right| + C$

40. $\displaystyle\int u^2\sqrt{u^2 - a^2}\, du = \frac{u}{8}(2u^2 - a^2)\sqrt{u^2 - a^2} - \frac{a^4}{8}\ln\left|u + \sqrt{u^2 - a^2}\right| + C$

41. $\displaystyle\int \frac{\sqrt{u^2 - a^2}}{u}\, du = \sqrt{u^2 - a^2} - a\cos^{-1}\frac{a}{|u|} + C$

42. $\displaystyle\int \frac{\sqrt{u^2 - a^2}}{u^2}\, du = -\frac{\sqrt{u^2 - a^2}}{u} + \ln\left|u + \sqrt{u^2 - a^2}\right| + C$

43. $\displaystyle\int \frac{du}{\sqrt{u^2 - a^2}} = \ln\left|u + \sqrt{u^2 - a^2}\right| + C$

44. $\displaystyle\int \frac{u^2\, du}{\sqrt{u^2 - a^2}} = \frac{u}{2}\sqrt{u^2 - a^2} + \frac{a^2}{2}\ln\left|u + \sqrt{u^2 - a^2}\right| + C$

45. $\displaystyle\int \frac{du}{u^2\sqrt{u^2 - a^2}} = \frac{\sqrt{u^2 - a^2}}{a^2 u} + C$

46. $\displaystyle\int \frac{du}{(u^2 - a^2)^{3/2}} = -\frac{u}{a^2\sqrt{u^2 - a^2}} + C$

TABLE OF INTEGRALS

Forms Involving $a + bu$

47. $\displaystyle\int \frac{u\,du}{a + bu} = \frac{1}{b^2}\left(a + bu - a \ln|a + bu|\right) + C$

48. $\displaystyle\int \frac{u^2\,du}{a + bu} = \frac{1}{2b^3}\left[(a + bu)^2 - 4a(a + bu) + 2a^2 \ln|a + bu|\right] + C$

49. $\displaystyle\int \frac{du}{u(a + bu)} = \frac{1}{a} \ln\left|\frac{u}{a + bu}\right| + C$

50. $\displaystyle\int \frac{du}{u^2(a + bu)} = -\frac{1}{au} + \frac{b}{a^2} \ln\left|\frac{a + bu}{u}\right| + C$

51. $\displaystyle\int \frac{u\,du}{(a + bu)^2} = \frac{a}{b^2(a + bu)} + \frac{1}{b^2} \ln|a + bu| + C$

52. $\displaystyle\int \frac{du}{u(a + bu)^2} = \frac{1}{a(a + bu)} - \frac{1}{a^2} \ln\left|\frac{a + bu}{u}\right| + C$

53. $\displaystyle\int \frac{u^2\,du}{(a + bu)^2} = \frac{1}{b^3}\left(a + bu - \frac{a^2}{a + bu} - 2a \ln|a + bu|\right) + C$

54. $\displaystyle\int u\sqrt{a + bu}\,du = \frac{2}{15b^2}(3bu - 2a)(a + bu)^{3/2} + C$

55. $\displaystyle\int \frac{u\,du}{\sqrt{a + bu}} = \frac{2}{3b^2}(bu - 2a)\sqrt{a + bu} + C$

56. $\displaystyle\int \frac{u^2\,du}{\sqrt{a + bu}} = \frac{2}{15b^3}(8a^2 + 3b^2u^2 - 4abu)\sqrt{a + bu} + C$

57. $\displaystyle\int \frac{du}{u\sqrt{a + bu}} = \frac{1}{\sqrt{a}} \ln\left|\frac{\sqrt{a + bu} - \sqrt{a}}{\sqrt{a + bu} + \sqrt{a}}\right| + C,\quad \text{if } a > 0$

$\displaystyle\qquad\qquad\quad = \frac{2}{\sqrt{-a}} \tan^{-1}\sqrt{\frac{a + bu}{-a}} + C,\qquad \text{if } a < 0$

58. $\displaystyle\int \frac{\sqrt{a + bu}}{u}\,du = 2\sqrt{a + bu} + a\int \frac{du}{u\sqrt{a + bu}}$

59. $\displaystyle\int \frac{\sqrt{a + bu}}{u^2}\,du = -\frac{\sqrt{a + bu}}{u} + \frac{b}{2}\int \frac{du}{u\sqrt{a + bu}}$

60. $\displaystyle\int u^n\sqrt{a + bu}\,du = \frac{2}{b(2n + 3)}\left[u^n(a + bu)^{3/2} - na\int u^{n-1}\sqrt{a + bu}\,du\right]$

61. $\displaystyle\int \frac{u^n\,du}{\sqrt{a + bu}} = \frac{2u^n\sqrt{a + bu}}{b(2n + 1)} - \frac{2na}{b(2n + 1)}\int \frac{u^{n-1}\,du}{\sqrt{a + bu}}$

62. $\displaystyle\int \frac{du}{u^n\sqrt{a + bu}} = -\frac{\sqrt{a + bu}}{a(n - 1)u^{n-1}} - \frac{b(2n - 3)}{2a(n - 1)}\int \frac{du}{u^{n-1}\sqrt{a + bu}}$

TABLE OF INTEGRALS

Trigonometric Forms

63. $\displaystyle\int \sin^2 u \, du = \tfrac{1}{2}u - \tfrac{1}{4}\sin 2u + C$

64. $\displaystyle\int \cos^2 u \, du = \tfrac{1}{2}u + \tfrac{1}{4}\sin 2u + C$

65. $\displaystyle\int \tan^2 u \, du = \tan u - u + C$

66. $\displaystyle\int \cot^2 u \, du = -\cot u - u + C$

67. $\displaystyle\int \sin^3 u \, du = -\tfrac{1}{3}(2 + \sin^2 u)\cos u + C$

68. $\displaystyle\int \cos^3 u \, du = \tfrac{1}{3}(2 + \cos^2 u)\sin u + C$

69. $\displaystyle\int \tan^3 u \, du = \tfrac{1}{2}\tan^2 u + \ln |\cos u| + C$

70. $\displaystyle\int \cot^3 u \, du = -\tfrac{1}{2}\cot^2 u - \ln |\sin u| + C$

71. $\displaystyle\int \sec^3 u \, du = \tfrac{1}{2}\sec u \tan u + \tfrac{1}{2}\ln |\sec u + \tan u| + C$

72. $\displaystyle\int \csc^3 u \, du = -\tfrac{1}{2}\csc u \cot u + \tfrac{1}{2}\ln |\csc u - \cot u| + C$

73. $\displaystyle\int \sin^n u \, du = -\frac{1}{n}\sin^{n-1}u \cos u + \frac{n-1}{n}\int \sin^{n-2}u \, du$

74. $\displaystyle\int \cos^n u \, du = \frac{1}{n}\cos^{n-1}u \sin u + \frac{n-1}{n}\int \cos^{n-2}u \, du$

75. $\displaystyle\int \tan^n u \, du = \frac{1}{n-1}\tan^{n-1}u - \int \tan^{n-2}u \, du$

76. $\displaystyle\int \cot^n u \, du = \frac{-1}{n-1}\cot^{n-1}u - \int \cot^{n-2}u \, du$

77. $\displaystyle\int \sec^n u \, du = \frac{1}{n-1}\tan u \sec^{n-2}u + \frac{n-2}{n-1}\int \sec^{n-2}u \, du$

78. $\displaystyle\int \csc^n u \, du = \frac{-1}{n-1}\cot u \csc^{n-2}u + \frac{n-2}{n-1}\int \csc^{n-2}u \, du$

79. $\displaystyle\int \sin au \sin bu \, du = \frac{\sin (a-b)u}{2(a-b)} - \frac{\sin (a+b)u}{2(a+b)} + C$

80. $\displaystyle\int \cos au \cos bu \, du = \frac{\sin (a-b)u}{2(a-b)} + \frac{\sin (a+b)u}{2(a+b)} + C$

81. $\displaystyle\int \sin au \cos bu \, du = -\frac{\cos (a-b)u}{2(a-b)} - \frac{\cos (a+b)u}{2(a+b)} + C$

82. $\displaystyle\int u \sin u \, du = \sin u - u \cos u + C$

83. $\displaystyle\int u \cos u \, du = \cos u + u \sin u + C$

84. $\displaystyle\int u^n \sin u \, du = -u^n \cos u + n \int u^{n-1}\cos u \, du$

85. $\displaystyle\int u^n \cos u \, du = u^n \sin u - n \int u^{n-1}\sin u \, du$

86. $\displaystyle\int \sin^n u \cos^m u \, du = -\frac{\sin^{n-1}u \cos^{m+1}u}{n+m} + \frac{n-1}{n+m}\int \sin^{n-2}u \cos^m u \, du$

$$= \frac{\sin^{n+1}u \cos^{m-1}u}{n+m} + \frac{m-1}{n+m}\int \sin^n u \cos^{m-2}u \, du$$

Inverse Trigonometric Forms

87. $\displaystyle\int \sin^{-1}u \, du = u \sin^{-1}u + \sqrt{1-u^2} + C$

88. $\displaystyle\int \cos^{-1}u \, du = u \cos^{-1}u - \sqrt{1-u^2} + C$

89. $\displaystyle\int \tan^{-1}u \, du = u \tan^{-1}u - \tfrac{1}{2}\ln(1+u^2) + C$

90. $\displaystyle\int u \sin^{-1}u \, du = \frac{2u^2-1}{4}\sin^{-1}u + \frac{u\sqrt{1-u^2}}{4} + C$

91. $\displaystyle\int u \cos^{-1}u \, du = \frac{2u^2-1}{4}\cos^{-1}u - \frac{u\sqrt{1-u^2}}{4} + C$

92. $\displaystyle\int u \tan^{-1}u \, du = \frac{u^2+1}{2}\tan^{-1}u - \frac{u}{2} + C$

93. $\displaystyle\int u^n \sin^{-1}u \, du = \frac{1}{n+1}\left[u^{n+1}\sin^{-1}u - \int \frac{u^{n+1}\,du}{\sqrt{1-u^2}}\right], \quad n \neq -1$

94. $\displaystyle\int u^n \cos^{-1}u \, du = \frac{1}{n+1}\left[u^{n+1}\cos^{-1}u + \int \frac{u^{n+1}\,du}{\sqrt{1-u^2}}\right], \quad n \neq -1$

95. $\displaystyle\int u^n \tan^{-1}u \, du = \frac{1}{n+1}\left[u^{n+1}\tan^{-1}u - \int \frac{u^{n+1}\,du}{1+u^2}\right], \quad n \neq -1$

TABLE OF INTEGRALS

Exponential and Logarithmic Forms

96. $\displaystyle\int ue^{au}\,du = \frac{1}{a^2}(au-1)e^{au} + C$

97. $\displaystyle\int u^n e^{au}\,du = \frac{1}{a}u^n e^{au} - \frac{n}{a}\int u^{n-1}e^{au}\,du$

98. $\displaystyle\int e^{au}\sin bu\,du = \frac{e^{au}}{a^2+b^2}(a\sin bu - b\cos bu) + C$

99. $\displaystyle\int e^{au}\cos bu\,du = \frac{e^{au}}{a^2+b^2}(a\cos bu + b\sin bu) + C$

100. $\displaystyle\int \ln u\,du = u\ln u - u + C$

101. $\displaystyle\int u^n \ln u\,du = \frac{u^{n+1}}{(n+1)^2}[(n+1)\ln u - 1] + C$

102. $\displaystyle\int \frac{1}{u\ln u}\,du = \ln|\ln u| + C$

Hyperbolic Forms

103. $\displaystyle\int \sinh u\,du = \cosh u + C$

104. $\displaystyle\int \cosh u\,du = \sinh u + C$

105. $\displaystyle\int \tanh u\,du = \ln \cosh u + C$

106. $\displaystyle\int \coth u\,du = \ln|\sinh u| + C$

107. $\displaystyle\int \operatorname{sech} u\,du = \tan^{-1}|\sinh u| + C$

108. $\displaystyle\int \operatorname{csch} u\,du = \ln\left|\tanh \tfrac{1}{2}u\right| + C$

109. $\displaystyle\int \operatorname{sech}^2 u\,du = \tanh u + C$

110. $\displaystyle\int \operatorname{csch}^2 u\,du = -\coth u + C$

111. $\displaystyle\int \operatorname{sech} u \tanh u\,du = -\operatorname{sech} u + C$

112. $\displaystyle\int \operatorname{csch} u \coth u\,du = -\operatorname{csch} u + C$

Forms Involving $\sqrt{2au - u^2}$, $a > 0$

113. $\displaystyle\int \sqrt{2au-u^2}\,du = \frac{u-a}{2}\sqrt{2au-u^2} + \frac{a^2}{2}\cos^{-1}\left(\frac{a-u}{a}\right) + C$

114. $\displaystyle\int u\sqrt{2au-u^2}\,du = \frac{2u^2-au-3a^2}{6}\sqrt{2au-u^2} + \frac{a^3}{2}\cos^{-1}\left(\frac{a-u}{a}\right) + C$

115. $\displaystyle\int \frac{\sqrt{2au-u^2}}{u}\,du = \sqrt{2au-u^2} + a\cos^{-1}\left(\frac{a-u}{a}\right) + C$

116. $\displaystyle\int \frac{\sqrt{2au-u^2}}{u^2}\,du = -\frac{2\sqrt{2au-u^2}}{u} - \cos^{-1}\left(\frac{a-u}{a}\right) + C$

117. $\displaystyle\int \frac{du}{\sqrt{2au-u^2}} = \cos^{-1}\left(\frac{a-u}{a}\right) + C$

118. $\displaystyle\int \frac{u\,du}{\sqrt{2au-u^2}} = -\sqrt{2au-u^2} + a\cos^{-1}\left(\frac{a-u}{a}\right) + C$

119. $\displaystyle\int \frac{u^2\,du}{\sqrt{2au-u^2}} = -\frac{(u+3a)}{2}\sqrt{2au-u^2} + \frac{3a^2}{2}\cos^{-1}\left(\frac{a-u}{a}\right) + C$

120. $\displaystyle\int \frac{du}{u\sqrt{2au-u^2}} = -\frac{\sqrt{2au-u^2}}{au} + C$

☐ DIAGNOSTIC TESTS

Test A   Algebra

1. (a) $(-3)^4 = (-3)(-3)(-3)(-3) = 81$

(b) $-3^4 = -(3)(3)(3)(3) = -81$

(c) $3^{-4} = \dfrac{1}{3^4} = \dfrac{1}{81}$

(d) $\dfrac{5^{23}}{5^{21}} = 5^{23-21} = 5^2 = 25$

(e) $\left(\frac{2}{3}\right)^{-2} = \left(\frac{3}{2}\right)^2 = \frac{9}{4}$

(f) $16^{-3/4} = \dfrac{1}{16^{3/4}} = \dfrac{1}{\left(\sqrt[4]{16}\right)^3} = \dfrac{1}{2^3} = \dfrac{1}{8}$

2. (a) Note that $\sqrt{200} = \sqrt{100 \cdot 2} = 10\sqrt{2}$ and $\sqrt{32} = \sqrt{16 \cdot 2} = 4\sqrt{2}$. Thus $\sqrt{200} - \sqrt{32} = 10\sqrt{2} - 4\sqrt{2} = 6\sqrt{2}$.

(b) $(3a^3b^3)(4ab^2)^2 = 3a^3b^3 16a^2b^4 = 48a^5b^7$

(c) $\left(\dfrac{3x^{3/2}y^3}{x^2y^{-1/2}}\right)^{-2} = \left(\dfrac{x^2y^{-1/2}}{3x^{3/2}y^3}\right)^2 = \dfrac{(x^2y^{-1/2})^2}{(3x^{3/2}y^3)^2} = \dfrac{x^4y^{-1}}{9x^3y^6} = \dfrac{x^4}{9x^3y^6y} = \dfrac{x}{9y^7}$

3. (a) $3(x+6) + 4(2x-5) = 3x + 18 + 8x - 20 = 11x - 2$

(b) $(x+3)(4x-5) = 4x^2 - 5x + 12x - 15 = 4x^2 + 7x - 15$

(c) $\left(\sqrt{a} + \sqrt{b}\right)\left(\sqrt{a} - \sqrt{b}\right) = \left(\sqrt{a}\right)^2 - \sqrt{a}\sqrt{b} + \sqrt{a}\sqrt{b} - \left(\sqrt{b}\right)^2 = a - b$

Or: Use the formula for the difference of two squares to see that $\left(\sqrt{a} + \sqrt{b}\right)\left(\sqrt{a} - \sqrt{b}\right) = \left(\sqrt{a}\right)^2 - \left(\sqrt{b}\right)^2 = a - b$.

(d) $(2x+3)^2 = (2x+3)(2x+3) = 4x^2 + 6x + 6x + 9 = 4x^2 + 12x + 9$.

Note: A quicker way to expand this binomial is to use the formula $(a+b)^2 = a^2 + 2ab + b^2$ with $a = 2x$ and $b = 3$:
$(2x+3)^2 = (2x)^2 + 2(2x)(3) + 3^2 = 4x^2 + 12x + 9$

(e) See Reference Page 1 for the binomial formula $(a+b)^3 = a^3 + 3a^2b + 3ab^2 + b^3$. Using it, we get
$(x+2)^3 = x^3 + 3x^2(2) + 3x(2^2) + 2^3 = x^3 + 6x^2 + 12x + 8$.

4. (a) Using the difference of two squares formula, $a^2 - b^2 = (a+b)(a-b)$, we have
$4x^2 - 25 = (2x)^2 - 5^2 = (2x+5)(2x-5)$.

(b) Factoring by trial and error, we get $2x^2 + 5x - 12 = (2x-3)(x+4)$.

(c) Using factoring by grouping and the difference of two squares formula, we have
$x^3 - 3x^2 - 4x + 12 = x^2(x-3) - 4(x-3) = (x^2-4)(x-3) = (x-2)(x+2)(x-3)$.

(d) $x^4 + 27x = x(x^3 + 27) = x(x+3)(x^2 - 3x + 9)$

This last expression was obtained using the sum of two cubes formula, $a^3 + b^3 = (a+b)(a^2 - ab + b^2)$ with $a = x$ and $b = 3$. [See Reference Page 1 in the textbook.]

(e) The smallest exponent on x is $-\frac{1}{2}$, so we will factor out $x^{-1/2}$.
$3x^{3/2} - 9x^{1/2} + 6x^{-1/2} = 3x^{-1/2}(x^2 - 3x + 2) = 3x^{-1/2}(x-1)(x-2)$

(f) $x^3y - 4xy = xy(x^2 - 4) = xy(x-2)(x+2)$

5. (a) $\dfrac{x^2 + 3x + 2}{x^2 - x - 2} = \dfrac{(x+1)(x+2)}{(x+1)(x-2)} = \dfrac{x+2}{x-2}$

(b) $\dfrac{2x^2 - x - 1}{x^2 - 9} \cdot \dfrac{x+3}{2x+1} = \dfrac{(2x+1)(x-1)}{(x-3)(x+3)} \cdot \dfrac{x+3}{2x+1} = \dfrac{x-1}{x-3}$

(c) $\dfrac{x^2}{x^2 - 4} - \dfrac{x+1}{x+2} = \dfrac{x^2}{(x-2)(x+2)} - \dfrac{x+1}{x+2} = \dfrac{x^2}{(x-2)(x+2)} - \dfrac{x+1}{x+2} \cdot \dfrac{x-2}{x-2} = \dfrac{x^2 - (x+1)(x-2)}{(x-2)(x+2)}$

$\qquad = \dfrac{x^2 - (x^2 - x - 2)}{(x+2)(x-2)} = \dfrac{x+2}{(x+2)(x-2)} = \dfrac{1}{x-2}$

(d) $\dfrac{\dfrac{y}{x} - \dfrac{x}{y}}{\dfrac{1}{y} - \dfrac{1}{x}} = \dfrac{\dfrac{y}{x} - \dfrac{x}{y}}{\dfrac{1}{y} - \dfrac{1}{x}} \cdot \dfrac{xy}{xy} = \dfrac{y^2 - x^2}{x - y} = \dfrac{(y-x)(y+x)}{-(y-x)} = \dfrac{y+x}{-1} = -(x+y)$

6. (a) $\dfrac{\sqrt{10}}{\sqrt{5} - 2} = \dfrac{\sqrt{10}}{\sqrt{5} - 2} \cdot \dfrac{\sqrt{5} + 2}{\sqrt{5} + 2} = \dfrac{\sqrt{50} + 2\sqrt{10}}{\left(\sqrt{5}\right)^2 - 2^2} = \dfrac{5\sqrt{2} + 2\sqrt{10}}{5 - 4} = 5\sqrt{2} + 2\sqrt{10}$

(b) $\dfrac{\sqrt{4+h} - 2}{h} = \dfrac{\sqrt{4+h} - 2}{h} \cdot \dfrac{\sqrt{4+h} + 2}{\sqrt{4+h} + 2} = \dfrac{4 + h - 4}{h\left(\sqrt{4+h} + 2\right)} = \dfrac{h}{h\left(\sqrt{4+h} + 2\right)} = \dfrac{1}{\sqrt{4+h} + 2}$

7. (a) $x^2 + x + 1 = \left(x^2 + x + \frac{1}{4}\right) + 1 - \frac{1}{4} = \left(x + \frac{1}{2}\right)^2 + \frac{3}{4}$

(b) $2x^2 - 12x + 11 = 2(x^2 - 6x) + 11 = 2(x^2 - 6x + 9 - 9) + 11 = 2(x^2 - 6x + 9) - 18 + 11 = 2(x-3)^2 - 7$

8. (a) $x + 5 = 14 - \frac{1}{2}x \Leftrightarrow x + \frac{1}{2}x = 14 - 5 \Leftrightarrow \frac{3}{2}x = 9 \Leftrightarrow x = \frac{2}{3} \cdot 9 \Leftrightarrow x = 6$

(b) $\dfrac{2x}{x+1} = \dfrac{2x-1}{x} \Rightarrow 2x^2 = (2x-1)(x+1) \Leftrightarrow 2x^2 = 2x^2 + x - 1 \Leftrightarrow x = 1$

(c) $x^2 - x - 12 = 0 \Leftrightarrow (x+3)(x-4) = 0 \Leftrightarrow x + 3 = 0 \text{ or } x - 4 = 0 \Leftrightarrow x = -3 \text{ or } x = 4$

(d) By the quadratic formula, $2x^2 + 4x + 1 = 0 \Leftrightarrow$

$$x = \dfrac{-4 \pm \sqrt{4^2 - 4(2)(1)}}{2(2)} = \dfrac{-4 \pm \sqrt{8}}{4} = \dfrac{-4 \pm 2\sqrt{2}}{4} = \dfrac{2\left(-2 \pm \sqrt{2}\right)}{4} = \dfrac{-2 \pm \sqrt{2}}{2} = -1 \pm \tfrac{1}{2}\sqrt{2}.$$

(e) $x^4 - 3x^2 + 2 = 0 \Leftrightarrow (x^2 - 1)(x^2 - 2) = 0 \Leftrightarrow x^2 - 1 = 0 \text{ or } x^2 - 2 = 0 \Leftrightarrow x^2 = 1 \text{ or } x^2 = 2 \Leftrightarrow$

$x = \pm 1 \text{ or } x = \pm\sqrt{2}$

(f) $3\,|x - 4| = 10 \Leftrightarrow |x - 4| = \frac{10}{3} \Leftrightarrow x - 4 = -\frac{10}{3} \text{ or } x - 4 = \frac{10}{3} \Leftrightarrow x = \frac{2}{3} \text{ or } x = \frac{22}{3}$

(g) Multiplying through $2x(4-x)^{-1/2} - 3\sqrt{4-x} = 0$ by $(4-x)^{1/2}$ gives $2x - 3(4-x) = 0 \Leftrightarrow$

$2x - 12 + 3x = 0 \Leftrightarrow 5x - 12 = 0 \Leftrightarrow 5x = 12 \Leftrightarrow x = \frac{12}{5}.$

9. (a) $-4 < 5 - 3x \leq 17 \Leftrightarrow -9 < -3x \leq 12 \Leftrightarrow 3 > x \geq -4 \text{ or } -4 \leq x < 3.$

In interval notation, the answer is $[-4, 3)$.

(b) $x^2 < 2x + 8 \Leftrightarrow x^2 - 2x - 8 < 0 \Leftrightarrow (x+2)(x-4) < 0$. Now, $(x+2)(x-4)$ will change sign at the critical

values $x = -2$ and $x = 4$. Thus the possible intervals of solution are $(-\infty, -2)$, $(-2, 4)$, and $(4, \infty)$. By choosing a

single test value from each interval, we see that $(-2, 4)$ is the only interval that satisfies the inequality.

(c) The inequality $x(x-1)(x+2) > 0$ has critical values of $-2, 0$, and 1. The corresponding possible intervals of solution are $(-\infty, -2)$, $(-2, 0)$, $(0, 1)$ and $(1, \infty)$. By choosing a single test value from each interval, we see that both intervals $(-2, 0)$ and $(1, \infty)$ satisfy the inequality. Thus, the solution is the union of these two intervals: $(-2, 0) \cup (1, \infty)$.

(d) $|x - 4| < 3 \Leftrightarrow -3 < x - 4 < 3 \Leftrightarrow 1 < x < 7$. In interval notation, the answer is $(1, 7)$.

(e) $\dfrac{2x-3}{x+1} \leq 1 \Leftrightarrow \dfrac{2x-3}{x+1} - 1 \leq 0 \Leftrightarrow \dfrac{2x-3}{x+1} - \dfrac{x+1}{x+1} \leq 0 \Leftrightarrow \dfrac{2x-3-x-1}{x+1} \leq 0 \Leftrightarrow \dfrac{x-4}{x+1} \leq 0.$

Now, the expression $\dfrac{x-4}{x+1}$ may change signs at the critical values $x = -1$ and $x = 4$, so the possible intervals of solution are $(-\infty, -1)$, $(-1, 4]$, and $[4, \infty)$. By choosing a single test value from each interval, we see that $(-1, 4]$ is the only interval that satisfies the inequality.

10. (a) False. In order for the statement to be true, it must hold for all real numbers, so, to show that the statement is false, pick $p = 1$ and $q = 2$ and observe that $(1 + 2)^2 \neq 1^2 + 2^2$. In general, $(p+q)^2 = p^2 + 2pq + q^2$.

(b) True as long as a and b are nonnegative real numbers. To see this, think in terms of the laws of exponents:
$$\sqrt{ab} = (ab)^{1/2} = a^{1/2}b^{1/2} = \sqrt{a}\,\sqrt{b}.$$

(c) False. To see this, let $p = 1$ and $q = 2$, then $\sqrt{1^2 + 2^2} \neq 1 + 2$.

(d) False. To see this, let $T = 1$ and $C = 2$, then $\dfrac{1 + 1(2)}{2} \neq 1 + 1$.

(e) False. To see this, let $x = 2$ and $y = 3$, then $\dfrac{1}{2 - 3} \neq \dfrac{1}{2} - \dfrac{1}{3}$.

(f) True since $\dfrac{1/x}{a/x - b/x} \cdot \dfrac{x}{x} = \dfrac{1}{a - b}$, as long as $x \neq 0$ and $a - b \neq 0$.

Test B   Analytic Geometry

1. (a) Using the point $(2, -5)$ and $m = -3$ in the point-slope equation of a line, $y - y_1 = m(x - x_1)$, we get
$$y - (-5) = -3(x - 2) \Rightarrow y + 5 = -3x + 6 \Rightarrow y = -3x + 1.$$

(b) A line parallel to the x-axis must be horizontal and thus have a slope of 0. Since the line passes through the point $(2, -5)$, the y-coordinate of every point on the line is -5, so the equation is $y = -5$.

(c) A line parallel to the y-axis is vertical with undefined slope. So the x-coordinate of every point on the line is 2 and so the equation is $x = 2$.

(d) Note that $2x - 4y = 3 \Rightarrow -4y = -2x + 3 \Rightarrow y = \frac{1}{2}x - \frac{3}{4}$. Thus the slope of the given line is $m = \frac{1}{2}$. Hence, the slope of the line we're looking for is also $\frac{1}{2}$ (since the line we're looking for is required to be parallel to the given line). So the equation of the line is $y - (-5) = \frac{1}{2}(x - 2) \Rightarrow y + 5 = \frac{1}{2}x - 1 \Rightarrow y = \frac{1}{2}x - 6$.

2. First we'll find the distance between the two given points in order to obtain the radius, r, of the circle:
$$r = \sqrt{[3 - (-1)]^2 + (-2 - 4)^2} = \sqrt{4^2 + (-6)^2} = \sqrt{52}.$$ Next use the standard equation of a circle, $(x - h)^2 + (y - k)^2 = r^2$, where (h, k) is the center, to get $(x + 1)^2 + (y - 4)^2 = 52$.

3. We must rewrite the equation in standard form in order to identify the center and radius. Note that
$x^2 + y^2 - 6x + 10y + 9 = 0 \quad \Rightarrow \quad x^2 - 6x + 9 + y^2 + 10y = 0$. For the left-hand side of the latter equation, we
factor the first three terms and complete the square on the last two terms as follows: $x^2 - 6x + 9 + y^2 + 10y = 0 \quad \Rightarrow$
$(x-3)^2 + y^2 + 10y + 25 = 25 \quad \Rightarrow \quad (x-3)^2 + (y+5)^2 = 25$. Thus, the center of the circle is $(3, -5)$ and the radius is 5.

4. (a) $A(-7, 4)$ and $B(5, -12) \quad \Rightarrow \quad m_{AB} = \dfrac{-12 - 4}{5 - (-7)} = \dfrac{-16}{12} = -\dfrac{4}{3}$

   (b) $y - 4 = -\frac{4}{3}[x - (-7)] \quad \Rightarrow \quad y - 4 = -\frac{4}{3}x - \frac{28}{3} \quad \Rightarrow \quad 3y - 12 = -4x - 28 \quad \Rightarrow \quad 4x + 3y + 16 = 0$. Putting $y = 0$,
   we get $4x + 16 = 0$, so the x-intercept is -4, and substituting 0 for x results in a y-intercept of $-\frac{16}{3}$.

   (c) The midpoint is obtained by averaging the corresponding coordinates of both points: $\left(\frac{-7+5}{2}, \frac{4+(-12)}{2}\right) = (-1, -4)$.

   (d) $d = \sqrt{[5 - (-7)]^2 + (-12 - 4)^2} = \sqrt{12^2 + (-16)^2} = \sqrt{144 + 256} = \sqrt{400} = 20$

   (e) The perpendicular bisector is the line that intersects the line segment $\overline{AB}$ at a right angle through its midpoint. Thus the
   perpendicular bisector passes through $(-1, -4)$ and has slope $\frac{3}{4}$ [the slope is obtained by taking the negative reciprocal of
   the answer from part (a)]. So the perpendicular bisector is given by $y + 4 = \frac{3}{4}[x - (-1)]$ or $3x - 4y = 13$.

   (f) The center of the required circle is the midpoint of $\overline{AB}$, and the radius is half the length of $\overline{AB}$, which is 10. Thus, the
   equation is $(x + 1)^2 + (y + 4)^2 = 100$.

5. (a) Graph the corresponding horizontal lines (given by the equations $y = -1$ and
   $y = 3$) as solid lines. The inequality $y \geq -1$ describes the points (x, y) that lie
   on or *above* the line $y = -1$. The inequality $y \leq 3$ describes the points (x, y)
   that lie on or *below* the line $y = 3$. So the pair of inequalities $-1 \leq y \leq 3$
   describes the points that lie on or *between* the lines $y = -1$ and $y = 3$.

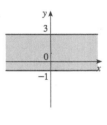

   (b) Note that the given inequalities can be written as $-4 < x < 4$ and $-2 < y < 2$,
   respectively. So the region lies between the vertical lines $x = -4$ and $x = 4$ and
   between the horizontal lines $y = -2$ and $y = 2$. As shown in the graph, the
   region common to both graphs is a rectangle (minus its edges) centered at the
   origin.

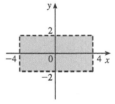

   (c) We first graph $y = 1 - \frac{1}{2}x$ as a dotted line. Since $y < 1 - \frac{1}{2}x$, the points in the
   region lie *below* this line.

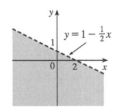

(d) We first graph the parabola $y = x^2 - 1$ using a solid curve. Since $y \geq x^2 - 1$, the points in the region lie on or *above* the parabola.

(e) We graph the circle $x^2 + y^2 = 4$ using a dotted curve. Since $\sqrt{x^2 + y^2} < 2$, the region consists of points whose distance from the origin is less than 2, that is, the points that lie *inside* the circle.

(f) The equation $9x^2 + 16y^2 = 144$ is an ellipse centered at $(0, 0)$. We put it in standard form by dividing by 144 and get $\dfrac{x^2}{16} + \dfrac{y^2}{9} = 1$. The x-intercepts are located at a distance of $\sqrt{16} = 4$ from the center while the y-intercepts are a distance of $\sqrt{9} = 3$ from the center (see the graph).

Test C   Functions

1. (a) Locate -1 on the x-axis and then go down to the point on the graph with an x-coordinate of -1. The corresponding y-coordinate is the value of the function at $x = -1$, which is -2. So, $f(-1) = -2$.

(b) Using the same technique as in part (a), we get $f(2) \approx 2.8$.

(c) Locate 2 on the y-axis and then go left and right to find all points on the graph with a y-coordinate of 2. The corresponding x-coordinates are the x-values we are searching for. So $x = -3$ and $x = 1$.

(d) Using the same technique as in part (c), we get $x \approx -2.5$ and $x \approx 0.3$.

(e) The domain is all the x-values for which the graph exists, and the range is all the y-values for which the graph exists. Thus, the domain is $[-3, 3]$, and the range is $[-2, 3]$.

2. Note that $f(2 + h) = (2 + h)^3$ and $f(2) = 2^3 = 8$. So the difference quotient becomes

$$\frac{f(2 + h) - f(2)}{h} = \frac{(2 + h)^3 - 8}{h} = \frac{8 + 12h + 6h^2 + h^3 - 8}{h} = \frac{12h + 6h^2 + h^3}{h} = \frac{h(12 + 6h + h^2)}{h} = 12 + 6h + h^2.$$

3. (a) Set the denominator equal to 0 and solve to find restrictions on the domain: $x^2 + x - 2 = 0 \Rightarrow$ $(x - 1)(x + 2) = 0 \Rightarrow x = 1$ or $x = -2$. Thus, the domain is all real numbers except 1 or -2 or, in interval notation, $(-\infty, -2) \cup (-2, 1) \cup (1, \infty)$.

(b) Note that the denominator is always greater than or equal to 1, and the numerator is defined for all real numbers. Thus, the domain is $(-\infty, \infty)$.

(c) Note that the function h is the sum of two root functions. So h is defined on the intersection of the domains of these two root functions. The domain of a square root function is found by setting its radicand greater than or equal to 0. Now,

$4 - x \geq 0 \Rightarrow x \leq 4$ and $x^2 - 1 \geq 0 \Rightarrow (x-1)(x+1) \geq 0 \Rightarrow x \leq -1$ or $x \geq 1$. Thus, the domain of h is $(-\infty, -1] \cup [1, 4]$.

4. (a) Reflect the graph of f about the x-axis.

(b) Stretch the graph of f vertically by a factor of 2, then shift 1 unit downward.

(c) Shift the graph of f right 3 units, then up 2 units.

5. (a) Make a table and then connect the points with a smooth curve:

x	-2	-1	0	1	2
y	-8	-1	0	1	8

(b) Shift the graph from part (a) left 1 unit.

(c) Shift the graph from part (a) right 2 units and up 3 units.

(d) First plot $y = x^2$. Next, to get the graph of $f(x) = 4 - x^2$, reflect f about the x-axis and then shift it upward 4 units.

(e) Make a table and then connect the points with a smooth curve:

x	0	1	4	9
y	0	1	2	3

(f) Stretch the graph from part (e) vertically by a factor of two.

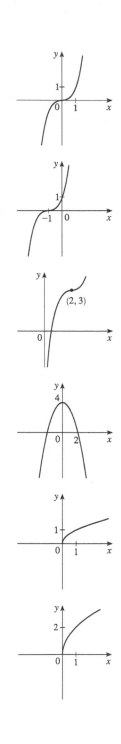

(g) First plot $y = 2^x$. Next, get the graph of $y = -2^x$ by reflecting the graph of

$y = 2^x$ about the x-axis.

(h) Note that $y = 1 + x^{-1} = 1 + 1/x$. So first plot $y = 1/x$ and then shift it

upward 1 unit.

6. (a) $f(-2) = 1 - (-2)^2 = -3$ and $f(1) = 2(1) + 1 = 3$

(b) For $x \leq 0$ plot $f(x) = 1 - x^2$ and, on the same plane, for $x > 0$ plot the graph

of $f(x) = 2x + 1$.

7. (a) $(f \circ g)(x) = f(g(x)) = f(2x - 3) = (2x - 3)^2 + 2(2x - 3) - 1 = 4x^2 - 12x + 9 + 4x - 6 - 1 = 4x^2 - 8x + 2$

(b) $(g \circ f)(x) = g(f(x)) = g(x^2 + 2x - 1) = 2(x^2 + 2x - 1) - 3 = 2x^2 + 4x - 2 - 3 = 2x^2 + 4x - 5$

(c) $(g \circ g \circ g)(x) = g(g(g(x))) = g(g(2x - 3)) = g(2(2x - 3) - 3) = g(4x - 9) = 2(4x - 9) - 3$

$= 8x - 18 - 3 = 8x - 21$

Test D   Trigonometry

1. (a) $300° = 300° \left(\dfrac{\pi}{180°} \right) = \dfrac{300\pi}{180} = \dfrac{5\pi}{3}$ (b) $-18° = -18° \left(\dfrac{\pi}{180°} \right) = -\dfrac{18\pi}{180} = -\dfrac{\pi}{10}$

2. (a) $\dfrac{5\pi}{6} = \dfrac{5\pi}{6} \left(\dfrac{180°}{\pi} \right) = 150°$ (b) $2 = 2 \left(\dfrac{180°}{\pi} \right) = \dfrac{360°}{\pi} \approx 114.6°$

3. We will use the arc length formula, $s = r\theta$, where s is arc length, r is the radius of the circle, and θ is the measure of the

central angle in radians. First, note that $30° = 30° \left(\dfrac{\pi}{180°} \right) = \dfrac{\pi}{6}$. So $s = (12) \left(\dfrac{\pi}{6} \right) = 2\pi$ cm.

4. (a) $\tan(\pi/3) = \sqrt{3}$ [You can read the value from a right triangle with sides 1, 2, and $\sqrt{3}$.]

(b) Note that $7\pi/6$ can be thought of as an angle in the third quadrant with reference angle $\pi/6$. Thus, $\sin(7\pi/6) = -\frac{1}{2}$,

since the sine function is negative in the third quadrant.

(c) Note that $5\pi/3$ can be thought of as an angle in the fourth quadrant with reference angle $\pi/3$. Thus,

$\sec(5\pi/3) = \dfrac{1}{\cos(5\pi/3)} = \dfrac{1}{1/2} = 2$, since the cosine function is positive in the fourth quadrant.

5. $\sin\theta = a/24 \ \Rightarrow \ a = 24\sin\theta$ and $\cos\theta = b/24 \ \Rightarrow \ b = 24\cos\theta$

6. $\sin x = \frac{1}{3}$ and $\sin^2 x + \cos^2 x = 1 \;\Rightarrow\; \cos x = \sqrt{1 - \frac{1}{9}} = \frac{2\sqrt{2}}{3}$. Also, $\cos y = \frac{4}{5} \;\Rightarrow\; \sin y = \sqrt{1 - \frac{16}{25}} = \frac{3}{5}$.

So, using the sum identity for the sine, we have

$$\sin(x+y) = \sin x \, \cos y + \cos x \, \sin y = \frac{1}{3} \cdot \frac{4}{5} + \frac{2\sqrt{2}}{3} \cdot \frac{3}{5} = \frac{4 + 6\sqrt{2}}{15} = \frac{1}{15}\left(4 + 6\sqrt{2}\right)$$

7. (a) $\tan\theta \, \sin\theta + \cos\theta = \dfrac{\sin\theta}{\cos\theta} \sin\theta + \cos\theta = \dfrac{\sin^2\theta}{\cos\theta} + \dfrac{\cos^2\theta}{\cos\theta} = \dfrac{1}{\cos\theta} = \sec\theta$

(b) $\dfrac{2\tan x}{1 + \tan^2 x} = \dfrac{2\sin x/(\cos x)}{\sec^2 x} = 2\,\dfrac{\sin x}{\cos x}\cos^2 x = 2\sin x \, \cos x = \sin 2x$

8. $\sin 2x = \sin x \;\Leftrightarrow\; 2\sin x \, \cos x = \sin x \;\Leftrightarrow\; 2\sin x \, \cos x - \sin x = 0 \;\Leftrightarrow\; \sin x\,(2\cos x - 1) = 0 \;\Leftrightarrow$

$\sin x = 0$ or $\cos x = \frac{1}{2} \;\Rightarrow\; x = 0, \frac{\pi}{3}, \pi, \frac{5\pi}{3}, 2\pi$.

9. We first graph $y = \sin 2x$ (by compressing the graph of $\sin x$ by a factor of 2) and then shift it upward 1 unit.

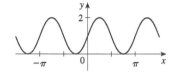

1 □ FUNCTIONS AND MODELS

1.1 Four Ways To Represent a Function

In exercises requiring estimations or approximations, your answers may vary slightly from the answers given here.

1. (a) The point $(1, 3)$ is on the graph of f, so $f(1) = 3$.

    (b) When $x = -1$, y is about -0.2, so $f(-1) \approx -0.2$.

    (c) $f(x) = 1$ is equivalent to $y = 1$. When $y = 1$, we have $x = 0$ and $x = 3$.

    (d) A reasonable estimate for x when $y = 0$ is $x = -0.8$.

    (e) The domain of f consists of all x-values on the graph of f. For this function, the domain is $-2 \le x \le 4$, or $[-2, 4]$.

    The range of f consists of all y-values on the graph of f. For this function, the range is $-1 \le y \le 3$, or $[-1, 3]$.

    (f) As x increases from -2 to 1, y increases from -1 to 3. Thus, f is increasing on the interval $[-2, 1]$.

3. From Figure 1 in the text, the lowest point occurs at about $(t, a) = (12, -85)$. The highest point occurs at about $(17, 115)$. Thus, the range of the vertical ground acceleration is $-85 \le a \le 115$. Written in interval notation, we get $[-85, 115]$.

5. No, the curve is not the graph of a function because a vertical line intersects the curve more than once. Hence, the curve fails the Vertical Line Test.

7. Yes, the curve is the graph of a function because it passes the Vertical Line Test. The domain is $[-3, 2]$ and the range is $[-3, -2) \cup [-1, 3]$.

9. The person's weight increased to about 160 pounds at age 20 and stayed fairly steady for 10 years. The person's weight dropped to about 120 pounds for the next 5 years, then increased rapidly to about 170 pounds. The next 30 years saw a gradual increase to 190 pounds. Possible reasons for the drop in weight at 30 years of age: diet, exercise, health problems.

11. The water will cool down almost to freezing as the ice melts. Then, when the ice has melted, the water will slowly warm up to room temperature.

13. (a) The power consumption at 6 AM is 500 MW, which is obtained by reading the value of power P when $t = 6$ from the graph. At 6 PM we read the value of P when $t = 18$, obtaining approximately 730 MW.

    (b) The minimum power consumption is determined by finding the time for the lowest point on the graph, $t = 4$, or 4 AM. The maximum power consumption corresponds to the highest point on the graph, which occurs just before $t = 12$, or right before noon. These times are reasonable, considering the power consumption schedules of most individuals and businesses.

15. Of course, this graph depends strongly on the geographical location!

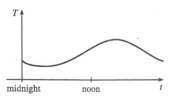

17. As the price increases, the amount sold decreases.

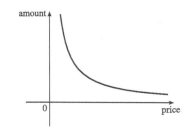

19.

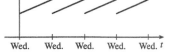

21. (a)

(b) From the graph, we estimate the number of US cell-phone subscribers to be about 126 million in 2001 and 207 million in 2005.

23. $f(x) = 3x^2 - x + 2$.

$f(2) = 3(2)^2 - 2 + 2 = 12 - 2 + 2 = 12$.

$f(-2) = 3(-2)^2 - (-2) + 2 = 12 + 2 + 2 = 16$.

$f(a) = 3a^2 - a + 2$.

$f(-a) = 3(-a)^2 - (-a) + 2 = 3a^2 + a + 2$.

$f(a+1) = 3(a+1)^2 - (a+1) + 2 = 3(a^2 + 2a + 1) - a - 1 + 2 = 3a^2 + 6a + 3 - a + 1 = 3a^2 + 5a + 4$.

$2f(a) = 2 \cdot f(a) = 2(3a^2 - a + 2) = 6a^2 - 2a + 4$.

$f(2a) = 3(2a)^2 - (2a) + 2 = 3(4a^2) - 2a + 2 = 12a^2 - 2a + 2$.

$f(a^2) = 3(a^2)^2 - (a^2) + 2 = 3(a^4) - a^2 + 2 = 3a^4 - a^2 + 2$.

$[f(a)]^2 = [3a^2 - a + 2]^2 = (3a^2 - a + 2)(3a^2 - a + 2)$
$= 9a^4 - 3a^3 + 6a^2 - 3a^3 + a^2 - 2a + 6a^2 - 2a + 4 = 9a^4 - 6a^3 + 13a^2 - 4a + 4$.

$f(a+h) = 3(a+h)^2 - (a+h) + 2 = 3(a^2 + 2ah + h^2) - a - h + 2 = 3a^2 + 6ah + 3h^2 - a - h + 2$.

25. $f(x) = 4 + 3x - x^2$, so $f(3+h) = 4 + 3(3+h) - (3+h)^2 = 4 + 9 + 3h - (9 + 6h + h^2) = 4 - 3h - h^2$,

and $\dfrac{f(3+h) - f(3)}{h} = \dfrac{(4 - 3h - h^2) - 4}{h} = \dfrac{h(-3-h)}{h} = -3 - h$.

27. $\dfrac{f(x) - f(a)}{x - a} = \dfrac{\dfrac{1}{x} - \dfrac{1}{a}}{x - a} = \dfrac{\dfrac{a - x}{xa}}{x - a} = \dfrac{a - x}{xa(x - a)} = \dfrac{-1(x - a)}{xa(x - a)} = -\dfrac{1}{ax}$

29. $f(x) = (x+4)/(x^2 - 9)$ is defined for all x except when $0 = x^2 - 9$ $\Leftrightarrow$ $0 = (x+3)(x-3)$ $\Leftrightarrow$ $x = -3$ or 3, so the

domain is $\{x \in \mathbb{R} \mid x \neq -3, 3\} = (-\infty, -3) \cup (-3, 3) \cup (3, \infty)$.

31. $f(t) = \sqrt[3]{2t - 1}$ is defined for all real numbres. In fact $\sqrt[3]{p(t)}$, where $p(t)$ is a polynomial, is defined for all real numbers.

Thus, the domain is $\mathbb{R}$, or $(-\infty, \infty)$.

33. $h(x) = 1 / \sqrt[4]{x^2 - 5x}$ is defined when $x^2 - 5x > 0$ $\Leftrightarrow$ $x(x - 5) > 0$. Note that $x^2 - 5x \neq 0$ since that would result in

division by zero. The expression $x(x - 5)$ is positive if $x < 0$ or $x > 5$. (See Appendix A for methods for solving

inequalities.) Thus, the domain is $(-\infty, 0) \cup (5, \infty)$.

35. $f(x) = 2 - 0.4x$ is defined for all real numbers, so the domain is $\mathbb{R}$,

or $(-\infty, \infty)$. The graph of f is a line with slope -0.4 and y-intercept 2.

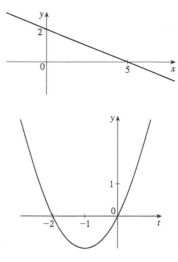

37. $f(t) = 2t + t^2$ is defined for all real numbers, so the domain is $\mathbb{R}$, or

$(-\infty, \infty)$. The graph of f is a parabola opening upward since the

coefficient of t^2 is positive. To find the t-intercepts, let $y = 0$ and solve

for t. $0 = 2t + t^2 = t(2 + t)$ $\Rightarrow$ $t = 0$ or $t = -2$. The t-coordinate of

the vertex is halfway between the t-intercepts, that is, at $t = -1$. Since

$f(-1) = 2(-1) + (-1)^2 = -2 + 1 = -1$, the vertex is $(-1, -1)$.

39. $g(x) = \sqrt{x - 5}$ is defined when $x - 5 \geq 0$ or $x \geq 5$, so the domain is $[5, \infty)$.

Since $y = \sqrt{x - 5}$ $\Rightarrow$ $y^2 = x - 5$ $\Rightarrow$ $x = y^2 + 5$, we see that g is the

top half of a parabola.

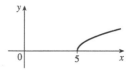

41. $G(x) = \dfrac{3x + |x|}{x}$. Since $|x| = \begin{cases} x & \text{if } x \geq 0 \\ -x & \text{if } x < 0 \end{cases}$, we have

$$G(x) = \begin{cases} \dfrac{3x + x}{x} & \text{if } x > 0 \\ \dfrac{3x - x}{x} & \text{if } x < 0 \end{cases} = \begin{cases} \dfrac{4x}{x} & \text{if } x > 0 \\ \dfrac{2x}{x} & \text{if } x < 0 \end{cases} = \begin{cases} 4 & \text{if } x > 0 \\ 2 & \text{if } x < 0 \end{cases}$$

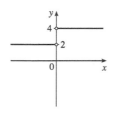

Note that G is not defined for $x = 0$. The domain is $(-\infty, 0) \cup (0, \infty)$.

43. $f(x) = \begin{cases} x + 2 & \text{if } x < 0 \\ 1 - x & \text{if } x \geq 0 \end{cases}$

The domain is $\mathbb{R}$.

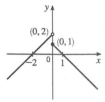

45. $f(x) = \begin{cases} x + 2 & \text{if } x \leq -1 \\ x^2 & \text{if } x > -1 \end{cases}$

Note that for $x = -1$, both $x + 2$ and x^2 are equal to 1.

The domain is $\mathbb{R}$.

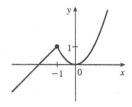

47. Recall that the slope m of a line between the two points (x_1, y_1) and (x_2, y_2) is $m = \dfrac{y_2 - y_1}{x_2 - x_1}$ and an equation of the line

connecting those two points is $y - y_1 = m(x - x_1)$. The slope of the line segment joining the points $(1, -3)$ and $(5, 7)$ is

$\dfrac{7 - (-3)}{5 - 1} = \dfrac{5}{2}$, so an equation is $y - (-3) = \frac{5}{2}(x - 1)$. The function is $f(x) = \frac{5}{2}x - \frac{11}{2}, 1 \leq x \leq 5$.

49. We need to solve the given equation for y. $x + (y - 1)^2 = 0 \iff (y - 1)^2 = -x \iff y - 1 = \pm\sqrt{-x} \iff$

$y = 1 \pm \sqrt{-x}$. The expression with the positive radical represents the top half of the parabola, and the one with the negative

radical represents the bottom half. Hence, we want $f(x) = 1 - \sqrt{-x}$. Note that the domain is $x \leq 0$.

51. For $0 \leq x \leq 3$, the graph is the line with slope -1 and y-intercept 3, that is, $y = -x + 3$. For $3 < x \leq 5$, the graph is the line

with slope 2 passing through $(3, 0)$; that is, $y - 0 = 2(x - 3)$, or $y = 2x - 6$. So the function is

$$f(x) = \begin{cases} -x + 3 & \text{if } 0 \leq x \leq 3 \\ 2x - 6 & \text{if } 3 < x \leq 5 \end{cases}$$

53. Let the length and width of the rectangle be L and W. Then the perimeter is $2L + 2W = 20$ and the area is $A = LW$.

Solving the first equation for W in terms of L gives $W = \dfrac{20 - 2L}{2} = 10 - L$. Thus, $A(L) = L(10 - L) = 10L - L^2$. Since

lengths are positive, the domain of A is $0 < L < 10$. If we further restrict L to be larger than W, then $5 < L < 10$ would be

the domain.

55. Let the length of a side of the equilateral triangle be x. Then by the Pythagorean Theorem, the height y of the triangle satisfies

$y^2 + \left(\frac{1}{2}x\right)^2 = x^2$, so that $y^2 = x^2 - \frac{1}{4}x^2 = \frac{3}{4}x^2$ and $y = \frac{\sqrt{3}}{2}x$. Using the formula for the area A of a triangle,

$A = \frac{1}{2}(\text{base})(\text{height})$, we obtain $A(x) = \frac{1}{2}(x)\left(\frac{\sqrt{3}}{2}x\right) = \frac{\sqrt{3}}{4}x^2$, with domain $x > 0$.

57. Let each side of the base of the box have length x, and let the height of the box be h. Since the volume is 2, we know that

$2 = hx^2$, so that $h = 2/x^2$, and the surface area is $S = x^2 + 4xh$. Thus, $S(x) = x^2 + 4x(2/x^2) = x^2 + (8/x)$, with

domain $x > 0$.

59. The height of the box is x and the length and width are $L = 20 - 2x$, $W = 12 - 2x$. Then $V = LWx$ and so

$$V(x) = (20 - 2x)(12 - 2x)(x) = 4(10 - x)(6 - x)(x) = 4x(60 - 16x + x^2) = 4x^3 - 64x^2 + 240x.$$

The sides L, W, and x must be positive. Thus, $L > 0$ $\Leftrightarrow$ $20 - 2x > 0$ $\Leftrightarrow$ $x < 10$;

$W > 0$ $\Leftrightarrow$ $12 - 2x > 0$ $\Leftrightarrow$ $x < 6$; and $x > 0$. Combining these restrictions gives us the domain $0 < x < 6$.

61. (a)

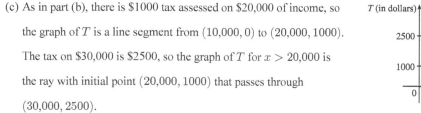

(b) On \$14,000, tax is assessed on \$4000, and $10\%(\$4000) = \$400$.

On \$26,000, tax is assessed on \$16,000, and

$10\%(\$10,000) + 15\%(\$6000) = \$1000 + \$900 = \$1900$.

(c) As in part (b), there is \$1000 tax assessed on \$20,000 of income, so

the graph of T is a line segment from $(10,000, 0)$ to $(20,000, 1000)$.

The tax on \$30,000 is \$2500, so the graph of T for $x > 20,000$ is

the ray with initial point $(20,000, 1000)$ that passes through

$(30,000, 2500)$.

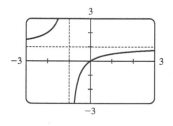

63. f is an odd function because its graph is symmetric about the origin. g is an even function because its graph is symmetric with

respect to the y-axis.

65. (a) Because an even function is symmetric with respect to the y-axis, and the point $(5, 3)$ is on the graph of this even function,

the point $(-5, 3)$ must also be on its graph.

(b) Because an odd function is symmetric with respect to the origin, and the point $(5, 3)$ is on the graph of this odd function,

the point $(-5, -3)$ must also be on its graph.

67. $f(x) = \dfrac{x}{x^2 + 1}$.

$f(-x) = \dfrac{-x}{(-x)^2 + 1} = \dfrac{-x}{x^2 + 1} = -\dfrac{x}{x^2 + 1} = -f(x)$.

So f is an odd function.

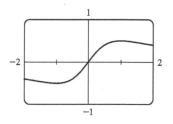

69. $f(x) = \dfrac{x}{x + 1}$, so $f(-x) = \dfrac{-x}{-x + 1} = \dfrac{x}{x - 1}$.

Since this is neither $f(x)$ nor $-f(x)$, the function f is

neither even nor odd.

71. $f(x) = 1 + 3x^2 - x^4$.

$f(-x) = 1 + 3(-x)^2 - (-x)^4 = 1 + 3x^2 - x^4 = f(x)$.

So f is an even function.

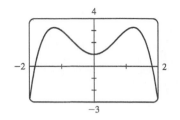

73. (i) If f and g are both even functions, then $f(-x) = f(x)$ and $g(-x) = g(x)$. Now

$(f + g)(-x) = f(-x) + g(-x) = f(x) + g(x) = (f + g)(x)$, so $f + g$ is an *even* function.

(ii) If f and g are both odd functions, then $f(-x) = -f(x)$ and $g(-x) = -g(x)$. Now

$(f + g)(-x) = f(-x) + g(-x) = -f(x) + [-g(x)] = -[f(x) + g(x)] = -(f + g)(x)$, so $f + g$ is an *odd* function.

(iii) If f is an even function and g is an odd function, then $(f + g)(-x) = f(-x) + g(-x) = f(x) + [-g(x)] = f(x) - g(x)$,

which is not $(f + g)(x)$ nor $-(f + g)(x)$, so $f + g$ is *neither* even nor odd. (Exception: if f is the zero function, then

$f + g$ will be *odd*. If g is the zero function, then $f + g$ will be *even*.)

1.2 Mathematical Models: A Catalog of Essential Functions

1. (a) $f(x) = \log_2 x$ is a logarithmic function.

(b) $g(x) = \sqrt[4]{x}$ is a root function with $n = 4$.

(c) $h(x) = \dfrac{2x^3}{1 - x^2}$ is a rational function because it is a ratio of polynomials.

(d) $u(t) = 1 - 1.1t + 2.54t^2$ is a polynomial of degree 2 (also called a *quadratic function*).

(e) $v(t) = 5^t$ is an exponential function.

(f) $w(\theta) = \sin \theta \, \cos^2 \theta$ is a trigonometric function.

3. We notice from the figure that g and h are even functions (symmetric with respect to the y-axis) and that f is an odd function

(symmetric with respect to the origin). So (b) $\left[y = x^5\right]$ must be f. Since g is flatter than h near the origin, we must have

(c) $\left[y = x^8\right]$ matched with g and (a) $\left[y = x^2\right]$ matched with h.

5. (a) An equation for the family of linear functions with slope 2

is $y = f(x) = 2x + b$, where b is the y-intercept.

(b) $f(2) = 1$ means that the point $(2, 1)$ is on the graph of f. We can use the point-slope form of a line to obtain an equation for the family of linear functions through the point $(2, 1)$. $y - 1 = m(x - 2)$, which is equivalent to $y = mx + (1 - 2m)$ in slope-intercept form.

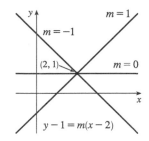

(c) To belong to both families, an equation must have slope $m = 2$, so the equation in part (b), $y = mx + (1 - 2m)$, becomes $y = 2x - 3$. It is the *only* function that belongs to both families.

7. All members of the family of linear functions $f(x) = c - x$ have graphs that are lines with slope -1. The y-intercept is c.

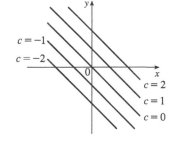

9. Since $f(-1) = f(0) = f(2) = 0$, f has zeros of $-1, 0$, and 2, so an equation for f is $f(x) = a[x - (-1)](x - 0)(x - 2)$, or $f(x) = ax(x + 1)(x - 2)$. Because $f(1) = 6$, we'll substitute 1 for x and 6 for $f(x)$.

$6 = a(1)(2)(-1) \Rightarrow -2a = 6 \Rightarrow a = -3$, so an equation for f is $f(x) = -3x(x + 1)(x - 2)$.

11. (a) $D = 200$, so $c = 0.0417D(a + 1) = 0.0417(200)(a + 1) = 8.34a + 8.34$. The slope is 8.34, which represents the change in mg of the dosage for a child for each change of 1 year in age.

(b) For a newborn, $a = 0$, so $c = 8.34$ mg.

13. (a)

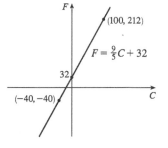

(b) The slope of $\frac{9}{5}$ means that F increases $\frac{9}{5}$ degrees for each increase of $1°C$. (Equivalently, F increases by 9 when C increases by 5 and F decreases by 9 when C decreases by 5.) The F-intercept of 32 is the Fahrenheit temperature corresponding to a Celsius temperature of 0.

15. (a) Using N in place of x and T in place of y, we find the slope to be $\dfrac{T_2 - T_1}{N_2 - N_1} = \dfrac{80 - 70}{173 - 113} = \dfrac{10}{60} = \dfrac{1}{6}$. So a linear

equation is $T - 80 = \frac{1}{6}(N - 173) \Leftrightarrow T - 80 = \frac{1}{6}N - \frac{173}{6} \Leftrightarrow T = \frac{1}{6}N + \frac{307}{6}$ $\left[\frac{307}{6} = 51.1\overline{6}\right]$.

(b) The slope of $\frac{1}{6}$ means that the temperature in Fahrenheit degrees increases one-sixth as rapidly as the number of cricket chirps per minute. Said differently, each increase of 6 cricket chirps per minute corresponds to an increase of $1°F$.

(c) When $N = 150$, the temperature is given approximately by $T = \frac{1}{6}(150) + \frac{307}{6} = 76.1\overline{6}\,°\text{F} \approx 76\,°\text{F}$.

17. (a) We are given $\dfrac{\text{change in pressure}}{10 \text{ feet change in depth}} = \dfrac{4.34}{10} = 0.434$. Using P for pressure and d for depth with the point

$(d, P) = (0, 15)$, we have the slope-intercept form of the line, $P = 0.434d + 15$.

(b) When $P = 100$, then $100 = 0.434d + 15 \iff 0.434d = 85 \iff d = \frac{85}{0.434} \approx 195.85$ feet. Thus, the pressure is

$100\,\text{lb/in}^2$ at a depth of approximately 196 feet.

19. (a) The data appear to be periodic and a sine or cosine function would make the best model. A model of the form

$f(x) = a\cos(bx) + c$ seems appropriate.

(b) The data appear to be decreasing in a linear fashion. A model of the form $f(x) = mx + b$ seems appropriate.

Exercises 21–24: Some values are given to many decimal places. These are the results given by several computer algebra systems — rounding is left to the reader.

21. (a)

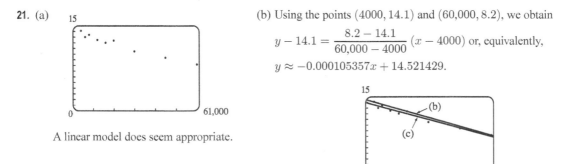

A linear model does seem appropriate.

(b) Using the points $(4000, 14.1)$ and $(60{,}000, 8.2)$, we obtain

$$y - 14.1 = \frac{8.2 - 14.1}{60{,}000 - 4000}(x - 4000) \text{ or, equivalently,}$$

$$y \approx -0.000105357x + 14.521429.$$

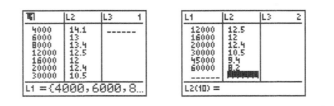

(c) Using a computing device, we obtain the least squares regression line $y = -0.0000997855x + 13.950764$.

The following commands and screens illustrate how to find the least squares regression line on a TI-84 Plus.

Enter the data into list one (L1) and list two (L2). Press [STAT] [1] to enter the editor.

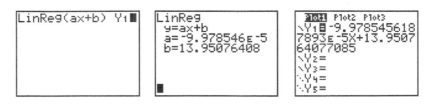

Find the regression line and store it in Y_1. Press [2nd] [QUIT] [STAT] [▶] [4] [VARS] [▶] [1] [1] [ENTER].

Note from the last figure that the regression line has been stored in Y_1 and that Plot1 has been turned on (Plot1 is highlighted). You can turn on Plot1 from the Y= menu by placing the cursor on Plot1 and pressing $\boxed{\text{ENTER}}$ or by pressing $\boxed{\text{2nd}}\ \boxed{\text{STAT PLOT}}\ \boxed{1}\ \boxed{\text{ENTER}}$.

Now press $\boxed{\text{ZOOM}}\ \boxed{9}$ to produce a graph of the data and the regression line. Note that choice 9 of the ZOOM menu automatically selects a window that displays all of the data.

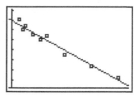

(d) When $x = 25{,}000$, $y \approx 11.456$; or about 11.5 per 100 population.

(e) When $x = 80{,}000$, $y \approx 5.968$; or about a 6% chance.

(f) When $x = 200{,}000$, y is negative, so the model does not apply.

23. (a) A linear model seems appropriate over the time interval considered.

(b) Using a computing device, we obtain the least squares regression line $y \approx 0.027t - 47.758$.

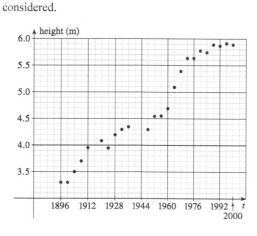

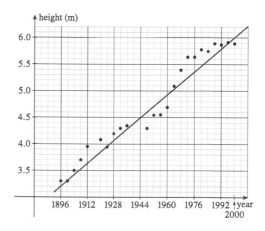

(c) When $t = 2004$, $y = 6.35$, which is higher than the actual winning height of 5.95 m.

(d) No, since the times appear to be leveling off and getting further away from the model.

25.

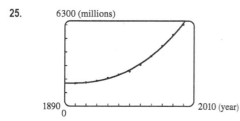

Using a computing device, we obtain the cubic function
$y = ax^3 + bx^2 + cx + d$ with $a = 0.0012937$,
$b = -7.06142$, $c = 12{,}823$, and $d = -7{,}743{,}770$. When
$x = 1925$, $y \approx 1914$ (million).

1.3 New Functions from Old Functions

1. (a) If the graph of f is shifted 3 units upward, its equation becomes $y = f(x) + 3$.

   (b) If the graph of f is shifted 3 units downward, its equation becomes $y = f(x) - 3$.

   (c) If the graph of f is shifted 3 units to the right, its equation becomes $y = f(x - 3)$.

   (d) If the graph of f is shifted 3 units to the left, its equation becomes $y = f(x + 3)$.

   (e) If the graph of f is reflected about the x-axis, its equation becomes $y = -f(x)$.

   (f) If the graph of f is reflected about the y-axis, its equation becomes $y = f(-x)$.

   (g) If the graph of f is stretched vertically by a factor of 3, its equation becomes $y = 3f(x)$.

   (h) If the graph of f is shrunk vertically by a factor of 3, its equation becomes $y = \frac{1}{3}f(x)$.

3. (a) (graph 3) The graph of f is shifted 4 units to the right and has equation $y = f(x - 4)$.

   (b) (graph 1) The graph of f is shifted 3 units upward and has equation $y = f(x) + 3$.

   (c) (graph 4) The graph of f is shrunk vertically by a factor of 3 and has equation $y = \frac{1}{3}f(x)$.

   (d) (graph 5) The graph of f is shifted 4 units to the left and reflected about the x-axis. Its equation is $y = -f(x + 4)$.

   (e) (graph 2) The graph of f is shifted 6 units to the left and stretched vertically by a factor of 2. Its equation is
   $y = 2f(x + 6)$.

5. (a) To graph $y = f(2x)$ we shrink the graph of f horizontally by a factor of 2.

   The point $(4, -1)$ on the graph of f corresponds to the point $\left(\frac{1}{2} \cdot 4, -1\right) = (2, -1)$.

   (b) To graph $y = f\left(\frac{1}{2}x\right)$ we stretch the graph of f horizontally by a factor of 2.

   The point $(4, -1)$ on the graph of f corresponds to the point $(2 \cdot 4, -1) = (8, -1)$.

   (c) To graph $y = f(-x)$ we reflect the graph of f about the y-axis.

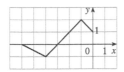

   The point $(4, -1)$ on the graph of f corresponds to the point $(-1 \cdot 4, -1) = (-4, -1)$.

   (d) To graph $y = -f(-x)$ we reflect the graph of f about the y-axis, then about the x-axis.

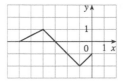

   The point $(4, -1)$ on the graph of f corresponds to the point $(-1 \cdot 4, -1 \cdot -1) = (-4, 1)$.

7. The graph of $y = f(x) = \sqrt{3x - x^2}$ has been shifted 4 units to the left, reflected about the x-axis, and shifted downward 1 unit. Thus, a function describing the graph is

$$y = \underbrace{-1 \cdot}_{\substack{\text{reflect} \\ \text{about } x\text{-axis}}} \underbrace{f\ (x + 4)}_{\substack{\text{shift} \\ 4 \text{ units left}}} \underbrace{-\ 1}_{\substack{\text{shift} \\ 1 \text{ unit left}}}$$

This function can be written as

$$y = -f(x+4) - 1 = -\sqrt{3(x+4) - (x+4)^2} - 1 = -\sqrt{3x + 12 - (x^2 + 8x + 16)} - 1 = -\sqrt{-x^2 - 5x - 4} - 1$$

9. $y = -x^3$: Start with the graph of $y = x^3$ and reflect about the x-axis. Note: Reflecting about the y-axis gives the same result since substituting $-x$ for x gives us $y = (-x)^3 = -x^3$.

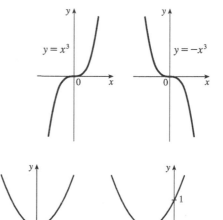

11. $y = (x+1)^2$: Start with the graph of $y = x^2$ and shift 1 unit to the left.

13. $y = 1 + 2\cos x$: Start with the graph of $y = \cos x$, stretch vertically by a factor of 2, and then shift 1 unit upward.

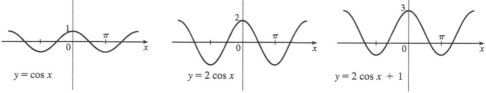

15. $y = \sin(x/2)$: Start with the graph of $y = \sin x$ and stretch horizontally by a factor of 2.

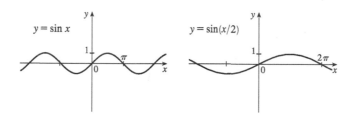

17. $y = \sqrt{x+3}$: Start with the graph of $y = \sqrt{x}$ and shift 3 units to the left.

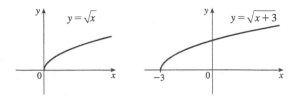

19. $y = \frac{1}{2}(x^2 + 8x) = \frac{1}{2}(x^2 + 8x + 16) - 8 = \frac{1}{2}(x+4)^2 - 8$: Start with the graph of $y = x^2$, compress vertically by a factor of 2, shift 4 units to the left, and then shift 8 units downward.

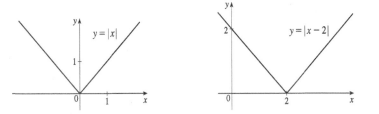

21. $y = |x - 2|$: Start with the graph of $y = |x|$ and shift 2 units to the right.

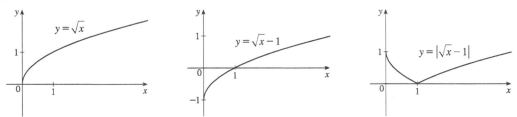

23. $y = |\sqrt{x} - 1|$: Start with the graph of $y = \sqrt{x}$, shift it 1 unit downward, and then reflect the portion of the graph below the x-axis about the x-axis.

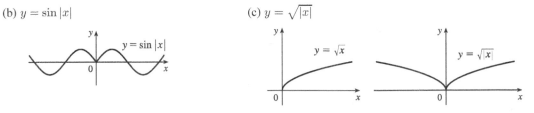

25. This is just like the solution to Example 4 except the amplitude of the curve (the 30°N curve in Figure 9 on June 21) is $14 - 12 = 2$. So the function is $L(t) = 12 + 2\sin\left[\frac{2\pi}{365}(t - 80)\right]$. March 31 is the 90th day of the year, so the model gives $L(90) \approx 12.34$ h. The daylight time (5:51 AM to 6:18 PM) is 12 hours and 27 minutes, or 12.45 h. The model value differs from the actual value by $\frac{12.45 - 12.34}{12.45} \approx 0.009$, less than 1%.

27. (a) To obtain $y = f(|x|)$, the portion of the graph of $y = f(x)$ to the right of the y-axis is reflected about the y-axis.

(b) $y = \sin|x|$ (c) $y = \sqrt{|x|}$

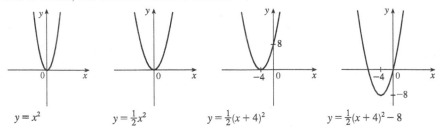

29. $f(x) = x^3 + 2x^2$; $g(x) = 3x^2 - 1$. $D = \mathbb{R}$ for both f and g.

(a) $(f + g)(x) = (x^3 + 2x^2) + (3x^2 - 1) = x^3 + 5x^2 - 1$, $D = \mathbb{R}$.

(b) $(f - g)(x) = (x^3 + 2x^2) - (3x^2 - 1) = x^3 - x^2 + 1$, $D = \mathbb{R}$.

(c) $(fg)(x) = (x^3 + 2x^2)(3x^2 - 1) = 3x^5 + 6x^4 - x^3 - 2x^2$, $D = \mathbb{R}$.

(d) $\left(\dfrac{f}{g}\right)(x) = \dfrac{x^3 + 2x^2}{3x^2 - 1}$, $D = \left\{x \mid x \neq \pm\dfrac{1}{\sqrt{3}}\right\}$ since $3x^2 - 1 \neq 0$.

31. $f(x) = x^2 - 1$, $D = \mathbb{R}$; $g(x) = 2x + 1$, $D = \mathbb{R}$.

(a) $(f \circ g)(x) = f(g(x)) = f(2x + 1) = (2x + 1)^2 - 1 = (4x^2 + 4x + 1) - 1 = 4x^2 + 4x$, $D = \mathbb{R}$.

(b) $(g \circ f)(x) = g(f(x)) = g(x^2 - 1) = 2(x^2 - 1) + 1 = (2x^2 - 2) + 1 = 2x^2 - 1$, $D = \mathbb{R}$.

(c) $(f \circ f)(x) = f(f(x)) = f(x^2 - 1) = (x^2 - 1)^2 - 1 = (x^4 - 2x^2 + 1) - 1 = x^4 - 2x^2$, $D = \mathbb{R}$.

(d) $(g \circ g)(x) = g(g(x)) = g(2x + 1) = 2(2x + 1) + 1 = (4x + 2) + 1 = 4x + 3$, $D = \mathbb{R}$.

33. $f(x) = 1 - 3x$; $g(x) = \cos x$. $D = \mathbb{R}$ for both f and g, and hence for their composites.

(a) $(f \circ g)(x) = f(g(x)) = f(\cos x) = 1 - 3\cos x$.

(b) $(g \circ f)(x) = g(f(x)) = g(1 - 3x) = \cos(1 - 3x)$.

(c) $(f \circ f)(x) = f(f(x)) = f(1 - 3x) = 1 - 3(1 - 3x) = 1 - 3 + 9x = 9x - 2$.

(d) $(g \circ g)(x) = g(g(x)) = g(\cos x) = \cos(\cos x)$ [Note that this is *not* $\cos x \cdot \cos x$.]

35. $f(x) = x + \dfrac{1}{x}$, $D = \{x \mid x \neq 0\}$; $g(x) = \dfrac{x + 1}{x + 2}$, $D = \{x \mid x \neq -2\}$

(a) $(f \circ g)(x) = f(g(x)) = f\left(\dfrac{x + 1}{x + 2}\right) = \dfrac{x + 1}{x + 2} + \dfrac{1}{\dfrac{x + 1}{x + 2}} = \dfrac{x + 1}{x + 2} + \dfrac{x + 2}{x + 1}$

$= \dfrac{(x + 1)(x + 1) + (x + 2)(x + 2)}{(x + 2)(x + 1)} = \dfrac{(x^2 + 2x + 1) + (x^2 + 4x + 4)}{(x + 2)(x + 1)} = \dfrac{2x^2 + 6x + 5}{(x + 2)(x + 1)}$

Since $g(x)$ is not defined for $x = -2$ and $f(g(x))$ is not defined for $x = -2$ and $x = -1$,

the domain of $(f \circ g)(x)$ is $D = \{x \mid x \neq -2, -1\}$.

(b) $(g \circ f)(x) = g(f(x)) = g\left(x + \dfrac{1}{x}\right) = \dfrac{\left(x + \dfrac{1}{x}\right) + 1}{\left(x + \dfrac{1}{x}\right) + 2} = \dfrac{\dfrac{x^2 + 1 + x}{x}}{\dfrac{x^2 + 1 + 2x}{x}} = \dfrac{x^2 + x + 1}{x^2 + 2x + 1} = \dfrac{x^2 + x + 1}{(x + 1)^2}$

Since $f(x)$ is not defined for $x = 0$ and $g(f(x))$ is not defined for $x = -1$,
the domain of $(g \circ f)(x)$ is $D = \{x \mid x \neq -1, 0\}$.

(c) $(f \circ f)(x) = f(f(x)) = f\left(x + \dfrac{1}{x}\right) = \left(x + \dfrac{1}{x}\right) + \dfrac{1}{x + \dfrac{1}{x}} = x + \dfrac{1}{x} + \dfrac{1}{\dfrac{x^2 + 1}{x}} = x + \dfrac{1}{x} + \dfrac{x}{x^2 + 1}$

$= \dfrac{x(x)\left(x^2 + 1\right) + 1\left(x^2 + 1\right) + x(x)}{x(x^2 + 1)} = \dfrac{x^4 + x^2 + x^2 + 1 + x^2}{x(x^2 + 1)}$

$= \dfrac{x^4 + 3x^2 + 1}{x(x^2 + 1)}$, $D = \{x \mid x \neq 0\}$

(d) $(g \circ g)(x) = g(g(x)) = g\left(\dfrac{x+1}{x+2}\right) = \dfrac{\dfrac{x+1}{x+2}+1}{\dfrac{x+1}{x+2}+2} = \dfrac{\dfrac{x+1+1(x+2)}{x+2}}{\dfrac{x+1+2(x+2)}{x+2}} = \dfrac{x+1+x+2}{x+1+2x+4} = \dfrac{2x+3}{3x+5}$

Since $g(x)$ is not defined for $x = -2$ and $g(g(x))$ is not defined for $x = -\frac{5}{3}$,

the domain of $(g \circ g)(x)$ is $D = \left\{x \mid x \neq -2, -\frac{5}{3}\right\}$.

37. $(f \circ g \circ h)(x) = f(g(h(x))) = f(g(x-1)) = f(2(x-1)) = 2(x-1)+1 = 2x-1$

39. $(f \circ g \circ h)(x) = f(g(h(x))) = f(g(x^3+2)) = f[(x^3+2)^2]$

$\qquad = f(x^6 + 4x^3 + 4) = \sqrt{(x^6 + 4x^3 + 4) - 3} = \sqrt{x^6 + 4x^3 + 1}$

41. Let $g(x) = 2x + x^2$ and $f(x) = x^4$. Then $(f \circ g)(x) = f(g(x)) = f(2x + x^2) = (2x + x^2)^4 = F(x)$.

43. Let $g(x) = \sqrt[3]{x}$ and $f(x) = \dfrac{x}{1+x}$. Then $(f \circ g)(x) = f(g(x)) = f(\sqrt[3]{x}) = \dfrac{\sqrt[3]{x}}{1 + \sqrt[3]{x}} = F(x)$.

45. Let $g(t) = \cos t$ and $f(t) = \sqrt{t}$. Then $(f \circ g)(t) = f(g(t)) = f(\cos t) = \sqrt{\cos t} = u(t)$.

47. Let $h(x) = x^2$, $g(x) = 3^x$, and $f(x) = 1 - x$. Then

$(f \circ g \circ h)(x) = f(g(h(x))) = f(g(x^2)) = f\left(3^{x^2}\right) = 1 - 3^{x^2} = H(x)$.

49. Let $h(x) = \sqrt{x}$, $g(x) = \sec x$, and $f(x) = x^4$. Then

$(f \circ g \circ h)(x) = f(g(h(x))) = f(g(\sqrt{x})) = f(\sec\sqrt{x}) = (\sec\sqrt{x})^4 = \sec^4(\sqrt{x}) = H(x)$.

51. (a) $g(2) = 5$, because the point $(2, 5)$ is on the graph of g. Thus, $f(g(2)) = f(5) = 4$, because the point $(5, 4)$ is on the graph of f.

(b) $g(f(0)) = g(0) = 3$

(c) $(f \circ g)(0) = f(g(0)) = f(3) = 0$

(d) $(g \circ f)(6) = g(f(6)) = g(6)$. This value is not defined, because there is no point on the graph of g that has x-coordinate 6.

(e) $(g \circ g)(-2) = g(g(-2)) = g(1) = 4$

(f) $(f \circ f)(4) = f(f(4)) = f(2) = -2$

53. (a) Using the relationship *distance = rate · time* with the radius r as the distance, we have $r(t) = 60t$.

(b) $A = \pi r^2 \;\Rightarrow\; (A \circ r)(t) = A(r(t)) = \pi(60t)^2 = 3600\pi t^2$. This formula gives us the extent of the rippled area (in cm^2) at any time t.

55. (a) From the figure, we have a right triangle with legs 6 and d, and hypotenuse s.

By the Pythagorean Theorem, $d^2 + 6^2 = s^2 \;\Rightarrow\; s = f(d) = \sqrt{d^2 + 36}$.

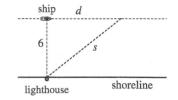

(b) Using $d = rt$, we get $d = (30 \text{ km/h})(t \text{ hours}) = 30t$ (in km). Thus,

$d = g(t) = 30t$.

(c) $(f \circ g)(t) = f(g(t)) = f(30t) = \sqrt{(30t)^2 + 36} = \sqrt{900t^2 + 36}$. This function represents the distance between the lighthouse and the ship as a function of the time elapsed since noon.

57. (a)   (b)

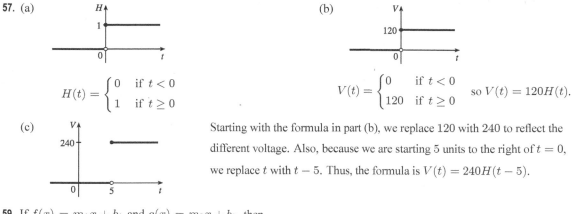

$$H(t) = \begin{cases} 0 & \text{if } t < 0 \\ 1 & \text{if } t \geq 0 \end{cases}$$

$$V(t) = \begin{cases} 0 & \text{if } t < 0 \\ 120 & \text{if } t \geq 0 \end{cases} \quad \text{so } V(t) = 120H(t).$$

(c)   Starting with the formula in part (b), we replace 120 with 240 to reflect the different voltage. Also, because we are starting 5 units to the right of $t = 0$, we replace t with $t - 5$. Thus, the formula is $V(t) = 240H(t - 5)$.

59. If $f(x) = m_1 x + b_1$ and $g(x) = m_2 x + b_2$, then

$$(f \circ g)(x) = f(g(x)) = f(m_2 x + b_2) = m_1(m_2 x + b_2) + b_1 = m_1 m_2 x + m_1 b_2 + b_1.$$

So $f \circ g$ is a linear function with slope $m_1 m_2$.

61. (a) By examining the variable terms in g and h, we deduce that we must square g to get the terms $4x^2$ and $4x$ in h. If we let

$f(x) = x^2 + c$, then $(f \circ g)(x) = f(g(x)) = f(2x + 1) = (2x + 1)^2 + c = 4x^2 + 4x + (1 + c)$. Since

$h(x) = 4x^2 + 4x + 7$, we must have $1 + c = 7$. So $c = 6$ and $f(x) = x^2 + 6$.

(b) We need a function g so that $f(g(x)) = 3(g(x)) + 5 = h(x)$. But

$h(x) = 3x^2 + 3x + 2 = 3(x^2 + x) + 2 = 3(x^2 + x - 1) + 5$, so we see that $g(x) = x^2 + x - 1$.

63. We need to examine $h(-x)$.

$$h(-x) = (f \circ g)(-x) = f(g(-x)) = f(g(x)) \quad \text{[because } g \text{ is even]} \quad = h(x)$$

Because $h(-x) = h(x)$, h is an even function.

1.4   Graphing Calculators and Computers

1. $f(x) = \sqrt{x^3 - 5x^2}$

(a) $[-5, 5]$ by $[-5, 5]$ (b) $[0, 10]$ by $[0, 2]$ (c) $[0, 10]$ by $[0, 10]$

   (There is no graph shown.)

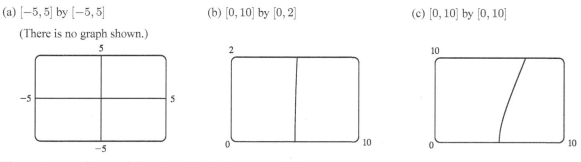

The most appropriate graph is produced in viewing rectangle (c).

3. Since the graph of $f(x) = x^2 - 36x + 32$ is a parabola opening upward, an appropriate viewing rectangle should include the minimum point. Completing the square, we get $f(x) = (x - 18)^2 - 292$, and so the minimum point is $(18, -292)$.

5. $f(x) = \sqrt[4]{81 - x^4}$ is defined when $81 - x^4 \geq 0 \Leftrightarrow x^4 \leq 81 \Leftrightarrow |x| \leq 3$, so the domain of f is $[-3, 3]$. Also $0 \leq \sqrt[4]{81 - x^4} \leq \sqrt[4]{81} = 3$, so the range is $[0, 3]$.

7. The graph of $f(x) = x^3 - 225x$ is symmetric with respect to the origin. Since $f(x) = x^3 - 225x = x(x^2 - 225) = x(x + 15)(x - 15)$, there are x-intercepts at 0, -15, and 15. $f(20) = 3500$.

9. The period of $g(x) = \sin(1000x)$ is $\frac{2\pi}{1000} \approx 0.0063$ and its range is $[-1, 1]$. Since $f(x) = \sin^2(1000x)$ is the square of g, its range is $[0, 1]$ and a viewing rectangle of $[-0.01, 0.01]$ by $[0, 1.1]$ seems appropriate.

11. The domain of $y = \sqrt{x}$ is $x \geq 0$, so the domain of $f(x) = \sin\sqrt{x}$ is $[0, \infty)$ and the range is $[-1, 1]$. With a little trial-and-error experimentation, we find that an Xmax of 100 illustrates the general shape of f, so an appropriate viewing rectangle is $[0, 100]$ by $[-1.5, 1.5]$.

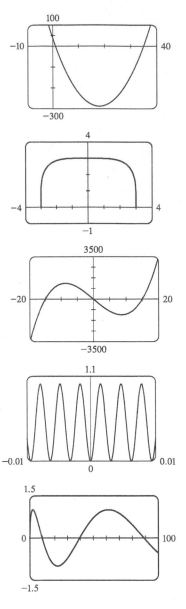

13. The first term, $10\sin x$, has period 2π and range $[-10, 10]$. It will be the dominant term in any "large" graph of $y = 10\sin x + \sin 100x$, as shown in the first figure. The second term, $\sin 100x$, has period $\frac{2\pi}{100} = \frac{\pi}{50}$ and range $[-1, 1]$. It causes the bumps in the first figure and will be the dominant term in any "small" graph, as shown in the view near the origin in the second figure.

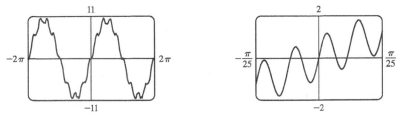

15. (a) The first figure shows the "big picture" for $f(x) = (x - 10)^3 2^{-x}$. The second figure shows a maximum near $x = 10$.

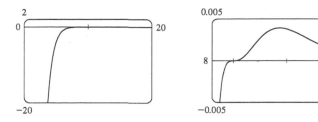

(b) You need more than one window because no single window can show what the function looks like globally and the detail of the function near $x = 10$.

17. We must solve the given equation for y to obtain equations for the upper and lower halves of the ellipse.

$$4x^2 + 2y^2 = 1 \quad \Leftrightarrow \quad 2y^2 = 1 - 4x^2 \quad \Leftrightarrow \quad y^2 = \frac{1 - 4x^2}{2} \quad \Leftrightarrow$$

$$y = \pm\sqrt{\frac{1 - 4x^2}{2}}$$

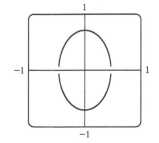

19. From the graph of $y = 3x^2 - 6x + 1$ and $y = 0.23x - 2.25$ in the viewing rectangle $[-1, 3]$ by $[-2.5, 1.5]$, it is difficult to see if the graphs intersect. If we zoom in on the fourth quadrant, we see the graphs do not intersect.

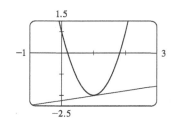
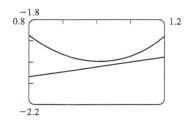

21. We see that the graphs of $f(x) = x^4 - x$ and $g(x) = 1$ intersect twice. The x-coordinates of these points (which are the solutions of the equations) are approximately -0.72 and 1.22. Alternatively, we could find these values by finding the zeros of $h(x) = x^4 - x - 1$.

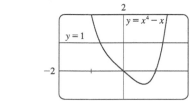

23. We see that the graphs of $f(x) = \tan x$ and $g(x) = \sqrt{1 - x^2}$ intersect once. Using an intersect feature or zooming in, we find this value to be approximately 0.65. Alternatively, we could find this value by finding the positive zero of $h(x) = \tan x - \sqrt{1 - x^2}$.

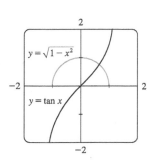

Note: After producing the graph on a TI-84 Plus, we can find the approximate value 0.65 by using the following keystrokes:

2nd CALC 5 ENTER ENTER .6 ENTER . The ".6" is just a guess for 0.65.

25. $g(x) = x^3/10$ is larger than $f(x) = 10x^2$ whenever $x > 100$.

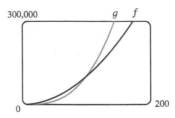

27.

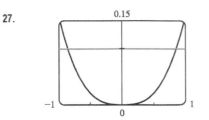

We see from the graphs of $y = |\sin x - x|$ and $y = 0.1$ that there are two solutions to the equation $|\sin x - x| = 0.1$: $x \approx -0.85$ and $x \approx 0.85$. The condition $|\sin x - x| < 0.1$ holds for any x lying between these two values, that is, $-0.85 < x < 0.85$.

29. (a) The root functions $y = \sqrt{x}$, $y = \sqrt[4]{x}$ and $y = \sqrt[6]{x}$

(b) The root functions $y = x$, $y = \sqrt[3]{x}$ and $y = \sqrt[5]{x}$

(c) The root functions $y = \sqrt{x}$, $y = \sqrt[3]{x}$, $y = \sqrt[4]{x}$ and $y = \sqrt[5]{x}$

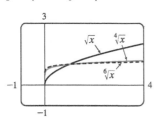

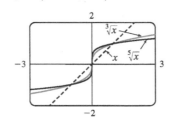

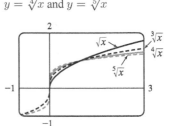

(d) ● For any n, the nth root of 0 is 0 and the nth root of 1 is 1; that is, all nth root functions pass through the points $(0,0)$ and $(1,1)$.

   ● For odd n, the domain of the nth root function is $\mathbb{R}$, while for even n, it is $\{x \in \mathbb{R} \mid x \geq 0\}$.

   ● Graphs of even root functions look similar to that of $\sqrt{x}$, while those of odd root functions resemble that of $\sqrt[3]{x}$.

   ● As n increases, the graph of $\sqrt[n]{x}$ becomes steeper near 0 and flatter for $x > 1$.

31. $f(x) = x^4 + cx^2 + x$. If $c < -1.5$, there are three humps: two minimum points and a maximum point. These humps get flatter as c increases, until at $c = -1.5$ two of the humps disappear and there is only one minimum point. This single hump then moves to the right and approaches the origin as c increases.

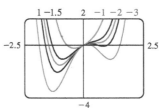

33. $y = x^n 2^{-x}$. As n increases, the maximum of the function moves further from the origin, and gets larger. Note, however, that regardless of n, the function approaches 0 as $x \to \infty$.

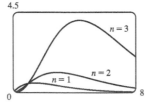

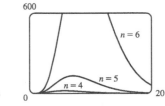

35. $y^2 = cx^3 + x^2$. If $c < 0$, the loop is to the right of the origin, and if c is positive, it is to the left. In both cases, the closer c is to 0, the larger the loop is. (In the limiting case, $c = 0$, the loop is "infinite," that is, it doesn't close.) Also, the larger $|c|$ is, the steeper the slope is on the loopless side of the origin.

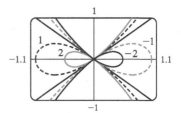

37. The graphing window is 95 pixels wide and we want to start with $x = 0$ and end with $x = 2\pi$. Since there are 94 "gaps" between pixels, the distance between pixels is $\frac{2\pi - 0}{94}$. Thus, the x-values that the calculator actually plots are $x = 0 + \frac{2\pi}{94} \cdot n$, where $n = 0, 1, 2, \ldots, 93, 94$. For $y = \sin 2x$, the actual points plotted by the calculator are $\left(\frac{2\pi}{94} \cdot n, \sin\left(2 \cdot \frac{2\pi}{94} \cdot n\right)\right)$ for $n = 0, 1, \ldots, 94$. For $y = \sin 96x$, the points plotted are $\left(\frac{2\pi}{94} \cdot n, \sin\left(96 \cdot \frac{2\pi}{94} \cdot n\right)\right)$ for $n = 0, 1, \ldots, 94$. But

$$\sin\left(96 \cdot \tfrac{2\pi}{94} \cdot n\right) = \sin\left(94 \cdot \tfrac{2\pi}{94} \cdot n + 2 \cdot \tfrac{2\pi}{94} \cdot n\right) = \sin\left(2\pi n + 2 \cdot \tfrac{2\pi}{94} \cdot n\right)$$

$$= \sin\left(2 \cdot \tfrac{2\pi}{94} \cdot n\right) \quad \text{[by periodicity of sine]}, \quad n = 0, 1, \ldots, 94$$

So the y-values, and hence the points, plotted for $y = \sin 96x$ are identical to those plotted for $y = \sin 2x$.

Note: Try graphing $y = \sin 94x$. Can you see why all the y-values are zero?

1.5   Exponential Functions

1. (a) $\dfrac{4^{-3}}{2^{-8}} = \dfrac{2^8}{4^3} = \dfrac{2^8}{(2^2)^3} = \dfrac{2^8}{2^6} = 2^{8-6} = 2^2 = 4$

(b) $\dfrac{1}{\sqrt[3]{x^4}} = \dfrac{1}{x^{4/3}} = x^{-4/3}$

3. (a) $b^8(2b)^4 = b^8 \cdot 2^4 b^4 = 16b^{12}$

(b) $\dfrac{(6y^3)^4}{2y^5} = \dfrac{6^4(y^3)^4}{2y^5} = \dfrac{1296y^{12}}{2y^5} = 648y^7$

5. (a) $f(x) = a^x$, $a > 0$ (b) $\mathbb{R}$ (c) $(0, \infty)$ (d) See Figures 4(c), 4(b), and 4(a), respectively.

7. All of these graphs approach 0 as $x \to -\infty$, all of them pass through the point $(0, 1)$, and all of them are increasing and approach ∞ as $x \to \infty$. The larger the base, the faster the function increases for $x > 0$, and the faster it approaches 0 as $x \to -\infty$.

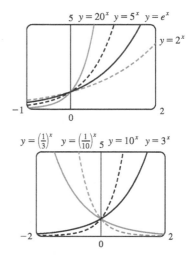

9. The functions with bases greater than 1 (3^x and 10^x) are increasing, while those with bases less than 1 $\left[\left(\frac{1}{3}\right)^x \text{ and } \left(\frac{1}{10}\right)^x\right]$ are decreasing. The graph of $\left(\frac{1}{3}\right)^x$ is the reflection of that of 3^x about the y-axis, and the graph of $\left(\frac{1}{10}\right)^x$ is the reflection of that of 10^x about the y-axis. The graph of 10^x increases more quickly than that of 3^x for $x > 0$, and approaches 0 faster as $x \to -\infty$.

11. We start with the graph of $y = 10^x$ (Figure 3) and shift it 2 units to the left to obtain the graph of $y = 10^{x+2}$.

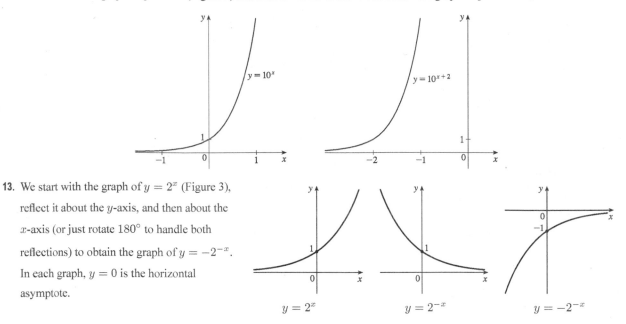

13. We start with the graph of $y = 2^x$ (Figure 3), reflect it about the y-axis, and then about the x-axis (or just rotate $180°$ to handle both reflections) to obtain the graph of $y = -2^{-x}$. In each graph, $y = 0$ is the horizontal asymptote.

$$y = 2^x \qquad y = 2^{-x} \qquad y = -2^{-x}$$

15. We start with the graph of $y = e^x$ (Figure 13) and reflect about the y-axis to get the graph of $y = e^{-x}$. Then we compress the graph vertically by a factor of 2 to obtain the graph of $y = \frac{1}{2}e^{-x}$ and then reflect about the x-axis to get the graph of $y = -\frac{1}{2}e^{-x}$. Finally, we shift the graph upward one unit to get the graph of $y = 1 - \frac{1}{2}e^{-x}$.

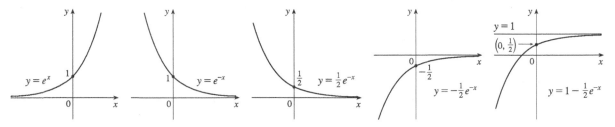

17. (a) To find the equation of the graph that results from shifting the graph of $y = e^x$ 2 units downward, we subtract 2 from the original function to get $y = e^x - 2$.

(b) To find the equation of the graph that results from shifting the graph of $y = e^x$ 2 units to the right, we replace x with $x - 2$ in the original function to get $y = e^{(x-2)}$.

(c) To find the equation of the graph that results from reflecting the graph of $y = e^x$ about the x-axis, we multiply the original function by -1 to get $y = -e^x$.

(d) To find the equation of the graph that results from reflecting the graph of $y = e^x$ about the y-axis, we replace x with $-x$ in the original function to get $y = e^{-x}$.

(e) To find the equation of the graph that results from reflecting the graph of $y = e^x$ about the x-axis and then about the y-axis, we first multiply the original function by -1 (to get $y = -e^x$) and then replace x with $-x$ in this equation to get $y = -e^{-x}$.

19. (a) The denominator is zero when $1 - e^{1-x^2} = 0$ ⇔ $e^{1-x^2} = 1$ ⇔ $1 - x^2 = 0$ ⇔ $x = \pm 1$. Thus,

the function $f(x) = \dfrac{1 - e^{x^2}}{1 - e^{1-x^2}}$ has domain $\{x \mid x \neq \pm 1\} = (-\infty, -1) \cup (-1, 1) \cup (1, \infty)$.

(b) The denominator is never equal to zero, so the function $f(x) = \dfrac{1+x}{e^{\cos x}}$ has domain $\mathbb{R}$, or $(-\infty, \infty)$.

21. Use $y = Ca^x$ with the points $(1, 6)$ and $(3, 24)$. $6 = Ca^1 \quad [C = \frac{6}{a}]$ and $24 = Ca^3$ ⇒ $24 = \left(\dfrac{6}{a}\right)a^3$ ⇒

$4 = a^2$ ⇒ $a = 2$ [since $a > 0$] and $C = \frac{6}{2} = 3$. The function is $f(x) = 3 \cdot 2^x$.

23. If $f(x) = 5^x$, then $\dfrac{f(x+h) - f(x)}{h} = \dfrac{5^{x+h} - 5^x}{h} = \dfrac{5^x 5^h - 5^x}{h} = \dfrac{5^x \left(5^h - 1\right)}{h} = 5^x \left(\dfrac{5^h - 1}{h}\right)$.

25. 2 ft = 24 in, $f(24) = 24^2$ in = 576 in = 48 ft. $g(24) = 2^{24}$ in = $2^{24}/(12 \cdot 5280)$ mi ≈ 265 mi

27. The graph of g finally surpasses that of f at $x \approx 35.8$.

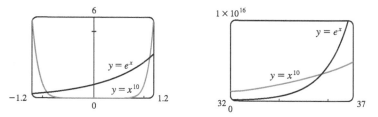

29. (a) Fifteen hours represents 5 doubling periods (one doubling period is three hours). $100 \cdot 2^5 = 3200$

(b) In t hours, there will be $t/3$ doubling periods. The initial population is 100,

so the population y at time t is $y = 100 \cdot 2^{t/3}$.

(c) $t = 20$ ⇒ $y = 100 \cdot 2^{20/3} \approx 10{,}159$

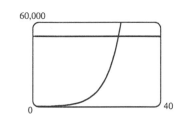

(d) We graph $y_1 = 100 \cdot 2^{x/3}$ and $y_2 = 50{,}000$. The two curves intersect at

$x \approx 26.9$, so the population reaches 50,000 in about 26.9 hours.

31. (a) Fifteen days represents 3 half-life periods (one half-life period is 5 days). $200 \left(\frac{1}{2}\right)^3 = 25$ mg

(b) In t hours, there will be $t/5$ half-life periods. The initial amount is 200 mg,

so the amount remaining after t days is $y = 200 \left(\frac{1}{2}\right)^{t/5}$, or equivalently,

$y = 200 \cdot 2^{-t/5}$.

(c) $t = 3$ weeks = 21 days ⇒ $y = 200 \cdot 2^{-21/5} \approx 10.9$ mg

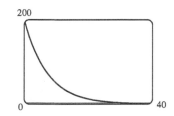

(d) We graph $y_1 = 200 \cdot 2^{-t/5}$ and $y_2 = 1$. The two curves intersect at

$t \approx 38.2$, so the mass will be reduced to 1 mg in about 38.2 days.

33. An exponential model is $y = ab^t$, where $a = 3.154832569 \times 10^{-12}$ and $b = 1.017764706$. This model gives $y(1993) \approx 5498$ million and $y(2010) \approx 7417$ million.

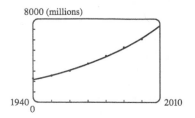

35.

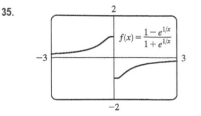

$$f(x) = \frac{1 - e^{1/x}}{1 + e^{1/x}}$$

From the graph, it appears that f is an odd function (f is undefined for $x = 0$).

To prove this, we must show that $f(-x) = -f(x)$.

$$f(-x) = \frac{1 - e^{1/(-x)}}{1 + e^{1/(-x)}} = \frac{1 - e^{(-1/x)}}{1 + e^{(-1/x)}} = \frac{1 - \dfrac{1}{e^{1/x}}}{1 + \dfrac{1}{e^{1/x}}} \cdot \frac{e^{1/x}}{e^{1/x}} = \frac{e^{1/x} - 1}{e^{1/x} + 1}$$

$$= -\frac{1 - e^{1/x}}{1 + e^{1/x}} = -f(x)$$

so f is an odd function.

1.6 Inverse Functions and Logarithms

1. (a) See Definition 1.

(b) It must pass the Horizontal Line Test.

3. f is not one-to-one because $2 \neq 6$, but $f(2) = 2.0 = f(6)$.

5. We could draw a horizontal line that intersects the graph in more than one point. Thus, by the Horizontal Line Test, the function is not one-to-one.

7. No horizontal line intersects the graph more than once. Thus, by the Horizontal Line Test, the function is one-to-one.

9. The graph of $f(x) = x^2 - 2x$ is a parabola with axis of symmetry $x = -\dfrac{b}{2a} = -\dfrac{-2}{2(1)} = 1$. Pick any x-values equidistant from 1 to find two equal function values. For example, $f(0) = 0$ and $f(2) = 0$, so f is not one-to-one.

11. $g(x) = 1/x$. $x_1 \neq x_2 \Rightarrow 1/x_1 \neq 1/x_2 \Rightarrow g(x_1) \neq g(x_2)$, so g is one-to-one.

Geometric solution: The graph of g is the hyperbola shown in Figure 14 in Section 1.2. It passes the Horizontal Line Test, so g is one-to-one.

13. A football will attain every height h up to its maximum height twice: once on the way up, and again on the way down. Thus, even if t_1 does not equal t_2, $f(t_1)$ may equal $f(t_2)$, so f is not 1-1.

15. Since $f(2) = 9$ and f is 1-1, we know that $f^{-1}(9) = 2$. Remember, if the point $(2, 9)$ is on the graph of f, then the point $(9, 2)$ is on the graph of f^{-1}.

17. First, we must determine x such that $g(x) = 4$. By inspection, we see that if $x = 0$, then $g(x) = 4$. Since g is 1-1 (g is an increasing function), it has an inverse, and $g^{-1}(4) = 0$.

19. We solve $C = \frac{5}{9}(F - 32)$ for F: $\frac{9}{5}C = F - 32 \implies F = \frac{9}{5}C + 32$. This gives us a formula for the inverse function, that is, the Fahrenheit temperature F as a function of the Celsius temperature C. $F \geq -459.67 \implies \frac{9}{5}C + 32 \geq -459.67 \implies \frac{9}{5}C \geq -491.67 \implies C \geq -273.15$, the domain of the inverse function.

21. $y = f(x) = 1 + \sqrt{2 + 3x}$ $(y \geq 1)$ $\implies$ $y - 1 = \sqrt{2 + 3x}$ $\implies$ $(y - 1)^2 = 2 + 3x$ $\implies$ $(y - 1)^2 - 2 = 3x$ $\implies$ $x = \frac{1}{3}(y - 1)^2 - \frac{2}{3}$. Interchange x and y: $y = \frac{1}{3}(x - 1)^2 - \frac{2}{3}$. So $f^{-1}(x) = \frac{1}{3}(x - 1)^2 - \frac{2}{3}$. Note that the domain of f^{-1} is $x \geq 1$.

23. $y = f(x) = e^{2x-1}$ $\implies$ $\ln y = 2x - 1$ $\implies$ $1 + \ln y = 2x$ $\implies$ $x = \frac{1}{2}(1 + \ln y)$.

Interchange x and y: $y = \frac{1}{2}(1 + \ln x)$. So $f^{-1}(x) = \frac{1}{2}(1 + \ln x)$.

25. $y = f(x) = \ln(x + 3)$ $\implies$ $x + 3 = e^y$ $\implies$ $x = e^y - 3$. Interchange x and y: $y = e^x - 3$. So $f^{-1}(x) = e^x - 3$.

27. $y = f(x) = x^4 + 1$ $\implies$ $y - 1 = x^4$ $\implies$ $x = \sqrt[4]{y - 1}$ [not $\pm$ since $x \geq 0$]. Interchange x and y: $y = \sqrt[4]{x - 1}$. So $f^{-1}(x) = \sqrt[4]{x - 1}$. The graph of $y = \sqrt[4]{x - 1}$ is just the graph of $y = \sqrt[4]{x}$ shifted right one unit. From the graph, we see that f and f^{-1} are reflections about the line $y = x$.

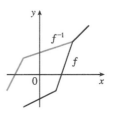

29. Reflect the graph of f about the line $y = x$. The points $(-1, -2)$, $(1, -1)$, $(2, 2)$, and $(3, 3)$ on f are reflected to $(-2, -1)$, $(-1, 1)$, $(2, 2)$, and $(3, 3)$ on f^{-1}.

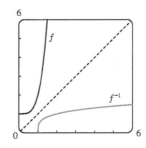

31. (a) $y = f(x) = \sqrt{1 - x^2}$ $(0 \leq x \leq 1$ and note that $y \geq 0)$ $\implies$ $y^2 = 1 - x^2$ $\implies$ $x^2 = 1 - y^2$ $\implies$ $x = \sqrt{1 - y^2}$. So $f^{-1}(x) = \sqrt{1 - x^2}$, $0 \leq x \leq 1$.   We see that f^{-1} and f are the same function.

(b) The graph of f is the portion of the circle $x^2 + y^2 = 1$ with $0 \leq x \leq 1$ and $0 \leq y \leq 1$ (quarter-circle in the first quadrant). The graph of f is symmetric with respect to the line $y = x$, so its reflection about $y = x$ is itself, that is, $f^{-1} = f$.

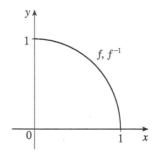

33. (a) It is defined as the inverse of the exponential function with base a, that is, $\log_a x = y \iff a^y = x$.

(b) $(0, \infty)$'   **(c)** $\mathbb{R}$ **(d)** See Figure 11.

35. (a) $\log_5 125 = 3$ since $5^3 = 125$.   **(b)** $\log_3 \dfrac{1}{27} = -3$ since $3^{-3} = \dfrac{1}{3^3} = \dfrac{1}{27}$.

37. (a) $\log_2 6 - \log_2 15 + \log_2 20 = \log_2\left(\frac{6}{15}\right) + \log_2 20$ [by Law 2]

$\qquad\qquad\qquad\qquad = \log_2\left(\frac{6}{15}\cdot 20\right)$ [by Law 1]

$\qquad\qquad\qquad\qquad = \log_2 8$, and $\log_2 8 = 3$ since $2^3 = 8$.

(b) $\log_3 100 - \log_3 18 - \log_3 50 = \log_3\left(\frac{100}{18}\right) - \log_3 50 = \log_3\left(\frac{100}{18\cdot 50}\right)$

$\qquad\qquad\qquad\qquad\qquad\qquad = \log_3\left(\frac{1}{9}\right)$, and $\log_3\left(\frac{1}{9}\right) = -2$ since $3^{-2} = \frac{1}{9}$.

39. $\ln 5 + 5\ln 3 = \ln 5 + \ln 3^5$ [by Law 3]

$\qquad\qquad\quad = \ln(5\cdot 3^5)$ [by Law 1]

$\qquad\qquad\quad = \ln 1215$

41. $\ln(1+x^2) + \frac{1}{2}\ln x - \ln\sin x = \ln(1+x^2) + \ln x^{1/2} - \ln\sin x = \ln[(1+x^2)\sqrt{x}\,] - \ln\sin x = \ln\dfrac{(1+x^2)\sqrt{x}}{\sin x}$

43. To graph these functions, we use $\log_{1.5} x = \dfrac{\ln x}{\ln 1.5}$ and $\log_{50} x = \dfrac{\ln x}{\ln 50}$.

These graphs all approach $-\infty$ as $x \to 0^+$, and they all pass through the

point $(1,0)$. Also, they are all increasing, and all approach ∞ as $x \to \infty$.

The functions with larger bases increase extremely slowly, and the ones with

smaller bases do so somewhat more quickly. The functions with large bases

approach the y-axis more closely as $x \to 0^+$.

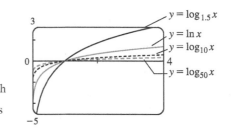

45. 3 ft $=$ 36 in, so we need x such that $\log_2 x = 36 \iff x = 2^{36} = 68{,}719{,}476{,}736$. In miles, this is

$68{,}719{,}476{,}736$ in $\cdot\dfrac{1\text{ ft}}{12\text{ in}}\cdot\dfrac{1\text{ mi}}{5280\text{ ft}} \approx 1{,}084{,}587.7$ mi.

47. (a) Shift the graph of $y = \log_{10} x$ five units to the left to   (b) Reflect the graph of $y = \ln x$ about the x-axis to obtain

obtain the graph of $y = \log_{10}(x+5)$. Note the vertical   the graph of $y = -\ln x$.

asymptote of $x = -5$.

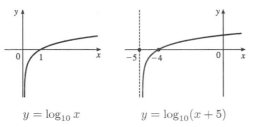

$y = \log_{10} x \qquad\qquad y = \log_{10}(x+5)$

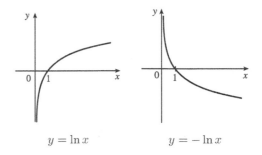

$y = \ln x \qquad\qquad\qquad y = -\ln x$

49. (a) $e^{7-4x} = 6 \iff 7 - 4x = \ln 6 \iff 7 - \ln 6 = 4x \iff x = \frac{1}{4}(7 - \ln 6)$

(b) $\ln(3x - 10) = 2 \iff 3x - 10 = e^2 \iff 3x = e^2 + 10 \iff x = \frac{1}{3}(e^2 + 10)$

51. (a) $2^{x-5} = 3 \iff \log_2 3 = x - 5 \iff x = 5 + \log_2 3$.

$\qquad$ *Or:* $2^{x-5} = 3 \iff \ln(2^{x-5}) = \ln 3 \iff (x-5)\ln 2 = \ln 3 \iff x - 5 = \dfrac{\ln 3}{\ln 2} \iff x = 5 + \dfrac{\ln 3}{\ln 2}$

(b) $\ln x + \ln(x-1) = \ln(x(x-1)) = 1 \;\Leftrightarrow\; x(x-1) = e^1 \;\Leftrightarrow\; x^2 - x - e = 0$. The quadratic formula (with $a = 1$, $b = -1$, and $c = -e$) gives $x = \frac{1}{2}\left(1 \pm \sqrt{1+4e}\right)$, but we reject the negative root since the natural logarithm is not defined for $x < 0$. So $x = \frac{1}{2}\left(1 + \sqrt{1+4e}\right)$.

53. (a) $e^x < 10 \;\Rightarrow\; \ln e^x < \ln 10 \;\Rightarrow\; x < \ln 10 \;\Rightarrow\; x \in (-\infty, \ln 10)$

(b) $\ln x > -1 \;\Rightarrow\; e^{\ln x} > e^{-1} \;\Rightarrow\; x > e^{-1} \;\Rightarrow\; x \in (1/e, \infty)$

55. (a) For $f(x) = \sqrt{3 - e^{2x}}$, we must have $3 - e^{2x} \geq 0 \;\Rightarrow\; e^{2x} \leq 3 \;\Rightarrow\; 2x \leq \ln 3 \;\Rightarrow\; x \leq \frac{1}{2}\ln 3$.

Thus, the domain of f is $(-\infty, \frac{1}{2}\ln 3]$.

(b) $y = f(x) = \sqrt{3 - e^{2x}}$ [note that $y \geq 0$] $\;\Rightarrow\; y^2 = 3 - e^{2x} \;\Rightarrow\; e^{2x} = 3 - y^2 \;\Rightarrow\; 2x = \ln(3 - y^2) \;\Rightarrow$

$x = \frac{1}{2}\ln(3 - y^2)$. Interchange x and y: $y = \frac{1}{2}\ln(3 - x^2)$. So $f^{-1}(x) = \frac{1}{2}\ln(3 - x^2)$. For the domain of f^{-1},

we must have $3 - x^2 > 0 \;\Rightarrow\; x^2 < 3 \;\Rightarrow\; |x| < \sqrt{3} \;\Rightarrow\; -\sqrt{3} < x < \sqrt{3} \;\Rightarrow\; 0 \leq x < \sqrt{3}$ since $x \geq 0$. Note

that the domain of f^{-1}, $[0, \sqrt{3})$, equals the range of f.

57. We see that the graph of $y = f(x) = \sqrt{x^3 + x^2 + x + 1}$ is increasing, so f is 1-1.

Enter $x = \sqrt{y^3 + y^2 + y + 1}$ and use your CAS to solve the equation for y.

Using Derive, we get two (irrelevant) solutions involving imaginary expressions,

as well as one which can be simplified to the following:

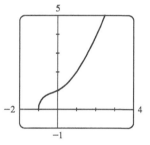

$y = f^{-1}(x) = -\frac{\sqrt[3]{4}}{6}\left(\sqrt[3]{D - 27x^2 + 20} - \sqrt[3]{D + 27x^2 - 20} + \sqrt[3]{2}\right)$

where $D = 3\sqrt{3}\sqrt{27x^4 - 40x^2 + 16}$.

Maple and Mathematica each give two complex expressions and one real expression, and the real expression is equivalent

to that given by Derive. For example, Maple's expression simplifies to $\dfrac{1}{6}\dfrac{M^{2/3} - 8 - 2M^{1/3}}{2M^{1/3}}$, where

$M = 108x^2 + 12\sqrt{48 - 120x^2 + 81x^4} - 80$.

59. (a) $n = 100 \cdot 2^{t/3} \;\Rightarrow\; \dfrac{n}{100} = 2^{t/3} \;\Rightarrow\; \log_2\left(\dfrac{n}{100}\right) = \dfrac{t}{3} \;\Rightarrow\; t = 3\log_2\left(\dfrac{n}{100}\right)$. Using formula (10), we can write

this as $t = f^{-1}(n) = 3 \cdot \dfrac{\ln(n/100)}{\ln 2}$. This function tells us how long it will take to obtain n bacteria (given the number n).

(b) $n = 50{,}000 \;\Rightarrow\; t = f^{-1}(50{,}000) = 3 \cdot \dfrac{\ln\left(\frac{50{,}000}{100}\right)}{\ln 2} = 3\left(\dfrac{\ln 500}{\ln 2}\right) \approx 26.9$ hours

61. (a) To find the equation of the graph that results from shifting the graph of $y = \ln x$ 3 units upward, we add 3 to the original function to get $y = \ln x + 3$.

(b) To find the equation of the graph that results from shifting the graph of $y = \ln x$ 3 units to the left, we replace x with $x + 3$ in the original function to get $y = \ln(x + 3)$.

(c) To find the equation of the graph that results from reflecting the graph of $y = \ln x$ about the x-axis, we multiply the original equation by -1 to get $y = -\ln x$.

(d) To find the equation of the graph that results from reflecting the graph of $y = \ln x$ about the y-axis, we replace x with $-x$ in the original equation to get $y = \ln(-x)$.

(e) To find the equation of the graph that results from reflecting the graph of $y = \ln x$ about the line $y = x$, we interchange x and y in the original equation to get $x = \ln y \iff y = e^x$.

(f) To find the equation of the graph that results from reflecting the graph of $y = \ln x$ about the x-axis and then about the line $y = x$, we first multiply the original equation by -1 [to get $y = -\ln x$] and then interchange x and y in this equation to get $x = -\ln y \iff \ln y = -x \iff y = e^{-x}$.

(g) To find the equation of the graph that results from reflecting the graph of $y = \ln x$ about the y-axis and then about the line $y = x$, we first replace x with $-x$ in the original equation [to get $y = \ln(-x)$] and then interchange x and y to get $x = \ln(-y) \iff -y = e^x \iff y = -e^x$.

(h) To find the equation of the graph that results from shifting the graph of $y = \ln x$ 3 units to the left and then reflecting it about the line $y = x$, we first replace x with $x + 3$ in the original equation [to get $y = \ln(x + 3)$] and then interchange x and y in this equation to get $x = \ln(y + 3) \iff y + 3 = e^x \iff y = e^x - 3$.

1.7 Parametric Curves

1. $x = t^2 + t$, $\quad y = t^2 - t$, $\quad -2 \le t \le 2$

t	-2	-1	0	1	2
x	2	0	0	2	6
y	6	2	0	0	2

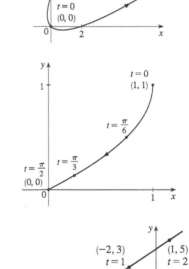

3. $x = \cos^2 t$, $\quad y = 1 - \sin t$, $\quad 0 \le t \le \pi/2$

t	0	$\pi/6$	$\pi/3$	$\pi/2$
x	1	3/4	1/4	0
y	1	1/2	$1 - \frac{\sqrt{3}}{2} \approx 0.13$	0

5. $x = 3t - 5$, $\quad y = 2t + 1$

(a)

t	-2	-1	0	1	2	3	4
x	-11	-8	-5	-2	1	4	7
y	-3	-1	1	3	5	7	9

(b) $x = 3t - 5 \implies 3t = x + 5 \implies t = \frac{1}{3}(x + 5) \implies$
$y = 2 \cdot \frac{1}{3}(x + 5) + 1$, so $y = \frac{2}{3}x + \frac{13}{3}$.

7. $x = \sqrt{t}$, $y = 1 - t$

(a)

t	0	1	2	3	4
x	0	1	1.414	1.732	2
y	1	0	−1	−2	−3

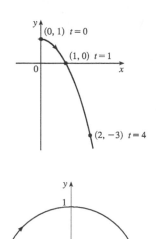

(b) $x = \sqrt{t}$ ⇒ $t = x^2$ ⇒ $y = 1 - t = 1 - x^2$. Since $t \geq 0$, $x \geq 0$.

So the curve is the right half of the parabola $y = 1 - x^2$.

9. (a) $x = \sin \frac{1}{2}\theta$, $y = \cos \frac{1}{2}\theta$, $-\pi \leq \theta \leq \pi$.

$x^2 + y^2 = \sin^2 \frac{1}{2}\theta + \cos^2 \frac{1}{2}\theta = 1$. For $-\pi \leq \theta \leq 0$, we have

$-1 \leq x \leq 0$ and $0 \leq y \leq 1$. For $0 < \theta \leq \pi$, we have $0 < x \leq 1$

and $1 > y \geq 0$. The graph is a semicircle.

(b)

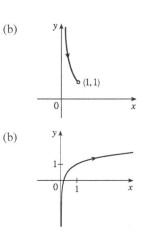

11. (a) $x = \sin t$, $y = \csc t$, $0 < t < \frac{\pi}{2}$. $y = \csc t = \dfrac{1}{\sin t} = \dfrac{1}{x}$.

For $0 < t < \frac{\pi}{2}$, we have $0 < x < 1$ and $y > 1$. Thus, the curve is the

portion of the hyperbola $y = 1/x$ with $y > 1$.

(b)

13. (a) $x = e^{2t}$ ⇒ $2t = \ln x$ ⇒ $t = \frac{1}{2} \ln x$.

$y = t + 1 = \frac{1}{2} \ln x + 1$.

(b)

15. (a) $x = \sin \theta$, $y = \cos 2\theta$.

$y = \cos^2 \theta - \sin^2 \theta = 1 - \sin^2 \theta - \sin^2 \theta$

$= 1 - 2\sin^2 \theta = 1 - 2x^2$.

Since $-1 \leq \sin \theta \leq 1$ and $-1 \leq \cos 2\theta \leq 1$, $-1 \leq x \leq 1$, and

$-1 \leq y \leq 1$. The point (x, y) moves back and forth infinitely often along

the parabola $y = 1 - 2x^2$ from $(1, -1)$ to $(-1, -1)$.

(b)

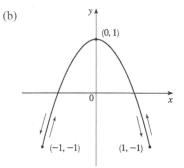

17. $x = 3 + 2\cos t$, $y = 1 + 2\sin t$, $\pi/2 \leq t \leq 3\pi/2$. By Example 4 with $r = 2$, $h = 3$, and $k = 1$, the motion of the particle

takes place on a circle centered at $(3, 1)$ with a radius of 2. As t goes from $\frac{\pi}{2}$ to $\frac{3\pi}{2}$, the particle starts at the point $(3, 3)$ and

moves counterclockwise to $(3, -1)$ [one-half of a circle].

19. $x = 5\sin t$, $y = 2\cos t$ $\Rightarrow$ $\sin t = \dfrac{x}{5}$, $\cos t = \dfrac{y}{2}$. $\sin^2 t + \cos^2 t = 1$ $\Rightarrow$ $\left(\dfrac{x}{5}\right)^2 + \left(\dfrac{y}{2}\right)^2 = 1$. The motion of the

particle takes place on an ellipse centered at $(0,0)$. As t goes from $-\pi$ to 5π, the particle starts at the point $(0,-2)$ and moves

clockwise around the ellipse 3 times.

21. We must have $1 \le x \le 4$ and $2 \le y \le 3$. So the graph of the curve must be contained in the rectangle $[1,4]$ by $[2,3]$.

23. When $t = -1$, $(x,y) = (0,-1)$. As t increases to 0, x decreases to -1 and y

increases to 0. As t increases from 0 to 1, x increases to 0 and y increases to 1.

As t increases beyond 1, both x and y increase. For $t < -1$, x is positive and

decreasing and y is negative and increasing. We could achieve greater accuracy

by estimating x- and y-values for selected values of t from the given graphs and

plotting the corresponding points.

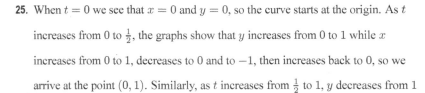

25. When $t = 0$ we see that $x = 0$ and $y = 0$, so the curve starts at the origin. As t

increases from 0 to $\frac{1}{2}$, the graphs show that y increases from 0 to 1 while x

increases from 0 to 1, decreases to 0 and to -1, then increases back to 0, so we

arrive at the point $(0,1)$. Similarly, as t increases from $\frac{1}{2}$ to 1, y decreases from 1

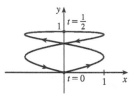

to 0 while x repeats its pattern, and we arrive back at the origin. We could achieve greater accuracy by estimating x- and

y-values for selected values of t from the given graphs and plotting the corresponding points.

27. Use $y = t$ and $x = t - 2\sin \pi t$ with a t-interval of $[-\pi, \pi]$.

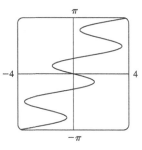

29. (a) $x = x_1 + (x_2 - x_1)t$, $y = y_1 + (y_2 - y_1)t$, $0 \le t \le 1$. Clearly the curve passes through $P_1(x_1, y_1)$ when $t = 0$ and

through $P_2(x_2, y_2)$ when $t = 1$. For $0 < t < 1$, x is strictly between x_1 and x_2 and y is strictly between y_1 and y_2. For

every value of t, x and y satisfy the relation $y - y_1 = \dfrac{y_2 - y_1}{x_2 - x_1}(x - x_1)$, which is the equation of the line through

$P_1(x_1, y_1)$ and $P_2(x_2, y_2)$.

Finally, any point (x,y) on that line satisfies $\dfrac{y - y_1}{y_2 - y_1} = \dfrac{x - x_1}{x_2 - x_1}$; if we call that common value t, then the given

parametric equations yield the point (x,y); and any (x,y) on the line between $P_1(x_1, y_1)$ and $P_2(x_2, y_2)$ yields a value of

t in $[0,1]$. So the given parametric equations exactly specify the line segment from $P_1(x_1, y_1)$ to $P_2(x_2, y_2)$.

(b) $x = -2 + [3 - (-2)]t = -2 + 5t$ and $y = 7 + (-1 - 7)t = 7 - 8t$ for $0 \le t \le 1$.

31. The circle $x^2 + (y-1)^2 = 4$ has center $(0, 1)$ and radius 2, so by Example 4 it can be represented by $x = 2\cos t$,
$y = 1 + 2\sin t$, $0 \le t \le 2\pi$. This representation gives us the circle with a counterclockwise orientation starting at $(2, 1)$.

    (a) To get a clockwise orientation, we could change the equations to $x = 2\cos t$, $y = 1 - 2\sin t$, $0 \le t \le 2\pi$.

    (b) To get three times around in the counterclockwise direction, we use the original equations $x = 2\cos t$, $y = 1 + 2\sin t$ with
the domain expanded to $0 \le t \le 6\pi$.

    (c) To start at $(0, 3)$ using the original equations, we must have $x_1 = 0$; that is, $2\cos t = 0$. Hence, $t = \frac{\pi}{2}$. So we use
$x = 2\cos t$, $y = 1 + 2\sin t$, $\frac{\pi}{2} \le t \le \frac{3\pi}{2}$.

       Alternatively, if we want t to start at 0, we could change the equations of the curve. For example, we could use
$x = -2\sin t$, $y = 1 + 2\cos t$, $0 \le t \le \pi$.

33. *Big circle:* It's centered at $(2, 2)$ with a radius of 2, so by Example 4, parametric equations are

$$x = 2 + 2\cos t, \qquad y = 2 + 2\sin t, \qquad 0 \le t \le 2\pi$$

Small circles: They are centered at $(1, 3)$ and $(3, 3)$ with a radius of 0.1. By Example 4, parametric equations are

              (left) $x = 1 + 0.1\cos t, \qquad y = 3 + 0.1\sin t, \qquad 0 \le t \le 2\pi$

and   *(right)* $x = 3 + 0.1\cos t, \qquad y = 3 + 0.1\sin t, \qquad 0 \le t \le 2\pi$

Semicircle: It's the lower half of a circle centered at $(2, 2)$ with radius 1. By Example 4, parametric equations are

$$x = 2 + 1\cos t, \qquad y = 2 + 1\sin t, \qquad \pi \le t \le 2\pi$$

To get all four graphs on the same screen with a typical graphing calculator, we need to change the last t-interval to $[0, 2\pi]$ in
order to match the others. We can do this by changing t to $0.5t$. This change gives us the upper half. There are several ways to
get the lower half—one is to change the "+" to a "−" in the y-assignment, giving us

$$x = 2 + 1\cos(0.5t), \qquad y = 2 - 1\sin(0.5t), \qquad 0 \le t \le 2\pi$$

35. (a) $x = t^3 \implies t = x^{1/3}$, so $y = t^2 = x^{2/3}$.   (b) $x = t^6 \implies t = x^{1/6}$, so $y = t^4 = x^{4/6} = x^{2/3}$.

    We get the entire curve $y = x^{2/3}$ traversed in a left to   Since $x = t^6 \ge 0$, we only get the right half of the

    right direction.   curve $y = x^{2/3}$.

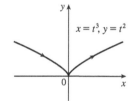

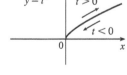

    (c) $x = e^{-3t} = (e^{-t})^3$ [so $e^{-t} = x^{1/3}$],

       $y = e^{-2t} = (e^{-t})^2 = (x^{1/3})^2 = x^{2/3}$.

    If $t < 0$, then x and y are both larger than 1. If $t > 0$, then x and y
are between 0 and 1. Since $x > 0$ and $y > 0$, the curve never quite
reaches the origin.

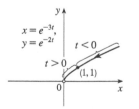

37. The case $\frac{\pi}{2} < \theta < \pi$ is illustrated. C has coordinates $(r\theta, r)$ as in Example 7, and Q has coordinates $(r\theta, r + r\cos(\pi - \theta)) = (r\theta, r(1 - \cos\theta))$ [since $\cos(\pi - \alpha) = \cos\pi\cos\alpha + \sin\pi\sin\alpha = -\cos\alpha$], so P has coordinates $(r\theta - r\sin(\pi - \theta), r(1 - \cos\theta)) = (r(\theta - \sin\theta), r(1 - \cos\theta))$ [since $\sin(\pi - \alpha) = \sin\pi\cos\alpha - \cos\pi\sin\alpha = \sin\alpha$]. Again we have the parametric equations $x = r(\theta - \sin\theta)$, $y = r(1 - \cos\theta)$.

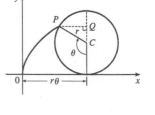
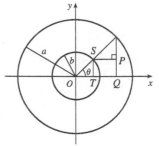

39. It is apparent that $x = |OQ|$ and $y = |QP| = |ST|$. From the diagram,

$x = |OQ| = a\cos\theta$ and $y = |ST| = b\sin\theta$. Thus, the parametric equations are

$x = a\cos\theta$ and $y = b\sin\theta$. To eliminate θ we rearrange: $\sin\theta = y/b \Rightarrow$

$\sin^2\theta = (y/b)^2$ and $\cos\theta = x/a \Rightarrow \cos^2\theta = (x/a)^2$. Adding the two

equations: $\sin^2\theta + \cos^2\theta = 1 = x^2/a^2 + y^2/b^2$. Thus, we have an ellipse.

41. (a)

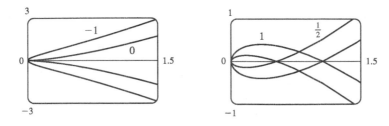

There are 2 points of intersection:

$(-3, 0)$ and approximately $(-2.1, 1.4)$.

(b) A collision point occurs when $x_1 = x_2$ and $y_1 = y_2$ for the same t. So solve the equations:

$$3\sin t = -3 + \cos t \quad \textbf{(1)}$$

$$2\cos t = 1 + \sin t \quad \textbf{(2)}$$

From **(2)**, $\sin t = 2\cos t - 1$. Substituting into **(1)**, we get $3(2\cos t - 1) = -3 + \cos t \Rightarrow 5\cos t = 0 \; (\star) \Rightarrow$

$\cos t = 0 \Rightarrow t = \frac{\pi}{2}$ or $\frac{3\pi}{2}$. We check that $t = \frac{3\pi}{2}$ satisfies **(1)** and **(2)** but $t = \frac{\pi}{2}$ does not. So the only collision point

occurs when $t = \frac{3\pi}{2}$, and this gives the point $(-3, 0)$. [We could check our work by graphing x_1 and x_2 together as

functions of t and, on another plot, y_1 and y_2 as functions of t. If we do so, we see that the only value of t for which *both*

pairs of graphs intersect is $t = \frac{3\pi}{2}$.]

(c) The circle is centered at $(3, 1)$ instead of $(-3, 1)$. There are still 2 intersection points: $(3, 0)$ and $(2.1, 1.4)$, but there are

no collision points, since $(\star)$ in part (b) becomes $5\cos t = 6 \Rightarrow \cos t = \frac{6}{5} > 1$.

43. $x = t^2$, $y = t^3 - ct$. We use a graphing device to produce the graphs for various values of c with $-\pi \le t \le \pi$. Note that all

the members of the family are symmetric about the x-axis. For $c < 0$, the graph does not cross itself, but for $c = 0$ it has a

cusp at $(0, 0)$ and for $c > 0$ the graph crosses itself at $x = c$, so the loop grows larger as c increases.

[Two graphs as described]

45. Note that all the Lissajous figures are symmetric about the x-axis. The parameters a and b simply stretch the graph in the x- and y-directions respectively. For $a = b = n = 1$ the graph is simply a circle with radius 1. For $n = 2$ the graph crosses itself at the origin and there are loops above and below the x-axis. In general, the figures have $n - 1$ points of intersection, all of which are on the y-axis, and a total of n closed loops.

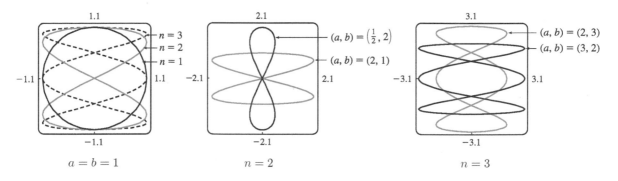

$$a = b = 1 \qquad\qquad n = 2 \qquad\qquad n = 3$$

1 Review

CONCEPT CHECK

1. (a) A **function** f is a rule that assigns to each element x in a set A exactly one element, called $f(x)$, in a set B. The set A is called the **domain** of the function. The **range** of f is the set of all possible values of $f(x)$ as x varies throughout the domain.

(b) If f is a function with domain A, then its **graph** is the set of ordered pairs $\{(x, f(x)) \mid x \in A\}$.

(c) Use the Vertical Line Test on page 17.

2. The four ways to represent a function are: verbally, numerically, visually, and algebraically. An example of each is given below.

Verbally: An assignment of students to chairs in a classroom (a description in words)

Numerically: A tax table that assigns an amount of tax to an income (a table of values)

Visually: A graphical history of the Dow Jones average (a graph)

Algebraically: A relationship between distance, rate, and time: $d = rt$ (an explicit formula)

3. (a) An **even function** f satisfies $f(-x) = f(x)$ for every number x in its domain. It is symmetric with respect to the y-axis.

(b) An **odd function** g satisfies $g(-x) = -g(x)$ for every number x in its domain. It is symmetric with respect to the origin.

4. A function f is called **increasing** on an interval I if $f(x_1) < f(x_2)$ whenever $x_1 < x_2$ in I.

5. A **mathematical model** is a mathematical description (often by means of a function or an equation) of a real-world phenomenon.

6. (a) Linear function: $f(x) = 2x + 1$, $f(x) = ax + b$

(b) Power function: $f(x) = x^2$, $f(x) = x^a$

(c) Exponential function: $f(x) = 2^x$, $f(x) = a^x$

(d) Quadratic function: $f(x) = x^2 + x + 1$, $f(x) = ax^2 + bx + c$

(e) Polynomial of degree 5: $f(x) = x^5 + 2$

(f) Rational function: $f(x) = \dfrac{x}{x+2}$, $f(x) = \dfrac{P(x)}{Q(x)}$ where $P(x)$ and $Q(x)$ are polynomials

7.

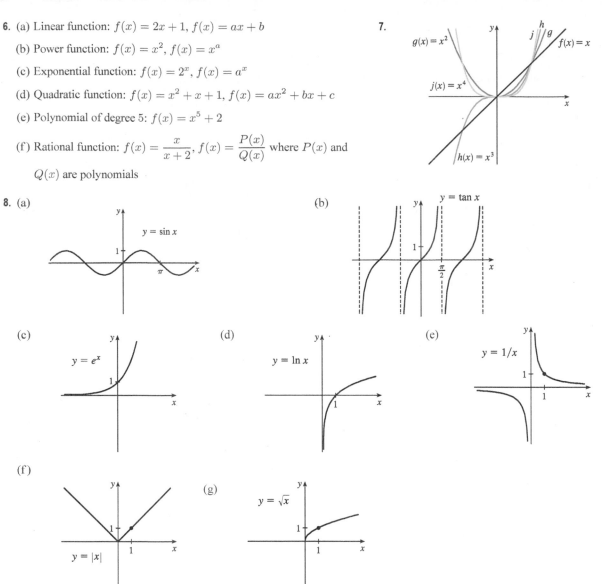

8. (a)

(b)

(c)

(d)

(e)

(f)

(g)

9. (a) The domain of $f + g$ is the intersection of the domain of f and the domain of g; that is, $A \cap B$.

(b) The domain of fg is also $A \cap B$.

(c) The domain of f/g must exclude values of x that make g equal to 0; that is, $\{x \in A \cap B \mid g(x) \neq 0\}$.

10. Given two functions f and g, the **composite** function $f \circ g$ is defined by $(f \circ g)(x) = f(g(x))$. The domain of $f \circ g$ is the set of all x in the domain of g such that $g(x)$ is in the domain of f.

11. (a) If the graph of f is shifted 2 units upward, its equation becomes $y = f(x) + 2$.

(b) If the graph of f is shifted 2 units downward, its equation becomes $y = f(x) - 2$.

(c) If the graph of f is shifted 2 units to the right, its equation becomes $y = f(x - 2)$.

(d) If the graph of f is shifted 2 units to the left, its equation becomes $y = f(x + 2)$.

(e) If the graph of f is reflected about the x-axis, its equation becomes $y = -f(x)$.

(f) If the graph of f is reflected about the y-axis, its equation becomes $y = f(-x)$.

(g) If the graph of f is stretched vertically by a factor of 2, its equation becomes $y = 2f(x)$.

(h) If the graph of f is shrunk vertically by a factor of 2, its equation becomes $y = \frac{1}{2}f(x)$.

(i) If the graph of f is stretched horizontally by a factor of 2, its equation becomes $y = f\left(\frac{1}{2}x\right)$.

(j) If the graph of f is shrunk horizontally by a factor of 2, its equation becomes $y = f(2x)$.

12. (a) A function f is called a *one-to-one function* if it never takes on the same value twice; that is, if $f(x_1) \neq f(x_2)$ whenever $x_1 \neq x_2$. (Or, f is 1-1 if each output corresponds to only one input.)

   Use the Horizontal Line Test: A function is one-to-one if and only if no horizontal line intersects its graph more than once.

(b) If f is a one-to-one function with domain A and range B, then its *inverse function* f^{-1} has domain B and range A and is defined by

$$f^{-1}(y) = x \quad \Leftrightarrow \quad f(x) = y$$

for any y in B. The graph of f^{-1} is obtained by reflecting the graph of f about the line $y = x$.

13. (a) A parametric curve is a set of points of the form $(x, y) = (f(t), g(t))$, where f and g are continuous functions of a variable t.

(b) Sketching a parametric curve, like sketching the graph of a function, is difficult to do in general. We can plot points on the curve by finding $f(t)$ and $g(t)$ for various values of t, either by hand or with a calculator or computer. Sometimes, when f and g are given by formulas, we can eliminate t from the equations $x = f(t)$ and $y = g(t)$ to get a Cartesian equation relating x and y. It may be easier to graph that equation than to work with the original formulas for x and y in terms of t.

(c) See the margin note on page 72.

TRUE-FALSE QUIZ

1. False.   Let $f(x) = x^2$, $s = -1$, and $t = 1$. Then $f(s + t) = (-1 + 1)^2 = 0^2 = 0$, but
$f(s) + f(t) = (-1)^2 + 1^2 = 2 \neq 0 = f(s + t)$.

3. False.   Let $f(x) = x^2$. Then $f(3x) = (3x)^2 = 9x^2$ and $3f(x) = 3x^2$. So $f(3x) \neq 3f(x)$.

5. True.   See the Vertical Line Test.

7. False.   Let $f(x) = x^3$. Then f is one-to-one and $f^{-1}(x) = \sqrt[3]{x}$. But $1/f(x) = 1/x^3$, which is not equal to $f^{-1}(x)$.

9. True.   The function $\ln x$ is an increasing function on $(0, \infty)$.

11. False.   Let $x = e^2$ and $a = e$. Then $\dfrac{\ln x}{\ln a} = \dfrac{\ln e^2}{\ln e} = \dfrac{2\ln e}{\ln e} = 2$ and $\ln \dfrac{x}{a} = \ln \dfrac{e^2}{e} = \ln e = 1$, so in general the statement is false. What *is* true, however, is that $\ln \dfrac{x}{a} = \ln x - \ln a$.

EXERCISES

1. (a) When $x = 2$, $y \approx 2.7$. Thus, $f(2) \approx 2.7$.   (b) $f(x) = 3 \;\Rightarrow\; x \approx 2.3, 5.6$

(c) The domain of f is $-6 \le x \le 6$, or $[-6, 6]$.   (d) The range of f is $-4 \le y \le 4$, or $[-4, 4]$.

(e) f is increasing on $[-4, 4]$, that is, on $-4 \le x \le 4$.

(f) f is not one-to-one since it fails the Horizontal Line Test.

(g) f is odd since its graph is symmetric about the origin.

3. $f(x) = x^2 - 2x + 3$, so $f(a + h) = (a + h)^2 - 2(a + h) + 3 = a^2 + 2ah + h^2 - 2a - 2h + 3$, and

$$\frac{f(a+h) - f(a)}{h} = \frac{(a^2 + 2ah + h^2 - 2a - 2h + 3) - (a^2 - 2a + 3)}{h} = \frac{h(2a + h - 2)}{h} = 2a + h - 2.$$

5. $f(x) = 2/(3x - 1)$.   Domain: $3x - 1 \ne 0 \;\Rightarrow\; 3x \ne 1 \;\Rightarrow\; x \ne \frac{1}{3}$. $D = \left(-\infty, \frac{1}{3}\right) \cup \left(\frac{1}{3}, \infty\right)$

Range: all reals except 0 ($y = 0$ is the horizontal asymptote for f.) $R = (-\infty, 0) \cup (0, \infty)$

7. $h(x) = \ln(x + 6)$.   Domain: $x + 6 > 0 \;\Rightarrow\; x > -6$. $D = (-6, \infty)$

Range: $x + 6 > 0$, so $\ln(x + 6)$ takes on all real numbers and, hence, the range is $\mathbb{R}$.

$R = (-\infty, \infty)$

9. (a) To obtain the graph of $y = f(x) + 8$, we shift the graph of $y = f(x)$ up 8 units.

(b) To obtain the graph of $y = f(x + 8)$, we shift the graph of $y = f(x)$ left 8 units.

(c) To obtain the graph of $y = 1 + 2f(x)$, we stretch the graph of $y = f(x)$ vertically by a factor of 2, and then shift the resulting graph 1 unit upward.

(d) To obtain the graph of $y = f(x - 2) - 2$, we shift the graph of $y = f(x)$ right 2 units (for the "-2" inside the parentheses), and then shift the resulting graph 2 units downward.

(e) To obtain the graph of $y = -f(x)$, we reflect the graph of $y = f(x)$ about the x-axis.

(f) To obtain the graph of $y = f^{-1}(x)$, we reflect the graph of $y = f(x)$ about the line $y = x$ (assuming f is one-to-one).

11. $y = -\sin 2x$: Start with the graph of $y = \sin x$, compress horizontally by a factor of 2, and reflect about the x-axis.

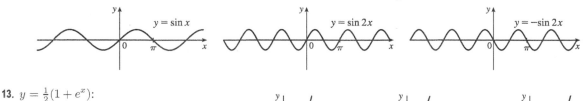

13. $y = \frac{1}{2}(1 + e^x)$:

Start with the graph of $y = e^x$,

shift 1 unit upward, and compress

vertically by a factor of 2.

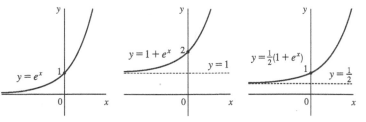

15. $f(x) = \dfrac{1}{x+2}$:

Start with the graph of $f(x) = 1/x$

and shift 2 units to the left.

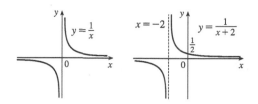

17. (a) The terms of f are a mixture of odd and even powers of x, so f is neither even nor odd.

(b) The terms of f are all odd powers of x, so f is odd.

(c) $f(-x) = e^{-(-x)^2} = e^{-x^2} = f(x)$, so f is even.

(d) $f(-x) = 1 + \sin(-x) = 1 - \sin x$. Now $f(-x) \neq f(x)$ and $f(-x) \neq -f(x)$, so f is neither even nor odd.

19. $f(x) = \ln x$, $\quad D = (0, \infty)$; $\quad g(x) = x^2 - 9$, $\quad D = \mathbb{R}$.

(a) $(f \circ g)(x) = f(g(x)) = f(x^2 - 9) = \ln(x^2 - 9)$.

Domain: $x^2 - 9 > 0 \;\Rightarrow\; x^2 > 9 \;\Rightarrow\; |x| > 3 \;\Rightarrow\; x \in (-\infty, -3) \cup (3, \infty)$

(b) $(g \circ f)(x) = g(f(x)) = g(\ln x) = (\ln x)^2 - 9$. Domain: $x > 0$, or $(0, \infty)$

(c) $(f \circ f)(x) = f(f(x)) = f(\ln x) = \ln(\ln x)$. Domain: $\ln x > 0 \;\Rightarrow\; x > e^0 = 1$, or $(1, \infty)$

(d) $(g \circ g)(x) = g(g(x)) = g(x^2 - 9) = (x^2 - 9)^2 - 9$. Domain: $x \in \mathbb{R}$, or $(-\infty, \infty)$

21.

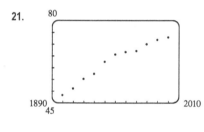

Many models appear to be plausible. Your choice depends on whether you think medical advances will keep increasing life expectancy, or if there is bound to be a natural leveling-off of life expectancy. A linear model, $y = 0.2493x - 423.4818$, gives us an estimate of 77.6 years for the year 2010.

23. We need to know the value of x such that $f(x) = 2x + \ln x = 2$. Since $x = 1$ gives us $y = 2$, $f^{-1}(2) = 1$.

25. (a) $e^{2 \ln 3} = (e^{\ln 3})^2 = 3^2 = 9$

(b) $\log_{10} 25 + \log_{10} 4 = \log_{10}(25 \cdot 4) = \log_{10} 100 = \log_{10} 10^2 = 2$

27. (a) After 4 days, $\frac{1}{2}$ gram remains; after 8 days, $\frac{1}{4}$ g; after 12 days, $\frac{1}{8}$ g; after 16 days, $\frac{1}{16}$ g.

(b) $m(4) = \dfrac{1}{2}$, $m(8) = \dfrac{1}{2^2}$, $m(12) = \dfrac{1}{2^3}$, $m(16) = \dfrac{1}{2^4}$. From the pattern, we see that $m(t) = \dfrac{1}{2^{t/4}}$, or $2^{-t/4}$.

(c) $m = 2^{-t/4} \;\Rightarrow\; \log_2 m = -t/4 \;\Rightarrow\; t = -4 \log_2 m$; this is the time elapsed when there are m grams of ^{100}Pd.

(d) $m = 0.01 \;\Rightarrow\; t = -4 \log_2 0.01 = -4 \left(\dfrac{\ln 0.01}{\ln 2} \right) \approx 26.6$ days

29. $f(x) = \ln(x^2 - c)$. If $c < 0$, the domain of f is $\mathbb{R}$. If $c = 0$, the

domain of f is $(-\infty, 0) \cup (0, \infty)$. If $c > 0$, the domain of f is

$(-\infty, -\sqrt{c}) \cup (\sqrt{c}, \infty)$. As c increases, the dip at $x = 0$ becomes

deeper. For $c \geq 0$, the graph has asymptotes at $x = \pm\sqrt{c}$.

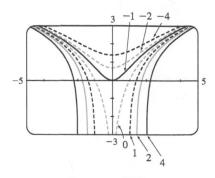

31. (a)

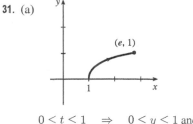

(b) $x = e^t \quad \Rightarrow \quad t = \ln x; y = \sqrt{t}$ so $y = \sqrt{\ln x}$.

$0 \leq t \leq 1 \quad \Rightarrow \quad 0 \leq y \leq 1$ and $1 \leq x \leq e$.

33. We sketch $x = t$, $y = 2t + \ln t$ (the function) and $x = 2t + \ln t$, $y = t$ (its inverse) for $t > 0$.

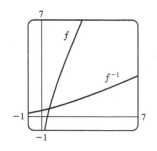

☐ PRINCIPLES OF PROBLEM SOLVING

1.

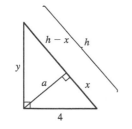

By using the area formula for a triangle, $\frac{1}{2}$ (base) (height), in two ways, we see that

$$\tfrac{1}{2}\,(4)\,(y) = \tfrac{1}{2}\,(h)\,(a),\ \text{so}\ a = \frac{4y}{h}.\ \text{Since}\ 4^2 + y^2 = h^2,\ y = \sqrt{h^2 - 16},\ \text{and}$$

$$a = \frac{4\sqrt{h^2 - 16}}{h}.$$

3. $|2x - 1| = \begin{cases} 2x - 1 & \text{if } x \geq \frac{1}{2} \\ 1 - 2x & \text{if } x < \frac{1}{2} \end{cases}$ and $|x + 5| = \begin{cases} x + 5 & \text{if } x \geq -5 \\ -x - 5 & \text{if } x < -5 \end{cases}$

Therefore, we consider the three cases $x < -5$, $-5 \leq x < \frac{1}{2}$, and $x \geq \frac{1}{2}$.

If $x < -5$, we must have $1 - 2x - (-x - 5) = 3 \iff x = 3$, which is false, since we are considering $x < -5$.

If $-5 \leq x < \frac{1}{2}$, we must have $1 - 2x - (x + 5) = 3 \iff x = -\frac{7}{3}$.

If $x \geq \frac{1}{2}$, we must have $2x - 1 - (x + 5) = 3 \iff x = 9$.

So the two solutions of the equation are $x = -\frac{7}{3}$ and $x = 9$.

5. $f(x) = \left|x^2 - 4\,|x| + 3\right|$. If $x \geq 0$, then $f(x) = \left|x^2 - 4x + 3\right| = |(x - 1)(x - 3)|$.

  Case (i):   If $0 < x \leq 1$, then $f(x) = x^2 - 4x + 3$.

  Case (ii):   If $1 < x \leq 3$, then $f(x) = -(x^2 - 4x + 3) = -x^2 + 4x - 3$.

  Case (iii): If $x > 3$, then $f(x) = x^2 - 4x + 3$.

This enables us to sketch the graph for $x \geq 0$. Then we use the fact that f is an even

function to reflect this part of the graph about the y-axis to obtain the entire graph. Or, we

could consider also the cases $x < -3$, $-3 \leq x < -1$, and $-1 \leq x < 0$.

7. Remember that $|a| = a$ if $a \geq 0$ and that $|a| = -a$ if $a < 0$. Thus,

$$x + |x| = \begin{cases} 2x & \text{if } x \geq 0 \\ 0 & \text{if } x < 0 \end{cases} \quad \text{and} \quad y + |y| = \begin{cases} 2y & \text{if } y \geq 0 \\ 0 & \text{if } y < 0 \end{cases}$$

We will consider the equation $x + |x| = y + |y|$ in four cases.

$(1)\ x \geq 0, y \geq 0$	$(2)\ x \geq 0, y < 0$	$(3)\ x < 0, y \geq 0$	$(4)\ x < 0, y < 0$
$2x = 2y$	$2x = 0$	$0 = 2y$	$0 = 0$
$x = y$	$x = 0$	$0 = y$	

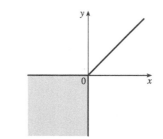

Case 1 gives us the line $y = x$ with nonnegative x and y.

Case 2 gives us the portion of the y-axis with y negative.

Case 3 gives us the portion of the x-axis with x negative.

Case 4 gives us the entire third quadrant.

9. $|x| + |y| \leq 1$. The boundary of the region has equation $|x| + |y| = 1$. In quadrants
I, II, III, and IV, this becomes the lines $x + y = 1$, $-x + y = 1$, $-x - y = 1$, and
$x - y = 1$ respectively.

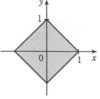

11. $(\log_2 3)(\log_3 4)(\log_4 5) \cdots (\log_{31} 32) = \left(\dfrac{\ln 3}{\ln 2}\right)\left(\dfrac{\ln 4}{\ln 3}\right)\left(\dfrac{\ln 5}{\ln 4}\right) \cdots \left(\dfrac{\ln 32}{\ln 31}\right) = \dfrac{\ln 32}{\ln 2} = \dfrac{\ln 2^5}{\ln 2} = \dfrac{5\ln 2}{\ln 2} = 5$

13. $\ln(x^2 - 2x - 2) \leq 0 \;\Rightarrow\; x^2 - 2x - 2 \leq e^0 = 1 \;\Rightarrow\; x^2 - 2x - 3 \leq 0 \;\Rightarrow\; (x - 3)(x + 1) \leq 0 \;\Rightarrow\; x \in [-1, 3]$.

Since the argument must be positive, $x^2 - 2x - 2 > 0 \;\Rightarrow\; \left[x - \left(1 - \sqrt{3}\right)\right]\left[x - \left(1 + \sqrt{3}\right)\right] > 0 \;\Rightarrow$

$x \in \left(-\infty, 1 - \sqrt{3}\right) \cup \left(1 + \sqrt{3}, \infty\right)$. The intersection of these intervals is $\left[-1, 1 - \sqrt{3}\right) \cup \left(1 + \sqrt{3}, 3\right]$.

15. Let d be the distance traveled on each half of the trip. Let t_1 and t_2 be the times taken for the first and second halves of the trip.

For the first half of the trip we have $t_1 = d/30$ and for the second half we have $t_2 = d/60$. Thus, the average speed for the

entire trip is $\dfrac{\text{total distance}}{\text{total time}} = \dfrac{2d}{t_1 + t_2} = \dfrac{2d}{\dfrac{d}{30} + \dfrac{d}{60}} \cdot \dfrac{60}{60} = \dfrac{120d}{2d + d} = \dfrac{120d}{3d} = 40$. The average speed for the entire trip

is 40 mi/h.

17. Let S_n be the statement that $7^n - 1$ is divisible by 6.

- S_1 is true because $7^1 - 1 = 6$ is divisible by 6.

- Assume S_k is true, that is, $7^k - 1$ is divisible by 6. In other words, $7^k - 1 = 6m$ for some positive integer m. Then

  $7^{k+1} - 1 = 7^k \cdot 7 - 1 = (6m + 1) \cdot 7 - 1 = 42m + 6 = 6(7m + 1)$, which is divisible by 6, so S_{k+1} is true.

- Therefore, by mathematical induction, $7^n - 1$ is divisible by 6 for every positive integer n.

19. $f_0(x) = x^2$ and $f_{n+1}(x) = f_0(f_n(x))$ for $n = 0, 1, 2, \ldots$.

$f_1(x) = f_0(f_0(x)) = f_0(x^2) = (x^2)^2 = x^4$, $f_2(x) = f_0(f_1(x)) = f_0(x^4) = (x^4)^2 = x^8$,

$f_3(x) = f_0(f_2(x)) = f_0(x^8) = (x^8)^2 = x^{16}, \ldots$. Thus, a general formula is $f_n(x) = x^{2^{n+1}}$.

2 ☐ LIMITS AND DERIVATIVES

2.1 The Tangent and Velocity Problems

1. (a) Using $P(15, 250)$, we construct the following table:

t	Q	slope $= m_{PQ}$
5	$(5, 694)$	$\frac{694-250}{5-15} = -\frac{444}{10} = -44.4$
10	$(10, 444)$	$\frac{444-250}{10-15} = -\frac{194}{5} = -38.8$
20	$(20, 111)$	$\frac{111-250}{20-15} = -\frac{139}{5} = -27.8$
25	$(25, 28)$	$\frac{28-250}{25-15} = -\frac{222}{10} = -22.2$
30	$(30, 0)$	$\frac{0-250}{30-15} = -\frac{250}{15} = -16.\overline{6}$

(b) Using the values of t that correspond to the points closest to P ($t = 10$ and $t = 20$), we have

$$\frac{-38.8 + (-27.8)}{2} = -33.3$$

(c) From the graph, we can estimate the slope of the tangent line at P to be $\frac{-300}{9} = -33.\overline{3}$.

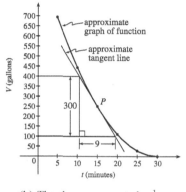

3. (a) $y = \dfrac{x}{1+x}$, $P(1, \frac{1}{2})$

	x	Q	m_{PQ}
(i)	0.5	$(0.5, 0.333333)$	0.333333
(ii)	0.9	$(0.9, 0.473684)$	0.263158
(iii)	0.99	$(0.99, 0.497487)$	0.251256
(iv)	0.999	$(0.999, 0.499750)$	0.250125
(v)	1.5	$(1.5, 0.6)$	0.2
(vi)	1.1	$(1.1, 0.523810)$	0.238095
(vii)	1.01	$(1.01, 0.502488)$	0.248756
(viii)	1.001	$(1.001, 0.500250)$	0.249875

(b) The slope appears to be $\frac{1}{4}$.

(c) $y - \frac{1}{2} = \frac{1}{4}(x - 1)$ or $y = \frac{1}{4}x + \frac{1}{4}$.

5. (a) $y = y(t) = 40t - 16t^2$. At $t = 2$, $y = 40(2) - 16(2)^2 = 16$. The average velocity between times 2 and $2 + h$ is

$$v_{\text{ave}} = \frac{y(2+h) - y(2)}{(2+h) - 2} = \frac{\left[40(2+h) - 16(2+h)^2\right] - 16}{h} = \frac{-24h - 16h^2}{h} = -24 - 16h, \ \text{if } h \neq 0.$$

(i) $[2, 2.5]$: $h = 0.5$, $v_{\text{ave}} = -32$ ft/s
(ii) $[2, 2.1]$: $h = 0.1$, $v_{\text{ave}} = -25.6$ ft/s

(iii) $[2, 2.05]$: $h = 0.05$, $v_{\text{ave}} = -24.8$ ft/s
(iv) $[2, 2.01]$: $h = 0.01$, $v_{\text{ave}} = -24.16$ ft/s

(b) The instantaneous velocity when $t = 2$ (h approaches 0) is -24 ft/s.

7. (a) (i) On the interval $[1, 3]$, $v_{\text{ave}} = \dfrac{s(3) - s(1)}{3 - 1} = \dfrac{10.7 - 1.4}{2} = \dfrac{9.3}{2} = 4.65$ m/s.

(ii) On the interval $[2, 3]$, $v_{\text{ave}} = \dfrac{s(3) - s(2)}{3 - 2} = \dfrac{10.7 - 5.1}{1} = 5.6$ m/s.

(iii) On the interval $[3, 5]$, $v_{\text{ave}} = \dfrac{s(5) - s(3)}{5 - 3} = \dfrac{25.8 - 10.7}{2} = \dfrac{15.1}{2} = 7.55$ m/s.

(iv) On the interval $[3, 4]$, $v_{\text{ave}} = \dfrac{s(4) - s(3)}{4 - 3} = \dfrac{17.7 - 10.7}{1} = 7$ m/s.

(b)

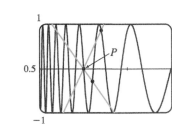

Using the points $(2, 4)$ and $(5, 23)$ from the approximate tangent line, the instantaneous velocity at $t = 3$ is about $\dfrac{23 - 4}{5 - 2} \approx 6.3$ m/s.

9. (a) For the curve $y = \sin(10\pi/x)$ and the point $P(1, 0)$:

x	Q	m_{PQ}
2	$(2, 0)$	0
1.5	$(1.5, 0.8660)$	1.7321
1.4	$(1.4, -0.4339)$	-1.0847
1.3	$(1.3, -0.8230)$	-2.7433
1.2	$(1.2, 0.8660)$	4.3301
1.1	$(1.1, -0.2817)$	-2.8173

x	Q	m_{PQ}
0.5	$(0.5, 0)$	0
0.6	$(0.6, 0.8660)$	-2.1651
0.7	$(0.7, 0.7818)$	-2.6061
0.8	$(0.8, 1)$	-5
0.9	$(0.9, -0.3420)$	3.4202

As x approaches 1, the slopes do not appear to be approaching any particular value.

(b)

We see that problems with estimation are caused by the frequent oscillations of the graph. The tangent is so steep at P that we need to take x-values much closer to 1 in order to get accurate estimates of its slope.

(c) If we choose $x = 1.001$, then the point Q is $(1.001, -0.0314)$ and $m_{PQ} \approx -31.3794$. If $x = 0.999$, then Q is $(0.999, 0.0314)$ and $m_{PQ} = -31.4422$. The average of these slopes is -31.4108. So we estimate that the slope of the tangent line at P is about -31.4.

2.2 The Limit of a Function

1. As x approaches 2, $f(x)$ approaches 5. [Or, the values of $f(x)$ can be made as close to 5 as we like by taking x sufficiently close to 2 (but $x \neq 2$).] Yes, the graph could have a hole at $(2, 5)$ and be defined such that $f(2) = 3$.

3. (a) $f(x)$ approaches 2 as x approaches 1 from the left, so $\lim\limits_{x \to 1^-} f(x) = 2$.

(b) $f(x)$ approaches 3 as x approaches 1 from the right, so $\lim\limits_{x \to 1^+} f(x) = 3$.

(c) $\lim\limits_{x \to 1} f(x)$ does not exist because the limits in part (a) and part (b) are not equal.

(d) $f(x)$ approaches 4 as x approaches 5 from the left and from the right, so $\lim\limits_{x \to 5} f(x) = 4$.

(e) $f(5)$ is not defined, so it doesn't exist.

5. (a) $\lim\limits_{t \to 0^-} g(t) = -1$ (b) $\lim\limits_{t \to 0^+} g(t) = -2$

(c) $\lim\limits_{t \to 0} g(t)$ does not exist because the limits in part (a) and part (b) are not equal.

(d) $\lim\limits_{t \to 2^-} g(t) = 2$ (e) $\lim\limits_{t \to 2^+} g(t) = 0$

(f) $\lim\limits_{t \to 2} g(t)$ does not exist because the limits in part (d) and part (e) are not equal.

(g) $g(2) = 1$ (h) $\lim\limits_{t \to 4} g(t) = 3$

7. From the graph of

$$f(x) = \begin{cases} 1 + x & \text{if } x < -1 \\ x^2 & \text{if } -1 \le x < 1, \\ 2 - x & \text{if } x \ge 1 \end{cases}$$

we see that $\lim\limits_{x \to a} f(x)$ exists for all a except $a = -1$. Notice that the

right and left limits are different at $a = -1$.

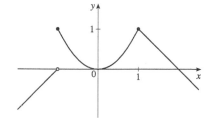

9. (a) $\lim\limits_{x \to 0^-} f(x) = 1$

(b) $\lim\limits_{x \to 0^+} f(x) = 0$

(c) $\lim\limits_{x \to 0} f(x)$ does not exist because the limits

in part (a) and part (b) are not equal.

11. (a) $\lim\limits_{x \to 0^-} f(x) = -2$

(b) $\lim\limits_{x \to 0^+} f(x) = 2$

(c) $\lim\limits_{x \to 0} f(x)$ does not exist because the limits

in part (a) and part (b) are not equal.

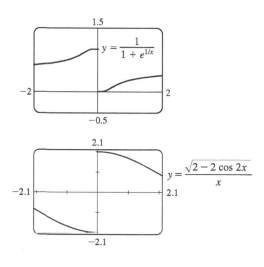

13. $\lim_{x\to 0^-} f(x) = -1$, $\quad \lim_{x\to 0^+} f(x) = 2$, $\quad f(0) = 1$

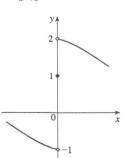

15. $\lim_{x\to 3^+} f(x) = 4$, $\quad \lim_{x\to 3^-} f(x) = 2$, $\lim_{x\to -2} f(x) = 2$,

$\quad f(3) = 3$, $\quad f(-2) = 1$

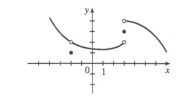

17. For $f(x) = \dfrac{x^2 - 2x}{x^2 - x - 2}$:

x	$f(x)$
2.5	0.714286
2.1	0.677419
2.05	0.672131
2.01	0.667774
2.005	0.667221
2.001	0.666778

x	$f(x)$
1.9	0.655172
1.95	0.661017
1.99	0.665552
1.995	0.666110
1.999	0.666556

It appears that $\lim_{x\to 2} \dfrac{x^2 - 2x}{x^2 - x - 2} = 0.\bar{6} = \dfrac{2}{3}$.

19. For $f(t) = \dfrac{e^{5t} - 1}{t}$:

t	$f(t)$
0.5	22.364988
0.1	6.487213
0.01	5.127110
0.001	5.012521
0.0001	5.001250

t	$f(t)$
−0.5	1.835830
−0.1	3.934693
−0.01	4.877058
−0.001	4.987521
−0.0001	4.998750

It appears that $\lim_{t\to 0} \dfrac{e^{5t} - 1}{t} = 5$.

21. For $f(x) = \dfrac{\sqrt{x+4} - 2}{x}$:

x	$f(x)$
1	0.236068
0.5	0.242641
0.1	0.248457
0.05	0.249224
0.01	0.249844

x	$f(x)$
−1	0.267949
−0.5	0.258343
−0.1	0.251582
−0.05	0.250786
−0.01	0.250156

It appears that $\lim_{x\to 0} \dfrac{\sqrt{x+4} - 2}{x} = 0.25 = \dfrac{1}{4}$.

23. For $f(x) = \dfrac{x^6 - 1}{x^{10} - 1}$:

x	$f(x)$
0.5	0.985337
0.9	0.719397
0.95	0.660186
0.99	0.612018
0.999	0.601200

x	$f(x)$
1.5	0.183369
1.1	0.484119
1.05	0.540783
1.01	0.588022
1.001	0.598800

It appears that $\lim_{x\to 1} \dfrac{x^6 - 1}{x^{10} - 1} = 0.6 = \dfrac{3}{5}$.

25. (a) From the graphs, it seems that $\lim_{x\to 0} \dfrac{\cos 2x - \cos x}{x^2} = -1.5$.

(b)

x	$f(x)$
±0.1	−1.493759
±0.01	−1.499938
±0.001	−1.499999
±0.0001	−1.500000

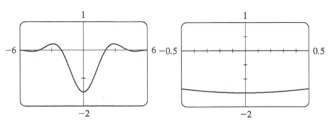

27. (a) Let $h(x) = (1+x)^{1/x}$.

x	$h(x)$
-0.001	2.71964
-0.0001	2.71842
-0.00001	2.71830
-0.000001	2.71828
0.000001	2.71828
0.00001	2.71827
0.0001	2.71815
0.001	2.71692

(b)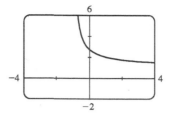

It appears that $\lim\limits_{x \to 0} (1+x)^{1/x} \approx 2.71828$, which is approximately e.

In Section 3.7 we will see that the value of the limit is exactly e.

29. For $f(x) = x^2 - (2^x/1000)$:

(a)

x	$f(x)$
1	0.998000
0.8	0.638259
0.6	0.358484
0.4	0.158680
0.2	0.038851
0.1	0.008928
0.05	0.001465

It appears that $\lim\limits_{x \to 0} f(x) = 0$.

(b)

x	$f(x)$
0.04	0.000572
0.02	-0.000614
0.01	-0.000907
0.005	-0.000978
0.003	-0.000993
0.001	-0.001000

It appears that $\lim\limits_{x \to 0} f(x) = -0.001$.

31. We need to have $5.8 < x^3 - 3x + 4 < 6.2$. From the graph we obtain the approximate points of intersection $P(1.9774, 5.8)$ and $Q(2.0219, 6.2)$. So if x is within 0.021 of 2, then y will be within 0.2 of 6. If we must have $x^3 - 3x + 4$ within 0.1 of 6, we get $P(1.9888, 5.9)$ and $Q(2.0110, 6.1)$. We would then need x to be within 0.011 of 2.

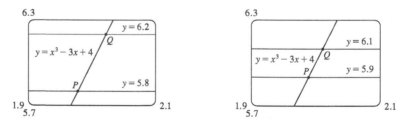

2.3 Calculating Limits Using the Limit Laws

1. (a) $\lim\limits_{x \to 2} [f(x) + 5g(x)] = \lim\limits_{x \to 2} f(x) + \lim\limits_{x \to 2} [5g(x)]$ [Limit Law 1]

$$= \lim\limits_{x \to 2} f(x) + 5 \lim\limits_{x \to 2} g(x)$$ [Limit Law 3]

$$= 4 + 5(-2) = -6$$

(b) $\lim\limits_{x \to 2} [g(x)]^3 = \left[\lim\limits_{x \to 2} g(x) \right]^3$ [Limit Law 6]

$$= (-2)^3 = -8$$

(c) $\lim\limits_{x \to 2} \sqrt{f(x)} = \sqrt{\lim\limits_{x \to 2} f(x)}$ [Limit Law 11]

$$= \sqrt{4} = 2$$

(d) $\lim\limits_{x \to 2} \dfrac{3f(x)}{g(x)} = \dfrac{\lim\limits_{x \to 2} [3f(x)]}{\lim\limits_{x \to 2} g(x)}$ [Limit Law 5]

$$= \dfrac{3 \lim\limits_{x \to 2} f(x)}{\lim\limits_{x \to 2} g(x)}$$ [Limit Law 3]

$$= \dfrac{3(4)}{-2} = -6$$

(e) Because the limit of the denominator is 0, we can't use Limit Law 5. The given limit, $\lim\limits_{x \to 2} \dfrac{g(x)}{h(x)}$, does not exist because the denominator approaches 0 while the numerator approaches a nonzero number.

(f) $\lim\limits_{x \to 2} \dfrac{g(x)\,h(x)}{f(x)} = \dfrac{\lim\limits_{x \to 2} [g(x)\,h(x)]}{\lim\limits_{x \to 2} f(x)}$ [Limit Law 5]

$$= \dfrac{\lim\limits_{x \to 2} g(x) \cdot \lim\limits_{x \to 2} h(x)}{\lim\limits_{x \to 2} f(x)}$$ [Limit Law 4]

$$= \dfrac{-2 \cdot 0}{4} = 0$$

3. $\lim\limits_{x \to -2} (3x^4 + 2x^2 - x + 1) = \lim\limits_{x \to -2} 3x^4 + \lim\limits_{x \to -2} 2x^2 - \lim\limits_{x \to -2} x + \lim\limits_{x \to -2} 1$ [Limit Laws 1 and 2]

$$= 3 \lim\limits_{x \to -2} x^4 + 2 \lim\limits_{x \to -2} x^2 - \lim\limits_{x \to -2} x + \lim\limits_{x \to -2} 1$$ [3]

$$= 3(-2)^4 + 2(-2)^2 - (-2) + (1)$$ [9, 8, and 7]

$$= 48 + 8 + 2 + 1 = 59$$

5. $\lim\limits_{x \to 8} (1 + \sqrt[3]{x})(2 - 6x^2 + x^3) = \lim\limits_{x \to 8} (1 + \sqrt[3]{x}) \cdot \lim\limits_{x \to 8} (2 - 6x^2 + x^3)$ [Limit Law 4]

$$= \left(\lim\limits_{x \to 8} 1 + \lim\limits_{x \to 8} \sqrt[3]{x} \right) \cdot \left(\lim\limits_{x \to 8} 2 - 6 \lim\limits_{x \to 8} x^2 + \lim\limits_{x \to 8} x^3 \right)$$ [1, 2, and 3]

$$= (1 + \sqrt[3]{8}) \cdot (2 - 6 \cdot 8^2 + 8^3)$$ [7, 10, 9]

$$= (3)(130) = 390$$

7. $\displaystyle\lim_{x\to 2}\sqrt{\frac{2x^2+1}{3x-2}} = \sqrt{\lim_{x\to 2}\frac{2x^2+1}{3x-2}}$ [Limit Law 11]

$$= \sqrt{\frac{\lim\limits_{x\to 2}(2x^2+1)}{\lim\limits_{x\to 2}(3x-2)}}$$ [5]

$$= \sqrt{\frac{2\lim\limits_{x\to 2}x^2 + \lim\limits_{x\to 2}1}{3\lim\limits_{x\to 2}x - \lim\limits_{x\to 2}2}}$$ [1, 2, and 3]

$$= \sqrt{\frac{2(2)^2+1}{3(2)-2}} = \sqrt{\frac{9}{4}} = \frac{3}{2}$$ [9, 8, and 7]

9. $\displaystyle\lim_{x\to 5}\frac{x^2-6x+5}{x-5} = \lim_{x\to 5}\frac{(x-5)(x-1)}{x-5} = \lim_{x\to 5}(x-1) = 5-1 = 4$

11. $\displaystyle\lim_{x\to 5}\frac{x^2-5x+6}{x-5}$ does not exist since $x-5\to 0$, but $x^2-5x+6\to 6$ as $x\to 5$.

13. $\displaystyle\lim_{t\to -3}\frac{t^2-9}{2t^2+7t+3} = \lim_{t\to -3}\frac{(t+3)(t-3)}{(2t+1)(t+3)} = \lim_{t\to -3}\frac{t-3}{2t+1} = \frac{-3-3}{2(-3)+1} = \frac{-6}{-5} = \frac{6}{5}$

15. $\displaystyle\lim_{h\to 0}\frac{(4+h)^2-16}{h} = \lim_{h\to 0}\frac{(16+8h+h^2)-16}{h} = \lim_{h\to 0}\frac{8h+h^2}{h} = \lim_{h\to 0}\frac{h(8+h)}{h} = \lim_{h\to 0}(8+h) = 8+0 = 8$

17. By the formula for the sum of cubes, we have

$$\lim_{x\to -2}\frac{x+2}{x^3+8} = \lim_{x\to -2}\frac{x+2}{(x+2)(x^2-2x+4)} = \lim_{x\to -2}\frac{1}{x^2-2x+4} = \frac{1}{4+4+4} = \frac{1}{12}.$$

19. $\displaystyle\lim_{x\to -4}\frac{\frac{1}{4}+\frac{1}{x}}{4+x} = \lim_{x\to -4}\frac{\frac{x+4}{4x}}{4+x} = \lim_{x\to -4}\frac{x+4}{4x(4+x)} = \lim_{x\to -4}\frac{1}{4x} = \frac{1}{4(-4)} = -\frac{1}{16}$

21. $\displaystyle\lim_{x\to 16}\frac{4-\sqrt{x}}{16x-x^2} = \lim_{x\to 16}\frac{(4-\sqrt{x})(4+\sqrt{x})}{(16x-x^2)(4+\sqrt{x})} = \lim_{x\to 16}\frac{16-x}{x(16-x)(4+\sqrt{x})}$

$$= \lim_{x\to 16}\frac{1}{x(4+\sqrt{x})} = \frac{1}{16(4+\sqrt{16})} = \frac{1}{16(8)} = \frac{1}{128}$$

23. $\displaystyle\lim_{t\to 0}\left(\frac{1}{t\sqrt{1+t}}-\frac{1}{t}\right) = \lim_{t\to 0}\frac{1-\sqrt{1+t}}{t\sqrt{1+t}} = \lim_{t\to 0}\frac{(1-\sqrt{1+t})(1+\sqrt{1+t})}{t\sqrt{t+1}(1+\sqrt{1+t})} = \lim_{t\to 0}\frac{-t}{t\sqrt{1+t}(1+\sqrt{1+t})}$

$$= \lim_{t\to 0}\frac{-1}{\sqrt{1+t}(1+\sqrt{1+t})} = \frac{-1}{\sqrt{1+0}(1+\sqrt{1+0})} = -\frac{1}{2}$$

25. (a)

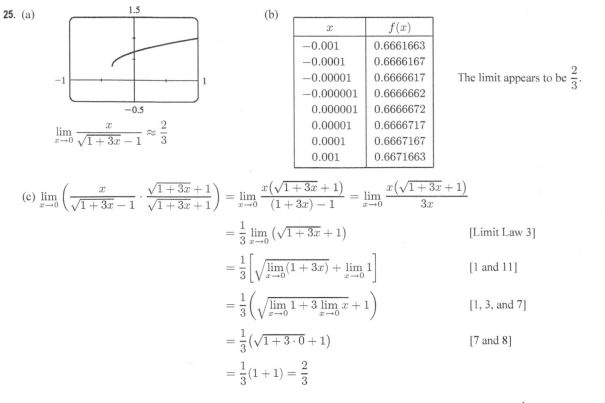

$$\lim_{x \to 0} \frac{x}{\sqrt{1+3x}-1} \approx \frac{2}{3}$$

(b)

x	$f(x)$
-0.001	0.6661663
-0.0001	0.6666167
-0.00001	0.6666617
-0.000001	0.6666662
0.000001	0.6666672
0.00001	0.6666717
0.0001	0.6667167
0.001	0.6671663

The limit appears to be $\dfrac{2}{3}$.

(c) $\displaystyle\lim_{x \to 0}\left(\frac{x}{\sqrt{1+3x}-1} \cdot \frac{\sqrt{1+3x}+1}{\sqrt{1+3x}+1}\right) = \lim_{x \to 0}\frac{x(\sqrt{1+3x}+1)}{(1+3x)-1} = \lim_{x \to 0}\frac{x(\sqrt{1+3x}+1)}{3x}$

$$= \frac{1}{3}\lim_{x \to 0}\left(\sqrt{1+3x}+1\right) \qquad\qquad \text{[Limit Law 3]}$$

$$= \frac{1}{3}\left[\sqrt{\lim_{x \to 0}(1+3x)} + \lim_{x \to 0}1\right] \qquad\qquad \text{[1 and 11]}$$

$$= \frac{1}{3}\left(\sqrt{\lim_{x \to 0}1 + 3\lim_{x \to 0}x} + 1\right) \qquad\qquad \text{[1, 3, and 7]}$$

$$= \frac{1}{3}\left(\sqrt{1+3\cdot 0}+1\right) \qquad\qquad \text{[7 and 8]}$$

$$= \frac{1}{3}(1+1) = \frac{2}{3}$$

27. Let $f(x) = -x^2$, $g(x) = x^2 \cos 20\pi x$ and $h(x) = x^2$. Then

$-1 \le \cos 20\pi x \le 1 \quad \Rightarrow \quad -x^2 \le x^2 \cos 20\pi x \le x^2 \quad \Rightarrow \quad f(x) \le g(x) \le h(x).$

So since $\displaystyle\lim_{x \to 0} f(x) = \lim_{x \to 0} h(x) = 0$, by the Squeeze Theorem we have

$$\lim_{x \to 0} g(x) = 0.$$

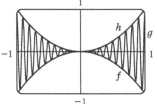

29. We have $\displaystyle\lim_{x \to 4}(4x-9) = 4(4)-9 = 7$ and $\displaystyle\lim_{x \to 4}(x^2-4x+7) = 4^2 - 4(4) + 7 = 7$. Since $4x - 9 \le f(x) \le x^2 - 4x + 7$

for $x \ge 0$, $\displaystyle\lim_{x \to 4} f(x) = 7$ by the Squeeze Theorem.

31. $-1 \le \cos(2/x) \le 1 \quad \Rightarrow \quad -x^4 \le x^4 \cos(2/x) \le x^4$. Since $\displaystyle\lim_{x \to 0}(-x^4) = 0$ and $\displaystyle\lim_{x \to 0}x^4 = 0$, we have

$$\lim_{x \to 0}\left[x^4 \cos(2/x)\right] = 0 \text{ by the Squeeze Theorem.}$$

33. $|x-3| = \begin{cases} x-3 & \text{if } x-3 \ge 0 \\ -(x-3) & \text{if } x-3 < 0 \end{cases} = \begin{cases} x-3 & \text{if } x \ge 3 \\ 3-x & \text{if } x < 3 \end{cases}$

Thus, $\displaystyle\lim_{x \to 3^+}(2x + |x-3|) = \lim_{x \to 3^+}(2x + x - 3) = \lim_{x \to 3^+}(3x - 3) = 3(3) - 3 = 6$ and

$\displaystyle\lim_{x \to 3^-}(2x + |x-3|) = \lim_{x \to 3^-}(2x + 3 - x) = \lim_{x \to 3^-}(x + 3) = 3 + 3 = 6.$ Since the left and right limits are equal,

$$\lim_{x \to 3}(2x + |x-3|) = 6.$$

35. Since $|x| = -x$ for $x < 0$, we have $\lim\limits_{x \to 0^-} \left(\dfrac{1}{x} - \dfrac{1}{|x|} \right) = \lim\limits_{x \to 0^-} \left(\dfrac{1}{x} - \dfrac{1}{-x} \right) = \lim\limits_{x \to 0^-} \dfrac{2}{x}$, which does not exist since the

denominator approaches 0 and the numerator does not.

37. (a) (i) $\lim\limits_{x \to 1^-} g(x) = \lim\limits_{x \to 1^-} x = 1$

    (ii) $\lim\limits_{x \to 1^+} g(x) = \lim\limits_{x \to 1^+} (2 - x^2) = 2 - 1^2 = 1$. Since $\lim\limits_{x \to 1^-} g(x) = 1$ and $\lim\limits_{x \to 1^+} g(x) = 1$, we have $\lim\limits_{x \to 1} g(x) = 1$.

        Note that the fact $g(1) = 3$ does not affect the value of the limit.

    (iii) When $x = 1$, $g(x) = 3$, so $g(1) = 3$.

    (iv) $\lim\limits_{x \to 2^-} g(x) = \lim\limits_{x \to 2^-} (2 - x^2) = 2 - 2^2 = 2 - 4 = -2$

    (v) $\lim\limits_{x \to 2^+} g(x) = \lim\limits_{x \to 2^+} (x - 3) = 2 - 3 = -1$

    (vi) $\lim\limits_{x \to 2} g(x)$ does not exist since $\lim\limits_{x \to 2^-} g(x) \neq \lim\limits_{x \to 2^+} g(x)$.

(b)
$$g(x) = \begin{cases} x & \text{if } x < 1 \\ 3 & \text{if } x = 1 \\ 2 - x^2 & \text{if } 1 < x \leq 2 \\ x - 3 & \text{if } x > 2 \end{cases}$$

39. (a) (i) $[\![x]\!] = -2$ for $-2 \leq x < -1$, so $\lim\limits_{x \to -2^+} [\![x]\!] = \lim\limits_{x \to -2^+} (-2) = -2$

    (ii) $[\![x]\!] = -3$ for $-3 \leq x < -2$, so $\lim\limits_{x \to -2^-} [\![x]\!] = \lim\limits_{x \to -2^-} (-3) = -3$.

        The right and left limits are different, so $\lim\limits_{x \to -2} [\![x]\!]$ does not exist.

    (iii) $[\![x]\!] = -3$ for $-3 \leq x < -2$, so $\lim\limits_{x \to -2.4} [\![x]\!] = \lim\limits_{x \to -2.4} (-3) = -3$.

  (b) (i) $[\![x]\!] = n - 1$ for $n - 1 \leq x < n$, so $\lim\limits_{x \to n^-} [\![x]\!] = \lim\limits_{x \to n^-} (n - 1) = n - 1$.

    (ii) $[\![x]\!] = n$ for $n \leq x < n + 1$, so $\lim\limits_{x \to n^+} [\![x]\!] = \lim\limits_{x \to n^+} n = n$.

  (c) $\lim\limits_{x \to a} [\![x]\!]$ exists $\quad \Leftrightarrow \quad a$ is not an integer.

41. The graph of $f(x) = [\![x]\!] + [\![-x]\!]$ is the same as the graph of $g(x) = -1$ with holes at each integer, since $f(a) = 0$ for any

integer a. Thus, $\lim\limits_{x \to 2^-} f(x) = -1$ and $\lim\limits_{x \to 2^+} f(x) = -1$, so $\lim\limits_{x \to 2} f(x) = -1$. However,

$$f(2) = [\![2]\!] + [\![-2]\!] = 2 + (-2) = 0, \text{ so } \lim\limits_{x \to 2} f(x) \neq f(2).$$

43. Since $p(x)$ is a polynomial, $p(x) = a_0 + a_1 x + a_2 x^2 + \cdots + a_n x^n$. Thus, by the Limit Laws,

$$\lim\limits_{x \to a} p(x) = \lim\limits_{x \to a} \left(a_0 + a_1 x + a_2 x^2 + \cdots + a_n x^n \right) = a_0 + a_1 \lim\limits_{x \to a} x + a_2 \lim\limits_{x \to a} x^2 + \cdots + a_n \lim\limits_{x \to a} x^n$$

$$= a_0 + a_1 a + a_2 a^2 + \cdots + a_n a^n = p(a)$$

Thus, for any polynomial p, $\lim\limits_{x \to a} p(x) = p(a)$.

45. $\lim\limits_{x \to 1} [f(x) - 8] = \lim\limits_{x \to 1} \left[\dfrac{f(x) - 8}{x - 1} \cdot (x - 1) \right] = \lim\limits_{x \to 1} \dfrac{f(x) - 8}{x - 1} \cdot \lim\limits_{x \to 1} (x - 1) = 10 \cdot 0 = 0.$

Thus, $\lim\limits_{x \to 1} f(x) = \lim\limits_{x \to 1} \{[f(x) - 8] + 8\} = \lim\limits_{x \to 1} [f(x) - 8] + \lim\limits_{x \to 1} 8 = 0 + 8 = 8.$

Note: The value of $\lim\limits_{x \to 1} \dfrac{f(x) - 8}{x - 1}$ does not affect the answer since it's multiplied by 0. What's important is that

$\lim\limits_{x \to 1} \dfrac{f(x) - 8}{x - 1}$ exists.

47. Let $f(x) = [\![x]\!]$ and $g(x) = -[\![x]\!]$. Then $\lim\limits_{x \to 3} f(x)$ and $\lim\limits_{x \to 3} g(x)$ do not exist   [Example 9]

but $\lim\limits_{x \to 3} [f(x) + g(x)] = \lim\limits_{x \to 3} ([\![x]\!] - [\![x]\!]) = \lim\limits_{x \to 3} 0 = 0.$

49. Since the denominator approaches 0 as $x \to -2$, the limit will exist only if the numerator also approaches

0 as $x \to -2$. In order for this to happen, we need $\lim\limits_{x \to -2} \left(3x^2 + ax + a + 3 \right) = 0 \iff$

$3(-2)^2 + a(-2) + a + 3 = 0 \iff 12 - 2a + a + 3 = 0 \iff a = 15.$ With $a = 15$, the limit becomes

$\lim\limits_{x \to -2} \dfrac{3x^2 + 15x + 18}{x^2 + x - 2} = \lim\limits_{x \to -2} \dfrac{3(x + 2)(x + 3)}{(x - 1)(x + 2)} = \lim\limits_{x \to -2} \dfrac{3(x + 3)}{x - 1} = \dfrac{3(-2 + 3)}{-2 - 1} = \dfrac{3}{-3} = -1.$

2.4   Continuity

1. From Definition 1, $\lim\limits_{x \to 4} f(x) = f(4).$

3. (a) f is discontinuous at -4 since $f(-4)$ is not defined and at -2, 2, and 4 since the limit does not exist (the left and right

limits are not the same).

(b) f is continuous from the left at -2 since $\lim\limits_{x \to -2^-} f(x) = f(-2)$. f is continuous from the right at 2 and 4 since

$\lim\limits_{x \to 2^+} f(x) = f(2)$ and $\lim\limits_{x \to 4^+} f(x) = f(4)$. It is continuous from neither side at -4 since $f(-4)$ is undefined.

5. The graph of $y = f(x)$ must have a discontinuity at

$x = 2$ and must show that $\lim\limits_{x \to 2^+} f(x) = f(2).$

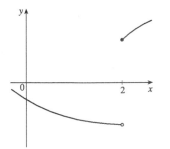

7. The graph of $y = f(x)$ must have a removable

discontinuity (a hole) at $x = 3$ and a jump discontinuity

at $x = 5$.

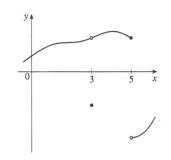

9. (a)

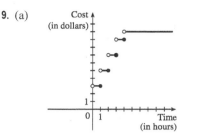

(b) There are discontinuities at times $t = 1, 2, 3,$ and 4. A person parking in the lot would want to keep in mind that the charge will jump at the beginning of each hour.

11. Since f and g are continuous functions,

$$\lim_{x \to 3} [2f(x) - g(x)] = 2 \lim_{x \to 3} f(x) - \lim_{x \to 3} g(x) \qquad \text{[by Limit Laws 2 and 3]}$$

$$= 2f(3) - g(3) \qquad \text{[by continuity of } f \text{ and } g \text{ at } x = 3]$$

$$= 2 \cdot 5 - g(3) = 10 - g(3)$$

Since it is given that $\lim_{x \to 3} [2f(x) - g(x)] = 4$, we have $10 - g(3) = 4$, so $g(3) = 6$.

13. $\lim_{x \to -1} f(x) = \lim_{x \to -1} (x + 2x^3)^4 = \left(\lim_{x \to -1} x + 2 \lim_{x \to -1} x^3\right)^4 = [-1 + 2(-1)^3]^4 = (-3)^4 = 81 = f(-1).$

By the definition of continuity, f is continuous at $a = -1$.

15. $f(x) = \begin{cases} e^x & \text{if } x < 0 \\ x^2 & \text{if } x \geq 0 \end{cases}$

The left-hand limit of f at $a = 0$ is $\lim_{x \to 0^-} f(x) = \lim_{x \to 0^-} e^x = 1$. The right-hand limit of f at $a = 0$ is $\lim_{x \to 0^+} f(x) = \lim_{x \to 0^+} x^2 = 0$. Since these limits are not equal, $\lim_{x \to 0} f(x)$ does not exist and f is discontinuous at 0.

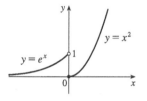

17. $f(x) = \begin{cases} \cos x & \text{if } x < 0 \\ 0 & \text{if } x = 0 \\ 1 - x^2 & \text{if } x > 0 \end{cases}$

$\lim_{x \to 0} f(x) = 1$, but $f(0) = 0 \neq 1$, so f is discontinuous at 0.

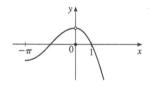

19. By Theorem 5, the polynomials x^2 and $2x - 1$ are continuous on $(-\infty, \infty)$. By Theorem 7, the root function $\sqrt{x}$ is continuous on $[0, \infty)$. By Theorem 9, the composite function $\sqrt{2x - 1}$ is continuous on its domain, $\left[\frac{1}{2}, \infty\right)$. By part 1 of Theorem 4, the sum $R(x) = x^2 + \sqrt{2x - 1}$ is continuous on $\left[\frac{1}{2}, \infty\right)$.

21. By Theorem 7, the exponential function e^{-5t} and the trigonometric function $\cos 2\pi t$ are continuous on $(-\infty, \infty)$. By part 4 of Theorem 4, $L(t) = e^{-5t} \cos 2\pi t$ is continuous on $(-\infty, \infty)$.

23. By Theorem 5, the polynomial $t^4 - 1$ is continuous on $(-\infty, \infty)$. By Theorem 7, $\ln x$ is continuous on its domain, $(0, \infty)$. By Theorem 9, $\ln(t^4 - 1)$ is continuous on its domain, which is

$$\{t \mid t^4 - 1 > 0\} = \{t \mid t^4 > 1\} = \{t \mid |t| > 1\} = (-\infty, -1) \cup (1, \infty)$$

25. The function $y = \dfrac{1}{1 + e^{1/x}}$ is discontinuous at $x = 0$ because the

left- and right-hand limits at $x = 0$ are different.

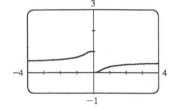

27. Because we are dealing with root functions, $5 + \sqrt{x}$ is continuous on $[0, \infty)$, $\sqrt{x+5}$ is continuous on $[-5, \infty)$, so the

quotient $f(x) = \dfrac{5 + \sqrt{x}}{\sqrt{5+x}}$ is continuous on $[0, \infty)$. Since f is continuous at $x = 4$, $\lim\limits_{x \to 4} f(x) = f(4) = \frac{7}{3}$.

29. Because $x^2 - x$ is continuous on $\mathbb{R}$, the composite function $f(x) = e^{x^2 - x}$ is continuous on $\mathbb{R}$, so

$\lim\limits_{x \to 1} f(x) = f(1) = e^{1-1} = e^0 = 1$.

31. $f(x) = \begin{cases} x^2 & \text{if } x < 1 \\ \sqrt{x} & \text{if } x \geq 1 \end{cases}$

By Theorem 5, since $f(x)$ equals the polynomial x^2 on $(-\infty, 1)$, f is continuous on $(-\infty, 1)$. By Theorem 7, since $f(x)$

equals the root function $\sqrt{x}$ on $(1, \infty)$, f is continuous on $(1, \infty)$. At $x = 1$, $\lim\limits_{x \to 1^-} f(x) = \lim\limits_{x \to 1^-} x^2 = 1$ and

$\lim\limits_{x \to 1^+} f(x) = \lim\limits_{x \to 1^+} \sqrt{x} = 1$. Thus, $\lim\limits_{x \to 1} f(x)$ exists and equals 1. Also, $f(1) = \sqrt{1} = 1$. Thus, f is continuous at $x = 1$.

We conclude that f is continuous on $(-\infty, \infty)$.

33. $f(x) = \begin{cases} x + 2 & \text{if } x < 0 \\ e^x & \text{if } 0 \leq x \leq 1 \\ 2 - x & \text{if } x > 1 \end{cases}$

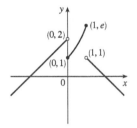

f is continuous on $(-\infty, 0)$ and $(1, \infty)$ since on each of these intervals

it is a polynomial; it is continuous on $(0, 1)$ since it is an exponential.

Now $\lim\limits_{x \to 0^-} f(x) = \lim\limits_{x \to 0^-} (x + 2) = 2$ and $\lim\limits_{x \to 0^+} f(x) = \lim\limits_{x \to 0^+} e^x = 1$, so f is discontinuous at 0. Since $f(0) = 1$, f is

continuous from the right at 0. Also $\lim\limits_{x \to 1^-} f(x) = \lim\limits_{x \to 1^-} e^x = e$ and $\lim\limits_{x \to 1^+} f(x) = \lim\limits_{x \to 1^+} (2 - x) = 1$, so f is discontinuous

at 1. Since $f(1) = e$, f is continuous from the left at 1.

35. $f(x) = \begin{cases} cx^2 + 2x & \text{if } x < 2 \\ x^3 - cx & \text{if } x \geq 2 \end{cases}$

f is continuous on $(-\infty, 2)$ and $(2, \infty)$. Now $\lim\limits_{x \to 2^-} f(x) = \lim\limits_{x \to 2^-} (cx^2 + 2x) = 4c + 4$ and

$\lim\limits_{x \to 2^+} f(x) = \lim\limits_{x \to 2^+} (x^3 - cx) = 8 - 2c$. So f is continuous $\Leftrightarrow$ $4c + 4 = 8 - 2c$ $\Leftrightarrow$ $6c = 4$ $\Leftrightarrow$ $c = \frac{2}{3}$. Thus, for f

to be continuous on $(-\infty, \infty)$, $c = \frac{2}{3}$.

37. (a) $f(x) = \dfrac{x^4 - 1}{x - 1} = \dfrac{(x^2 + 1)(x^2 - 1)}{x - 1} = \dfrac{(x^2 + 1)(x + 1)(x - 1)}{x - 1} = (x^2 + 1)(x + 1)$ [or $x^3 + x^2 + x + 1$]

for $x \neq 1$. The discontinuity is removable and $g(x) = x^3 + x^2 + x + 1$ agrees with f for $x \neq 1$ and is continuous on $\mathbb{R}$.

(b) $f(x) = \dfrac{x^3 - x^2 - 2x}{x - 2} = \dfrac{x(x^2 - x - 2)}{x - 2} = \dfrac{x(x - 2)(x + 1)}{x - 2} = x(x + 1)$ [or $x^2 + x$]   for $x \neq 2$. The discontinuity

is removable and $g(x) = x^2 + x$ agrees with f for $x \neq 2$ and is continuous on $\mathbb{R}$.

(c) $\lim\limits_{x \to \pi^-} f(x) = \lim\limits_{x \to \pi^-} [\![\sin x]\!] = \lim\limits_{x \to \pi^-} 0 = 0$ and $\lim\limits_{x \to \pi^+} f(x) = \lim\limits_{x \to \pi^+} [\![\sin x]\!] = \lim\limits_{x \to \pi^+} (-1) = -1$, so $\lim\limits_{x \to \pi} f(x)$ does not

exist. The discontinuity at $x = \pi$ is a jump discontinuity.

39. $f(x) = x^2 + 10\sin x$ is continuous on the interval $[31, 32]$, $f(31) \approx 957$, and $f(32) \approx 1030$. Since $957 < 1000 < 1030$,

there is a number c in $(31, 32)$ such that $f(c) = 1000$ by the Intermediate Value Theorem. *Note:* There is also a number c in

$(-32, -31)$ such that $f(c) = 1000$.

41. $f(x) = x^4 + x - 3$ is continuous on the interval $[1, 2]$, $f(1) = -1$, and $f(2) = 15$. Since $-1 < 0 < 15$, there is a number c

in $(1, 2)$ such that $f(c) = 0$ by the Intermediate Value Theorem. Thus, there is a root of the equation $x^4 + x - 3 = 0$ in the

interval $(1, 2)$.

43. The equation $e^x = 3 - 2x$ is equivalent to the equation $e^x + 2x - 3 = 0$. $f(x) = e^x + 2x - 3$ is continuous on the interval

$[0, 1]$, $f(0) = -2$, and $f(1) = e - 1 \approx 1.72$. Since $-2 < 0 < e - 1$, there is a number c in $(0, 1)$ such that $f(c) = 0$ by the

Intermediate Value Theorem. Thus, there is a root of the equation $e^x + 2x - 3 = 0$, or $e^x = 3 - 2x$, in the interval $(0, 1)$.

45. (a) $f(x) = \cos x - x^3$ is continuous on the interval $[0, 1]$, $f(0) = 1 > 0$, and $f(1) = \cos 1 - 1 \approx -0.46 < 0$. Since

$1 > 0 > -0.46$, there is a number c in $(0, 1)$ such that $f(c) = 0$ by the Intermediate Value Theorem. Thus, there is a root

of the equation $\cos x - x^3 = 0$, or $\cos x = x^3$, in the interval $(0, 1)$.

(b) $f(0.86) \approx 0.016 > 0$ and $f(0.87) \approx -0.014 < 0$, so there is a root between 0.86 and 0.87, that is, in the interval

$(0.86, 0.87)$.

47. (a) Let $f(x) = 100e^{-x/100} - 0.01x^2$. Then $f(0) = 100 > 0$ and

$f(100) = 100e^{-1} - 100 \approx -63.2 < 0$. So by the Intermediate

Value Theorem, there is a number c in $(0, 100)$ such that $f(c) = 0$.

This implies that $100e^{-c/100} = 0.01c^2$.

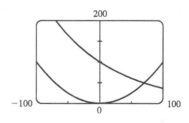

(b) Using the intersect feature of the graphing device, we find that the

root of the equation is $x = 70.347$, correct to three decimal places.

49. $\lim\limits_{h \to 0} \sin(a + h) = \lim\limits_{h \to 0} (\sin a \cos h + \cos a \sin h) = \lim\limits_{h \to 0} (\sin a \cos h) + \lim\limits_{h \to 0} (\cos a \sin h)$

$= \left(\lim\limits_{h \to 0} \sin a \right) \left(\lim\limits_{h \to 0} \cos h \right) + \left(\lim\limits_{h \to 0} \cos a \right) \left(\lim\limits_{h \to 0} \sin h \right) = (\sin a)(1) + (\cos a)(0) = \sin a$

51. If there is such a number, it satisfies the equation $x^3 + 1 = x \Leftrightarrow x^3 - x + 1 = 0$. Let the left-hand side of this equation be

called $f(x)$. Now $f(-2) = -5 < 0$, and $f(-1) = 1 > 0$. Note also that $f(x)$ is a polynomial, and thus continuous. So by the

Intermediate Value Theorem, there is a number c between -2 and -1 such that $f(c) = 0$, so that $c = c^3 + 1$.

53. $f(x) = x^4 \sin(1/x)$ is continuous on $(-\infty, 0) \cup (0, \infty)$ since it is the product of a polynomial and a composite of a

trigonometric function and a rational function. Now since $-1 \le \sin(1/x) \le 1$, we have $-x^4 \le x^4 \sin(1/x) \le x^4$. Because

$\lim\limits_{x \to 0}(-x^4) = 0$ and $\lim\limits_{x \to 0} x^4 = 0$, the Squeeze Theorem gives us $\lim\limits_{x \to 0}(x^4 \sin(1/x)) = 0$, which equals $f(0)$. Thus, f is

continuous at 0 and, hence, on $(-\infty, \infty)$.

55. Define $u(t)$ to be the monk's distance from the monastery, as a function of time, on the first day, and define $d(t)$ to be his

distance from the monastery, as a function of time, on the second day. Let D be the distance from the monastery to the top of

the mountain. From the given information we know that $u(0) = 0$, $u(12) = D$, $d(0) = D$ and $d(12) = 0$. Now consider the

function $u - d$, which is clearly continuous. We calculate that $(u - d)(0) = -D$ and $(u - d)(12) = D$. So by the

Intermediate Value Theorem, there must be some time t_0 between 0 and 12 such that $(u - d)(t_0) = 0 \quad \Leftrightarrow \quad u(t_0) = d(t_0)$.

So at time t_0 after 7:00 AM, the monk will be at the same place on both days.

2.5 Limits Involving Infinity

1. (a) As x approaches 2 (from the right or the left), the values of $f(x)$ become large.

(b) As x approaches 1 from the right, the values of $f(x)$ become large negative.

(c) As x becomes large, the values of $f(x)$ approach 5.

(d) As x becomes large negative, the values of $f(x)$ approach 3.

3. (a) $\lim\limits_{x \to 2} f(x) = \infty$ (b) $\lim\limits_{x \to -1^-} f(x) = \infty$ (c) $\lim\limits_{x \to -1^+} f(x) = -\infty$ (d) $\lim\limits_{x \to \infty} f(x) = 1$

(e) $\lim\limits_{x \to -\infty} f(x) = 2$ (f) Vertical: $x = -1$, $x = 2$; Horizontal: $y = 1$, $y = 2$

5. $\lim\limits_{x \to 0} f(x) = -\infty$,   **7.** $\lim\limits_{x \to 2} f(x) = -\infty$, $\lim\limits_{x \to \infty} f(x) = \infty$,   **9.** $f(0) = 3$, $\lim\limits_{x \to 0^-} f(x) = 4$,

     $\lim\limits_{x \to -\infty} f(x) = 5$, $\lim\limits_{x \to -\infty} f(x) = 0$, $\lim\limits_{x \to 0^+} f(x) = \infty$, $\lim\limits_{x \to 0^+} f(x) = 2$,

     $\lim\limits_{x \to \infty} f(x) = -5$ $\lim\limits_{x \to 0^-} f(x) = -\infty$ $\lim\limits_{x \to -\infty} f(x) = -\infty$, $\lim\limits_{x \to 4^-} f(x) = $

                                                     $-\infty$,

                                             $\lim\limits_{x \to 4^+} f(x) = \infty$, $\lim\limits_{x \to \infty} f(x) = 3$

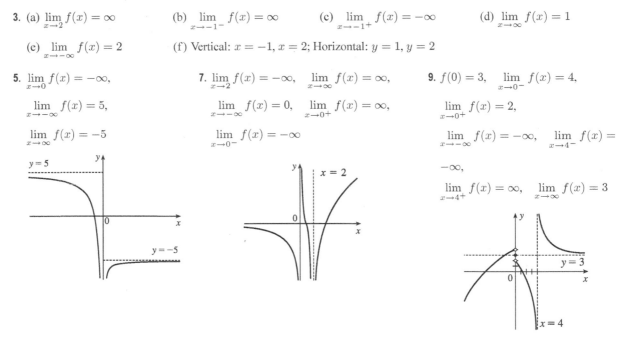

11. If $f(x) = x^2/2^x$, then a calculator gives $f(0) = 0$, $f(1) = 0.5$, $f(2) = 1$, $f(3) = 1.125$, $f(4) = 1$, $f(5) = 0.78125$,

$f(6) = 0.5625$, $f(7) = 0.3828125$, $f(8) = 0.25$, $f(9) = 0.158203125$, $f(10) = 0.09765625$, $f(20) \approx 0.00038147$,

$f(50) \approx 2.2204 \times 10^{-12}$, $f(100) \approx 7.8886 \times 10^{-27}$.

It appears that $\lim\limits_{x \to \infty} (x^2/2^x) = 0$.

13. Vertical: $x \approx -1.62$, $x \approx 0.62$, $x = 1$;

Horizontal: $y = 1$

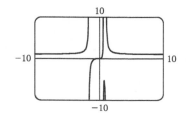

15. $\lim\limits_{x \to 1} \dfrac{2-x}{(x-1)^2} = \infty$ since the numerator is positive and the denominator approaches 0 through positive values as $x \to 1$.

17. Let $t = 3/(2-x)$. As $x \to 2^+$, $t \to -\infty$. So $\lim\limits_{x \to 2^+} e^{3/(2-x)} = \lim\limits_{t \to -\infty} e^t = 0$ by (7).

19. Let $t = x^2 - 9$. Then as $x \to 3^+$, $t \to 0^+$, and $\lim\limits_{x \to 3^+} \ln(x^2 - 9) = \lim\limits_{t \to 0^+} \ln t = -\infty$ by (3).

21. $\lim\limits_{x \to 2\pi^-} x \csc x = \lim\limits_{x \to 2\pi^-} \dfrac{x}{\sin x} = -\infty$ since the numerator is positive and the denominator approaches 0 through negative

values as $x \to 2\pi^-$.

23. Divide both the numerator and denominator by x^3 (the highest power of x that occurs in the denominator).

$$\lim_{x \to \infty} \frac{x^3 + 5x}{2x^3 - x^2 + 4} = \lim_{x \to \infty} \frac{\dfrac{x^3 + 5x}{x^3}}{\dfrac{2x^3 - x^2 + 4}{x^3}} = \lim_{x \to \infty} \frac{1 + \dfrac{5}{x^2}}{2 - \dfrac{1}{x} + \dfrac{4}{x^3}} = \frac{\lim\limits_{x \to \infty} \left(1 + \dfrac{5}{x^2}\right)}{\lim\limits_{x \to \infty} \left(2 - \dfrac{1}{x} + \dfrac{4}{x^3}\right)}$$

$$= \frac{\lim\limits_{x \to \infty} 1 + 5 \lim\limits_{x \to \infty} \dfrac{1}{x^2}}{\lim\limits_{x \to \infty} 2 - \lim\limits_{x \to \infty} \dfrac{1}{x} + 4 \lim\limits_{x \to \infty} \dfrac{1}{x^3}} = \frac{1 + 5(0)}{2 - 0 + 4(0)} = \frac{1}{2}$$

25. First, multiply the factors in the denominator. Then divide both the numerator and denominator by u^4.

$$\lim_{u \to \infty} \frac{4u^4 + 5}{(u^2 - 2)(2u^2 - 1)} = \lim_{u \to \infty} \frac{4u^4 + 5}{2u^4 - 5u^2 + 2} = \lim_{u \to \infty} \frac{\dfrac{4u^4 + 5}{u^4}}{\dfrac{2u^4 - 5u^2 + 2}{u^4}} = \lim_{u \to \infty} \frac{4 + \dfrac{5}{u^4}}{2 - \dfrac{5}{u^2} + \dfrac{2}{u^4}}$$

$$= \frac{\lim\limits_{u \to \infty} \left(4 + \dfrac{5}{u^4}\right)}{\lim\limits_{u \to \infty} \left(2 - \dfrac{5}{u^2} + \dfrac{2}{u^4}\right)} = \frac{\lim\limits_{u \to \infty} 4 + 5 \lim\limits_{u \to \infty} \dfrac{1}{u^4}}{\lim\limits_{u \to \infty} 2 - 5 \lim\limits_{u \to \infty} \dfrac{1}{u^2} + 2 \lim\limits_{u \to \infty} \dfrac{1}{u^4}} = \frac{4 + 5(0)}{2 - 5(0) + 2(0)} = \frac{4}{2} = 2$$

27. $\lim\limits_{x \to \infty} \left(\sqrt{9x^2 + x} - 3x\right) = \lim\limits_{x \to \infty} \dfrac{\left(\sqrt{9x^2 + x} - 3x\right)\left(\sqrt{9x^2 + x} + 3x\right)}{\sqrt{9x^2 + x} + 3x} = \lim\limits_{x \to \infty} \dfrac{\left(\sqrt{9x^2 + x}\right)^2 - (3x)^2}{\sqrt{9x^2 + x} + 3x}$

$= \lim\limits_{x \to \infty} \dfrac{(9x^2 + x) - 9x^2}{\sqrt{9x^2 + x} + 3x} = \lim\limits_{x \to \infty} \dfrac{x}{\sqrt{9x^2 + x} + 3x} \cdot \dfrac{1/x}{1/x}$

$= \lim\limits_{x \to \infty} \dfrac{x/x}{\sqrt{9x^2/x^2 + x/x^2} + 3x/x} = \lim\limits_{x \to \infty} \dfrac{1}{\sqrt{9 + 1/x} + 3} = \dfrac{1}{\sqrt{9} + 3} = \dfrac{1}{3 + 3} = \dfrac{1}{6}$

29. Let $t = -x^2$. As $x \to \infty$, $t \to -\infty$. So $\lim\limits_{x \to \infty} e^{-x^2} = \lim\limits_{t \to -\infty} e^t = 0$ by (7).

31. $\lim\limits_{x \to \infty} \cos x$ does not exist because as x increases $\cos x$ does not approach any one value, but oscillates between 1 and -1.

33. Since $-1 \le \cos x \le 1$ and $e^{-2x} > 0$, we have $-e^{-2x} \le e^{-2x} \cos x \le e^{-2x}$. We know that $\lim\limits_{x \to \infty} (-e^{-2x}) = 0$ and

$\lim\limits_{x \to \infty} (e^{-2x}) = 0$, so by the Squeeze Theorem, $\lim\limits_{x \to \infty} (e^{-2x} \cos x) = 0$.

35. $\lim\limits_{x \to -\infty} (x^4 + x^5) = \lim\limits_{x \to -\infty} x^5(\frac{1}{x} + 1)$ [factor out the largest power of x] $= -\infty$ because $x^5 \to -\infty$ and $1/x + 1 \to 1$

as $x \to -\infty$.

Or: $\lim\limits_{x \to -\infty} (x^4 + x^5) = \lim\limits_{x \to -\infty} x^4(1 + x) = -\infty$.

37. $\lim\limits_{x \to \infty} \dfrac{x + x^3 + x^5}{1 - x^2 + x^4} = \lim\limits_{x \to \infty} \dfrac{(x + x^3 + x^5)/x^4}{(1 - x^2 + x^4)/x^4}$ [divide by the highest power of x in the denominator]

$= \lim\limits_{x \to \infty} \dfrac{1/x^3 + 1/x + x}{1/x^4 - 1/x^2 + 1} = \infty$

because $(1/x^3 + 1/x + x) \to \infty$ and $(1/x^4 - 1/x^2 + 1) \to 1$ as $x \to \infty$.

39. $\lim\limits_{x \to \infty} \dfrac{2x^2 + x - 1}{x^2 + x - 2} = \lim\limits_{x \to \infty} \dfrac{\dfrac{2x^2 + x - 1}{x^2}}{\dfrac{x^2 + x - 2}{x^2}} = \lim\limits_{x \to \infty} \dfrac{2 + \dfrac{1}{x} - \dfrac{1}{x^2}}{1 + \dfrac{1}{x} - \dfrac{2}{x^2}} = \dfrac{\lim\limits_{x \to \infty} \left(2 + \dfrac{1}{x} - \dfrac{1}{x^2}\right)}{\lim\limits_{x \to \infty} \left(1 + \dfrac{1}{x} - \dfrac{2}{x^2}\right)}$

$= \dfrac{\lim\limits_{x \to \infty} 2 + \lim\limits_{x \to \infty} \dfrac{1}{x} - \lim\limits_{x \to \infty} \dfrac{1}{x^2}}{\lim\limits_{x \to \infty} 1 + \lim\limits_{x \to \infty} \dfrac{1}{x} - 2 \lim\limits_{x \to \infty} \dfrac{1}{x^2}} = \dfrac{2 + 0 - 0}{1 + 0 - 2(0)} = 2$,   so $y = 2$ is a horizontal asymptote.

$y = f(x) = \dfrac{2x^2 + x - 1}{x^2 + x - 2} = \dfrac{(2x - 1)(x + 1)}{(x + 2)(x - 1)}$, so $\lim\limits_{x \to -2^-} f(x) = \infty$,

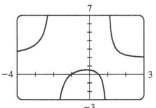

$\lim\limits_{x \to -2^+} f(x) = -\infty$, $\lim\limits_{x \to 1^-} f(x) = -\infty$, and $\lim\limits_{x \to 1^+} f(x) = \infty$. Thus, $x = -2$

and $x = 1$ are vertical asymptotes. The graph confirms our work.

41. $y = f(x) = \dfrac{x^3 - x}{x^2 - 6x + 5} = \dfrac{x(x^2 - 1)}{(x - 1)(x - 5)} = \dfrac{x(x + 1)(x - 1)}{(x - 1)(x - 5)} = \dfrac{x(x + 1)}{x - 5} = g(x)$ for $x \ne 1$.

The graph of g is the same as the graph of f with the exception of a hole in the

graph of f at $x = 1$. By long division, $g(x) = \dfrac{x^2 + x}{x - 5} = x + 6 + \dfrac{30}{x - 5}$.

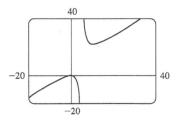

As $x \to \pm\infty$, $g(x) \to \pm\infty$, so there is no horizontal asymptote. The denominator

of g is zero when $x = 5$. $\lim\limits_{x \to 5^-} g(x) = -\infty$ and $\lim\limits_{x \to 5^+} g(x) = \infty$, so $x = 5$ is a

vertical asymptote. The graph confirms our work.

43. (a)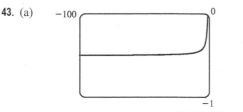

(b)

x	$f(x)$
$-10{,}000$	-0.4999625
$-100{,}000$	-0.4999962
$-1{,}000{,}000$	-0.4999996

From the graph of $f(x) = \sqrt{x^2 + x + 1} + x$, we estimate the value of $\lim\limits_{x \to -\infty} f(x)$ to be -0.5.

From the table, we estimate the limit to be -0.5.

(c) $\displaystyle\lim_{x \to -\infty} \left(\sqrt{x^2 + x + 1} + x \right) = \lim_{x \to -\infty} \left(\sqrt{x^2 + x + 1} + x \right) \left[\frac{\sqrt{x^2 + x + 1} - x}{\sqrt{x^2 + x + 1} - x} \right] = \lim_{x \to -\infty} \frac{(x^2 + x + 1) - x^2}{\sqrt{x^2 + x + 1} - x}$

$\displaystyle = \lim_{x \to -\infty} \frac{(x + 1)(1/x)}{\left(\sqrt{x^2 + x + 1} - x\right)(1/x)} = \lim_{x \to -\infty} \frac{1 + (1/x)}{-\sqrt{1 + (1/x) + (1/x^2)} - 1}$

$\displaystyle = \frac{1 + 0}{-\sqrt{1 + 0 + 0} - 1} = -\frac{1}{2}$

Note that for $x < 0$, we have $\sqrt{x^2} = |x| = -x$, so when we divide the radical by x, with $x < 0$, we get

$\dfrac{1}{x}\sqrt{x^2 + x + 1} = -\dfrac{1}{\sqrt{x^2}}\sqrt{x^2 + x + 1} = -\sqrt{1 + (1/x) + (1/x^2)}.$

45. From the graph, it appears $y = 1$ is a horizontal asymptote.

$\displaystyle\lim_{x \to \infty} \frac{3x^3 + 500x^2}{x^3 + 500x^2 + 100x + 2000} = \lim_{x \to \infty} \frac{\dfrac{3x^3 + 500x^2}{x^3}}{\dfrac{x^3 + 500x^2 + 100x + 2000}{x^3}} = \lim_{x \to \infty} \frac{3 + (500/x)}{1 + (500/x) + (100/x^2) + (2000/x^3)}$

$\displaystyle = \frac{3 + 0}{1 + 0 + 0 + 0} = 3, \quad$ so $y = 3$ is a horizontal asymptote.

The discrepancy can be explained by the choice of the viewing window. Try $[-100{,}000, 100{,}000]$ by $[-1, 4]$ to get a graph that lends credibility to our calculation that $y = 3$ is a horizontal asymptote.

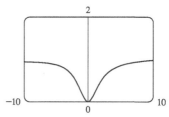

47. Let's look for a rational function.

(1) $\lim\limits_{x \to \pm\infty} f(x) = 0 \quad \Rightarrow \quad$ degree of numerator < degree of denominator

(2) $\lim\limits_{x \to 0} f(x) = -\infty \quad \Rightarrow \quad$ there is a factor of x^2 in the denominator (not just x, since that would produce a sign change at $x = 0$), and the function is negative near $x = 0$.

(3) $\lim\limits_{x \to 3^-} f(x) = \infty$ and $\lim\limits_{x \to 3^+} f(x) = -\infty \quad \Rightarrow \quad$ vertical asymptote at $x = 3$; there is a factor of $(x - 3)$ in the denominator.

(4) $f(2) = 0 \quad \Rightarrow \quad$ 2 is an x-intercept; there is at least one factor of $(x - 2)$ in the numerator.

Combining all of this information and putting in a negative sign to give us the desired left- and right-hand limits gives us $f(x) = \dfrac{2 - x}{x^2(x - 3)}$ as one possibility.

49. (a) We must first find the function f. Since f has a vertical asymptote $x = 4$ and x-intercept $x = 1$, $x - 4$ is a factor of the

denominator and $x - 1$ is a factor of the numerator. There is a removable discontinuity at $x = -1$, so $x - (-1) = x + 1$ is

a factor of both the numerator and denominator. Thus, f now looks like this: $f(x) = \dfrac{a(x-1)(x+1)}{(x-4)(x+1)}$, where a is still to

be determined. Then $\lim\limits_{x \to -1} f(x) = \lim\limits_{x \to -1} \dfrac{a(x-1)(x+1)}{(x-4)(x+1)} = \lim\limits_{x \to -1} \dfrac{a(x-1)}{x-4} = \dfrac{a(-1-1)}{(-1-4)} = \dfrac{2}{5}a$, so $\dfrac{2}{5}a = 2$, and

$a = 5$. Thus $f(x) = \dfrac{5(x-1)(x+1)}{(x-4)(x+1)}$ is a ratio of quadratic functions satisfying all the given conditions and

$f(0) = \dfrac{5(-1)(1)}{(-4)(1)} = \dfrac{5}{4}$.

(b) $\lim\limits_{x \to \infty} f(x) = 5 \lim\limits_{x \to \infty} \dfrac{x^2 - 1}{x^2 - 3x - 4} = 5 \lim\limits_{x \to \infty} \dfrac{(x^2/x^2) - (1/x^2)}{(x^2/x^2) - (3x/x^2) - (4/x^2)} = 5\dfrac{1 - 0}{1 - 0 - 0} = 5(1) = 5$

51. (a) Divide the numerator and the denominator by the highest power of x in $Q(x)$.

(a) If $\deg P < \deg Q$, then the numerator $\to 0$ but the denominator doesn't. So $\lim\limits_{x \to \infty} [P(x)/Q(x)] = 0$.

(b) If $\deg P > \deg Q$, then the numerator $\to \pm\infty$ but the denominator doesn't, so $\lim\limits_{x \to \infty} [P(x)/Q(x)] = \pm\infty$

(depending on the ratio of the leading coefficients of P and Q).

53. $\lim\limits_{x \to \infty} \dfrac{5\sqrt{x}}{\sqrt{x-1}} \cdot \dfrac{1/\sqrt{x}}{1/\sqrt{x}} = \lim\limits_{x \to \infty} \dfrac{5}{\sqrt{1 - (1/x)}} = \dfrac{5}{\sqrt{1-0}} = 5$ and

$\lim\limits_{x \to \infty} \dfrac{10e^x - 21}{2e^x} \cdot \dfrac{1/e^x}{1/e^x} = \lim\limits_{x \to \infty} \dfrac{10 - (21/e^x)}{2} = \dfrac{10 - 0}{2} = 5$. Since $\dfrac{10e^x - 21}{2e^x} < f(x) < \dfrac{5\sqrt{x}}{\sqrt{x-1}}$,

we have $\lim\limits_{x \to \infty} f(x) = 5$ by the Squeeze Theorem.

55. (a) After t minutes, $25t$ liters of brine with 30 g of salt per liter has been pumped into the tank, so it contains

$(5000 + 25t)$ liters of water and $25t \cdot 30 = 750t$ grams of salt. Therefore, the salt concentration at time t will be

$C(t) = \dfrac{750t}{5000 + 25t} = \dfrac{30t}{200 + t} \dfrac{\text{g}}{\text{L}}$.

(b) $\lim\limits_{t \to \infty} C(t) = \lim\limits_{t \to \infty} \dfrac{30t}{200 + t} = \lim\limits_{t \to \infty} \dfrac{30t/t}{200/t + t/t} = \dfrac{30}{0 + 1} = 30$. So the salt concentration approaches that of the brine

being pumped into the tank.

57. (a) If $t = -x/10$, then $x = -10t$ and as $x \to \infty$, $t \to -\infty$. Thus, $\lim\limits_{x \to \infty} e^{-x/10} = \lim\limits_{t \to -\infty} e^t = 0$ by Equation 7.

(b) $y = e^{-x/10}$ and $y = 0.1$ intersect at $x_1 \approx 23.03$.

If $x > x_1$, then $e^{-x/10} < 0.1$.

(c) $e^{-x/10} < 0.1 \;\Rightarrow\; -x/10 < \ln 0.1 \;\Rightarrow$

$x > -10\ln\frac{1}{10} = -10\ln 10^{-1} = 10\ln 10 \approx 23.03$

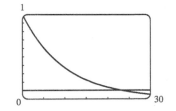

2.6 Derivatives and Rates of Change

1. (a) This is just the slope of the line through two points: $m_{PQ} = \dfrac{\Delta y}{\Delta x} = \dfrac{f(x) - f(3)}{x - 3}$.

(b) This is the limit of the slope of the secant line PQ as Q approaches P: $m = \lim\limits_{x \to 3} \dfrac{f(x) - f(3)}{x - 3}$.

3. (a) (i) Using Definition 1 with $f(x) = 4x - x^2$ and $P(1, 3)$,

$$m = \lim_{x \to a} \frac{f(x) - f(a)}{x - a} = \lim_{x \to 1} \frac{(4x - x^2) - 3}{x - 1} = \lim_{x \to 1} \frac{-(x^2 - 4x + 3)}{x - 1} = \lim_{x \to 1} \frac{-(x - 1)(x - 3)}{x - 1}$$

$$= \lim_{x \to 1} (3 - x) = 3 - 1 = 2$$

(ii) Using Equation 2 with $f(x) = 4x - x^2$ and $P(1, 3)$,

$$m = \lim_{h \to 0} \frac{f(a + h) - f(a)}{h} = \lim_{h \to 0} \frac{f(1 + h) - f(1)}{h} = \lim_{h \to 0} \frac{[4(1 + h) - (1 + h)^2] - 3}{h}$$

$$= \lim_{h \to 0} \frac{4 + 4h - 1 - 2h - h^2 - 3}{h} = \lim_{h \to 0} \frac{-h^2 + 2h}{h} = \lim_{h \to 0} \frac{h(-h + 2)}{h} = \lim_{h \to 0} (-h + 2) = 2$$

(b) An equation of the tangent line is $y - f(a) = f'(a)(x - a) \Rightarrow y - f(1) = f'(1)(x - 1) \Rightarrow y - 3 = 2(x - 1)$, or $y = 2x + 1$.

(c)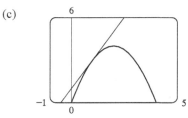

The graph of $y = 2x + 1$ is tangent to the graph of $y = 4x - x^2$ at the point $(1, 3)$. Now zoom in toward the point $(1, 3)$ until the parabola and the tangent line are indistiguishable.

5. Using (1) with $f(x) = 4x - 3x^2$ and $P(2, -4)$ [we could also use (2)],

$$m = \lim_{x \to a} \frac{f(x) - f(a)}{x - a} = \lim_{x \to 2} \frac{(4x - 3x^2) - (-4)}{x - 2} = \lim_{x \to 2} \frac{-3x^2 + 4x + 4}{x - 2}$$

$$= \lim_{x \to 2} \frac{(-3x - 2)(x - 2)}{x - 2} = \lim_{x \to 2} (-3x - 2) = -3(2) - 2 = -8$$

Tangent line: $y - (-4) = -8(x - 2) \Leftrightarrow y + 4 = -8x + 16 \Leftrightarrow y = -8x + 12$.

7. Using (1), $m = \lim\limits_{x \to 1} \dfrac{\sqrt{x} - \sqrt{1}}{x - 1} = \lim\limits_{x \to 1} \dfrac{(\sqrt{x} - 1)(\sqrt{x} + 1)}{(x - 1)(\sqrt{x} + 1)} = \lim\limits_{x \to 1} \dfrac{x - 1}{(x - 1)(\sqrt{x} + 1)} = \lim\limits_{x \to 1} \dfrac{1}{\sqrt{x} + 1} = \dfrac{1}{2}$.

Tangent line: $y - 1 = \frac{1}{2}(x - 1) \Leftrightarrow y = \frac{1}{2}x + \frac{1}{2}$

9. (a) Using (2) with $y = f(x) = 3 + 4x^2 - 2x^3$,

$$m = \lim_{h \to 0} \frac{f(a + h) - f(a)}{h} = \lim_{h \to 0} \frac{3 + 4(a + h)^2 - 2(a + h)^3 - (3 + 4a^2 - 2a^3)}{h}$$

$$= \lim_{h \to 0} \frac{3 + 4(a^2 + 2ah + h^2) - 2(a^3 + 3a^2h + 3ah^2 + h^3) - 3 - 4a^2 + 2a^3}{h}$$

$$= \lim_{h \to 0} \frac{3 + 4a^2 + 8ah + 4h^2 - 2a^3 - 6a^2h - 6ah^2 - 2h^3 - 3 - 4a^2 + 2a^3}{h}$$

$$= \lim_{h \to 0} \frac{8ah + 4h^2 - 6a^2h - 6ah^2 - 2h^3}{h} = \lim_{h \to 0} \frac{h(8a + 4h - 6a^2 - 6ah - 2h^2)}{h}$$

$$= \lim_{h \to 0} (8a + 4h - 6a^2 - 6ah - 2h^2) = 8a - 6a^2$$

(b) At $(1, 5)$: $m = 8(1) - 6(1)^2 = 2$, so an equation of the tangent line

is $y - 5 = 2(x - 1)$ ⇔ $y = 2x + 3$.

At $(2, 3)$: $m = 8(2) - 6(2)^2 = -8$, so an equation of the tangent

line is $y - 3 = -8(x - 2)$ ⇔ $y = -8x + 19$.

(c)

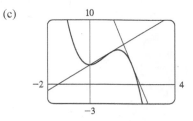

11. (a) The particle is moving to the right when s is increasing; that is, on the intervals $(0, 1)$ and $(4, 6)$. The particle is moving to

the left when s is decreasing; that is, on the interval $(2, 3)$. The particle is standing still when s is constant; that is, on the

intervals $(1, 2)$ and $(3, 4)$.

(b) The velocity of the particle is equal to the slope of the tangent line of the

graph. Note that there is no slope at the corner points on the graph. On the

interval $(0, 1)$, the slope is $\dfrac{3 - 0}{1 - 0} = 3$. On the interval $(2, 3)$, the slope is

$\dfrac{1 - 3}{3 - 2} = -2$. On the interval $(4, 6)$, the slope is $\dfrac{3 - 1}{6 - 4} = 1$.

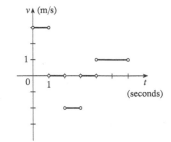

13. Let $s(t) = 40t - 16t^2$.

$$v(2) = \lim_{t \to 2} \frac{s(t) - s(2)}{t - 2} = \lim_{t \to 2} \frac{\left(40t - 16t^2\right) - 16}{t - 2} = \lim_{t \to 2} \frac{-16t^2 + 40t - 16}{t - 2} = \lim_{t \to 2} \frac{-8\left(2t^2 - 5t + 2\right)}{t - 2}$$

$$= \lim_{t \to 2} \frac{-8(t - 2)(2t - 1)}{t - 2} = -8 \lim_{t \to 2} (2t - 1) = -8(3) = -24$$

Thus, the instantaneous velocity when $t = 2$ is -24 ft/s.

15. $v(a) = \lim\limits_{h \to 0} \dfrac{s(a + h) - s(a)}{h} = \lim\limits_{h \to 0} \dfrac{\dfrac{1}{(a + h)^2} - \dfrac{1}{a^2}}{h} = \lim\limits_{h \to 0} \dfrac{\dfrac{a^2 - (a + h)^2}{a^2(a + h)^2}}{h} = \lim\limits_{h \to 0} \dfrac{a^2 - (a^2 + 2ah + h^2)}{ha^2(a + h)^2}$

$= \lim\limits_{h \to 0} \dfrac{-(2ah + h^2)}{ha^2(a + h)^2} = \lim\limits_{h \to 0} \dfrac{-h(2a + h)}{ha^2(a + h)^2} = \lim\limits_{h \to 0} \dfrac{-(2a + h)}{a^2(a + h)^2} = \dfrac{-2a}{a^2 \cdot a^2} = \dfrac{-2}{a^3}$ m/s

So $v(1) = \dfrac{-2}{1^3} = -2$ m/s, $v(2) = \dfrac{-2}{2^3} = -\dfrac{1}{4}$ m/s, and $v(3) = \dfrac{-2}{3^3} = -\dfrac{2}{27}$ m/s.

17. $g'(0)$ is the only negative value. The slope at $x = 4$ is smaller than the slope at $x = 2$ and both are smaller than the slope

at $x = -2$. Thus, $g'(0) < 0 < g'(4) < g'(2) < g'(-2)$.

19. For the tangent line $y = 4x - 5$: when $x = 2$, $y = 4(2) - 5 = 3$ and its slope is 4 (the coefficient of x). At the point of

tangency, these values are shared with the curve $y = f(x)$; that is, $f(2) = 3$ and $f'(2) = 4$.

21. We begin by drawing a curve through the origin with a slope of 3 to satisfy $f(0) = 0$ and $f'(0) = 3$. Since $f'(1) = 0$, we will round off our figure so that there is a horizontal tangent directly over $x = 1$. Last, we make sure that the curve has a slope of -1 as we pass over $x = 2$. Two of the many possibilities are shown.

23. Using (4) with $f(x) = 3x^2 - x^3$ and $a = 1$,

$$f'(1) = \lim_{h \to 0} \frac{f(1+h) - f(1)}{h} = \lim_{h \to 0} \frac{[3(1+h)^2 - (1+h)^3] - 2}{h}$$

$$= \lim_{h \to 0} \frac{(3 + 6h + 3h^2) - (1 + 3h + 3h^2 + h^3) - 2}{h} = \lim_{h \to 0} \frac{3h - h^3}{h} = \lim_{h \to 0} \frac{h(3 - h^2)}{h}$$

$$= \lim_{h \to 0} (3 - h^2) = 3 - 0 = 3$$

Tangent line: $y - 2 = 3(x - 1)$ $\Leftrightarrow$ $y - 2 = 3x - 3$ $\Leftrightarrow$ $y = 3x - 1$

25. (a) Using (4) with $F(x) = 5x/(1 + x^2)$ and the point $(2, 2)$, we have

(b)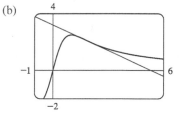

$$F'(2) = \lim_{h \to 0} \frac{F(2+h) - F(2)}{h} = \lim_{h \to 0} \frac{\dfrac{5(2+h)}{1 + (2+h)^2} - 2}{h}$$

$$= \lim_{h \to 0} \frac{\dfrac{5h + 10}{h^2 + 4h + 5} - 2}{h} = \lim_{h \to 0} \frac{\dfrac{5h + 10 - 2(h^2 + 4h + 5)}{h^2 + 4h + 5}}{h}$$

$$= \lim_{h \to 0} \frac{-2h^2 - 3h}{h(h^2 + 4h + 5)} = \lim_{h \to 0} \frac{h(-2h - 3)}{h(h^2 + 4h + 5)} = \lim_{h \to 0} \frac{-2h - 3}{h^2 + 4h + 5} = \frac{-3}{5}$$

So an equation of the tangent line at $(2, 2)$ is $y - 2 = -\frac{3}{5}(x - 2)$ or $y = -\frac{3}{5}x + \frac{16}{5}$.

27. Use (4) with $f(x) = 3x^2 - 4x + 1$.

$$f'(a) = \lim_{h \to 0} \frac{f(a+h) - f(a)}{h} = \lim_{h \to 0} \frac{[3(a+h)^2 - 4(a+h) + 1] - (3a^2 - 4a + 1)}{h}$$

$$= \lim_{h \to 0} \frac{3a^2 + 6ah + 3h^2 - 4a - 4h + 1 - 3a^2 + 4a - 1}{h} = \lim_{h \to 0} \frac{6ah + 3h^2 - 4h}{h}$$

$$= \lim_{h \to 0} \frac{h(6a + 3h - 4)}{h} = \lim_{h \to 0} (6a + 3h - 4) = 6a - 4$$

29. Use (4) with $f(t) = (2t + 1)/(t + 3)$.

$$f'(a) = \lim_{h \to 0} \frac{f(a+h) - f(a)}{h} = \lim_{h \to 0} \frac{\dfrac{2(a+h) + 1}{(a+h) + 3} - \dfrac{2a + 1}{a + 3}}{h} = \lim_{h \to 0} \frac{(2a + 2h + 1)(a + 3) - (2a + 1)(a + h + 3)}{h(a + h + 3)(a + 3)}$$

$$= \lim_{h \to 0} \frac{(2a^2 + 6a + 2ah + 6h + a + 3) - (2a^2 + 2ah + 6a + a + h + 3)}{h(a + h + 3)(a + 3)}$$

$$= \lim_{h \to 0} \frac{5h}{h(a + h + 3)(a + 3)} = \lim_{h \to 0} \frac{5}{(a + h + 3)(a + 3)} = \frac{5}{(a + 3)^2}$$

31. Use (4) with $f(x) = \sqrt{1 - 2x}$.

$$f'(a) = \lim_{h \to 0} \frac{f(a+h) - f(a)}{h} = \lim_{h \to 0} \frac{\sqrt{1 - 2(a+h)} - \sqrt{1 - 2a}}{h}$$

$$= \lim_{h \to 0} \frac{\sqrt{1 - 2(a+h)} - \sqrt{1 - 2a}}{h} \cdot \frac{\sqrt{1 - 2(a+h)} + \sqrt{1 - 2a}}{\sqrt{1 - 2(a+h)} + \sqrt{1 - 2a}} = \lim_{h \to 0} \frac{\left(\sqrt{1 - 2(a+h)}\right)^2 - \left(\sqrt{1 - 2a}\right)^2}{h\left(\sqrt{1 - 2(a+h)} + \sqrt{1 - 2a}\right)}$$

$$= \lim_{h \to 0} \frac{(1 - 2a - 2h) - (1 - 2a)}{h\left(\sqrt{1 - 2(a+h)} + \sqrt{1 - 2a}\right)} = \lim_{h \to 0} \frac{-2h}{h\left(\sqrt{1 - 2(a+h)} + \sqrt{1 - 2a}\right)}$$

$$= \lim_{h \to 0} \frac{-2}{\sqrt{1 - 2(a+h)} + \sqrt{1 - 2a}} = \frac{-2}{\sqrt{1 - 2a} + \sqrt{1 - 2a}} = \frac{-2}{2\sqrt{1 - 2a}} = \frac{-1}{\sqrt{1 - 2a}}$$

Note that the answers to Exercises 33 – 38 are not unique.

33. By (4), $\lim_{h \to 0} \frac{(1 + h)^{10} - 1}{h} = f'(1)$, where $f(x) = x^{10}$ and $a = 1$.

   Or: By (4), $\lim_{h \to 0} \frac{(1 + h)^{10} - 1}{h} = f'(0)$, where $f(x) = (1 + x)^{10}$ and $a = 0$.

35. By Equation 5, $\lim_{x \to 5} \frac{2^x - 32}{x - 5} = f'(5)$, where $f(x) = 2^x$ and $a = 5$.

37. By (4), $\lim_{h \to 0} \frac{\cos(\pi + h) + 1}{h} = f'(\pi)$, where $f(x) = \cos x$ and $a = \pi$.

   Or: By (4), $\lim_{h \to 0} \frac{\cos(\pi + h) + 1}{h} = f'(0)$, where $f(x) = \cos(\pi + x)$ and $a = 0$.

39. $v(5) = f'(5) = \lim_{h \to 0} \frac{f(5 + h) - f(5)}{h} = \lim_{h \to 0} \frac{[100 + 50(5 + h) - 4.9(5 + h)^2] - [100 + 50(5) - 4.9(5)^2]}{h}$

   $= \lim_{h \to 0} \frac{(100 + 250 + 50h - 4.9h^2 - 49h - 122.5) - (100 + 250 - 122.5)}{h} = \lim_{h \to 0} \frac{-4.9h^2 + h}{h}$

   $= \lim_{h \to 0} \frac{h(-4.9h + 1)}{h} = \lim_{h \to 0} (-4.9h + 1) = 1 \text{ m/s}$

   The speed when $t = 5$ is $|1| = 1$ m/s.

41. The sketch shows the graph for a room temperature of $72°$ and a refrigerator temperature of $38°$. The initial rate of change is greater in magnitude than the rate of change after an hour.

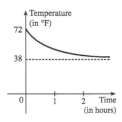

43. (a) (i) $[2002, 2006]$: $\frac{N(2006) - N(2002)}{2006 - 2002} = \frac{233 - 141}{4} = \frac{92}{4} = 23$ millions of cell phone subscribers per year

   (ii) $[2002, 2004]$: $\frac{N(2004) - N(2002)}{2004 - 2002} = \frac{182 - 141}{2} = \frac{41}{2} = 20.5$ millions of cell phone subscribers per year

   (iii) $[2000, 2002]$: $\frac{N(2002) - N(2000)}{2002 - 2000} = \frac{141 - 109}{2} = \frac{32}{2} = 16$ millions of cell phone subscribers per year

(b) Using the values from (ii) and (iii), we have $\dfrac{20.5 + 16}{2} = 18.25$ millions of cell phone subscribers per year.

(c) Estimating A as $(2000, 107)$ and B as $(2004, 175)$, the slope at 2002

is $\dfrac{175 - 107}{2004 - 2000} = \dfrac{68}{4} = 17$ millions of cell phone subscribers per year.

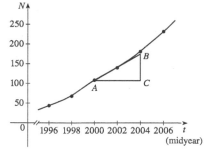

45. (a) (i) $\dfrac{\Delta C}{\Delta x} = \dfrac{C(105) - C(100)}{105 - 100} = \dfrac{6601.25 - 6500}{5} = \$20.25/\text{unit.}$

(ii) $\dfrac{\Delta C}{\Delta x} = \dfrac{C(101) - C(100)}{101 - 100} = \dfrac{6520.05 - 6500}{1} = \$20.05/\text{unit.}$

(b) $\dfrac{C(100 + h) - C(100)}{h} = \dfrac{\left[5000 + 10(100 + h) + 0.05(100 + h)^2\right] - 6500}{h} = \dfrac{20h + 0.05h^2}{h}$

$= 20 + 0.05h, \; h \neq 0$

So the instantaneous rate of change is $\displaystyle\lim_{h \to 0} \dfrac{C(100 + h) - C(100)}{h} = \lim_{h \to 0}(20 + 0.05h) = \$20/\text{unit.}$

47. (a) $f'(x)$ is the rate of change of the production cost with respect to the number of ounces of gold produced. Its units are dollars per ounce.

(b) After 800 ounces of gold have been produced, the rate at which the production cost is increasing is \$17/ounce. So the cost of producing the 800th (or 801st) ounce is about \$17.

(c) In the short term, the values of $f'(x)$ will decrease because more efficient use is made of start-up costs as x increases. But eventually $f'(x)$ might increase due to large-scale operations.

49. $T'(10)$ is the rate at which the temperature is changing at 10:00 AM. To estimate the value of $T'(10)$, we will average the

difference quotients obtained using the times $t = 8$ and $t = 12$. Let $A = \dfrac{T(8) - T(10)}{8 - 10} = \dfrac{65 - 76}{-2} = 5.5$ and

$B = \dfrac{T(12) - T(10)}{12 - 10} = \dfrac{85 - 76}{2} = 4.5$. Then $T'(10) = \displaystyle\lim_{t \to 10} \dfrac{T(t) - T(10)}{t - 10} \approx \dfrac{A + B}{2} = \dfrac{5.5 + 4.5}{2} = 5°\text{F/h.}$

51. (a) $S'(T)$ is the rate at which the oxygen solubility changes with respect to the water temperature. Its units are $(\text{mg/L})/°\text{C}$.

(b) For $T = 16°\text{C}$, it appears that the tangent line to the curve goes through the points $(0, 14)$ and $(32, 6)$. So

$S'(16) \approx \dfrac{6 - 14}{32 - 0} = -\dfrac{8}{32} = -0.25 \; (\text{mg/L})/°\text{C}$. This means that as the temperature increases past $16°\text{C}$, the oxygen

solubility is decreasing at a rate of $0.25 \; (\text{mg/L})/°\text{C}$.

53. Since $f(x) = x \sin(1/x)$ when $x \neq 0$ and $f(0) = 0$, we have

$f'(0) = \displaystyle\lim_{h \to 0} \dfrac{f(0 + h) - f(0)}{h} = \lim_{h \to 0} \dfrac{h \sin(1/h) - 0}{h} = \lim_{h \to 0} \sin(1/h)$. This limit does not exist since $\sin(1/h)$ takes the

values -1 and 1 on any interval containing 0. (Compare with Example 4 in Section 2.2.)

2.7 The Derivative as a Function

1. It appears that f is an odd function, so f' will be an even function—that is, $f'(-a) = f'(a)$.

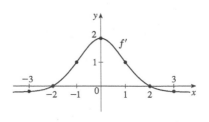

(a) $f'(-3) \approx -0.2$

(b) $f'(-2) \approx 0$

(c) $f'(-1) \approx 1$

(d) $f'(0) \approx 2$

(e) $f'(1) \approx 1$

(f) $f'(2) \approx 0$

(g) $f'(3) \approx -0.2$

3. (a)' = II, since from left to right, the slopes of the tangents to graph (a) start out negative, become 0, then positive, then 0, then negative again. The actual function values in graph II follow the same pattern.

(b)' = IV, since from left to right, the slopes of the tangents to graph (b) start out at a fixed positive quantity, then suddenly become negative, then positive again. The discontinuities in graph IV indicate sudden changes in the slopes of the tangents.

(c)' = I, since the slopes of the tangents to graph (c) are negative for $x < 0$ and positive for $x > 0$, as are the function values of graph I.

(d)' = III, since from left to right, the slopes of the tangents to graph (d) are positive, then 0, then negative, then 0, then positive, then 0, then negative again, and the function values in graph III follow the same pattern.

Hints for Exercises 4–11: First plot x-intercepts on the graph of f' for any horizontal tangents on the graph of f. Look for any corners on the graph of f—there will be a discontinuity on the graph of f'. On any interval where f has a tangent with positive (or negative) slope, the graph of f' will be positive (or negative). If the graph of the function is linear, the graph of f' will be a horizontal line.

5.

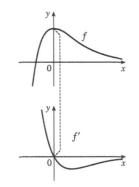

7.

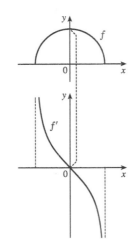

9.

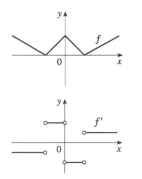

11.

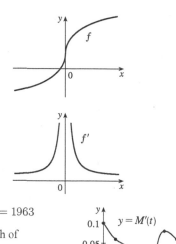

13. It appears that there are horizontal tangents on the graph of M for $t = 1963$ and $t = 1971$. Thus, there are zeros for those values of t on the graph of M'. The derivative is negative for the years 1963 to 1971.

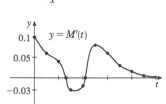

15.

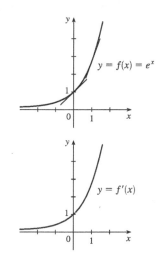

The slope at 0 appears to be 1 and the slope at 1 appears to be 2.7. As x decreases, the slope gets closer to 0. Since the graphs are so similar, we might guess that $f'(x) = e^x$.

17. (a) By zooming in, we estimate that $f'(0) = 0$, $f'\left(\frac{1}{2}\right) = 1$, $f'(1) = 2$, and $f'(2) = 4$.

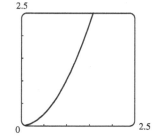

(b) By symmetry, $f'(-x) = -f'(x)$. So $f'\left(-\frac{1}{2}\right) = -1$, $f'(-1) = -2$, and $f'(-2) = -4$.

(c) It appears that $f'(x)$ is twice the value of x, so we guess that $f'(x) = 2x$.

(d) $f'(x) = \lim_{h \to 0} \dfrac{f(x+h) - f(x)}{h} = \lim_{h \to 0} \dfrac{(x+h)^2 - x^2}{h}$

$= \lim_{h \to 0} \dfrac{(x^2 + 2hx + h^2) - x^2}{h} = \lim_{h \to 0} \dfrac{2hx + h^2}{h} = \lim_{h \to 0} \dfrac{h(2x + h)}{h} = \lim_{h \to 0} (2x + h) = 2x$

19. $f'(x) = \lim\limits_{h \to 0} \dfrac{f(x+h) - f(x)}{h} = \lim\limits_{h \to 0} \dfrac{\left[\frac{1}{2}(x+h) - \frac{1}{3}\right] - \left(\frac{1}{2}x - \frac{1}{3}\right)}{h} = \lim\limits_{h \to 0} \dfrac{\frac{1}{2}x + \frac{1}{2}h - \frac{1}{3} - \frac{1}{2}x + \frac{1}{3}}{h}$

$= \lim\limits_{h \to 0} \dfrac{\frac{1}{2}h}{h} = \lim\limits_{h \to 0} \frac{1}{2} = \frac{1}{2}$

Domain of f = domain of f' = $\mathbb{R}$.

21. $f'(t) = \lim\limits_{h \to 0} \dfrac{f(t+h) - f(t)}{h} = \lim\limits_{h \to 0} \dfrac{\left[5(t+h) - 9(t+h)^2\right] - (5t - 9t^2)}{h}$

$= \lim\limits_{h \to 0} \dfrac{5t + 5h - 9(t^2 + 2th + h^2) - 5t + 9t^2}{h} = \lim\limits_{h \to 0} \dfrac{5t + 5h - 9t^2 - 18th - 9h^2 - 5t + 9t^2}{h}$

$= \lim\limits_{h \to 0} \dfrac{5h - 18th - 9h^2}{h} = \lim\limits_{h \to 0} \dfrac{h(5 - 18t - 9h)}{h} = \lim\limits_{h \to 0} (5 - 18t - 9h) = 5 - 18t$

Domain of f = domain of f' = $\mathbb{R}$.

23. $f'(x) = \lim\limits_{h \to 0} \dfrac{f(x+h) - f(x)}{h} = \lim\limits_{h \to 0} \dfrac{\left[(x+h)^2 - 2(x+h)^3\right] - (x^2 - 2x^3)}{h}$

$= \lim\limits_{h \to 0} \dfrac{x^2 + 2xh + h^2 - 2x^3 - 6x^2h - 6xh^2 - 2h^3 - x^2 + 2x^3}{h}$

$= \lim\limits_{h \to 0} \dfrac{2xh + h^2 - 6x^2h - 6xh^2 - 2h^3}{h} = \lim\limits_{h \to 0} \dfrac{h(2x + h - 6x^2 - 6xh - 2h^2)}{h}$

$= \lim\limits_{h \to 0} (2x + h - 6x^2 - 6xh - 2h^2) = 2x - 6x^2$

Domain of f = domain of f' = $\mathbb{R}$.

25. $g'(x) = \lim\limits_{h \to 0} \dfrac{g(x+h) - g(x)}{h} = \lim\limits_{h \to 0} \dfrac{\sqrt{1 + 2(x+h)} - \sqrt{1 + 2x}}{h} \left[\dfrac{\sqrt{1 + 2(x+h)} + \sqrt{1 + 2x}}{\sqrt{1 + 2(x+h)} + \sqrt{1 + 2x}}\right]$

$= \lim\limits_{h \to 0} \dfrac{(1 + 2x + 2h) - (1 + 2x)}{h\left[\sqrt{1 + 2(x+h)} + \sqrt{1 + 2x}\right]} = \lim\limits_{h \to 0} \dfrac{2}{\sqrt{1 + 2x + 2h} + \sqrt{1 + 2x}} = \dfrac{2}{2\sqrt{1 + 2x}} = \dfrac{1}{\sqrt{1 + 2x}}$

Domain of g = $\left[-\frac{1}{2}, \infty\right)$, domain of g' = $\left(-\frac{1}{2}, \infty\right)$.

27. $G'(t) = \lim\limits_{h \to 0} \dfrac{G(t+h) - G(t)}{h} = \lim\limits_{h \to 0} \dfrac{\dfrac{4(t+h)}{(t+h)+1} - \dfrac{4t}{t+1}}{h} = \lim\limits_{h \to 0} \dfrac{\dfrac{4(t+h)(t+1) - 4t(t+h+1)}{(t+h+1)(t+1)}}{h}$

$= \lim\limits_{h \to 0} \dfrac{\left(4t^2 + 4ht + 4t + 4h\right) - \left(4t^2 + 4ht + 4t\right)}{h(t+h+1)(t+1)} = \lim\limits_{h \to 0} \dfrac{4h}{h(t+h+1)(t+1)}$

$= \lim\limits_{h \to 0} \dfrac{4}{(t+h+1)(t+1)} = \dfrac{4}{(t+1)^2}$

Domain of G = domain of G' = $(-\infty, -1) \cup (-1, \infty)$.

29. $f'(x) = \lim\limits_{h \to 0} \dfrac{f(x+h) - f(x)}{h} = \lim\limits_{h \to 0} \dfrac{(x+h)^4 - x^4}{h} = \lim\limits_{h \to 0} \dfrac{\left(x^4 + 4x^3h + 6x^2h^2 + 4xh^3 + h^4\right) - x^4}{h}$

$= \lim\limits_{h \to 0} \dfrac{4x^3h + 6x^2h^2 + 4xh^3 + h^4}{h} = \lim\limits_{h \to 0} \left(4x^3 + 6x^2h + 4xh^2 + h^3\right) = 4x^3$

Domain of f = domain of f' = $\mathbb{R}$.

31. (a) $f'(x) = \lim\limits_{h \to 0} \dfrac{f(x+h) - f(x)}{h} = \lim\limits_{h \to 0} \dfrac{[(x+h)^4 + 2(x+h)] - (x^4 + 2x)}{h}$

$= \lim\limits_{h \to 0} \dfrac{x^4 + 4x^3h + 6x^2h^2 + 4xh^3 + h^4 + 2x + 2h - x^4 - 2x}{h}$

$= \lim\limits_{h \to 0} \dfrac{4x^3h + 6x^2h^2 + 4xh^3 + h^4 + 2h}{h} = \lim\limits_{h \to 0} \dfrac{h(4x^3 + 6x^2h + 4xh^2 + h^3 + 2)}{h}$

$= \lim\limits_{h \to 0} (4x^3 + 6x^2h + 4xh^2 + h^3 + 2) = 4x^3 + 2$

(b) Notice that $f'(x) = 0$ when f has a horizontal tangent, $f'(x)$ is

positive when the tangents have positive slope, and $f'(x)$ is

negative when the tangents have negative slope.

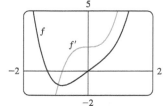

33. (a) $U'(t)$ is the rate at which the unemployment rate is changing with respect to time. Its units are percent per year.

(b) To find $U'(t)$, we use $\lim\limits_{h \to 0} \dfrac{U(t+h) - U(t)}{h} \approx \dfrac{U(t+h) - U(t)}{h}$ for small values of h.

For 1998: $U'(1998) \approx \dfrac{U(1999) - U(1998)}{1999 - 1998} = \dfrac{4.2 - 4.5}{1} = -0.30$

For 1999: We estimate $U'(1999)$ by using $h = -1$ and $h = 1$, and then average the two results to obtain a final estimate.

$h = -1 \quad \Rightarrow \quad U'(1999) \approx \dfrac{U(1998) - U(1999)}{1998 - 1999} = \dfrac{4.5 - 4.2}{-1} = -0.30;$

$h = 1 \quad \Rightarrow \quad U'(1999) \approx \dfrac{U(2000) - U(1999)}{2000 - 1999} = \dfrac{4.0 - 4.2}{1} = -0.20.$

So we estimate that $U'(1999) \approx \frac{1}{2}[(-0.30) + (-0.20)] = -0.25.$

t	1998	1999	2000	2001	2002	2003	2004	2005	2006	2007
$U'(t)$	−0.30	−0.25	0.25	0.90	0.65	−0.15	−0.45	−0.45	−0.25	0.00

35. f is not differentiable at $x = -4$, because the graph has a corner there, and at $x = 0$, because there is a discontinuity there.

37. f is not differentiable at $x = -1$, because the graph has a vertical tangent there, and at $x = 4$, because the graph has a corner there.

39. As we zoom in toward $(-1, 0)$, the curve appears more and more like a straight

line, so $f(x) = x + \sqrt{|x|}$ is differentiable at $x = -1$. But no matter how much

we zoom in toward the origin, the curve doesn't straighten out—we can't

eliminate the sharp point (a cusp). So f is not differentiable at $x = 0$.

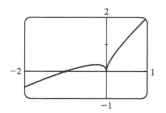

41. $a = f$, $b = f'$, $c = f''$. We can see this because where a has a horizontal tangent, $b = 0$, and where b has a horizontal tangent,

$c = 0$. We can immediately see that c can be neither f nor f', since at the points where c has a horizontal tangent, neither a

nor b is equal to 0.

43. We can immediately see that a is the graph of the acceleration function, since at the points where a has a horizontal tangent, neither c nor b is equal to 0. Next, we note that $a = 0$ at the point where b has a horizontal tangent, so b must be the graph of the velocity function, and hence, $b' = a$. We conclude that c is the graph of the position function.

45. $f'(x) = \lim\limits_{h \to 0} \dfrac{f(x+h) - f(x)}{h} = \lim\limits_{h \to 0} \dfrac{[3(x+h)^2 + 2(x+h) + 1] - (3x^2 + 2x + 1)}{h}$

$= \lim\limits_{h \to 0} \dfrac{(3x^2 + 6xh + 3h^2 + 2x + 2h + 1) - (3x^2 + 2x + 1)}{h} = \lim\limits_{h \to 0} \dfrac{6xh + 3h^2 + 2h}{h}$

$= \lim\limits_{h \to 0} \dfrac{h(6x + 3h + 2)}{h} = \lim\limits_{h \to 0} (6x + 3h + 2) = 6x + 2$

$f''(x) = \lim\limits_{h \to 0} \dfrac{f'(x+h) - f'(x)}{h} = \lim\limits_{h \to 0} \dfrac{[6(x+h) + 2] - (6x + 2)}{h} = \lim\limits_{h \to 0} \dfrac{(6x + 6h + 2) - (6x + 2)}{h}$

$= \lim\limits_{h \to 0} \dfrac{6h}{h} = \lim\limits_{h \to 0} 6 = 6$

We see from the graph that our answers are reasonable because the graph of f' is that of a linear function and the graph of f'' is that of a constant function.

47. $f'(x) = \lim\limits_{h \to 0} \dfrac{f(x+h) - f(x)}{h} = \lim\limits_{h \to 0} \dfrac{[2(x+h)^2 - (x+h)^3] - (2x^2 - x^3)}{h}$

$= \lim\limits_{h \to 0} \dfrac{h(4x + 2h - 3x^2 - 3xh - h^2)}{h} = \lim\limits_{h \to 0} (4x + 2h - 3x^2 - 3xh - h^2) = 4x - 3x^2$

$f''(x) = \lim\limits_{h \to 0} \dfrac{f'(x+h) - f'(x)}{h} = \lim\limits_{h \to 0} \dfrac{[4(x+h) - 3(x+h)^2] - (4x - 3x^2)}{h} = \lim\limits_{h \to 0} \dfrac{h(4 - 6x - 3h)}{h}$

$= \lim\limits_{h \to 0} (4 - 6x - 3h) = 4 - 6x$

$f'''(x) = \lim\limits_{h \to 0} \dfrac{f''(x+h) - f''(x)}{h} = \lim\limits_{h \to 0} \dfrac{[4 - 6(x+h)] - (4 - 6x)}{h} = \lim\limits_{h \to 0} \dfrac{-6h}{h} = \lim\limits_{h \to 0} (-6) = -6$

$f^{(4)}(x) = \lim\limits_{h \to 0} \dfrac{f'''(x+h) - f'''(x)}{h} = \lim\limits_{h \to 0} \dfrac{-6 - (-6)}{h} = \lim\limits_{h \to 0} \dfrac{0}{h} = \lim\limits_{h \to 0} (0) = 0$

The graphs are consistent with the geometric interpretations of the derivatives because f' has zeros where f has a local minimum and a local maximum, f'' has a zero where f' has a local maximum, and f''' is a constant function equal to the slope of f''.

49. (a) Note that we have factored $x - a$ as the difference of two cubes in the third step.

$f'(a) = \lim\limits_{x \to a} \dfrac{f(x) - f(a)}{x - a} = \lim\limits_{x \to a} \dfrac{x^{1/3} - a^{1/3}}{x - a} = \lim\limits_{x \to a} \dfrac{x^{1/3} - a^{1/3}}{(x^{1/3} - a^{1/3})(x^{2/3} + x^{1/3}a^{1/3} + a^{2/3})}$

$= \lim\limits_{x \to a} \dfrac{1}{x^{2/3} + x^{1/3}a^{1/3} + a^{2/3}} = \dfrac{1}{3a^{2/3}}$ or $\tfrac{1}{3}a^{-2/3}$

(b) $f'(0) = \lim\limits_{h \to 0} \dfrac{f(0+h) - f(0)}{h} = \lim\limits_{h \to 0} \dfrac{\sqrt[3]{h} - 0}{h} = \lim\limits_{h \to 0} \dfrac{1}{h^{2/3}}$. This function increases without bound, so the limit does not

exist, and therefore $f'(0)$ does not exist.

(c) $\lim\limits_{x \to 0} |f'(x)| = \lim\limits_{x \to 0} \dfrac{1}{3x^{2/3}} = \infty$ and f is continuous at $x = 0$ (root function), so f has a vertical tangent at $x = 0$.

51. $f(x) = |x - 6| = \begin{cases} x - 6 & \text{if } x - 6 \geq 6 \\ -(x - 6) & \text{if } x - 6 < 0 \end{cases} = \begin{cases} x - 6 & \text{if } x \geq 6 \\ 6 - x & \text{if } x < 6 \end{cases}$

So the right-hand limit is $\lim\limits_{x \to 6^+} \dfrac{f(x) - f(6)}{x - 6} = \lim\limits_{x \to 6^+} \dfrac{|x - 6| - 0}{x - 6} = \lim\limits_{x \to 6^+} \dfrac{x - 6}{x - 6} = \lim\limits_{x \to 6^+} 1 = 1$, and the left-hand limit

is $\lim\limits_{x \to 6^-} \dfrac{f(x) - f(6)}{x - 6} = \lim\limits_{x \to 6^-} \dfrac{|x - 6| - 0}{x - 6} = \lim\limits_{x \to 6^-} \dfrac{6 - x}{x - 6} = \lim\limits_{x \to 6^-} (-1) = -1$. Since these limits are not equal,

$f'(6) = \lim\limits_{x \to 6} \dfrac{f(x) - f(6)}{x - 6}$ does not exist and f is not differentiable at 6.

However, a formula for f' is $f'(x) = \begin{cases} 1 & \text{if } x > 6 \\ -1 & \text{if } x < 6 \end{cases}$.

Another way of writing the formula is $f'(x) = \dfrac{x - 6}{|x - 6|}$.

53. (a) If f is even, then

$$f'(-x) = \lim\limits_{h \to 0} \dfrac{f(-x + h) - f(-x)}{h} = \lim\limits_{h \to 0} \dfrac{f[-(x - h)] - f(-x)}{h}$$

$$= \lim\limits_{h \to 0} \dfrac{f(x - h) - f(x)}{h} = -\lim\limits_{h \to 0} \dfrac{f(x - h) - f(x)}{-h} \qquad [\text{let } \Delta x = -h]$$

$$= -\lim\limits_{\Delta x \to 0} \dfrac{f(x + \Delta x) - f(x)}{\Delta x} = -f'(x)$$

Therefore, f' is odd.

(b) If f is odd, then

$$f'(-x) = \lim\limits_{h \to 0} \dfrac{f(-x + h) - f(-x)}{h} = \lim\limits_{h \to 0} \dfrac{f[-(x - h)] - f(-x)}{h}$$

$$= \lim\limits_{h \to 0} \dfrac{-f(x - h) + f(x)}{h} = \lim\limits_{h \to 0} \dfrac{f(x - h) - f(x)}{-h} \qquad [\text{let } \Delta x = -h]$$

$$= \lim\limits_{\Delta x \to 0} \dfrac{f(x + \Delta x) - f(x)}{\Delta x} = f'(x)$$

Therefore, f' is even.

55.

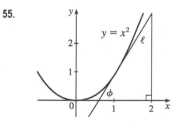

In the right triangle in the diagram, let Δy be the side opposite angle ϕ and Δx the side adjacent angle ϕ. Then the slope of the tangent line ℓ is $m = \Delta y/\Delta x = \tan\phi$. Note that $0 < \phi < \frac{\pi}{2}$. We know (see Exercise 17) that the derivative of $f(x) = x^2$ is $f'(x) = 2x$. So the slope of the tangent to the curve at the point $(1, 1)$ is 2. Thus, ϕ is the angle between 0 and $\frac{\pi}{2}$ whose tangent is 2; that is, $\phi = \tan^{-1} 2 \approx 63°$.

2.8 What Does f' Say about f?

1. (a) Since $f'(x) < 0$ on $(1, 4)$, f is decreasing on this interval. Since $f'(x) > 0$ on $(0, 1)$ and $(4, 5)$, f is increasing on these

intervals.

(b) At $x = 1$, $f'(x) = 0$ and f' changes from positive to negative there, f changes from increasing to decreasing and has a

local maximum at $x = 1$. At $x = 4$, $f'(x) = 0$ and f' changes from negative to positive there, f changes from decreasing

to increasing and has local minimum at $x = 4$.

(c) Since $f(0) = 0$, start at the origin. Draw an increasing function on $(0, 1)$

with a local maximum at $x = 1$. Now draw a decreasing function on $(1, 4)$

and the steepest slope should occur at $x = 2.5$ since that's where the

smallest value of f' occurs. Last, draw an increasing function on $(4, 5)$

making sure you have a local minimum at $x = 4$.

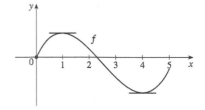

3. (a) $f'(x) > 0$ and f is increasing on $(-2, -1)$, $(0, 1)$, and $(2, 3)$. $f'(x) < 0$

and f is decreasing on $(-1, 0)$ and $(1, 2)$.

(b) At $x = -1$ and $x = 1$, $f'(x) = 0$ and f' changes from positive to negative,

so f has local maxima at $x = -1$ and $x = 1$. At $x = 0$ and $x = 2$,

$f'(x) = 0$ and f' changes from negative to positive, so f has local minima

at $x = 0$ and $x = 2$.

(c)

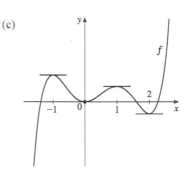

5. The derivative f' is increasing when the slopes of the tangent lines of f are becoming larger as x increases. This seems to be

the case on the interval $(2, 5)$. The derivative is decreasing when the slopes of the tangent lines of f are becoming smaller as x

increases, and this seems to be the case on $(-\infty, 2)$ and $(5, \infty)$. So f' is increasing on $(2, 5)$ and decreasing on $(-\infty, 2)$

and $(5, \infty)$.

7. Call the curve with the positive y-intercept g and the other curve h. Notice that g has a maximum (horizontal tangent) at

$x = 0$, but $h \neq 0$, so h cannot be the derivative of g. Also notice that where g is positive, h is increasing. Thus, $h = f$ and

$g = f'$. Now $f'(-1)$ is negative since f' is below the x-axis there and $f''(1)$ is positive since f is concave upward at $x = 1$.

Therefore, $f''(1)$ is greater than $f'(-1)$.

9. If $D(t)$ is the size of the deficit as a function of time, then at the time of the speech $D'(t) > 0$, but $D''(t) < 0$ because

$D''(t) = (D')'(t)$ is the rate of change of $D'(t)$.

11. (a) The rate of increase of the population is initially very small, then increases rapidly until about 1932 when it starts decreasing. The rate becomes negative by 1936, peaks in magnitude in 1937, and approaches 0 in 1940.

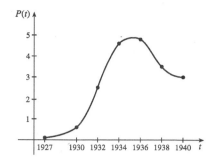

(b) Inflection points (IP) appear to be at $(1932, 2.5)$ and $(1937, 4.3)$. The rate of change of population density starts to decrease in 1932 and starts to increase in 1937. The rates of population increase and decrease have their maximum values at those points.

13. Most students learn more in the third hour of studying than in the eighth hour, so $K(3) - K(2)$ is larger than $K(8) - K(7)$. In other words, as you begin studying for a test, the rate of knowledge gain is large and then starts to taper off, so $K'(t)$ decreases and the graph of K is concave downward.

15. (a) f is increasing where f' is positive, that is, on $(0, 2)$, $(4, 6)$, and $(8, \infty)$; and decreasing where f' is negative, that is, on $(2, 4)$ and $(6, 8)$.

(b) f has local maxima where f' changes from positive to negative, at $x = 2$ and at $x = 6$, and local minima where f' changes from negative to positive, at $x = 4$ and at $x = 8$.

(c) f is concave upward (CU) where f' is increasing, that is, on $(3, 6)$ and $(6, \infty)$, and concave downward (CD) where f' is decreasing, that is, on $(0, 3)$.

(d) There is a point of inflection where f changes from being CD to being CU, that is, at $x = 3$.

(e)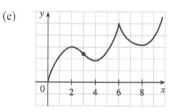

17. The function must be always decreasing (since the first derivative is always negative) and concave downward (since the second derivative is always negative).

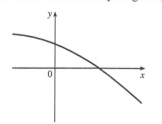

19. $f'(0) = f'(4) = 0 \Rightarrow$ horizontal tangents at $x = 0, 4$.

$f'(x) > 0$ if $x < 0 \Rightarrow f$ is increasing on $(-\infty, 0)$.

$f'(x) < 0$ if $0 < x < 4$ or if $x > 4 \Rightarrow f$ is decreasing on $(0, 4)$ and $(4, \infty)$.

$f''(x) > 0$ if $2 < x < 4 \Rightarrow f$ is concave upward on $(2, 4)$.

$f''(x) < 0$ if $x < 2$ or $x > 4 \Rightarrow f$ is concave downward on $(-\infty, 2)$

and $(4, \infty)$. There are inflection points when $x = 2$ and 4.

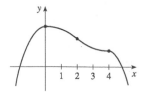

21. $f'(0) = f'(2) = f'(4) = 0 \Rightarrow$ horizontal tangents at $x = 0, 2, 4$.

$f'(x) > 0$ if $x < 0$ or $2 < x < 4 \Rightarrow f$ is increasing on $(-\infty, 0)$ and $(2, 4)$.

$f'(x) < 0$ if $0 < x < 2$ or $x > 4 \Rightarrow f$ is decreasing on $(0, 2)$ and $(4, \infty)$.

$f''(x) > 0$ if $1 < x < 3 \Rightarrow f$ is concave upward on $(1, 3)$.

$f''(x) < 0$ if $x < 1$ or $x > 3 \Rightarrow f$ is concave downward on $(-\infty, 1)$

and $(3, \infty)$. There are inflection points when $x = 1$ and 3.

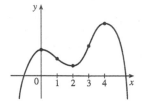

23. $f'(x) > 0$ if $|x| < 2 \Rightarrow f$ is increasing on $(-2, 2)$.

$f'(x) < 0$ if $|x| > 2 \Rightarrow f$ is decreasing on $(-\infty, -2)$

and $(2, \infty)$. $\qquad f'(-2) = 0 \Rightarrow$ horizontal tangent at

$x = -2$. $\lim_{x \to 2} |f'(x)| = \infty \Rightarrow$ there is a vertical

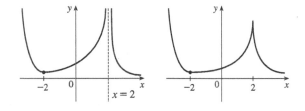

asymptote or vertical tangent (cusp) at $x = 2$. $f''(x) > 0$ if $x \neq 2 \Rightarrow f$ is concave upward on $(-\infty, 2)$ and $(2, \infty)$.

25. (a) Since e^{-x^2} is positive for all x, $f'(x) = xe^{-x^2}$ is positive where $x > 0$ and negative where $x < 0$. Thus, f is increasing

on $(0, \infty)$ and decreasing on $(-\infty, 0)$.

(b) Since f changes from decreasing to increasing at $x = 0$, f has a minimum value there.

27. (a) To find the intervals on which f is increasing, we need to find the intervals on which $f'(x) = 3x^2 - 1$ is positive.

$3x^2 - 1 > 0 \Leftrightarrow 3x^2 > 1 \Leftrightarrow x^2 > \frac{1}{3} \Leftrightarrow |x| > \sqrt{\frac{1}{3}}$, so $x \in \left(-\infty, -\sqrt{\frac{1}{3}}\right) \cup \left(\sqrt{\frac{1}{3}}, \infty\right)$. Thus, f is

increasing on $\left(-\infty, -\sqrt{\frac{1}{3}}\right)$ and on $\left(\sqrt{\frac{1}{3}}, \infty\right)$. In a similar fashion, f is decreasing on $\left(-\sqrt{\frac{1}{3}}, \sqrt{\frac{1}{3}}\right)$.

(b) To find the intervals on which f is concave upward, we need to find the intervals on which $f''(x) = 6x$ is positive.

$6x > 0 \Leftrightarrow x > 0$. So f is concave upward on $(0, \infty)$ and f is concave downward on $(-\infty, 0)$.

(c) There is an inflection point at $(0, 0)$ since f changes its direction of concavity at $x = 0$.

29. b is the antiderivative of f. For small x, f is negative, so the graph of its antiderivative must be decreasing. But both a and c

are increasing for small x, so only b can be f's antiderivative. Also, f is positive where b is increasing, which supports our

conclusion.

31.

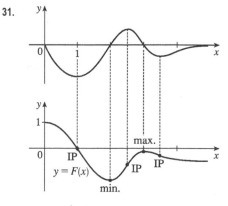

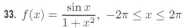

The graph of F must start at $(0, 1)$. Where the given graph, $y = f(x)$, has a local minimum or maximum, the graph of F will have an inflection point. Where f is negative (positive), F is decreasing (increasing).

Where f changes from negative to positive, F will have a minimum.

Where f changes from positive to negative, F will have a maximum.

Where f is decreasing (increasing), F is concave downward (upward).

33. $f(x) = \dfrac{\sin x}{1 + x^2}$, $-2\pi \le x \le 2\pi$

Note that the graph of f is one of an odd function, so the graph of F will be one of an even function.

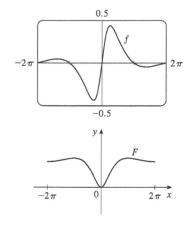

2 Review

CONCEPT CHECK

1. (a) $\lim_{x \to a} f(x) = L$: See Definition 2.2.1 and Figures 1 and 2 in Section 2.2.

(b) $\lim_{x \to a^+} f(x) = L$: See the paragraph after Definition 2.2.2 and Figure 9(b) in Section 2.2.

(c) $\lim_{x \to a^-} f(x) = L$: See Definition 2.2.2 and Figure 9(a) in Section 2.2.

(d) $\lim_{x \to a} f(x) = \infty$: See Definition 2.5.1 and Figure 2 in Section 2.5.

(e) $\lim_{x \to \infty} f(x) = L$: See Definition 2.5.4 and Figure 9 in Section 2.5.

2. In general, the limit of a function fails to exist when the function does not approach a fixed number. For each of the following functions, the limit fails to exist at $x = 2$.

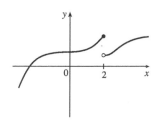

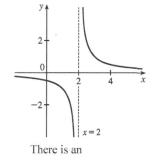

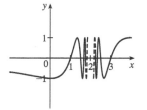

The left- and right-hand limits are not equal.

There is an infinite discontinuity.

There are an infinite number of oscillations.

3. (a)–(g) See the statements of Limit Laws 1–6 and 11 in Section 2.3.

4. See Theorem 3 in Section 2.3.

5. (a) See Definition 2.5.2 and Figures 2–4 in Section 2.5.

   (b) See Definition 2.5.5 and Figures 9 and 10 in Section 2.5.

6. (a) $y = x^4$: No asymptote

   (b) $y = \sin x$: No asymptote

   (c) $y = \tan x$: Vertical asymptotes $x = \frac{\pi}{2} + \pi n$, n an integer

   (d) $y = e^x$: Horizontal asymptote $y = 0$ $\left(\lim\limits_{x \to -\infty} e^x = 0 \right)$

   (e) $y = \ln x$: Vertical asymptote $x = 0$ $\left(\lim\limits_{x \to 0^+} \ln x = -\infty \right)$

   (f) $y = 1/x$: Vertical asymptote $x = 0$, horizontal asymptote $y = 0$

   (g) $y = \sqrt{x}$: No asymptote

7. (a) A function f is continuous at a number a if $f(x)$ approaches $f(a)$ as x approaches a; that is, $\lim\limits_{x \to a} f(x) = f(a)$.

   (b) A function f is continuous on the interval $(-\infty, \infty)$ if f is continuous at every real number a. The graph of such a
   function has no breaks and every vertical line crosses it.

8. See Theorem 2.4.10.

9. See Definition 2.6.1.

10. See the paragraph containing Formula 3 in Section 2.6.

11. (a) The average rate of change of y with respect to x over the interval $[x_1, x_2]$ is $\dfrac{f(x_2) - f(x_1)}{x_2 - x_1}$.

   (b) The instantaneous rate of change of y with respect to x at $x = x_1$ is $\lim\limits_{x_2 \to x_1} \dfrac{f(x_2) - f(x_1)}{x_2 - x_1}$.

12. See Definition 2.7.2. The pages following the definition discuss interpretations of $f'(a)$ as the slope of a tangent line to the
   graph of f at $x = a$ and as an instantaneous rate of change of $f(x)$ with respect to x when $x = a$.

13. See the paragraphs before and after Example 7 in Section 2.7.

14. (a) A function f is differentiable at a number a if its derivative f' exists
   at $x = a$; that is, if $f'(a)$ exists.

   (b) See Theorem 2.7.4. This theorem also tells us that if f is *not*
   continuous at a, then f is *not* differentiable at a.

(c)

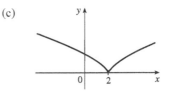

15. See the discussion and Figure 8 on page 152.

16. (a) See the first box in Section 2.8.

   (b) See the second box in Section 2.8.

17. (a) An antiderivative of a function f is a function F such that $F' = f$.

(b) The antiderivative of a velocity function is a position function (the derivative of a position function is a velocity function). The antiderivative of an acceleration function is a velocity function (the derivative of a velocity function is an acceleration function).

TRUE-FALSE QUIZ

1. False. Limit Law 2 applies only if the individual limits exist (these don't).

3. True. Limit Law 5 applies.

5. False. Consider $\lim\limits_{x \to 5} \dfrac{x(x-5)}{x-5}$ or $\lim\limits_{x \to 5} \dfrac{\sin(x-5)}{x-5}$. The first limit exists and is equal to 5. By Example 3 in Section 2.2, we know that the latter limit exists (and it is equal to 1).

7. True. A polynomial is continuous everywhere, so $\lim\limits_{x \to b} p(x)$ exists and is equal to $p(b)$.

9. True. See Figure 11 in Section 2.5.

11. False. Consider $f(x) = \begin{cases} 1/(x-1) & \text{if } x \neq 1 \\ 2 & \text{if } x = 1 \end{cases}$

13. True. Use Theorem 2.4.8 with $a = 2$, $b = 5$, and $g(x) = 4x^2 - 11$. Note that $f(4) = 3$ is not needed.

15. False. See the note after Theorem 4 in Section 2.7.

17. False. $\dfrac{d^2y}{dx^2}$ is the second derivative while $\left(\dfrac{dy}{dx}\right)^2$ is the first derivative squared. For example, if $y = x$, then $\dfrac{d^2y}{dx^2} = 0$, but $\left(\dfrac{dy}{dx}\right)^2 = 1$.

EXERCISES

1. (a) (i) $\lim\limits_{x \to 2^+} f(x) = 3$ (ii) $\lim\limits_{x \to -3^+} f(x) = 0$

(iii) $\lim\limits_{x \to -3} f(x)$ does not exist since the left and right limits are not equal. (The left limit is -2.)

(iv) $\lim\limits_{x \to 4} f(x) = 2$

(v) $\lim\limits_{x \to 0} f(x) = \infty$ (vi) $\lim\limits_{x \to 2^-} f(x) = -\infty$

(vii) $\lim\limits_{x \to \infty} f(x) = 4$ (viii) $\lim\limits_{x \to -\infty} f(x) = -1$

(b) The equations of the horizontal asymptotes are $y = -1$ and $y = 4$.

(c) The equations of the vertical asymptotes are $x = 0$ and $x = 2$.

(d) f is discontinuous at $x = -3, 0, 2$, and 4. The discontinuities are jump, infinite, infinite, and removable, respectively.

3. Since the exponential function is continuous, $\lim\limits_{x \to 1} e^{x^3 - x} = e^{1-1} = e^0 = 1$.

5. $\lim\limits_{x \to -3} \dfrac{x^2 - 9}{x^2 + 2x - 3} = \lim\limits_{x \to -3} \dfrac{(x+3)(x-3)}{(x+3)(x-1)} = \lim\limits_{x \to -3} \dfrac{x-3}{x-1} = \dfrac{-3-3}{-3-1} = \dfrac{-6}{-4} = \dfrac{3}{2}$

7. $\lim\limits_{h \to 0} \dfrac{(h-1)^3 + 1}{h} = \lim\limits_{h \to 0} \dfrac{(h^3 - 3h^2 + 3h - 1) + 1}{h} = \lim\limits_{h \to 0} \dfrac{h^3 - 3h^2 + 3h}{h} = \lim\limits_{h \to 0} (h^2 - 3h + 3) = 3$

Another solution: Factor the numerator as a sum of two cubes and then simplify.

$$\lim\limits_{h \to 0} \dfrac{(h-1)^3 + 1}{h} = \lim\limits_{h \to 0} \dfrac{(h-1)^3 + 1^3}{h} = \lim\limits_{h \to 0} \dfrac{[(h-1) + 1]\left[(h-1)^2 - 1(h-1) + 1^2\right]}{h}$$

$$= \lim\limits_{h \to 0} \left[(h-1)^2 - h + 2\right] = 1 - 0 + 2 = 3$$

9. $\lim\limits_{r \to 9} \dfrac{\sqrt{r}}{(r-9)^4} = \infty$ since $(r-9)^4 \to 0$ as $r \to 9$ and $\dfrac{\sqrt{r}}{(r-9)^4} > 0$ for $r \neq 9$.

11. $\lim\limits_{u \to 1} \dfrac{u^4 - 1}{u^3 + 5u^2 - 6u} = \lim\limits_{u \to 1} \dfrac{(u^2 + 1)(u^2 - 1)}{u(u^2 + 5u - 6)} = \lim\limits_{u \to 1} \dfrac{(u^2 + 1)(u+1)(u-1)}{u(u+6)(u-1)} = \lim\limits_{u \to 1} \dfrac{(u^2 + 1)(u+1)}{u(u+6)} = \dfrac{2(2)}{1(7)} = \dfrac{4}{7}$

13. Let $t = \sin x$. Then as $x \to \pi^-$, $\sin x \to 0^+$, so $t \to 0^+$. Thus, $\lim\limits_{x \to \pi^-} \ln(\sin x) = \lim\limits_{t \to 0^+} \ln t = -\infty$.

15. Since x is positive, $\sqrt{x^2} = |x| = x$. Thus,

$$\lim\limits_{x \to \infty} \dfrac{\sqrt{x^2 - 9}}{2x - 6} = \lim\limits_{x \to \infty} \dfrac{\sqrt{x^2 - 9}/\sqrt{x^2}}{(2x-6)/x} = \lim\limits_{x \to \infty} \dfrac{\sqrt{1 - 9/x^2}}{2 - 6/x} = \dfrac{\sqrt{1 - 0}}{2 - 0} = \dfrac{1}{2}$$

17. $\lim\limits_{x \to \infty} \left(\sqrt{x^2 + 4x + 1} - x\right) = \lim\limits_{x \to \infty} \left[\dfrac{\sqrt{x^2 + 4x + 1} - x}{1} \cdot \dfrac{\sqrt{x^2 + 4x + 1} + x}{\sqrt{x^2 + 4x + 1} + x}\right] = \lim\limits_{x \to \infty} \dfrac{(x^2 + 4x + 1) - x^2}{\sqrt{x^2 + 4x + 1} + x}$

$$= \lim\limits_{x \to \infty} \dfrac{(4x + 1)/x}{\left(\sqrt{x^2 + 4x + 1} + x\right)/x} \qquad \left[\text{divide by } x = \sqrt{x^2} \text{ for } x > 0\right]$$

$$= \lim\limits_{x \to \infty} \dfrac{4 + 1/x}{\sqrt{1 + 4/x + 1/x^2} + 1} = \dfrac{4 + 0}{\sqrt{1 + 0 + 0} + 1} = \dfrac{4}{2} = 2$$

19. From the graph of $y = (\cos^2 x)/x^2$, it appears that $y = 0$ is the horizontal

asymptote and $x = 0$ is the vertical asymptote. Now $0 \le (\cos x)^2 \le 1 \Rightarrow$

$\dfrac{0}{x^2} \le \dfrac{\cos^2 x}{x^2} \le \dfrac{1}{x^2} \Rightarrow 0 \le \dfrac{\cos^2 x}{x^2} \le \dfrac{1}{x^2}$. But $\lim\limits_{x \to \pm\infty} 0 = 0$ and

$\lim\limits_{x \to \pm\infty} \dfrac{1}{x^2} = 0$, so by the Squeeze Theorem, $\lim\limits_{x \to \pm\infty} \dfrac{\cos^2 x}{x^2} = 0$.

Thus, $y = 0$ is the horizontal asymptote. $\lim\limits_{x \to 0} \dfrac{\cos^2 x}{x^2} = \infty$ because $\cos^2 x \to 1$ and $x^2 \to 0$ as $x \to 0$, so $x = 0$ is the

vertical asymptote.

21. Since $2x - 1 \le f(x) \le x^2$ for $0 < x < 3$ and $\lim\limits_{x \to 1}(2x - 1) = 1 = \lim\limits_{x \to 1} x^2$, we have $\lim\limits_{x \to 1} f(x) = 1$ by the Squeeze Theorem.

23. (a) $f(x) = \sqrt{-x}$ if $x < 0$, $f(x) = 3 - x$ if $0 \le x < 3$, $f(x) = (x-3)^2$ if $x > 3$.

(i) $\displaystyle\lim_{x \to 0^+} f(x) = \lim_{x \to 0^+} (3-x) = 3$ 　　　　(ii) $\displaystyle\lim_{x \to 0^-} f(x) = \lim_{x \to 0^-} \sqrt{-x} = 0$

(iii) Because of (i) and (ii), $\displaystyle\lim_{x \to 0} f(x)$ does not exist. 　　(iv) $\displaystyle\lim_{x \to 3^-} f(x) = \lim_{x \to 3^-} (3-x) = 0$

(v) $\displaystyle\lim_{x \to 3^+} f(x) = \lim_{x \to 3^+} (x-3)^2 = 0$ 　　　　(vi) Because of (iv) and (v), $\displaystyle\lim_{x \to 3} f(x) = 0$.

(b) f is discontinuous at 0 since $\displaystyle\lim_{x \to 0} f(x)$ does not exist. 　　(c)

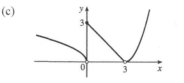

　　f is discontinuous at 3 since $f(3)$ does not exist.

25. $f(x) = 2x^3 + x^2 + 2$ is a polynomial, so it is continuous on $[-2, -1]$ and $f(-2) = -10 < 0 < 1 = f(-1)$. So by the

Intermediate Value Theorem there is a number c in $(-2, -1)$ such that $f(c) = 0$, that is, the equation $2x^3 + x^2 + 2 = 0$ has a

root in $(-2, -1)$.

27. (a) $s = s(t) = 1 + 2t + t^2/4$. The average velocity over the time interval $[1, 1 + h]$ is

$$v_{\text{ave}} = \frac{s(1+h) - s(1)}{(1+h) - 1} = \frac{1 + 2(1+h) + (1+h)^2/4 - 13/4}{h} = \frac{10h + h^2}{4h} = \frac{10 + h}{4}$$

So for the following intervals the average velocities are:

(i) $[1, 3]$: $h = 2$, $v_{\text{ave}} = (10 + 2)/4 = 3$ m/s 　　　　(ii) $[1, 2]$: $h = 1$, $v_{\text{ave}} = (10 + 1)/4 = 2.75$ m/s

(iii) $[1, 1.5]$: $h = 0.5$, $v_{\text{ave}} = (10 + 0.5)/4 = 2.625$ m/s 　　(iv) $[1, 1.1]$: $h = 0.1$, $v_{\text{ave}} = (10 + 0.1)/4 = 2.525$ m/s

(b) When $t = 1$, the instantaneous velocity is $\displaystyle\lim_{h \to 0} \frac{s(1+h) - s(1)}{h} = \lim_{h \to 0} \frac{10 + h}{4} = \frac{10}{4} = 2.5$ m/s.

29. Estimating the slopes of the tangent lines at $x = 2, 3$, and 5, we obtain approximate values 0.4, 2, and 0.1. Since the

graph is concave downward at $x = 5$, $f''(5)$ is negative. Arranging the numbers in increasing order, we have:

$$f''(5) < 0 < f'(5) < f'(2) < 1 < f'(3).$$

31. (a) Estimating $f'(1)$ from the triangle in the graph,

we get $\dfrac{\Delta y}{\Delta x} \approx \dfrac{-0.37}{0.50} = -0.74$.

To estimate $f'(1)$ numerically, we have

$$f'(1) = \lim_{h \to 0} \frac{f(1+h) - f(1)}{h} = \lim_{h \to 0} \frac{e^{-(1+h)^2} - e^{-1}}{h} = y$$

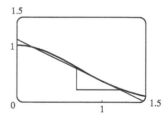

From the table, we have $f'(1) \approx -0.736$.

h	y
0.01	−0.732
0.001	−0.735
0.0001	−0.736
−0.01	−0.739
−0.001	−0.736
−0.0001	−0.736

(b) $y - e^{-1} \approx -0.736(x - 1)$ or $y \approx -0.736x + 1.104$

(c) See the graph in part (a).

33. (a) $f'(r)$ is the rate at which the total cost changes with respect to the interest rate. Its units are dollars/(percent per year).

(b) The total cost of paying off the loan is increasing by $1200/(percent per year) as the interest rate reaches 10%. So if the interest rate goes up from 10% to 11%, the cost goes up approximately $1200.

(c) As r increases, C increases. So $f'(r)$ will always be positive.

35.

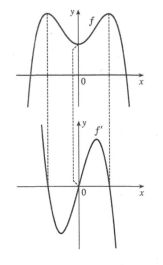

37. (a) $f'(x) = \lim\limits_{h \to 0} \dfrac{f(x+h) - f(x)}{h} = \lim\limits_{h \to 0} \dfrac{\sqrt{3 - 5(x+h)} - \sqrt{3 - 5x}}{h} \cdot \dfrac{\sqrt{3 - 5(x+h)} + \sqrt{3 - 5x}}{\sqrt{3 - 5(x+h)} + \sqrt{3 - 5x}}$

$= \lim\limits_{h \to 0} \dfrac{[3 - 5(x+h)] - (3 - 5x)}{h\left(\sqrt{3 - 5(x+h)} + \sqrt{3 - 5x}\right)} = \lim\limits_{h \to 0} \dfrac{-5}{\sqrt{3 - 5(x+h)} + \sqrt{3 - 5x}} = \dfrac{-5}{2\sqrt{3 - 5x}}$

(b) Domain of f: (the radicand must be nonnegative) $3 - 5x \geq 0 \implies$

$5x \leq 3 \implies x \in \left(-\infty, \frac{3}{5}\right]$

Domain of f': exclude $\frac{3}{5}$ because it makes the denominator zero;

$x \in \left(-\infty, \frac{3}{5}\right)$

(c) Our answer to part (a) is reasonable because $f'(x)$ is always negative and f is always decreasing.

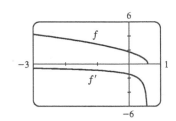

39. f is not differentiable: at $x = -4$ because f is not continuous, at $x = -1$ because f has a corner, at $x = 2$ because f is not continuous, and at $x = 5$ because f has a vertical tangent.

41. $C'(1990)$ is the rate at which the total value of US currency in circulation is changing in billions of dollars per year. To estimate the value of $C'(1990)$, we will average the difference quotients obtained using the times $t = 1985$ and $t = 1995$.

Let $A = \dfrac{C(1985) - C(1990)}{1985 - 1990} = \dfrac{187.3 - 271.9}{-5} = \dfrac{-84.6}{-5} = 16.92$ and

$B = \dfrac{C(1995) - C(1990)}{1995 - 1990} = \dfrac{409.3 - 271.9}{5} = \dfrac{137.4}{5} = 27.48$. Then

$C'(1990) = \lim\limits_{t \to 1990} \dfrac{C(t) - C(1990)}{t - 1990} \approx \dfrac{A + B}{2} = \dfrac{16.92 + 27.48}{2} = \dfrac{44.4}{2} = 22.2$ billion dollars/year.

43. (a) $f'(x) > 0$ on $(-2, 0)$ and $(2, \infty)$ $\Rightarrow$ f is increasing on those intervals. $f'(x) < 0$ on $(-\infty, -2)$ and $(0, 2)$ $\Rightarrow$ f is decreasing on those intervals.

(b) $f'(x) = 0$ at $x = -2$, 0, and 2, so these are where local maxima or minima will occur. At $x = \pm 2$, f' changes from negative to positive, so f has local minima at those values. At $x = 0$, f' changes from positive to negative, so f has a local maximum there.

(c) f' is increasing on $(-\infty, -1)$ and $(1, \infty)$ $\Rightarrow$ (d)

$f'' > 0$ and f is concave upward on those intervals.

f' is decreasing on $(-1, 1)$ $\Rightarrow$ $f'' < 0$ and f is concave downward on this interval.

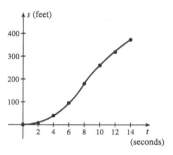

45. $f(0) = 0$, $f'(-2) = f'(1) = f'(9) = 0$, $\lim_{x \to \infty} f(x) = 0$, $\lim_{x \to 6} f(x) = -\infty$,

$f'(x) < 0$ on $(-\infty, -2)$, $(1, 6)$, and $(9, \infty)$, $f'(x) > 0$ on $(-2, 1)$ and $(6, 9)$,

$f''(x) > 0$ on $(-\infty, 0)$ and $(12, \infty)$, $f''(x) < 0$ on $(0, 6)$ and $(6, 12)$

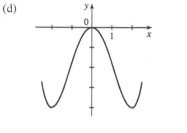

47. (a) Using the data closest to $t = 6$, we have $\dfrac{s(8) - s(6)}{8 - 6} = \dfrac{180 - 95}{2} = 42.5$

and $\dfrac{s(4) - s(6)}{4 - 6} = \dfrac{40 - 95}{-2} = 27.5$. Averaging these two values gives us

$\dfrac{42.5 + 27.5}{2} = 35$ ft/s as an estimate for the speed of the car after

6 seconds.

(b) From the graph, it appears that the inflection point is at $(8, 180)$.

(c) The velocity of the car is at a maximum at the inflection point.

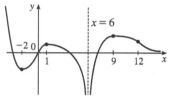

1. Let $t = \sqrt[6]{x}$, so $x = t^6$. Then $t \to 1$ as $x \to 1$, so

$$\lim_{x \to 1} \frac{\sqrt[3]{x} - 1}{\sqrt{x} - 1} = \lim_{t \to 1} \frac{t^2 - 1}{t^3 - 1} = \lim_{t \to 1} \frac{(t-1)(t+1)}{(t-1)(t^2+t+1)} = \lim_{t \to 1} \frac{t+1}{t^2+t+1} = \frac{1+1}{1^2+1+1} = \frac{2}{3}.$$

Another method: Multiply both the numerator and the denominator by $(\sqrt{x} + 1)\left(\sqrt[3]{x^2} + \sqrt[3]{x} + 1\right)$.

3. For $-\frac{1}{2} < x < \frac{1}{2}$, we have $2x - 1 < 0$ and $2x + 1 > 0$, so $|2x - 1| = -(2x - 1)$ and $|2x + 1| = 2x + 1$.

Therefore, $\displaystyle\lim_{x \to 0} \frac{|2x - 1| - |2x + 1|}{x} = \lim_{x \to 0} \frac{-(2x-1) - (2x+1)}{x} = \lim_{x \to 0} \frac{-4x}{x} = \lim_{x \to 0} (-4) = -4.$

5. Since $[\![x]\!] \le x < [\![x]\!] + 1$, we have $\dfrac{[\![x]\!]}{[\![x]\!]} \le \dfrac{x}{[\![x]\!]} < \dfrac{[\![x]\!] + 1}{[\![x]\!]}$ $\Rightarrow$ $1 \le \dfrac{x}{[\![x]\!]} < 1 + \dfrac{1}{[\![x]\!]}$ for $x \ge 1$. As $x \to \infty$, $[\![x]\!] \to \infty$,

so $\dfrac{1}{[\![x]\!]} \to 0$ and $1 + \dfrac{1}{[\![x]\!]} \to 1$. Thus, $\displaystyle\lim_{x \to \infty} \frac{x}{[\![x]\!]} = 1$ by the Squeeze Theorem.

7. f is continuous on $(-\infty, a)$ and (a, ∞). To make f continuous on $\mathbb{R}$, we must have continuity at a. Thus,

$$\lim_{x \to a^+} f(x) = \lim_{x \to a^-} f(x) \quad \Rightarrow \quad \lim_{x \to a^+} x^2 = \lim_{x \to a^-} (x+1) \quad \Rightarrow \quad a^2 = a + 1 \quad \Rightarrow \quad a^2 - a - 1 = 0 \quad \Rightarrow$$

[by the quadratic formula] $a = \left(1 \pm \sqrt{5}\right)/2 \approx 1.618$ or -0.618.

9. (a) Consider $G(x) = T(x + 180°) - T(x)$. Fix any number a. If $G(a) = 0$, we are done: Temperature at a = Temperature

at $a + 180°$. If $G(a) > 0$, then $G(a + 180°) = T(a + 360°) - T(a + 180°) = T(a) - T(a + 180°) = -G(a) < 0$.

Also, G is continuous since temperature varies continuously. So, by the Intermediate Value Theorem, G has a zero on the

interval $[a, a + 180°]$. If $G(a) < 0$, then a similar argument applies.

(b) Yes. The same argument applies.

(c) The same argument applies for quantities that vary continuously, such as barometric pressure. But one could argue that

altitude above sea level is sometimes discontinuous, so the result might not always hold for that quantity.

11. Let a be the x-coordinate of Q. Since the derivative of $y = 1 - x^2$ is $y' = -2x$, the slope at Q is $-2a$. But since the triangle

is equilateral, $\overline{AO}/\overline{OC} = \sqrt{3}/1$, so the slope at Q is $-\sqrt{3}$. Therefore, we must have that $-2a = -\sqrt{3}$ $\Rightarrow$ $a = \frac{\sqrt{3}}{2}$.

Thus, the point Q has coordinates $\left(\frac{\sqrt{3}}{2}, 1 - \left(\frac{\sqrt{3}}{2}\right)^2\right) = \left(\frac{\sqrt{3}}{2}, \frac{1}{4}\right)$ and by symmetry, P has coordinates $\left(-\frac{\sqrt{3}}{2}, \frac{1}{4}\right)$.

13. (a) Put $x = 0$ and $y = 0$ in the equation: $f(0 + 0) = f(0) + f(0) + 0^2 \cdot 0 + 0 \cdot 0^2$ $\Rightarrow$ $f(0) = 2f(0)$.

Subtracting $f(0)$ from each side of this equation gives $f(0) - 0$.

(b) $f'(0) = \lim\limits_{h \to 0} \dfrac{f(0 + h) - f(0)}{h} = \lim\limits_{h \to 0} \dfrac{[f(0) + f(h) + 0^2 h + 0h^2] - f(0)}{h} = \lim\limits_{h \to 0} \dfrac{f(h)}{h} = \lim\limits_{x \to 0} \dfrac{f(x)}{x} = 1$

(c) $f'(x) = \lim\limits_{h \to 0} \dfrac{f(x + h) - f(x)}{h} = \lim\limits_{h \to 0} \dfrac{[f(x) + f(h) + x^2 h + xh^2] - f(x)}{h} = \lim\limits_{h \to 0} \dfrac{f(h) + x^2 h + xh^2}{h}$

$\qquad = \lim\limits_{h \to 0} \left[\dfrac{f(h)}{h} + x^2 + xh \right] = 1 + x^2$

15. $\lim\limits_{x \to a} f(x) = \lim\limits_{x \to a} \left(\frac{1}{2} [f(x) + g(x)] + \frac{1}{2} [f(x) - g(x)] \right) = \frac{1}{2} \lim\limits_{x \to a} [f(x) + g(x)] + \frac{1}{2} \lim\limits_{x \to a} [f(x) - g(x)]$

$\qquad = \frac{1}{2} \cdot 2 + \frac{1}{2} \cdot 1 = \frac{3}{2}$,

and $\lim\limits_{x \to a} g(x) = \lim\limits_{x \to a} \left([f(x) + g(x)] - f(x) \right) = \lim\limits_{x \to a} [f(x) + g(x)] - \lim\limits_{x \to a} f(x) = 2 - \frac{3}{2} = \frac{1}{2}$.

So $\lim\limits_{x \to a} [f(x) g(x)] = \left[\lim\limits_{x \to a} f(x) \right] \left[\lim\limits_{x \to a} g(x) \right] = \frac{3}{2} \cdot \frac{1}{2} = \frac{3}{4}$.

Another solution: Since $\lim\limits_{x \to a} [f(x) + g(x)]$ and $\lim\limits_{x \to a} [f(x) - g(x)]$ exist, we must have

$\lim\limits_{x \to a} [f(x) + g(x)]^2 = \left(\lim\limits_{x \to a} [f(x) + g(x)] \right)^2$ and $\lim\limits_{x \to a} [f(x) - g(x)]^2 = \left(\lim\limits_{x \to a} [f(x) - g(x)] \right)^2$, so

$\lim\limits_{x \to a} [f(x) g(x)] = \lim\limits_{x \to a} \frac{1}{4} \left([f(x) + g(x)]^2 - [f(x) - g(x)]^2 \right)$ [because all of the f^2 and g^2 cancel]

$\qquad = \frac{1}{4} \left(\lim\limits_{x \to a} [f(x) + g(x)]^2 - \lim\limits_{x \to a} [f(x) - g(x)]^2 \right) = \frac{1}{4} \left(2^2 - 1^2 \right) = \frac{3}{4}$.

17. We are given that $|f(x)| \le x^2$ for all x. In particular, $|f(0)| \le 0$, but $|a| \ge 0$ for all a. The only conclusion is

that $f(0) = 0$. Now $\left| \dfrac{f(x) - f(0)}{x - 0} \right| = \left| \dfrac{f(x)}{x} \right| = \dfrac{|f(x)|}{|x|} \le \dfrac{x^2}{|x|} = \dfrac{|x^2|}{|x|} = |x| \quad \Rightarrow \quad -|x| \le \dfrac{f(x) - f(0)}{x - 0} \le |x|$.

But $\lim\limits_{x \to 0} (-|x|) = 0 = \lim\limits_{x \to 0} |x|$, so by the Squeeze Theorem, $\lim\limits_{x \to 0} \dfrac{f(x) - f(0)}{x - 0} = 0$. So by the definition of a derivative,

f is differentiable at 0 and, furthermore, $f'(0) = 0$.

3 ☐ DIFFERENTIATION RULES

3.1 Derivatives of Polynomials and Exponential Functions

1. (a) e is the number such that $\lim\limits_{h \to 0} \dfrac{e^h - 1}{h} = 1$.

(b)

x	$\dfrac{2.7^x - 1}{x}$
-0.001	0.9928
-0.0001	0.9932
0.001	0.9937
0.0001	0.9933

x	$\dfrac{2.8^x - 1}{x}$
-0.001	1.0291
-0.0001	1.0296
0.001	1.0301
0.0001	1.0297

From the tables (to two decimal places),

$\lim\limits_{h \to 0} \dfrac{2.7^h - 1}{h} = 0.99$ and $\lim\limits_{h \to 0} \dfrac{2.8^h - 1}{h} = 1.03$.

Since $0.99 < 1 < 1.03$, $2.7 < e < 2.8$.

3. $f(x) = 186.5$ is a constant function, so its derivative is 0, that is, $f'(x) = 0$.

5. $f(t) = 2 - \frac{2}{3}t \quad \Rightarrow \quad f'(t) = 0 - \frac{2}{3} = -\frac{2}{3}$

7. $f(x) = x^3 - 4x + 6 \quad \Rightarrow \quad f'(x) = 3x^2 - 4(1) + 0 = 3x^2 - 4$

9. $f(t) = \frac{1}{4}(t^4 + 8) \quad \Rightarrow \quad f'(t) = \frac{1}{4}(t^4 + 8)' = \frac{1}{4}(4t^{4-1} + 0) = t^3$

11. $A(s) = -\dfrac{12}{s^5} = -12s^{-5} \quad \Rightarrow \quad A'(s) = -12(-5s^{-6}) = 60s^{-6} \quad$ or $\quad 60/s^6$

13. $g(t) = 2t^{-3/4} \quad \Rightarrow \quad g'(t) = 2(-\frac{3}{4}t^{-7/4}) = -\frac{3}{2}t^{-7/4}$

15. $y = 3e^x + \dfrac{4}{\sqrt[3]{x}} = 3e^x + 4x^{-1/3} \quad \Rightarrow \quad y' = 3(e^x) + 4(-\frac{1}{3})x^{-4/3} = 3e^x - \frac{4}{3}x^{-4/3}$

17. $F(x) = \left(\frac{1}{2}x\right)^5 = \left(\frac{1}{2}\right)^5 x^5 = \frac{1}{32}x^5 \quad \Rightarrow \quad F'(x) = \frac{1}{32}(5x^4) = \frac{5}{32}x^4$

19. $y = \dfrac{x^2 + 4x + 3}{\sqrt{x}} = x^{3/2} + 4x^{1/2} + 3x^{-1/2} \quad \Rightarrow$

$y' = \frac{3}{2}x^{1/2} + 4\left(\frac{1}{2}\right)x^{-1/2} + 3\left(-\frac{1}{2}\right)x^{-3/2} = \frac{3}{2}\sqrt{x} + \dfrac{2}{\sqrt{x}} - \dfrac{3}{2x\sqrt{x}} \quad \left[\text{note that } x^{3/2} = x^{2/2} \cdot x^{1/2} = x\sqrt{x}\right]$

The last expression can be written as $\dfrac{3x^2}{2x\sqrt{x}} + \dfrac{4x}{2x\sqrt{x}} - \dfrac{3}{2x\sqrt{x}} = \dfrac{3x^2 + 4x - 3}{2x\sqrt{x}}$.

21. $y = 4\pi^2 \quad \Rightarrow \quad y' = 0$ since $4\pi^2$ is a constant.

23. $u = \sqrt[5]{t} + 4\sqrt{t^5} = t^{1/5} + 4t^{5/2} \quad \Rightarrow \quad u' = \frac{1}{5}t^{-4/5} + 4\left(\frac{5}{2}t^{3/2}\right) = \frac{1}{5}t^{-4/5} + 10t^{3/2} \quad$ or $\quad 1/\left(5\sqrt[5]{t^4}\right) + 10\sqrt{t^3}$

25. $z = \dfrac{A}{y^{10}} + Be^y = Ay^{-10} + Be^y \quad \Rightarrow \quad z' = -10Ay^{-11} + Be^y = -\dfrac{10A}{y^{11}} + Be^y$

27. $y = \sqrt[4]{x} = x^{1/4}$ $\Rightarrow$ $y' = \frac{1}{4}x^{-3/4} = \dfrac{1}{4\sqrt[4]{x^3}}$. At $(1, 1)$, $y' = \frac{1}{4}$ and an equation of the tangent line is

$y - 1 = \frac{1}{4}(x - 1)$ or $y = \frac{1}{4}x + \frac{3}{4}$.

29. $y = x^4 + 2e^x$ $\Rightarrow$ $y' = 4x^3 + 2e^x$. At $(0, 2)$, $y' = 2$ and an equation of the tangent line is $y - 2 = 2(x - 0)$

or $y = 2x + 2$. The slope of the normal line is $-\frac{1}{2}$ (the negative reciprocal of 2) and an equation of the normal line is

$y - 2 = -\frac{1}{2}(x - 0)$ or $y = -\frac{1}{2}x + 2$.

31. $y = 3x^2 - x^3$ $\Rightarrow$ $y' = 6x - 3x^2$.

At $(1, 2)$, $y' = 6 - 3 = 3$, so an equation of the tangent line is

$y - 2 = 3(x - 1)$ or $y = 3x - 1$.

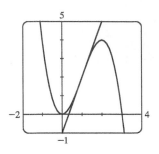

33. $f(x) = e^x - 5x$ $\Rightarrow$ $f'(x) = e^x - 5$.

Notice that $f'(x) = 0$ when f has a horizontal tangent, f' is positive

when f is increasing, and f' is negative when f is decreasing.

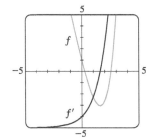

35. $f(x) = 3x^{15} - 5x^3 + 3$ $\Rightarrow$ $f'(x) = 45x^{14} - 15x^2$.

Notice that $f'(x) = 0$ when f has a horizontal tangent, f' is positive

when f is increasing, and f' is negative when f is decreasing.

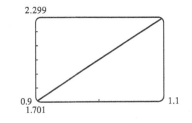

37. To graphically estimate the value of $f'(1)$ for $f(x) = 3x^2 - x^3$, we'll graph f in the viewing rectangle $[1 - 0.1, 1 + 0.1]$ by

$[f(0.9), f(1.1)]$, as shown in the figure. [When assigning values to the window variables, it is convenient to use $Y_1(0.9)$ for

$Y_{\min}$ and $Y_1(1.1)$ for $Y_{\max}$.] If we have sufficiently zoomed in on the graph of f, we should obtain a graph that looks like a

diagonal line; if not, graph again with $1 - 0.01$ and $1 + 0.01$, etc.

Estimated value:

$f'(1) \approx \dfrac{2.299 - 1.701}{1.1 - 0.9} = \dfrac{0.589}{0.2} = 2.99$.

Exact value: $f(x) = 3x^2 - x^3$ $\Rightarrow$ $f'(x) = 6x - 3x^2$,

so $f'(1) = 6 - 3 = 3$.

39. (a)

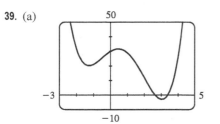

(b) From the graph in part (a), it appears that f' is zero at $x_1 \approx -1.25$, $x_2 \approx 0.5$, and $x_3 \approx 3$. The slopes are negative (so f' is negative) on $(-\infty, x_1)$ and (x_2, x_3). The slopes are positive (so f' is positive) on (x_1, x_2) and (x_3, ∞).

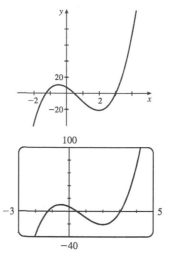

(c) $f(x) = x^4 - 3x^3 - 6x^2 + 7x + 30 \Rightarrow$

$f'(x) = 4x^3 - 9x^2 - 12x + 7$

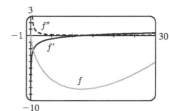

41. $f(x) = 10x^{10} + 5x^5 - x \Rightarrow f'(x) = 100x^9 + 25x^4 - 1 \Rightarrow f''(x) = 900x^8 + 100x^3$

43. $f(x) = 2x - 5x^{3/4} \Rightarrow f'(x) = 2 - \frac{15}{4}x^{-1/4} \Rightarrow f''(x) = \frac{15}{16}x^{-5/4}$

Note that f' is negative when f is decreasing and positive when f is increasing. f'' is always positive since f' is always increasing.

45. (a) $s = t^3 - 3t \Rightarrow v(t) = s'(t) = 3t^2 - 3 \Rightarrow a(t) = v'(t) = 6t$

(b) $a(2) = 6(2) = 12 \text{ m/s}^2$

(c) $v(t) = 3t^2 - 3 = 0$ when $t^2 = 1$, that is, $t = 1$ and $a(1) = 6 \text{ m/s}^2$.

47. $f(x) = 5x - e^x \Rightarrow f'(x) = 5 - e^x$. $f'(x) > 0 \Rightarrow 5 - e^x > 0 \Rightarrow e^x < 5 \Rightarrow x < \ln 5 \approx 1.61$.

f is increasing when f' is positive; that is, on $(-\infty, \ln 5)$.

49. The curve $y = 2x^3 + 3x^2 - 12x + 1$ has a horizontal tangent when $y' = 6x^2 + 6x - 12 = 0 \Leftrightarrow 6(x^2 + x - 2) = 0 \Leftrightarrow 6(x+2)(x-1) = 0 \Leftrightarrow x = -2$ or $x = 1$. The points on the curve are $(-2, 21)$ and $(1, -6)$.

51. $y = 6x^3 + 5x - 3 \Rightarrow m = y' = 18x^2 + 5$, but $x^2 \geq 0$ for all x, so $m \geq 5$ for all x.

53. The slope of the line $12x - y = 1$ (or $y = 12x - 1$) is 12, so the slope of both lines tangent to the curve is 12.

$y = 1 + x^3 \Rightarrow y' = 3x^2$. Thus, $3x^2 = 12 \Rightarrow x^2 = 4 \Rightarrow x = \pm 2$, which are the x-coordinates at which the tangent lines have slope 12. The points on the curve are $(2, 9)$ and $(-2, -7)$, so the tangent line equations are $y - 9 = 12(x - 2)$ or $y = 12x - 15$ and $y + 7 = 12(x + 2)$ or $y = 12x + 17$.

55. The slope of $y = x^2 - 5x + 4$ is given by $m = y' = 2x - 5$. The slope of $x - 3y = 5$ $\Leftrightarrow$ $y = \frac{1}{3}x - \frac{5}{3}$ is $\frac{1}{3}$,

so the desired normal line must have slope $\frac{1}{3}$, and hence, the tangent line to the parabola must have slope -3. This occurs if

$2x - 5 = -3$ $\Rightarrow$ $2x = 2$ $\Rightarrow$ $x = 1$. When $x = 1$, $y = 1^2 - 5(1) + 4 = 0$, and an equation of the normal line is

$y - 0 = \frac{1}{3}(x - 1)$ or $y = \frac{1}{3}x - \frac{1}{3}$.

57.

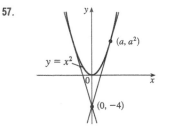

Let (a, a^2) be a point on the parabola at which the tangent line passes

through the point $(0, -4)$. The tangent line has slope $2a$ and equation

$y - (-4) = 2a(x - 0)$ $\Leftrightarrow$ $y = 2ax - 4$. Since (a, a^2) also lies on the

line, $a^2 = 2a(a) - 4$, or $a^2 = 4$. So $a = \pm 2$ and the points are $(2, 4)$

and $(-2, 4)$.

59. $f'(x) = \lim\limits_{h \to 0} \dfrac{f(x + h) - f(x)}{h} = \lim\limits_{h \to 0} \dfrac{\frac{1}{x + h} - \frac{1}{x}}{h} = \lim\limits_{h \to 0} \dfrac{x - (x + h)}{hx(x + h)} = \lim\limits_{h \to 0} \dfrac{-h}{hx(x + h)} = \lim\limits_{h \to 0} \dfrac{-1}{x(x + h)} = -\dfrac{1}{x^2}$

61. Let $P(x) = ax^2 + bx + c$. Then $P'(x) = 2ax + b$ and $P''(x) = 2a$. $P''(2) = 2$ $\Rightarrow$ $2a = 2$ $\Rightarrow$ $a = 1$.

$P'(2) = 3$ $\Rightarrow$ $2(1)(2) + b = 3$ $\Rightarrow$ $4 + b = 3$ $\Rightarrow$ $b = -1$.

$P(2) = 5$ $\Rightarrow$ $1(2)^2 + (-1)(2) + c = 5$ $\Rightarrow$ $2 + c = 5$ $\Rightarrow$ $c = 3$. So $P(x) = x^2 - x + 3$.

63. (a) At this stage, we would guess that an antiderivative of x^2 must have x^3 in it. Differentiating x^3 gives us $3x^2$, so we know

that we must divide x^3 by 3. That gives us $F(x) = \frac{1}{3}x^3$. Checking, we have $F'(x) = \frac{1}{3}(3x^2) = x^2 = f(x)$. Because we

can add an arbitrary constant C to F without changing its derivative, we have an infinite number of antiderivatives of the

form $F(x) = \frac{1}{3}x^3 + C$.

(b) As in part (a), antiderivatives of $f(x) = x^3$ and $f(x) = x^4$ are $F(x) = \frac{1}{4}x^4 + C$ and $F(x) = \frac{1}{5}x^5 + C$.

(c) Similarly, an antiderivative for $f(x) = x^n$ is $F(x) = \dfrac{1}{n + 1}x^{n+1} + C$, since then

$F'(x) = \dfrac{1}{n + 1}[(n + 1)x^n] = x^n = f(x)$ for $n \neq -1$.

65. Substituting $x = 1$ and $y = 1$ into $y = ax^2 + bx$ gives us $a + b = 1$ **(1)**. The slope of the tangent line $y = 3x - 2$ is 3 and the

slope of the tangent to the parabola at (x, y) is $y' = 2ax + b$. At $x = 1$, $y' = 3$ $\Rightarrow$ $3 = 2a + b$ **(2)**. Subtracting **(1)** from

(2) gives us $2 = a$ and it follows that $b = -1$. The parabola has equation $y = 2x^2 - x$.

67. $y = f(x) = ax^3 + bx^2 + cx + d$ $\Rightarrow$ $f'(x) = 3ax^2 + 2bx + c$. The point $(-2, 6)$ is on f, so $f(-2) = 6$ $\Rightarrow$

$-8a + 4b - 2c + d = 6$ **(1)**. The point $(2, 0)$ is on f, so $f(2) = 0$ $\Rightarrow$ $8a + 4b + 2c + d = 0$ **(2)**. Since there are

horizontal tangents at $(-2, 6)$ and $(2, 0)$, $f'(\pm 2) = 0$. $f'(-2) = 0$ $\Rightarrow$ $12a - 4b + c = 0$ **(3)** and $f'(2) = 0$ $\Rightarrow$

$12a + 4b + c = 0$ **(4)**. Subtracting equation **(3)** from **(4)** gives $8b = 0$ $\Rightarrow$ $b = 0$. Adding **(1)** and **(2)** gives $8b + 2d = 6$, so $d = 3$ since $b = 0$. From **(3)** we have $c = -12a$, so **(2)** becomes $8a + 4(0) + 2(-12a) + 3 = 0 \Rightarrow 3 = 16a \Rightarrow$

$a = \frac{3}{16}$. Now $c = -12a = -12\left(\frac{3}{16}\right) = -\frac{9}{4}$ and the desired cubic function is $y = \frac{3}{16}x^3 - \frac{9}{4}x + 3$.

69. $y = f(x) = ax^2 \Rightarrow f'(x) = 2ax$. So the slope of the tangent to the parabola at $x = 2$ is $m = 2a(2) = 4a$. The slope

of the given line, $2x + y = b \Leftrightarrow y = -2x + b$, is seen to be -2, so we must have $4a = -2 \Leftrightarrow a = -\frac{1}{2}$. So when

$x = 2$, the point in question has y-coordinate $-\frac{1}{2} \cdot 2^2 = -2$. Now we simply require that the given line, whose equation is

$2x + y = b$, pass through the point $(2, -2)$: $2(2) + (-2) = b \Leftrightarrow b = 2$. So we must have $a = -\frac{1}{2}$ and $b = 2$.

71. *Solution 1:* Let $f(x) = x^{1000}$. Then, by the definition of a derivative, $f'(1) = \lim\limits_{x \to 1} \dfrac{f(x) - f(1)}{x - 1} = \lim\limits_{x \to 1} \dfrac{x^{1000} - 1}{x - 1}$.

But this is just the limit we want to find, and we know (from the Power Rule) that $f'(x) = 1000x^{999}$, so

$f'(1) = 1000(1)^{999} = 1000$. So $\lim\limits_{x \to 1} \dfrac{x^{1000} - 1}{x - 1} = 1000$.

Solution 2: Note that $(x^{1000} - 1) = (x - 1)(x^{999} + x^{998} + x^{997} + \cdots + x^2 + x + 1)$. So

$$\lim_{x \to 1} \frac{x^{1000} - 1}{x - 1} = \lim_{x \to 1} \frac{(x - 1)(x^{999} + x^{998} + x^{997} + \cdots + x^2 + x + 1)}{x - 1} = \lim_{x \to 1} (x^{999} + x^{998} + x^{997} + \cdots + x^2 + x + 1)$$

$$= \underbrace{1 + 1 + 1 + \cdots + 1 + 1 + 1}_{1000 \text{ ones}} = 1000, \text{ as above.}$$

73. $y = x^2 \Rightarrow y' = 2x$, so the slope of a tangent line at the point (a, a^2) is $y' = 2a$ and the slope of a normal line is $-1/(2a)$,

for $a \neq 0$. The slope of the normal line through the points (a, a^2) and $(0, c)$ is $\dfrac{a^2 - c}{a - 0}$, so $\dfrac{a^2 - c}{a} = -\dfrac{1}{2a} \Rightarrow$

$a^2 - c = -\frac{1}{2} \Rightarrow a^2 = c - \frac{1}{2}$. The last equation has two solutions if $c > \frac{1}{2}$, one solution if $c = \frac{1}{2}$, and no solution if

$c < \frac{1}{2}$. Since the y-axis is normal to $y = x^2$ regardless of the value of c (this is the case for $a = 0$), we have three normal lines

if $c > \frac{1}{2}$ and one normal line if $c \leq \frac{1}{2}$.

3.2 The Product and Quotient Rules

1. Product Rule: $f(x) = (1 + 2x^2)(x - x^2) \Rightarrow$

$$f'(x) = (1 + 2x^2)(1 - 2x) + (x - x^2)(4x) = 1 - 2x + 2x^2 - 4x^3 + 4x^2 - 4x^3 = 1 - 2x + 6x^2 - 8x^3.$$

Multiplying first: $f(x) = (1 + 2x^2)(x - x^2) = x - x^2 + 2x^3 - 2x^4 \Rightarrow f'(x) = 1 - 2x + 6x^2 - 8x^3$ (equivalent).

3. By the Product Rule, $f(x) = (x^3 + 2x)e^x \Rightarrow$

$$f'(x) = (x^3 + 2x)(e^x)' + e^x(x^3 + 2x)' = (x^3 + 2x)e^x + e^x(3x^2 + 2)$$

$$= e^x[(x^3 + 2x) + (3x^2 + 2)] = e^x(x^3 + 3x^2 + 2x + 2)$$

5. By the Quotient Rule, $y = \dfrac{e^x}{x^2} \Rightarrow y' = \dfrac{x^2 \dfrac{d}{dx}(e^x) - e^x \dfrac{d}{dx}(x^2)}{(x^2)^2} = \dfrac{x^2(e^x) - e^x(2x)}{x^4} = \dfrac{xe^x(x - 2)}{x^4} = \dfrac{e^x(x - 2)}{x^3}$.

The notations $\overset{PR}{\Rightarrow}$ and $\overset{QR}{\Rightarrow}$ indicate the use of the Product and Quotient Rules, respectively.

7. $g(x) = \dfrac{3x-1}{2x+1}$ $\overset{QR}{\Rightarrow}$ $g'(x) = \dfrac{(2x+1)(3) - (3x-1)(2)}{(2x+1)^2} = \dfrac{6x+3-6x+2}{(2x+1)^2} = \dfrac{5}{(2x+1)^2}$

9. $F(y) = \left(\dfrac{1}{y^2} - \dfrac{3}{y^4}\right)(y+5y^3) = (y^{-2} - 3y^{-4})(y+5y^3)$ $\overset{PR}{\Rightarrow}$

$F'(y) = (y^{-2} - 3y^{-4})(1+15y^2) + (y+5y^3)(-2y^{-3} + 12y^{-5})$

$\qquad = (y^{-2} + 15 - 3y^{-4} - 45y^{-2}) + (-2y^{-2} + 12y^{-4} - 10 + 60y^{-2})$

$\qquad = 5 + 14y^{-2} + 9y^{-4}$ or $5 + 14/y^2 + 9/y^4$

11. $y = \dfrac{x^3}{1-x^2}$ $\overset{QR}{\Rightarrow}$ $y' = \dfrac{(1-x^2)(3x^2) - x^3(-2x)}{(1-x^2)^2} = \dfrac{x^2(3 - 3x^2 + 2x^2)}{(1-x^2)^2} = \dfrac{x^2(3-x^2)}{(1-x^2)^2}$

13. $y = \dfrac{t^2+2}{t^4 - 3t^2 + 1}$ $\overset{QR}{\Rightarrow}$

$y' = \dfrac{(t^4 - 3t^2 + 1)(2t) - (t^2+2)(4t^3 - 6t)}{(t^4 - 3t^2 + 1)^2} = \dfrac{2t[(t^4 - 3t^2 + 1) - (t^2 + 2)(2t^2 - 3)]}{(t^4 - 3t^2 + 1)^2}$

$\quad = \dfrac{2t(t^4 - 3t^2 + 1 - 2t^4 - 4t^2 + 3t^2 + 6)}{(t^4 - 3t^2 + 1)^2} = \dfrac{2t(-t^4 - 4t^2 + 7)}{(t^4 - 3t^2 + 1)^2}$

15. $y = (r^2 - 2r)e^r$ $\overset{PR}{\Rightarrow}$ $y' = (r^2 - 2r)(e^r) + e^r(2r - 2) = e^r(r^2 - 2r + 2r - 2) = e^r(r^2 - 2)$

17. $y = \dfrac{v^3 - 2v\sqrt{v}}{v} = v^2 - 2\sqrt{v} = v^2 - 2v^{1/2}$ $\Rightarrow$ $y' = 2v - 2(\tfrac{1}{2})v^{-1/2} = 2v - v^{-1/2}$.

We can change the form of the answer as follows: $2v - v^{-1/2} = 2v - \dfrac{1}{\sqrt{v}} = \dfrac{2v\sqrt{v} - 1}{\sqrt{v}} = \dfrac{2v^{3/2} - 1}{\sqrt{v}}$

19. $f(t) = \dfrac{2t}{2 + \sqrt{t}}$ $\overset{QR}{\Rightarrow}$ $f'(t) = \dfrac{(2 + t^{1/2})(2) - 2t\left(\frac{1}{2}t^{-1/2}\right)}{(2 + \sqrt{t})^2} = \dfrac{4 + 2t^{1/2} - t^{1/2}}{(2 + \sqrt{t})^2} = \dfrac{4 + t^{1/2}}{(2 + \sqrt{t})^2}$ or $\dfrac{4 + \sqrt{t}}{(2 + \sqrt{t})^2}$

21. $f(x) = \dfrac{A}{B + Ce^x}$ $\overset{QR}{\Rightarrow}$ $f'(x) = \dfrac{(B + Ce^x) \cdot 0 - A(Ce^x)}{(B + Ce^x)^2} = -\dfrac{ACe^x}{(B + Ce^x)^2}$

23. $f(x) = \dfrac{x}{x + c/x}$ $\Rightarrow$ $f'(x) = \dfrac{(x + c/x)(1) - x(1 - c/x^2)}{\left(x + \dfrac{c}{x}\right)^2} = \dfrac{x + c/x - x + c/x}{\left(\dfrac{x^2+c}{x}\right)^2} = \dfrac{2c/x}{\dfrac{(x^2+c)^2}{x^2}} \cdot \dfrac{x^2}{x^2} = \dfrac{2cx}{(x^2+c)^2}$

25. $f(x) = x^4 e^x$ $\Rightarrow$ $f'(x) = x^4 e^x + e^x \cdot 4x^3 = (x^4 + 4x^3)e^x$ $\left[\text{or } x^3 e^x(x+4)\right]$ $\Rightarrow$

$f''(x) = (x^4 + 4x^3)e^x + e^x(4x^3 + 12x^2) = (x^4 + 4x^3 + 4x^3 + 12x^2)e^x$

$\qquad = (x^4 + 8x^3 + 12x^2)e^x$ $\left[\text{or } x^2 e^x(x+2)(x+6)\right]$

27. $f(x) = \dfrac{x^2}{1+2x} \;\Rightarrow\; f'(x) = \dfrac{(1+2x)(2x) - x^2(2)}{(1+2x)^2} = \dfrac{2x + 4x^2 - 2x^2}{(1+2x)^2} = \dfrac{2x^2 + 2x}{(1+2x)^2} \;\Rightarrow\;$

$f''(x) = \dfrac{(1+2x)^2(4x+2) - (2x^2 + 2x)(1 + 4x + 4x^2)'}{[(1+2x)^2]^2} = \dfrac{2(1+2x)^2(2x+1) - 2x(x+1)(4+8x)}{(1+2x)^4}$

$= \dfrac{2(1+2x)[(1+2x)^2 - 4x(x+1)]}{(1+2x)^4} = \dfrac{2(1 + 4x + 4x^2 - 4x^2 - 4x)}{(1+2x)^3} = \dfrac{2}{(1+2x)^3}$

29. $y = \dfrac{2x}{x+1} \;\Rightarrow\; y' = \dfrac{(x+1)(2) - (2x)(1)}{(x+1)^2} = \dfrac{2}{(x+1)^2}.$

At $(1,1)$, $y' = \frac{1}{2}$, and an equation of the tangent line is $y - 1 = \frac{1}{2}(x-1)$, or $y = \frac{1}{2}x + \frac{1}{2}$.

31. $y = 2xe^x \;\Rightarrow\; y' = 2(x \cdot e^x + e^x \cdot 1) = 2e^x(x+1).$

At $(0,0)$, $y' = 2e^0(0+1) = 2 \cdot 1 \cdot 1 = 2$, and an equation of the tangent line is $y - 0 = 2(x-0)$, or $y = 2x$. The slope of

the normal line is $-\frac{1}{2}$, so an equation of the normal line is $y - 0 = -\frac{1}{2}(x-0)$, or $y = -\frac{1}{2}x$.

33. (a) $y = f(x) = \dfrac{1}{1+x^2} \;\Rightarrow\;$

(b)

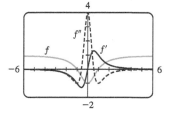

$f'(x) = \dfrac{(1+x^2)(0) - 1(2x)}{(1+x^2)^2} = \dfrac{-2x}{(1+x^2)^2}$. So the slope of the

tangent line at the point $\left(-1, \frac{1}{2}\right)$ is $f'(-1) = \dfrac{2}{2^2} = \frac{1}{2}$ and its

equation is $y - \frac{1}{2} = \frac{1}{2}(x+1)$ or $y = \frac{1}{2}x + 1$.

35. (a) $f(x) = (x^3 - x)e^x \;\Rightarrow\; f'(x) = (x^3 - x)e^x + e^x(3x^2 - 1) = e^x(x^3 + 3x^2 - x - 1)$

(b)

$f' = 0$ when f has a horizontal tangent line, f' is negative when f is

decreasing, and f' is positive when f is increasing.

37. (a) $f(x) = \dfrac{x^2 - 1}{x^2 + 1} \;\Rightarrow\;$

$f'(x) = \dfrac{(x^2+1)(2x) - (x^2-1)(2x)}{(x^2+1)^2} = \dfrac{(2x)[(x^2+1) - (x^2-1)]}{(x^2+1)^2} = \dfrac{(2x)(2)}{(x^2+1)^2} = \dfrac{4x}{(x^2+1)^2} \;\Rightarrow\;$

$f''(x) = \dfrac{(x^2+1)^2(4) - 4x(x^4 + 2x^2 + 1)'}{[(x^2+1)^2]^2} = \dfrac{4(x^2+1)^2 - 4x(4x^3 + 4x)}{(x^2+1)^4}$

$= \dfrac{4(x^2+1)^2 - 16x^2(x^2+1)}{(x^2+1)^4} = \dfrac{4(x^2+1)[(x^2+1) - 4x^2]}{(x^2+1)^4} = \dfrac{4(1 - 3x^2)}{(x^2+1)^3}$

(b)

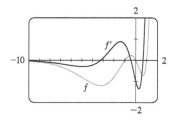

$f' = 0$ when f has a horizontal tangent and $f'' = 0$ when f' has a

horizontal tangent. f' is negative when f is decreasing and positive when f

is increasing. f'' is negative when f' is decreasing and positive when f' is

increasing. f'' is negative when f is concave down and positive when f is

concave up.

39. $f(x) = \dfrac{x^2}{1+x}$ $\Rightarrow$ $f'(x) = \dfrac{(1+x)(2x) - x^2(1)}{(1+x)^2} = \dfrac{2x + 2x^2 - x^2}{(1+x)^2} = \dfrac{x^2 + 2x}{x^2 + 2x + 1}$ $\Rightarrow$

$$f''(x) = \frac{(x^2 + 2x + 1)(2x+2) - (x^2+2x)(2x+2)}{(x^2+2x+1)^2} = \frac{(2x+2)(x^2+2x+1-x^2-2x)}{[(x+1)^2]^2}$$

$$= \frac{2(x+1)(1)}{(x+1)^4} = \frac{2}{(x+1)^3},$$

so $f''(1) = \dfrac{2}{(1+1)^3} = \dfrac{2}{8} = \dfrac{1}{4}$.

41. We are given that $f(5) = 1$, $f'(5) = 6$, $g(5) = -3$, and $g'(5) = 2$.

(a) $(fg)'(5) = f(5)g'(5) + g(5)f'(5) = (1)(2) + (-3)(6) = 2 - 18 = -16$

(b) $\left(\dfrac{f}{g}\right)'(5) = \dfrac{g(5)f'(5) - f(5)g'(5)}{[g(5)]^2} = \dfrac{(-3)(6) - (1)(2)}{(-3)^2} = -\dfrac{20}{9}$

(c) $\left(\dfrac{g}{f}\right)'(5) = \dfrac{f(5)g'(5) - g(5)f'(5)}{[f(5)]^2} = \dfrac{(1)(2) - (-3)(6)}{(1)^2} = 20$

43. $f(x) = e^x g(x)$ $\Rightarrow$ $f'(x) = e^x g'(x) + g(x)e^x = e^x[g'(x) + g(x)]$. $f'(0) = e^0[g'(0) + g(0)] = 1(5 + 2) = 7$

45. (a) From the graphs of f and g, we obtain the following values: $f(1) = 2$ since the point $(1, 2)$ is on the graph of f;

$g(1) = 1$ since the point $(1, 1)$ is on the graph of g; $f'(1) = 2$ since the slope of the line segment between $(0, 0)$ and

$(2, 4)$ is $\dfrac{4 - 0}{2 - 0} = 2$; $g'(1) = -1$ since the slope of the line segment between $(-2, 4)$ and $(2, 0)$ is $\dfrac{0 - 4}{2 - (-2)} = -1$.

Now $u(x) = f(x)g(x)$, so $u'(1) = f(1)g'(1) + g(1)f'(1) = 2 \cdot (-1) + 1 \cdot 2 = 0$.

(b) $v(x) = f(x)/g(x)$, so $v'(5) = \dfrac{g(5)f'(5) - f(5)g'(5)}{[g(5)]^2} = \dfrac{2\left(-\frac{1}{3}\right) - 3 \cdot \frac{2}{3}}{2^2} = \dfrac{-\frac{8}{3}}{4} = -\dfrac{2}{3}$

47. (a) $y = xg(x)$ $\Rightarrow$ $y' = xg'(x) + g(x) \cdot 1 = xg'(x) + g(x)$

(b) $y = \dfrac{x}{g(x)}$ $\Rightarrow$ $y' = \dfrac{g(x) \cdot 1 - xg'(x)}{[g(x)]^2} = \dfrac{g(x) - xg'(x)}{[g(x)]^2}$

(c) $y = \dfrac{g(x)}{x}$ $\Rightarrow$ $y' = \dfrac{xg'(x) - g(x) \cdot 1}{(x)^2} = \dfrac{xg'(x) - g(x)}{x^2}$

49. If $P(t)$ denotes the population at time t and $A(t)$ the average annual income, then $T(t) = P(t)A(t)$ is the total personal

income. The rate at which $T(t)$ is rising is given by $T'(t) = P(t)A'(t) + A(t)P'(t)$ $\Rightarrow$

$$T'(1999) = P(1999)A'(1999) + A(1999)P'(1999) = (961{,}400)(\$1400/\text{yr}) + (\$30{,}593)(9200/\text{yr})$$

$$= \$1{,}345{,}960{,}000/\text{yr} + \$281{,}455{,}600/\text{yr} = \$1{,}627{,}415{,}600/\text{yr}$$

So the total personal income was rising by about $1.627 billion per year in 1999.

The term $P(t)A'(t) \approx \$1.346$ billion represents the portion of the rate of change of total income due to the existing

population's increasing income. The term $A(t)P'(t) \approx \$281$ million represents the portion of the rate of change of total

income due to increasing population.

51. f is increasing when f' is positive. $f(x) = x^3 e^x \Rightarrow f'(x) = x^3 e^x + e^x(3x^2) = x^2 e^x(x+3)$. Now $x^2 \geq 0$ and $e^x > 0$

for all x, so $f'(x) > 0$ when $x + 3 > 0$ and $x \neq 0$; that is, when $x \in (-3, 0) \cup (0, \infty)$. So f is increasing on $(-3, \infty)$.

53. If $y = f(x) = \dfrac{x}{x+1}$, then $f'(x) = \dfrac{(x+1)(1) - x(1)}{(x+1)^2} = \dfrac{1}{(x+1)^2}$. When $x = a$, the equation of the tangent line is

$y - \dfrac{a}{a+1} = \dfrac{1}{(a+1)^2}(x-a)$. This line passes through $(1, 2)$ when $2 - \dfrac{a}{a+1} = \dfrac{1}{(a+1)^2}(1-a) \Leftrightarrow$

$2(a+1)^2 - a(a+1) = 1 - a \Leftrightarrow 2a^2 + 4a + 2 - a^2 - a - 1 + a = 0 \Leftrightarrow a^2 + 4a + 1 = 0$.

The quadratic formula gives the roots of this equation as $a = \dfrac{-4 \pm \sqrt{4^2 - 4(1)(1)}}{2(1)} = \dfrac{-4 \pm \sqrt{12}}{2} = -2 \pm \sqrt{3}$,

so there are two such tangent lines. Since

$$f\left(-2 \pm \sqrt{3}\right) = \frac{-2 \pm \sqrt{3}}{-2 \pm \sqrt{3} + 1} = \frac{-2 \pm \sqrt{3}}{-1 \pm \sqrt{3}} \cdot \frac{-1 \mp \sqrt{3}}{-1 \mp \sqrt{3}}$$

$$= \frac{2 \pm 2\sqrt{3} \mp \sqrt{3} - 3}{1 - 3} = \frac{-1 \pm \sqrt{3}}{-2} = \frac{1 \mp \sqrt{3}}{2},$$

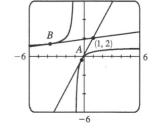

the lines touch the curve at $A\left(-2 + \sqrt{3}, \frac{1-\sqrt{3}}{2}\right) \approx (-0.27, -0.37)$

and $B\left(-2 - \sqrt{3}, \frac{1+\sqrt{3}}{2}\right) \approx (-3.73, 1.37)$.

55. $R = \dfrac{f}{g} \Rightarrow R' = \dfrac{gf' - fg'}{g^2}$. For $f(x) = x - 3x^3 + 5x^5$, $f'(x) = 1 - 9x^2 + 25x^4$,

and for $g(x) = 1 + 3x^3 + 6x^6 + 9x^9$, $g'(x) = 9x^2 + 36x^5 + 81x^8$.

Thus, $R'(0) = \dfrac{g(0)f'(0) - f(0)g'(0)}{[g(0)]^2} = \dfrac{1 \cdot 1 - 0 \cdot 0}{1^2} = \dfrac{1}{1} = 1$.

57. (a) $(fgh)' = [(fg)h]' = (fg)'h + (fg)h' = (f'g + fg')h + (fg)h' = f'gh + fg'h + fgh'$

(b) Putting $f = g = h$ in part (a), we have $\dfrac{d}{dx}[f(x)]^3 = (fff)' = f'ff + ff'f + fff' = 3fff' = 3[f(x)]^2 f'(x)$.

(c) $\dfrac{d}{dx}(e^{3x}) = \dfrac{d}{dx}(e^x)^3 = 3(e^x)^2 e^x = 3e^{2x}e^x = 3e^{3x}$

59. For $f(x) = x^2 e^x$, $f'(x) = x^2 e^x + e^x(2x) = e^x(x^2 + 2x)$. Similarly, we have

$$f''(x) = e^x(x^2 + 4x + 2)$$
$$f'''(x) = e^x(x^2 + 6x + 6)$$
$$f^{(4)}(x) = e^x(x^2 + 8x + 12)$$
$$f^{(5)}(x) = e^x(x^2 + 10x + 20)$$

It appears that the coefficient of x in the quadratic term increases by 2 with each differentiation. The pattern for the

constant terms seems to be $0 = 1 \cdot 0$, $2 = 2 \cdot 1$, $6 = 3 \cdot 2$, $12 = 4 \cdot 3$, $20 = 5 \cdot 4$. So a reasonable guess is that

$f^{(n)}(x) = e^x[x^2 + 2nx + n(n-1)]$.

[continued]

Proof: Let S_n be the statement that $f^{(n)}(x) = e^x[x^2 + 2nx + n(n-1)]$.

1. S_1 is true because $f'(x) = e^x(x^2 + 2x)$.

2. Assume that S_k is true; that is, $f^{(k)}(x) = e^x[x^2 + 2kx + k(k-1)]$. Then

$$f^{(k+1)}(x) = \frac{d}{dx}\left[f^{(k)}(x)\right] = e^x(2x + 2k) + [x^2 + 2kx + k(k-1)]e^x$$
$$= e^x[x^2 + (2k+2)x + (k^2 + k)] = e^x[x^2 + 2(k+1)x + (k+1)k]$$

This shows that S_{k+1} is true.

3. Therefore, by mathematical induction, S_n is true for all n; that is, $f^{(n)}(x) = e^x[x^2 + 2nx + n(n-1)]$ for every positive integer n.

3.3 Derivatives of Trigonometric Functions

1. $f(x) = 3x^2 - 2\cos x \Rightarrow f'(x) = 6x - 2(-\sin x) = 6x + 2\sin x$

3. $f(x) = \sin x + \frac{1}{2}\cot x \Rightarrow f'(x) = \cos x - \frac{1}{2}\csc^2 x$

5. $y = \sec\theta\tan\theta \Rightarrow y' = \sec\theta(\sec^2\theta) + \tan\theta(\sec\theta\tan\theta) = \sec\theta(\sec^2\theta + \tan^2\theta)$. Using the identity

$1 + \tan^2\theta = \sec^2\theta$, we can write alternative forms of the answer as $\sec\theta(1 + 2\tan^2\theta)$ or $\sec\theta(2\sec^2\theta - 1)$.

7. $y = c\cos t + t^2\sin t \Rightarrow y' = c(-\sin t) + t^2(\cos t) + \sin t(2t) = -c\sin t + t(t\cos t + 2\sin t)$

9. $y = \dfrac{x}{2 - \tan x} \Rightarrow y' = \dfrac{(2 - \tan x)(1) - x(-\sec^2 x)}{(2 - \tan x)^2} = \dfrac{2 - \tan x + x\sec^2 x}{(2 - \tan x)^2}$

11. $f(\theta) = \dfrac{\sec\theta}{1 + \sec\theta} \Rightarrow$

$$f'(\theta) = \frac{(1 + \sec\theta)(\sec\theta\tan\theta) - (\sec\theta)(\sec\theta\tan\theta)}{(1 + \sec\theta)^2} = \frac{(\sec\theta\tan\theta)[(1 + \sec\theta) - \sec\theta]}{(1 + \sec\theta)^2} = \frac{\sec\theta\tan\theta}{(1 + \sec\theta)^2}$$

13. Using Exercise 3.2.57(a), $f(x) = xe^x\csc x \Rightarrow$

$f'(x) = (x)'e^x\csc x + x(e^x)'\csc x + xe^x(\csc x)' = 1e^x\csc x + xe^x\csc x + xe^x(-\cot x\csc x)$
$= e^x\csc x(1 + x - x\cot x)$

15. $\dfrac{d}{dx}(\csc x) = \dfrac{d}{dx}\left(\dfrac{1}{\sin x}\right) = \dfrac{(\sin x)(0) - 1(\cos x)}{\sin^2 x} = \dfrac{-\cos x}{\sin^2 x} = -\dfrac{1}{\sin x}\cdot\dfrac{\cos x}{\sin x} = -\csc x\cot x$

17. $\dfrac{d}{dx}(\cot x) = \dfrac{d}{dx}\left(\dfrac{\cos x}{\sin x}\right) = \dfrac{(\sin x)(-\sin x) - (\cos x)(\cos x)}{\sin^2 x} = -\dfrac{\sin^2 x + \cos^2 x}{\sin^2 x} = -\dfrac{1}{\sin^2 x} = -\csc^2 x$

19. $y = \sec x \Rightarrow y' = \sec x\tan x$, so $y'(\frac{\pi}{3}) = \sec\frac{\pi}{3}\tan\frac{\pi}{3} = 2\sqrt{3}$. An equation of the tangent line to the curve $y = \sec x$

at the point $(\frac{\pi}{3}, 2)$ is $y - 2 = 2\sqrt{3}\left(x - \frac{\pi}{3}\right)$ or $y = 2\sqrt{3}x + 2 - \frac{2}{3}\sqrt{3}\pi$.

21. $y = x + \cos x \quad \Rightarrow \quad y' = 1 - \sin x$. At $(0, 1)$, $y' = 1$, and an equation of the tangent line is $y - 1 = 1(x - 0)$, or $y = x + 1$.

23. (a) $y = 2x \sin x \quad \Rightarrow \quad y' = 2(x \cos x + \sin x \cdot 1)$. At $\left(\frac{\pi}{2}, \pi\right)$,

$y' = 2\left(\frac{\pi}{2} \cos \frac{\pi}{2} + \sin \frac{\pi}{2}\right) = 2(0 + 1) = 2$, and an equation of the

tangent line is $y - \pi = 2\left(x - \frac{\pi}{2}\right)$, or $y = 2x$.

(b)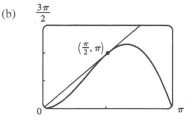

25. (a) $f(x) = \sec x - x \quad \Rightarrow \quad f'(x) = \sec x \tan x - 1$

(b)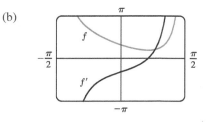

Note that $f' = 0$ where f has a minimum. Also note that f' is negative when f is decreasing and f' is positive when f is increasing.

27. $H(\theta) = \theta \sin \theta \quad \Rightarrow \quad H'(\theta) = \theta (\cos \theta) + (\sin \theta) \cdot 1 = \theta \cos \theta + \sin \theta \quad \Rightarrow$

$H''(\theta) = \theta (-\sin \theta) + (\cos \theta) \cdot 1 + \cos \theta = -\theta \sin \theta + 2 \cos \theta$

29. (a) $f(x) = \dfrac{\tan x - 1}{\sec x} \quad \Rightarrow$

$f'(x) = \dfrac{\sec x (\sec^2 x) - (\tan x - 1)(\sec x \tan x)}{(\sec x)^2} = \dfrac{\sec x (\sec^2 x - \tan^2 x + \tan x)}{\sec^2 x} = \dfrac{1 + \tan x}{\sec x}$

(b) $f(x) = \dfrac{\tan x - 1}{\sec x} = \dfrac{\dfrac{\sin x}{\cos x} - 1}{\dfrac{1}{\cos x}} = \dfrac{\dfrac{\sin x - \cos x}{\cos x}}{\dfrac{1}{\cos x}} = \sin x - \cos x \quad \Rightarrow \quad f'(x) = \cos x - (-\sin x) = \cos x + \sin x$

(c) From part (a), $f'(x) = \dfrac{1 + \tan x}{\sec x} = \dfrac{1}{\sec x} + \dfrac{\tan x}{\sec x} = \cos x + \sin x$, which is the expression for $f'(x)$ in part (b).

31. $f(x) = x + 2 \sin x$ has a horizontal tangent when $f'(x) = 0 \quad \Leftrightarrow \quad 1 + 2 \cos x = 0 \quad \Leftrightarrow \quad \cos x = -\frac{1}{2} \quad \Leftrightarrow$

$x = \frac{2\pi}{3} + 2\pi n$ or $\frac{4\pi}{3} + 2\pi n$, where n is an integer. Note that $\frac{4\pi}{3}$ and $\frac{2\pi}{3}$ are $\pm \frac{\pi}{3}$ units from π. This allows us to write the

solutions in the more compact equivalent form $(2n + 1)\pi \pm \frac{\pi}{3}$, n an integer.

33. $f(x) = x - 2 \sin x$, $0 \le x \le 2\pi$. $f'(x) = 1 - 2 \cos x$. So $f'(x) > 0 \quad \Leftrightarrow \quad 1 - 2 \cos x > 0 \quad \Leftrightarrow \quad -2 \cos x > -1 \quad \Leftrightarrow$

$\cos x < \frac{1}{2} \quad \Leftrightarrow \quad \frac{\pi}{3} < x < \frac{5\pi}{3} \quad \Rightarrow \quad f$ is increasing on $\left(\frac{\pi}{3}, \frac{5\pi}{3}\right)$.

35. (a) $x(t) = 8 \sin t \quad \Rightarrow \quad v(t) = x'(t) = 8 \cos t \quad \Rightarrow \quad a(t) = x''(t) = -8 \sin t$

(b) The mass at time $t = \frac{2\pi}{3}$ has position $x\left(\frac{2\pi}{3}\right) = 8 \sin \frac{2\pi}{3} = 8\left(\frac{\sqrt{3}}{2}\right) = 4\sqrt{3}$, velocity $v\left(\frac{2\pi}{3}\right) = 8 \cos \frac{2\pi}{3} = 8\left(-\frac{1}{2}\right) = -4$,

and acceleration $a\left(\frac{2\pi}{3}\right) = -8 \sin \frac{2\pi}{3} = -8\left(\frac{\sqrt{3}}{2}\right) = -4\sqrt{3}$. Since $v\left(\frac{2\pi}{3}\right) < 0$, the particle is moving to the left.

37. 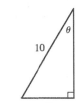 From the diagram we can see that $\sin\theta = x/10 \iff x = 10\sin\theta$. We want to find the rate of change of x with respect to θ, that is, $dx/d\theta$. Taking the derivative of $x = 10\sin\theta$, we get $dx/d\theta = 10(\cos\theta)$. So when $\theta = \frac{\pi}{3}$, $\frac{dx}{d\theta} = 10\cos\frac{\pi}{3} = 10\left(\frac{1}{2}\right) = 5$ ft/rad.

39. $\frac{d}{dx}(\sin x) = \cos x \implies \frac{d^2}{dx^2}(\sin x) = -\sin x \implies \frac{d^3}{dx^3}(\sin x) = -\cos x \implies \frac{d^4}{dx^4}(\sin x) = \sin x.$

The derivatives of $\sin x$ occur in a cycle of four. Since $99 = 4(24) + 3$, we have $\frac{d^{99}}{dx^{99}}(\sin x) = \frac{d^3}{dx^3}(\sin x) = -\cos x.$

41. $y = A\sin x + B\cos x \implies y' = A\cos x - B\sin x \implies y'' = -A\sin x - B\cos x.$ Substituting these expressions for y, y', and y'' into the given differential equation $y'' + y' - 2y = \sin x$ gives us

$(-A\sin x - B\cos x) + (A\cos x - B\sin x) - 2(A\sin x + B\cos x) = \sin x \iff$

$-3A\sin x - B\sin x + A\cos x - 3B\cos x = \sin x \iff (-3A - B)\sin x + (A - 3B)\cos x = 1\sin x$, so we must have

$-3A - B = 1$ and $A - 3B = 0$ (since 0 is the coefficient of $\cos x$ on the right side). Solving for A and B, we add the first

equation to three times the second to get $B = -\frac{1}{10}$ and $A = -\frac{3}{10}$.

43. $\displaystyle\lim_{t\to 0}\frac{\tan 6t}{\sin 2t} = \lim_{t\to 0}\left(\frac{\sin 6t}{t}\cdot\frac{1}{\cos 6t}\cdot\frac{t}{\sin 2t}\right) = \lim_{t\to 0}\frac{6\sin 6t}{6t}\cdot\lim_{t\to 0}\frac{1}{\cos 6t}\cdot\lim_{t\to 0}\frac{2t}{2\sin 2t}$

$\qquad = 6\lim_{t\to 0}\frac{\sin 6t}{6t}\cdot\lim_{t\to 0}\frac{1}{\cos 6t}\cdot\frac{1}{2}\lim_{t\to 0}\frac{2t}{\sin 2t} = 6(1)\cdot\frac{1}{1}\cdot\frac{1}{2}(1) = 3$

45. $\displaystyle\lim_{\theta\to 0}\frac{\sin\theta}{\theta + \tan\theta} = \frac{\displaystyle\lim_{\theta\to 0}\frac{\sin\theta}{\theta}}{\displaystyle\lim_{\theta\to 0}\frac{\theta + \tan\theta}{\theta}} = \frac{1}{\displaystyle\lim_{\theta\to 0}\left(1 + \frac{\sin\theta}{\theta}\cdot\frac{1}{\cos\theta}\right)} = \frac{1}{1 + 1\cdot 1} = \frac{1}{2}$

47. (a) $\frac{d}{dx}\tan x = \frac{d}{dx}\frac{\sin x}{\cos x} \implies \sec^2 x = \frac{\cos x\cos x - \sin x(-\sin x)}{\cos^2 x} = \frac{\cos^2 x + \sin^2 x}{\cos^2 x}$. So $\sec^2 x = \frac{1}{\cos^2 x}$.

(b) $\frac{d}{dx}\sec x = \frac{d}{dx}\frac{1}{\cos x} \implies \sec x\tan x = \frac{(\cos x)(0) - 1(-\sin x)}{\cos^2 x}$. So $\sec x\tan x = \frac{\sin x}{\cos^2 x}$.

(c) $\frac{d}{dx}(\sin x + \cos x) = \frac{d}{dx}\frac{1 + \cot x}{\csc x} \implies$

$\cos x - \sin x = \frac{\csc x(-\csc^2 x) - (1 + \cot x)(-\csc x\cot x)}{\csc^2 x} = \frac{\csc x[-\csc^2 x + (1 + \cot x)\cot x]}{\csc^2 x}$

$\qquad = \frac{-\csc^2 x + \cot^2 x + \cot x}{\csc x} = \frac{-1 + \cot x}{\csc x}$

So $\cos x - \sin x = \frac{\cot x - 1}{\csc x}$.

49. By the definition of radian measure, $s = r\theta$, where r is the radius of the circle. By drawing the bisector of the angle θ, we can

see that $\sin \dfrac{\theta}{2} = \dfrac{d/2}{r} \;\Rightarrow\; d = 2r \sin \dfrac{\theta}{2}$. So $\displaystyle\lim_{\theta \to 0^+} \dfrac{s}{d} = \lim_{\theta \to 0^+} \dfrac{r\theta}{2r\sin(\theta/2)} = \lim_{\theta \to 0^+} \dfrac{2 \cdot (\theta/2)}{2\sin(\theta/2)} = \lim_{\theta \to 0} \dfrac{\theta/2}{\sin(\theta/2)} = 1.$

[This is just the reciprocal of the limit $\displaystyle\lim_{x \to 0} \dfrac{\sin x}{x} = 1$ combined with the fact that as $\theta \to 0$, $\tfrac{\theta}{2} \to 0$ also.]

3.4   The Chain Rule

1. Let $u = g(x) = 1 + 4x$ and $y = f(u) = \sqrt[3]{u}$. Then $\dfrac{dy}{dx} = \dfrac{dy}{du}\dfrac{du}{dx} = (\tfrac{1}{3}u^{-2/3})(4) = \dfrac{4}{3\sqrt[3]{(1+4x)^2}}$.

3. Let $u = g(x) = \pi x$ and $y = f(u) = \tan u$. Then $\dfrac{dy}{dx} = \dfrac{dy}{du}\dfrac{du}{dx} = (\sec^2 u)(\pi) = \pi \sec^2 \pi x$.

5. Let $u = g(x) = \sqrt{x}$ and $y = f(u) = e^u$. Then $\dfrac{dy}{dx} = \dfrac{dy}{du}\dfrac{du}{dx} = (e^u)\left(\tfrac{1}{2}x^{-1/2}\right) = e^{\sqrt{x}} \cdot \dfrac{1}{2\sqrt{x}} = \dfrac{e^{\sqrt{x}}}{2\sqrt{x}}$.

7. $F(x) = (x^4 + 3x^2 - 2)^5 \;\Rightarrow\; F'(x) = 5(x^4 + 3x^2 - 2)^4 \cdot \dfrac{d}{dx}\left(x^4 + 3x^2 - 2\right) = 5(x^4 + 3x^2 - 2)^4(4x^3 + 6x)$

$\left[\text{or } 10x(x^4 + 3x^2 - 2)^4(2x^2 + 3)\right]$

9. $F(x) = \sqrt{1 - 2x} = (1 - 2x)^{1/2} \;\Rightarrow\; F'(x) = \tfrac{1}{2}(1 - 2x)^{-1/2}(-2) = -\dfrac{1}{\sqrt{1 - 2x}}$

11. $f(z) = \dfrac{1}{z^2 + 1} = (z^2 + 1)^{-1} \;\Rightarrow\; f'(z) = -1(z^2 + 1)^{-2}(2z) = -\dfrac{2z}{(z^2 + 1)^2}$

13. $y = \cos(a^3 + x^3) \;\Rightarrow\; y' = -\sin(a^3 + x^3) \cdot 3x^2 \quad [a^3 \text{ is just a constant}] \quad = -3x^2 \sin(a^3 + x^3)$

15. $h(t) = t^3 - 3^t \;\Rightarrow\; h'(t) = 3t^2 - 3^t \ln 3 \quad$ [by Formula 5]

17. $y = xe^{-kx} \;\Rightarrow\; y' = x\left[e^{-kx}(-k)\right] + e^{-kx} \cdot 1 = e^{-kx}(-kx + 1) \quad \left[\text{or } (1 - kx)e^{-kx}\right]$

19. $y = (2x - 5)^4(8x^2 - 5)^{-3} \;\Rightarrow\;$

$y' = 4(2x - 5)^3(2)(8x^2 - 5)^{-3} + (2x - 5)^4(-3)(8x^2 - 5)^{-4}(16x)$

$= 8(2x - 5)^3(8x^2 - 5)^{-3} - 48x(2x - 5)^4(8x^2 - 5)^{-4}$

[This simplifies to $8(2x - 5)^3(8x^2 - 5)^{-4}(-4x^2 + 30x - 5)$.]

21. $y = e^{x\cos x} \;\Rightarrow\; y' = e^{x\cos x} \cdot \dfrac{d}{dx}(x \cos x) = e^{x\cos x}[x(-\sin x) + (\cos x) \cdot 1] = e^{x\cos x}(\cos x - x\sin x)$

23. $y = \left(\dfrac{x^2 + 1}{x^2 - 1}\right)^3 \;\Rightarrow\;$

$y' = 3\left(\dfrac{x^2 + 1}{x^2 - 1}\right)^2 \cdot \dfrac{d}{dx}\left(\dfrac{x^2 + 1}{x^2 - 1}\right) = 3\left(\dfrac{x^2 + 1}{x^2 - 1}\right)^2 \cdot \dfrac{(x^2 - 1)(2x) - (x^2 + 1)(2x)}{(x^2 - 1)^2}$

$= 3\left(\dfrac{x^2 + 1}{x^2 - 1}\right)^2 \cdot \dfrac{2x[x^2 - 1 - (x^2 + 1)]}{(x^2 - 1)^2} = 3\left(\dfrac{x^2 + 1}{x^2 - 1}\right)^2 \cdot \dfrac{2x(-2)}{(x^2 - 1)^2} = \dfrac{-12x(x^2 + 1)^2}{(x^2 - 1)^4}$

25. $y = \sec^2 x + \tan^2 x = (\sec x)^2 + (\tan x)^2 \Rightarrow$

$y' = 2(\sec x)(\sec x \tan x) + 2(\tan x)(\sec^2 x) = 2\sec^2 x \tan x + 2\sec^2 x \tan x = 4\sec^2 x \tan x$

27. $y = \dfrac{r}{\sqrt{r^2+1}} \Rightarrow$

$y' = \dfrac{\sqrt{r^2+1}\,(1) - r \cdot \frac{1}{2}(r^2+1)^{-1/2}(2r)}{\left(\sqrt{r^2+1}\right)^2} = \dfrac{\sqrt{r^2+1} - \dfrac{r^2}{\sqrt{r^2+1}}}{\left(\sqrt{r^2+1}\right)^2} = \dfrac{\dfrac{\sqrt{r^2+1}\sqrt{r^2+1} - r^2}{\sqrt{r^2+1}}}{\left(\sqrt{r^2+1}\right)^2}$

$= \dfrac{(r^2+1) - r^2}{\left(\sqrt{r^2+1}\right)^3} = \dfrac{1}{(r^2+1)^{3/2}} \text{ or } (r^2+1)^{-3/2}$

Another solution: Write y as a product and make use of the Product Rule. $y = r(r^2+1)^{-1/2} \Rightarrow$

$y' = r \cdot -\frac{1}{2}(r^2+1)^{-3/2}(2r) + (r^2+1)^{-1/2} \cdot 1 = (r^2+1)^{-3/2}[-r^2 + (r^2+1)^1] = (r^2+1)^{-3/2}(1) = (r^2+1)^{-3/2}.$

The step that students usually have trouble with is factoring out $(r^2+1)^{-3/2}$. But this is no different than factoring out x^2 from $x^2 + x^5$; that is, we are just factoring out a factor with the *smallest* exponent that appears on it. In this case, $-\frac{3}{2}$ is smaller than $-\frac{1}{2}$.

29. $y = \sin(\tan 2x) \Rightarrow y' = \cos(\tan 2x) \cdot \dfrac{d}{dx}(\tan 2x) = \cos(\tan 2x) \cdot \sec^2(2x) \cdot \dfrac{d}{dx}(2x) = 2\cos(\tan 2x)\sec^2(2x)$

31. Using Formula 5 and the Chain Rule, $y = 2^{\sin \pi x} \Rightarrow$

$y' = 2^{\sin \pi x}(\ln 2) \cdot \dfrac{d}{dx}(\sin \pi x) = 2^{\sin \pi x}(\ln 2) \cdot \cos \pi x \cdot \pi = 2^{\sin \pi x}(\pi \ln 2)\cos \pi x$

33. $y = \cot^2(\sin \theta) = [\cot(\sin \theta)]^2 \Rightarrow$

$y' = 2[\cot(\sin \theta)] \cdot \dfrac{d}{d\theta}[\cot(\sin \theta)] = 2\cot(\sin \theta) \cdot [-\csc^2(\sin \theta) \cdot \cos \theta] = -2\cos \theta \cot(\sin \theta) \csc^2(\sin \theta)$

35. $y = \cos\sqrt{\sin(\tan \pi x)} = \cos(\sin(\tan \pi x))^{1/2} \Rightarrow$

$y' = -\sin(\sin(\tan \pi x))^{1/2} \cdot \dfrac{d}{dx}(\sin(\tan \pi x))^{1/2} = -\sin(\sin(\tan \pi x))^{1/2} \cdot \frac{1}{2}(\sin(\tan \pi x))^{-1/2} \cdot \dfrac{d}{dx}(\sin(\tan \pi x))$

$= \dfrac{-\sin\sqrt{\sin(\tan \pi x)}}{2\sqrt{\sin(\tan \pi x)}} \cdot \cos(\tan \pi x) \cdot \dfrac{d}{dx}\tan \pi x = \dfrac{-\sin\sqrt{\sin(\tan \pi x)}}{2\sqrt{\sin(\tan \pi x)}} \cdot \cos(\tan \pi x) \cdot \sec^2(\pi x) \cdot \pi$

$= \dfrac{-\pi \cos(\tan \pi x)\sec^2(\pi x)\sin\sqrt{\sin(\tan \pi x)}}{2\sqrt{\sin(\tan \pi x)}}$

37. $y = \cos(x^2) \Rightarrow y' = -\sin(x^2) \cdot 2x = -2x\sin(x^2) \Rightarrow$

$y'' = -2x\cos(x^2) \cdot 2x + \sin(x^2) \cdot (-2) = -4x^2\cos(x^2) - 2\sin(x^2)$

39. $y = e^{\alpha x}\sin \beta x \Rightarrow y' = e^{\alpha x} \cdot \beta \cos \beta x + \sin \beta x \cdot \alpha e^{\alpha x} = e^{\alpha x}(\beta \cos \beta x + \alpha \sin \beta x) \Rightarrow$

$y'' = e^{\alpha x}(-\beta^2 \sin \beta x + \alpha\beta \cos \beta x) + (\beta \cos \beta x + \alpha \sin \beta x) \cdot \alpha e^{\alpha x}$

$= e^{\alpha x}(-\beta^2 \sin \beta x + \alpha\beta \cos \beta x + \alpha\beta \cos \beta x + \alpha^2 \sin \beta x) = e^{\alpha x}(\alpha^2 \sin \beta x - \beta^2 \sin \beta x + 2\alpha\beta \cos \beta x)$

$= e^{\alpha x}\left[(\alpha^2 - \beta^2)\sin \beta x + 2\alpha\beta \cos \beta x\right]$

41. $y = (1 + 2x)^{10}$ $\Rightarrow$ $y' = 10(1 + 2x)^9 \cdot 2 = 20(1 + 2x)^9$.

At $(0, 1)$, $y' = 20(1 + 0)^9 = 20$, and an equation of the tangent line is $y - 1 = 20(x - 0)$, or $y = 20x + 1$.

43. $y = \sin(\sin x)$ $\Rightarrow$ $y' = \cos(\sin x) \cdot \cos x$. At $(\pi, 0)$, $y' = \cos(\sin \pi) \cdot \cos \pi = \cos(0) \cdot (-1) = 1(-1) = -1$, and an

equation of the tangent line is $y - 0 = -1(x - \pi)$, or $y = -x + \pi$.

45. (a) $y = \dfrac{2}{1 + e^{-x}}$ $\Rightarrow$ $y' = \dfrac{(1 + e^{-x})(0) - 2(-e^{-x})}{(1 + e^{-x})^2} = \dfrac{2e^{-x}}{(1 + e^{-x})^2}$.   **(b)**

At $(0, 1)$, $y' = \dfrac{2e^0}{(1 + e^0)^2} = \dfrac{2(1)}{(1 + 1)^2} = \dfrac{2}{2^2} = \dfrac{1}{2}$. So an equation of the

tangent line is $y - 1 = \frac{1}{2}(x - 0)$ or $y = \frac{1}{2}x + 1$.

47. (a) $f(x) = x\sqrt{2 - x^2} = x(2 - x^2)^{1/2}$ $\Rightarrow$

$$f'(x) = x \cdot \tfrac{1}{2}(2 - x^2)^{-1/2}(-2x) + (2 - x^2)^{1/2} \cdot 1 = (2 - x^2)^{-1/2}\left[-x^2 + (2 - x^2)\right] = \dfrac{2 - 2x^2}{\sqrt{2 - x^2}}$$

(b)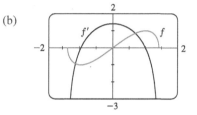

$f' = 0$ when f has a horizontal tangent line, f' is negative when f is

decreasing, and f' is positive when f is increasing.

49. For the tangent line to be horizontal, $f'(x) = 0$. $f(x) = 2\sin x + \sin^2 x$ $\Rightarrow$ $f'(x) = 2\cos x + 2\sin x \cos x = 0$ $\Leftrightarrow$

$2\cos x(1 + \sin x) = 0$ $\Leftrightarrow$ $\cos x = 0$ or $\sin x = -1$, so $x = \frac{\pi}{2} + 2n\pi$ or $\frac{3\pi}{2} + 2n\pi$, where n is any integer. Now

$f\left(\frac{\pi}{2}\right) = 3$ and $f\left(\frac{3\pi}{2}\right) = -1$, so the points on the curve with a horizontal tangent are $\left(\frac{\pi}{2} + 2n\pi, 3\right)$ and $\left(\frac{3\pi}{2} + 2n\pi, -1\right)$,

where n is any integer.

51. $F(x) = f(g(x))$ $\Rightarrow$ $F'(x) = f'(g(x)) \cdot g'(x)$, so $F'(5) = f'(g(5)) \cdot g'(5) = f'(-2) \cdot 6 = 4 \cdot 6 = 24$

53. (a) $h(x) = f(g(x))$ $\Rightarrow$ $h'(x) = f'(g(x)) \cdot g'(x)$, so $h'(1) = f'(g(1)) \cdot g'(1) = f'(2) \cdot 6 = 5 \cdot 6 = 30$.

(b) $H(x) = g(f(x))$ $\Rightarrow$ $H'(x) = g'(f(x)) \cdot f'(x)$, so $H'(1) = g'(f(1)) \cdot f'(1) = g'(3) \cdot 4 = 9 \cdot 4 = 36$.

55. (a) $u(x) = f(g(x))$ $\Rightarrow$ $u'(x) = f'(g(x))g'(x)$. So $u'(1) = f'(g(1))g'(1) = f'(3)g'(1)$. To find $f'(3)$, note that f is

linear from $(2, 4)$ to $(6, 3)$, so its slope is $\dfrac{3 - 4}{6 - 2} = -\dfrac{1}{4}$. To find $g'(1)$, note that g is linear from $(0, 6)$ to $(2, 0)$, so its slope

is $\dfrac{0 - 6}{2 - 0} = -3$. Thus, $f'(3)g'(1) = \left(-\frac{1}{4}\right)(-3) = \frac{3}{4}$.

(b) $v(x) = g(f(x))$ $\Rightarrow$ $v'(x) = g'(f(x))f'(x)$. So $v'(1) = g'(f(1))f'(1) = g'(2)f'(1)$, which does not exist since

$g'(2)$ does not exist.

(c) $w(x) = g(g(x))$ $\Rightarrow$ $w'(x) = g'(g(x))g'(x)$. So $w'(1) = g'(g(1))g'(1) = g'(3)g'(1)$. To find $g'(3)$, note that g is

linear from $(2, 0)$ to $(5, 2)$, so its slope is $\dfrac{2 - 0}{5 - 2} = \dfrac{2}{3}$. Thus, $g'(3)g'(1) = \left(\frac{2}{3}\right)(-3) = -2$.

57. $h(x) = f(g(x)) \quad \Rightarrow \quad h'(x) = f'(g(x))g'(x)$. So $h'(0.5) = f'(g(0.5))g'(0.5) = f'(0.1)g'(0.5)$.

We can estimate the derivatives by taking the average of two secant slopes.

For $f'(0.1)$: $m_1 = \dfrac{14.8 - 12.6}{0.1 - 0} = 22$, $m_2 = \dfrac{18.4 - 14.8}{0.2 - 0.1} = 36$. So $f'(0.1) \approx \dfrac{m_1 + m_2}{2} = \dfrac{22 + 36}{2} = 29$.

For $g'(0.5)$: $m_1 = \dfrac{0.10 - 0.17}{0.5 - 0.4} = -0.7$, $m_2 = \dfrac{0.05 - 0.10}{0.6 - 0.5} = -0.5$. So $g'(0.5) \approx \dfrac{m_1 + m_2}{2} = -0.6$.

Hence, $h'(0.5) = f'(0.1)g'(0.5) \approx (29)(-0.6) = -17.4$.

59. (a) $F(x) = f(e^x) \quad \Rightarrow \quad F'(x) = f'(e^x)\dfrac{d}{dx}(e^x) = f'(e^x)e^x$

(b) $G(x) = e^{f(x)} \quad \Rightarrow \quad G'(x) = e^{f(x)}\dfrac{d}{dx}f(x) = e^{f(x)}f'(x)$

61. $r(x) = f(g(h(x))) \quad \Rightarrow \quad r'(x) = f'(g(h(x))) \cdot g'(h(x)) \cdot h'(x)$, so

$r'(1) = f'(g(h(1))) \cdot g'(h(1)) \cdot h'(1) = f'(g(2)) \cdot g'(2) \cdot 4 = f'(3) \cdot 5 \cdot 4 = 6 \cdot 5 \cdot 4 = 120$

63. $F(x) = f(3f(4f(x))) \quad \Rightarrow$

$$F'(x) = f'(3f(4f(x))) \cdot \frac{d}{dx}(3f(4f(x))) = f'(3f(4f(x))) \cdot 3f'(4f(x)) \cdot \frac{d}{dx}(4f(x))$$

$$= f'(3f(4f(x))) \cdot 3f'(4f(x)) \cdot 4f'(x), \quad \text{so}$$

$$F'(0) = f'(3f(4f(0))) \cdot 3f'(4f(0)) \cdot 4f'(0) = f'(3f(4 \cdot 0)) \cdot 3f'(4 \cdot 0) \cdot 4 \cdot 2 = f'(3 \cdot 0) \cdot 3 \cdot 2 \cdot 4 \cdot 2 = 2 \cdot 3 \cdot 2 \cdot 4 \cdot 2 = 96.$$

65. $y = e^{2x}(A \cos 3x + B \sin 3x) \quad \Rightarrow$

$$y' = e^{2x}(-3A \sin 3x + 3B \cos 3x) + (A \cos 3x + B \sin 3x) \cdot 2e^{2x}$$

$$= e^{2x}(-3A \sin 3x + 3B \cos 3x + 2A \cos 3x + 2B \sin 3x)$$

$$= e^{2x}[(2A + 3B) \cos 3x + (2B - 3A) \sin 3x] \quad \Rightarrow$$

$$y'' = e^{2x}[-3(2A + 3B) \sin 3x + 3(2B - 3A) \cos 3x] + [(2A + 3B) \cos 3x + (2B - 3A) \sin 3x] \cdot 2e^{2x}$$

$$= e^{2x}\{[-3(2A + 3B) + 2(2B - 3A)] \sin 3x + [3(2B - 3A) + 2(2A + 3B)] \cos 3x\}$$

$$= e^{2x}[(-12A - 5B) \sin 3x + (-5A + 12B) \cos 3x]$$

Substitute the expressions for y, y', and y'' in $y'' - 4y' + 13y$ to get

$$y'' - 4y' + 13y = e^{2x}[(-12A - 5B) \sin 3x + (-5A + 12B) \cos 3x]$$

$$- 4e^{2x}[(2A + 3B) \cos 3x + (2B - 3A) \sin 3x] + 13e^{2x}(A \cos 3x + B \sin 3x)$$

$$= e^{2x}[(-12A - 5B - 8B + 12A + 13B) \sin 3x + (-5A + 12B - 8A - 12B + 13A) \cos 3x]$$

$$= e^{2x}[(0) \sin 3x + (0) \cos 3x] = 0$$

Thus, the function y satisfies the differential equation $y'' - 4y' + 13y = 0$.

67. The use of D, D^2, ..., D^n is just a derivative notation (see text page 150). In general, $Df(2x) = 2f'(2x)$,

$D^2 f(2x) = 4f''(2x)$, ..., $D^n f(2x) = 2^n f^{(n)}(2x)$. Since $f(x) = \cos x$ and $50 = 4(12) + 2$, we have

$f^{(50)}(x) = f^{(2)}(x) = -\cos x$, so $D^{50} \cos 2x = -2^{50} \cos 2x$.

69. $s(t) = 10 + \frac{1}{4}\sin(10\pi t)$ ⇒ the velocity after t seconds is $v(t) = s'(t) = \frac{1}{4}\cos(10\pi t)(10\pi) = \frac{5\pi}{2}\cos(10\pi t)$ cm/s.

71. (a) $B(t) = 4.0 + 0.35\sin\dfrac{2\pi t}{5.4}$ ⇒ $\dfrac{dB}{dt} = \left(0.35\cos\dfrac{2\pi t}{5.4}\right)\left(\dfrac{2\pi}{5.4}\right) = \dfrac{0.7\pi}{5.4}\cos\dfrac{2\pi t}{5.4} = \dfrac{7\pi}{54}\cos\dfrac{2\pi t}{5.4}$

(b) At $t = 1$, $\dfrac{dB}{dt} = \dfrac{7\pi}{54}\cos\dfrac{2\pi}{5.4} \approx 0.16$.

73. $s(t) = 2e^{-1.5t}\sin 2\pi t$ ⇒

$v(t) = s'(t) = 2[e^{-1.5t}(\cos 2\pi t)(2\pi) + (\sin 2\pi t)e^{-1.5t}(-1.5)] = 2e^{-1.5t}(2\pi\cos 2\pi t - 1.5\sin 2\pi t)$

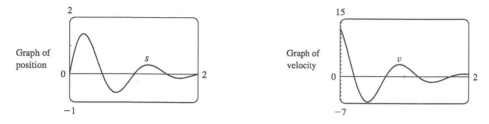

75. By the Chain Rule, $a(t) = \dfrac{dv}{dt} = \dfrac{dv}{ds}\dfrac{ds}{dt} = \dfrac{dv}{ds}v(t) = v(t)\dfrac{dv}{ds}$. The derivative dv/dt is the rate of change of the velocity

with respect to time (in other words, the acceleration) whereas the derivative dv/ds is the rate of change of the velocity with respect to the displacement.

77. (a) Using a calculator or CAS, we obtain the model $Q = ab^t$ with $a \approx 100.0124369$ and $b \approx 0.000045145933$.

(b) Use $Q'(t) = ab^t\ln b$ (from Formula 5) to get $Q'(0.04) \approx -670.63$ μA. The result of Example 2 in Section 2.1 was -670 μA.

79. $x = t^4 + 1$, $y = t^3 + t$; $t = -1$. $\dfrac{dy}{dt} = 3t^2 + 1$, $\dfrac{dx}{dt} = 4t^3$, and $\dfrac{dy}{dx} = \dfrac{dy/dt}{dx/dt} = \dfrac{3t^2 + 1}{4t^3}$. When $t = -1$,

$(x, y) = (2, -2)$ and $dy/dx = \frac{4}{-4} = -1$, so an equation of the tangent to the curve at the point corresponding to $t = -1$

is $y - (-2) = (-1)(x - 2)$, or $y = -x$.

81. $x = e^{\sqrt{t}}$, $y = t - \ln t^2$; $t = 1$. $\dfrac{dy}{dt} = 1 - \dfrac{2t}{t^2} = 1 - \dfrac{2}{t}$, $\dfrac{dx}{dt} = \dfrac{e^{\sqrt{t}}}{2\sqrt{t}}$, and $\dfrac{dy}{dx} = \dfrac{dy/dt}{dx/dt} = \dfrac{1 - 2/t}{e^{\sqrt{t}}/(2\sqrt{t})} \cdot \dfrac{2t}{2t} = \dfrac{2t - 4}{\sqrt{t}e^{\sqrt{t}}}$.

When $t = 1$, $(x, y) = (e, 1)$ and $\dfrac{dy}{dx} = -\dfrac{2}{e}$, so an equation of the tangent line is $y - 1 = -\dfrac{2}{e}(x - e)$, or $y = -\dfrac{2}{e}x + 3$.

83. $x = 10 - t^2$, $y = t^3 - 12t$. $\dfrac{dy}{dt} = 3t^2 - 12 = 3(t + 2)(t - 2)$, so $\dfrac{dy}{dt} = 0$ ⇔ $t = \pm 2$ ⇔

$(x, y) = (6, \mp 16)$. $\dfrac{dx}{dt} = -2t$, so $\dfrac{dx}{dt} = 0$ ⇔ $t = 0$ ⇔ $(x, y) = (10, 0)$. The curve has horizontal tangents at $(6, \pm 16)$

and a vertical tangent at $(10, 0)$.

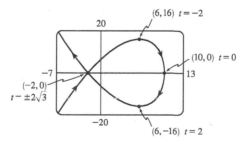

85. (a) $x = t^2$, $y = t^3 - 3t$ $\Rightarrow$ $\dfrac{dy}{dx} = \dfrac{dy/dt}{dx/dt} = \dfrac{3t^2 - 3}{2t}$. At the point $(3, 0)$, $x = 3$ $\Rightarrow$ $t^2 = 3$ $\Rightarrow$ $t = \pm\sqrt{3}$ $\Rightarrow$

$\dfrac{dy}{dx} = \dfrac{3(\pm\sqrt{3})^2 - 3}{2(\pm\sqrt{3})} = \dfrac{6}{2(\pm\sqrt{3})} = \pm\dfrac{3}{\sqrt{3}} = \pm\sqrt{3}$. When $t = \sqrt{3}$, an equation of the tangent line is

$y - 0 = \sqrt{3}\,(x - 3)$ or $y = \sqrt{3}\,x - 3\sqrt{3}$. When $t = -\sqrt{3}$, an equation of the tangent line is $y - 0 = -\sqrt{3}\,(x - 3)$

or $y = -\sqrt{3}\,x + 3\sqrt{3}$.

(b) Horizontal tangent: $dy/dx = 0$ $\Leftrightarrow$ $3t^2 - 3 = 0$ $\Leftrightarrow$

$3(t^2 - 1) = 0$ $\Leftrightarrow$ $t^2 = 1$ $\Leftrightarrow$ $t = \pm 1$. $t = 1$ corresponds to

the point $(x, y) = (t^2, t^3 - 3t) = (1^2, 1^3 - 3 \cdot 1) = (1, -2)$

and $t = -1$ to $(1, 2)$.

Vertical tangent: dy/dx is undefined $\Leftrightarrow$ $2t = 0$ $\Leftrightarrow$ $t = 0$.

The value $t = 0$ corresponds to the origin; that is, $(0, 0)$.

(c)

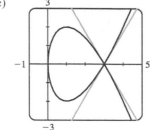

87. (a) Derive gives $g'(t) = \dfrac{45(t - 2)^8}{(2t + 1)^{10}}$ without simplifying. With either Maple or Mathematica, we first get

$g'(t) = 9\dfrac{(t - 2)^8}{(2t + 1)^9} - 18\dfrac{(t - 2)^9}{(2t + 1)^{10}}$, and the simplification command results in the expression given by Derive.

(b) Derive gives $y' = 2(x^3 - x + 1)^3(2x + 1)^4(17x^3 + 6x^2 - 9x + 3)$ without simplifying. With either Maple or

Mathematica, we first get $y' = 10(2x + 1)^4(x^3 - x + 1)^4 + 4(2x + 1)^5(x^3 - x + 1)^3(3x^2 - 1)$. If we use

Mathematica's Factor or Simplify, or Maple's factor, we get the above expression, but Maple's simplify gives

the polynomial expansion instead. For locating horizontal tangents, the factored form is the most helpful.

89. (a) $\dfrac{d}{dx}(\sin^n x \cos nx) = n\sin^{n-1} x \cos x \cos nx + \sin^n x\,(-n\sin nx)$ [Product Rule]

$\qquad = n\sin^{n-1} x\,(\cos nx \cos x - \sin nx \sin x)$ [factor out $n\sin^{n-1} x$]

$\qquad = n\sin^{n-1} x \cos(nx + x)$ [Addition Formula for cosine]

$\qquad = n\sin^{n-1} x \cos[(n + 1)x]$ [factor out x]

(b) $\dfrac{d}{dx}(\cos^n x \cos nx) = n\cos^{n-1} x\,(-\sin x)\cos nx + \cos^n x\,(-n\sin nx)$ [Product Rule]

$\qquad = -n\cos^{n-1} x\,(\cos nx \sin x + \sin nx \cos x)$ [factor out $-n\cos^{n-1} x$]

$\qquad = -n\cos^{n-1} x \sin(nx + x)$ [Addition Formula for sine]

$\qquad = -n\cos^{n-1} x \sin[(n + 1)x]$ [factor out x]

91. Since $\theta° = \left(\frac{\pi}{180}\right)\theta$ rad, we have $\dfrac{d}{d\theta}(\sin\theta°) = \dfrac{d}{d\theta}\left(\sin\frac{\pi}{180}\theta\right) = \frac{\pi}{180}\cos\frac{\pi}{180}\theta = \frac{\pi}{180}\cos\theta°$.

93. $\dfrac{d^2y}{dx^2} = \dfrac{d}{dx}\left(\dfrac{dy}{dx}\right)$ [Leibniz notation for the second derivative]

$\qquad\quad = \dfrac{d}{dx}\left(\dfrac{dy}{du}\dfrac{du}{dx}\right)$ [Chain Rule]

$\qquad\quad = \dfrac{dy}{du}\cdot\dfrac{d}{dx}\left(\dfrac{du}{dx}\right) + \dfrac{du}{dx}\cdot\dfrac{d}{dx}\left(\dfrac{dy}{du}\right)$ [Product Rule]

$\qquad\quad = \dfrac{dy}{du}\cdot\dfrac{d^2u}{dx^2} + \dfrac{du}{dx}\cdot\dfrac{d}{du}\left(\dfrac{dy}{du}\right)\cdot\dfrac{du}{dx}$ [dy/du is a function of u]

$\qquad\quad = \dfrac{dy}{du}\dfrac{d^2u}{dx^2} + \dfrac{d^2y}{du^2}\left(\dfrac{du}{dx}\right)^2$

Or: Using function notation for $y = f(u)$ and $u = g(x)$, we have $y = f(g(x))$, so

$y' = f'(g(x))\cdot g'(x)$ [by the Chain Rule] $\Rightarrow$

$(y')' = [f'(g(x))\cdot g'(x)]' = f'(g(x))\cdot g''(x) + g'(x)\cdot f''(g(x))\cdot g'(x) = f'(g(x))\cdot g''(x) + f''(g(x))\cdot [g'(x)]^2.$

3.5 Implicit Differentiation

1. (a) $\dfrac{d}{dx}(xy + 2x + 3x^2) = \dfrac{d}{dx}(4) \ \Rightarrow\ (x\cdot y' + y\cdot 1) + 2 + 6x = 0 \ \Rightarrow\ xy' = -y - 2 - 6x \ \Rightarrow$

$\qquad y' = \dfrac{-y - 2 - 6x}{x}$ or $y' = -6 - \dfrac{y+2}{x}$.

(b) $xy + 2x + 3x^2 = 4 \ \Rightarrow\ xy = 4 - 2x - 3x^2 \ \Rightarrow\ y = \dfrac{4 - 2x - 3x^2}{x} = \dfrac{4}{x} - 2 - 3x$, so $y' = -\dfrac{4}{x^2} - 3$.

(c) From part (a), $y' = \dfrac{-y - 2 - 6x}{x} = \dfrac{-(4/x - 2 - 3x) - 2 - 6x}{x} = \dfrac{-4/x - 3x}{x} = -\dfrac{4}{x^2} - 3$.

3. $\dfrac{d}{dx}(x^3 + y^3) = \dfrac{d}{dx}(1) \ \Rightarrow\ 3x^2 + 3y^2\cdot y' = 0 \ \Rightarrow\ 3y^2 y' = -3x^2 \ \Rightarrow\ y' = -\dfrac{x^2}{y^2}$

5. $\dfrac{d}{dx}(x^2 + xy - y^2) = \dfrac{d}{dx}(4) \ \Rightarrow\ 2x + x\cdot y' + y\cdot 1 - 2y y' = 0 \ \Rightarrow$

$\qquad xy' - 2y y' = -2x - y \ \Rightarrow\ (x - 2y)y' = -2x - y \ \Rightarrow\ y' = \dfrac{-2x - y}{x - 2y} = \dfrac{2x + y}{2y - x}$

7. $\dfrac{d}{dx}[x^4(x + y)] = \dfrac{d}{dx}[y^2(3x - y)] \ \Rightarrow\ x^4(1 + y') + (x + y)\cdot 4x^3 = y^2(3 - y') + (3x - y)\cdot 2y y' \ \Rightarrow$

$\qquad x^4 + x^4 y' + 4x^4 + 4x^3 y = 3y^2 - y^2 y' + 6xy y' - 2y^2 y' \ \Rightarrow\ x^4 y' + 3y^2 y' - 6xy y' = 3y^2 - 5x^4 - 4x^3 y \ \Rightarrow$

$\qquad (x^4 + 3y^2 - 6xy)y' = 3y^2 - 5x^4 - 4x^3 y \ \Rightarrow\ y' = \dfrac{3y^2 - 5x^4 - 4x^3 y}{x^4 + 3y^2 - 6xy}$

9. $\dfrac{d}{dx}(x^2 y^2 + x\sin y) = \dfrac{d}{dx}(4) \ \Rightarrow\ x^2\cdot 2y y' + y^2\cdot 2x + x\cos y\cdot y' + \sin y\cdot 1 = 0 \ \Rightarrow$

$\qquad 2x^2 y y' + x\cos y\cdot y' = -2xy^2 - \sin y \ \Rightarrow\ (2x^2 y + x\cos y)y' = -2xy^2 - \sin y \ \Rightarrow\ y' = \dfrac{-2xy^2 - \sin y}{2x^2 y + x\cos y}$

11. $\dfrac{d}{dx}(4\cos x \sin y) = \dfrac{d}{dx}(1) \Rightarrow 4[\cos x \cdot \cos y \cdot y' + \sin y \cdot (-\sin x)] = 0 \Rightarrow$

$y'(4\cos x \cos y) = 4\sin x \sin y \Rightarrow y' = \dfrac{4\sin x \sin y}{4\cos x \cos y} = \tan x \tan y$

13. $\dfrac{d}{dx}(e^{x/y}) = \dfrac{d}{dx}(x - y) \Rightarrow e^{x/y} \cdot \dfrac{d}{dx}\left(\dfrac{x}{y}\right) = 1 - y' \Rightarrow$

$e^{x/y} \cdot \dfrac{y \cdot 1 - x \cdot y'}{y^2} = 1 - y' \Rightarrow e^{x/y} \cdot \dfrac{1}{y} - \dfrac{xe^{x/y}}{y^2} \cdot y' = 1 - y' \Rightarrow y' - \dfrac{xe^{x/y}}{y^2} \cdot y' = 1 - \dfrac{e^{x/y}}{y} \Rightarrow$

$y'\left(1 - \dfrac{xe^{x/y}}{y^2}\right) = \dfrac{y - e^{x/y}}{y} \Rightarrow y' = \dfrac{\dfrac{y - e^{x/y}}{y}}{\dfrac{y^2 - xe^{x/y}}{y^2}} = \dfrac{y(y - e^{x/y})}{y^2 - xe^{x/y}}$

15. $\dfrac{d}{dx}(e^y \cos x) = \dfrac{d}{dx}[1 + \sin(xy)] \Rightarrow e^y(-\sin x) + \cos x \cdot e^y \cdot y' = \cos(xy) \cdot (xy' + y \cdot 1) \Rightarrow$

$-e^y \sin x + e^y \cos x \cdot y' = x\cos(xy) \cdot y' + y\cos(xy) \Rightarrow e^y \cos x \cdot y' - x\cos(xy) \cdot y' = e^y \sin x + y\cos(xy) \Rightarrow$

$[e^y \cos x - x\cos(xy)]\, y' = e^y \sin x + y\cos(xy) \Rightarrow y' = \dfrac{e^y \sin x + y\cos(xy)}{e^y \cos x - x\cos(xy)}$

17. $\dfrac{d}{dx}\{f(x) + x^2[f(x)]^3\} = \dfrac{d}{dx}(10) \Rightarrow f'(x) + x^2 \cdot 3[f(x)]^2 \cdot f'(x) + [f(x)]^3 \cdot 2x = 0.$ If $x = 1$, we have

$f'(1) + 1^2 \cdot 3[f(1)]^2 \cdot f'(1) + [f(1)]^3 \cdot 2(1) = 0 \Rightarrow f'(1) + 1 \cdot 3 \cdot 2^2 \cdot f'(1) + 2^3 \cdot 2 = 0 \Rightarrow$

$f'(1) + 12f'(1) = -16 \Rightarrow 13f'(1) = -16 \Rightarrow f'(1) = -\frac{16}{13}.$

19. $\dfrac{d}{dy}(x^4y^2 - x^3y + 2xy^3) = \dfrac{d}{dy}(0) \Rightarrow x^4 \cdot 2y + y^2 \cdot 4x^3 x' - (x^3 \cdot 1 + y \cdot 3x^2 x') + 2(x \cdot 3y^2 + y^3 \cdot x') = 0 \Rightarrow$

$4x^3y^2 x' - 3x^2y x' + 2y^3 x' = -2x^4y + x^3 - 6xy^2 \Rightarrow (4x^3y^2 - 3x^2y + 2y^3) x' = -2x^4y + x^3 - 6xy^2 \Rightarrow$

$x' = \dfrac{dx}{dy} = \dfrac{-2x^4y + x^3 - 6xy^2}{4x^3y^2 - 3x^2y + 2y^3}$

21. $y\sin 2x = x\cos 2y \Rightarrow y \cdot \cos 2x \cdot 2 + \sin 2x \cdot y' = x(-\sin 2y \cdot 2y') + \cos(2y) \cdot 1 \Rightarrow$

$\sin 2x \cdot y' + 2x\sin 2y \cdot y' = -2y\cos 2x + \cos 2y \Rightarrow$

$y'(\sin 2x + 2x\sin 2y) = -2y\cos 2x + \cos 2y \Rightarrow y' = \dfrac{-2y\cos 2x + \cos 2y}{\sin 2x + 2x\sin 2y}$. When $x = \frac{\pi}{2}$ and $y = \frac{\pi}{4}$, we have

$y' = \dfrac{(-\pi/2)(-1) + 0}{0 + \pi \cdot 1} = \dfrac{\pi/2}{\pi} = \dfrac{1}{2}$, so an equation of the tangent line is $y - \frac{\pi}{4} = \frac{1}{2}(x - \frac{\pi}{2})$, or $y = \frac{1}{2}x$.

23. $x^2 + xy + y^2 = 3 \Rightarrow 2x + xy' + y \cdot 1 + 2yy' = 0 \Rightarrow xy' + 2yy' = -2x - y \Rightarrow y'(x + 2y) = -2x - y \Rightarrow$

$y' = \dfrac{-2x - y}{x + 2y}$. When $x = 1$ and $y = 1$, we have $y' = \dfrac{-2 - 1}{1 + 2 \cdot 1} = \dfrac{-3}{3} = -1$, so an equation of the tangent line is

$y - 1 = -1(x - 1)$ or $y = -x + 2$.

25. $x^2 + y^2 = (2x^2 + 2y^2 - x)^2 \;\Rightarrow\; 2x + 2y\,y' = 2(2x^2 + 2y^2 - x)(4x + 4y\,y' - 1)$. When $x = 0$ and $y = \frac{1}{2}$, we have

$0 + y' = 2(\frac{1}{2})(2y' - 1) \;\Rightarrow\; y' = 2y' - 1 \;\Rightarrow\; y' = 1$, so an equation of the tangent line is $y - \frac{1}{2} = 1(x - 0)$

or $y = x + \frac{1}{2}$.

27. $2(x^2 + y^2)^2 = 25(x^2 - y^2) \;\Rightarrow\; 4(x^2 + y^2)(2x + 2y\,y') = 25(2x - 2y\,y') \;\Rightarrow$

$4(x + y\,y')(x^2 + y^2) = 25(x - y\,y') \;\Rightarrow\; 4y\,y'(x^2 + y^2) + 25yy' = 25x - 4x(x^2 + y^2) \;\Rightarrow$

$y' = \dfrac{25x - 4x(x^2 + y^2)}{25y + 4y(x^2 + y^2)}$. When $x = 3$ and $y = 1$, we have $y' = \frac{75 - 120}{25 + 40} = -\frac{45}{65} = -\frac{9}{13}$,

so an equation of the tangent line is $y - 1 = -\frac{9}{13}(x - 3)$ or $y = -\frac{9}{13}x + \frac{40}{13}$.

29. (a) $y^2 = 5x^4 - x^2 \;\Rightarrow\; 2y\,y' = 5(4x^3) - 2x \;\Rightarrow\; y' = \dfrac{10x^3 - x}{y}$. (b)

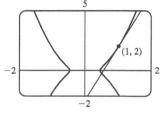

So at the point $(1, 2)$ we have $y' = \dfrac{10(1)^3 - 1}{2} = \dfrac{9}{2}$, and an equation

of the tangent line is $y - 2 = \frac{9}{2}(x - 1)$ or $y = \frac{9}{2}x - \frac{5}{2}$.

31. $9x^2 + y^2 = 9 \;\Rightarrow\; 18x + 2y\,y' = 0 \;\Rightarrow\; 2y\,y' = -18x \;\Rightarrow\; y' = -9x/y \;\Rightarrow$

$y'' = -9\left(\dfrac{y \cdot 1 - x \cdot y'}{y^2}\right) = -9\left(\dfrac{y - x(-9x/y)}{y^2}\right) = -9 \cdot \dfrac{y^2 + 9x^2}{y^3} = -9 \cdot \dfrac{9}{y^3}$ [since x and y must satisfy the

original equation, $9x^2 + y^2 = 9$]. Thus, $y'' = -81/y^3$.

33. $x^3 + y^3 = 1 \;\Rightarrow\; 3x^2 + 3y^2\,y' = 0 \;\Rightarrow\; y' = -\dfrac{x^2}{y^2} \;\Rightarrow$

$y'' = -\dfrac{y^2(2x) - x^2 \cdot 2y\,y'}{(y^2)^2} = -\dfrac{2xy^2 - 2x^2y(-x^2/y^2)}{y^4} = -\dfrac{2xy^4 + 2x^4y}{y^6} = -\dfrac{2xy(y^3 + x^3)}{y^6} = -\dfrac{2x}{y^5}$,

since x and y must satisfy the original equation, $x^3 + y^3 = 1$.

35. If $x = 0$ in $xy + e^y = e$, then we get $0 + e^y = e$, so $y = 1$ and the point where $x = 0$ is $(0, 1)$. Differentiating implicitly

with respect to x gives us $xy' + y \cdot 1 + e^y y' = 0$. Substituting 0 for x and 1 for y gives us

$0 + 1 + ey' = 0 \;\Rightarrow\; ey' = -1 \;\Rightarrow\; y' = -1/e$. Differentiating $xy' + y + e^y y' = 0$ implicitly with respect to x gives

us $xy'' + y' \cdot 1 + y' + e^y y'' + y' \cdot e^y y' = 0$. Now substitute 0 for x, 1 for y, and $-1/e$ for y'.

$0 + \left(-\dfrac{1}{e}\right) + \left(-\dfrac{1}{e}\right) + ey'' + \left(-\dfrac{1}{e}\right)(e)\left(-\dfrac{1}{e}\right) = 0 \;\Rightarrow\; -\dfrac{2}{e} + ey'' + \dfrac{1}{e} = 0 \;\Rightarrow\; ey'' = \dfrac{1}{e} \;\Rightarrow\; y'' = \dfrac{1}{e^2}$.

37. (a) There are eight points with horizontal tangents: four at $x \approx 1.57735$ and

four at $x \approx 0.42265$.

(b) $y' = \dfrac{3x^2 - 6x + 2}{2(2y^3 - 3y^2 - y + 1)} \;\Rightarrow\; y' = -1$ at $(0, 1)$ and $y' = \frac{1}{3}$ at $(0, 2)$.

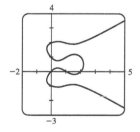

Equations of the tangent lines are $y = -x + 1$ and $y = \frac{1}{3}x + 2$.

(c) $y' = 0 \;\Rightarrow\; 3x^2 - 6x + 2 = 0 \;\Rightarrow\; x = 1 \pm \frac{1}{3}\sqrt{3}$

(d) By multiplying the right side of the equation by $x - 3$, we obtain the first graph. By modifying the equation in other ways, we can generate the other graphs.

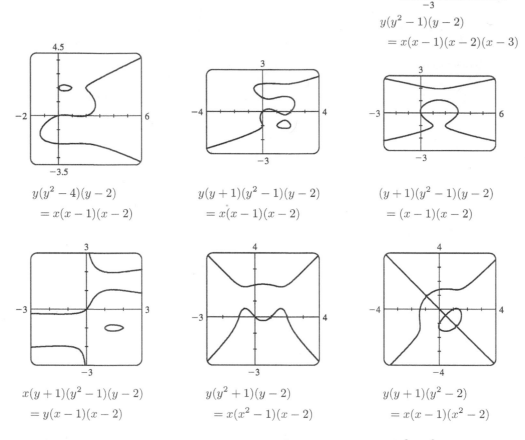

$$y(y^2 - 1)(y - 2)$$
$$= x(x - 1)(x - 2)(x - 3)$$

$$y(y^2 - 4)(y - 2)$$
$$= x(x - 1)(x - 2)$$

$$y(y + 1)(y^2 - 1)(y - 2)$$
$$= x(x - 1)(x - 2)$$

$$(y + 1)(y^2 - 1)(y - 2)$$
$$= (x - 1)(x - 2)$$

$$x(y + 1)(y^2 - 1)(y - 2)$$
$$= y(x - 1)(x - 2)$$

$$y(y^2 + 1)(y - 2)$$
$$= x(x^2 - 1)(x - 2)$$

$$y(y + 1)(y^2 - 2)$$
$$= x(x - 1)(x^2 - 2)$$

39. From Exercise 27, a tangent to the lemniscate will be horizontal if $y' = 0$ $\Rightarrow$ $25x - 4x(x^2 + y^2) = 0$ $\Rightarrow$ $x[25 - 4(x^2 + y^2)] = 0$ $\Rightarrow$ $x^2 + y^2 = \frac{25}{4}$ **(1)**. (Note that when x is 0, y is also 0, and there is no horizontal tangent at the origin.) Substituting $\frac{25}{4}$ for $x^2 + y^2$ in the equation of the lemniscate, $2(x^2 + y^2)^2 = 25(x^2 - y^2)$, we get $x^2 - y^2 = \frac{25}{8}$ **(2)**. Solving **(1)** and **(2)**, we have $x^2 = \frac{75}{16}$ and $y^2 = \frac{25}{16}$, so the four points are $\left(\pm\frac{5\sqrt{3}}{4}, \pm\frac{5}{4}\right)$.

41. $x^2 + y^2 = r^2$ is a circle with center O and $ax + by = 0$ is a line through O [assume a and b are not both zero]. $x^2 + y^2 = r^2$ $\Rightarrow$ $2x + 2yy' = 0$ $\Rightarrow$ $y' = -x/y$, so the slope of the tangent line at $P_0\,(x_0, y_0)$ is $-x_0/y_0$. The slope of the line OP_0 is y_0/x_0, which is the negative reciprocal of $-x_0/y_0$. Hence, the curves are orthogonal, and the families of curves are orthogonal trajectories of each other.

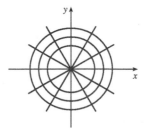

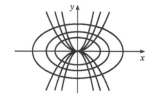

43. $y = cx^2 \Rightarrow y' = 2cx$ and $x^2 + 2y^2 = k$ [assume $k > 0$] $\Rightarrow 2x + 4yy' = 0 \Rightarrow$

$2yy' = -x \Rightarrow y' = -\dfrac{x}{2(y)} = -\dfrac{x}{2(cx^2)} = -\dfrac{1}{2cx}$, so the curves are orthogonal if

$c \neq 0$. If $c = 0$, then the horizontal line $y = cx^2 = 0$ intersects $x^2 + 2y^2 = k$ orthogonally

at $\left(\pm\sqrt{k}, 0 \right)$, since the ellipse $x^2 + 2y^2 = k$ has vertical tangents at those two points.

45. Since $A^2 < a^2$, we are assured that there are four points of intersection.

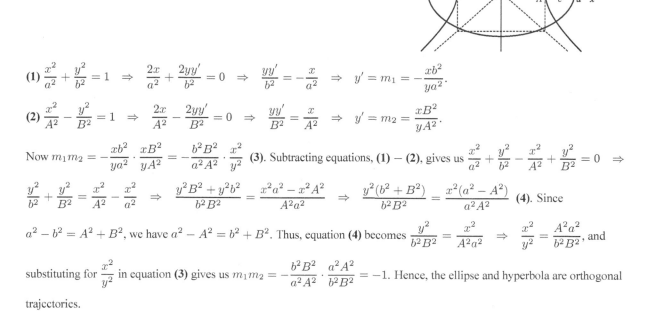

(1) $\dfrac{x^2}{a^2} + \dfrac{y^2}{b^2} = 1 \Rightarrow \dfrac{2x}{a^2} + \dfrac{2yy'}{b^2} = 0 \Rightarrow \dfrac{yy'}{b^2} = -\dfrac{x}{a^2} \Rightarrow y' = m_1 = -\dfrac{xb^2}{ya^2}$.

(2) $\dfrac{x^2}{A^2} - \dfrac{y^2}{B^2} = 1 \Rightarrow \dfrac{2x}{A^2} - \dfrac{2yy'}{B^2} = 0 \Rightarrow \dfrac{yy'}{B^2} = \dfrac{x}{A^2} \Rightarrow y' = m_2 = \dfrac{xB^2}{yA^2}$.

Now $m_1 m_2 = -\dfrac{xb^2}{ya^2} \cdot \dfrac{xB^2}{yA^2} = -\dfrac{b^2 B^2}{a^2 A^2} \cdot \dfrac{x^2}{y^2}$ **(3)**. Subtracting equations, **(1)** $-$ **(2)**, gives us $\dfrac{x^2}{a^2} + \dfrac{y^2}{b^2} - \dfrac{x^2}{A^2} + \dfrac{y^2}{B^2} = 0 \Rightarrow$

$\dfrac{y^2}{b^2} + \dfrac{y^2}{B^2} = \dfrac{x^2}{A^2} - \dfrac{x^2}{a^2} \Rightarrow \dfrac{y^2 B^2 + y^2 b^2}{b^2 B^2} = \dfrac{x^2 a^2 - x^2 A^2}{A^2 a^2} \Rightarrow \dfrac{y^2(b^2 + B^2)}{b^2 B^2} = \dfrac{x^2(a^2 - A^2)}{a^2 A^2}$ **(4)**. Since

$a^2 - b^2 = A^2 + B^2$, we have $a^2 - A^2 = b^2 + B^2$. Thus, equation **(4)** becomes $\dfrac{y^2}{b^2 B^2} = \dfrac{x^2}{A^2 a^2} \Rightarrow \dfrac{x^2}{y^2} = \dfrac{A^2 a^2}{b^2 B^2}$, and

substituting for $\dfrac{x^2}{y^2}$ in equation **(3)** gives us $m_1 m_2 = -\dfrac{b^2 B^2}{a^2 A^2} \cdot \dfrac{a^2 A^2}{b^2 B^2} = -1$. Hence, the ellipse and hyperbola are orthogonal

trajectories.

47. (a) $\left(P + \dfrac{n^2 a}{V^2} \right)(V - nb) = nRT \Rightarrow PV - Pnb + \dfrac{n^2 a}{V} - \dfrac{n^3 ab}{V^2} = nRT \Rightarrow$

$\dfrac{d}{dP}(PV - Pnb + n^2 aV^{-1} - n^3 abV^{-2}) = \dfrac{d}{dP}(nRT) \Rightarrow$

$PV' + V \cdot 1 - nb - n^2 aV^{-2} \cdot V' + 2n^3 abV^{-3} \cdot V' = 0 \Rightarrow V'(P - n^2 aV^{-2} + 2n^3 abV^{-3}) = nb - V \Rightarrow$

$V' = \dfrac{nb - V}{P - n^2 aV^{-2} + 2n^3 abV^{-3}}$ or $\dfrac{dV}{dP} = \dfrac{V^3(nb - V)}{PV^3 - n^2 aV + 2n^3 ab}$

(b) Using the last expression for dV/dP from part (a), we get

$\dfrac{dV}{dP} = \dfrac{(10 \text{ L})^3 [(1 \text{ mole})(0.04267 \text{ L/mole}) - 10 \text{ L}]}{\left[\begin{array}{c} (2.5 \text{ atm})(10 \text{ L})^3 - (1 \text{ mole})^2 (3.592 \text{ L}^2\text{-atm/ mole}^2)(10 \text{ L}) \\ + 2(1 \text{ mole})^3 (3.592 \text{ L}^2\text{-atm/ mole}^2)(0.04267 \text{ L/ mole}) \end{array} \right]}$

$= \dfrac{-9957.33 \text{ L}^4}{2464.386541 \text{ L}^3\text{-atm}} \approx -4.04 \text{ L/ atm}.$

49. If the circle has radius r, its equation is $x^2 + y^2 = r^2$ $\Rightarrow$ $2x + 2yy' = 0$ $\Rightarrow$ $y' = -\dfrac{x}{y}$, so the slope of the tangent line

at $P(x_0, y_0)$ is $-\dfrac{x_0}{y_0}$. The negative reciprocal of that slope is $\dfrac{-1}{-x_0/y_0} = \dfrac{y_0}{x_0}$, which is the slope of OP, so the tangent line at

P is perpendicular to the radius OP.

51. To find the points at which the ellipse $x^2 - xy + y^2 = 3$ crosses the x-axis, let $y = 0$ and solve for x.

$y = 0$ $\Rightarrow$ $x^2 - x(0) + 0^2 = 3$ $\Leftrightarrow$ $x = \pm\sqrt{3}$. So the graph of the ellipse crosses the x-axis at the points $(\pm\sqrt{3}, 0)$.

Using implicit differentiation to find y', we get $2x - xy' - y + 2yy' = 0$ $\Rightarrow$ $y'(2y - x) = y - 2x$ $\Leftrightarrow$ $y' = \dfrac{y - 2x}{2y - x}$.

So y' at $(\sqrt{3}, 0)$ is $\dfrac{0 - 2\sqrt{3}}{2(0) - \sqrt{3}} = 2$ and y' at $(-\sqrt{3}, 0)$ is $\dfrac{0 + 2\sqrt{3}}{2(0) + \sqrt{3}} = 2$. Thus, the tangent lines at these points are parallel.

53. $x^2 y^2 + xy = 2$ $\Rightarrow$ $x^2 \cdot 2yy' + y^2 \cdot 2x + x \cdot y' + y \cdot 1 = 0$ $\Leftrightarrow$ $y'(2x^2 y + x) = -2xy^2 - y$ $\Leftrightarrow$

$y' = -\dfrac{2xy^2 + y}{2x^2 y + x}$. So $-\dfrac{2xy^2 + y}{2x^2 y + x} = -1$ $\Leftrightarrow$ $2xy^2 + y = 2x^2 y + x$ $\Leftrightarrow$ $y(2xy + 1) = x(2xy + 1)$ $\Leftrightarrow$

$y(2xy + 1) - x(2xy + 1) = 0$ $\Leftrightarrow$ $(2xy + 1)(y - x) = 0$ $\Leftrightarrow$ $xy = -\frac{1}{2}$ or $y = x$. But $xy = -\frac{1}{2}$ $\Rightarrow$

$x^2 y^2 + xy = \frac{1}{4} - \frac{1}{2} \neq 2$, so we must have $x = y$. Then $x^2 y^2 + xy = 2$ $\Rightarrow$ $x^4 + x^2 = 2$ $\Leftrightarrow$ $x^4 + x^2 - 2 = 0$ $\Leftrightarrow$

$(x^2 + 2)(x^2 - 1) = 0$. So $x^2 = -2$, which is impossible, or $x^2 = 1$ $\Leftrightarrow$ $x = \pm 1$. Since $x = y$, the points on the curve

where the tangent line has a slope of -1 are $(-1, -1)$ and $(1, 1)$.

55. (a) $y = J(x)$ and $xy'' + y' + xy = 0$ $\Rightarrow$ $xJ''(x) + J'(x) + xJ(x) = 0$. If $x = 0$, we have $0 + J'(0) + 0 = 0$,

so $J'(0) = 0$.

(b) Differentiating $xy'' + y' + xy = 0$ implicitly, we get $xy''' + y'' \cdot 1 + y'' + xy' + y \cdot 1 = 0$ $\Rightarrow$

$xy''' + 2y'' + xy' + y = 0$, so $xJ'''(x) + 2J''(x) + xJ'(x) + J(x) = 0$. If $x = 0$, we have

$0 + 2J''(0) + 0 + 1$ $[J(0) = 1$ is given$]$ $= 0$ $\Rightarrow$ $2J''(0) = -1$ $\Rightarrow$ $J''(0) = -\frac{1}{2}$.

3.6 Inverse Trigonometric Functions and Their Derivatives

1. (a) $\sin^{-1}\left(\frac{\sqrt{3}}{2}\right) = \frac{\pi}{3}$ since $\sin\frac{\pi}{3} = \frac{\sqrt{3}}{2}$ and $\frac{\pi}{3}$ is in $\left[-\frac{\pi}{2}, \frac{\pi}{2}\right]$.

(b) $\cos^{-1}(-1) = \pi$ since $\cos\pi = -1$ and π is in $[0, \pi]$.

3. (a) $\arctan 1 = \frac{\pi}{4}$ since $\tan\frac{\pi}{4} = 1$ and $\frac{\pi}{4}$ is in $\left(-\frac{\pi}{2}, \frac{\pi}{2}\right)$.

(b) $\sin^{-1}\frac{1}{\sqrt{2}} = \frac{\pi}{4}$ since $\sin\frac{\pi}{4} = \frac{1}{\sqrt{2}}$ and $\frac{\pi}{4}$ is in $\left[-\frac{\pi}{2}, \frac{\pi}{2}\right]$.

5. Let $\theta = \sin^{-1}\left(\frac{2}{3}\right)$.

Then $\tan\left(\sin^{-1}\left(\frac{2}{3}\right)\right) = \tan\theta = \dfrac{2}{\sqrt{5}}$.

7. Let $\theta = \tan^{-1}\sqrt{2}$. Then

$$\sin\left(2\tan^{-1}\sqrt{2}\right) = \sin(2\theta) = 2\sin = 2\left(\frac{\sqrt{2}}{\sqrt{3}}\right)\left(\frac{1}{\sqrt{3}}\right) = \frac{2\sqrt{2}}{3}$$

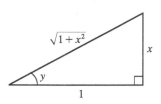

9. Let $y = \sin^{-1}x$. Then $-\frac{\pi}{2} \le y \le \frac{\pi}{2}$ $\Rightarrow$ $\cos y \ge 0$, so $\cos(\sin^{-1}x) = \cos y = \sqrt{1 - \sin^2 y} = \sqrt{1 - x^2}$.

11. Let $y = \tan^{-1}x$. Then $\tan y = x$, so from the triangle we see that

$$\sin(\tan^{-1}x) = \sin y = \frac{x}{\sqrt{1+x^2}}.$$

13.

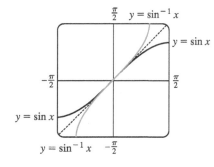

The graph of $\sin^{-1}x$ is the reflection of the graph of $\sin x$ about the line $y = x$.

15. Let $y = \cos^{-1}x$. Then $\cos y = x$ and $0 \le y \le \pi$ $\Rightarrow$ $-\sin y\,\dfrac{dy}{dx} = 1$ $\Rightarrow$

$$\frac{dy}{dx} = -\frac{1}{\sin y} = -\frac{1}{\sqrt{1 - \cos^2 y}} = -\frac{1}{\sqrt{1 - x^2}}. \quad \text{[Note that } \sin y \ge 0 \text{ for } 0 \le y \le \pi.\text{]}$$

17. $y = (\tan^{-1}x)^2$ $\Rightarrow$ $y' = 2(\tan^{-1}x)^1 \cdot \dfrac{d}{dx}(\tan^{-1}x) = 2\tan^{-1}x \cdot \dfrac{1}{1+x^2} = \dfrac{2\tan^{-1}x}{1+x^2}$

19. $y = \sin^{-1}(2x+1)$ $\Rightarrow$

$$y' = \frac{1}{\sqrt{1 - (2x+1)^2}} \cdot \frac{d}{dx}(2x+1) = \frac{1}{\sqrt{1 - (4x^2 + 4x + 1)}} \cdot 2 = \frac{2}{\sqrt{-4x^2 - 4x}} = \frac{1}{\sqrt{-x^2 - x}}$$

21. $G(x) = \sqrt{1-x^2}\,\arccos x$ $\Rightarrow$ $G'(x) = \sqrt{1-x^2}\cdot\dfrac{-1}{\sqrt{1-x^2}} + \arccos x\cdot\dfrac{1}{2}(1-x^2)^{-1/2}(-2x) = -1 - \dfrac{x\arccos x}{\sqrt{1-x^2}}$

23. $y = \cos^{-1}(e^{2x})$ $\Rightarrow$ $y' = -\dfrac{1}{\sqrt{1 - (e^{2x})^2}} \cdot \dfrac{d}{dx}(e^{2x}) = -\dfrac{2e^{2x}}{\sqrt{1 - e^{4x}}}$

25. $y = \arctan(\cos\theta)$ $\Rightarrow$ $y' = \dfrac{1}{1 + (\cos\theta)^2}(-\sin\theta) = -\dfrac{\sin\theta}{1 + \cos^2\theta}$

27. $y = x\sin^{-1}x + \sqrt{1-x^2}$ $\Rightarrow$

$$y' = x \cdot \frac{1}{\sqrt{1-x^2}} + (\sin^{-1}x)(1) + \frac{1}{2}(1-x^2)^{-1/2}(-2x) = \frac{x}{\sqrt{1-x^2}} + \sin^{-1}x - \frac{x}{\sqrt{1-x^2}} = \sin^{-1}x$$

29. $y = \arccos\left(\dfrac{b + a\cos x}{a + b\cos x}\right)$ $\Rightarrow$

$$y' = -\frac{1}{\sqrt{1 - \left(\dfrac{b + a\cos x}{a + b\cos x}\right)^2}} \frac{(a + b\cos x)(-a\sin x) - (b + a\cos x)(-b\sin x)}{(a + b\cos x)^2}$$

$$= \frac{1}{\sqrt{a^2 + b^2\cos^2 x - b^2 - a^2\cos^2 x}} \frac{(a^2 - b^2)\sin x}{|a + b\cos x|}$$

$$= \frac{1}{\sqrt{a^2 - b^2}\sqrt{1 - \cos^2 x}} \frac{(a^2 - b^2)\sin x}{|a + b\cos x|} = \frac{\sqrt{a^2 - b^2}}{|a + b\cos x|} \frac{\sin x}{|\sin x|}$$

But $0 \le x \le \pi$, so $|\sin x| = \sin x$. Also $a > b > 0$ $\Rightarrow$ $b\cos x \ge -b > -a$, so $a + b\cos x > 0$. Thus $y' = \dfrac{\sqrt{a^2 - b^2}}{a + b\cos x}$.

31. $g(x) = \cos^{-1}(3 - 2x)$ $\Rightarrow$ $g'(x) = -\dfrac{1}{\sqrt{1 - (3 - 2x)^2}}(-2) = \dfrac{2}{\sqrt{1 - (3 - 2x)^2}}$.

Domain$(g) = \{x \mid -1 \le 3 - 2x \le 1\} = \{x \mid -4 \le -2x \le -2\} = \{x \mid 2 \ge x \ge 1\} = [1, 2]$.

Domain$(g') = \{x \mid 1 - (3 - 2x)^2 > 0\} = \{x \mid (3 - 2x)^2 < 1\} = \{x \mid |3 - 2x| < 1\}$

$$= \{x \mid -1 < 3 - 2x < 1\} = \{x \mid -4 < -2x < -2\} = \{x \mid 2 > x > 1\} = (1, 2)$$

33. $g(x) = x\sin^{-1}\left(\dfrac{x}{4}\right) + \sqrt{16 - x^2}$ $\Rightarrow$ $g'(x) = \sin^{-1}\left(\dfrac{x}{4}\right) + \dfrac{x}{4\sqrt{1 - (x/4)^2}} - \dfrac{x}{\sqrt{16 - x^2}} = \sin^{-1}\left(\dfrac{x}{4}\right)$ $\Rightarrow$

$g'(2) = \sin^{-1}\left(\frac{1}{2}\right) = \frac{\pi}{6}$

35. $f(x) = \sqrt{1 - x^2}\arcsin x$ $\Rightarrow$ $f'(x) = \sqrt{1 - x^2} \cdot \dfrac{1}{\sqrt{1 - x^2}} + \arcsin x \cdot \dfrac{1}{2}\left(1 - x^2\right)^{-1/2}(-2x) = 1 - \dfrac{x\arcsin x}{\sqrt{1 - x^2}}$

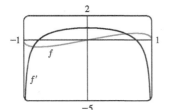

Note that $f' = 0$ where the graph of f has a horizontal tangent. Also note that f' is negative when f is decreasing and f' is positive when f is increasing.

37. $\displaystyle\lim_{x \to -1^+} \sin^{-1} x = \sin^{-1}(-1) = -\frac{\pi}{2}$

39. Let $t = e^x$. As $x \to \infty$, $t \to \infty$. $\displaystyle\lim_{x \to \infty} \arctan(e^x) = \lim_{t \to \infty} \arctan t = \frac{\pi}{2}$ by (3).

41. (a) If $y = f^{-1}(x)$, then $f(y) = x$. Differentiating implicitly with respect to x and remembering that y is a function of x,

we get $f'(y)\dfrac{dy}{dx} = 1$, so $\dfrac{dy}{dx} = \dfrac{1}{f'(y)}$ $\Rightarrow$ $\left(f^{-1}\right)'(x) = \dfrac{1}{f'(f^{-1}(x))}$.

(b) $f(4) = 5$ $\Rightarrow$ $f^{-1}(5) = 4$. By part (a), $\left(f^{-1}\right)'(5) = \dfrac{1}{f'(f^{-1}(5))} = \dfrac{1}{f'(4)} = 1/\left(\frac{2}{3}\right) = \frac{3}{2}$.

43. (a) Let $f(x) = \sin x$, so $f^{-1}(x) = \sin^{-1} x$ and $f'(x) = \cos x$.

$$(f^{-1})'(x) = \frac{1}{f'(f^{-1}(x))} \quad \Rightarrow$$

$$\frac{d}{dx}(\sin^{-1} x) = \frac{1}{\cos(\sin^{-1} x)} = \frac{1}{\sqrt{1-x^2}/1} = \frac{1}{\sqrt{1-x^2}}, \text{ which is Formula 1.}$$

(Note that we could have used the result of Exercise 9.)

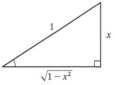

(b) Let $f(x) = \tan x$, so $f^{-1}(x) = \tan^{-1} x$ and $f'(x) = \sec^2 x$.

$$(f^{-1})'(x) = \frac{1}{f'(f^{-1}(x))} \quad \Rightarrow$$

$$\frac{d}{dx}(\tan^{-1} x) = \frac{1}{\sec^2(\tan^{-1} x)} = \frac{1}{[\sec(\tan^{-1} x)]^2} = \frac{1}{(\sqrt{1+x^2})^2} = \frac{1}{1+x^2},$$

which is Formula 4.

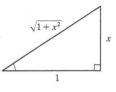

3.7   Derivatives of Logarithmic Functions

1. The differentiation formula for logarithmic functions, $\dfrac{d}{dx}(\log_a x) = \dfrac{1}{x \ln a}$, is simplest when $a = e$ because $\ln e = 1$.

3. $f(x) = \sin(\ln x) \quad \Rightarrow \quad f'(x) = \cos(\ln x) \cdot \dfrac{d}{dx} \ln x = \cos(\ln x) \cdot \dfrac{1}{x} = \dfrac{\cos(\ln x)}{x}$

5. $f(x) = \log_2(1 - 3x) \quad \Rightarrow \quad f'(x) = \dfrac{1}{(1-3x)\ln 2} \dfrac{d}{dx}(1-3x) = \dfrac{-3}{(1-3x)\ln 2}$ or $\dfrac{3}{(3x-1)\ln 2}$

7. $f(x) = \sqrt[5]{\ln x} = (\ln x)^{1/5} \quad \Rightarrow \quad f'(x) = \frac{1}{5}(\ln x)^{-4/5}\dfrac{d}{dx}(\ln x) = \dfrac{1}{5(\ln x)^{4/5}} \cdot \dfrac{1}{x} = \dfrac{1}{5x\sqrt[5]{(\ln x)^4}}$

9. $f(x) = \sin x \ln(5x) \quad \Rightarrow \quad f'(x) = \sin x \cdot \dfrac{1}{5x} \cdot \dfrac{d}{dx}(5x) + \ln(5x) \cdot \cos x = \dfrac{\sin x \cdot 5}{5x} + \cos x \ln(5x) = \dfrac{\sin x}{x} + \cos x \ln(5x)$

11. $F(t) = \ln \dfrac{(2t+1)^3}{(3t-1)^4} = \ln(2t+1)^3 - \ln(3t-1)^4 = 3\ln(2t+1) - 4\ln(3t-1) \quad \Rightarrow$

$$F'(t) = 3 \cdot \dfrac{1}{2t+1} \cdot 2 - 4 \cdot \dfrac{1}{3t-1} \cdot 3 = \dfrac{6}{2t+1} - \dfrac{12}{3t-1}, \text{ or combined, } \dfrac{-6(t+3)}{(2t+1)(3t-1)}.$$

13. $g(x) = \ln\left(x\sqrt{x^2-1}\right) = \ln x + \ln(x^2-1)^{1/2} = \ln x + \frac{1}{2}\ln(x^2-1) \quad \Rightarrow$

$$g'(x) = \dfrac{1}{x} + \dfrac{1}{2} \cdot \dfrac{1}{x^2-1} \cdot 2x = \dfrac{1}{x} + \dfrac{x}{x^2-1} = \dfrac{x^2 - 1 + x \cdot x}{x(x^2-1)} = \dfrac{2x^2 - 1}{x(x^2-1)}$$

15. $y = \ln|2 - x - 5x^2| \quad \Rightarrow \quad y' = \dfrac{1}{2-x-5x^2} \cdot (-1-10x) = \dfrac{-10x-1}{2-x-5x^2}$ or $\dfrac{10x+1}{5x^2+x-2}$

17. $y = \ln(e^{-x} + xe^{-x}) = \ln(e^{-x}(1+x)) = \ln(e^{-x}) + \ln(1+x) = -x + \ln(1+x) \quad \Rightarrow$

$$y' = -1 + \dfrac{1}{1+x} = \dfrac{-1-x+1}{1+x} = -\dfrac{x}{1+x}$$

19. $y = 2x \log_{10} \sqrt{x} = 2x \log_{10} x^{1/2} = 2x \cdot \frac{1}{2} \log_{10} x = x \log_{10} x \quad \Rightarrow \quad y' = x \cdot \frac{1}{x \ln 10} + \log_{10} x \cdot 1 = \frac{1}{\ln 10} + \log_{10} x$

Note: $\frac{1}{\ln 10} = \frac{\ln e}{\ln 10} = \log_{10} e$, so the answer could be written as $\frac{1}{\ln 10} + \log_{10} x = \log_{10} e + \log_{10} x = \log_{10} ex$.

21. $y = x^2 \ln(2x) \quad \Rightarrow \quad y' = x^2 \cdot \frac{1}{2x} \cdot 2 + \ln(2x) \cdot (2x) = x + 2x \ln(2x) \quad \Rightarrow$

$y'' = 1 + 2x \cdot \frac{1}{2x} \cdot 2 + \ln(2x) \cdot 2 = 1 + 2 + 2\ln(2x) = 3 + 2\ln(2x)$

23. $f(x) = \dfrac{x}{1 - \ln(x-1)} \quad \Rightarrow$

$f'(x) = \dfrac{[1 - \ln(x-1)] \cdot 1 - x \cdot \frac{-1}{x-1}}{[1 - \ln(x-1)]^2} = \dfrac{\frac{(x-1)[1 - \ln(x-1)] + x}{x-1}}{[1 - \ln(x-1)]^2} = \dfrac{x - 1 - (x-1)\ln(x-1) + x}{(x-1)[1 - \ln(x-1)]^2}$

$= \dfrac{2x - 1 - (x-1)\ln(x-1)}{(x-1)[1 - \ln(x-1)]^2}$

$\text{Dom}(f) = \{x \mid x - 1 > 0 \quad \text{and} \quad 1 - \ln(x-1) \neq 0\} = \{x \mid x > 1 \quad \text{and} \quad \ln(x-1) \neq 1\}$

$= \{x \mid x > 1 \quad \text{and} \quad x - 1 \neq e^1\} = \{x \mid x > 1 \quad \text{and} \quad x \neq 1 + e\} = (1, 1 + e) \cup (1 + e, \infty)$

25. $y = \ln(x^2 - 3x + 1) \quad \Rightarrow \quad y' = \dfrac{1}{x^2 - 3x + 1} \cdot (2x - 3) \quad \Rightarrow \quad y'(3) = \frac{1}{1} \cdot 3 = 3$, so an equation of a tangent line at

$(3, 0)$ is $y - 0 = 3(x - 3)$, or $y = 3x - 9$.

27. $y = \ln\left(xe^{x^2}\right) = \ln x + \ln e^{x^2} = \ln x + x^2 \quad \Rightarrow \quad y' = \dfrac{1}{x} + 2x$. At $(1, 1)$, the slope of the tangent line is

$y'(1) = 1 + 2 = 3$, and an equation of the tangent line is $y - 1 = 3(x - 1)$, or $y = 3x - 2$.

29. (a) The domain of $f(x) = x \ln x$ is $(0, \infty)$. $f'(x) = x(1/x) + (\ln x) \cdot 1 = 1 + \ln x$. So $f'(x) < 0$ when

$1 + \ln x < 0 \quad \Leftrightarrow \quad \ln x < -1 \quad \Leftrightarrow \quad x < e^{-1}$. Therefore, f is decreasing on $(0, 1/e)$.

(b) $f'(x) = 1 + \ln x \quad \Rightarrow \quad f''(x) = 1/x > 0$ for $x > 0$. So the curve is concave upward on $(0, \infty)$.

31. $f(x) = cx + \ln(\cos x) \quad \Rightarrow \quad f'(x) = c + \dfrac{1}{\cos x} \cdot (-\sin x) = c - \tan x$.

$f'(\frac{\pi}{4}) = 6 \quad \Rightarrow \quad c - \tan \frac{\pi}{4} = 6 \quad \Rightarrow \quad c - 1 = 6 \quad \Rightarrow \quad c = 7$.

33. $y = (2x + 1)^5 (x^4 - 3)^6 \quad \Rightarrow \quad \ln y = \ln\left((2x + 1)^5 (x^4 - 3)^6\right) \quad \Rightarrow \quad \ln y = 5\ln(2x + 1) + 6\ln(x^4 - 3) \quad \Rightarrow$

$\dfrac{1}{y} y' = 5 \cdot \dfrac{1}{2x + 1} \cdot 2 + 6 \cdot \dfrac{1}{x^4 - 3} \cdot 4x^3 \quad \Rightarrow$

$y' = y\left(\dfrac{10}{2x + 1} + \dfrac{24x^3}{x^4 - 3}\right) = (2x + 1)^5 (x^4 - 3)^6 \left(\dfrac{10}{2x + 1} + \dfrac{24x^3}{x^4 - 3}\right)$.

[The answer could be simplified to $y' = 2(2x + 1)^4 (x^4 - 3)^5 (29x^4 + 12x^3 - 15)$, but this is unnecessary.]

35. $y = \dfrac{\sin^2 x \tan^4 x}{(x^2+1)^2}$ $\Rightarrow$ $\ln y = \ln(\sin^2 x \tan^4 x) - \ln(x^2+1)^2$ $\Rightarrow$

$\ln y = \ln(\sin x)^2 + \ln(\tan x)^4 - \ln(x^2+1)^2$ $\Rightarrow$ $\ln y = 2\ln|\sin x| + 4\ln|\tan x| - 2\ln(x^2+1)$ $\Rightarrow$

$\dfrac{1}{y}\, y' = 2 \cdot \dfrac{1}{\sin x} \cdot \cos x + 4 \cdot \dfrac{1}{\tan x} \cdot \sec^2 x - 2 \cdot \dfrac{1}{x^2+1} \cdot 2x$ $\Rightarrow$ $y' = \dfrac{\sin^2 x \tan^4 x}{(x^2+1)^2}\left(2\cot x + \dfrac{4\sec^2 x}{\tan x} - \dfrac{4x}{x^2+1}\right)$

37. $y = x^x$ $\Rightarrow$ $\ln y = \ln x^x$ $\Rightarrow$ $\ln y = x\ln x$ $\Rightarrow$ $y'/y = x(1/x) + (\ln x) \cdot 1$ $\Rightarrow$ $y' = y(1 + \ln x)$ $\Rightarrow$

$y' = x^x(1 + \ln x)$

39. $y = (\cos x)^x$ $\Rightarrow$ $\ln y = \ln(\cos x)^x$ $\Rightarrow$ $\ln y = x\ln\cos x$ $\Rightarrow$ $\dfrac{1}{y}\, y' = x \cdot \dfrac{1}{\cos x} \cdot (-\sin x) + \ln\cos x \cdot 1$ $\Rightarrow$

$y' = y\left(\ln\cos x - \dfrac{x\sin x}{\cos x}\right)$ $\Rightarrow$ $y' = (\cos x)^x (\ln\cos x - x\tan x)$

41. $y = (\tan x)^{1/x}$ $\Rightarrow$ $\ln y = \ln(\tan x)^{1/x}$ $\Rightarrow$ $\ln y = \dfrac{1}{x}\ln\tan x$ $\Rightarrow$

$\dfrac{1}{y}\, y' = \dfrac{1}{x} \cdot \dfrac{1}{\tan x} \cdot \sec^2 x + \ln\tan x \cdot \left(-\dfrac{1}{x^2}\right)$ $\Rightarrow$ $y' = y\left(\dfrac{\sec^2 x}{x\tan x} - \dfrac{\ln\tan x}{x^2}\right)$ $\Rightarrow$

$y' = (\tan x)^{1/x}\left(\dfrac{\sec^2 x}{x\tan x} - \dfrac{\ln\tan x}{x^2}\right)$ or $y' = (\tan x)^{1/x} \cdot \dfrac{1}{x}\left(\csc x \sec x - \dfrac{\ln\tan x}{x}\right)$

43. $y = \ln(x^2 + y^2)$ $\Rightarrow$ $y' = \dfrac{1}{x^2+y^2}\dfrac{d}{dx}(x^2+y^2)$ $\Rightarrow$ $y' = \dfrac{2x + 2yy'}{x^2+y^2}$ $\Rightarrow$ $x^2 y' + y^2 y' = 2x + 2yy'$ $\Rightarrow$

$x^2 y' + y^2 y' - 2yy' = 2x$ $\Rightarrow$ $(x^2 + y^2 - 2y)y' = 2x$ $\Rightarrow$ $y' = \dfrac{2x}{x^2 + y^2 - 2y}$

45. $f(x) = \ln(x-1)$ $\Rightarrow$ $f'(x) = \dfrac{1}{(x-1)} = (x-1)^{-1}$ $\Rightarrow$ $f''(x) = -(x-1)^{-2}$ $\Rightarrow$ $f'''(x) = 2(x-1)^{-3}$ $\Rightarrow$

$f^{(4)}(x) = -2 \cdot 3(x-1)^{-4}$ $\Rightarrow$ $\cdots$ $\Rightarrow$ $f^{(n)}(x) = (-1)^{n-1} \cdot 2 \cdot 3 \cdot 4 \cdots \cdot (n-1)(x-1)^{-n} = (-1)^{n-1}\dfrac{(n-1)!}{(x-1)^n}$

47. If $f(x) = \ln(1+x)$, then $f'(x) = \dfrac{1}{1+x}$, so $f'(0) = 1$.

Thus, $\displaystyle\lim_{x\to 0}\dfrac{\ln(1+x)}{x} = \lim_{x\to 0}\dfrac{f(x)}{x} = \lim_{x\to 0}\dfrac{f(x) - f(0)}{x - 0} = f'(0) = 1$.

3.8   Rates of Change in the Natural and Social Sciences

1. (a) $s = f(t) = t^3 - 12t^2 + 36t$ $\Rightarrow$ $v(t) = f'(t) = 3t^2 - 24t + 36$

(b) $v(3) = 27 - 72 + 36 = -9$ ft/s

(c) The particle is at rest when $v(t) = 0$. $3t^2 - 24t + 36 = 0$ $\Leftrightarrow$ $3(t-2)(t-6) = 0$ $\Leftrightarrow$ $t = 2$ s or 6 s.

(d) The particle is moving in the positive direction when $v(t) > 0$. $3(t-2)(t-6) > 0$ $\Leftrightarrow$ $0 \le t < 2$ or $t > 6$.

(e) Since the particle is moving in the positive direction and in the negative direction, we need to calculate the distance traveled in the intervals $[0, 2]$, $[2, 6]$, and $[6, 8]$ separately.

$$|f(2) - f(0)| = |32 - 0| = 32.$$

$$|f(6) - f(2)| = |0 - 32| = 32.$$

$$|f(8) - f(6)| = |32 - 0| = 32.$$

The total distance is $32 + 32 + 32 = 96$ ft.

(f)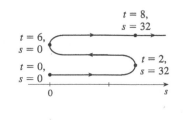
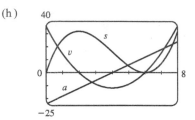

(g) $v(t) = 3t^2 - 24t + 36 \quad \Rightarrow$

$a(t) = v'(t) = 6t - 24.$

$a(3) = 6(3) - 24 = -6$ (ft/s)/s or ft/s^2.

(h)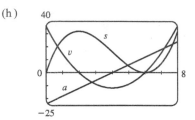

(i) The particle is speeding up when v and a have the same sign. This occurs when $2 < t < 4$ [v and a are both negative] and when $t > 6$ [v and a are both positive]. It is slowing down when v and a have opposite signs; that is, when $0 \le t < 2$ and when $4 < t < 6$.

3. (a) $s = f(t) = \cos(\pi t/4) \quad \Rightarrow \quad v(t) = f'(t) = -\sin(\pi t/4) \cdot (\pi/4)$

(b) $v(3) = -\frac{\pi}{4} \sin \frac{3\pi}{4} = -\frac{\pi}{4} \cdot \frac{\sqrt{2}}{2} = -\frac{\pi\sqrt{2}}{8}$ ft/s $[\approx -0.56]$

(c) The particle is at rest when $v(t) = 0$. $-\frac{\pi}{4} \sin \frac{\pi t}{4} = 0 \quad \Rightarrow \quad \sin \frac{\pi t}{4} = 0 \quad \Rightarrow \quad \frac{\pi t}{4} = \pi n \quad \Rightarrow \quad t = 0, 4, 8$ s.

(d) The particle is moving in the positive direction when $v(t) > 0$. $-\frac{\pi}{4} \sin \frac{\pi t}{4} > 0 \quad \Rightarrow \quad \sin \frac{\pi t}{4} < 0 \quad \Rightarrow \quad 4 < t < 8.$

(e) From part (c), $v(t) = 0$ for $t = 0, 4, 8$. As in Exercise 1, we'll find the distance traveled in the intervals $[0, 4]$ and $[4, 8]$.

$$|f(4) - f(0)| = |-1 - 1| = 2$$

$$|f(8) - f(4)| = |1 - (-1)| = 2.$$

The total distance is $2 + 2 = 4$ ft.

(f)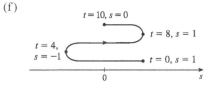

(g) $v(t) = -\dfrac{\pi}{4} \sin \dfrac{\pi t}{4} \quad \Rightarrow$

$a(t) = v'(t) = -\dfrac{\pi}{4} \cos \dfrac{\pi t}{4} \cdot \dfrac{\pi}{4} = -\dfrac{\pi^2}{16} \cos \dfrac{\pi t}{4}.$

$a(3) = -\dfrac{\pi^2}{16} \cos \dfrac{3\pi}{4} = -\dfrac{\pi^2}{16}\left(-\dfrac{\sqrt{2}}{2}\right) = \dfrac{\pi^2\sqrt{2}}{32}$ (ft/s)/s or ft/s^2.

(h)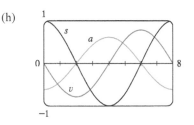

(i) The particle is speeding up when v and a have the same sign. This occurs when $0 < t < 2$ or $8 < t < 10$ [v and a are both negative] and when $4 < t < 6$ [v and a are both positive]. It is slowing down when v and a have opposite signs; that is, when $2 < t < 4$ and when $6 < t < 8$.

5. (a) From the figure, the velocity v is positive on the interval $(0, 2)$ and negative on the interval $(2, 3)$. The acceleration a is positive (negative) when the slope of the tangent line is positive (negative), so the acceleration is positive on the interval

$(0, 1)$, and negative on the interval $(1, 3)$. The particle is speeding up when v and a have the same sign, that is, on the interval $(0, 1)$ when $v > 0$ and $a > 0$, and on the interval $(2, 3)$ when $v < 0$ and $a < 0$. The particle is slowing down when v and a have opposite signs, that is, on the interval $(1, 2)$ when $v > 0$ and $a < 0$.

(b) $v > 0$ on $(0, 3)$ and $v < 0$ on $(3, 4)$. $a > 0$ on $(1, 2)$ and $a < 0$ on $(0, 1)$ and $(2, 4)$. The particle is speeding up on $(1, 2)$ $[v > 0, a > 0]$ and on $(3, 4)$ $[v < 0, a < 0]$. The particle is slowing down on $(0, 1)$ and $(2, 3)$ $[v > 0, a < 0]$.

7. (a) $s(t) = t^3 - 4.5t^2 - 7t$ $\Rightarrow$ $v(t) = s'(t) = 3t^2 - 9t - 7 = 5$ $\Leftrightarrow$ $3t^2 - 9t - 12 = 0$ $\Leftrightarrow$

   $3(t - 4)(t + 1) = 0$ $\Leftrightarrow$ $t = 4$ or -1. Since $t \geq 0$, the particle reaches a velocity of 5 m/s at $t = 4$ s.

   (b) $a(t) = v'(t) = 6t - 9 = 0$ $\Leftrightarrow$ $t = 1.5$. The acceleration changes from negative to positive, so the velocity changes from decreasing to increasing. Thus, at $t = 1.5$ s, the velocity has its minimum value.

9. (a) $h = 10t - 0.83t^2$ $\Rightarrow$ $v(t) = \dfrac{dh}{dt} = 10 - 1.66t$, so $v(3) = 10 - 1.66(3) = 5.02$ m/s.

   (b) $h = 25$ $\Rightarrow$ $10t - 0.83t^2 = 25$ $\Rightarrow$ $0.83t^2 - 10t + 25 = 0$ $\Rightarrow$ $t = \frac{10 \pm \sqrt{17}}{1.66} \approx 3.54$ or 8.51.

   The value $t_1 = \frac{10 - \sqrt{17}}{1.66}$ corresponds to the time it takes for the stone to rise 25 m and $t_2 = \frac{10 + \sqrt{17}}{1.66}$ corresponds to the

   time when the stone is 25 m high on the way down. Thus, $v(t_1) = 10 - 1.66\left(\frac{10 - \sqrt{17}}{1.66}\right) = \sqrt{17} \approx 4.12$ m/s.

11. (a) $A(x) = x^2$ $\Rightarrow$ $A'(x) = 2x$. $A'(15) = 30$ mm²/mm is the rate at which the area is increasing with respect to the side length as x reaches 15 mm.

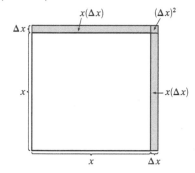

   (b) The perimeter is $P(x) = 4x$, so $A'(x) = 2x = \frac{1}{2}(4x) = \frac{1}{2}P(x)$. The figure suggests that if Δx is small, then the change in the area of the square is approximately half of its perimeter (2 of the 4 sides) times Δx. From the figure, $\Delta A = 2x\,(\Delta x) + (\Delta x)^2$. If Δx is small, then $\Delta A \approx 2x\,(\Delta x)$ and so $\Delta A / \Delta x \approx 2x$.

13. (a) Using $A(r) = \pi r^2$, we find that the average rate of change is:

   (i) $\dfrac{A(3) - A(2)}{3 - 2} = \dfrac{9\pi - 4\pi}{1} = 5\pi$

   (ii) $\dfrac{A(2.5) - A(2)}{2.5 - 2} = \dfrac{6.25\pi - 4\pi}{0.5} = 4.5\pi$

   (iii) $\dfrac{A(2.1) - A(2)}{2.1 - 2} = \dfrac{4.41\pi - 4\pi}{0.1} = 4.1\pi$

   (b) $A(r) = \pi r^2$ $\Rightarrow$ $A'(r) = 2\pi r$, so $A'(2) = 4\pi$.

   (c) The circumference is $C(r) = 2\pi r = A'(r)$. The figure suggests that if Δr is small, then the change in the area of the circle (a ring around the outside) is approximately equal to its circumference times Δr. Straightening out this ring gives us a shape that is approximately rectangular with length $2\pi r$ and width Δr, so $\Delta A \approx 2\pi r(\Delta r)$. Algebraically, $\Delta A = A(r + \Delta r) - A(r) = \pi(r + \Delta r)^2 - \pi r^2 = 2\pi r(\Delta r) + \pi(\Delta r)^2$. So we see that if Δr is small, then $\Delta A \approx 2\pi r(\Delta r)$ and therefore, $\Delta A / \Delta r \approx 2\pi r$.

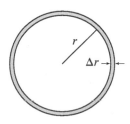

15. $S(r) = 4\pi r^2 \;\Rightarrow\; S'(r) = 8\pi r \;\Rightarrow$

(a) $S'(1) = 8\pi$ ft²/ft   (b) $S'(2) = 16\pi$ ft²/ft   (c) $S'(3) = 24\pi$ ft²/ft

As the radius increases, the surface area grows at an increasing rate. In fact, the rate of change is linear with respect to the radius.

17. The mass is $f(x) = 3x^2$, so the linear density at x is $\rho(x) = f'(x) = 6x$.

(a) $\rho(1) = 6$ kg/m   (b) $\rho(2) = 12$ kg/m   (c) $\rho(3) = 18$ kg/m

Since ρ is an increasing function, the density will be the highest at the right end of the rod and lowest at the left end.

19. The quantity of charge is $Q(t) = t^3 - 2t^2 + 6t + 2$, so the current is $Q'(t) = 3t^2 - 4t + 6$.

(a) $Q'(0.5) = 3(0.5)^2 - 4(0.5) + 6 = 4.75$ A   (b) $Q'(1) = 3(1)^2 - 4(1) + 6 = 5$ A

The current is lowest when Q' has a minimum. $Q''(t) = 6t - 4 < 0$ when $t < \frac{2}{3}$. So the current decreases when $t < \frac{2}{3}$ and increases when $t > \frac{2}{3}$. Thus, the current is lowest at $t = \frac{2}{3}$ s.

21. (a) To find the rate of change of volume with respect to pressure, we first solve for V in terms of P.

$$PV = C \;\Rightarrow\; V = \frac{C}{P} \;\Rightarrow\; \frac{dV}{dP} = -\frac{C}{P^2}.$$

(b) From the formula for dV/dP in part (a), we see that as P increases, the absolute value of dV/dP decreases.

Thus, the volume is decreasing more rapidly at the beginning.

(c) $\beta = -\dfrac{1}{V}\dfrac{dV}{dP} = -\dfrac{1}{V}\left(-\dfrac{C}{P^2}\right) = \dfrac{C}{(PV)P} = \dfrac{C}{CP} = \dfrac{1}{P}$

23. In Example 6, the population function was $n = 2^t n_0$. Since we are tripling instead of doubling and the initial population is 400, the population function is $n(t) = 400 \cdot 3^t$. The rate of growth is $n'(t) = 400 \cdot 3^t \cdot \ln 3$, so the rate of growth after 2.5 hours is $n'(2.5) = 400 \cdot 3^{2.5} \cdot \ln 3 \approx 6850$ bacteria/hour.

25. (a) **1920:** $m_1 = \dfrac{1860 - 1750}{1920 - 1910} = \dfrac{110}{10} = 11, \; m_2 = \dfrac{2070 - 1860}{1930 - 1920} = \dfrac{210}{10} = 21,$

$(m_1 + m_2)/2 = (11 + 21)/2 = 16$ million/year

1980: $m_1 = \dfrac{4450 - 3710}{1980 - 1970} = \dfrac{740}{10} = 74, \; m_2 = \dfrac{5280 - 4450}{1990 - 1980} = \dfrac{830}{10} = 83,$

$(m_1 + m_2)/2 = (74 + 83)/2 = 78.5$ million/year

(b) $P(t) = at^3 + bt^2 + ct + d$ (in millions of people), where $a \approx 0.0012937063$, $b \approx -7.061421911$, $c \approx 12{,}822.97902$, and $d \approx -7{,}743{,}770.396$.

(c) $P(t) = at^3 + bt^2 + ct + d \;\Rightarrow\; P'(t) = 3at^2 + 2bt + c$ (in millions of people per year)

(d) $P'(1920) = 3(0.0012937063)(1920)^2 + 2(-7.061421911)(1920) + 12{,}822.97902$

≈ 14.48 million/year [smaller than the answer in part (a), but close to it]

$P'(1980) \approx 75.29$ million/year (smaller, but close)

(e) $P'(1985) \approx 81.62$ million/year, so the rate of growth in 1985 was about 81.62 million/year.

27. (a) Using $v = \dfrac{P}{4\eta l}(R^2 - r^2)$ with $R = 0.01$, $l = 3$, $P = 3000$, and $\eta = 0.027$, we have v as a function of r:

$$v(r) = \frac{3000}{4(0.027)3}(0.01^2 - r^2). \quad v(0) = 0.\overline{925} \text{ cm/s}, \ v(0.005) = 0.69\overline{4} \text{ cm/s}, \ v(0.01) = 0.$$

(b) $v(r) = \dfrac{P}{4\eta l}(R^2 - r^2) \ \Rightarrow \ v'(r) = \dfrac{P}{4\eta l}(-2r) = -\dfrac{Pr}{2\eta l}.$ When $l = 3$, $P = 3000$, and $\eta = 0.027$, we have

$$v'(r) = -\frac{3000r}{2(0.027)3}. \quad v'(0) = 0, \ v'(0.005) = -92.\overline{592} \text{ (cm/s)/cm, and } v'(0.01) = -185.\overline{185} \text{ (cm/s)/cm.}$$

(c) The velocity is greatest where $r = 0$ (at the center) and the velocity is changing most where $r = R = 0.01$ cm

(at the edge).

29. (a) $C(x) = 1200 + 12x - 0.1x^2 + 0.0005x^3 \ \Rightarrow \ C'(x) = 12 - 0.2x + 0.0015x^2$ \$/yard, which is the marginal cost

function.

(b) $C'(200) = 12 - 0.2(200) + 0.0015(200)^2 = \$32$/yard, and this is the rate at which costs are increasing with respect to

the production level when $x = 200$. $C'(200)$ predicts the cost of producing the 201st yard.

(c) The cost of manufacturing the 201st yard of fabric is $C(201) - C(200) = 3632.2005 - 3600 \approx \$32.20$, which is

approximately $C'(200)$.

31. (a) $A(x) = \dfrac{p(x)}{x} \ \Rightarrow \ A'(x) = \dfrac{xp'(x) - p(x) \cdot 1}{x^2} = \dfrac{xp'(x) - p(x)}{x^2}.$

$A'(x) > 0 \ \Rightarrow \ A(x)$ is increasing; that is, the average productivity increases as the size of the workforce increases.

(b) $p'(x)$ is greater than the average productivity $\ \Rightarrow \ p'(x) > A(x) \ \Rightarrow \ p'(x) > \dfrac{p(x)}{x} \ \Rightarrow \ xp'(x) > p(x) \ \Rightarrow$

$$xp'(x) - p(x) > 0 \ \Rightarrow \ \frac{xp'(x) - p(x)}{x^2} > 0 \ \Rightarrow \ A'(x) > 0.$$

33. $PV = nRT \ \Rightarrow \ T = \dfrac{PV}{nR} = \dfrac{PV}{(10)(0.0821)} = \dfrac{1}{0.821}(PV).$ Using the Product Rule, we have

$$\frac{dT}{dt} = \frac{1}{0.821}[P(t)V'(t) + V(t)P'(t)] = \frac{1}{0.821}[(8)(-0.15) + (10)(0.10)] \approx -0.2436 \text{ K/min.}$$

35. (a) If the populations are stable, then the growth rates are neither positive nor negative; that is, $\dfrac{dC}{dt} = 0$ and $\dfrac{dW}{dt} = 0$.

(b) "The caribou go extinct" means that the population is zero, or mathematically, $C = 0$.

(c) We have the equations $\dfrac{dC}{dt} = aC - bCW$ and $\dfrac{dW}{dt} = -cW + dCW$. Let $dC/dt = dW/dt = 0$, $a = 0.05$, $b = 0.001$,

$c = 0.05$, and $d = 0.0001$ to obtain $0.05C - 0.001CW = 0$ **(1)** and $-0.05W + 0.0001CW = 0$ **(2)**. Adding 10 times

(2) to **(1)** eliminates the CW-terms and gives us $0.05C - 0.5W = 0 \ \Rightarrow \ C = 10W$. Substituting $C = 10W$ into **(1)**

results in $0.05(10W) - 0.001(10W)W = 0 \ \Leftrightarrow \ 0.5W - 0.01W^2 = 0 \ \Leftrightarrow \ 50W - W^2 = 0 \ \Leftrightarrow$

$W(50 - W) = 0 \ \Leftrightarrow \ W = 0$ or 50. Since $C = 10W$, $C = 0$ or 500. Thus, the population pairs (C, W) that lead to

stable populations are $(0, 0)$ and $(500, 50)$. So it is possible for the two species to live in harmony.

3.9 Linear Approximations and Differentials

1. As in Example 1, $T(0) = 185$, $T(10) = 172$, $T(20) = 160$, and

$$T'(20) \approx \frac{T(10) - T(20)}{10 - 20} = \frac{172 - 160}{-10} = -1.2°\text{F/min}.$$

$$T(30) \approx T(20) + T'(20)(30 - 20) \approx 160 - 1.2(10) = 148°\text{F}.$$

We would expect the temperature of the turkey to get closer to $75°\text{F}$ as time

increases. Since the temperature decreased $13°\text{F}$ in the first 10 minutes and $12°\text{F}$

in the second 10 minutes, we can assume that the slopes of the tangent line are

increasing through negative values: $-1.3, -1.2, \ldots$. Hence, the tangent lines are

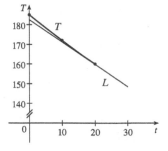

under the curve and $148°\text{F}$ is an underestimate. From the figure, we estimate the slope of the tangent line at $t = 20$ to be

$\frac{184 - 147}{0 - 30} = -\frac{37}{30}$. Then the linear approximation becomes $T(30) \approx T(20) + T'(20) \cdot 10 \approx 160 - \frac{37}{30}(10) = 147\frac{2}{3} \approx 147.7$.

3. Extend the tangent line at the point $(2030, 21)$ to the t-axis. Answers

will vary based on this approximation—we'll use $t = 1900$ as our

t-intercept. The linearization is then

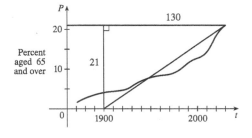

$$P(t) \approx P(2030) + P'(2030)(t - 2030) \approx 21 + \frac{21}{130}(t - 2030)$$

$$P(2040) = 21 + \frac{21}{130}(2040 - 2030) \approx 22.6\%$$

$$P(2050) = 21 + \frac{21}{130}(2050 - 2030) \approx 24.2\%$$

These predictions are probably too high since the tangent line lies above the graph at $t = 2030$.

5. $f(x) = x^4 + 3x^2 \Rightarrow f'(x) = 4x^3 + 6x$, so $f(-1) = 4$ and $f'(-1) = -10$.

Thus, $L(x) = f(-1) + f'(-1)(x - (-1)) = 4 + (-10)(x + 1) = -10x - 6$.

7. $f(x) = \cos x \Rightarrow f'(x) = -\sin x$, so $f\left(\frac{\pi}{2}\right) = 0$ and $f'\left(\frac{\pi}{2}\right) = -1$.

Thus, $L(x) = f\left(\frac{\pi}{2}\right) + f'\left(\frac{\pi}{2}\right)\left(x - \frac{\pi}{2}\right) = 0 - 1\left(x - \frac{\pi}{2}\right) = -x + \frac{\pi}{2}$.

9. $f(x) = \sqrt{1 - x} \Rightarrow f'(x) = \frac{-1}{2\sqrt{1 - x}}$, so $f(0) = 1$ and $f'(0) = -\frac{1}{2}$.

Therefore,

$$\sqrt{1 - x} = f(x) \approx f(0) + f'(0)(x - 0) = 1 + \left(-\frac{1}{2}\right)(x - 0) = 1 - \frac{1}{2}x.$$

So $\sqrt{0.9} = \sqrt{1 - 0.1} \approx 1 - \frac{1}{2}(0.1) = 0.95$

and $\sqrt{0.99} = \sqrt{1 - 0.01} \approx 1 - \frac{1}{2}(0.01) = 0.995$.

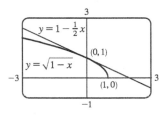

11. $f(x) = \sqrt[3]{1 - x} = (1 - x)^{1/3} \Rightarrow f'(x) = -\frac{1}{3}(1 - x)^{-2/3}$, so $f(0) = 1$

and $f'(0) = -\frac{1}{3}$. Thus, $f(x) \approx f(0) + f'(0)(x - 0) = 1 - \frac{1}{3}x$. We need

$\sqrt[3]{1 - x} - 0.1 < 1 - \frac{1}{3}x < \sqrt[3]{1 - x} + 0.1$, which is true when

$-1.204 < x < 0.706$.

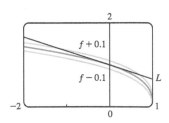

13. $f(x) = \dfrac{1}{(1 + 2x)^4} = (1 + 2x)^{-4}$ $\Rightarrow$

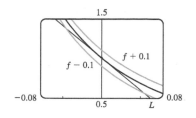

$f'(x) = -4(1 + 2x)^{-5}(2) = \dfrac{-8}{(1 + 2x)^5}$, so $f(0) = 1$ and $f'(0) = -8$.

Thus, $f(x) \approx f(0) + f'(0)(x - 0) = 1 + (-8)(x - 0) = 1 - 8x$.

We need $\dfrac{1}{(1 + 2x)^4} - 0.1 < 1 - 8x < \dfrac{1}{(1 + 2x)^4} + 0.1$, which is true

when $-0.045 < x < 0.055$.

15. To estimate $(2.001)^5$, we'll find the linearization of $f(x) = x^5$ at $a = 2$. Since $f'(x) = 5x^4$, $f(2) = 32$, and $f'(2) = 80$,

we have $L(x) = 32 + 80(x - 2) = 80x - 128$. Thus, $x^5 \approx 80x - 128$ when x is near 2 , so

$(2.001)^5 \approx 80(2.001) - 128 = 160.08 - 128 = 32.08$.

17. To estimate $(8.06)^{2/3}$, we'll find the linearization of $f(x) = x^{2/3}$ at $a = 8$. Since $f'(x) = \frac{2}{3}x^{-1/3} = 2/\left(3\sqrt[3]{x}\right)$,

$f(8) = 4$, and $f'(8) = \frac{1}{3}$, we have $L(x) = 4 + \frac{1}{3}(x - 8) = \frac{1}{3}x + \frac{4}{3}$. Thus, $x^{2/3} \approx \frac{1}{3}x + \frac{4}{3}$ when x is near 8, so

$(8.06)^{2/3} \approx \frac{1}{3}(8.06) + \frac{4}{3} = \frac{12.06}{3} = 4.02$.

19. $y = f(x) = \sec x$ $\Rightarrow$ $f'(x) = \sec x \tan x$, so $f(0) = 1$ and $f'(0) = 1 \cdot 0 = 0$. The linear approximation of f at 0 is

$f(0) + f'(0)(x - 0) = 1 + 0(x) = 1$. Since 0.08 is close to 0, approximating $\sec 0.08$ with 1 is reasonable.

21. $y = f(x) = \ln x$ $\Rightarrow$ $f'(x) = 1/x$, so $f(1) = 0$ and $f'(1) = 1$. The linear approximation of f at 1 is

$f(1) + f'(1)(x - 1) = 0 + 1(x - 1) = x - 1$. Now $f(1.05) = \ln 1.05 \approx 1.05 - 1 = 0.05$, so the approximation

is reasonable.

23. (a) For $y = f(u) = \dfrac{u + 1}{u - 1}$, $f'(u) = \dfrac{(u - 1)(1) - (u + 1)(1)}{(u - 1)^2} = \dfrac{-2}{(u - 1)^2}$, so $dy = \dfrac{-2}{(u - 1)^2}\,du$.

(b) For $y = f(r) = (1 + r^3)^{-2}$, $f'(r) = -2(1 + r^3)^{-3}(3r^2) = \dfrac{-6r^2}{(1 + r^3)^3}$, so $dy = \dfrac{-6r^2}{(1 + r^3)^3}\,dr$.

25. (a) $y = e^{x/10}$ $\Rightarrow$ $dy = e^{x/10} \cdot \frac{1}{10}\,dx = \frac{1}{10}e^{x/10}dx$

(b) $x = 0$ and $dx = 0.1$ $\Rightarrow$ $dy = \frac{1}{10}e^{0/10}(0.1) = 0.01$.

$\Delta y = f(x + \Delta x) - f(x) = e^{0 + 0.1} - e^0 = e^{0.1} - 1 \approx 0.0101$.

27. (a) If x is the edge length, then $V = x^3$ $\Rightarrow$ $dV = 3x^2\,dx$. When $x = 30$ and $dx = 0.1$, $dV = 3(30)^2(0.1) = 270$, so the

maximum possible error in computing the volume of the cube is about 270 cm^3. The relative error is calculated by dividing

the change in V, ΔV, by V. We approximate ΔV with dV.

Relative error $= \dfrac{\Delta V}{V} \approx \dfrac{dV}{V} = \dfrac{3x^2\,dx}{x^3} = 3\,\dfrac{dx}{x} = 3\left(\dfrac{0.1}{30}\right) = 0.01$.

Percentage error $=$ relative error $\times$ 100% $= 0.01 \times$ 100% $=$ 1%.

(b) $S = 6x^2 \;\Rightarrow\; dS = 12x\,dx$. When $x = 30$ and $dx = 0.1$, $dS = 12(30)(0.1) = 36$, so the maximum possible error in computing the surface area of the cube is about 36 cm^2.

$$\text{Relative error} = \frac{\Delta S}{S} \approx \frac{dS}{S} = \frac{12x\,dx}{6x^2} = 2\frac{dx}{x} = 2\left(\frac{0.1}{30}\right) = 0.00\overline{6}.$$

Percentage error $=$ relative error $\times\, 100\% = 0.00\overline{6} \times 100\% = 0.\overline{6}\%$.

29. (a) For a sphere of radius r, the circumference is $C = 2\pi r$ and the surface area is $S = 4\pi r^2$, so

$$r = \frac{C}{2\pi} \;\Rightarrow\; S = 4\pi\left(\frac{C}{2\pi}\right)^2 = \frac{C^2}{\pi} \;\Rightarrow\; dS = \frac{2}{\pi}C\,dC. \text{ When } C = 84 \text{ and } dC = 0.5,\ dS = \frac{2}{\pi}(84)(0.5) = \frac{84}{\pi},$$

so the maximum error is about $\dfrac{84}{\pi} \approx 27$ cm^2. Relative error $\approx \dfrac{dS}{S} = \dfrac{84/\pi}{84^2/\pi} = \dfrac{1}{84} \approx 0.012$

(b) $V = \dfrac{4}{3}\pi r^3 = \dfrac{4}{3}\pi\left(\dfrac{C}{2\pi}\right)^3 = \dfrac{C^3}{6\pi^2} \;\Rightarrow\; dV = \dfrac{1}{2\pi^2}C^2\,dC.$ When $C = 84$ and $dC = 0.5$,

$dV = \dfrac{1}{2\pi^2}(84)^2(0.5) = \dfrac{1764}{\pi^2}$, so the maximum error is about $\dfrac{1764}{\pi^2} \approx 179$ cm^3.

The relative error is approximately $\dfrac{dV}{V} = \dfrac{1764/\pi^2}{(84)^3/(6\pi^2)} = \dfrac{1}{56} \approx 0.018$.

31. (a) $V = \pi r^2 h \;\Rightarrow\; \Delta V \approx dV = 2\pi rh\,dr = 2\pi rh\,\Delta r$

(b) The error is

$$\Delta V - dV = [\pi(r + \Delta r)^2 h - \pi r^2 h] - 2\pi rh\,\Delta r = \pi r^2 h + 2\pi rh\,\Delta r + \pi(\Delta r)^2 h - \pi r^2 h - 2\pi rh\,\Delta r = \pi(\Delta r)^2 h.$$

33. $F = kR^4 \;\Rightarrow\; dF = 4kR^3\,dR \;\Rightarrow\; \dfrac{dF}{F} = \dfrac{4kR^3\,dR}{kR^4} = 4\left(\dfrac{dR}{R}\right)$. Thus, the relative change in F is about 4 times the relative change in R. So a 5% increase in the radius corresponds to a 20% increase in blood flow.

35. (a) The graph shows that $f'(1) = 2$, so $L(x) = f(1) + f'(1)(x-1) = 5 + 2(x-1) = 2x + 3$.

$f(0.9) \approx L(0.9) = 4.8$ and $f(1.1) \approx L(1.1) = 5.2$.

(b) From the graph, we see that $f'(x)$ is positive and decreasing. This means that the slopes of the tangent lines are positive, but the tangents are becoming less steep. So the tangent lines lie *above* the curve. Thus, the estimates in part (a) are too large.

3 Review

CONCEPT CHECK

1. (a) The Power Rule: If n is any real number, then $\dfrac{d}{dx}(x^n) = nx^{n-1}$. The derivative of a variable base raised to a constant power is the power times the base raised to the power minus one.

(b) The Constant Multiple Rule: If c is a constant and f is a differentiable function, then $\dfrac{d}{dx}[cf(x)] = c\dfrac{d}{dx}f(x)$.

The derivative of a constant times a function is the constant times the derivative of the function.

(c) The Sum Rule: If f and g are both differentiable, then $\dfrac{d}{dx}\,[f(x)+g(x)] = \dfrac{d}{dx}\,f(x) + \dfrac{d}{dx}\,g(x)$. The derivative of a sum of functions is the sum of the derivatives.

(d) The Difference Rule: If f and g are both differentiable, then $\dfrac{d}{dx}\,[f(x)-g(x)] = \dfrac{d}{dx}\,f(x) - \dfrac{d}{dx}\,g(x)$. The derivative of a difference of functions is the difference of the derivatives.

(e) The Product Rule: If f and g are both differentiable, then $\dfrac{d}{dx}\,[f(x)\,g(x)] = f(x)\dfrac{d}{dx}\,g(x) + g(x)\dfrac{d}{dx}\,f(x)$. The derivative of a product of two functions is the first function times the derivative of the second function plus the second function times the derivative of the first function.

(f) The Quotient Rule: If f and g are both differentiable, then $\dfrac{d}{dx}\left[\dfrac{f(x)}{g(x)}\right] = \dfrac{g(x)\dfrac{d}{dx}\,f(x) - f(x)\dfrac{d}{dx}\,g(x)}{[g(x)]^2}$.

The derivative of a quotient of functions is the denominator times the derivative of the numerator minus the numerator times the derivative of the denominator, all divided by the square of the denominator.

(g) The Chain Rule: If f and g are both differentiable and $F = f \circ g$ is the composite function defined by $F(x) = f(g(x))$, then F is differentiable and F' is given by the product $F'(x) = f'(g(x))\,g'(x)$. The derivative of a composite function is the derivative of the outer function evaluated at the inner function times the derivative of the inner function.

2. (a) $y = x^n \;\Rightarrow\; y' = nx^{n-1}$

   (b) $y = e^x \;\Rightarrow\; y' = e^x$

   (c) $y = a^x \;\Rightarrow\; y' = a^x \ln a$

   (d) $y = \ln x \;\Rightarrow\; y' = 1/x$

   (e) $y = \log_a x \;\Rightarrow\; y' = 1/(x\ln a)$

   (f) $y = \sin x \;\Rightarrow\; y' = \cos x$

   (g) $y = \cos x \;\Rightarrow\; y' = -\sin x$

   (h) $y = \tan x \;\Rightarrow\; y' = \sec^2 x$

   (i) $y = \csc x \;\Rightarrow\; y' = -\csc x \cot x$

   (j) $y = \sec x \;\Rightarrow\; y' = \sec x \tan x$

   (k) $y = \cot x \;\Rightarrow\; y' = -\csc^2 x$

   (l) $y = \sin^{-1} x \;\Rightarrow\; y' = 1/\sqrt{1-x^2}$

   (m) $y = \cos^{-1} x \;\Rightarrow\; y' = -1/\sqrt{1-x^2}$

   (n) $y = \tan^{-1} x \;\Rightarrow\; y' = 1/(1+x^2)$

3. (a) e is the number such that $\displaystyle\lim_{h\to 0}\frac{e^h - 1}{h} = 1$.

   (b) $e = \displaystyle\lim_{x\to 0}(1+x)^{1/x}$

   (c) The differentiation formula for $y = a^x$ $\;[y' = a^x \ln a]\;$ is simplest when $a = e$ because $\ln e = 1$.

   (d) The differentiation formula for $y = \log_a x$ $\;[y' = 1/(x\ln a)]\;$ is simplest when $a = e$ because $\ln e = 1$.

4. (a) Implicit differentiation consists of differentiating both sides of an equation involving x and y with respect to x, and then solving the resulting equation for y'. Use implicit differentiation when it is difficult to solve an equation for y in terms of x.

   (b) Logarithmic differentiation consists of taking natural logarithms of both sides of an equation $y = f(x)$, simplifying, differentiating implicitly with respect to x, and then solving the resulting equation for y'. Use logarithmic differentiation when the calculation of derivatives of complicated functions involving products, quotients, or powers can be simplified by taking logarithms.

5. You can find $\dfrac{dy}{dx}$ as a function of t by calculating $\dfrac{dy}{dx} = \dfrac{dy/dt}{dx/dt} = \dfrac{g'(t)}{f'(t)}$ [if $dx/dt = f'(t) \neq 0$].

6. The linearization L of f at $x = a$ is $L(x) = f(a) + f'(a)(x - a)$.

TRUE-FALSE QUIZ

1. True.   This is the Sum Rule.

3. True.   This is the Chain Rule.

5. False. $\dfrac{d}{dx} f(\sqrt{x}) = \dfrac{f'(\sqrt{x})}{2\sqrt{x}}$ by the Chain Rule.

7. False. $\dfrac{d}{dx} 10^x = 10^x \ln 10$

9. True. $\dfrac{d}{dx}(\tan^2 x) = 2\tan x \sec^2 x$, and $\dfrac{d}{dx}(\sec^2 x) = 2\sec x(\sec x \tan x) = 2\tan x \sec^2 x$.

   Or: $\dfrac{d}{dx}(\sec^2 x) = \dfrac{d}{dx}(1 + \tan^2 x) = \dfrac{d}{dx}(\tan^2 x)$.

11. True. $g(x) = x^5 \Rightarrow g'(x) = 5x^4 \Rightarrow g'(2) = 5(2)^4 = 80$, and by the definition of the derivative,

   $\displaystyle\lim_{x \to 2} \dfrac{g(x) - g(2)}{x - 2} = g'(2) = 80$.

EXERCISES

1. $y = (x^4 - 3x^2 + 5)^3 \Rightarrow$

   $y' = 3(x^4 - 3x^2 + 5)^2 \dfrac{d}{dx}(x^4 - 3x^2 + 5) = 3(x^4 - 3x^2 + 5)^2(4x^3 - 6x) = 6x(x^4 - 3x^2 + 5)^2(2x^2 - 3)$

3. $y = \sqrt{x} + \dfrac{1}{\sqrt[3]{x^4}} = x^{1/2} + x^{-4/3} \Rightarrow y' = \frac{1}{2}x^{-1/2} - \frac{4}{3}x^{-7/3} = \dfrac{1}{2\sqrt{x}} - \dfrac{4}{3\sqrt[3]{x^7}}$

5. $y = 2x\sqrt{x^2 + 1} \Rightarrow$

   $y' = 2x \cdot \frac{1}{2}(x^2 + 1)^{-1/2}(2x) + \sqrt{x^2 + 1}\,(2) = \dfrac{2x^2}{\sqrt{x^2 + 1}} + 2\sqrt{x^2 + 1} = \dfrac{2x^2 + 2(x^2 + 1)}{\sqrt{x^2 + 1}} = \dfrac{2(2x^2 + 1)}{\sqrt{x^2 + 1}}$

7. $y = e^{\sin 2\theta} \Rightarrow y' = e^{\sin 2\theta}\dfrac{d}{d\theta}(\sin 2\theta) = e^{\sin 2\theta}(\cos 2\theta)(2) = 2\cos 2\theta\, e^{\sin 2\theta}$

9. $y = \dfrac{t}{1 - t^2} \Rightarrow y' = \dfrac{(1 - t^2)(1) - t(-2t)}{(1 - t^2)^2} = \dfrac{1 - t^2 + 2t^2}{(1 - t^2)^2} = \dfrac{t^2 + 1}{(1 - t^2)^2}$

11. $y = \dfrac{e^{1/x}}{x^2} \Rightarrow y' = \dfrac{x^2(e^{1/x})' - e^{1/x}\,(x^2)'}{(x^2)^2} = \dfrac{x^2(e^{1/x})(-1/x^2) - e^{1/x}(2x)}{x^4} = \dfrac{-e^{1/x}(1 + 2x)}{x^4}$

13. $\dfrac{d}{dx}(xy^4 + x^2y) = \dfrac{d}{dx}(x + 3y) \Rightarrow x \cdot 4y^3y' + y^4 \cdot 1 + x^2 \cdot y' + y \cdot 2x = 1 + 3y' \Rightarrow$

   $y'(4xy^3 + x^2 - 3) = 1 - y^4 - 2xy \Rightarrow y' = \dfrac{1 - y^4 - 2xy}{4xy^3 + x^2 - 3}$

15. $y = \dfrac{\sec 2\theta}{1 + \tan 2\theta}$ ⟹

$$y' = \frac{(1 + \tan 2\theta)(\sec 2\theta \tan 2\theta \cdot 2) - (\sec 2\theta)(\sec^2 2\theta \cdot 2)}{(1 + \tan 2\theta)^2} = \frac{2\sec 2\theta\,[(1 + \tan 2\theta)\tan 2\theta - \sec^2 2\theta]}{(1 + \tan 2\theta)^2}$$

$$= \frac{2\sec 2\theta\,(\tan 2\theta + \tan^2 2\theta - \sec^2 2\theta)}{(1 + \tan 2\theta)^2} = \frac{2\sec 2\theta\,(\tan 2\theta - 1)}{(1 + \tan 2\theta)^2} \qquad [1 + \tan^2 x = \sec^2 x]$$

17. $y = e^{cx}(c\sin x - \cos x)$ ⟹

$$y' = e^{cx}(c\cos x + \sin x) + ce^{cx}(c\sin x - \cos x) = e^{cx}(c^2\sin x - c\cos x + c\cos x + \sin x)$$

$$= e^{cx}(c^2\sin x + \sin x) = e^{cx}\sin x\,(c^2 + 1)$$

19. $y = \log_5(1 + 2x)$ ⟹ $y' = \dfrac{1}{(1 + 2x)\ln 5}\dfrac{d}{dx}(1 + 2x) = \dfrac{2}{(1 + 2x)\ln 5}$

21. $\sin(xy) = x^2 - y$ ⟹ $\cos(xy)(xy' + y\cdot 1) = 2x - y'$ ⟹ $x\cos(xy)y' + y' = 2x - y\cos(xy)$ ⟹

$$y'[x\cos(xy) + 1] = 2x - y\cos(xy) \quad \Rightarrow \quad y' = \frac{2x - y\cos(xy)}{x\cos(xy) + 1}$$

23. $y = 3^{x\ln x}$ ⟹ $y' = 3^{x\ln x}(\ln 3)\dfrac{d}{dx}(x\ln x) = 3^{x\ln x}(\ln 3)\left(x\cdot\dfrac{1}{x} + \ln x\cdot 1\right) = 3^{x\ln x}(\ln 3)(1 + \ln x)$

25. $y = \ln\sin x - \tfrac{1}{2}\sin^2 x$ ⟹ $y' = \dfrac{1}{\sin x}\cdot\cos x - \tfrac{1}{2}\cdot 2\sin x\cdot\cos x = \cot x - \sin x\cos x$

27. $y = x\tan^{-1}(4x)$ ⟹ $y' = x\cdot\dfrac{1}{1 + (4x)^2}\cdot 4 + \tan^{-1}(4x)\cdot 1 = \dfrac{4x}{1 + 16x^2} + \tan^{-1}(4x)$

29. $y = \ln|\sec 5x + \tan 5x|$ ⟹

$$y' = \frac{1}{\sec 5x + \tan 5x}(\sec 5x\tan 5x\cdot 5 + \sec^2 5x\cdot 5) = \frac{5\sec 5x\,(\tan 5x + \sec 5x)}{\sec 5x + \tan 5x} = 5\sec 5x$$

31. $y = \tan^2(\sin\theta) = [\tan(\sin\theta)]^2$ ⟹ $y' = 2[\tan(\sin\theta)]\cdot\sec^2(\sin\theta)\cdot\cos\theta$

33. $y = \sin\!\left(\tan\sqrt{1 + x^3}\right)$ ⟹ $y' = \cos\!\left(\tan\sqrt{1 + x^3}\right)\!\left(\sec^2\sqrt{1 + x^3}\right)\!\left[3x^2/\!\left(2\sqrt{1 + x^3}\right)\right]$

35. $y = \cos\!\left(e^{\sqrt{\tan 3x}}\right)$ ⟹

$$y' = -\sin\!\left(e^{\sqrt{\tan 3x}}\right)\cdot\left(e^{\sqrt{\tan 3x}}\right)' = -\sin\!\left(e^{\sqrt{\tan 3x}}\right)e^{\sqrt{\tan 3x}}\cdot\tfrac{1}{2}(\tan 3x)^{-1/2}\cdot\sec^2(3x)\cdot 3$$

$$= \frac{-3\sin\!\left(e^{\sqrt{\tan 3x}}\right)e^{\sqrt{\tan 3x}}\sec^2(3x)}{2\sqrt{\tan 3x}}$$

37. $f(t) = \sqrt{4t + 1}$ ⟹ $f'(t) = \tfrac{1}{2}(4t + 1)^{-1/2}\cdot 4 = 2(4t + 1)^{-1/2}$ ⟹

$$f''(t) = 2(-\tfrac{1}{2})(4t + 1)^{-3/2}\cdot 4 = -4/(4t + 1)^{3/2}, \text{ so } f''(2) = -4/9^{3/2} = -\tfrac{4}{27}.$$

39. $f(x) = 2^x$ ⟹ $f'(x) = 2^x\ln 2$ ⟹ $f''(x) = (2^x\ln 2)\ln 2 = 2^x(\ln 2)^2$ ⟹

$$f'''(x) = (2^x\ln 2)(\ln 2)^2 = 2^x(\ln 2)^3 \quad \Rightarrow \quad \cdots \quad \Rightarrow \quad f^{(n)}(x) = (2^x\ln 2)(\ln 2)^{n-1} = 2^x(\ln 2)^n$$

41. $y = 4\sin^2 x \Rightarrow y' = 4 \cdot 2\sin x \cos x$. At $\left(\frac{\pi}{6}, 1\right)$, $y' = 8 \cdot \frac{1}{2} \cdot \frac{\sqrt{3}}{2} = 2\sqrt{3}$, so an equation of the tangent line

is $y - 1 = 2\sqrt{3}\left(x - \frac{\pi}{6}\right)$, or $y = 2\sqrt{3}\,x + 1 - \pi\sqrt{3}/3$.

43. $x = \ln t$, $y = t^2 + 1$, $(0, 2)$. If $(x, y) = (0, 2)$, then $x = \ln t = 0 \Rightarrow t = 1$.

$$\frac{dy}{dt} = 2t, \quad \frac{dx}{dt} = \frac{1}{t}, \text{ and } \frac{dy}{dx} = \frac{dy/dt}{dx/dt} = \frac{2t}{1/t} = 2t^2, \text{ so } \frac{dy}{dx} = 2 \text{ when } t = 1.$$

An equation of the tangent to the curve at $(0, 2)$ is $y - 2 = 2(x - 0)$, or $y = 2x + 2$.

45. $y = (2 + x)e^{-x} \Rightarrow y' = (2 + x)(-e^{-x}) + e^{-x} \cdot 1 = e^{-x}[-(2 + x) + 1] = e^{-x}(-x - 1)$.

At $(0, 2)$, $y' = 1(-1) = -1$, so an equation of the tangent line is $y - 2 = -1(x - 0)$, or $y = -x + 2$.

The slope of the normal line is 1, so an equation of the normal line is $y - 2 = 1(x - 0)$, or $y = x + 2$.

47. (a) $f(x) = x\sqrt{5 - x} \Rightarrow$

$$f'(x) = x\left[\frac{1}{2}(5 - x)^{-1/2}(-1)\right] + \sqrt{5 - x} = \frac{-x}{2\sqrt{5 - x}} + \sqrt{5 - x} \cdot \frac{2\sqrt{5 - x}}{2\sqrt{5 - x}} = \frac{-x}{2\sqrt{5 - x}} + \frac{2(5 - x)}{2\sqrt{5 - x}}$$

$$= \frac{-x + 10 - 2x}{2\sqrt{5 - x}} = \frac{10 - 3x}{2\sqrt{5 - x}}$$

(b) At $(1, 2)$: $f'(1) = \frac{7}{4}$.

So an equation of the tangent line is $y - 2 = \frac{7}{4}(x - 1)$ or $y = \frac{7}{4}x + \frac{1}{4}$.

At $(4, 4)$: $f'(4) = -\frac{2}{2} = -1$.

So an equation of the tangent line is $y - 4 = -1(x - 4)$ or $y = -x + 8$.

(c)

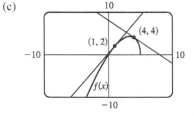

(d)

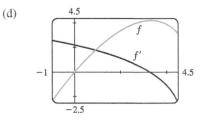

The graphs look reasonable, since f' is positive where f has tangents with

positive slope, and f' is negative where f has tangents with negative slope.

49. $f(x) = xe^{\sin x} \Rightarrow f'(x) = x[e^{\sin x}(\cos x)] + e^{\sin x}(1) = e^{\sin x}(x\cos x + 1)$. As a check on our work, we notice from the

graphs that $f'(x) > 0$ when f is increasing. Also, we see in the larger viewing rectangle a certain similarity in the graphs of f

and f': the sizes of the oscillations of f and f' are linked.

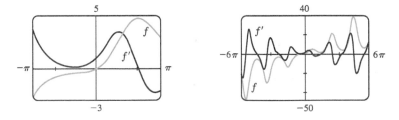

51. (a) $h(x) = f(x) g(x) \quad \Rightarrow \quad h'(x) = f(x) g'(x) + g(x) f'(x) \quad \Rightarrow$

$h'(2) = f(2) g'(2) + g(2) f'(2) = (3)(4) + (5)(-2) = 12 - 10 = 2$

(b) $F(x) = f(g(x)) \quad \Rightarrow \quad F'(x) = f'(g(x)) g'(x) \quad \Rightarrow \quad F'(2) = f'(g(2)) g'(2) = f'(5)(4) = 11 \cdot 4 = 44$

53. $f(x) = x^2 g(x) \quad \Rightarrow \quad f'(x) = x^2 g'(x) + g(x)(2x) = x[xg'(x) + 2g(x)]$

55. $f(x) = [g(x)]^2 \quad \Rightarrow \quad f'(x) = 2[g(x)] \cdot g'(x) = 2g(x) g'(x)$

57. $f(x) = g(e^x) \quad \Rightarrow \quad f'(x) = g'(e^x) e^x$

59. $f(x) = \ln|g(x)| \quad \Rightarrow \quad f'(x) = \dfrac{1}{g(x)} g'(x) = \dfrac{g'(x)}{g(x)}$

61. $h(x) = \dfrac{f(x) g(x)}{f(x) + g(x)} \quad \Rightarrow$

$h'(x) = \dfrac{[f(x) + g(x)] [f(x) g'(x) + g(x) f'(x)] - f(x) g(x) [f'(x) + g'(x)]}{[f(x) + g(x)]^2}$

$= \dfrac{[f(x)]^2 g'(x) + f(x) g(x) f'(x) + f(x) g(x) g'(x) + [g(x)]^2 f'(x) - f(x) g(x) f'(x) - f(x) g(x) g'(x)}{[f(x) + g(x)]^2}$

$= \dfrac{f'(x) [g(x)]^2 + g'(x) [f(x)]^2}{[f(x) + g(x)]^2}$

63. $y = [\ln(x+4)]^2 \quad \Rightarrow \quad y' = 2[\ln(x+4)]^1 \cdot \dfrac{1}{x+4} \cdot 1 = 2\dfrac{\ln(x+4)}{x+4}$ and $y' = 0 \quad \Leftrightarrow \quad \ln(x+4) = 0 \quad \Leftrightarrow$

$x + 4 = e^0 \quad \Rightarrow \quad x + 4 = 1 \quad \Leftrightarrow \quad x = -3$, so the tangent is horizontal at the point $(-3, 0)$.

65. $x^2 + 2y^2 = 1 \quad \Rightarrow \quad 2x + 4yy' = 0 \quad \Rightarrow \quad y' = -x/(2y) = 1 \quad \Leftrightarrow \quad x = -2y$. Since the points lie on the ellipse,

we have $(-2y)^2 + 2y^2 = 1 \quad \Rightarrow \quad 6y^2 = 1 \quad \Rightarrow \quad y = \pm\dfrac{1}{\sqrt{6}}$. The points are $\left(-\dfrac{2}{\sqrt{6}}, \dfrac{1}{\sqrt{6}}\right)$ and $\left(\dfrac{2}{\sqrt{6}}, -\dfrac{1}{\sqrt{6}}\right)$.

67. $y = f(x) = ax^2 + bx + c \quad \Rightarrow \quad f'(x) = 2ax + b$. We know that $f'(-1) = 6$ and $f'(5) = -2$, so $-2a + b = 6$ and

$10a + b = -2$. Subtracting the first equation from the second gives $12a = -8 \quad \Rightarrow \quad a = -\dfrac{2}{3}$. Substituting $-\dfrac{2}{3}$ for a in the

first equation gives $b = \dfrac{14}{3}$. Now $f(1) = 4 \quad \Rightarrow \quad 4 = a + b + c$, so $c = 4 + \dfrac{2}{3} - \dfrac{14}{3} = 0$ and hence, $f(x) = -\dfrac{2}{3}x^2 + \dfrac{14}{3}x$.

69. $s(t) = Ae^{-ct} \cos(\omega t + \delta) \quad \Rightarrow$

$v(t) = s'(t) = A\{e^{-ct} [-\omega \sin(\omega t + \delta)] + \cos(\omega t + \delta)(-ce^{-ct})\} = -Ae^{-ct} [\omega \sin(\omega t + \delta) + c \cos(\omega t + \delta)] \quad \Rightarrow$

$a(t) = v'(t) = -A\{e^{-ct}[\omega^2 \cos(\omega t + \delta) - c\omega \sin(\omega t + \delta)] + [\omega \sin(\omega t + \delta) + c \cos(\omega t + \delta)](-ce^{-ct})\}$

$= -Ae^{-ct}[\omega^2 \cos(\omega t + \delta) - c\omega \sin(\omega t + \delta) - c\omega \sin(\omega t + \delta) - c^2 \cos(\omega t + \delta)]$

$= -Ae^{-ct}[(\omega^2 - c^2) \cos(\omega t + \delta) - 2c\omega \sin(\omega t + \delta)] = Ae^{-ct}[(c^2 - \omega^2) \cos(\omega t + \delta) + 2c\omega \sin(\omega t + \delta)]$

71. The linear density ρ is the rate of change of mass m with respect to length x.

$$m = x\left(1 + \sqrt{x}\right) = x + x^{3/2} \quad \Rightarrow \quad \rho = dm/dx = 1 + \tfrac{3}{2}\sqrt{x},$$ so the linear density when $x = 4$ is $1 + \tfrac{3}{2}\sqrt{4} = 4$ kg/m.

73. (a) $C(x) = 920 + 2x - 0.02x^2 + 0.00007x^3 \quad \Rightarrow \quad C'(x) = 2 - 0.04x + 0.00021x^2$

(b) $C'(100) = 2 - 4 + 2.1 = \$0.10/$unit. This value represents the rate at which costs are increasing as the hundredth unit is produced, and is the approximate cost of producing the 101st unit.

(c) The cost of producing the 101st item is $C(101) - C(100) = 990.10107 - 990 = \$0.10107$, slightly larger than $C'(100)$.

(d) $C''(x) = -0.04 + 0.00042x = 0 \quad \Rightarrow \quad x = \frac{0.04}{0.00042} \approx 95.24$ and C'' changes from negative to positive at this value of x. This is the value of x at which the marginal cost is minimized.

75. (a) $f(x) = \sqrt[3]{1 + 3x} = (1 + 3x)^{1/3} \quad \Rightarrow \quad f'(x) = (1 + 3x)^{-2/3}$, so the linearization of f at $a = 0$ is

$$L(x) = f(0) + f'(0)(x - 0) = 1^{1/3} + 1^{-2/3}x = 1 + x. \text{ Thus, } \sqrt[3]{1 + 3x} \approx 1 + x \quad \Rightarrow$$

$$\sqrt[3]{1.03} = \sqrt[3]{1 + 3(0.01)} \approx 1 + (0.01) = 1.01.$$

(b) The linear approximation is $\sqrt[3]{1 + 3x} \approx 1 + x$, so for the required accuracy we want $\sqrt[3]{1 + 3x} - 0.1 < 1 + x < \sqrt[3]{1 + 3x} + 0.1$. From the graph, it appears that this is true when $-0.23 < x < 0.40$.

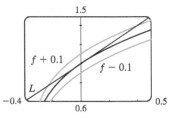

77. $\displaystyle \lim_{\theta \to \pi/3} \frac{\cos\theta - 0.5}{\theta - \pi/3} = \left[\frac{d}{d\theta}\cos\theta\right]_{\theta = \pi/3} = -\sin\frac{\pi}{3} = -\frac{\sqrt{3}}{2}$

79. $\displaystyle \lim_{x \to 0} \frac{\sqrt{1 + \tan x} - \sqrt{1 + \sin x}}{x^3} = \lim_{x \to 0} \frac{\left(\sqrt{1 + \tan x} - \sqrt{1 + \sin x}\right)\left(\sqrt{1 + \tan x} + \sqrt{1 + \sin x}\right)}{x^3\left(\sqrt{1 + \tan x} + \sqrt{1 + \sin x}\right)}$

$$= \lim_{x \to 0} \frac{(1 + \tan x) - (1 + \sin x)}{x^3\left(\sqrt{1 + \tan x} + \sqrt{1 + \sin x}\right)} = \lim_{x \to 0} \frac{\sin x\,(1/\cos x - 1)}{x^3\left(\sqrt{1 + \tan x} + \sqrt{1 + \sin x}\right)} \cdot \frac{\cos x}{\cos x}$$

$$= \lim_{x \to 0} \frac{\sin x\,(1 - \cos x)}{x^3\left(\sqrt{1 + \tan x} + \sqrt{1 + \sin x}\right)\cos x} \cdot \frac{1 + \cos x}{1 + \cos x}$$

$$= \lim_{x \to 0} \frac{\sin x \cdot \sin^2 x}{x^3\left(\sqrt{1 + \tan x} + \sqrt{1 + \sin x}\right)\cos x\,(1 + \cos x)}$$

$$= \left(\lim_{x \to 0} \frac{\sin x}{x}\right)^3 \lim_{x \to 0} \frac{1}{\left(\sqrt{1 + \tan x} + \sqrt{1 + \sin x}\right)\cos x\,(1 + \cos x)}$$

$$= 1^3 \cdot \frac{1}{\left(\sqrt{1} + \sqrt{1}\right) \cdot 1 \cdot (1 + 1)} = \frac{1}{4}$$

☐ FOCUS ON PROBLEM SOLVING

1. We must find a value x_0 such that the normal lines to the parabola $y = x^2$ at $x = \pm x_0$ intersect at a point one unit from the

points $(\pm x_0, x_0^2)$. The normals to $y = x^2$ at $x = \pm x_0$ have slopes $-\dfrac{1}{\pm 2x_0}$ and pass through $(\pm x_0, x_0^2)$ respectively, so the

normals have the equations $y - x_0^2 = -\dfrac{1}{2x_0}(x - x_0)$ and $y - x_0^2 = \dfrac{1}{2x_0}(x + x_0)$. The common y-intercept is $x_0^2 + \dfrac{1}{2}$.

We want to find the value of x_0 for which the distance from $\left(0, x_0^2 + \frac{1}{2}\right)$ to $\left(x_0, x_0^2\right)$ equals 1. The square of the distance is

$(x_0 - 0)^2 + \left[x_0^2 - \left(x_0^2 + \frac{1}{2}\right)\right]^2 = x_0^2 + \frac{1}{4} = 1 \;\Leftrightarrow\; x_0 = \pm\frac{\sqrt{3}}{2}$. For these values of x_0, the y-intercept is $x_0^2 + \frac{1}{2} = \frac{5}{4}$, so

the center of the circle is at $\left(0, \frac{5}{4}\right)$.

Another solution: Let the center of the circle be $(0, a)$. Then the equation of the circle is $x^2 + (y - a)^2 = 1$.

Solving with the equation of the parabola, $y = x^2$, we get $x^2 + (x^2 - a)^2 = 1 \;\Leftrightarrow\; x^2 + x^4 - 2ax^2 + a^2 = 1 \;\Leftrightarrow\;$

$x^4 + (1 - 2a)x^2 + a^2 - 1 = 0$. The parabola and the circle will be tangent to each other when this quadratic equation in x^2

has equal roots; that is, when the discriminant is 0. Thus, $(1 - 2a)^2 - 4(a^2 - 1) = 0 \;\Leftrightarrow\;$

$1 - 4a + 4a^2 - 4a^2 + 4 = 0 \;\Leftrightarrow\; 4a = 5$, so $a = \frac{5}{4}$. The center of the circle is $\left(0, \frac{5}{4}\right)$.

3.

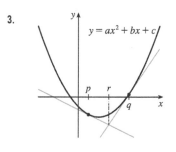

We must show that r (in the figure) is halfway between p and q, that is,

$r = (p + q)/2$. For the parabola $y = ax^2 + bx + c$, the slope of the tangent line is

given by $y' = 2ax + b$. An equation of the tangent line at $x = p$ is

$y - (ap^2 + bp + c) = (2ap + b)(x - p)$. Solving for y gives us

$$y = (2ap + b)x - 2ap^2 - bp + (ap^2 + bp + c)$$

or $\qquad y = (2ap + b)x + c - ap^2 \qquad \textbf{(1)}$

Similarly, an equation of the tangent line at $x = q$ is $\quad y = (2aq + b)x + c - aq^2 \qquad \textbf{(2)}$

We can eliminate y and solve for x by subtracting equation **(1)** from equation **(2)**.

$$[(2aq + b) - (2ap + b)]x - aq^2 + ap^2 = 0$$

$$(2aq - 2ap)x = aq^2 - ap^2$$

$$2a(q - p)x = a(q^2 - p^2)$$

$$x = \frac{a(q + p)(q - p)}{2a(q - p)} = \frac{p + q}{2}$$

Thus, the x-coordinate of the point of intersection of the two tangent lines, namely r, is $(p + q)/2$.

5. Using $f'(a) = \lim\limits_{x \to a} \dfrac{f(x) - f(a)}{x - a}$, we recognize the given expression, $f(x) = \lim\limits_{t \to x} \dfrac{\sec t - \sec x}{t - x}$, as

$g'(x)$ with $g(x) = \sec x$. Now $f'\left(\frac{\pi}{4}\right) = g''\left(\frac{\pi}{4}\right)$, so we will find $g''(x)$.

$g'(x) = \sec x \tan x \;\Rightarrow\; g''(x) = \sec x \sec^2 x + \tan x \sec x \tan x = \sec x(\sec^2 x + \tan^2 x)$, so

$g''\left(\frac{\pi}{4}\right) = \sqrt{2}\left(\sqrt{2}^2 + 1^2\right) = \sqrt{2}(2 + 1) = 3\sqrt{2}$.

7. We can assume without loss of generality that $\theta = 0$ at time $t = 0$, so that $\theta = 12\pi t$ rad. [The angular velocity of the wheel is 360 rpm $= 360 \cdot (2\pi \text{ rad})/(60 \text{ s}) = 12\pi$ rad/s.] Then the position of A as a function of time is

$$A = (40\cos\theta, 40\sin\theta) = (40\cos 12\pi t, 40\sin 12\pi t), \text{ so } \sin\alpha = \frac{y}{1.2 \text{ m}} = \frac{40\sin\theta}{120} = \frac{\sin\theta}{3} = \frac{1}{3}\sin 12\pi t.$$

(a) Differentiating the expression for $\sin\alpha$, we get $\cos\alpha \cdot \dfrac{d\alpha}{dt} = \dfrac{1}{3} \cdot 12\pi \cdot \cos 12\pi t = 4\pi\cos\theta$. When $\theta = \dfrac{\pi}{3}$, we have

$$\sin\alpha = \frac{1}{3}\sin\theta = \frac{\sqrt{3}}{6}, \text{ so } \cos\alpha = \sqrt{1 - \left(\frac{\sqrt{3}}{6}\right)^2} = \sqrt{\frac{11}{12}} \text{ and } \frac{d\alpha}{dt} = \frac{4\pi\cos\frac{\pi}{3}}{\cos\alpha} = \frac{2\pi}{\sqrt{11/12}} = \frac{4\pi\sqrt{3}}{\sqrt{11}} \approx 6.56 \text{ rad/s}.$$

(b) By the Law of Cosines, $|AP|^2 = |OA|^2 + |OP|^2 - 2|OA||OP|\cos\theta \;\Rightarrow$

$$120^2 = 40^2 + |OP|^2 - 2\cdot 40|OP|\cos\theta \;\Rightarrow\; |OP|^2 - (80\cos\theta)|OP| - 12{,}800 = 0 \;\Rightarrow$$

$$|OP| = \tfrac{1}{2}\left(80\cos\theta \pm \sqrt{6400\cos^2\theta + 51{,}200}\right) = 40\cos\theta \pm 40\sqrt{\cos^2\theta + 8} = 40\left(\cos\theta + \sqrt{8 + \cos^2\theta}\right) \text{ cm}$$

[since $|OP| > 0$]. As a check, note that $|OP| = 160$ cm when $\theta = 0$ and $|OP| = 80\sqrt{2}$ cm when $\theta = \frac{\pi}{2}$.

(c) By part (b), the x-coordinate of P is given by $x = 40\left(\cos\theta + \sqrt{8 + \cos^2\theta}\right)$, so

$$\frac{dx}{dt} = \frac{dx}{d\theta}\frac{d\theta}{dt} = 40\left(-\sin\theta - \frac{2\cos\theta\sin\theta}{2\sqrt{8 + \cos^2\theta}}\right)\cdot 12\pi = -480\pi\sin\theta\left(1 + \frac{\cos\theta}{\sqrt{8 + \cos^2\theta}}\right) \text{ cm/s}.$$

In particular, $dx/dt = 0$ cm/s when $\theta = 0$ and $dx/dt = -480\pi$ cm/s when $\theta = \frac{\pi}{2}$.

9. Consider the statement that $\dfrac{d^n}{dx^n}(e^{ax}\sin bx) = r^n e^{ax}\sin(bx + n\theta)$. For $n = 1$,

$$\frac{d}{dx}(e^{ax}\sin bx) = ae^{ax}\sin bx + be^{ax}\cos bx, \text{ and}$$

$$re^{ax}\sin(bx + \theta) = re^{ax}[\sin bx\cos\theta + \cos bx\sin\theta] = re^{ax}\left(\frac{a}{r}\sin bx + \frac{b}{r}\cos bx\right) = ae^{ax}\sin bx + be^{ax}\cos bx$$

since $\tan\theta = \dfrac{b}{a} \;\Rightarrow\; \sin\theta = \dfrac{b}{r}$ and $\cos\theta = \dfrac{a}{r}$. So the statement is true for $n = 1$.

Assume it is true for $n = k$. Then

$$\frac{d^{k+1}}{dx^{k+1}}(e^{ax}\sin bx) = \frac{d}{dx}\left[r^k e^{ax}\sin(bx + k\theta)\right] = r^k ae^{ax}\sin(bx + k\theta) + r^k e^{ax}b\cos(bx + k\theta)$$

$$= r^k e^{ax}[a\sin(bx + k\theta) + b\cos(bx + k\theta)]$$

But

$$\sin[bx + (k+1)\theta] = \sin[(bx + k\theta) + \theta] = \sin(bx + k\theta)\cos\theta + \sin\theta\cos(bx + k\theta)$$

$$= \tfrac{a}{r}\sin(bx + k\theta) + \tfrac{b}{r}\cos(bx + k\theta).$$

Hence, $a\sin(bx + k\theta) + b\cos(bx + k\theta) = r\sin[bx + (k+1)\theta]$. So

$$\frac{d^{k+1}}{dx^{k+1}}(e^{ax}\sin bx) = r^k e^{ax}[a\sin(bx+k\theta)+b\cos(bx+k\theta)] = r^k e^{ax}[r\sin(bx+(k+1)\theta)] = r^{k+1}e^{ax}[\sin(bx+(k+1)\theta)].$$

Therefore, the statement is true for all n by mathematical induction.

11. It seems from the figure that as P approaches the point $(0, 2)$ from the right, $x_T \to \infty$ and $y_T \to 2^+$. As P approaches the point $(3, 0)$ from the left, it appears that $x_T \to 3^+$ and $y_T \to \infty$. So we guess that $x_T \in (3, \infty)$ and $y_T \in (2, \infty)$. It is more difficult to estimate the range of values for x_N and y_N. We might perhaps guess that $x_N \in (0, 3)$, and $y_N \in (-\infty, 0)$ or $(-2, 0)$.

In order to actually solve the problem, we implicitly differentiate the equation of the ellipse to find the equation of the tangent line: $\dfrac{x^2}{9} + \dfrac{y^2}{4} = 1 \Rightarrow \dfrac{2x}{9} + \dfrac{2y}{4}y' = 0$, so $y' = -\dfrac{4}{9}\dfrac{x}{y}$. So at the point (x_0, y_0) on the ellipse, an equation of the tangent line is $y - y_0 = -\dfrac{4}{9}\dfrac{x_0}{y_0}(x - x_0)$ or $4x_0 x + 9y_0 y = 4x_0^2 + 9y_0^2$. This can be written as $\dfrac{x_0 x}{9} + \dfrac{y_0 y}{4} = \dfrac{x_0^2}{9} + \dfrac{y_0^2}{4} = 1$, because (x_0, y_0) lies on the ellipse. So an equation of the tangent line is $\dfrac{x_0 x}{9} + \dfrac{y_0 y}{4} = 1$.

Therefore, the x-intercept x_T for the tangent line is given by $\dfrac{x_0 x_T}{9} = 1 \Leftrightarrow x_T = \dfrac{9}{x_0}$, and the y-intercept y_T is given by $\dfrac{y_0 y_T}{4} = 1 \Leftrightarrow y_T = \dfrac{4}{y_0}$.

So as x_0 takes on all values in $(0, 3)$, x_T takes on all values in $(3, \infty)$, and as y_0 takes on all values in $(0, 2)$, y_T takes on all values in $(2, \infty)$. At the point (x_0, y_0) on the ellipse, the slope of the normal line is $-\dfrac{1}{y'(x_0, y_0)} = \dfrac{9}{4}\dfrac{y_0}{x_0}$, and its equation is $y - y_0 = \dfrac{9}{4}\dfrac{y_0}{x_0}(x - x_0)$. So the x-intercept x_N for the normal line is given by $0 - y_0 = \dfrac{9}{4}\dfrac{y_0}{x_0}(x_N - x_0) \Rightarrow x_N = -\dfrac{4x_0}{9} + x_0 = \dfrac{5x_0}{9}$, and the y-intercept y_N is given by $y_N - y_0 = \dfrac{9}{4}\dfrac{y_0}{x_0}(0 - x_0) \Rightarrow y_N = -\dfrac{9y_0}{4} + y_0 = -\dfrac{5y_0}{4}$.

So as x_0 takes on all values in $(0, 3)$, x_N takes on all values in $\left(0, \dfrac{5}{3}\right)$, and as y_0 takes on all values in $(0, 2)$, y_N takes on all values in $\left(-\dfrac{5}{2}, 0\right)$.

13. $y = \dfrac{x}{\sqrt{a^2 - 1}} - \dfrac{2}{\sqrt{a^2 - 1}} \arctan \dfrac{\sin x}{a + \sqrt{a^2 - 1} + \cos x}$. Let $k = a + \sqrt{a^2 - 1}$. Then

$$y' = \dfrac{1}{\sqrt{a^2 - 1}} - \dfrac{2}{\sqrt{a^2 - 1}} \cdot \dfrac{1}{1 + \sin^2 x/(k + \cos x)^2} \cdot \dfrac{\cos x(k + \cos x) + \sin^2 x}{(k + \cos x)^2}$$

$$= \dfrac{1}{\sqrt{a^2 - 1}} - \dfrac{2}{\sqrt{a^2 - 1}} \cdot \dfrac{k \cos x + \cos^2 x + \sin^2 x}{(k + \cos x)^2 + \sin^2 x} = \dfrac{1}{\sqrt{a^2 - 1}} - \dfrac{2}{\sqrt{a^2 - 1}} \cdot \dfrac{k \cos x + 1}{k^2 + 2k \cos x + 1}$$

$$= \dfrac{k^2 + 2k \cos x + 1 - 2k \cos x - 2}{\sqrt{a^2 - 1}\,(k^2 + 2k \cos x + 1)} = \dfrac{k^2 - 1}{\sqrt{a^2 - 1}\,(k^2 + 2k \cos x + 1)}$$

But $k^2 = 2a^2 + 2a\sqrt{a^2 - 1} - 1 = 2a\left(a + \sqrt{a^2 - 1}\right) - 1 = 2ak - 1$, so $k^2 + 1 = 2ak$, and $k^2 - 1 = 2(ak - 1)$.

So $y' = \dfrac{2(ak - 1)}{\sqrt{a^2 - 1}\,(2ak + 2k \cos x)} = \dfrac{ak - 1}{\sqrt{a^2 - 1}\,k\,(a + \cos x)}$. But $ak - 1 = a^2 + a\sqrt{a^2 - 1} - 1 = k\sqrt{a^2 - 1}$, so $y' = 1/(a + \cos x)$.

15.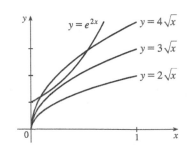

Let $f(x) = e^{2x}$ and $g(x) = k\sqrt{x}$ $[k > 0]$. From the graphs of f and g, we see that f will intersect g exactly once when f and g share a tangent line. Thus, we must have $f = g$ and $f' = g'$ at $x = a$.

$$f(a) = g(a) \quad \Rightarrow \quad e^{2a} = k\sqrt{a} \quad (\star)$$

and $\quad f'(a) = g'(a) \quad \Rightarrow \quad 2e^{2a} = \dfrac{k}{2\sqrt{a}} \quad \Rightarrow \quad e^{2a} = \dfrac{k}{4\sqrt{a}}$.

So we must have $k\sqrt{a} = \dfrac{k}{4\sqrt{a}} \quad \Rightarrow \quad \left(\sqrt{a}\right)^2 = \dfrac{k}{4k} \quad \Rightarrow \quad a = \frac{1}{4}$. From $(\star)$, $e^{2(1/4)} = k\sqrt{1/4} \quad \Rightarrow$

$k = 2e^{1/2} = 2\sqrt{e} \approx 3.297$.

17. (a) If the two lines L_1 and L_2 have slopes m_1 and m_2 and angles of inclination ϕ_1 and ϕ_2, then $m_1 = \tan\phi_1$ and $m_2 = \tan\phi_2$. The triangle in the figure shows that $\phi_1 + \alpha + (180° - \phi_2) = 180°$ and so $\alpha = \phi_2 - \phi_1$. Therefore, using the identity for $\tan(x - y)$, we have

$$\tan\alpha = \tan(\phi_2 - \phi_1) = \frac{\tan\phi_2 - \tan\phi_1}{1 + \tan\phi_2\tan\phi_1} \text{ and so } \tan\alpha = \frac{m_2 - m_1}{1 + m_1 m_2}.$$

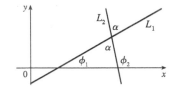

(b) (i) The parabolas intersect when $x^2 = (x-2)^2 \quad \Rightarrow \quad x = 1$. If $y = x^2$, then $y' = 2x$, so the slope of the tangent to $y = x^2$ at $(1, 1)$ is $m_1 = 2(1) = 2$. If $y = (x-2)^2$, then $y' = 2(x-2)$, so the slope of the tangent to

$y = (x-2)^2$ at $(1, 1)$ is $m_2 = 2(1 - 2) = -2$. Therefore, $\tan\alpha = \dfrac{m_2 - m_1}{1 + m_1 m_2} = \dfrac{-2 - 2}{1 + 2(-2)} = \dfrac{4}{3}$ and

so $\alpha = \tan^{-1}\left(\frac{4}{3}\right) \approx 53°$ [or $127°$].

(ii) $x^2 - y^2 = 3$ and $x^2 - 4x + y^2 + 3 = 0$ intersect when $x^2 - 4x + (x^2 - 3) + 3 = 0 \quad \Leftrightarrow \quad 2x(x - 2) = 0 \quad \Rightarrow$

$x = 0$ or 2, but 0 is extraneous. If $x = 2$, then $y = \pm 1$. If $x^2 - y^2 = 3$ then $2x - 2yy' = 0 \quad \Rightarrow \quad y' = x/y$ and

$x^2 - 4x + y^2 + 3 = 0 \quad \Rightarrow \quad 2x - 4 + 2yy' = 0 \quad \Rightarrow \quad y' = \dfrac{2 - x}{y}$. At $(2, 1)$ the slopes are $m_1 = 2$ and

$m_2 = 0$, so $\tan\alpha = \frac{0 - 2}{1 + 2\cdot 0} = -2 \quad \Rightarrow \quad \alpha \approx 117°$. At $(2, -1)$ the slopes are $m_1 = -2$ and $m_2 = 0$,

so $\tan\alpha = \dfrac{0 - (-2)}{1 + (-2)(0)} = 2 \quad \Rightarrow \quad \alpha \approx 63°$ [or $117°$].

19. Since $\angle ROQ = \angle OQP = \theta$, the triangle QOR is isosceles, so

$|QR| = |RO| = x$. By the Law of Cosines, $x^2 = x^2 + r^2 - 2rx\cos\theta$. Hence,

$2rx\cos\theta = r^2$, so $x = \dfrac{r^2}{2r\cos\theta} = \dfrac{r}{2\cos\theta}$. Note that as $y \to 0^+$, $\theta \to 0^+$ (since

$\sin\theta = y/r$), and hence $x \to \dfrac{r}{2\cos 0} = \dfrac{r}{2}$. Thus, as P is taken closer and closer

to the x-axis, the point R approaches the midpoint of the radius AO.

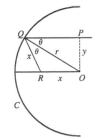

21. $y = x^4 - 2x^2 - x \implies y' = 4x^3 - 4x - 1$. The equation of the tangent line at $x = a$ is

$y - (a^4 - 2a^2 - a) = (4a^3 - 4a - 1)(x - a)$ or $y = (4a^3 - 4a - 1)x + (-3a^4 + 2a^2)$ and similarly for $x = b$. So if at

$x = a$ and $x = b$ we have the same tangent line, then $4a^3 - 4a - 1 = 4b^3 - 4b - 1$ and $-3a^4 + 2a^2 = -3b^4 + 2b^2$. The first

equation gives $a^3 - b^3 = a - b \implies (a - b)(a^2 + ab + b^2) = (a - b)$. Assuming $a \neq b$, we have $1 = a^2 + ab + b^2$.

The second equation gives $3(a^4 - b^4) = 2(a^2 - b^2) \implies 3(a^2 - b^2)(a^2 + b^2) = 2(a^2 - b^2)$ which is true if $a = -b$.

Substituting into $1 = a^2 + ab + b^2$ gives $1 = a^2 - a^2 + a^2 \implies a = \pm 1$ so that $a = 1$ and $b = -1$ or vice versa. Thus,

the points $(1, -2)$ and $(-1, 0)$ have a common tangent line.

As long as there are only two such points, we are done. So we show that these are in fact the only two such points.

Suppose that $a^2 - b^2 \neq 0$. Then $3(a^2 - b^2)(a^2 + b^2) = 2(a^2 - b^2)$ gives $3(a^2 + b^2) = 2$ or $a^2 + b^2 = \frac{2}{3}$.

Thus, $ab = (a^2 + ab + b^2) - (a^2 + b^2) = 1 - \frac{2}{3} = \frac{1}{3}$, so $b = \frac{1}{3a}$. Hence, $a^2 + \frac{1}{9a^2} = \frac{2}{3}$, so $9a^4 + 1 = 6a^2 \implies$

$0 = 9a^4 - 6a^2 + 1 = (3a^2 - 1)^2$. So $3a^2 - 1 = 0 \implies a^2 = \frac{1}{3} \implies b^2 = \frac{1}{9a^2} = \frac{1}{3} = a^2$, contradicting our assumption

that $a^2 \neq b^2$.

23. Because of the periodic nature of the lattice points, it suffices to consider the points in the 5×2 grid shown. We can see that

the minimum value of r occurs when there is a line with slope $\frac{2}{5}$ which touches the circle centered at $(3, 1)$ and the circles

centered at $(0, 0)$ and $(5, 2)$.

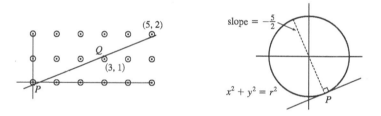

To find P, the point at which the line is tangent to the circle at $(0, 0)$, we simultaneously solve $x^2 + y^2 = r^2$ and

$y = -\frac{5}{2}x \implies x^2 + \frac{25}{4}x^2 = r^2 \implies x^2 = \frac{4}{29}r^2 \implies x = \frac{2}{\sqrt{29}}r, y = -\frac{5}{\sqrt{29}}r$. To find Q, we either use symmetry or

solve $(x - 3)^2 + (y - 1)^2 = r^2$ and $y - 1 = -\frac{5}{2}(x - 3)$. As above, we get $x = 3 - \frac{2}{\sqrt{29}}r, y = 1 + \frac{5}{\sqrt{29}}r$. Now the slope of

the line PQ is $\frac{2}{5}$, so $m_{PQ} = \dfrac{1 + \frac{5}{\sqrt{29}}r - \left(-\frac{5}{\sqrt{29}}r\right)}{3 - \frac{2}{\sqrt{29}}r - \frac{2}{\sqrt{29}}r} = \dfrac{1 + \frac{10}{\sqrt{29}}r}{3 - \frac{4}{\sqrt{29}}r} = \dfrac{\sqrt{29} + 10r}{3\sqrt{29} - 4r} = \dfrac{2}{5} \implies$

$5\sqrt{29} + 50r = 6\sqrt{29} - 8r \iff 58r = \sqrt{29} \iff r = \frac{\sqrt{29}}{58}$. So the minimum value of r for which any line with slope $\frac{2}{5}$

intersects circles with radius r centered at the lattice points on the plane is $r = \frac{\sqrt{29}}{58} \approx 0.093$.

4 □ APPLICATIONS OF DIFFERENTIATION

4.1 Related Rates

1. $V = x^3 \quad \Rightarrow \quad \dfrac{dV}{dt} = \dfrac{dV}{dx}\dfrac{dx}{dt} = 3x^2\dfrac{dx}{dt}$

3. Let s denote the side of a square. The square's area A is given by $A = s^2$. Differentiating with respect to t gives us $\dfrac{dA}{dt} = 2s\dfrac{ds}{dt}$. When $A = 16$, $s = 4$. Substituting 4 for s and 6 for $\dfrac{ds}{dt}$ gives us $\dfrac{dA}{dt} = 2(4)(6) = 48\text{ cm}^2/\text{s}$.

5. $V = \pi r^2 h = \pi(5)^2 h = 25\pi h \quad \Rightarrow \quad \dfrac{dV}{dt} = 25\pi\dfrac{dh}{dt} \quad \Rightarrow \quad 3 = 25\pi\dfrac{dh}{dt} \quad \Rightarrow \quad \dfrac{dh}{dt} = \dfrac{3}{25\pi}\text{ m/min}.$

7. (a) $y = \sqrt{2x+1}$ and $\dfrac{dx}{dt} = 3 \quad \Rightarrow \quad \dfrac{dy}{dt} = \dfrac{dy}{dx}\dfrac{dx}{dt} = \dfrac{1}{2}(2x+1)^{-1/2}\cdot 2\cdot 3 = \dfrac{3}{\sqrt{2x+1}}$. When $x = 4$, $\dfrac{dy}{dt} = \dfrac{3}{\sqrt{9}} = 1$.

  (b) $y = \sqrt{2x+1} \quad \Rightarrow \quad y^2 = 2x+1 \quad \Rightarrow \quad 2x = y^2 - 1 \quad \Rightarrow \quad x = \tfrac{1}{2}y^2 - \tfrac{1}{2}$ and $\dfrac{dy}{dt} = 5 \quad \Rightarrow$

  $\dfrac{dx}{dt} = \dfrac{dx}{dy}\dfrac{dy}{dt} = y\cdot 5 = 5y$. When $x = 12$, $y = \sqrt{25} = 5$, so $\dfrac{dx}{dt} = 5(5) = 25$.

9. $z^2 = x^2 + y^2 \quad \Rightarrow \quad 2z\dfrac{dz}{dt} = 2x\dfrac{dx}{dt} + 2y\dfrac{dy}{dt} \quad \Rightarrow \quad \dfrac{dz}{dt} = \dfrac{1}{z}\left(x\dfrac{dx}{dt} + y\dfrac{dy}{dt}\right)$. When $x = 5$ and $y = 12$,

  $z^2 = 5^2 + 12^2 \quad \Rightarrow \quad z^2 = 169 \quad \Rightarrow \quad z = \pm 13$. For $\dfrac{dx}{dt} = 2$ and $\dfrac{dy}{dt} = 3$, $\dfrac{dz}{dt} = \dfrac{1}{\pm 13}(5\cdot 2 + 12\cdot 3) = \pm\dfrac{46}{13}$.

11. (a) Given: the rate of decrease of the surface area is $1\text{ cm}^2/\text{min}$. If we let t be time (in minutes) and S be the surface area (in cm^2), then we are given that $dS/dt = -1\text{ cm}^2/\text{s}$.

  (b) Unknown: the rate of decrease of the diameter when the diameter is 10 cm. If we let x be the diameter, then we want to find dx/dt when $x = 10$ cm.

  (c)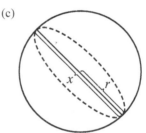

  (d) If the radius is r and the diameter $x = 2r$, then $r = \tfrac{1}{2}x$ and

  $S = 4\pi r^2 = 4\pi\left(\tfrac{1}{2}x\right)^2 = \pi x^2 \quad \Rightarrow \quad \dfrac{dS}{dt} = \dfrac{dS}{dx}\dfrac{dx}{dt} = 2\pi x\dfrac{dx}{dt}.$

  (e) $-1 = \dfrac{dS}{dt} = 2\pi x\dfrac{dx}{dt} \quad \Rightarrow \quad \dfrac{dx}{dt} = -\dfrac{1}{2\pi x}$. When $x = 10$, $\dfrac{dx}{dt} = -\dfrac{1}{20\pi}$. So the rate of decrease is $\dfrac{1}{20\pi}\text{ cm/min}$.

13. (a) Given: a plane flying horizontally at an altitude of 1 mi and a speed of 500 mi/h passes directly over a radar station. If we let t be time (in hours) and x be the horizontal distance traveled by the plane (in mi), then we are given that $dx/dt = 500$ mi/h.

  (b) Unknown: the rate at which the distance from the plane to the station is increasing when it is 2 mi from the station. If we let y be the distance from the plane to the station, then we want to find dy/dt when $y = 2$ mi.

  (c)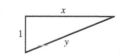

(d) By the Pythagorean Theorem, $y^2 = x^2 + 1 \Rightarrow 2y \, (dy/dt) = 2x \, (dx/dt)$.

(e) $\dfrac{dy}{dt} = \dfrac{x}{y}\dfrac{dx}{dt} = \dfrac{x}{y}(500)$. Since $y^2 = x^2 + 1$, when $y = 2$, $x = \sqrt{3}$, so $\dfrac{dy}{dt} = \dfrac{\sqrt{3}}{2}(500) = 250\sqrt{3} \approx 433$ mi/h.

15.

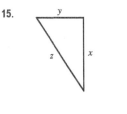

We are given that $\dfrac{dx}{dt} = 60$ mi/h and $\dfrac{dy}{dt} = 25$ mi/h. $z^2 = x^2 + y^2 \Rightarrow$

$$2z\,\frac{dz}{dt} = 2x\,\frac{dx}{dt} + 2y\,\frac{dy}{dt} \Rightarrow z\,\frac{dz}{dt} = x\,\frac{dx}{dt} + y\,\frac{dy}{dt} \Rightarrow \frac{dz}{dt} = \frac{1}{z}\left(x\,\frac{dx}{dt} + y\,\frac{dy}{dt}\right).$$

After 2 hours, $x = 2\,(60) = 120$ and $y = 2\,(25) = 50 \Rightarrow z = \sqrt{120^2 + 50^2} = 130$,

so $\dfrac{dz}{dt} = \dfrac{1}{z}\left(x\,\dfrac{dx}{dt} + y\,\dfrac{dy}{dt}\right) = \dfrac{120(60) + 50(25)}{130} = 65$ mi/h.

17.

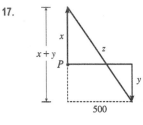

We are given that $\dfrac{dx}{dt} = 4$ ft/s and $\dfrac{dy}{dt} = 5$ ft/s. $z^2 = (x+y)^2 + 500^2 \Rightarrow$

$2z\,\dfrac{dz}{dt} = 2(x+y)\left(\dfrac{dx}{dt} + \dfrac{dy}{dt}\right)$. 15 minutes after the woman starts, we have

$x = (4 \text{ ft/s})(20 \text{ min})(60 \text{ s/min}) = 4800$ ft and $y = 5 \cdot 15 \cdot 60 = 4500 \Rightarrow$

$z = \sqrt{(4800 + 4500)^2 + 500^2} = \sqrt{86{,}740{,}000}$, so

$\dfrac{dz}{dt} = \dfrac{x+y}{z}\left(\dfrac{dx}{dt} + \dfrac{dy}{dt}\right) = \dfrac{4800 + 4500}{\sqrt{86{,}740{,}000}}(4+5) = \dfrac{837}{\sqrt{8674}} \approx 8.99$ ft/s.

19. $A = \frac{1}{2}bh$, where b is the base and h is the altitude. We are given that $\dfrac{dh}{dt} = 1$ cm/min and $\dfrac{dA}{dt} = 2$ cm^2/min. Using the

Product Rule, we have $\dfrac{dA}{dt} = \dfrac{1}{2}\left(b\,\dfrac{dh}{dt} + h\,\dfrac{db}{dt}\right)$. When $h = 10$ and $A = 100$, we have $100 = \frac{1}{2}b(10) \Rightarrow \frac{1}{2}b = 10 \Rightarrow$

$b = 20$, so $2 = \dfrac{1}{2}\left(20 \cdot 1 + 10\,\dfrac{db}{dt}\right) \Rightarrow 4 = 20 + 10\,\dfrac{db}{dt} \Rightarrow \dfrac{db}{dt} = \dfrac{4-20}{10} = -1.6$ cm/min.

21.

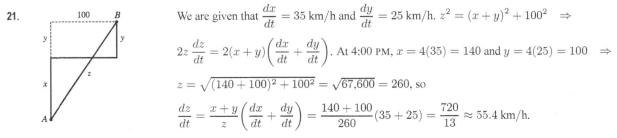

We are given that $\dfrac{dx}{dt} = 35$ km/h and $\dfrac{dy}{dt} = 25$ km/h. $z^2 = (x+y)^2 + 100^2 \Rightarrow$

$2z\,\dfrac{dz}{dt} = 2(x+y)\left(\dfrac{dx}{dt} + \dfrac{dy}{dt}\right)$. At 4:00 PM, $x = 4(35) = 140$ and $y = 4(25) = 100 \Rightarrow$

$z = \sqrt{(140 + 100)^2 + 100^2} = \sqrt{67{,}600} = 260$, so

$\dfrac{dz}{dt} = \dfrac{x+y}{z}\left(\dfrac{dx}{dt} + \dfrac{dy}{dt}\right) = \dfrac{140 + 100}{260}(35 + 25) = \dfrac{720}{13} \approx 55.4$ km/h.

23. From the figure and given information, we have $x^2 + y^2 = L^2$, $\dfrac{dy}{dt} = -0.15$ m/s, and

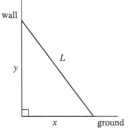

$\dfrac{dx}{dt} = 0.2$ m/s when $x = 3$ m. Differentiating implicitly with respect to t, we get

$x^2 + y^2 = L^2 \Rightarrow 2x\,\dfrac{dx}{dt} + 2y\,\dfrac{dy}{dt} = 0 \Rightarrow y\,\dfrac{dy}{dt} = -x\,\dfrac{dx}{dt}$. Substituting the given

information gives us $y(-0.15) = -3(0.2) \Rightarrow y = 4$ m. Thus, $3^2 + 4^2 = L^2 \Rightarrow$

$L^2 = 25 \Rightarrow L = 5$ m.

25. Using Q for the origin, we are given $\dfrac{dx}{dt} = -2$ ft/s and need to find $\dfrac{dy}{dt}$ when $x = -5$.

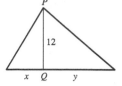

Using the Pythagorean Theorem twice, we have $\sqrt{x^2 + 12^2} + \sqrt{y^2 + 12^2} = 39$,

the total length of the rope. Differentiating with respect to t, we get

$$\frac{x}{\sqrt{x^2+12^2}}\frac{dx}{dt} + \frac{y}{\sqrt{y^2+12^2}}\frac{dy}{dt} = 0, \text{ so } \frac{dy}{dt} = -\frac{x\sqrt{y^2+12^2}}{y\sqrt{x^2+12^2}}\frac{dx}{dt}.$$

Now when $x = -5$, $39 = \sqrt{(-5)^2 + 12^2} + \sqrt{y^2 + 12^2} = 13 + \sqrt{y^2 + 12^2}$ $\Leftrightarrow$ $\sqrt{y^2 + 12^2} = 26$, and

$y = \sqrt{26^2 - 12^2} = \sqrt{532}$. So when $x = -5$, $\dfrac{dy}{dt} = -\dfrac{(-5)(26)}{\sqrt{532}\,(13)}(-2) = -\dfrac{10}{\sqrt{133}} \approx -0.87$ ft/s.

So cart B is moving towards Q at about 0.87 ft/s.

27. By similar triangles, $\dfrac{3}{1} = \dfrac{b}{h}$, so $b = 3h$. The trough has volume

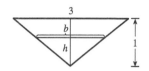

$$V = \tfrac{1}{2}bh(10) = 5(3h)h = 15h^2 \quad\Rightarrow\quad 12 = \frac{dV}{dt} = 30h\frac{dh}{dt} \quad\Rightarrow\quad \frac{dh}{dt} = \frac{2}{5h}.$$

When $h = \tfrac{1}{2}$, $\dfrac{dh}{dt} = \dfrac{2}{5 \cdot \tfrac{1}{2}} = \dfrac{4}{5}$ ft/min.

29. We are given that $\dfrac{dV}{dt} = 30$ ft^3/min. $V = \dfrac{1}{3}\pi r^2 h = \dfrac{1}{3}\pi\left(\dfrac{h}{2}\right)^2 h = \dfrac{\pi h^3}{12}$ $\Rightarrow$

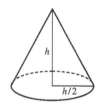

$$\frac{dV}{dt} = \frac{dV}{dh}\frac{dh}{dt} \quad\Rightarrow\quad 30 = \frac{\pi h^2}{4}\frac{dh}{dt} \quad\Rightarrow\quad \frac{dh}{dt} = \frac{120}{\pi h^2}.$$

When $h = 10$ ft, $\dfrac{dh}{dt} = \dfrac{120}{10^2\pi} = \dfrac{6}{5\pi} \approx 0.38$ ft/min.

31. $A = \tfrac{1}{2}bh$, but $b = 5$ m and $\sin\theta = \dfrac{h}{4}$ $\Rightarrow$ $h = 4\sin\theta$, so $A = \tfrac{1}{2}(5)(4\sin\theta) = 10\sin\theta$.

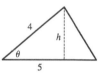

We are given $\dfrac{d\theta}{dl} = 0.06$ rad/s, so $\dfrac{dA}{dt} = \dfrac{dA}{d\theta}\dfrac{d\theta}{dt} = (10\cos\theta)(0.06) = 0.6\cos\theta$.

When $\theta = \dfrac{\pi}{3}$, $\dfrac{dA}{dt} = 0.6\left(\cos\dfrac{\pi}{3}\right) = (0.6)\left(\tfrac{1}{2}\right) = 0.3$ m^2/s.

33. Differentiating both sides of $PV = C$ with respect to t and using the Product Rule gives us $P\dfrac{dV}{dt} + V\dfrac{dP}{dt} = 0$ $\Rightarrow$

$\dfrac{dV}{dt} = -\dfrac{V}{P}\dfrac{dP}{dt}$. When $V = 600$, $P = 150$ and $\dfrac{dP}{dt} = 20$, so we have $\dfrac{dV}{dt} = -\dfrac{600}{150}(20) = -80$. Thus, the volume is

decreasing at a rate of 80 cm^3/min.

35. With $R_1 = 80$ and $R_2 = 100$, $\dfrac{1}{R} = \dfrac{1}{R_1} + \dfrac{1}{R_2} = \dfrac{1}{80} + \dfrac{1}{100} = \dfrac{180}{8000} = \dfrac{9}{400}$, so $R = \dfrac{400}{9}$. Differentiating $\dfrac{1}{R} = \dfrac{1}{R_1} + \dfrac{1}{R_2}$

with respect to t, we have $-\dfrac{1}{R^2}\dfrac{dR}{dt} = -\dfrac{1}{R_1^2}\dfrac{dR_1}{dt} - \dfrac{1}{R_2^2}\dfrac{dR_2}{dt}$ $\Rightarrow$ $\dfrac{dR}{dt} = R^2\left(\dfrac{1}{R_1^2}\dfrac{dR_1}{dt} + \dfrac{1}{R_2^2}\dfrac{dR_2}{dt}\right)$. When $R_1 = 80$ and

$R_2 = 100$, $\dfrac{dR}{dt} = \dfrac{400^2}{9^2}\left[\dfrac{1}{80^2}(0.3) + \dfrac{1}{100^2}(0.2)\right] = \dfrac{107}{810} \approx 0.132\ \Omega/\text{s}$.

37. (a) By the Pythagorean Theorem, $4000^2 + y^2 = \ell^2$. Differentiating with respect to t,

we obtain $2y\dfrac{dy}{dt} = 2\ell\dfrac{d\ell}{dt}$. We know that $\dfrac{dy}{dt} = 600$ ft/s, so when $y = 3000$ ft,

$\ell = \sqrt{4000^2 + 3000^2} = \sqrt{25{,}000{,}000} = 5000$ ft

and $\dfrac{d\ell}{dt} = \dfrac{y}{\ell}\dfrac{dy}{dt} = \dfrac{3000}{5000}(600) = \dfrac{1800}{5} = 360$ ft/s.

(b) Here $\tan\theta = \dfrac{y}{4000} \ \Rightarrow\ \dfrac{d}{dt}(\tan\theta) = \dfrac{d}{dt}\left(\dfrac{y}{4000}\right) \ \Rightarrow\ \sec^2\theta\,\dfrac{d\theta}{dt} = \dfrac{1}{4000}\dfrac{dy}{dt} \ \Rightarrow\ \dfrac{d\theta}{dt} = \dfrac{\cos^2\theta}{4000}\dfrac{dy}{dt}$. When

$y = 3000$ ft, $\dfrac{dy}{dt} = 600$ ft/s, $\ell = 5000$ and $\cos\theta = \dfrac{4000}{\ell} = \dfrac{4000}{5000} = \dfrac{4}{5}$, so $\dfrac{d\theta}{dt} = \dfrac{(4/5)^2}{4000}(600) = 0.096$ rad/s.

39. $\cot\theta = \dfrac{x}{5} \ \Rightarrow\ -\csc^2\theta\,\dfrac{d\theta}{dt} = \dfrac{1}{5}\dfrac{dx}{dt} \ \Rightarrow\ -\left(\csc\dfrac{\pi}{3}\right)^2\left(-\dfrac{\pi}{6}\right) = \dfrac{1}{5}\dfrac{dx}{dt} \ \Rightarrow$

$\dfrac{dx}{dt} = \dfrac{5\pi}{6}\left(\dfrac{2}{\sqrt{3}}\right)^2 = \dfrac{10}{9}\pi$ km/min $[\approx 130$ mi/h$]$

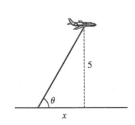

41. We are given that $\dfrac{dx}{dt} = 300$ km/h. By the Law of Cosines,

$y^2 = x^2 + 1^2 - 2(1)(x)\cos 120° = x^2 + 1 - 2x\left(-\tfrac{1}{2}\right) = x^2 + x + 1$, so

$2y\dfrac{dy}{dt} = 2x\dfrac{dx}{dt} + \dfrac{dx}{dt} \ \Rightarrow\ \dfrac{dy}{dt} = \dfrac{2x+1}{2y}\dfrac{dx}{dt}$. After 1 minute, $x = \frac{300}{60} = 5$ km $\ \Rightarrow$

$y = \sqrt{5^2 + 5 + 1} = \sqrt{31}$ km $\ \Rightarrow\ \dfrac{dy}{dt} = \dfrac{2(5)+1}{2\sqrt{31}}(300) = \dfrac{1650}{\sqrt{31}} \approx 296$ km/h.

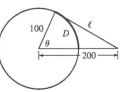

43. Let the distance between the runner and the friend be ℓ. Then by the Law of Cosines,

$\ell^2 = 200^2 + 100^2 - 2\cdot 200\cdot 100\cdot\cos\theta = 50{,}000 - 40{,}000\cos\theta$ $(\star)$. Differentiating

implicitly with respect to t, we obtain $2\ell\dfrac{d\ell}{dt} = -40{,}000(-\sin\theta)\dfrac{d\theta}{dt}$. Now if D is the

distance run when the angle is θ radians, then by the formula for the length of an arc

on a circle, $s = r\theta$, we have $D = 100\theta$, so $\theta = \dfrac{1}{100}D \ \Rightarrow\ \dfrac{d\theta}{dt} = \dfrac{1}{100}\dfrac{dD}{dt} = \dfrac{7}{100}$. To substitute into the expression for

$\dfrac{d\ell}{dt}$, we must know $\sin\theta$ at the time when $\ell = 200$, which we find from $(\star)$: $200^2 = 50{,}000 - 40{,}000\cos\theta \ \Leftrightarrow$

$\cos\theta = \tfrac{1}{4} \ \Rightarrow\ \sin\theta = \sqrt{1-\left(\tfrac{1}{4}\right)^2} = \dfrac{\sqrt{15}}{4}$. Substituting, we get $2(200)\dfrac{d\ell}{dt} = 40{,}000\dfrac{\sqrt{15}}{4}\left(\tfrac{7}{100}\right) \ \Rightarrow$

$d\ell/dt = \dfrac{7\sqrt{15}}{4} \approx 6.78$ m/s. Whether the distance between them is increasing or decreasing depends on the direction in which

the runner is running.

4.2   Maximum and Minimum Values

1. A function f has an **absolute minimum** at $x = c$ if $f(c)$ is the smallest function value on the entire domain of f, whereas f has a **local minimum** at c if $f(c)$ is the smallest function value when x is near c.

3. Absolute maximum at s, absolute minimum at r, local maximum at c, local minima at b and r, neither a maximum nor a minimum at a and d.

5. Absolute maximum value is $f(4) = 5$; there is no absolute minimum value; local maximum values are $f(4) = 5$ and $f(6) = 4$; local minimum values are $f(2) = 2$ and $f(1) = f(5) = 3$.

7. Absolute minimum at 2, absolute maximum at 3, local minimum at 4

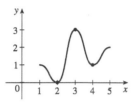

9. Absolute maximum at 5, absolute minimum at 2, local maximum at 3, local minima at 2 and 4

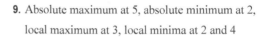

11. (a)

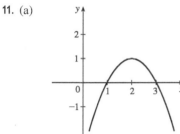

(b)

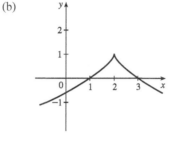

(c)

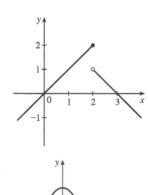

13. (a) *Note:* By the Extreme Value Theorem, f must *not* be continuous; because if it were, it would attain an absolute minimum.

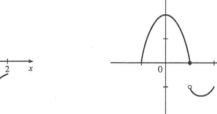

(b)

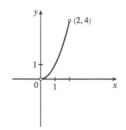

15. $f(x) = \frac{1}{2}(3x - 1)$, $x \le 3$. Absolute maximum $f(3) = 4$; no local maximum. No absolute or local minimum.

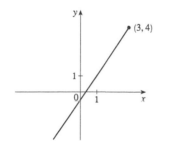

17. $f(x) = x^2$, $0 < x < 2$. No absolute or local maximum or minimum value.

19. $f(x) = \ln x$, $0 < x \le 2$. Absolute maximum $f(2) = \ln 2 \approx 0.69$; no local maximum. No absolute or local minimum.

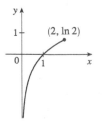

21. $f(x) = 1 - \sqrt{x}$. Absolute maximum $f(0) = 1$; no local maximum. No absolute or local minimum.

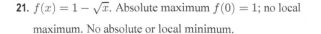
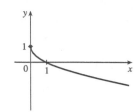

23. $f(x) = 4 + \frac{1}{3}x - \frac{1}{2}x^2$ $\Rightarrow$ $f'(x) = \frac{1}{3} - x$. $f'(x) = 0$ $\Rightarrow$ $x = \frac{1}{3}$. This is the only critical number.

25. $f(x) = x^3 + 3x^2 - 24x$ $\Rightarrow$ $f'(x) = 3x^2 + 6x - 24 = 3(x^2 + 2x - 8)$.

$f'(x) = 0$ $\Rightarrow$ $3(x + 4)(x - 2) = 0$ $\Rightarrow$ $x = -4, 2$. These are the only critical numbers.

27. $s(t) = 3t^4 + 4t^3 - 6t^2$ $\Rightarrow$ $s'(t) = 12t^3 + 12t^2 - 12t$. $s'(t) = 0$ $\Rightarrow$ $12t(t^2 + t - 1)$ $\Rightarrow$

$t = 0$ or $t^2 + t - 1 = 0$. Using the quadratic formula to solve the latter equation gives us

$$t = \frac{-1 \pm \sqrt{1^2 - 4(1)(-1)}}{2(1)} = \frac{-1 \pm \sqrt{5}}{2} \approx 0.618, -1.618.$$ The three critical numbers are 0, $\dfrac{-1 \pm \sqrt{5}}{2}$.

29. $g(y) = \dfrac{y - 1}{y^2 - y + 1}$ $\Rightarrow$

$$g'(y) = \frac{(y^2 - y + 1)(1) - (y - 1)(2y - 1)}{(y^2 - y + 1)^2} = \frac{y^2 - y + 1 - (2y^2 - 3y + 1)}{(y^2 - y + 1)^2} = \frac{-y^2 + 2y}{(y^2 - y + 1)^2} = \frac{y(2 - y)}{(y^2 - y + 1)^2}.$$

$g'(y) = 0$ $\Rightarrow$ $y = 0, 2$. The expression $y^2 - y + 1$ is never equal to 0, so $g'(y)$ exists for all real numbers.
The critical numbers are 0 and 2.

31. $h(t) = t^{3/4} - 2t^{1/4}$ $\Rightarrow$ $h'(t) = \frac{3}{4}t^{-1/4} - \frac{2}{4}t^{-3/4} = \frac{1}{4}t^{-3/4}(3t^{1/2} - 2) = \dfrac{3\sqrt{t} - 2}{4\sqrt[4]{t^3}}$.

$h'(t) = 0$ $\Rightarrow$ $3\sqrt{t} = 2$ $\Rightarrow$ $\sqrt{t} = \frac{2}{3}$ $\Rightarrow$ $t = \frac{4}{9}$. $h'(t)$ does not exist at $t = 0$, so the critical numbers are 0 and $\frac{4}{9}$.

33. $F(x) = x^{4/5}(x - 4)^2$ $\Rightarrow$

$$F'(x) = x^{4/5} \cdot 2(x - 4) + (x - 4)^2 \cdot \frac{4}{5}x^{-1/5} = \frac{1}{5}x^{-1/5}(x - 4)[5 \cdot x \cdot 2 + (x - 4) \cdot 4]$$

$$= \frac{(x - 4)(14x - 16)}{5x^{1/5}} = \frac{2(x - 4)(7x - 8)}{5x^{1/5}}$$

$F'(x) = 0$ $\Rightarrow$ $x = 4, \frac{8}{7}$. $F'(0)$ does not exist. Thus, the three critical numbers are 0, $\frac{8}{7}$, and 4.

35. $f(\theta) = 2\cos\theta + \sin^2\theta$ $\Rightarrow$ $f'(\theta) = -2\sin\theta + 2\sin\theta\cos\theta$. $f'(\theta) = 0$ $\Rightarrow$ $2\sin\theta(\cos\theta - 1) = 0$ $\Rightarrow$ $\sin\theta = 0$

or $\cos\theta = 1$ $\Rightarrow$ $\theta = n\pi$ [n an integer] or $\theta = 2n\pi$. The solutions $\theta = n\pi$ include the solutions $\theta = 2n\pi$, so the critical numbers are $\theta = n\pi$.

37. $f(x) = x^2 e^{-3x}$ ⇒ $f'(x) = x^2(-3e^{-3x}) + e^{-3x}(2x) = xe^{-3x}(-3x+2)$. $f'(x) = 0$ ⇒ $x = 0, \frac{2}{3}$

[e^{-3x} is never equal to 0]. $f'(x)$ always exists, so the critical numbers are 0 and $\frac{2}{3}$.

39. The graph of $f'(x) = 5e^{-0.1|x|} \sin x - 1$ has 10 zeros and exists

everywhere, so f has 10 critical numbers.

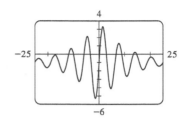

41. $f(x) = 12 + 4x - x^2$, $[0, 5]$. $f'(x) = 4 - 2x = 0$ ⇔ $x = 2$. $f(0) = 12$, $f(2) = 16$, and $f(5) = 7$.

So $f(2) = 16$ is the absolute maximum value and $f(5) = 7$ is the absolute minimum value.

43. $f(x) = 2x^3 - 3x^2 - 12x + 1$, $[-2, 3]$. $f'(x) = 6x^2 - 6x - 12 = 6(x^2 - x - 2) = 6(x - 2)(x + 1) = 0$ ⇔

$x = 2, -1$. $f(-2) = -3$, $f(-1) = 8$, $f(2) = -19$, and $f(3) = -8$. So $f(-1) = 8$ is the absolute maximum value and

$f(2) = -19$ is the absolute minimum value.

45. $f(x) = x^4 - 2x^2 + 3$, $[-2, 3]$. $f'(x) = 4x^3 - 4x = 4x(x^2 - 1) = 4x(x + 1)(x - 1) = 0$ ⇔ $x = -1, 0, 1$.

$f(-2) = 11$, $f(-1) = 2$, $f(0) = 3$, $f(1) = 2$, $f(3) = 66$. So $f(3) = 66$ is the absolute maximum value and $f(\pm 1) = 2$ is

the absolute minimum value.

47. $f(t) = t\sqrt{4 - t^2}$, $[-1, 2]$.

$f'(t) = t \cdot \frac{1}{2}(4 - t^2)^{-1/2}(-2t) + (4 - t^2)^{1/2} \cdot 1 = \frac{-t^2}{\sqrt{4 - t^2}} + \sqrt{4 - t^2} = \frac{-t^2 + (4 - t^2)}{\sqrt{4 - t^2}} = \frac{4 - 2t^2}{\sqrt{4 - t^2}}$.

$f'(t) = 0$ ⇒ $4 - 2t^2 = 0$ ⇒ $t^2 = 2$ ⇒ $t = +\sqrt{2}$, but $t = -\sqrt{2}$ is not in the given interval, $[-1, 2]$.

$f'(t)$ does not exist if $4 - t^2 = 0$ ⇒ $t = \pm 2$, but -2 is not in the given interval. $f(-1) = -\sqrt{3}$, $f(\sqrt{2}) = 2$, and

$f(2) = 0$. So $f(\sqrt{2}) = 2$ is the absolute maximum value and $f(-1) = -\sqrt{3}$ is the absolute minimum value.

49. $f(x) = xe^{-x^2/8}$, $[-1, 4]$. $f'(x) = x \cdot e^{-x^2/8} \cdot (-\frac{x}{4}) + e^{-x^2/8} \cdot 1 = e^{-x^2/8}(-\frac{x^2}{4} + 1)$. Since $e^{-x^2/8}$ is never 0,

$f'(x) = 0$ ⇒ $-x^2/4 + 1 = 0$ ⇒ $1 = x^2/4$ ⇒ $x^2 = 4$ ⇒ $x = \pm 2$, but -2 is not in the given interval, $[-1, 4]$.

$f(-1) = -e^{-1/8} \approx -0.88$, $f(2) = 2e^{-1/2} \approx 1.21$, and $f(4) = 4e^{-2} \approx 0.54$. So $f(2) = 2e^{-1/2} = 2/\sqrt{e}$ is the absolute

maximum value and $f(-1) = -e^{-1/8} = -1/\sqrt[8]{e}$ is the absolute minimum value.

51. $f(x) = \ln(x^2 + x + 1)$, $[-1, 1]$. $f'(x) = \frac{1}{x^2 + x + 1} \cdot (2x + 1) = 0$ ⇔ $x = -\frac{1}{2}$. Since $x^2 + x + 1 > 0$ for all x, the

domain of f and f' is $\mathbb{R}$. $f(-1) = \ln 1 = 0$, $f(-\frac{1}{2}) = \ln \frac{3}{4} \approx -0.29$, and $f(1) = \ln 3 \approx 1.10$. So $f(1) = \ln 3 \approx 1.10$ is

the absolute maximum value and $f(-\frac{1}{2}) = \ln \frac{3}{4} \approx -0.29$ is the absolute minimum value.

53. $f(t) = 2\cos t + \sin 2t, \quad [0, \pi/2]$.

$f'(t) = -2\sin t + \cos 2t \cdot 2 = -2\sin t + 2(1 - 2\sin^2 t) = -2(2\sin^2 t + \sin t - 1) = -2(2\sin t - 1)(\sin t + 1)$.

$f'(t) = 0 \implies \sin t = \frac{1}{2}$ or $\sin t = -1 \implies t = \frac{\pi}{6}$. $f(0) = 2$, $f(\frac{\pi}{6}) = \sqrt{3} + \frac{1}{2}\sqrt{3} = \frac{3}{2}\sqrt{3} \approx 2.60$, and $f(\frac{\pi}{2}) = 0$.

So $f(\frac{\pi}{6}) = \frac{3}{2}\sqrt{3}$ is the absolute maximum value and $f(\frac{\pi}{2}) = 0$ is the absolute minimum value.

55. $f(x) = x^a(1-x)^b, \quad 0 \le x \le 1, a > 0, b > 0$.

$f'(x) = x^a \cdot b(1-x)^{b-1}(-1) + (1-x)^b \cdot ax^{a-1} = x^{a-1}(1-x)^{b-1}[x \cdot b(-1) + (1-x) \cdot a]$

$\qquad = x^{a-1}(1-x)^{b-1}(a - ax - bx)$

At the endpoints, we have $f(0) = f(1) = 0$ [the minimum value of f]. In the interval $(0, 1)$, $f'(x) = 0 \iff x = \dfrac{a}{a+b}$.

$$f\left(\frac{a}{a+b}\right) = \left(\frac{a}{a+b}\right)^a \left(1 - \frac{a}{a+b}\right)^b = \frac{a^a}{(a+b)^a}\left(\frac{a+b-a}{a+b}\right)^b = \frac{a^a}{(a+b)^a} \cdot \frac{b^b}{(a+b)^b} = \frac{a^a b^b}{(a+b)^{a+b}}.$$

So $f\left(\dfrac{a}{a+b}\right) = \dfrac{a^a b^b}{(a+b)^{a+b}}$ is the absolute maximum value.

57. (a)

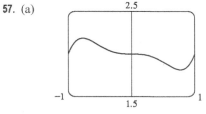

From the graph, it appears that the absolute maximum value is about $f(-0.77) = 2.19$, and the absolute minimum value is about $f(0.77) = 1.81$.

(b) $f(x) = x^5 - x^3 + 2 \implies f'(x) = 5x^4 - 3x^2 = x^2(5x^2 - 3)$. So $f'(x) = 0 \implies x = 0, \pm\sqrt{\frac{3}{5}}$.

$$f\left(-\sqrt{\tfrac{3}{5}}\right) = \left(-\sqrt{\tfrac{3}{5}}\right)^5 - \left(-\sqrt{\tfrac{3}{5}}\right)^3 + 2 = -\left(\tfrac{3}{5}\right)^2 \sqrt{\tfrac{3}{5}} + \tfrac{3}{5}\sqrt{\tfrac{3}{5}} + 2$$

$$= \left(\tfrac{3}{5} - \tfrac{9}{25}\right)\sqrt{\tfrac{3}{5}} + 2 = \tfrac{6}{25}\sqrt{\tfrac{3}{5}} + 2 \quad \text{(maximum)}$$

and similarly, $f\left(\sqrt{\tfrac{3}{5}}\right) = -\tfrac{6}{25}\sqrt{\tfrac{3}{5}} + 2$ (minimum).

59. (a)

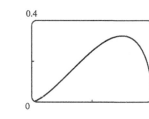

From the graph, it appears that the absolute maximum value is about $f(0.75) = 0.32$, and the absolute minimum value is $f(0) = f(1) = 0$; that is, at both endpoints.

(b) $f(x) = x\sqrt{x - x^2} \implies f'(x) = x \cdot \dfrac{1 - 2x}{2\sqrt{x - x^2}} + \sqrt{x - x^2} = \dfrac{(x - 2x^2) + (2x - 2x^2)}{2\sqrt{x - x^2}} = \dfrac{3x - 4x^2}{2\sqrt{x - x^2}}$.

So $f'(x) = 0 \implies 3x - 4x^2 = 0 \implies x(3 - 4x) = 0 \implies x = 0$ or $\frac{3}{4}$.

$f(0) = f(1) = 0$ (minimum), and $f\left(\tfrac{3}{4}\right) = \tfrac{3}{4}\sqrt{\tfrac{3}{4} - \left(\tfrac{3}{4}\right)^2} = \tfrac{3}{4}\sqrt{\tfrac{3}{16}} = \tfrac{3\sqrt{3}}{16}$ (maximum).

61. The density is defined as $\rho = \dfrac{\text{mass}}{\text{volume}} = \dfrac{1000}{V(T)}$ (in g/cm^3). But a critical point of ρ will also be a critical point of V

[since $\dfrac{d\rho}{dT} = -1000V^{-2}\dfrac{dV}{dT}$ and V is never 0], and V is easier to differentiate than ρ.

$V(T) = 999.87 - 0.06426T + 0.0085043T^2 - 0.0000679T^3 \;\Rightarrow\; V'(T) = -0.06426 + 0.0170086T - 0.0002037T^2$.

Setting this equal to 0 and using the quadratic formula to find T, we get

$$T = \frac{-0.0170086 \pm \sqrt{0.0170086^2 - 4 \cdot 0.0002037 \cdot 0.06426}}{2(-0.0002037)} \approx 3.9665°C \;\text{ or }\; 79.5318°C. \text{ Since we are only interested}$$

in the region $0°C \le T \le 30°C$, we check the density ρ at the endpoints and at $3.9665°C$: $\rho(0) \approx \dfrac{1000}{999.87} \approx 1.00013$;

$\rho(30) \approx \dfrac{1000}{1003.7628} \approx 0.99625$; $\rho(3.9665) \approx \dfrac{1000}{999.7447} \approx 1.000255$. So water has its maximum density at

about $3.9665°C$.

63. Let $a = -0.000\,032\,37$, $b = 0.000\,903\,7$, $c = -0.008\,956$, $d = 0.03629$, $e = -0.04458$, and $f = 0.4074$.

Then $S(t) = at^5 + bt^4 + ct^3 + dt^2 + et + f$ and $S'(t) = 5at^4 + 4bt^3 + 3ct^2 + 2dt + e$.

We now apply the Closed Interval Method to the continuous function S on the interval $0 \le t \le 10$. Since S' exists for all t,

the only critical numbers of S occur when $S'(t) = 0$. We use a rootfinder on a CAS (or a graphing device) to find that

$S'(t) = 0$ when $t_1 \approx 0.855$, $t_2 \approx 4.618$, $t_3 \approx 7.292$, and $t_4 \approx 9.570$. The values of S at these critical numbers are

$S(t_1) \approx 0.39$, $S(t_2) \approx 0.43645$, $S(t_3) \approx 0.427$, and $S(t_4) \approx 0.43641$. The values of S at the endpoints of the interval are

$S(0) \approx 0.41$ and $S(10) \approx 0.435$. Comparing the six numbers, we see that sugar was most expensive at $t_2 \approx 4.618$

(corresponding roughly to March 1998) and cheapest at $t_1 \approx 0.855$ (June 1994).

65. (a) $v(r) = k(r_0 - r)r^2 = kr_0r^2 - kr^3 \;\Rightarrow\; v'(r) = 2kr_0r - 3kr^2$. $\;\;v'(r) = 0 \;\Rightarrow\; kr(2r_0 - 3r) = 0 \;\Rightarrow\;$

$r = 0$ or $\frac{2}{3}r_0$ (but 0 is not in the interval). Evaluating v at $\frac{1}{2}r_0$, $\frac{2}{3}r_0$, and r_0, we get $v\left(\frac{1}{2}r_0\right) = \frac{1}{8}kr_0^3$, $v\left(\frac{2}{3}r_0\right) = \frac{4}{27}kr_0^3$,

and $v(r_0) = 0$. Since $\frac{4}{27} > \frac{1}{8}$, v attains its maximum value at $r = \frac{2}{3}r_0$. This supports the statement in the text.

(b) From part (a), the maximum value of v is $\frac{4}{27}kr_0^3$.

(c)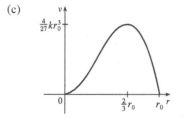

4.3 Derivatives and the Shapes of Curves

1. $\dfrac{f(8) - f(0)}{8 - 0} = \dfrac{6 - 4}{8} = \dfrac{1}{4}$. The values of c which satisfy

   $f'(c) = \frac{1}{4}$ seem to be about $c = 0.8$, 3.2, 4.4, and 6.1.

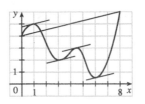

3. (a) Use the Increasing/Decreasing (I/D) Test.

   (b) Use the Concavity Test.

   (c) At any value of x where the concavity changes, we have an inflection point at $(x, f(x))$.

5. (a) There is an IP at $x = 3$ because the graph of f changes from CD to CU there. There is an IP at $x = 5$ because the graph

   of f changes from CU to CD there.

   (b) There is an IP at $x = 2$ and at $x = 6$ because $f'(x)$ has a maximum value there, and so $f''(x)$ changes from positive to

   negative there. There is an IP at $x = 4$ because $f'(x)$ has a minimum value there and so $f''(x)$ changes from negative to

   positive there.

   (c) There is an inflection point at $x = 1$ because $f''(x)$ changes from negative to positive there, and so the graph of f changes

   from concave downward to concave upward. There is an inflection point at $x = 7$ because $f''(x)$ changes from positive to

   negative there, and so the graph of f changes from concave upward to concave downward.

7. (a) $f(x) = 2x^3 + 3x^2 - 36x \;\Rightarrow\; f'(x) = 6x^2 + 6x - 36 = 6(x^2 + x - 6) = 6(x + 3)(x - 2)$.

   We don't need to include the "6" in the chart to determine the sign of $f'(x)$.

Interval	$x + 3$	$x - 2$	$f'(x)$	f
$x < -3$	$-$	$-$	$+$	increasing on $(-\infty, -3)$
$-3 < x < 2$	$+$	$-$	$-$	decreasing on $(-3, 2)$
$x > 2$	$+$	$+$	$+$	increasing on $(2, \infty)$

   (b) f changes from increasing to decreasing at $x = -3$ and from decreasing to increasing at $x = 2$. Thus, $f(-3) = 81$ is a

   local maximum value and $f(2) = -44$ is a local minimum value.

   (c) $f'(x) = 6x^2 + 6x - 36 \;\Rightarrow\; f''(x) = 12x + 6$. $f''(x) = 0$ at $x = -\frac{1}{2}$, $f''(x) > 0 \;\Leftrightarrow\; x > -\frac{1}{2}$, and

   $f''(x) < 0 \;\Leftrightarrow\; x < -\frac{1}{2}$. Thus, f is concave upward on $\left(-\frac{1}{2}, \infty\right)$ and concave downward on $\left(-\infty, -\frac{1}{2}\right)$. There is an

   inflection point at $\left(-\frac{1}{2}, f\left(-\frac{1}{2}\right)\right) = \left(-\frac{1}{2}, \frac{37}{2}\right)$.

9. (a) $f(x) = x^4 - 2x^2 + 3$ ⇒ $f'(x) = 4x^3 - 4x = 4x(x^2 - 1) = 4x(x + 1)(x - 1)$.

Interval	$x+1$	x	$x-1$	$f'(x)$	f
$x < -1$	$-$	$-$	$-$	$-$	decreasing on $(-\infty, -1)$
$-1 < x < 0$	$+$	$-$	$-$	$+$	increasing on $(-1, 0)$
$0 < x < 1$	$+$	$+$	$-$	$-$	decreasing on $(0, 1)$
$x > 1$	$+$	$+$	$+$	$+$	increasing on $(1, \infty)$

(b) f changes from increasing to decreasing at $x = 0$ and from decreasing to increasing at $x = -1$ and $x = 1$. Thus, $f(0) = 3$ is a local maximum value and $f(\pm 1) = 2$ are local minimum values.

(c) $f''(x) = 12x^2 - 4 = 12\left(x^2 - \frac{1}{3}\right) = 12\left(x + 1/\sqrt{3}\right)\left(x - 1/\sqrt{3}\right)$. $f''(x) > 0$ ⇔ $x < -1/\sqrt{3}$ or $x > 1/\sqrt{3}$ and $f''(x) < 0$ ⇔ $-1/\sqrt{3} < x < 1/\sqrt{3}$. Thus, f is concave upward on $\left(-\infty, -\sqrt{3}/3\right)$ and $\left(\sqrt{3}/3, \infty\right)$ and concave downward on $\left(-\sqrt{3}/3, \sqrt{3}/3\right)$. There are inflection points at $\left(\pm\sqrt{3}/3, \frac{22}{9}\right)$.

11. (a) $f(x) = \sin x + \cos x$, $0 \le x \le 2\pi$. $f'(x) = \cos x - \sin x = 0$ ⇒ $\cos x = \sin x$ ⇒ $1 = \dfrac{\sin x}{\cos x}$ ⇒
$\tan x = 1$ ⇒ $x = \frac{\pi}{4}$ or $\frac{5\pi}{4}$. Thus, $f'(x) > 0$ ⇔ $\cos x - \sin x > 0$ ⇔ $\cos x > \sin x$ ⇔ $0 < x < \frac{\pi}{4}$ or
$\frac{5\pi}{4} < x < 2\pi$ and $f'(x) < 0$ ⇔ $\cos x < \sin x$ ⇔ $\frac{\pi}{4} < x < \frac{5\pi}{4}$. So f is increasing on $\left(0, \frac{\pi}{4}\right)$ and $\left(\frac{5\pi}{4}, 2\pi\right)$ and f is decreasing on $\left(\frac{\pi}{4}, \frac{5\pi}{4}\right)$.

(b) f changes from increasing to decreasing at $x = \frac{\pi}{4}$ and from decreasing to increasing at $x = \frac{5\pi}{4}$. Thus, $f\left(\frac{\pi}{4}\right) = \sqrt{2}$ is a local maximum value and $f\left(\frac{5\pi}{4}\right) = -\sqrt{2}$ is a local minimum value.

(c) $f''(x) = -\sin x - \cos x = 0$ ⇒ $-\sin x = \cos x$ ⇒ $\tan x = -1$ ⇒ $x = \frac{3\pi}{4}$ or $\frac{7\pi}{4}$. Divide the interval $(0, 2\pi)$ into subintervals with these numbers as endpoints and complete a second derivative chart.

Interval	$f''(x) = -\sin x - \cos x$	Concavity
$\left(0, \frac{3\pi}{4}\right)$	$f''\left(\frac{\pi}{2}\right) = -1 < 0$	downward
$\left(\frac{3\pi}{4}, \frac{7\pi}{4}\right)$	$f''(\pi) = 1 > 0$	upward
$\left(\frac{7\pi}{4}, 2\pi\right)$	$f''\left(\frac{11\pi}{6}\right) = \frac{1}{2} - \frac{1}{2}\sqrt{3} < 0$	downward

There are inflection points at $\left(\frac{3\pi}{4}, 0\right)$ and $\left(\frac{7\pi}{4}, 0\right)$.

13. (a) $f(x) = e^{2x} + e^{-x}$ ⇒ $f'(x) = 2e^{2x} - e^{-x}$. $f'(x) > 0$ ⇔ $2e^{2x} > e^{-x}$ ⇔ $e^{3x} > \frac{1}{2}$ ⇔ $3x > \ln \frac{1}{2}$ ⇔
$x > \frac{1}{3}(\ln 1 - \ln 2)$ ⇔ $x > -\frac{1}{3}\ln 2$ [≈ -0.23] and $f'(x) < 0$ if $x < -\frac{1}{3}\ln 2$. So f is increasing on $\left(-\frac{1}{3}\ln 2, \infty\right)$ and f is decreasing on $\left(-\infty, -\frac{1}{3}\ln 2\right)$.

(b) f changes from decreasing to increasing at $x = -\frac{1}{3}\ln 2$. Thus,
$$f\left(-\tfrac{1}{3}\ln 2\right) = f\left(\ln \sqrt[3]{1/2}\right) = e^{2\ln \sqrt[3]{1/2}} + e^{-\ln \sqrt[3]{1/2}} = e^{\ln \sqrt[3]{1/4}} + e^{\ln \sqrt[3]{2}} = \sqrt[3]{1/4} + \sqrt[3]{2} = 2^{-2/3} + 2^{1/3} \ [\approx 1.89]$$
is a local minimum value.

(c) $f''(x) = 4e^{2x} + e^{-x} > 0$ [the sum of two positive terms]. Thus, f is concave upward on $(-\infty, \infty)$ and there is no point of inflection.

15. (a) $y = f(x) = \dfrac{\ln x}{\sqrt{x}}$. (Note that f is only defined for $x > 0$.)

$$f'(x) = \frac{\sqrt{x}\,(1/x) - \ln x \left(\frac{1}{2}x^{-1/2}\right)}{x} = \frac{\dfrac{1}{\sqrt{x}} - \dfrac{\ln x}{2\sqrt{x}}}{x} \cdot \frac{2\sqrt{x}}{2\sqrt{x}} = \frac{2 - \ln x}{2x^{3/2}} > 0 \quad \Leftrightarrow \quad 2 - \ln x > 0 \quad \Leftrightarrow$$

$\ln x < 2 \quad \Leftrightarrow \quad x < e^2$. Therefore f is increasing on $\left(0, e^2\right)$ and decreasing on $\left(e^2, \infty\right)$.

(b) f changes from increasing to decreasing at $x = e^2$, so $f(e^2) = \dfrac{\ln e^2}{\sqrt{e^2}} = \dfrac{2}{e}$ is a local maximum value.

(c) $f''(x) = \dfrac{2x^{3/2}(-1/x) - (2 - \ln x)(3x^{1/2})}{\left(2x^{3/2}\right)^2} = \dfrac{-2x^{1/2} + 3x^{1/2}(\ln x - 2)}{4x^3} = \dfrac{x^{1/2}(-2 + 3\ln x - 6)}{4x^3} = \dfrac{3\ln x - 8}{4x^{5/2}}$

$f''(x) = 0 \quad \Leftrightarrow \quad \ln x = \frac{8}{3} \quad \Leftrightarrow \quad x = e^{8/3}$. $\quad f''(x) > 0 \quad \Leftrightarrow \quad x > e^{8/3}$, so f is concave upward on $\left(e^{8/3}, \infty\right)$ and

concave downward on $\left(0, e^{8/3}\right)$. There is an inflection point at $\left(e^{8/3}, \frac{8}{3}e^{-4/3}\right) \approx (14.39, 0.70)$.

17. $f(x) = x + \sqrt{1 - x} \quad \Rightarrow \quad f'(x) = 1 + \frac{1}{2}(1 - x)^{-1/2}(-1) = 1 - \dfrac{1}{2\sqrt{1 - x}}$. Note that f is defined for $1 - x \geq 0$; that is,

for $x \leq 1$. $f'(x) = 0 \quad \Rightarrow \quad 2\sqrt{1 - x} = 1 \quad \Rightarrow \quad \sqrt{1 - x} = \frac{1}{2} \quad \Rightarrow \quad 1 - x = \frac{1}{4} \quad \Rightarrow \quad x = \frac{3}{4}$. f' does not exist at $x = 1$,

but we can't have a local maximum or minimum at an endpoint.

First Derivative Test: $f'(x) > 0 \quad \Rightarrow \quad x < \frac{3}{4}$ and $f'(x) < 0 \quad \Rightarrow \quad \frac{3}{4} < x < 1$. Since f' changes from positive to

negative at $x = \frac{3}{4}$, $f\left(\frac{3}{4}\right) = \frac{5}{4}$ is a local maximum value.

Second Derivative Test: $f''(x) = -\frac{1}{2}\left(-\frac{1}{2}\right)(1 - x)^{-3/2}(-1) = -\dfrac{1}{4\left(\sqrt{1 - x}\right)^3}$.

$f''\left(\frac{3}{4}\right) = -2 < 0 \quad \Rightarrow \quad f\left(\frac{3}{4}\right) = \frac{5}{4}$ is a local maximum value.

Preference: The First Derivative Test may be slightly easier to apply in this case.

19. (a) By the Second Derivative Test, if $f'(2) = 0$ and $f''(2) = -5 < 0$, f has a local maximum at $x = 2$.

(b) If $f'(6) = 0$, we know that f has a horizontal tangent at $x = 6$. Knowing that $f''(6) = 0$ does not provide any additional

information since the Second Derivative Test fails. For example, the first and second derivatives of $y = (x - 6)^4$,

$y = -(x - 6)^4$, and $y = (x - 6)^3$ all equal zero for $x = 6$, but the first has a local minimum at $x = 6$, the second has a

local maximum at $x = 6$, and the third has an inflection point at $x = 6$.

21. (a) $f(x) = 2x^3 - 3x^2 - 12x \quad \Rightarrow \quad f'(x) = 6x^2 - 6x - 12 = 6(x^2 - x - 2) = 6(x - 2)(x + 1)$.

$f'(x) > 0 \quad \Leftrightarrow \quad x < -1$ or $x > 2$ and $f'(x) < 0 \quad \Leftrightarrow \quad -1 < x < 2$. So f is increasing on $(-\infty, -1)$ and $(2, \infty)$,

and f is decreasing on $(-1, 2)$.

(b) Since f changes from increasing to decreasing at $x = -1$, $f(-1) = 7$ is a local

maximum value. Since f changes from decreasing to increasing at $x = 2$,

$f(2) = -20$ is a local minimum value.

(d)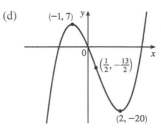

(c) $f''(x) = 6(2x - 1)$ ⇒ $f''(x) > 0$ on $\left(\frac{1}{2}, \infty\right)$ and $f''(x) < 0$ on $\left(-\infty, \frac{1}{2}\right)$.

So f is concave upward on $\left(\frac{1}{2}, \infty\right)$ and concave downward on $\left(-\infty, \frac{1}{2}\right)$. There

is a change in concavity at $x = \frac{1}{2}$, and we have an inflection point at $\left(\frac{1}{2}, -\frac{13}{2}\right)$.

23. (a) $f(x) = 2 + 2x^2 - x^4$ ⇒ $f'(x) = 4x - 4x^3 = 4x(1 - x^2) = 4x(1 + x)(1 - x)$. $f'(x) > 0$ ⇔ $x < -1$ or

$0 < x < 1$ and $f'(x) < 0$ ⇔ $-1 < x < 0$ or $x > 1$. So f is increasing on $(-\infty, -1)$ and $(0, 1)$ and f is decreasing

on $(-1, 0)$ and $(1, \infty)$.

(b) f changes from increasing to decreasing at $x = -1$ and $x = 1$, so $f(-1) = 3$ and $f(1) = 3$ are local maximum values.

f changes from decreasing to increasing at $x = 0$, so $f(0) = 2$ is a local minimum value.

(c) $f''(x) = 4 - 12x^2 = 4(1 - 3x^2)$. $f''(x) = 0$ ⇔ $1 - 3x^2 = 0$ ⇔

$x^2 = \frac{1}{3}$ ⇔ $x = \pm 1/\sqrt{3}$. $f''(x) > 0$ on $\left(-1/\sqrt{3}, 1/\sqrt{3}\right)$ and $f''(x) < 0$

on $\left(-\infty, -1/\sqrt{3}\right)$ and $\left(1/\sqrt{3}, \infty\right)$. So f is concave upward on

$\left(-1/\sqrt{3}, 1/\sqrt{3}\right)$ and f is concave downward on $\left(-\infty, -1/\sqrt{3}\right)$ and

$\left(1/\sqrt{3}, \infty\right)$. $f\left(\pm 1/\sqrt{3}\right) = 2 + \frac{2}{3} - \frac{1}{9} = \frac{23}{9}$. There are points of inflection

at $\left(\pm 1/\sqrt{3}, \frac{23}{9}\right)$.

(d)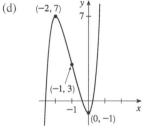

25. (a) $h(x) = (x + 1)^5 - 5x - 2$ ⇒ $h'(x) = 5(x + 1)^4 - 5$. $h'(x) = 0$ ⇔ $5(x + 1)^4 = 5$ ⇔ $(x + 1)^4 = 1$ ⇒

$(x + 1)^2 = 1$ ⇒ $x + 1 = 1$ or $x + 1 = -1$ ⇒ $x = 0$ or $x = -2$. $h'(x) > 0$ ⇔ $x < -2$ or $x > 0$ and

$h'(x) < 0$ ⇔ $-2 < x < 0$. So h is increasing on $(-\infty, -2)$ and $(0, \infty)$ and h is decreasing on $(-2, 0)$.

(b) $h(-2) = 7$ is a local maximum value and $h(0) = -1$ is a local minimum value.

(c) $h''(x) = 20(x + 1)^3 = 0$ ⇔ $x = -1$. $h''(x) > 0$ ⇔ $x > -1$ and

$h''(x) < 0$ ⇔ $x < -1$, so h is CU on $(-1, \infty)$ and h is CD on $(-\infty, -1)$.

There is a point of inflection at $(-1, h(-1)) = (-1, 3)$.

(d) *(graph with points (-2, 7), (-1, 3), (0, -1))*

27. (a) $A(x) = x\sqrt{x + 3}$ ⇒ $A'(x) = x \cdot \frac{1}{2}(x + 3)^{-1/2} + \sqrt{x + 3} \cdot 1 = \dfrac{x}{2\sqrt{x + 3}} + \sqrt{x + 3} = \dfrac{x + 2(x + 3)}{2\sqrt{x + 3}} = \dfrac{3x + 6}{2\sqrt{x + 3}}$.

The domain of A is $[-3, \infty)$. $A'(x) > 0$ for $x > -2$ and $A'(x) < 0$ for $-3 < x < -2$, so A is increasing on $(-2, \infty)$

and decreasing on $(-3, -2)$.

(b) $A(-2) = -2$ is a local minimum value.

(c) $A''(x) = \dfrac{2\sqrt{x + 3} \cdot 3 - (3x + 6) \cdot \dfrac{1}{\sqrt{x + 3}}}{\left(2\sqrt{x + 3}\right)^2}$

$= \dfrac{6(x + 3) - (3x + 6)}{4(x + 3)^{3/2}} = \dfrac{3x + 12}{4(x + 3)^{3/2}} = \dfrac{3(x + 4)}{4(x + 3)^{3/2}}$

(d)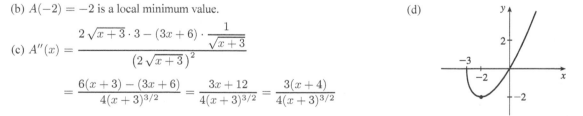

$A''(x) > 0$ for all $x > -3$, so A is concave upward on $(-3, \infty)$. There is no inflection point.

29. (a) $C(x) = x^{1/3}(x+4) = x^{4/3} + 4x^{1/3}$ $\Rightarrow$ $C'(x) = \frac{4}{3}x^{1/3} + \frac{4}{3}x^{-2/3} = \frac{4}{3}x^{-2/3}(x+1) = \frac{4(x+1)}{3\sqrt[3]{x^2}}$. $C'(x) > 0$ if

$-1 < x < 0$ or $x > 0$ and $C'(x) < 0$ for $x < -1$, so C is increasing on $(-1, \infty)$ and C is decreasing on $(-\infty, -1)$.

(b) $C(-1) = -3$ is a local minimum value.

(d)

(c) $C''(x) = \frac{4}{9}x^{-2/3} - \frac{8}{9}x^{-5/3} = \frac{4}{9}x^{-5/3}(x-2) = \frac{4(x-2)}{9\sqrt[3]{x^5}}$.

$C''(x) < 0$ for $0 < x < 2$ and $C''(x) > 0$ for $x < 0$ and $x > 2$, so C is

concave downward on $(0, 2)$ and concave upward on $(-\infty, 0)$ and $(2, \infty)$.

There are inflection points at $(0, 0)$ and $(2, 6\sqrt[3]{2}) \approx (2, 7.56)$.

31. (a) $f(\theta) = 2\cos\theta + \cos^2\theta$, $0 \le \theta \le 2\pi$ $\Rightarrow$ $f'(\theta) = -2\sin\theta + 2\cos\theta(-\sin\theta) = -2\sin\theta(1 + \cos\theta)$.

$f'(\theta) = 0$ $\Leftrightarrow$ $\theta = 0, \pi$, and 2π. $f'(\theta) > 0$ $\Leftrightarrow$ $\pi < \theta < 2\pi$ and $f'(\theta) < 0$ $\Leftrightarrow$ $0 < \theta < \pi$. So f is increasing

on $(\pi, 2\pi)$ and f is decreasing on $(0, \pi)$.

(b) $f(\pi) = -1$ is a local minimum value.

(c) $f'(\theta) = -2\sin\theta(1 + \cos\theta)$ $\Rightarrow$

$$f''(\theta) = -2\sin\theta(-\sin\theta) + (1 + \cos\theta)(-2\cos\theta) = 2\sin^2\theta - 2\cos\theta - 2\cos^2\theta$$

$$= 2(1 - \cos^2\theta) - 2\cos\theta - 2\cos^2\theta = -4\cos^2\theta - 2\cos\theta + 2$$

$$= -2(2\cos^2\theta + \cos\theta - 1) = -2(2\cos\theta - 1)(\cos\theta + 1)$$

Since $-2(\cos\theta + 1) < 0$ [for $\theta \ne \pi$], $f''(\theta) > 0$ $\Rightarrow$ $2\cos\theta - 1 < 0$ $\Rightarrow$ $\cos\theta < \frac{1}{2}$ $\Rightarrow$ $\frac{\pi}{3} < \theta < \frac{5\pi}{3}$ and

$f''(\theta) < 0$ $\Rightarrow$ $\cos\theta > \frac{1}{2}$ $\Rightarrow$ $0 < \theta < \frac{\pi}{3}$ or $\frac{5\pi}{3} < \theta < 2\pi$. So f is CU on $\left(\frac{\pi}{3}, \frac{5\pi}{3}\right)$ and f is CD on $\left(0, \frac{\pi}{3}\right)$ and

$\left(\frac{5\pi}{3}, 2\pi\right)$. There are points of inflection at $\left(\frac{\pi}{3}, f\left(\frac{\pi}{3}\right)\right) = \left(\frac{\pi}{3}, \frac{5}{4}\right)$ and $\left(\frac{5\pi}{3}, f\left(\frac{5\pi}{3}\right)\right) = \left(\frac{5\pi}{3}, \frac{5}{4}\right)$.

(d)

33. $f(x) = \dfrac{x^2}{x^2 - 1} = \dfrac{x^2}{(x+1)(x-1)}$ has domain $(-\infty, -1) \cup (-1, 1) \cup (1, \infty)$.

(a) $\displaystyle\lim_{x \to \pm\infty} f(x) = \lim_{x \to \pm\infty} \frac{x^2/x^2}{(x^2 - 1)/x^2} = \lim_{x \to \pm\infty} \frac{1}{1 - 1/x^2} = \frac{1}{1 - 0} = 1$, so $y = 1$ is a HA.

$\displaystyle\lim_{x \to -1^-} \frac{x^2}{x^2 - 1} = \infty$ since $x^2 \to 1$ and $(x^2 - 1) \to 0^+$ as $x \to -1^-$, so $x = -1$ is a VA.

$\displaystyle\lim_{x \to 1^+} \frac{x^2}{x^2 - 1} = \infty$ since $x^2 \to 1$ and $(x^2 - 1) \to 0^+$ as $x \to 1^+$, so $x = 1$ is a VA.

(b) $f(x) = \dfrac{x^2}{x^2 - 1}$ $\Rightarrow$ $f'(x) = \dfrac{(x^2 - 1)(2x) - x^2(2x)}{(x^2 - 1)^2} = \dfrac{2x[(x^2 - 1) - x^2]}{(x^2 - 1)^2} = \dfrac{-2x}{(x^2 - 1)^2}$. Since $(x^2 - 1)^2$ is

positive for all x in the domain of f, the sign of the derivative is determined by the sign of $-2x$. Thus, $f'(x) > 0$ if $x < 0$

$(x \ne -1)$ and $f'(x) < 0$ if $x > 0$ $(x \ne 1)$. So f is increasing on $(-\infty, -1)$ and $(-1, 0)$, and f is decreasing on $(0, 1)$

and $(1, \infty)$.

(c) $f'(x) = 0 \;\Rightarrow\; x = 0$ and $f(0) = 0$ is a local maximum value.

(d) $f''(x) = \dfrac{(x^2-1)^2(-2) - (-2x) \cdot 2(x^2-1)(2x)}{[(x^2-1)^2]^2}$

$= \dfrac{2(x^2-1)[-(x^2-1)+4x^2]}{(x^2-1)^4} = \dfrac{2(3x^2+1)}{(x^2-1)^3}.$

The sign of $f''(x)$ is determined by the denominator; that is, $f''(x) > 0$ if

$|x| > 1$ and $f''(x) < 0$ if $|x| < 1$. Thus, f is CU on $(-\infty, -1)$ and $(1, \infty)$,

and f is CD on $(-1, 1)$. There are no inflection points.

(e)

35. (a) $\displaystyle\lim_{x \to -\infty} \left(\sqrt{x^2+1} - x\right) = \infty$ and

$\displaystyle\lim_{x \to \infty} \left(\sqrt{x^2+1} - x\right) = \lim_{x \to \infty} \left(\sqrt{x^2+1} - x\right) \dfrac{\sqrt{x^2+1}+x}{\sqrt{x^2+1}+x} = \lim_{x \to \infty} \dfrac{1}{\sqrt{x^2+1}+x} = 0$, so $y = 0$ is a HA.

(b) $f(x) = \sqrt{x^2+1} - x \;\Rightarrow\; f'(x) = \dfrac{x}{\sqrt{x^2+1}} - 1$. Since $\dfrac{x}{\sqrt{x^2+1}} < 1$ for all x, $f'(x) < 0$, so f is decreasing on $\mathbb{R}$.

(c) No minimum or maximum

(d) $f''(x) = \dfrac{(x^2+1)^{1/2}(1) - x \cdot \frac{1}{2}(x^2+1)^{-1/2}(2x)}{\left(\sqrt{x^2+1}\right)^2}$

(e)

$= \dfrac{(x^2+1)^{1/2} - \dfrac{x^2}{(x^2+1)^{1/2}}}{x^2+1} = \dfrac{(x^2+1)-x^2}{(x^2+1)^{3/2}} = \dfrac{1}{(x^2+1)^{3/2}} > 0,$

so f is CU on $\mathbb{R}$. No IP

37. $f(x) = \ln(1 - \ln x)$ is defined when $x > 0$ (so that $\ln x$ is defined) and $1 - \ln x > 0$ [so that $\ln(1 - \ln x)$ is defined].

The second condition is equivalent to $1 > \ln x \;\Leftrightarrow\; x < e$, so f has domain $(0, e)$.

(a) As $x \to 0^+$, $\ln x \to -\infty$, so $1 - \ln x \to \infty$ and $f(x) \to \infty$. As $x \to e^-$, $\ln x \to 1^-$, so $1 - \ln x \to 0^+$ and

$f(x) \to -\infty$. Thus, $x = 0$ and $x = e$ are vertical asymptotes. There is no horizontal asymptote.

(b) $f'(x) = \dfrac{1}{1 - \ln x}\left(-\dfrac{1}{x}\right) = -\dfrac{1}{x(1 - \ln x)} < 0$ on $(0, e)$. Thus, f is decreasing on its domain, $(0, e)$.

(c) $f'(x) \neq 0$ on $(0, e)$, so f has no local maximum or minimum value.

(e)

(d) $f''(x) = -\dfrac{-[x(1 - \ln x)]'}{[x(1 - \ln x)]^2} = \dfrac{x(-1/x) + (1 - \ln x)}{x^2(1 - \ln x)^2}$

$= -\dfrac{\ln x}{x^2(1 - \ln x)^2}$

so $f''(x) > 0 \;\Leftrightarrow\; \ln x < 0 \;\Leftrightarrow\; 0 < x < 1$. Thus, f is CU on $(0, 1)$

and CD on $(1, e)$. There is an inflection point at $(1, 0)$.

39. (a) $\displaystyle\lim_{x \to \pm\infty} e^{-1/(x+1)} = 1$ since $-1/(x+1) \to 0$, so $y = 1$ is a HA. $\displaystyle\lim_{x \to -1^+} e^{-1/(x+1)} = 0$ since $-1/(x+1) \to -\infty$,

$\displaystyle\lim_{x \to -1^-} e^{-1/(x+1)} = \infty$ since $-1/(x+1) \to \infty$, so $x = -1$ is a VA.

(b) $f(x) = e^{-1/(x+1)}$ $\Rightarrow$ $f'(x) = e^{-1/(x+1)} \left[-(-1)\dfrac{1}{(x+1)^2} \right]$ [Reciprocal Rule] $= e^{-1/(x+1)}/(x+1)^2$ $\Rightarrow$

$f'(x) > 0$ for all x except -1, so f is increasing on $(-\infty, -1)$ and $(-1, \infty)$.

(c) There is no local maximum or minimum.

(d) $f''(x) = \dfrac{(x+1)^2 e^{-1/(x+1)} \left[1/(x+1)^2 \right] - e^{-1/(x+1)} \left[2(x+1) \right]}{\left[(x+1)^2 \right]^2}$ (e)

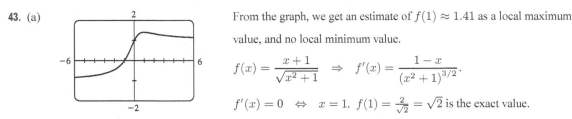

$= \dfrac{e^{-1/(x+1)} \left[1 - (2x+2) \right]}{(x+1)^4} = -\dfrac{e^{-1/(x+1)}(2x+1)}{(x+1)^4}$ $\Rightarrow$

$f''(x) > 0$ $\Leftrightarrow$ $2x + 1 < 0$ $\Leftrightarrow$ $x < -\frac{1}{2}$, so f is CU on $(-\infty, -1)$

and $\left(-1, -\frac{1}{2} \right)$, and CD on $\left(-\frac{1}{2}, \infty \right)$. f has an IP at $\left(-\frac{1}{2}, e^{-2} \right)$.

41. The nonnegative factors $(x+1)^2$ and $(x-6)^4$ do not affect the sign of $f'(x) = (x+1)^2 (x-3)^5 (x-6)^4$.

So $f'(x) > 0$ $\Rightarrow$ $(x-3)^5 > 0$ $\Rightarrow$ $x - 3 > 0$ $\Rightarrow$ $x > 3$. Thus, f is increasing on the interval $(3, \infty)$.

43. (a)

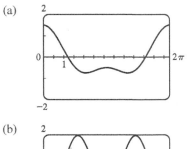

From the graph, we get an estimate of $f(1) \approx 1.41$ as a local maximum value, and no local minimum value.

$f(x) = \dfrac{x+1}{\sqrt{x^2+1}}$ $\Rightarrow$ $f'(x) = \dfrac{1-x}{(x^2+1)^{3/2}}$.

$f'(x) = 0$ $\Leftrightarrow$ $x = 1$. $f(1) = \frac{2}{\sqrt{2}} = \sqrt{2}$ is the exact value.

(b) From the graph in part (a), f increases most rapidly somewhere between $x = -\frac{1}{2}$ and $x = -\frac{1}{4}$. To find the exact value,

we need to find the maximum value of f', which we can do by finding the critical numbers of f'.

$f''(x) = \dfrac{2x^2 - 3x - 1}{(x^2+1)^{5/2}} = 0$ $\Leftrightarrow$ $x = \dfrac{3 \pm \sqrt{17}}{4}$. $x = \dfrac{3 + \sqrt{17}}{4}$ corresponds to the *minimum* value of f'.

The maximum value of f' occurs at $x = \dfrac{3 - \sqrt{17}}{4} \approx -0.28$.

45. $f(x) = \cos x + \frac{1}{2}\cos 2x$ $\Rightarrow$ $f'(x) = -\sin x - \sin 2x$ $\Rightarrow$ $f''(x) = -\cos x - 2\cos 2x$

(a)

From the graph of f, it seems that f is CD on $(0, 1)$, CU on $(1, 2.5)$, CD on $(2.5, 3.7)$, CU on $(3.7, 5.3)$, and CD on $(5.3, 2\pi)$. The points of inflection appear to be at $(1, 0.4)$, $(2.5, -0.6)$, $(3.7, -0.6)$, and $(5.3, 0.4)$.

(b)

From the graph of f'' (and zooming in near the zeros), it seems that f is CD on $(0, 0.94)$, CU on $(0.94, 2.57)$, CD on $(2.57, 3.71)$, CU on $(3.71, 5.35)$, and CD on $(5.35, 2\pi)$. Refined estimates of the inflection points are $(0.94, 0.44)$, $(2.57, -0.63)$, $(3.71, -0.63)$, and $(5.35, 0.44)$.

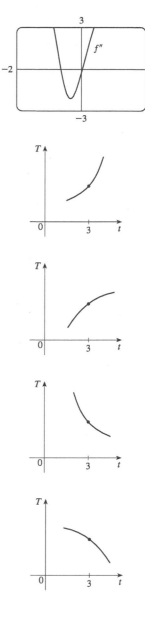

47. In Maple, we define f and then use the command

`plot(diff(diff(f,x),x),x=-2..2);`. In Mathematica, we define f

and then use `Plot[Dt[Dt[f,x],x],{x,-2,2}]`. We see that $f'' > 0$ for

$x < -0.6$ and $x > 0.0$ [≈ 0.03] and $f'' < 0$ for $-0.6 < x < 0.0$. So f is CU

on $(-\infty, -0.6)$ and $(0.0, \infty)$ and CD on $(-0.6, 0.0)$.

49. (a) I'm very unhappy. It's uncomfortably hot and $f'(3) = 2$ indicates that the

temperature is increasing, and $f''(3) = 4$ indicates that the rate of increase

is increasing. (The temperature is rapidly getting warmer.)

(b) I'm still unhappy, but not as unhappy as in part (a). It's uncomfortably hot

and $f'(3) = 2$ indicates that the temperature is increasing, but $f''(3) = -4$

indicates that the rate of increase is decreasing. (The temperature is slowly

getting warmer.)

(c) I'm somewhat happy. It's uncomfortably hot and $f'(3) = -2$ indicates that

the temperature is decreasing, but $f''(3) = 4$ indicates that the rate of

change is increasing. (The rate of change is negative but it's becoming less

negative. The temperature is slowly getting cooler.)

(d) I'm very happy. It's uncomfortably hot and $f'(3) = -2$ indicates that the

temperature is decreasing, and $f''(3) = -4$ indicates that the rate of change

is decreasing, that is, becoming more negative. (The temperature is rapidly

getting cooler.)

51. $x = t^3 - 12t, \ \ y = t^2 - 1 \ \ \Rightarrow \ \ \dfrac{dy}{dx} = \dfrac{dy/dt}{dx/dt} = \dfrac{2t}{3t^2 - 12} \ \ \Rightarrow$

$$\frac{d^2y}{dx^2} = \frac{\dfrac{d}{dt}\left(\dfrac{dy}{dx}\right)}{dx/dt} = \frac{\dfrac{(3t^2 - 12) \cdot 2 - 2t(6t)}{(3t^2 - 12)^2}}{3t^2 - 12} = \frac{-6t^2 - 24}{(3t^2 - 12)^3} = \frac{-6(t^2 + 4)}{3^3(t^2 - 4)^3} = \frac{-2(t^2 + 4)}{9(t^2 - 4)^3}.$$

Thus, the curve is CU when $t^2 - 4 < 0 \ \ \Rightarrow \ \ |t| < 2 \ \ \Rightarrow \ \ -2 < t < 2.$

53. $m = f(v) = \dfrac{m_0}{\sqrt{1 - v^2/c^2}}$. The m-intercept is $f(0) = m_0$. There are no v-intercepts. $\lim\limits_{v \to c^-} f(v) = \infty$, so $v = c$ is a VA.

$$f'(v) = -\tfrac{1}{2}m_0(1 - v^2/c^2)^{-3/2}(-2v/c^2) = \dfrac{m_0 v}{c^2(1 - v^2/c^2)^{3/2}} = \dfrac{m_0 v}{c^2 \dfrac{(c^2 - v^2)^{3/2}}{c^3}} = \dfrac{m_0 c v}{(c^2 - v^2)^{3/2}} > 0, \text{ so } f \text{ is}$$

increasing on $(0, c)$. There are no local extreme values.

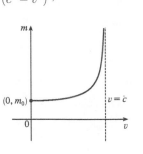

$$f''(v) = \dfrac{(c^2 - v^2)^{3/2}(m_0 c) - m_0 c v \cdot \frac{3}{2}(c^2 - v^2)^{1/2}(-2v)}{[(c^2 - v^2)^{3/2}]^2}$$

$$= \dfrac{m_0 c (c^2 - v^2)^{1/2}[(c^2 - v^2) + 3v^2]}{(c^2 - v^2)^3} = \dfrac{m_0 c (c^2 + 2v^2)}{(c^2 - v^2)^{5/2}} > 0,$$

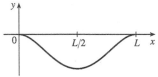

so f is CU on $(0, c)$. There are no inflection points.

55. $y = -\dfrac{W}{24EI}x^4 + \dfrac{WL}{12EI}x^3 - \dfrac{WL^2}{24EI}x^2 = -\dfrac{W}{24EI}x^2\left(x^2 - 2Lx + L^2\right)$

$$= \dfrac{-W}{24EI}x^2(x - L)^2 = cx^2(x - L)^2$$

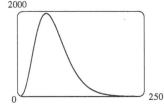

where $c = -\dfrac{W}{24EI}$ is a negative constant and $0 \le x \le L$. We sketch

$f(x) = cx^2(x - L)^2$ for $c = -1$. $f(0) = f(L) = 0$.

$f'(x) = cx^2[2(x - L)] + (x - L)^2(2cx) = 2cx(x - L)[x + (x - L)] = 2cx(x - L)(2x - L)$. So for $0 < x < L$,

$f'(x) > 0 \iff x(x - L)(2x - L) < 0$ [since $c < 0$] $\iff L/2 < x < L$ and $f'(x) < 0 \iff 0 < x < L/2$.

Thus, f is increasing on $(L/2, L)$ and decreasing on $(0, L/2)$, and there is a local and absolute

minimum at the point $(L/2, f(L/2)) = (L/2, cL^4/16)$. $f'(x) = 2c[x(x - L)(2x - L)] \Rightarrow$

$f''(x) = 2c[1(x - L)(2x - L) + x(1)(2x - L) + x(x - L)(2)] = 2c(6x^2 - 6Lx + L^2) = 0 \iff$

$x = \dfrac{6L \pm \sqrt{12L^2}}{12} = \frac{1}{2}L \pm \frac{\sqrt{3}}{6}L$, and these are the x-coordinates of the two inflection points.

57. $S(t) = At^p e^{-kt}$ with $A = 0.01$, $p = 4$, and $k = 0.07$. We will find the

zeros of f'' for $f(t) = t^p e^{-kt}$.

$f'(t) = t^p(-ke^{-kt}) + e^{-kt}(pt^{p-1}) = e^{-kt}(-kt^p + pt^{p-1})$

$f''(t) = e^{-kt}(-kpt^{p-1} + p(p - 1)t^{p-2}) + (-kt^p + pt^{p-1})(-ke^{-kt})$

$\quad = t^{p-2}e^{-kt}[-kpt + p(p - 1) + k^2t^2 - kpt]$

$\quad = t^{p-2}e^{-kt}(k^2t^2 - 2kpt + p^2 - p)$

Using the given values of p and k gives us $f''(t) = t^2 e^{-0.07t}(0.0049t^2 - 0.56t + 12)$. So $S''(t) = 0.01f''(t)$ and its zeros

are $t = 0$ and the solutions of $0.0049t^2 - 0.56t + 12 = 0$, which are $t_1 = \frac{200}{7} \approx 28.57$ and $t_2 = \frac{600}{7} \approx 85.71$.

At t_1 minutes, the rate of increase of the level of medication in the bloodstream is at its greatest and at t_2 minutes, the rate of

decrease is the greatest.

59. $f(x) = ax^3 + bx^2 + cx + d \quad \Rightarrow \quad f'(x) = 3ax^2 + 2bx + c$.

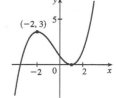

We are given that $f(1) = 0$ and $f(-2) = 3$, so $f(1) = a + b + c + d = 0$ and

$f(-2) = -8a + 4b - 2c + d = 3$. Also $f'(1) = 3a + 2b + c = 0$ and

$f'(-2) = 12a - 4b + c = 0$ by Fermat's Theorem. Solving these four equations, we get

$a = \frac{2}{9}, b = \frac{1}{3}, c = -\frac{4}{3}, d = \frac{7}{9}$, so the function is $f(x) = \frac{1}{9}\left(2x^3 + 3x^2 - 12x + 7\right)$.

61. $f(x) = \tan x - x \quad \Rightarrow \quad f'(x) = \sec^2 x - 1 > 0$ for $0 < x < \frac{\pi}{2}$ since $\sec^2 x > 1$ for $0 < x < \frac{\pi}{2}$. So f is increasing

on $\left(0, \frac{\pi}{2}\right)$. Thus, $f(x) > f(0) = 0$ for $0 < x < \frac{\pi}{2} \quad \Rightarrow \quad \tan x - x > 0 \quad \Rightarrow \quad \tan x > x$ for $0 < x < \frac{\pi}{2}$.

63. We are given that f is differentiable (and therefore continuous) everywhere. In particular, we can apply the Mean Value

Theorem on the interval $[0, 4]$. There exists a number c in $(0, 4)$ such that $f(4) - f(0) = f'(c)(4 - 0)$, so

$f(4) = f(0) + 4f'(c) = -3 + 4f'(c)$. We are given that $f'(x) \le 5$ for all x, so in particular we know that $f'(c) \le 5$.

Multiplying both sides of this inequality by 4, we have $4f'(c) \le 20$, so $f(4) = -3 + 4f'(c) \le -3 + 20 = 17$. The largest

possible value for $f(4)$ is 17.

65. Let $g(t)$ and $h(t)$ be the position functions of the two runners and let $f(t) = g(t) - h(t)$. By hypothesis,

$f(0) = g(0) - h(0) = 0$ and $f(b) = g(b) - h(b) = 0$, where b is the finishing time. Then by the Mean Value Theorem,

there is a time c, with $0 < c < b$, such that $f'(c) = \dfrac{f(b) - f(0)}{b - 0}$. But $f(b) = f(0) = 0$, so $f'(c) = 0$. Since

$f'(c) = g'(c) - h'(c) = 0$, we have $g'(c) = h'(c)$. So at time c, both runners have the same speed $g'(c) = h'(c)$.

67. $y = \dfrac{1+x}{1+x^2} \quad \Rightarrow \quad y' = \dfrac{(1+x^2)(1) - (1+x)(2x)}{(1+x^2)^2} = \dfrac{1 - 2x - x^2}{(1+x^2)^2} \quad \Rightarrow$

$y'' = \dfrac{(1+x^2)^2(-2 - 2x) - (1 - 2x - x^2) \cdot 2(1+x^2)(2x)}{[(1+x^2)^2]^2} = \dfrac{2(1+x^2)[(1+x^2)(-1-x) - (1-2x-x^2)(2x)]}{(1+x^2)^4}$

$= \dfrac{2(-1 - x - x^2 - x^3 - 2x + 4x^2 + 2x^3)}{(1+x^2)^3} = \dfrac{2(x^3 + 3x^2 - 3x - 1)}{(1+x^2)^3} = \dfrac{2(x-1)(x^2 + 4x + 1)}{(1+x^2)^3}$

So $y'' = 0 \quad \Rightarrow \quad x = 1, -2 \pm \sqrt{3}$. Let $a = -2 - \sqrt{3}, b = -2 + \sqrt{3}$, and $c = 1$. We can show that $f(a) = \frac{1}{4}\left(1 - \sqrt{3}\right)$,

$f(b) = \frac{1}{4}\left(1 + \sqrt{3}\right)$, and $f(c) = 1$. To show that these three points of inflection lie on one straight line, we'll show that the

slopes m_{ac} and m_{bc} are equal.

$$m_{ac} = \frac{f(c) - f(a)}{c - a} = \frac{1 - \frac{1}{4}\left(1 - \sqrt{3}\right)}{1 - \left(-2 - \sqrt{3}\right)} = \frac{\frac{3}{4} + \frac{1}{4}\sqrt{3}}{3 + \sqrt{3}} = \frac{1}{4}$$

$$m_{bc} = \frac{f(c) - f(b)}{c - b} = \frac{1 - \frac{1}{4}\left(1 + \sqrt{3}\right)}{1 - \left(-2 + \sqrt{3}\right)} = \frac{\frac{3}{4} - \frac{1}{4}\sqrt{3}}{3 - \sqrt{3}} = \frac{1}{4}$$

69. Let the cubic function be $f(x) = ax^3 + bx^2 + cx + d \quad \Rightarrow \quad f'(x) = 3ax^2 + 2bx + c \quad \Rightarrow \quad f''(x) = 6ax + 2b$.

So f is CU when $6ax + 2b > 0 \quad \Leftrightarrow \quad x > -b/(3a)$, CD when $x < -b/(3a)$, and so the only point of inflection occurs when

$x = -b/(3a)$. If the graph has three x-intercepts x_1, x_2 and x_3, then the expression for $f(x)$ must factor as

$f(x) = a(x - x_1)(x - x_2)(x - x_3)$. Multiplying these factors together gives us

$$f(x) = a[x^3 - (x_1 + x_2 + x_3)x^2 + (x_1x_2 + x_1x_3 + x_2x_3)x - x_1x_2x_3]$$

Equating the coefficients of the x^2-terms for the two forms of f gives us $b = -a(x_1 + x_2 + x_3)$. Hence, the x-coordinate of

the point of inflection is $-\dfrac{b}{3a} = -\dfrac{-a(x_1 + x_2 + x_3)}{3a} = \dfrac{x_1 + x_2 + x_3}{3}$.

71. (a) $f(x) = x^3 + ax^2 + bx \;\Rightarrow\; f'(x) = 3x^2 + 2ax + b$. f has the local minimum value $-\frac{2}{9}\sqrt{3}$ at $x = 1/\sqrt{3}$, so

$f'\left(\frac{1}{\sqrt{3}}\right) = 0 \;\Rightarrow\; 1 + \frac{2}{\sqrt{3}}a + b = 0$ **(1)**   and $f\left(\frac{1}{\sqrt{3}}\right) = -\frac{2}{9}\sqrt{3} \;\Rightarrow\; \frac{1}{9}\sqrt{3} + \frac{1}{3}a + \frac{1}{3}\sqrt{3}b = -\frac{2}{9}\sqrt{3}$ **(2)**.

Rewrite the system of equations as

$$\frac{2}{3}\sqrt{3}a \;+\; b \;=\; -1 \qquad \textbf{(3)}$$

$$\frac{1}{3}a \;+\; \frac{1}{3}\sqrt{3}b \;=\; -\frac{1}{3}\sqrt{3} \qquad \textbf{(4)}$$

and then multiplying **(4)** by $-2\sqrt{3}$ gives us the system

$$\frac{2}{3}\sqrt{3}a \;+\; b \;=\; -1$$

$$-\frac{2}{3}\sqrt{3}a \;-\; 2b \;=\; 2$$

Adding the equations gives us $-b = 1 \;\Rightarrow\; b = -1$. Substituting -1 for b into **(3)** gives us

$\frac{2}{3}\sqrt{3}a - 1 = -1 \;\Rightarrow\; \frac{2}{3}\sqrt{3}a = 0 \;\Rightarrow\; a = 0$. Thus, $f(x) = x^3 - x$.

(b) To find the smallest slope, we want to find the minimum of the slope function, f', so we'll find the critical

numbers of f'. $f(x) = x^3 - x \;\Rightarrow\; f'(x) = 3x^2 - 1 \;\Rightarrow\; f''(x) = 6x$. $f''(x) = 0 \;\Leftrightarrow\; x = 0$.

At $x = 0$, $y = 0$, $f'(x) = -1$, and f'' changes from negative to positive. Thus, we have a minimum for f' and

$y - 0 = -1(x - 0)$, or $y = -x$, is the tangent line that has the smallest slope.

4.4 Graphing with Calculus *and* Calculators

1. $f(x) = 4x^4 - 32x^3 + 89x^2 - 95x + 29 \;\Rightarrow\; f'(x) = 16x^3 - 96x^2 + 178x - 95 \;\Rightarrow\; f''(x) = 48x^2 - 192x + 178$.

$f(x) = 0 \;\Leftrightarrow\; x \approx 0.5,\ 1.60;\ f'(x) = 0 \;\Leftrightarrow\; x \approx 0.92,\ 2.5,\ 2.58$ and $f''(x) = 0 \;\Leftrightarrow\; x \approx 1.46,\ 2.54$.

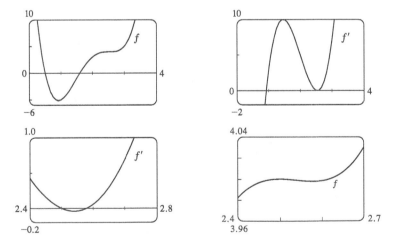

From the graphs of f', we estimate that $f' < 0$ and that f is decreasing on $(-\infty, 0.92)$ and $(2.5, 2.58)$, and that $f' > 0$ and f

is increasing on $(0.92, 2.5)$ and $(2.58, \infty)$ with local minimum values $f(0.92) \approx -5.12$ and $f(2.58) \approx 3.998$ and local maximum value $f(2.5) = 4$. The graphs of f' make it clear that f has a maximum and a minimum near $x = 2.5$, shown more clearly in the fourth graph.

From the graph of f'', we estimate that $f'' > 0$ and that f is CU on $(-\infty, 1.46)$ and $(2.54, \infty)$, and that $f'' < 0$ and f is CD on $(1.46, 2.54)$. There are inflection points at about $(1.46, -1.40)$ and $(2.54, 3.999)$.

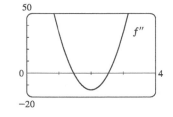

3. $f(x) = x^6 - 10x^5 - 400x^4 + 2500x^3 \quad \Rightarrow \quad f'(x) = 6x^5 - 50x^4 - 1600x^3 + 7500x^2 \quad \Rightarrow$

$f''(x) = 30x^4 - 200x^3 - 4800x^2 + 1500x$

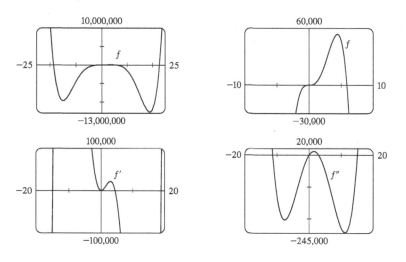

From the graph of f', we estimate that f is decreasing on $(-\infty, -15)$, increasing on $(-15, 4.40)$, decreasing on $(4.40, 18.93)$, and increasing on $(18.93, \infty)$, with local minimum values of $f(-15) \approx -9{,}700{,}000$ and $f(18.93) \approx -12{,}700{,}000$ and local maximum value $f(4.40) \approx 53{,}800$. From the graph of f'', we estimate that f is CU on $(-\infty, -11.34)$, CD on $(-11.34, 0)$, CU on $(0, 2.92)$, CD on $(2.92, 15.08)$, and CU on $(15.08, \infty)$. There is an inflection point at $(0, 0)$ and at about $(-11.34, -6{,}250{,}000)$, $(2.92, 31{,}800)$, and $(15.08, -8{,}150{,}000)$.

5. $f(x) = \dfrac{x}{x^3 - x^2 - 4x + 1} \quad \Rightarrow \quad f'(x) = \dfrac{-2x^3 + x^2 + 1}{(x^3 - x^2 - 4x + 1)^2} \quad \Rightarrow \quad f''(x) = \dfrac{2(3x^5 - 3x^4 + 5x^3 - 6x^2 + 3x + 4)}{(x^3 - x^2 - 4x + 1)^3}$

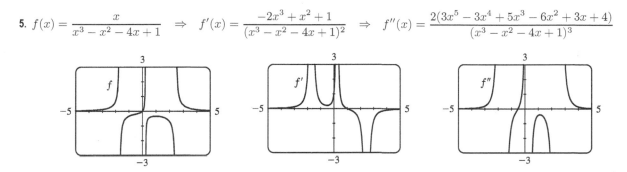

We estimate from the graph of f that $y = 0$ is a horizontal asymptote, and that there are vertical asymptotes at $x = -1.7$,

$x = 0.24$, and $x = 2.46$. From the graph of f', we estimate that f is increasing on $(-\infty, -1.7)$, $(-1.7, 0.24)$, and $(0.24, 1)$, and that f is decreasing on $(1, 2.46)$ and $(2.46, \infty)$. There is a local maximum value at $f(1) = -\frac{1}{3}$. From the graph of f'', we estimate that f is CU on $(-\infty, -1.7)$, $(-0.506, 0.24)$, and $(2.46, \infty)$, and that f is CD on $(-1.7, -0.506)$ and $(0.24, 2.46)$. There is an inflection point at $(-0.506, -0.192)$.

7. $f(x) = x^2 - 4x + 7\cos x$, $-4 \le x \le 4$. $\quad f'(x) = 2x - 4 - 7\sin x \quad \Rightarrow \quad f''(x) = 2 - 7\cos x$.

$f(x) = 0 \iff x \approx 1.10$; $f'(x) = 0 \iff x \approx -1.49, -1.07$, or 2.89; $f''(x) = 0 \iff x = \pm\cos^{-1}\left(\frac{2}{7}\right) \approx \pm 1.28$.

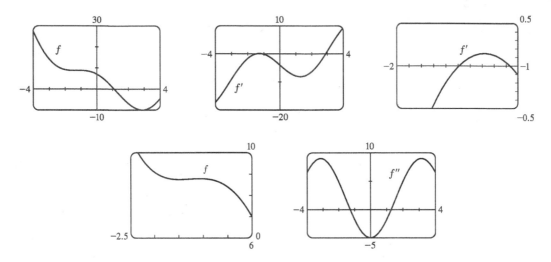

From the graphs of f', we estimate that f is decreasing ($f' < 0$) on $(-4, -1.49)$, increasing on $(-1.49, -1.07)$, decreasing on $(-1.07, 2.89)$, and increasing on $(2.89, 4)$, with local minimum values $f(-1.49) \approx 8.75$ and $f(2.89) \approx -9.99$ and local maximum value $f(-1.07) \approx 8.79$ (notice the second graph of f). From the graph of f'', we estimate that f is CU ($f'' > 0$) on $(-4, -1.28)$, CD on $(-1.28, 1.28)$, and CU on $(1.28, 4)$. There are inflection points at about $(-1.28, 8.77)$ and $(1.28, -1.48)$.

9. $f(x) = 1 + \dfrac{1}{x} + \dfrac{8}{x^2} + \dfrac{1}{x^3} \quad \Rightarrow \quad f'(x) = -\dfrac{1}{x^2} - \dfrac{16}{x^3} - \dfrac{3}{x^4} = -\dfrac{1}{x^4}(x^2 + 16x + 3) \quad \Rightarrow$

$f''(x) = \dfrac{2}{x^3} + \dfrac{48}{x^4} + \dfrac{12}{x^5} = \dfrac{2}{x^5}(x^2 + 24x + 6)$.

From the graphs, it appears that f increases on $(-15.8, -0.2)$ and decreases on $(-\infty, -15.8)$, $(-0.2, 0)$, and $(0, \infty)$; that f has a local minimum value of $f(-15.8) \approx 0.97$ and a local maximum value of $f(-0.2) \approx 72$; that f is CD on $(-\infty, -24)$ and $(-0.25, 0)$ and is CU on $(-24, -0.25)$ and $(0, \infty)$; and that f has IPs at $(-24, 0.97)$ and $(-0.25, 60)$.

To find the exact values, note that $f' = 0 \Rightarrow x = \dfrac{-16 \pm \sqrt{256 - 12}}{2} = -8 \pm \sqrt{61}$ [≈ -0.19 and -15.81].

f' is positive (f is increasing) on $\left(-8 - \sqrt{61}, -8 + \sqrt{61}\,\right)$ and f' is negative (f is decreasing) on $\left(-\infty, -8 - \sqrt{61}\,\right)$,

$\left(-8 + \sqrt{61}, 0\right)$, and $(0, \infty)$. $f'' = 0 \Rightarrow x = \dfrac{-24 \pm \sqrt{576 - 24}}{2} = -12 \pm \sqrt{138}$ [≈ -0.25 and -23.75]. f'' is

positive (f is CU) on $\left(-12 - \sqrt{138}, -12 + \sqrt{138}\,\right)$ and $(0, \infty)$ and f'' is negative (f is CD) on $\left(-\infty, -12 - \sqrt{138}\,\right)$

and $\left(-12 + \sqrt{138}, 0\right)$.

11.

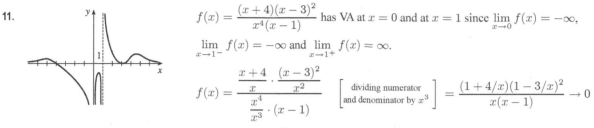

$f(x) = \dfrac{(x+4)(x-3)^2}{x^4(x-1)}$ has VA at $x = 0$ and at $x = 1$ since $\displaystyle\lim_{x \to 0} f(x) = -\infty$,

$\displaystyle\lim_{x \to 1^-} f(x) = -\infty$ and $\displaystyle\lim_{x \to 1^+} f(x) = \infty$.

$$f(x) = \dfrac{\dfrac{x+4}{x} \cdot \dfrac{(x-3)^2}{x^2}}{\dfrac{x^4}{x^3} \cdot (x-1)} \quad \begin{bmatrix} \text{dividing numerator} \\ \text{and denominator by } x^3 \end{bmatrix} = \dfrac{(1 + 4/x)(1 - 3/x)^2}{x(x-1)} \to 0$$

as $x \to \pm\infty$, so f is asymptotic to the x-axis.

Since f is undefined at $x = 0$, it has no y-intercept. $f(x) = 0 \Rightarrow (x+4)(x-3)^2 = 0 \Rightarrow x = -4$ or $x = 3$, so f has

x-intercepts -4 and 3. Note, however, that the graph of f is only tangent to the x-axis and does not cross it at $x = 3$, since f is

positive as $x \to 3^-$ and as $x \to 3^+$.

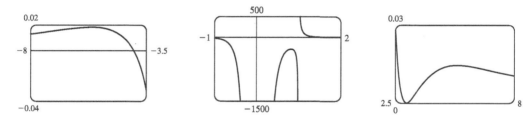

From these graphs, it appears that f has three maximum values and one minimum value. The maximum values are

approximately $f(-5.6) = 0.0182$, $f(0.82) = -281.5$ and $f(5.2) = 0.0145$ and we know (since the graph is tangent to the

x-axis at $x = 3$) that the minimum value is $f(3) = 0$.

13. $f(x) = \dfrac{x^2(x+1)^3}{(x-2)^2(x-4)^4} \Rightarrow f'(x) = -\dfrac{x(x+1)^2(x^3 + 18x^2 - 44x - 16)}{(x-2)^3(x-4)^5}$ [from CAS].

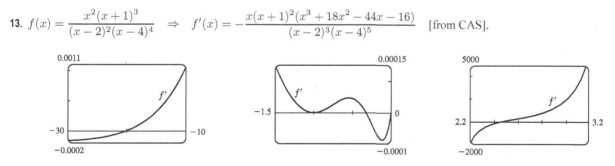

From the graphs of f', it seems that the critical points which indicate extrema occur at $x \approx -20$, -0.3, and 2.5, as estimated

in Example 3. (There is another critical point at $x = -1$, but the sign of f' does not change there.) We differentiate again,

obtaining $f''(x) = 2\dfrac{(x+1)(x^6 + 36x^5 + 6x^4 - 628x^3 + 684x^2 + 672x + 64)}{(x-2)^4(x-4)^6}$.

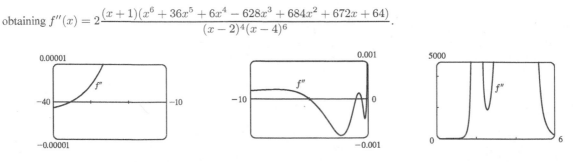

From the graphs of f'', it appears that f is CU on $(-35.3, -5.0)$, $(-1, -0.5)$, $(-0.1, 2)$, $(2, 4)$ and $(4, \infty)$ and CD on $(-\infty, -35.3)$, $(-5.0, -1)$ and $(-0.5, -0.1)$. We check back on the graphs of f to find the y-coordinates of the inflection points, and find that these points are approximately $(-35.3, -0.015)$, $(-5.0, -0.005)$, $(-1, 0)$, $(-0.5, 0.00001)$, and $(-0.1, 0.0000066)$.

15. $y = f(x) = \dfrac{\sqrt{x}}{x^2 + x + 1}$. From a CAS, $y' = -\dfrac{3x^2 + x - 1}{2\sqrt{x}\,(x^2 + x + 1)^2}$ and $y'' = \dfrac{15x^4 + 10x^3 - 15x^2 - 6x - 1}{4x^{3/2}(x^2 + x + 1)^3}$.

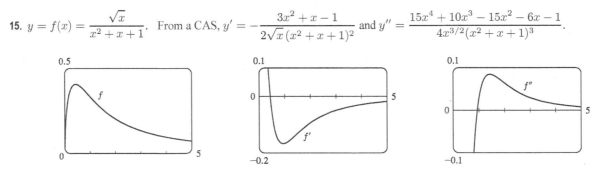

$f'(x) = 0 \Leftrightarrow x \approx 0.43$, so f is increasing on $(0, 0.43)$ and decreasing on $(0.43, \infty)$. There is a local maximum value of $f(0.43) \approx 0.41$. $f''(x) = 0 \Leftrightarrow x \approx 0.94$, so f is CD on $(0, 0.94)$ and CU on $(0.94, \infty)$. There is an inflection point at $(0.94, 0.34)$.

17. $y = f(x) = \sqrt{x + 5 \sin x}$, $x \le 20$.

From a CAS, $y' = \dfrac{5 \cos x + 1}{2\sqrt{x + 5 \sin x}}$ and $y'' = -\dfrac{10 \cos x + 25 \sin^2 x + 10x \sin x + 26}{4(x + 5 \sin x)^{3/2}}$.

We'll start with a graph of $g(x) = x + 5 \sin x$. Note that $f(x) = \sqrt{g(x)}$ is only defined if $g(x) \ge 0$. $g(x) = 0 \Leftrightarrow x = 0$ or $x \approx -4.91, -4.10, 4.10$, and 4.91. Thus, the domain of f is $[-4.91, -4.10] \cup [0, 4.10] \cup [4.91, 20]$.

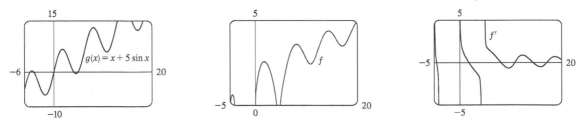

From the expression for y', we see that $y' = 0 \Leftrightarrow 5 \cos x + 1 = 0 \Rightarrow x_1 = \cos^{-1}\left(-\frac{1}{5}\right) \approx 1.77$ and

$x_2 = 2\pi - x_1 \approx -4.51$ (not in the domain of f). The leftmost zero of f' is $x_1 - 2\pi \approx -4.51$. Moving to the right, the zeros of f' are x_1, $x_1 + 2\pi$, $x_2 + 2\pi$, $x_1 + 4\pi$, and $x_2 + 4\pi$. Thus, f is increasing on $(-4.91, -4.51)$, decreasing on $(-4.51, -4.10)$, increasing on $(0, 1.77)$, decreasing on $(1.77, 4.10)$, increasing on $(4.91, 8.06)$, decreasing on $(8.06, 10.79)$, increasing on $(10.79, 14.34)$, decreasing on $(14.34, 17.08)$, and increasing on $(17.08, 20)$. The local maximum values are $f(-4.51) \approx 0.62$, $f(1.77) \approx 2.58$, $f(8.06) \approx 3.60$, and $f(14.34) \approx 4.39$. The local minimum values are $f(10.79) \approx 2.43$ and $f(17.08) \approx 3.49$.

f is CD on $(-4.91, -4.10)$, $(0, 4.10)$, $(4.91, 9.60)$, CU on $(9.60, 12.25)$, CD on $(12.25, 15.81)$, CU on $(15.81, 18.65)$, and CD on $(18.65, 20)$. There are inflection points at $(9.60, 2.95)$, $(12.25, 3.27)$, $(15.81, 3.91)$, and $(18.65, 4.20)$.

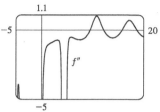

19. $y = f(x) = \dfrac{1 - e^{1/x}}{1 + e^{1/x}}$. From a CAS, $y' = \dfrac{2e^{1/x}}{x^2(1 + e^{1/x})^2}$ and $y'' = \dfrac{-2e^{1/x}(1 - e^{1/x} + 2x + 2xe^{1/x})}{x^4(1 + e^{1/x})^3}$.

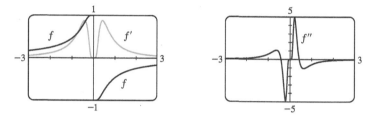

f is an odd function defined on $(-\infty, 0) \cup (0, \infty)$. Its graph has no x- or y-intercepts. Since $\lim\limits_{x \to \pm\infty} f(x) = 0$, the x-axis is a HA. $f'(x) > 0$ for $x \neq 0$, so f is increasing on $(-\infty, 0)$ and $(0, \infty)$. It has no local extreme values.

$f''(x) = 0$ for $x \approx \pm 0.417$, so f is CU on $(-\infty, -0.417)$, CD on $(-0.417, 0)$, CU on $(0, 0.417)$, and CD on $(0.417, \infty)$. f has IPs at $(-0.417, 0.834)$ and $(0.417, -0.834)$.

21.

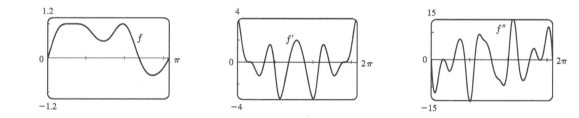

From the graph of $f(x) = \sin(x + \sin 3x)$ in the viewing rectangle $[0, \pi]$ by $[-1.2, 1.2]$, it looks like f has two maxima and two minima. If we calculate and graph $f'(x) = [\cos(x + \sin 3x)](1 + 3\cos 3x)$ on $[0, 2\pi]$, we see that the graph of f' appears to be almost tangent to the x-axis at about $x = 0.7$. The graph of

$$f'' = -[\sin(x + \sin 3x)](1 + 3\cos 3x)^2 + \cos(x + \sin 3x)(-9\sin 3x)$$

is even more interesting near this x-value: it seems to just touch the x-axis.

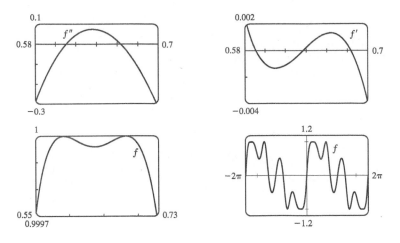

If we zoom in on this place on the graph of f'', we see that f'' actually does cross the axis twice near $x = 0.65$, indicating a change in concavity for a very short interval. If we look at the graph of f' on the same interval, we see that it changes sign three times near $x = 0.65$, indicating that what we had thought was a broad extremum at about $x = 0.7$ actually consists of three extrema (two maxima and a minimum). These maximum values are roughly $f(0.59) = 1$ and $f(0.68) = 1$, and the minimum value is roughly $f(0.64) = 0.99996$. There are also a maximum value of about $f(1.96) = 1$ and minimum values of about $f(1.46) = 0.49$ and $f(2.73) = -0.51$. The points of inflection on $(0, \pi)$ are about $(0.61, 0.99998)$, $(0.66, 0.99998)$, $(1.17, 0.72)$, $(1.75, 0.77)$, and $(2.28, 0.34)$. On $(\pi, 2\pi)$, they are about $(4.01, -0.34)$, $(4.54, -0.77)$, $(5.11, -0.72)$, $(5.62, -0.99998)$, and $(5.67, -0.99998)$. There are also IP at $(0, 0)$ and $(\pi, 0)$. Note that the function is odd and periodic with period 2π, and it is also rotationally symmetric about all points of the form $((2n + 1)\pi, 0)$, n an integer.

23.

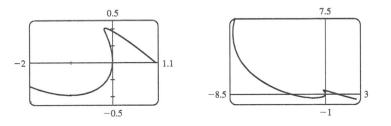

We graph the curve $x = t^4 - 2t^3 - 2t^2$, $y = t^3 - t$ in the viewing rectangle $[-2, 1.1]$ by $[-0.5, 0.5]$. This rectangle corresponds approximately to $t \in [-1, 0.8]$. We estimate that the curve has horizontal tangents at about $(-1, -0.4)$ and $(-0.17, 0.39)$ and vertical tangents at about $(0, 0)$ and $(-0.19, 0.37)$. We calculate $\dfrac{dy}{dx} = \dfrac{dy/dt}{dx/dt} = \dfrac{3t^2 - 1}{4t^3 - 6t^2 - 4t}$. The horizontal tangents occur when $dy/dt = 3t^2 - 1 = 0 \iff t = \pm\frac{1}{\sqrt{3}}$, so both horizontal tangents are shown in our graph.

$t = \frac{1}{\sqrt{3}}$ corresponds to the point $\left(\frac{-2\sqrt{3}-5}{9}, \frac{-2\sqrt{3}}{9}\right) \approx (-0.94, -0.38)$ and $t = -\frac{1}{\sqrt{3}}$ corresponds to

$\left(\frac{2\sqrt{3}-5}{9}, \frac{2\sqrt{3}}{9}\right) \approx (-0.17, 0.38)$. The vertical tangents occur when $dx/dt = 2t(2t^2 - 3t - 2) = 0 \Leftrightarrow$

$2t(2t+1)(t-2) = 0 \Leftrightarrow t = 0, -\frac{1}{2}$ or 2. It seems that we have missed one vertical tangent, and indeed if we plot the

curve on the t-interval $[-1.2, 2.2]$ we see that there is another vertical tangent at $(-8, 6)$. The t-values and points at which

there are vertical tangents are $t = 0$, $(0,0)$; $t = -\frac{1}{2}$, $\left(-\frac{3}{16}, \frac{3}{8}\right)$; and $t = 2$, $(-8, 6)$.

25. $x = t^3 - ct$, $y = t^2$. For $c = 0$, there is a cusp at $(0, 0)$. For $c < 0$, there is a local minimum at $(0, 0)$. For $c > 0$, there is a

loop whose size increases as c increases ($c = \frac{1}{2}$ and $c = 1$ are shown in the figure). The curve intersects itself on the y-axis;

that is, when $x = 0 \Leftrightarrow t^3 - ct = 0 \Leftrightarrow t(t^2 - c) = 0 \Leftrightarrow t = 0, \pm\sqrt{c}$. Substituting $\pm\sqrt{c}$ for t gives us $y = c$, so

the point of intersection is $(0, c)$.

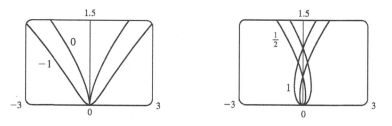

From the second figure, we see that the left- and rightmost points of the loop occur when there are vertical tangent lines.

$dx/dt = 0 \Rightarrow 3t^2 - c = 0 \Rightarrow t = \pm\sqrt{c/3}$. The rightmost point occurs when $t = -\sqrt{c/3}$ and has coordinates

$\left(\frac{2c\sqrt{3c}}{9}, \frac{c}{3}\right)$. The leftmost point occurs when $t = \sqrt{c/3}$ and has coordinates $\left(-\frac{2c\sqrt{3c}}{9}, \frac{c}{3}\right)$.

27. $f(x) = x^4 + cx^2 = x^2(x^2 + c)$. Note that f is an even function. For $c \geq 0$, the only x-intercept is the point $(0, 0)$. We

calculate $f'(x) = 4x^3 + 2cx = 4x\left(x^2 + \frac{1}{2}c\right) \Rightarrow f''(x) = 12x^2 + 2c$. If $c \geq 0$, $x = 0$ is the only critical point and there

is no inflection point. As we can see from the examples, there is no change in the basic shape of the graph for $c \geq 0$; it merely

becomes steeper as c increases. For $c = 0$, the graph is the simple curve $y = x^4$. For $c < 0$, there are x-intercepts at 0 and

at $\pm\sqrt{-c}$. Also, there is a maximum at $(0, 0)$, and there are minima

at $\left(\pm\sqrt{-\frac{1}{2}c}, -\frac{1}{4}c^2\right)$. As $c \to -\infty$, the x-coordinates of these

minima get larger in absolute value, and the minimum points move

downward. There are inflection points at $\left(\pm\sqrt{-\frac{1}{6}c}, -\frac{5}{36}c^2\right)$, which

also move away from the origin as $c \to -\infty$.

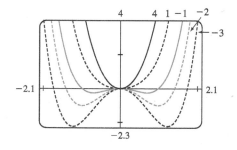

29. $f(x) = e^x + ce^{-x}$. $f = 0 \Rightarrow ce^{-x} = -e^x \Rightarrow c = -e^{2x} \Rightarrow 2x = \ln(-c) \Rightarrow x = \frac{1}{2}\ln(-c)$.

$f'(x) = e^x - ce^{-x}$. $f' = 0 \Rightarrow ce^{-x} = e^x \Rightarrow c = e^{2x} \Rightarrow 2x = \ln c \Rightarrow x = \frac{1}{2}\ln c$.

$f''(x) = e^x + ce^{-x} = f(x)$.

The only transitional value of c is 0. As c increases from $-\infty$ to 0, $\frac{1}{2}\ln(-c)$ is both the the x-intercept and inflection point,

and this decreases from ∞ to $-\infty$. Also $f' > 0$, so f is increasing. When $c = 0$, $f(x) = f'(x) = f''(x) = e^x$, f is positive,

increasing, and concave upward. As c increases from 0 to ∞, the absolute minimum occurs at $x = \frac{1}{2}\ln c$, which increases

from $-\infty$ to ∞. Also, $f = f'' > 0$, so f is positive and concave upward. The

value of the y-intercept is $f(0) = 1 + c$, and this increases as c increases from

$-\infty$ to ∞.

Note: The minimum point $\left(\frac{1}{2}\ln c, 2\sqrt{c}\right)$ can be parameterized by $x = \frac{1}{2}\ln c$,

$y = 2\sqrt{c}$, and after eliminating the parameter c, we see that the minimum point

lies on the graph of $y = 2e^x$.

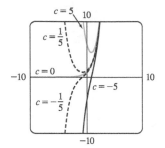

31. Note that $c = 0$ is a transitional value at which the graph consists of the x-axis. Also, we can see that if we substitute $-c$ for c,

the function $f(x) = \dfrac{cx}{1 + c^2x^2}$ will be reflected in the x-axis, so we investigate only positive values of c (except $c = -1$, as a

demonstration of this reflective property). Also, f is an odd function. $\displaystyle\lim_{x \to \pm\infty} f(x) = 0$, so $y = 0$ is a horizontal asymptote

for all c. We calculate $f'(x) = \dfrac{(1 + c^2x^2)c - cx(2c^2x)}{(1 + c^2x^2)^2} = -\dfrac{c(c^2x^2 - 1)}{(1 + c^2x^2)^2}$. $f'(x) = 0 \Leftrightarrow c^2x^2 - 1 = 0 \Leftrightarrow$

$x = \pm 1/c$. So there is an absolute maximum value of $f(1/c) = \frac{1}{2}$ and an absolute minimum value of $f(-1/c) = -\frac{1}{2}$.

These extrema have the same value regardless of c, but the maximum points move closer to the y-axis as c increases.

$$f''(x) = \frac{(-2c^3x)(1 + c^2x^2)^2 - (-c^3x^2 + c)[2(1 + c^2x^2)(2c^2x)]}{(1 + c^2x^2)^4}$$

$$= \frac{(-2c^3x)(1 + c^2x^2) + (c^3x^2 - c)(4c^2x)}{(1 + c^2x^2)^3} = \frac{2c^3x(c^2x^2 - 3)}{(1 + c^2x^2)^3}$$

$f''(x) = 0 \Leftrightarrow x = 0$ or $\pm\sqrt{3}/c$, so there are inflection points at $(0, 0)$ and

at $\left(\pm\sqrt{3}/c, \pm\sqrt{3}/4\right)$. Again, the y-coordinate of the inflection points does not depend on c, but as c increases, both inflection

points approach the y-axis.

33. $f(x) = cx + \sin x \Rightarrow f'(x) = c + \cos x \Rightarrow f''(x) = -\sin x$

$f(-x) = -f(x)$, so f is an odd function and its graph is symmetric with respect to the origin.

$f(x) = 0 \Leftrightarrow \sin x = -cx$, so 0 is always an x-intercept.

$f'(x) = 0 \Leftrightarrow \cos x = -c$, so there is no critical number when $|c| > 1$. If $|c| \le 1$, then there are infinitely many critical numbers. If x_1 is the unique solution of $\cos x = -c$ in the interval $[0, \pi]$, then the critical numbers are $2n\pi \pm x_1$, where n ranges over the integers. (Special cases: When $c = 1$, $x_1 = 0$; when $c = 0$, $x = \frac{\pi}{2}$; and when $c = -1$, $x_1 = \pi$.)

$f''(x) < 0 \iff \sin x > 0$, so f is CD on intervals of the form $(2n\pi, (2n+1)\pi)$. f is CU on intervals of the form $((2n-1)\pi, 2n\pi)$. The inflection points of f are the points $(2n\pi, 2n\pi c)$, where n is an integer.

If $c \geq 1$, then $f'(x) \geq 0$ for all x, so f is increasing and has no extremum. If $c \leq -1$, then $f'(x) \leq 0$ for all x, so f is decreasing and has no extremum. If $|c| < 1$, then $f'(x) > 0 \iff \cos x > -c \iff x$ is in an interval of the form $(2n\pi - x_1, 2n\pi + x_1)$ for some integer n. These are the intervals on which f is increasing. Similarly, we find that f is decreasing on the intervals of the form $(2n\pi + x_1, 2(n+1)\pi - x_1)$. Thus, f has local maxima at the points $2n\pi + x_1$, where f has the values $c(2n\pi + x_1) + \sin x_1 = c(2n\pi + x_1) + \sqrt{1 - c^2}$, and f has local minima at the points $2n\pi - x_1$, where we have $f(2n\pi - x_1) = c(2n\pi - x_1) - \sin x_1 = c(2n\pi - x_1) - \sqrt{1 - c^2}$.

The transitional values of c are -1 and 1. The inflection points move vertically, but not horizontally, when c changes.

When $|c| \geq 1$, there is no extremum. For $|c| < 1$, the maxima are spaced 2π apart horizontally, as are the minima. The horizontal spacing between maxima and adjacent minima is regular (and equals π) when $c = 0$, but the horizontal space between a local maximum and the nearest local minimum shrinks as $|c|$ approaches 1.

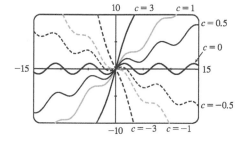

35. (a) $f(x) = cx^4 - 2x^2 + 1$. For $c = 0$, $f(x) = -2x^2 + 1$, a parabola whose vertex, $(0, 1)$, is the absolute maximum. For $c > 0$, $f(x) = cx^4 - 2x^2 + 1$ opens upward with two minimum points. As $c \to 0$, the minimum points spread apart and move downward; they are below the x-axis for $0 < c < 1$ and above for $c > 1$. For $c < 0$, the graph opens downward, and has an absolute maximum at $x = 0$ and no local minimum.

(b) $f'(x) = 4cx^3 - 4x = 4cx(x^2 - 1/c)$ $[c \neq 0]$. If $c \leq 0$, 0 is the only critical number.

$f''(x) = 12cx^2 - 4$, so $f''(0) = -4$ and there is a local maximum at $(0, f(0)) = (0, 1)$, which lies on $y = 1 - x^2$. If $c > 0$, the critical numbers are 0 and $\pm 1/\sqrt{c}$. As before, there is a local maximum at $(0, f(0)) = (0, 1)$, which lies on $y = 1 - x^2$.

$f''\left(\pm 1/\sqrt{c}\right) = 12 - 4 = 8 > 0$, so there is a local minimum at $x = \pm 1/\sqrt{c}$. Here $f\left(\pm 1/\sqrt{c}\right) = c(1/c^2) - 2/c + 1 = -1/c + 1$.

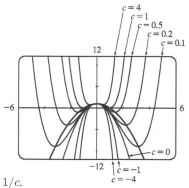

But $\left(\pm 1/\sqrt{c}, -1/c + 1\right)$ lies on $y = 1 - x^2$ since $1 - \left(\pm 1/\sqrt{c}\right)^2 = 1 - 1/c$.

4.5 Indeterminate Forms and l'Hospital's Rule

Note: The use of l'Hospital's Rule is indicated by an H above the equal sign: $\overset{H}{=}$

1. (a) $\lim\limits_{x \to a} \dfrac{f(x)}{g(x)}$ is an indeterminate form of type $\dfrac{0}{0}$.

   (b) $\lim\limits_{x \to a} \dfrac{f(x)}{p(x)} = 0$ because the numerator approaches 0 while the denominator becomes large.

   (c) $\lim\limits_{x \to a} \dfrac{h(x)}{p(x)} = 0$ because the numerator approaches a finite number while the denominator becomes large.

   (d) If $\lim\limits_{x \to a} p(x) = \infty$ and $f(x) \to 0$ through positive values, then $\lim\limits_{x \to a} \dfrac{p(x)}{f(x)} = \infty$. [For example, take $a = 0$, $p(x) = 1/x^2$,

   and $f(x) = x^2$.] If $f(x) \to 0$ through negative values, then $\lim\limits_{x \to a} \dfrac{p(x)}{f(x)} = -\infty$. [For example, take $a = 0$, $p(x) = 1/x^2$,

   and $f(x) = -x^2$.] If $f(x) \to 0$ through both positive and negative values, then the limit might not exist. [For example,

   take $a = 0$, $p(x) = 1/x^2$, and $f(x) = x$.]

   (e) $\lim\limits_{x \to a} \dfrac{p(x)}{q(x)}$ is an indeterminate form of type $\dfrac{\infty}{\infty}$.

3. (a) When x is near a, $f(x)$ is near 0 and $p(x)$ is large, so $f(x) - p(x)$ is large negative. Thus, $\lim\limits_{x \to a} [f(x) - p(x)] = -\infty$.

   (b) $\lim\limits_{x \to a} [p(x) - q(x)]$ is an indeterminate form of type $\infty - \infty$.

   (c) When x is near a, $p(x)$ and $q(x)$ are both large, so $p(x) + q(x)$ is large. Thus, $\lim\limits_{x \to a} [p(x) + q(x)] = \infty$.

5. This limit has the form $\frac{0}{0}$. We can simply factor and simplify to evaluate the limit.

$$\lim_{x \to 1} \frac{x^2 - 1}{x^2 - x} = \lim_{x \to 1} \frac{(x+1)(x-1)}{x(x-1)} = \lim_{x \to 1} \frac{x+1}{x} = \frac{1+1}{1} = 2$$

7. This limit has the form $\frac{0}{0}$. $\lim\limits_{x \to (\pi/2)^+} \dfrac{\cos x}{1 - \sin x} \overset{H}{=} \lim\limits_{x \to (\pi/2)^+} \dfrac{-\sin x}{-\cos x} = \lim\limits_{x \to (\pi/2)^+} \tan x = -\infty$.

9. This limit has the form $\frac{0}{0}$. $\lim\limits_{t \to 0} \dfrac{e^t - 1}{t^3} \overset{H}{=} \lim\limits_{t \to 0} \dfrac{e^t}{3t^2} = \infty$ since $e^t \to 1$ and $3t^2 \to 0^+$ as $t \to 0$.

11. This limit has the form $\frac{\infty}{\infty}$. $\lim\limits_{x \to \infty} \dfrac{\ln x}{\sqrt{x}} \overset{H}{=} \lim\limits_{x \to \infty} \dfrac{1/x}{\frac{1}{2}x^{-1/2}} = \lim\limits_{x \to \infty} \dfrac{2}{\sqrt{x}} = 0$

13. $\lim\limits_{x \to 0^+} [(\ln x)/x] = -\infty$ since $\ln x \to -\infty$ as $x \to 0^+$ and dividing by small values of x just increases the magnitude of the

    quotient $(\ln x)/x$. L'Hospital's Rule does not apply.

15. This limit has the form $\frac{0}{0}$.

$$\lim_{x \to 0} \frac{\sqrt{1 + 2x} - \sqrt{1 - 4x}}{x} \overset{H}{=} \lim_{x \to 0} \frac{\frac{1}{2}(1 + 2x)^{-1/2} \cdot 2 - \frac{1}{2}(1 - 4x)^{-1/2}(-4)}{1}$$

$$= \lim_{x \to 0} \left(\frac{1}{\sqrt{1 + 2x}} + \frac{2}{\sqrt{1 - 4x}} \right) = \frac{1}{\sqrt{1}} + \frac{2}{\sqrt{1}} = 3$$

17. This limit has the form $\frac{0}{0}$. $\displaystyle\lim_{t\to 0}\frac{5^t-3^t}{t}\overset{\text{H}}{=}\lim_{t\to 0}\frac{5^t\ln 5-3^t\ln 3}{1}=\ln 5-\ln 3=\ln\tfrac{5}{3}$

19. This limit has the form $\frac{0}{0}$. $\displaystyle\lim_{x\to 0}\frac{e^x-1-x}{x^2}\overset{\text{H}}{=}\lim_{x\to 0}\frac{e^x-1}{2x}\overset{\text{H}}{=}\lim_{x\to 0}\frac{e^x}{2}=\frac{1}{2}$

21. This limit has the form $\frac{0}{0}$. $\displaystyle\lim_{x\to 1}\frac{1-x+\ln x}{1+\cos\pi x}\overset{\text{H}}{=}\lim_{x\to 1}\frac{-1+1/x}{-\pi\sin\pi x}\overset{\text{H}}{=}\lim_{x\to 1}\frac{-1/x^2}{-\pi^2\cos\pi x}=\frac{-1}{-\pi^2(-1)}=-\frac{1}{\pi^2}$

23. This limit has the form $\frac{0}{0}$. $\displaystyle\lim_{x\to 1}\frac{x^a-ax+a-1}{(x-1)^2}\overset{\text{H}}{=}\lim_{x\to 1}\frac{ax^{a-1}-a}{2(x-1)}\overset{\text{H}}{=}\lim_{x\to 1}\frac{a(a-1)x^{a-2}}{2}=\frac{a(a-1)}{2}$

25. This limit has the form $\frac{0}{0}$. $\displaystyle\lim_{x\to 0}\frac{\cos x-1+\frac{1}{2}x^2}{x^4}\overset{\text{H}}{=}\lim_{x\to 0}\frac{-\sin x+x}{4x^3}\overset{\text{H}}{=}\lim_{x\to 0}\frac{-\cos x+1}{12x^2}\overset{\text{H}}{=}\lim_{x\to 0}\frac{\sin x}{24x}\overset{\text{H}}{=}\lim_{x\to 0}\frac{\cos x}{24}=\frac{1}{24}$

27. This limit has the form $\infty\cdot 0$.

$$\lim_{x\to\infty}x\sin(\pi/x)=\lim_{x\to\infty}\frac{\sin(\pi/x)}{1/x}\overset{\text{H}}{=}\lim_{x\to\infty}\frac{\cos(\pi/x)(-\pi/x^2)}{-1/x^2}=\pi\lim_{x\to\infty}\cos(\pi/x)=\pi(1)=\pi$$

29. This limit has the form $\infty\cdot 0$. We'll change it to the form $\frac{0}{0}$.

$$\lim_{x\to 0}\cot 2x\sin 6x=\lim_{x\to 0}\frac{\sin 6x}{\tan 2x}\overset{\text{H}}{=}\lim_{x\to 0}\frac{6\cos 6x}{2\sec^2 2x}=\frac{6(1)}{2(1)^2}=3$$

31. This limit has the form $\infty\cdot 0$. $\displaystyle\lim_{x\to\infty}x^3e^{-x^2}=\lim_{x\to\infty}\frac{x^3}{e^{x^2}}\overset{\text{H}}{=}\lim_{x\to\infty}\frac{3x^2}{2xe^{x^2}}=\lim_{x\to\infty}\frac{3x}{2e^{x^2}}\overset{\text{H}}{=}\lim_{x\to\infty}\frac{3}{4xe^{x^2}}=0$

33. This limit has the form $\infty-\infty$.

$$\lim_{x\to 1}\left(\frac{x}{x-1}-\frac{1}{\ln x}\right)-\lim_{x\to 1}\frac{x\ln x-(x-1)}{(x-1)\ln x}\overset{\text{H}}{=}\lim_{x\to 1}\frac{x(1/x)+\ln x-1}{(x-1)(1/x)+\ln x}=\lim_{x\to 1}\frac{\ln x}{1-(1/x)+\ln x}$$

$$\overset{\text{H}}{=}\lim_{x\to 1}\frac{1/x}{1/x^2+1/x}\cdot\frac{x^2}{x^2}=\lim_{x\to 1}\frac{x}{1+x}=\frac{1}{1+1}=\frac{1}{2}$$

35. We will multiply and divide by the conjugate of the expression to change the form of the expression.

$$\lim_{x\to\infty}\left(\sqrt{x^2+x}-x\right)=\lim_{x\to\infty}\left(\frac{\sqrt{x^2+x}-x}{1}\cdot\frac{\sqrt{x^2+x}+x}{\sqrt{x^2+x}+x}\right)=\lim_{x\to\infty}\frac{(x^2+x)-x^2}{\sqrt{x^2+x}+x}$$

$$=\lim_{x\to\infty}\frac{x}{\sqrt{x^2+x}+x}=\lim_{x\to\infty}\frac{1}{\sqrt{1+1/x}+1}=\frac{1}{\sqrt{1}+1}=\frac{1}{2}$$

As an alternate solution, write $\sqrt{x^2+x}-x$ as $\sqrt{x^2+x}-\sqrt{x^2}$, factor out $\sqrt{x^2}$, rewrite as $(\sqrt{1+1/x}-1)/(1/x)$, and apply l'Hospital's Rule.

37. The limit has the form $\infty-\infty$ and we will change the form to a product by factoring out x.

$$\lim_{x\to\infty}(x-\ln x)=\lim_{x\to\infty}x\left(1-\frac{\ln x}{x}\right)=\infty\text{ since }\lim_{x\to\infty}\frac{\ln x}{x}\overset{\text{H}}{=}\lim_{x\to\infty}\frac{1/x}{1}=0.$$

39. $y=x^{x^2}\ \Rightarrow\ \ln y=x^2\ln x$, so $\displaystyle\lim_{x\to 0^+}\ln y=\lim_{x\to 0^+}x^2\ln x=\lim_{x\to 0^+}\frac{\ln x}{1/x^2}\overset{\text{H}}{=}\lim_{x\to 0^+}\frac{1/x}{-2/x^3}=\lim_{x\to 0^+}\left(-\frac{1}{2}x^2\right)=0\ \Rightarrow$

$$\lim_{x\to 0^+}x^{x^2}=\lim_{x\to 0^+}e^{\ln y}=e^0=1.$$

41. $y = (1 - 2x)^{1/x}$ $\Rightarrow$ $\ln y = \dfrac{1}{x}\ln(1 - 2x)$, so $\lim\limits_{x \to 0} \ln y = \lim\limits_{x \to 0} \dfrac{\ln(1 - 2x)}{x} \overset{\text{H}}{=} \lim\limits_{x \to 0} \dfrac{-2/(1 - 2x)}{1} = -2$ $\Rightarrow$

$\lim\limits_{x \to 0}(1 - 2x)^{1/x} = \lim\limits_{x \to 0} e^{\ln y} = e^{-2}$.

43. $y = x^{1/x}$ $\Rightarrow$ $\ln y = (1/x)\ln x$ $\Rightarrow$ $\lim\limits_{x \to \infty} \ln y = \lim\limits_{x \to \infty} \dfrac{\ln x}{x} \overset{\text{H}}{=} \lim\limits_{x \to \infty} \dfrac{1/x}{1} = 0$ $\Rightarrow$

$\lim\limits_{x \to \infty} x^{1/x} = \lim\limits_{x \to \infty} e^{\ln y} = e^0 = 1$

45. $y = (4x + 1)^{\cot x}$ $\Rightarrow$ $\ln y = \cot x \ln(4x + 1)$, so $\lim\limits_{x \to 0^+} \ln y = \lim\limits_{x \to 0^+} \dfrac{\ln(4x + 1)}{\tan x} \overset{\text{H}}{=} \lim\limits_{x \to 0^+} \dfrac{\dfrac{4}{4x + 1}}{\sec^2 x} = 4$ $\Rightarrow$

$\lim\limits_{x \to 0^+}(4x + 1)^{\cot x} = \lim\limits_{x \to 0^+} e^{\ln y} = e^4$.

47.

From the graph, if $x = 500$, $y \approx 7.36$. The limit has the form 1^∞.

Now $y = \left(1 + \dfrac{2}{x}\right)^x$ $\Rightarrow$ $\ln y = x \ln\left(1 + \dfrac{2}{x}\right)$ $\Rightarrow$

$\lim\limits_{x \to \infty} \ln y = \lim\limits_{x \to \infty} \dfrac{\ln(1 + 2/x)}{1/x} \overset{\text{H}}{=} \lim\limits_{x \to \infty} \dfrac{\dfrac{1}{1 + 2/x}\left(-\dfrac{2}{x^2}\right)}{-1/x^2}$

$= 2\lim\limits_{x \to \infty} \dfrac{1}{1 + 2/x} = 2(1) = 2$ $\Rightarrow$

$\lim\limits_{x \to \infty}\left(1 + \dfrac{2}{x}\right)^x = \lim\limits_{x \to \infty} e^{\ln y} = e^2 \; [\approx 7.39]$

49.

From the graph, it appears that $\lim\limits_{x \to 0} \dfrac{f(x)}{g(x)} = \lim\limits_{x \to 0} \dfrac{f'(x)}{g'(x)} = 0.25$.

We calculate $\lim\limits_{x \to 0} \dfrac{f(x)}{g(x)} = \lim\limits_{x \to 0} \dfrac{e^x - 1}{x^3 + 4x} \overset{\text{H}}{=} \lim\limits_{x \to 0} \dfrac{e^x}{3x^2 + 4} = \dfrac{1}{4}$.

51. $\lim\limits_{x \to \infty} xe^{-x} = \lim\limits_{x \to \infty}(x/e^x) \overset{\text{H}}{=} \lim\limits_{x \to \infty}(1/e^x) = 0$, so $y = 0$ is a HA. $\lim\limits_{x \to -\infty} xe^{-x} = -\infty$. $f(x) = xe^{-x}$ $\Rightarrow$

$f'(x) = x\left(-e^{-x}\right) + e^{-x}\cdot 1 = e^{-x}(1 - x) > 0$ $\Leftrightarrow$ $1 - x > 0$ $\Leftrightarrow$ $x < 1$,

so f is increasing on $(-\infty, 1)$ and decreasing on $(1, \infty)$. By the FDT, $f(1) = 1/e$ is a

local maximum.

$f''(x) = e^{-x}(-1) + (1 - x)\left(-e^{-x}\right) = e^{-x}(-1 - 1 + x) = e^{-x}(x - 2) > 0$ $\Leftrightarrow$

$x - 2 > 0$ $\Leftrightarrow$ $x > 2$, so f is CU on $(2, \infty)$ and CD on $(-\infty, 2)$. IP is $\left(2, 2/e^2\right)$.

53.

$\lim\limits_{x \to \infty} \dfrac{\ln x}{x} \overset{\text{H}}{=} \lim\limits_{x \to \infty} \dfrac{1/x}{1} = 0$, so $y = 0$ is a HA. Also $\lim\limits_{x \to 0^+} \dfrac{\ln x}{x} = -\infty$

since $\ln x \to -\infty$ and $x \to 0^+$, so $x = 0$ is a VA.

$f(x) = \dfrac{\ln x}{x}$ $\Rightarrow$ $f'(x) = \dfrac{x(1/x) - (\ln x)(1)}{x^2} = \dfrac{1 - \ln x}{x^2} = 0$

when $\ln x = 1$ $\Leftrightarrow$ $x = e$.

[continued]

$f'(x) > 0 \Leftrightarrow 1 - \ln x > 0 \Leftrightarrow \ln x < 1 \Leftrightarrow 0 < x < e.\; f'(x) < 0 \Leftrightarrow x > e.$

So f is increasing on $(0, e)$ and decreasing on (e, ∞). By the FDT, $f(e) = 1/e$ is a local maximum.

$f''(x) = \dfrac{x^2(-1/x) - (1 - \ln x)(2x)}{(x^2)^2} = \dfrac{x(-1 - 2 + 2\ln x)}{x^4} = \dfrac{2\ln x - 3}{x^3}$, so $f''(x) > 0 \Leftrightarrow 2\ln x - 3 > 0 \Leftrightarrow$

$\ln x > \frac{3}{2} \Leftrightarrow x > e^{3/2}.\; f''(x) < 0 \Leftrightarrow 0 < x < e^{3/2}.$ So f is CU on $\left(e^{3/2}, \infty\right)$ and CD on $\left(0, e^{3/2}\right).$ There is an

inflection point at $\left(e^{3/2}, \frac{3}{2}e^{-3/2}\right).$

55. (a) $f(x) = x^2 \ln x.$ The domain of f is $(0, \infty).$

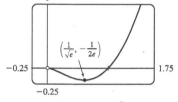

(b) $\displaystyle\lim_{x \to 0^+} x^2 \ln x = \lim_{x \to 0^+} \dfrac{\ln x}{1/x^2} \overset{\text{H}}{=} \lim_{x \to 0^+} \dfrac{1/x}{-2/x^3} = \lim_{x \to 0^+}\left(-\dfrac{x^2}{2}\right) = 0.$

There is a hole at $(0, 0).$

(c) It appears that there is an IP at about $(0.2, -0.06)$ and a local minimum at $(0.6, -0.18).\; f(x) = x^2 \ln x \Rightarrow$

$f'(x) = x^2(1/x) + (\ln x)(2x) = x(2\ln x + 1) > 0 \Leftrightarrow \ln x > -\frac{1}{2} \Leftrightarrow x > e^{-1/2},$ so f is increasing on

$\left(1/\sqrt{e}, \infty\right),$ decreasing on $\left(0, 1/\sqrt{e}\right).$ By the FDT, $f\left(1/\sqrt{e}\right) = -1/(2e)$ is a local minimum value. This point is

approximately $(0.6065, -0.1839),$ which agrees with our estimate.

$\qquad f''(x) = x(2/x) + (2\ln x + 1) = 2\ln x + 3 > 0 \Leftrightarrow \ln x > -\frac{3}{2} \Leftrightarrow x > e^{-3/2},$ so f is CU on $(e^{-3/2}, \infty)$

and CD on $(0, e^{-3/2}).$ IP is $(e^{-3/2}, -3/(2e^3)) \approx (0.2231, -0.0747).$

57. (a) $f(x) = x^{1/x}$

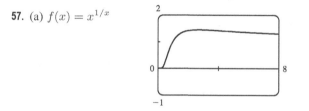

(b) Recall that $a^b = e^{b \ln a}.\; \displaystyle\lim_{x \to 0^+} x^{1/x} = \lim_{x \to 0^+} e^{(1/x)\ln x}.$ As $x \to 0^+,\; \dfrac{\ln x}{x} \to -\infty,$ so $x^{1/x} = e^{(1/x)\ln x} \to 0.$ This

indicates that there is a hole at $(0, 0).$ As $x \to \infty,$ we have the indeterminate form $\infty^0.\; \displaystyle\lim_{x \to \infty} x^{1/x} = \lim_{x \to \infty} e^{(1/x)\ln x},$

but $\displaystyle\lim_{x \to \infty} \dfrac{\ln x}{x} \overset{\text{H}}{=} \lim_{x \to \infty} \dfrac{1/x}{1} = 0,$ so $\displaystyle\lim_{x \to \infty} x^{1/x} = e^0 = 1.$ This indicates that $y = 1$ is a HA.

(c) Estimated maximum: $(2.72, 1.45).$ No estimated minimum. We use logarithmic differentiation to find any critical

numbers. $y = x^{1/x} \Rightarrow \ln y = \dfrac{1}{x}\ln x \Rightarrow \dfrac{y'}{y} = \dfrac{1}{x}\cdot\dfrac{1}{x} + (\ln x)\left(-\dfrac{1}{x^2}\right) \Rightarrow y' = x^{1/x}\left(\dfrac{1 - \ln x}{x^2}\right) = 0 \Rightarrow$

$\ln x = 1 \Rightarrow x = e.$ For $0 < x < e,\; y' > 0$ and for $x > e,\; y' < 0,$ so $f(e) = e^{1/e}$ is a local maximum value. This

point is approximately $(2.7183, 1.4447),$ which agrees with our estimate.

(d)

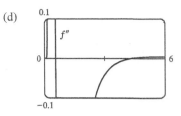

From the graph, we see that $f''(x) = 0$ at $x \approx 0.58$ and $x \approx 4.37$. Since f'' changes sign at these values, they are x-coordinates of inflection points.

59. If $c < 0$, then $\lim\limits_{x \to -\infty} f(x) = \lim\limits_{x \to -\infty} xe^{-cx} = \lim\limits_{x \to -\infty} \dfrac{x}{e^{cx}} \overset{H}{=} \lim\limits_{x \to -\infty} \dfrac{1}{ce^{cx}} = 0$, and $\lim\limits_{x \to \infty} f(x) = \infty$.

If $c > 0$, then $\lim\limits_{x \to -\infty} f(x) = -\infty$, and $\lim\limits_{x \to \infty} f(x) \overset{H}{=} \lim\limits_{x \to \infty} \dfrac{1}{ce^{cx}} = 0$.

If $c = 0$, then $f(x) = x$, so $\lim\limits_{x \to \pm\infty} f(x) = \pm\infty$, respectively.

So we see that $c = 0$ is a transitional value. We now exclude the case $c = 0$, since we know how the function behaves in that case. To find the maxima and minima of f, we differentiate: $f(x) = xe^{-cx}$ $\Rightarrow$

$f'(x) = x(-ce^{-cx}) + e^{-cx} = (1 - cx)e^{-cx}$. This is 0 when $1 - cx = 0$ $\Leftrightarrow$ $x = 1/c$. If $c < 0$ then this represents a minimum value of $f(1/c) = 1/(ce)$, since $f'(x)$ changes from negative to positive at $x = 1/c$;

and if $c > 0$, it represents a maximum value. As $|c|$ increases, the maximum or minimum point gets closer to the origin. To find the inflection points, we differentiate again: $f'(x) = e^{-cx}(1 - cx)$ $\Rightarrow$

$f''(x) = e^{-cx}(-c) + (1 - cx)(-ce^{-cx}) = (cx - 2)ce^{-cx}$. This changes sign when $cx - 2 = 0$ $\Leftrightarrow$ $x = 2/c$. So as $|c|$ increases, the points of inflection get closer to the origin.

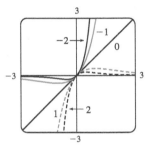

61. $\lim\limits_{x \to \infty} \dfrac{x}{\sqrt{x^2 + 1}} \overset{H}{=} \lim\limits_{x \to \infty} \dfrac{1}{\frac{1}{2}(x^2 + 1)^{-1/2}(2x)} = \lim\limits_{x \to \infty} \dfrac{\sqrt{x^2 + 1}}{x}$. Repeated applications of l'Hospital's Rule result in the original limit or the limit of the reciprocal of the function. Another method is to try dividing the numerator and denominator

by x: $\lim\limits_{x \to \infty} \dfrac{x}{\sqrt{x^2 + 1}} = \lim\limits_{x \to \infty} \dfrac{x/x}{\sqrt{x^2/x^2 + 1/x^2}} = \lim\limits_{x \to \infty} \dfrac{1}{\sqrt{1 + 1/x^2}} = \dfrac{1}{1} = 1$

63. $\lim\limits_{x \to \infty} \dfrac{e^x}{x^n} \overset{H}{=} \lim\limits_{x \to \infty} \dfrac{e^x}{nx^{n-1}} \overset{H}{=} \lim\limits_{x \to \infty} \dfrac{e^x}{n(n-1)x^{n-2}} \overset{H}{=} \cdots \overset{H}{=} \lim\limits_{x \to \infty} \dfrac{e^x}{n!} = \infty$

65. First we will find $\lim\limits_{n \to \infty} \left(1 + \dfrac{r}{n}\right)^{nt}$, which is of the form 1^{∞}. $y = \left(1 + \dfrac{r}{n}\right)^{nt}$ $\Rightarrow$ $\ln y = nt \ln\left(1 + \dfrac{r}{n}\right)$, so

$\lim\limits_{n \to \infty} \ln y = \lim\limits_{n \to \infty} nt \ln\left(1 + \dfrac{r}{n}\right) = t \lim\limits_{n \to \infty} \dfrac{\ln(1 + r/n)}{1/n} \overset{H}{=} t \lim\limits_{n \to \infty} \dfrac{(-r/n^2)}{(1 + r/n)(-1/n^2)} = t \lim\limits_{n \to \infty} \dfrac{r}{1 + i/n} = tr$ $\Rightarrow$

$\lim\limits_{n \to \infty} y = e^{rt}$. Thus, as $n \to \infty$, $A = A_0\left(1 + \dfrac{r}{n}\right)^{nt} \to A_0 e^{rt}$.

67. $\displaystyle\lim_{E\to 0^+} P(E) = \lim_{E\to 0^+}\left(\frac{e^E+e^{-E}}{e^E-e^{-E}}-\frac{1}{E}\right)$

$\displaystyle = \lim_{E\to 0^+}\frac{E(e^E+e^{-E})-1(e^E-e^{-E})}{(e^E-e^{-E})\,E} = \lim_{E\to 0^+}\frac{Ee^E+Ee^{-E}-e^E+e^{-E}}{Ee^E-Ee^{-E}}$ [form is $\frac{0}{0}$]

$\displaystyle \overset{\text{H}}{=} \lim_{E\to 0^+}\frac{Ee^E+e^E\cdot 1+E(-e^{-E})+e^{-E}\cdot 1-e^E+(-e^{-E})}{Ee^E+e^E\cdot 1-[E(-e^{-E})+e^{-E}\cdot 1]}$

$\displaystyle = \lim_{E\to 0^+}\frac{Ee^E-Ee^{-E}}{Ee^E+e^E+Ee^{-E}-e^{-E}} = \lim_{E\to 0^+}\frac{e^E-e^{-E}}{e^E+\dfrac{e^E}{E}+e^{-E}-\dfrac{e^{-E}}{E}}$ [divide by E]

$\displaystyle = \frac{0}{2+L}\,,$ where $L=\displaystyle\lim_{E\to 0^+}\frac{e^E-e^{-E}}{E}$ [form is $\frac{0}{0}$] $\displaystyle\overset{\text{H}}{=}\lim_{E\to 0^+}\frac{e^E+e^{-E}}{1}=\frac{1+1}{1}=2$

Thus, $\displaystyle\lim_{E\to 0^+}P(E)=\frac{0}{2+2}=0$.

69. We see that both numerator and denominator approach 0, so we can use l'Hospital's Rule:

$\displaystyle\lim_{x\to a}\frac{\sqrt{2a^3x-x^4}-a\sqrt[3]{aax}}{a-\sqrt[4]{ax^3}}\overset{\text{H}}{=}\lim_{x\to a}\frac{\frac{1}{2}(2a^3x-x^4)^{-1/2}(2a^3-4x^3)-a\left(\frac{1}{3}\right)(aax)^{-2/3}a^2}{-\frac{1}{4}(ax^3)^{-3/4}(3ax^2)}$

$\displaystyle = \frac{\frac{1}{2}(2a^3a-a^4)^{-1/2}(2a^3-4a^3)-\frac{1}{3}a^3(a^2a)^{-2/3}}{-\frac{1}{4}(aa^3)^{-3/4}(3aa^2)}$

$\displaystyle = \frac{(a^4)^{-1/2}(-a^3)-\frac{1}{3}a^3(a^3)^{-2/3}}{-\frac{3}{4}a^{3}(a^4)^{-3/4}} = \frac{-a-\frac{1}{3}a}{-\frac{3}{4}} = \frac{4}{3}\left(\frac{4}{3}a\right)=\frac{16}{9}a$

71. The limit, $L=\displaystyle\lim_{x\to\infty}\left[x-x^2\ln\left(\frac{1+x}{x}\right)\right]=\lim_{x\to\infty}\left[x-x^2\ln\left(\frac{1}{x}+1\right)\right]$. Let $t=1/x$, so as $x\to\infty$, $t\to 0^+$.

$\displaystyle L=\lim_{t\to 0^+}\left[\frac{1}{t}-\frac{1}{t^2}\ln(t+1)\right]=\lim_{t\to 0^+}\frac{t-\ln(t+1)}{t^2}\overset{\text{H}}{=}\lim_{t\to 0^+}\frac{1-\dfrac{1}{t+1}}{2t}=\lim_{t\to 0^+}\frac{t/(t+1)}{2t}=\lim_{t\to 0^+}\frac{1}{2\,(t+1)}=\frac{1}{2}$

Note: Starting the solution by factoring x or x^2 leads to a more complicated solution.

73. Since $f(2)=0$, the given limit has the form $\frac{0}{0}$.

$\displaystyle\lim_{x\to 0}\frac{f(2+3x)+f(2+5x)}{x}\overset{\text{H}}{=}\lim_{x\to 0}\frac{f'(2+3x)\cdot 3+f'(2+5x)\cdot 5}{1}=f'(2)\cdot 3+f'(2)\cdot 5=8f'(2)=8\cdot 7=56$

75. Since $\displaystyle\lim_{h\to 0}[f(x+h)-f(x-h)]=f(x)-f(x)=0$ (f is differentiable and hence continuous) and $\displaystyle\lim_{h\to 0}2h=0$, we use

l'Hospital's Rule:

$\displaystyle\lim_{h\to 0}\frac{f(x+h)-f(x-h)}{2h}\overset{\text{H}}{=}\lim_{h\to 0}\frac{f'(x+h)(1)-f'(x-h)(-1)}{2}=\frac{f'(x)+f'(x)}{2}=\frac{2f'(x)}{2}=f'(x)$

$\dfrac{f(x+h)-f(x-h)}{2h}$ is the slope of the secant line between

$(x-h,f(x-h))$ and $(x+h,f(x+h))$. As $h\to 0$, this line gets closer

to the tangent line and its slope approaches $f'(x)$.

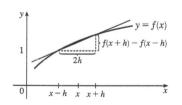

4.6 Optimization Problems

1. (a)

First Number	Second Number	Product
1	22	22
2	21	42
3	20	60
4	19	76
5	18	90
6	17	102
7	16	112
8	15	120
9	14	126
10	13	130
11	12	132

We needn't consider pairs where the first number is larger than the second, since we can just interchange the numbers in such cases. The answer appears to be 11 and 12, but we have considered only integers in the table.

(b) Call the two numbers x and y. Then $x + y = 23$, so $y = 23 - x$. Call the product P. Then

$P = xy = x(23 - x) = 23x - x^2$, so we wish to maximize the function $P(x) = 23x - x^2$. Since $P'(x) = 23 - 2x$,

we see that $P'(x) = 0 \iff x = \frac{23}{2} = 11.5$. Thus, the maximum value of P is $P(11.5) = (11.5)^2 = 132.25$ and it

occurs when $x = y = 11.5$.

Or: Note that $P''(x) = -2 < 0$ for all x, so P is everywhere concave downward and the local maximum at $x = 11.5$

must be an absolute maximum.

3. The two numbers are x and $\dfrac{100}{x}$, where $x > 0$. Minimize $f(x) = x + \dfrac{100}{x}$. $f'(x) = 1 - \dfrac{100}{x^2} = \dfrac{x^2 - 100}{x^2}$. The critical

number is $x = 10$. Since $f'(x) < 0$ for $0 < x < 10$ and $f'(x) > 0$ for $x > 10$, there is an absolute minimum at $x = 10$.

The numbers are 10 and 10.

5. If the rectangle has dimensions x and y, then its perimeter is $2x + 2y = 100$ m, so $y = 50 - x$. Thus, the area is

$A = xy = x(50 - x)$. We wish to maximize the function $A(x) = x(50 - x) = 50x - x^2$, where $0 < x < 50$. Since

$A'(x) = 50 - 2x = -2(x - 25)$, $A'(x) > 0$ for $0 < x < 25$ and $A'(x) < 0$ for $25 < x < 50$. Thus, A has an absolute

maximum at $x = 25$, and $A(25) = 25^2 = 625$ m². The dimensions of the rectangle that maximize its area are $x = y = 25$ m.

(The rectangle is a square.)

7. We need to maximize Y for $N \geq 0$. $Y(N) = \dfrac{kN}{1 + N^2} \Rightarrow$

$Y'(N) = \dfrac{(1 + N^2)k - kN(2N)}{(1 + N^2)^2} = \dfrac{k(1 - N^2)}{(1 + N^2)^2} = \dfrac{k(1 + N)(1 - N)}{(1 + N^2)^2}$. $Y'(N) > 0$ for $0 < N < 1$ and $Y'(N) < 0$

for $N > 1$. Thus, Y has an absolute maximum of $Y(1) = \frac{1}{2}k$ at $N = 1$.

9. (a)

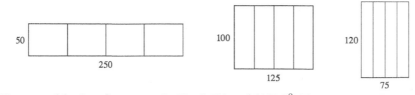

The areas of the three figures are 12,500, 12,500, and 9000 ft². There appears to be a maximum area of at least 12,500 ft².

(b) Let x denote the length of each of two sides and three dividers.

Let y denote the length of the other two sides.

(c) Area A = length × width = $y \cdot x$

(d) Length of fencing = 750 $\Rightarrow$ $5x + 2y = 750$

(e) $5x + 2y = 750$ $\Rightarrow$ $y = 375 - \frac{5}{2}x$ $\Rightarrow$ $A(x) = \left(375 - \frac{5}{2}x\right)x = 375x - \frac{5}{2}x^2$

(f) $A'(x) = 375 - 5x = 0$ $\Rightarrow$ $x = 75$. Since $A''(x) = -5 < 0$ there is an absolute maximum when $x = 75$. Then

$y = \frac{375}{2} = 187.5$. The largest area is $75\left(\frac{375}{2}\right) = 14{,}062.5 \text{ ft}^2$. These values of x and y are between the values in the first

and second figures in part (a). Our original estimate was low.

11. Let b be the length of the base of the box and h the height. The surface area is $1200 = b^2 + 4hb$ $\Rightarrow$ $h = (1200 - b^2)/(4b)$.

The volume is $V = b^2 h = b^2(1200 - b^2)/4b = 300b - b^3/4$ $\Rightarrow$ $V'(b) = 300 - \frac{3}{4}b^2$.

$V'(b) = 0$ $\Rightarrow$ $300 = \frac{3}{4}b^2$ $\Rightarrow$ $b^2 = 400$ $\Rightarrow$ $b = \sqrt{400} = 20$. Since $V'(b) > 0$ for $0 < b < 20$ and $V'(b) < 0$ for

$b > 20$, there is an absolute maximum when $b = 20$ by the First Derivative Test for Absolute Extreme Values (see page 302).

If $b = 20$, then $h = (1200 - 20^2)/(4 \cdot 20) = 10$, so the largest possible volume is $b^2 h = (20)^2(10) = 4000 \text{ cm}^3$.

13. (a) Let the rectangle have sides x and y and area A, so $A = xy$ or $y = A/x$. The problem is to minimize the

perimeter = $2x + 2y = 2x + 2A/x = P(x)$. Now $P'(x) = 2 - 2A/x^2 = 2(x^2 - A)/x^2$. So the critical number is

$x = \sqrt{A}$. Since $P'(x) < 0$ for $0 < x < \sqrt{A}$ and $P'(x) > 0$ for $x > \sqrt{A}$, there is an absolute minimum at $x = \sqrt{A}$.

The sides of the rectangle are $\sqrt{A}$ and $A/\sqrt{A} = \sqrt{A}$, so the rectangle is a square.

(b) Let p be the perimeter and x and y the lengths of the sides, so $p = 2x + 2y$ $\Rightarrow$ $2y = p - 2x$ $\Rightarrow$ $y = \frac{1}{2}p - x$.

The area is $A(x) = x\left(\frac{1}{2}p - x\right) = \frac{1}{2}px - x^2$. Now $A'(x) = 0$ $\Rightarrow$ $\frac{1}{2}p - 2x = 0$ $\Rightarrow$ $2x = \frac{1}{2}p$ $\Rightarrow$ $x = \frac{1}{4}p$. Since

$A''(x) = -2 < 0$, there is an absolute maximum for A when $x = \frac{1}{4}p$ by the Second Derivative Test. The sides of the

rectangle are $\frac{1}{4}p$ and $\frac{1}{2}p - \frac{1}{4}p = \frac{1}{4}p$, so the rectangle is a square.

15.

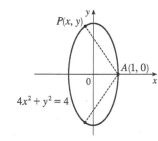

From the figure, we see that there are two points that are farthest away from

$A(1, 0)$. The distance d from A to an arbitrary point $P(x, y)$ on the ellipse is

$d = \sqrt{(x - 1)^2 + (y - 0)^2}$ and the square of the distance is

$S = d^2 = x^2 - 2x + 1 + y^2 = x^2 - 2x + 1 + (4 - 4x^2) = -3x^2 - 2x + 5$.

$S' = -6x - 2$ and $S' = 0$ $\Rightarrow$ $x = -\frac{1}{3}$. Now $S'' = -6 < 0$, so we know

that S has a maximum at $x = -\frac{1}{3}$. Since $-1 \le x \le 1$, $S(-1) = 4$,

$S\left(-\frac{1}{3}\right) = \frac{16}{3}$, and $S(1) = 0$, we see that the maximum distance is $\sqrt{\frac{16}{3}}$. The corresponding y-values are

$y = \pm\sqrt{4 - 4\left(-\frac{1}{3}\right)^2} = \pm\sqrt{\frac{32}{9}} = \pm\frac{4}{3}\sqrt{2} \approx \pm 1.89$. The points are $\left(-\frac{1}{3}, \pm\frac{4}{3}\sqrt{2}\right)$.

17.

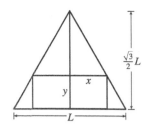

The height h of the equilateral triangle with sides of length L is $\frac{\sqrt{3}}{2}L$,

since $h^2 + (L/2)^2 = L^2 \Rightarrow h^2 = L^2 - \frac{1}{4}L^2 = \frac{3}{4}L^2 \Rightarrow$

$h = \frac{\sqrt{3}}{2}L$. Using similar triangles, $\dfrac{\frac{\sqrt{3}}{2}L - y}{x} = \dfrac{\frac{\sqrt{3}}{2}L}{L/2} = \sqrt{3} \Rightarrow$

$\sqrt{3}\,x = \dfrac{\sqrt{3}}{2}L - y \Rightarrow y = \dfrac{\sqrt{3}}{2}L - \sqrt{3}\,x \Rightarrow y = \dfrac{\sqrt{3}}{2}(L - 2x).$

The area of the inscribed rectangle is $A(x) = (2x)y = \sqrt{3}\,x(L - 2x) = \sqrt{3}\,Lx - 2\sqrt{3}\,x^2$, where $0 \le x \le L/2$. Now

$0 = A'(x) = \sqrt{3}\,L - 4\sqrt{3}\,x \Rightarrow x = \sqrt{3}\,L/(4\sqrt{3}) = L/4$. Since $A(0) = A(L/2) = 0$, the maximum occurs when

$x = L/4$, and $y = \frac{\sqrt{3}}{2}L - \frac{\sqrt{3}}{4}L = \frac{\sqrt{3}}{4}L$, so the dimensions are $L/2$ and $\frac{\sqrt{3}}{4}L$.

19.

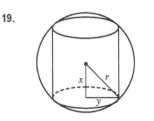

The cylinder has volume $V = \pi y^2 (2x)$. Also $x^2 + y^2 = r^2 \Rightarrow y^2 = r^2 - x^2$, so

$V(x) = \pi(r^2 - x^2)(2x) = 2\pi(r^2 x - x^3)$, where $0 \le x \le r$.

$V'(x) = 2\pi(r^2 - 3x^2) = 0 \Rightarrow x = r/\sqrt{3}$. Now $V(0) = V(r) = 0$, so there is a

maximum when $x = r/\sqrt{3}$ and $V(r/\sqrt{3}) = \pi(r^2 - r^2/3)(2r/\sqrt{3}) = 4\pi r^3/(3\sqrt{3})$.

21.

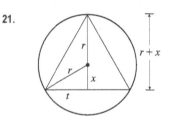

The area of the triangle is

$A(x) = \frac{1}{2}(2t)(r + x) = t(r + x) = \sqrt{r^2 - x^2}(r + x)$. Then

$0 = A'(x) = r\dfrac{-2x}{2\sqrt{r^2 - x^2}} + \sqrt{r^2 - x^2} + x\dfrac{-2x}{2\sqrt{r^2 - x^2}}$

$\quad = -\dfrac{x^2 + rx}{\sqrt{r^2 - x^2}} + \sqrt{r^2 - x^2} \Rightarrow$

$\dfrac{x^2 + rx}{\sqrt{r^2 - x^2}} = \sqrt{r^2 - x^2} \Rightarrow x^2 + rx = r^2 - x^2 \Rightarrow 0 = 2x^2 + rx - r^2 = (2x - r)(x + r) \Rightarrow$

$x = \frac{1}{2}r$ or $x = -r$. Now $A(r) = 0 = A(-r) \Rightarrow$ the maximum occurs where $x = \frac{1}{2}r$, so the triangle has

height $r + \frac{1}{2}r = \frac{3}{2}r$ and base $2\sqrt{r^2 - \left(\frac{1}{2}r\right)^2} = 2\sqrt{\frac{3}{4}r^2} = \sqrt{3}\,r.$

23.

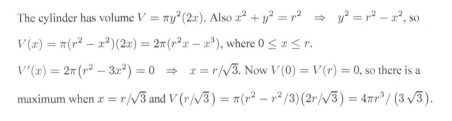

Perimeter $= 30 \Rightarrow 2y + x + \pi\left(\dfrac{x}{2}\right) = 30 \Rightarrow$

$y = \dfrac{1}{2}\left(30 - x - \dfrac{\pi x}{2}\right) = 15 - \dfrac{x}{2} - \dfrac{\pi x}{4}$. The area is the area of the rectangle plus the area of

the semicircle, or $xy + \frac{1}{2}\pi\left(\dfrac{x}{2}\right)^2$, so $A(x) = x\left(15 - \dfrac{x}{2} - \dfrac{\pi x}{4}\right) + \frac{1}{8}\pi x^2 = 15x - \frac{1}{2}x^2 - \frac{\pi}{8}x^2.$

$A'(x) = 15 - \left(1 + \frac{\pi}{4}\right)x = 0 \Rightarrow x = \dfrac{15}{1 + \pi/4} = \dfrac{60}{4 + \pi}$. $A''(x) = -\left(1 + \dfrac{\pi}{4}\right) < 0$, so this gives a maximum.

The dimensions are $x = \dfrac{60}{4 + \pi}$ ft and $y = 15 - \dfrac{30}{4 + \pi} - \dfrac{15\pi}{4 + \pi} = \dfrac{60 + 15\pi - 30 - 15\pi}{4 + \pi} = \dfrac{30}{4 + \pi}$ ft, so the height of the

rectangle is half the base.

25.

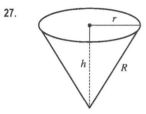

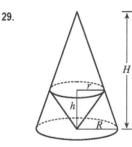

Let x be the length of the wire used for the square. The total area is

$$A(x) = \left(\frac{x}{4}\right)^2 + \frac{1}{2}\left(\frac{10-x}{3}\right)\frac{\sqrt{3}}{2}\left(\frac{10-x}{3}\right)$$

$$= \frac{1}{16}x^2 + \frac{\sqrt{3}}{36}(10-x)^2, \quad 0 \le x \le 10$$

$$A'(x) = \frac{1}{8}x - \frac{\sqrt{3}}{18}(10-x) = 0 \quad \Leftrightarrow \quad \frac{9}{72}x + \frac{4\sqrt{3}}{72}x - \frac{40\sqrt{3}}{72} = 0 \quad \Leftrightarrow \quad x = \frac{40\sqrt{3}}{9+4\sqrt{3}}.$$

Now $A(0) = \left(\frac{\sqrt{3}}{36}\right)100 \approx 4.81$, $A(10) = \frac{100}{16} = 6.25$ and $A\left(\frac{40\sqrt{3}}{9+4\sqrt{3}}\right) \approx 2.72$, so

(a) The maximum area occurs when $x = 10$ m, and all the wire is used for the square.

(b) The minimum area occurs when $x = \frac{40\sqrt{3}}{9+4\sqrt{3}} \approx 4.35$ m.

27.

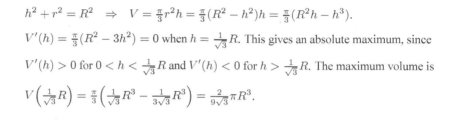

$h^2 + r^2 = R^2 \quad \Rightarrow \quad V = \frac{\pi}{3}r^2h = \frac{\pi}{3}(R^2 - h^2)h = \frac{\pi}{3}(R^2h - h^3).$

$V'(h) = \frac{\pi}{3}(R^2 - 3h^2) = 0$ when $h = \frac{1}{\sqrt{3}}R$. This gives an absolute maximum, since

$V'(h) > 0$ for $0 < h < \frac{1}{\sqrt{3}}R$ and $V'(h) < 0$ for $h > \frac{1}{\sqrt{3}}R$. The maximum volume is

$V\left(\frac{1}{\sqrt{3}}R\right) = \frac{\pi}{3}\left(\frac{1}{\sqrt{3}}R^3 - \frac{1}{3\sqrt{3}}R^3\right) = \frac{2}{9\sqrt{3}}\pi R^3.$

29.

By similar triangles, $\dfrac{H}{R} = \dfrac{H-h}{r}$ **(1)**. The volume of the inner cone is $V = \frac{1}{3}\pi r^2 h$,

so we'll solve **(1)** for h. $\dfrac{Hr}{R} = H - h \quad \Rightarrow$

$h = H - \dfrac{Hr}{R} = \dfrac{HR - Hr}{R} = \dfrac{H}{R}(R-r)$ **(2)**.

Thus, $V(r) = \dfrac{\pi}{3}r^2 \cdot \dfrac{H}{R}(R-r) = \dfrac{\pi H}{3R}(Rr^2 - r^3) \quad \Rightarrow$

$V'(r) = \dfrac{\pi H}{3R}(2Rr - 3r^2) = \dfrac{\pi H}{3R}r(2R - 3r).$

$V'(r) = 0 \quad \Rightarrow \quad r = 0$ or $2R = 3r \quad \Rightarrow \quad r = \frac{2}{3}R$ and from **(2)**, $h = \dfrac{H}{R}\left(R - \frac{2}{3}R\right) = \dfrac{H}{R}\left(\frac{1}{3}R\right) = \frac{1}{3}H.$

$V'(r)$ changes from positive to negative at $r = \frac{2}{3}R$, so the inner cone has a maximum volume of

$V = \frac{1}{3}\pi r^2 h = \frac{1}{3}\pi\left(\frac{2}{3}R\right)^2\left(\frac{1}{3}H\right) = \frac{4}{27} \cdot \frac{1}{3}\pi R^2 H$, which is approximately 15% of the volume of the larger cone.

31. $P(R) = \dfrac{E^2 R}{(R+r)^2} \quad \Rightarrow$

$P'(R) = \dfrac{(R+r)^2 \cdot E^2 - E^2 R \cdot 2(R+r)}{[(R+r)^2]^2} = \dfrac{(R^2 + 2Rr + r^2)E^2 - 2E^2R^2 - 2E^2Rr}{(R+r)^4}$

$= \dfrac{E^2r^2 - E^2R^2}{(R+r)^4} = \dfrac{E^2(r^2 - R^2)}{(R+r)^4} = \dfrac{E^2(r+R)(r-R)}{(R+r)^4} = \dfrac{E^2(r-R)}{(R+r)^3}$

$P'(R) = 0 \quad \Rightarrow \quad R = r \quad \Rightarrow \quad P(r) = \dfrac{E^2 r}{(r+r)^2} = \dfrac{E^2 r}{4r^2} = \dfrac{E^2}{4r}.$

The expression for $P'(R)$ shows that $P'(R) > 0$ for $R < r$ and $P'(R) < 0$ for $R > r$. Thus, the maximum value of the power is $E^2/(4r)$, and this occurs when $R = r$.

33. $S = 6sh - \frac{3}{2}s^2 \cot\theta + 3s^2 \frac{\sqrt{3}}{2} \csc\theta$

(a) $\dfrac{dS}{d\theta} = \frac{3}{2}s^2 \csc^2\theta - 3s^2 \frac{\sqrt{3}}{2} \csc\theta \cot\theta$ or $\frac{3}{2}s^2 \csc\theta \left(\csc\theta - \sqrt{3}\cot\theta\right)$.

(b) $\dfrac{dS}{d\theta} = 0$ when $\csc\theta - \sqrt{3}\cot\theta = 0 \;\Rightarrow\; \dfrac{1}{\sin\theta} - \sqrt{3}\dfrac{\cos\theta}{\sin\theta} = 0 \;\Rightarrow\; \cos\theta = \frac{1}{\sqrt{3}}$. The First Derivative Test shows

that the minimum surface area occurs when $\theta = \cos^{-1}\left(\frac{1}{\sqrt{3}}\right) \approx 55°$.

(c)

If $\cos\theta = \frac{1}{\sqrt{3}}$, then $\cot\theta = \frac{1}{\sqrt{2}}$ and $\csc\theta = \frac{\sqrt{3}}{\sqrt{2}}$, so the surface area is

$$S = 6sh - \frac{3}{2}s^2 \frac{1}{\sqrt{2}} + 3s^2 \frac{\sqrt{3}}{2}\frac{\sqrt{3}}{\sqrt{2}} = 6sh - \frac{3}{2\sqrt{2}}s^2 + \frac{9}{2\sqrt{2}}s^2$$

$$= 6sh + \frac{6}{2\sqrt{2}}s^2 = 6s\left(h + \frac{1}{2\sqrt{2}}s\right)$$

35. There are $(6-x)$ km over land and $\sqrt{x^2+4}$ km under the river.

We need to minimize the cost C (measured in \$100,000) of the pipeline.

$C(x) = (6-x)(4) + \left(\sqrt{x^2+4}\right)(8) \;\Rightarrow$

$C'(x) = -4 + 8\cdot\frac{1}{2}(x^2+4)^{-1/2}(2x) = -4 + \dfrac{8x}{\sqrt{x^2+4}}.$

$C'(x) = 0 \;\Rightarrow\; 4 = \dfrac{8x}{\sqrt{x^2+4}} \;\Rightarrow\; \sqrt{x^2+4} = 2x \;\Rightarrow\; x^2+4 = 4x^2 \;\Rightarrow\; 4 = 3x^2 \;\Rightarrow\; x^2 = \frac{4}{3} \;\Rightarrow$

$x = 2/\sqrt{3}$ $[0 \le x \le 6]$. Compare the costs for $x = 0$, $2/\sqrt{3}$, and 6. $C(0) = 24 + 16 = 40$,

$C\left(2/\sqrt{3}\right) = 24 - 8/\sqrt{3} + 32/\sqrt{3} = 24 + 24/\sqrt{3} \approx 37.9$, and $C(6) = 0 + 8\sqrt{40} \approx 50.6$. So the minimum cost is about

\$3.79 million when P is $6 - 2/\sqrt{3} \approx 4.85$ km east of the refinery.

37.

The total illumination is $I(x) = \dfrac{3k}{x^2} + \dfrac{k}{(10-x)^2}$, $0 < x < 10$. Then

$$I'(x) = \dfrac{-6k}{x^3} + \dfrac{2k}{(10-x)^3} = 0 \;\Rightarrow\; 6k(10-x)^3 = 2kx^3 \;\Rightarrow$$

$3(10-x)^3 = x^3 \;\Rightarrow\; \sqrt[3]{3}\,(10-x) = x \;\Rightarrow\; 10\sqrt[3]{3} - \sqrt[3]{3}\,x = x \;\Rightarrow\; 10\sqrt[3]{3} = x + \sqrt[3]{3}\,x \;\Rightarrow$

$10\sqrt[3]{3} = \left(1 + \sqrt[3]{3}\right)x \;\Rightarrow\; x = \dfrac{10\sqrt[3]{3}}{1 + \sqrt[3]{3}} \approx 5.9$ ft. This gives a minimum since $I''(x) > 0$ for $0 < x < 10$.

39.

The line with slope m (where $m < 0$) through $(3,5)$ has equation $y - 5 = m(x-3)$ or

$y = mx + (5 - 3m)$. The y-intercept is $5 - 3m$ and the x-intercept is $-5/m + 3$. So the

triangle has area $A(m) = \frac{1}{2}(5 - 3m)(-5/m + 3) = 15 - 25/(2m) - \frac{9}{2}m$. Now

$$A'(m) = \dfrac{25}{2m^2} - \dfrac{9}{2} = 0 \;\Leftrightarrow\; m^2 = \frac{25}{9} \;\Rightarrow\; m = -\frac{5}{3} \text{ (since } m < 0).$$

$A''(m) = -\dfrac{25}{m^3} > 0$, so there is an absolute minimum when $m = -\frac{5}{3}$. Thus, an equation of the line is $y - 5 = -\frac{5}{3}(x-3)$

or $y = -\frac{5}{3}x + 10$.

41. $y = \dfrac{3}{x}$ $\Rightarrow$ $y' = -\dfrac{3}{x^2}$, so an equation of the tangent line at the point $\left(a, \frac{3}{a}\right)$ is

$y - \dfrac{3}{a} = -\dfrac{3}{a^2}(x - a)$, or $y = -\dfrac{3}{a^2}x + \dfrac{6}{a}$. The y-intercept $[x = 0]$ is $6/a$. The

x-intercept $[y = 0]$ is $2a$. The distance d of the line segment that has endpoints at the

intercepts is $d = \sqrt{(2a - 0)^2 + (0 - 6/a)^2}$. Let $S = d^2$, so $S = 4a^2 + \dfrac{36}{a^2}$ $\Rightarrow$

$S' = 8a - \dfrac{72}{a^3}$. $S' = 0$ $\Leftrightarrow$ $\dfrac{72}{a^3} = 8a$ $\Leftrightarrow$ $a^4 = 9$ $\Leftrightarrow$ $a^2 = 3$ $\Rightarrow$ $a = \sqrt{3}$.

$S'' = 8 + \dfrac{216}{a^4} > 0$, so there is an absolute minimum at $a = \sqrt{3}$. Thus, $S = 4(3) + \frac{36}{3} = 12 + 12 = 24$ and

hence, $d = \sqrt{24} = 2\sqrt{6}$.

43. (a) If $c(x) = \dfrac{C(x)}{x}$, then, by Quotient Rule, we have $c'(x) = \dfrac{xC'(x) - C(x)}{x^2}$. Now $c'(x) = 0$ when $xC'(x) - C(x) = 0$

and this gives $C'(x) = \dfrac{C(x)}{x} = c(x)$. Therefore, the marginal cost equals the average cost.

(b) (i) $C(x) = 16{,}000 + 200x + 4x^{3/2}$, $C(1000) = 16{,}000 + 200{,}000 + 40{,}000\sqrt{10} \approx 216{,}000 + 126{,}491$, so

$C(1000) \approx \$342{,}491$. $c(x) = C(x)/x = \dfrac{16{,}000}{x} + 200 + 4x^{1/2}$, $c(1000) \approx \$342.49/\text{unit}$. $C'(x) = 200 + 6x^{1/2}$,

$C'(1000) = 200 + 60\sqrt{10} \approx \$389.74/\text{unit}$.

(ii) We must have $C'(x) = c(x)$ $\Leftrightarrow$ $200 + 6x^{1/2} = \dfrac{16{,}000}{x} + 200 + 4x^{1/2}$ $\Leftrightarrow$ $2x^{3/2} = 16{,}000$ $\Leftrightarrow$

$x = (8{,}000)^{2/3} = 400$ units. To check that this is a minimum, we calculate

$c'(x) = \dfrac{-16{,}000}{x^2} + \dfrac{2}{\sqrt{x}} = \dfrac{2}{x^2}\left(x^{3/2} - 8000\right)$. This is negative for $x < (8000)^{2/3} = 400$, zero at $x = 400$,

and positive for $x > 400$, so c is decreasing on $(0, 400)$ and increasing on $(400, \infty)$. Thus, c has an absolute minimum

at $x = 400$. [*Note:* $c''(x)$ is *not* positive for all $x > 0$.]

(iii) The minimum average cost is $c(400) = 40 + 200 + 80 = \$320/\text{unit}$.

45. (a) We are given that the demand function p is linear and $p(27{,}000) = 10$, $p(33{,}000) = 8$, so the slope is

$\dfrac{10 - 8}{27{,}000 - 33{,}000} = -\dfrac{1}{3000}$ and an equation of the line is $y - 10 = \left(-\dfrac{1}{3000}\right)(x - 27{,}000)$ $\Rightarrow$

$y = p(x) = -\dfrac{1}{3000}x + 19 = 19 - (x/3000)$.

(b) The revenue is $R(x) = xp(x) = 19x - (x^2/3000)$ $\Rightarrow$ $R'(x) = 19 - (x/1500) = 0$ when $x = 28{,}500$. Since

$R''(x) = -1/1500 < 0$, the maximum revenue occurs when $x = 28{,}500$ $\Rightarrow$ the price is $p(28{,}500) = \$9.50$.

47. (a) As in Example 6, we see that the demand function p is linear. We are given that $p(1000) = 450$ and deduce that

$p(1100) = 440$, since a \$10 reduction in price increases sales by 100 per week. The slope for p is $\dfrac{440 - 450}{1100 - 1000} = -\dfrac{1}{10}$,

so an equation is $p - 450 = -\dfrac{1}{10}(x - 1000)$ or $p(x) = -\dfrac{1}{10}x + 550$.

(b) $R(x) = xp(x) = -\frac{1}{10}x^2 + 550x$. $R'(x) = -\frac{1}{5}x + 550 = 0$ when $x = 5(550) = 2750$.

$p(2750) = 275$, so the rebate should be $450 - 275 = \$175$.

(c) $C(x) = 68{,}000 + 150x \;\Rightarrow\; P(x) = R(x) - C(x) = -\frac{1}{10}x^2 + 550x - 68{,}000 - 150x = -\frac{1}{10}x^2 + 400x - 68{,}000$,

$P'(x) = -\frac{1}{5}x + 400 = 0$ when $x = 2000$. $p(2000) = 350$. Therefore, the rebate to maximize profits should be

$450 - 350 = \$100$.

49.

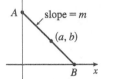

Every line segment in the first quadrant passing through (a, b) with endpoints on the x- and y-axes satisfies an equation of the form $y - b = m(x - a)$, where $m < 0$. By setting $x = 0$ and then $y = 0$, we find its endpoints, $A(0, b - am)$ and $B\left(a - \frac{b}{m}, 0\right)$. The distance d from A to B is given by $d = \sqrt{\left[\left(a - \frac{b}{m}\right) - 0\right]^2 + \left[0 - (b - am)\right]^2}$.

It follows that the square of the length of the line segment, as a function of m, is given by

$$S(m) = \left(a - \frac{b}{m}\right)^2 + (am - b)^2 = a^2 - \frac{2ab}{m} + \frac{b^2}{m^2} + a^2m^2 - 2abm + b^2.\ \text{Thus,}$$

$$S'(m) = \frac{2ab}{m^2} - \frac{2b^2}{m^3} + 2a^2m - 2ab = \frac{2}{m^3}(abm - b^2 + a^2m^4 - abm^3)$$

$$= \frac{2}{m^3}[b(am - b) + am^3(am - b)] = \frac{2}{m^3}(am - b)(b + am^3)$$

Thus, $S'(m) = 0 \;\Leftrightarrow\; m = b/a$ or $m = -\sqrt[3]{\frac{b}{a}}$. Since $b/a > 0$ and $m < 0$, m must equal $-\sqrt[3]{\frac{b}{a}}$. Since $\frac{2}{m^3} < 0$, we see

that $S'(m) < 0$ for $m < -\sqrt[3]{\frac{b}{a}}$ and $S'(m) > 0$ for $m > -\sqrt[3]{\frac{b}{a}}$. Thus, S has its absolute minimum value when $m = -\sqrt[3]{\frac{b}{a}}$.

That value is

$$S\left(-\sqrt[3]{\frac{b}{a}}\right) = \left(a + b\sqrt[3]{\frac{a}{b}}\right)^2 + \left(-a\sqrt[3]{\frac{b}{a}} - b\right)^2 = \left(a + \sqrt[3]{ab^2}\right)^2 + \left(\sqrt[3]{a^2b} + b\right)^2$$

$$= a^2 + 2a^{4/3}b^{2/3} + a^{2/3}b^{4/3} + a^{4/3}b^{2/3} + 2a^{2/3}b^{4/3} + b^2 = a^2 + 3a^{4/3}b^{2/3} + 3a^{2/3}b^{4/3} + b^2$$

The last expression is of the form $x^3 + 3x^2y + 3xy^2 + y^3 \;\; [= (x + y)^3]$ with $x = a^{2/3}$ and $y = b^{2/3}$,

so we can write it as $(a^{2/3} + b^{2/3})^3$ and the shortest such line segment has length $\sqrt{S} = (a^{2/3} + b^{2/3})^{3/2}$.

51.

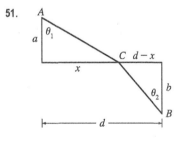

The total time is

$$T(x) = (\text{time from } A \text{ to } C) + (\text{time from } C \text{ to } B)$$

$$= \frac{\sqrt{a^2 + x^2}}{v_1} + \frac{\sqrt{b^2 + (d - x)^2}}{v_2}, \;\; 0 < x < d$$

$$T'(x) = \frac{x}{v_1\sqrt{a^2 + x^2}} - \frac{d - x}{v_2\sqrt{b^2 + (d - x)^2}} = \frac{\sin\theta_1}{v_1} - \frac{\sin\theta_2}{v_2}$$

The minimum occurs when $T'(x) = 0 \;\Rightarrow\; \dfrac{\sin\theta_1}{v_1} = \dfrac{\sin\theta_2}{v_2}$.

[*Note:* $T''(x) > 0$]

53.

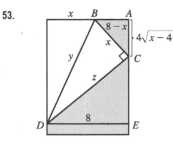

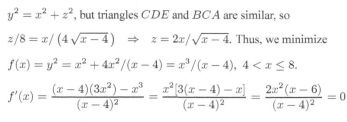

$y^2 = x^2 + z^2$, but triangles CDE and BCA are similar, so

$z/8 = x/\left(4\sqrt{x-4}\right)$ $\Rightarrow$ $z = 2x/\sqrt{x-4}$. Thus, we minimize

$f(x) = y^2 = x^2 + 4x^2/(x-4) = x^3/(x-4)$, $4 < x \leq 8$.

$f'(x) = \dfrac{(x-4)(3x^2) - x^3}{(x-4)^2} = \dfrac{x^2[3(x-4) - x]}{(x-4)^2} = \dfrac{2x^2(x-6)}{(x-4)^2} = 0$

when $x = 6$. $f'(x) < 0$ when $x < 6$, $f'(x) > 0$ when $x > 6$, so the minimum

occurs when $x = 6$ in.

55.

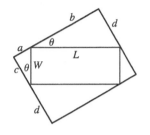

In the small triangle with sides a and c and hypotenuse W, $\sin\theta = \dfrac{a}{W}$ and

$\cos\theta = \dfrac{c}{W}$. In the triangle with sides b and d and hypotenuse L, $\sin\theta = \dfrac{d}{L}$ and

$\cos\theta = \dfrac{b}{L}$. Thus, $a = W\sin\theta$, $c = W\cos\theta$, $d = L\sin\theta$, and $b = L\cos\theta$, so the

area of the circumscribed rectangle is

$$
\begin{aligned}
A(\theta) &= (a+b)(c+d) = (W\sin\theta + L\cos\theta)(W\cos\theta + L\sin\theta)\\
&= W^2\sin\theta\,\cos\theta + WL\sin^2\theta + LW\cos^2\theta + L^2\sin\theta\,\cos\theta\\
&= LW\sin^2\theta + LW\cos^2\theta + (L^2 + W^2)\sin\theta\,\cos\theta\\
&= LW(\sin^2\theta + \cos^2\theta) + (L^2 + W^2)\cdot\tfrac{1}{2}\cdot 2\sin\theta\,\cos\theta = LW + \tfrac{1}{2}(L^2 + W^2)\sin 2\theta,\ 0 \leq \theta \leq \tfrac{\pi}{2}
\end{aligned}
$$

This expression shows, without calculus, that the maximum value of $A(\theta)$ occurs when $\sin 2\theta = 1$ $\Leftrightarrow$ $2\theta = \tfrac{\pi}{2}$ $\Rightarrow$

$\theta = \tfrac{\pi}{4}$. So the maximum area is $A\left(\tfrac{\pi}{4}\right) = LW + \tfrac{1}{2}(L^2 + W^2) = \tfrac{1}{2}(L^2 + 2LW + W^2) = \tfrac{1}{2}(L + W)^2$.

57.

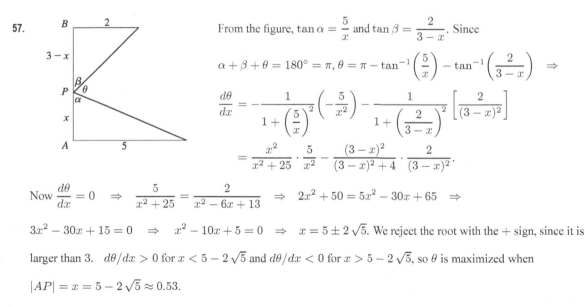

From the figure, $\tan\alpha = \dfrac{5}{x}$ and $\tan\beta = \dfrac{2}{3-x}$. Since

$$
\alpha + \beta + \theta = 180° = \pi,\ \theta = \pi - \tan^{-1}\left(\frac{5}{x}\right) - \tan^{-1}\left(\frac{2}{3-x}\right) \Rightarrow
$$

$$
\frac{d\theta}{dx} = -\frac{1}{1 + \left(\dfrac{5}{x}\right)^2}\left(-\frac{5}{x^2}\right) - \frac{1}{1 + \left(\dfrac{2}{3-x}\right)^2}\left[\frac{2}{(3-x)^2}\right]
$$

$$
= \frac{x^2}{x^2 + 25}\cdot\frac{5}{x^2} - \frac{(3-x)^2}{(3-x)^2 + 4}\cdot\frac{2}{(3-x)^2}.
$$

Now $\dfrac{d\theta}{dx} = 0$ $\Rightarrow$ $\dfrac{5}{x^2 + 25} = \dfrac{2}{x^2 - 6x + 13}$ $\Rightarrow$ $2x^2 + 50 = 5x^2 - 30x + 65$ $\Rightarrow$

$3x^2 - 30x + 15 = 0$ $\Rightarrow$ $x^2 - 10x + 5 = 0$ $\Rightarrow$ $x = 5 \pm 2\sqrt{5}$. We reject the root with the $+$ sign, since it is

larger than 3. $d\theta/dx > 0$ for $x < 5 - 2\sqrt{5}$ and $d\theta/dx < 0$ for $x > 5 - 2\sqrt{5}$, so θ is maximized when

$|AP| = x = 5 - 2\sqrt{5} \approx 0.53$.

59. (a)

If $k =$ energy/km over land, then energy/km over water $= 1.4k$.

So the total energy is $E = 1.4k\sqrt{25 + x^2} + k(13 - x)$, $0 \le x \le 13$,

and so $\dfrac{dE}{dx} = \dfrac{1.4kx}{(25 + x^2)^{1/2}} - k$.

Set $\dfrac{dE}{dx} = 0$: $1.4kx = k(25 + x^2)^{1/2}$ $\Rightarrow$ $1.96x^2 = x^2 + 25$ $\Rightarrow$ $0.96x^2 = 25$ $\Rightarrow$ $x = \dfrac{5}{\sqrt{0.96}} \approx 5.1$.

Testing against the value of E at the endpoints: $E(0) = 1.4k(5) + 13k = 20k$, $E(5.1) \approx 17.9k$, $E(13) \approx 19.5k$.

Thus, to minimize energy, the bird should fly to a point about 5.1 km from B.

(b) If W/L is large, the bird would fly to a point C that is closer to B than to D to minimize the energy used flying over water.

If W/L is small, the bird would fly to a point C that is closer to D than to B to minimize the distance of the flight.

$E = W\sqrt{25 + x^2} + L(13 - x)$ $\Rightarrow$ $\dfrac{dE}{dx} = \dfrac{Wx}{\sqrt{25 + x^2}} - L = 0$ when $\dfrac{W}{L} = \dfrac{\sqrt{25 + x^2}}{x}$. By the same sort of

argument as in part (a), this ratio will give the minimal expenditure of energy if the bird heads for the point x km from B.

(c) For flight direct to D, $x = 13$, so from part (b), $W/L = \dfrac{\sqrt{25 + 13^2}}{13} \approx 1.07$. There is no value of W/L for which the bird

should fly directly to B. But note that $\displaystyle\lim_{x \to 0^+}(W/L) = \infty$, so if the point at which E is a minimum is close to B, then

W/L is large.

(d) Assuming that the birds instinctively choose the path that minimizes the energy expenditure, we can use the equation for

$dE/dx = 0$ from part (a) with $1.4k = c$, $x = 4$, and $k = 1$: $c(4) = 1 \cdot (25 + 4^2)^{1/2}$ $\Rightarrow$ $c = \sqrt{41}/4 \approx 1.6$.

61. (a) Distance = rate × time, so time = distance/rate. $T_1 = \dfrac{D}{c_1}$, $T_2 = \dfrac{2\,|PR|}{c_1} + \dfrac{|RS|}{c_2} = \dfrac{2h\sec\theta}{c_1} + \dfrac{D - 2h\tan\theta}{c_2}$,

$T_3 = \dfrac{2\sqrt{h^2 + D^2/4}}{c_1} = \dfrac{\sqrt{4h^2 + D^2}}{c_1}$.

(b) $\dfrac{dT_2}{d\theta} = \dfrac{2h}{c_1} \cdot \sec\theta\tan\theta - \dfrac{2h}{c_2}\sec^2\theta = 0$ when $2h\sec\theta\left(\dfrac{1}{c_1}\tan\theta - \dfrac{1}{c_2}\sec\theta\right) = 0$ $\Rightarrow$

$\dfrac{1}{c_1}\dfrac{\sin\theta}{\cos\theta} - \dfrac{1}{c_2}\dfrac{1}{\cos\theta} = 0$ $\Rightarrow$ $\dfrac{\sin\theta}{c_1\cos\theta} = \dfrac{1}{c_2\cos\theta}$ $\Rightarrow$ $\sin\theta = \dfrac{c_1}{c_2}$. The First Derivative Test shows that this gives

a minimum.

(c) Using part (a) with $D = 1$ and $T_1 = 0.26$, we have $T_1 = \dfrac{D}{c_1}$ $\Rightarrow$ $c_1 = \dfrac{1}{0.26} \approx 3.85$ km/s. $T_3 = \dfrac{\sqrt{4h^2 + D^2}}{c_1}$ $\Rightarrow$

$4h^2 + D^2 = T_3^2 c_1^2$ $\Rightarrow$ $h = \tfrac{1}{2}\sqrt{T_3^2 c_1^2 - D^2} = \tfrac{1}{2}\sqrt{(0.34)^2(1/0.26)^2 - 1^2} \approx 0.42$ km. To find c_2, we use $\sin\theta = \dfrac{c_1}{c_2}$

from part (b) and $T_2 = \dfrac{2h\sec\theta}{c_1} + \dfrac{D - 2h\tan\theta}{c_2}$ from part (a). From the figure,

$\sin\theta = \dfrac{c_1}{c_2}$ $\Rightarrow$ $\sec\theta = \dfrac{c_2}{\sqrt{c_2^2 - c_1^2}}$ and $\tan\theta = \dfrac{c_1}{\sqrt{c_2^2 - c_1^2}}$, so

$T_2 = \dfrac{2hc_2}{c_1\sqrt{c_2^2 - c_1^2}} + \dfrac{D\sqrt{c_2^2 - c_1^2} - 2hc_1}{c_2\sqrt{c_2^2 - c_1^2}}$. Using the values for T_2 [given as 0.32],

h, c_1, and D, we can graph $Y_1 = T_2$ and $Y_2 = \dfrac{2hc_2}{c_1\sqrt{c_2^2 - c_1^2}} + \dfrac{D\sqrt{c_2^2 - c_1^2} - 2hc_1}{c_2\sqrt{c_2^2 - c_1^2}}$ and find their intersection points.

Doing so gives us $c_2 \approx 4.10$ and 7.66, but if $c_2 = 4.10$, then $\theta = \arcsin(c_1/c_2) \approx 69.6°$, which implies that point S is to the left of point R in the diagram. So $c_2 = 7.66$ km/s.

4.7 Newton's Method

1. (a)

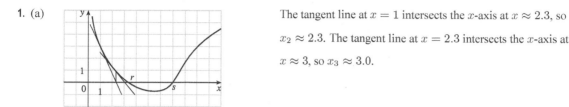

The tangent line at $x = 1$ intersects the x-axis at $x \approx 2.3$, so $x_2 \approx 2.3$. The tangent line at $x = 2.3$ intersects the x-axis at $x \approx 3$, so $x_3 \approx 3.0$.

(b) $x_1 = 5$ would *not* be a better first approximation than $x_1 = 1$ since the tangent line is nearly horizontal. In fact, the second approximation for $x_1 = 5$ appears to be to the left of $x = 1$.

3. Since $x_1 = 3$ and $y = 5x - 4$ is tangent to $y = f(x)$ at $x = 3$, we simply need to find where the tangent line intersects the x-axis. $y = 0 \;\Rightarrow\; 5x_2 - 4 = 0 \;\Rightarrow\; x_2 = \frac{4}{5}$.

5. $f(x) = x^3 + 2x - 4 \;\Rightarrow\; f'(x) = 3x^2 + 2$, so $x_{n+1} = x_n - \dfrac{x_n^3 + 2x_n - 4}{3x_n^2 + 2}$. Now $x_1 = 1 \;\Rightarrow$

$$x_2 = 1 - \frac{1 + 2 - 4}{3 \cdot 1^2 + 2} = 1 - \frac{-1}{5} = 1.2 \;\Rightarrow\; x_3 = 1.2 - \frac{(1.2)^3 + 2(1.2) - 4}{3(1.2)^2 + 2} \approx 1.1797.$$

7. $f(x) = x^5 - x - 1 \;\Rightarrow\; f'(x) = 5x^4 - 1$, so $x_{n+1} = x_n - \dfrac{x_n^5 - x_n - 1}{5x_n^4 - 1}$. Now $x_1 = 1 \;\Rightarrow$

$$x_2 = 1 - \frac{1}{5 - 1} = 1 - \left(-\tfrac{1}{4}\right) = 1.25 \;\Rightarrow\; x_3 = 1.25 - \frac{(1.25)^5 - 1.25 - 1}{5(1.25)^4 - 1} \approx 1.1785.$$

9. $f(x) = x^3 + x + 3 \;\Rightarrow\; f'(x) = 3x^2 + 1$, so $x_{n+1} = x_n - \dfrac{x_n^3 + x_n + 3}{3x_n^2 + 1}$.

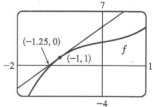

Now $x_1 = -1 \;\Rightarrow$

$$x_2 = -1 - \frac{(-1)^3 + (-1) + 3}{3(-1)^2 + 1} = -1 - \frac{-1 - 1 + 3}{3 + 1} = -1 - \frac{1}{4} = -1.25.$$

Newton's method follows the tangent line at $(-1, 1)$ down to its intersection with the x-axis at $(-1.25, 0)$, giving the second approximation $x_2 = -1.25$.

11. To approximate $x = \sqrt[5]{20}$ (so that $x^5 = 20$), we can take $f(x) = x^5 - 20$. So $f'(x) = 5x^4$, and thus,

$x_{n+1} = x_n - \dfrac{x_n^5 - 20}{5x_n^4}$. Since $\sqrt[5]{32} = 2$ and 32 is reasonably close to 20, we'll use $x_1 = 2$. We need to find approximations

until they agree to eight decimal places. $x_1 - 2 \;\Rightarrow\; x_2 = 1.85$, $x_3 \approx 1.82148614$, $x_4 \approx 1.82056514$,

$x_5 \approx 1.82056420 \approx x_6$. So $\sqrt[5]{20} \approx 1.82056420$, to eight decimal places.   [continued]

Here is a quick and easy method for finding the iterations for Newton's method on a programmable calculator. (The screens shown are from the TI-84 Plus, but the method is similar on other calculators.) Assign $f(x) = x^5 - 20$ to Y_1, and $f'(x) = 5x^4$ to Y_2. Now store $x_1 = 2$ in X and then enter $X - Y_1/Y_2 \rightarrow X$ to get $x_2 = 1.85$. By successively pressing the ENTER key, you get the approximations $x_3, x_4, \ldots$.

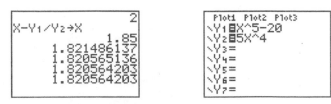

In Derive, load the utility file SOLVE. Enter NEWTON(x^5-20,x,2) and then APPROXIMATE to get [2, 1.85, 1.82148614, 1.82056514, 1.82056420]. You can request a specific iteration by adding a fourth argument. For example, NEWTON(x^5-20,x,2,2) gives [2, 1.85, 1.82148614].

In Maple, make the assignments $f := x \rightarrow x\hat{\ }5 - 20;$, $g := x \rightarrow x - f(x)/D(f)(x);$, and $x := 2.;$. Repeatedly execute the command $x := g(x);$ to generate successive approximations.

In Mathematica, make the assignments $f[x\_] := x\hat{\ }5 - 20$, $g[x\_] := x - f[x]/f'[x]$, and $x = 2$. Repeatedly execute the command $x = g[x]$ to generate successive approximations.

13.

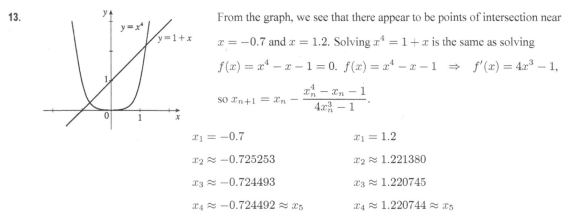

From the graph, we see that there appear to be points of intersection near $x = -0.7$ and $x = 1.2$. Solving $x^4 = 1 + x$ is the same as solving $f(x) = x^4 - x - 1 = 0$. $f(x) = x^4 - x - 1 \Rightarrow f'(x) = 4x^3 - 1$,

so $x_{n+1} = x_n - \dfrac{x_n^4 - x_n - 1}{4x_n^3 - 1}$.

$x_1 = -0.7$	$x_1 = 1.2$
$x_2 \approx -0.725253$	$x_2 \approx 1.221380$
$x_3 \approx -0.724493$	$x_3 \approx 1.220745$
$x_4 \approx -0.724492 \approx x_5$	$x_4 \approx 1.220744 \approx x_5$

To six decimal places, the roots of the equation are -0.724492 and 1.220744.

15.

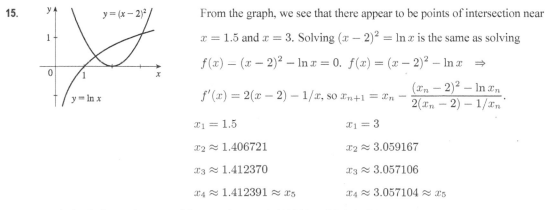

From the graph, we see that there appear to be points of intersection near $x = 1.5$ and $x = 3$. Solving $(x - 2)^2 = \ln x$ is the same as solving $f(x) = (x - 2)^2 - \ln x = 0$. $f(x) = (x - 2)^2 - \ln x \Rightarrow$

$f'(x) = 2(x - 2) - 1/x$, so $x_{n+1} = x_n - \dfrac{(x_n - 2)^2 - \ln x_n}{2(x_n - 2) - 1/x_n}$.

$x_1 = 1.5$	$x_1 = 3$
$x_2 \approx 1.406721$	$x_2 \approx 3.059167$
$x_3 \approx 1.412370$	$x_3 \approx 3.057106$
$x_4 \approx 1.412391 \approx x_5$	$x_4 \approx 3.057104 \approx x_5$

To six decimal places, the roots of the equation are 1.412391 and 3.057104.

17.

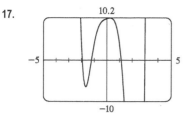

$f(x) = x^6 - x^5 - 6x^4 - x^2 + x + 10 \quad \Rightarrow$

$f'(x) = 6x^5 - 5x^4 - 24x^3 - 2x + 1 \quad \Rightarrow$

$x_{n+1} = x_n - \dfrac{x_n^6 - x_n^5 - 6x_n^4 - x_n^2 + x_n + 10}{6x_n^5 - 5x_n^4 - 24x_n^3 - 2x_n + 1}.$

From the graph of f, there appear to be roots near $-1.9, -1.2, 1.1,$ and 3.

$x_1 = -1.9$	$x_1 = -1.2$	$x_1 = 1.1$	$x_1 = 3$
$x_2 \approx -1.94278290$	$x_2 \approx -1.22006245$	$x_2 \approx 1.14111662$	$x_2 \approx 2.99$
$x_3 \approx -1.93828380$	$x_3 \approx -1.21997997 \approx x_4$	$x_3 \approx 1.13929741$	$x_3 \approx 2.98984106$
$x_4 \approx -1.93822884$		$x_4 \approx 1.13929375 \approx x_5$	$x_4 \approx 2.98984102 \approx x_5$
$x_5 \approx -1.93822883 \approx x_6$			

To eight decimal places, the roots of the equation are $-1.93822883, -1.21997997, 1.13929375,$ and 2.98984102.

19.

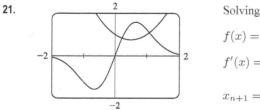

From the graph, $y = x^2\sqrt{2 - x - x^2}$ and $y = 1$ intersect twice, at $x \approx -2$ and

at $x \approx -1$. $f(x) = x^2\sqrt{2 - x - x^2} - 1 \quad \Rightarrow$

$f'(x) = x^2 \cdot \frac{1}{2}(2 - x - x^2)^{-1/2}(-1 - 2x) + (2 - x - x^2)^{1/2} \cdot 2x$

$= \frac{1}{2}x(2 - x - x^2)^{-1/2}[x(-1 - 2x) + 4(2 - x - x^2)]$

$= \dfrac{x(8 - 5x - 6x^2)}{2\sqrt{(2 + x)(1 - x)}},$

so $x_{n+1} = x_n - \dfrac{x_n^2\sqrt{2 - x_n - x_n^2} - 1}{\dfrac{x_n(8 - 5x_n - 6x_n^2)}{2\sqrt{(2 + x_n)(1 - x_n)}}}.$ Trying $x_1 = -2$ won't work because $f'(-2)$ is undefined, so we'll

try $x_1 = \quad 1.95$.

$x_1 = -1.95$	$x_1 = -0.8$
$x_2 \approx -1.98580357$	$x_2 \approx -0.82674444$
$x_3 \approx -1.97899778$	$x_3 \approx -0.82646236$
$x_4 \approx -1.97807848$	$x_4 \approx -0.82646233 \approx x_5$
$x_5 \approx -1.97806682$	
$x_6 \approx -1.97806681 \approx x_7$	

To eight decimal places, the roots of the equation are -1.97806681 and -0.82646233.

21.

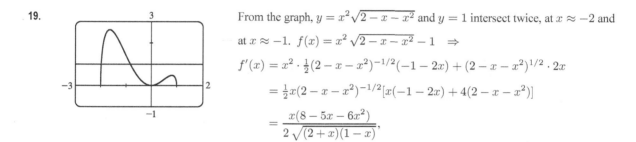

Solving $4e^{-x^2}\sin x = x^2 - x + 1$ is the same as solving

$f(x) = 4e^{-x^2}\sin x - x^2 + x - 1 = 0$.

$f'(x) = 4e^{-x^2}(\cos x - 2x\sin x) - 2x + 1 \quad \Rightarrow$

$x_{n+1} = x_n - \dfrac{4e^{-x_n^2}\sin x_n - x_n^2 + x_n - 1}{4e^{-x_n^2}(\cos x_n - 2x_n\sin x_n) - 2x_n + 1}.$

From the figure, we see that the graphs intersect at approximately $x = 0.2$ and $x = 1.1$.

$$x_1 = 0.2 \qquad\qquad\qquad x_1 = 1.1$$

$$x_2 \approx 0.21883273 \qquad\qquad x_2 \approx 1.08432830$$

$$x_3 \approx 0.21916357 \qquad\qquad x_3 \approx 1.08422462 \approx x_4$$

$$x_4 \approx 0.21916368 \approx x_5$$

To eight decimal places, the roots of the equation are 0.21916368 and 1.08422462.

23. (a) $f(x) = x^2 - a \;\Rightarrow\; f'(x) = 2x$, so Newton's method gives

$$x_{n+1} = x_n - \frac{x_n^2 - a}{2x_n} = x_n - \frac{1}{2}x_n + \frac{a}{2x_n} = \frac{1}{2}x_n + \frac{a}{2x_n} = \frac{1}{2}\left(x_n + \frac{a}{x_n}\right).$$

(b) Using (a) with $a = 1000$ and $x_1 = \sqrt{900} = 30$, we get $x_2 \approx 31.666667$, $x_3 \approx 31.622807$, and $x_4 \approx 31.622777 \approx x_5$.
So $\sqrt{1000} \approx 31.622777$.

25. $f(x) = x^3 - 3x + 6 \;\Rightarrow\; f'(x) = 3x^2 - 3$. If $x_1 = 1$, then $f'(x_1) = 0$ and the tangent line used for approximating x_2 is
horizontal. Attempting to find x_2 results in trying to divide by zero.

27. For $f(x) = x^{1/3}$, $f'(x) = \frac{1}{3}x^{-2/3}$ and

$$x_{n+1} = x_n - \frac{f(x_n)}{f'(x_n)} = x_n - \frac{x_n^{1/3}}{\frac{1}{3}x_n^{-2/3}} = x_n - 3x_n = -2x_n.$$

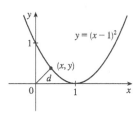

Therefore, each successive approximation becomes twice as large as the
previous one in absolute value, so the sequence of approximations fails to
converge to the root, which is 0. In the figure, we have $x_1 = 0.5$,
$x_2 = -2(0.5) = -1$, and $x_3 = -2(-1) = 2$.

29.

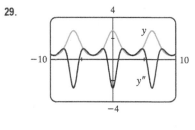

From the figure, we see that $y = f(x) = e^{\cos x}$ is periodic with period 2π. To
find the x-coordinates of the IP, we only need to approximate the zeros of y''
on $[0, \pi]$. $f'(x) = -e^{\cos x} \sin x \;\Rightarrow\; f''(x) = e^{\cos x}\left(\sin^2 x - \cos x\right)$. Since
$e^{\cos x} \neq 0$, we will use Newton's method with $g(x) = \sin^2 x - \cos x$,
$g'(x) = 2\sin x \cos x + \sin x$, and $x_1 = 1$. $x_2 \approx 0.904173$,
$x_3 \approx 0.904557 \approx x_4$. Thus, $(0.904557, 1.855277)$ is the IP.

31. We need to minimize the distance from $(0, 0)$ to an arbitrary point (x, y) on the

curve $y = (x - 1)^2$. $d = \sqrt{x^2 + y^2} \;\Rightarrow$

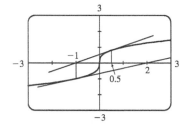

$d(x) = \sqrt{x^2 + [(x-1)^2]^2} = \sqrt{x^2 + (x-1)^4}$. When $d' = 0$, d will be
minimized and equivalently, $s = d^2$ will be minimized, so we will use Newton's
method with $f = s'$ and $f' = s''$.

$f(x) = 2x + 4(x-1)^3 \;\Rightarrow\; f'(x) = 2 + 12(x-1)^2$, so $x_{n+1} = x_n - \dfrac{2x_n + 4(x_n - 1)^3}{2 + 12(x_n - 1)^2}$. Try $x_1 = 0.5 \;\Rightarrow$

$x_2 = 0.4$, $x_3 \approx 0.410127$, $x_4 \approx 0.410245 \approx x_5$. Now $d(0.410245) \approx 0.537841$ is the minimum distance and the point on
the parabola is $(0.410245, 0.347810)$, correct to six decimal places.

33. In this case, $A = 18{,}000$, $R = 375$, and $n = 5(12) = 60$. So the formula $A = \dfrac{R}{i}\left[1 - (1+i)^{-n}\right]$ becomes

$$18{,}000 = \frac{375}{x}\left[1 - (1+x)^{-60}\right] \quad \Leftrightarrow \quad 48x = 1 - (1+x)^{-60} \quad \text{[multiply each term by } (1+x)^{60}] \quad \Leftrightarrow$$

$48x(1+x)^{60} - (1+x)^{60} + 1 = 0$. Let the LHS be called $f(x)$, so that

$$f'(x) = 48x(60)(1+x)^{59} + 48(1+x)^{60} - 60(1+x)^{59}$$

$$= 12(1+x)^{59}[4x(60) + 4(1+x) - 5] = 12(1+x)^{59}(244x - 1)$$

$x_{n+1} = x_n - \dfrac{48x_n(1+x_n)^{60} - (1+x_n)^{60} + 1}{12(1+x_n)^{59}(244x_n - 1)}$. An interest rate of 1% per month seems like a reasonable estimate for

$x = i$. So let $x_1 = 1\% = 0.01$, and we get $x_2 \approx 0.0082202$, $x_3 \approx 0.0076802$, $x_4 \approx 0.0076291$, $x_5 \approx 0.0076286 \approx x_6$.

Thus, the dealer is charging a monthly interest rate of 0.76286% (or 9.55% per year, compounded monthly).

4.8 Antiderivatives

1. $f(x) = \frac{1}{2} + \frac{3}{4}x^2 - \frac{4}{5}x^3 \ \Rightarrow\ F(x) = \frac{1}{2}x + \frac{3}{4}\dfrac{x^{2+1}}{2+1} - \frac{4}{5}\dfrac{x^{3+1}}{3+1} + C = \frac{1}{2}x + \frac{1}{4}x^3 - \frac{1}{5}x^4 + C$

Check: $F'(x) = \frac{1}{2} + \frac{1}{4}(3x^2) - \frac{1}{5}(4x^3) + 0 = \frac{1}{2} + \frac{3}{4}x^2 - \frac{4}{5}x^3 = f(x)$

3. $f(x) = (x+1)(2x-1) = 2x^2 + x - 1 \ \Rightarrow\ F(x) = 2\left(\frac{1}{3}x^3\right) + \frac{1}{2}x^2 - x + C = \frac{2}{3}x^3 + \frac{1}{2}x^2 - x + C$

5. $f(x) = 5x^{1/4} - 7x^{3/4} \ \Rightarrow\ F(x) = 5\dfrac{x^{1/4+1}}{\frac{1}{4}+1} - 7\dfrac{x^{3/4+1}}{\frac{3}{4}+1} + C = 5\dfrac{x^{5/4}}{5/4} - 7\dfrac{x^{7/4}}{7/4} + C = 4x^{5/4} - 4x^{7/4} + C$

7. $f(x) = 6\sqrt{x} - \sqrt[6]{x} = 6x^{1/2} - x^{1/6} \ \Rightarrow$

$F(x) = 6\dfrac{x^{1/2+1}}{\frac{1}{2}+1} - \dfrac{x^{1/6+1}}{\frac{1}{6}+1} + C = 6\dfrac{x^{3/2}}{3/2} - \dfrac{x^{7/6}}{7/6} + C = 4x^{3/2} - \frac{6}{7}x^{7/6} + C$

9. $f(x) = \dfrac{10}{x^9} = 10x^{-9}$ has domain $(-\infty, 0) \cup (0, \infty)$, so $F(x) = \begin{cases} \dfrac{10x^{-8}}{-8} + C_1 = -\dfrac{5}{4x^8} + C_1 & \text{if } x < 0 \\[2mm] -\dfrac{5}{4x^8} + C_2 & \text{if } x > 0 \end{cases}$

See Example 1(b) for a similar problem.

11. $f(u) = \dfrac{u^4 + 3\sqrt{u}}{u^2} = \dfrac{u^4}{u^2} + \dfrac{3u^{1/2}}{u^2} = u^2 + 3u^{-3/2} \ \Rightarrow$

$F(u) = \dfrac{u^3}{3} + 3\dfrac{u^{-3/2+1}}{-3/2+1} + C = \frac{1}{3}u^3 + 3\dfrac{u^{-1/2}}{-1/2} + C = \frac{1}{3}u^3 - \dfrac{6}{\sqrt{u}} + C$

13. $g(\theta) = \cos\theta - 5\sin\theta \ \Rightarrow\ G(\theta) = \sin\theta - 5(-\cos\theta) + C = \sin\theta + 5\cos\theta + C$

15. $f(x) = \dfrac{x^5 - x^3 + 2x}{x^4} = x - \dfrac{1}{x} + \dfrac{2}{x^3} = x - \dfrac{1}{x} + 2x^{-3} \ \Rightarrow$

$F(x) = \dfrac{x^2}{2} - \ln|x| + 2\left(\dfrac{x^{-3+1}}{-3+1}\right) + C = \frac{1}{2}x^2 - \ln|x| - \dfrac{1}{x^2} + C$

17. $f(x) = 5x^4 - 2x^5 \quad \Rightarrow \quad F(x) = 5 \cdot \dfrac{x^5}{5} - 2 \cdot \dfrac{x^6}{6} + C = x^5 - \frac{1}{3}x^6 + C.$

$F(0) = 4 \quad \Rightarrow \quad 0^5 - \frac{1}{3} \cdot 0^6 + C = 4 \quad \Rightarrow \quad C = 4,$ so $F(x) = x^5 - \frac{1}{3}x^6 + 4.$

The graph confirms our answer since $f(x) = 0$ when F has a local maximum, f is

positive when F is increasing, and f is negative when F is decreasing.

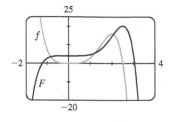

19. $f''(x) = 6x + 12x^2 \quad \Rightarrow \quad f'(x) = 6 \cdot \dfrac{x^2}{2} + 12 \cdot \dfrac{x^3}{3} + C = 3x^2 + 4x^3 + C \quad \Rightarrow$

$f(x) = 3 \cdot \dfrac{x^3}{3} + 4 \cdot \dfrac{x^4}{4} + Cx + D = x^3 + x^4 + Cx + D \qquad$ [C and D are just arbitrary constants]

21. $f''(x) = \frac{2}{3}x^{2/3} \quad \Rightarrow \quad f'(x) = \dfrac{2}{3}\left(\dfrac{x^{5/3}}{5/3}\right) + C = \frac{2}{5}x^{5/3} + C \quad \Rightarrow \quad f(x) = \dfrac{2}{5}\left(\dfrac{x^{8/3}}{8/3}\right) + Cx + D = \frac{3}{20}x^{8/3} + Cx + D$

23. $f'(x) = 1 - 6x \quad \Rightarrow \quad f(x) = x - 3x^2 + C.$ $f(0) = C$ and $f(0) = 8 \quad \Rightarrow \quad C = 8,$ so $f(x) = x - 3x^2 + 8.$

25. $f'(x) = \sqrt{x}(6 + 5x) = 6x^{1/2} + 5x^{3/2} \quad \Rightarrow \quad f(x) = 4x^{3/2} + 2x^{5/2} + C.$

$f(1) = 6 + C$ and $f(1) = 10 \quad \Rightarrow \quad C = 4,$ so $f(x) = 4x^{3/2} + 2x^{5/2} + 4.$

27. $f'(t) = 2\cos t + \sec^2 t \quad \Rightarrow \quad f(t) = 2\sin t + \tan t + C$ because $-\pi/2 < t < \pi/2.$

$f\left(\frac{\pi}{3}\right) = 2(\sqrt{3}/2) + \sqrt{3} + C = 2\sqrt{3} + C$ and $f\left(\frac{\pi}{3}\right) = 4 \quad \Rightarrow \quad C = 4 - 2\sqrt{3},$ so $f(t) = 2\sin t + \tan t + 4 - 2\sqrt{3}.$

29. $f''(x) = -2 + 12x - 12x^2 \quad \Rightarrow \quad f'(x) = -2x + 6x^2 - 4x^3 + C.$ $f'(0) = C$ and $f'(0) = 12 \quad \Rightarrow \quad C = 12,$ so

$f'(x) = -2x + 6x^2 - 4x^3 + 12$ and hence, $f(x) = -x^2 + 2x^3 - x^4 + 12x + D.$ $f(0) = D$ and $f(0) = 4 \quad \Rightarrow \quad D = 4,$

so $f(x) = -x^2 + 2x^3 - x^4 + 12x + 4.$

31. $f''(\theta) = \sin\theta + \cos\theta \quad \Rightarrow \quad f'(\theta) = -\cos\theta + \sin\theta + C.$ $f'(0) = -1 + C$ and $f'(0) = 4 \quad \Rightarrow \quad C = 5,$ so

$f'(\theta) = -\cos\theta + \sin\theta + 5$ and hence, $f(\theta) = -\sin\theta - \cos\theta + 5\theta + D.$ $f(0) = -1 + D$ and $f(0) = 3 \quad \Rightarrow \quad D = 4,$

so $f(\theta) = -\sin\theta - \cos\theta + 5\theta + 4.$

33. $f''(x) = 2 - 12x \quad \Rightarrow \quad f'(x) = 2x - 6x^2 + C \quad \Rightarrow \quad f(x) = x^2 - 2x^3 + Cx + D.$

$f(0) = D$ and $f(0) = 9 \quad \Rightarrow \quad D = 9.$ $f(2) = 4 - 16 + 2C + 9 = 2C - 3$ and $f(2) = 15 \quad \Rightarrow \quad 2C = 18 \quad \Rightarrow$

$C = 9,$ so $f(x) = x^2 - 2x^3 + 9x + 9.$

35. $f''(x) = 2 + \cos x \quad \Rightarrow \quad f'(x) = 2x + \sin x + C \quad \Rightarrow \quad f(x) = x^2 - \cos x + Cx + D.$

$f(0) = -1 + D$ and $f(0) = -1 \quad \Rightarrow \quad D = 0.$ $f\left(\frac{\pi}{2}\right) = \pi^2/4 + \left(\frac{\pi}{2}\right)C$ and $f\left(\frac{\pi}{2}\right) = 0 \quad \Rightarrow \quad \left(\frac{\pi}{2}\right)C = -\pi^2/4 \quad \Rightarrow$

$C = -\frac{\pi}{2},$ so $f(x) = x^2 - \cos x - \left(\frac{\pi}{2}\right)x.$

37. Given $f'(x) = 2x + 1,$ we have $f(x) = x^2 + x + C.$ Since f passes through $(1, 6),$ $f(1) = 6 \quad \Rightarrow \quad 1^2 + 1 + C = 6 \quad \Rightarrow$

$C = 4.$ Therefore, $f(x) = x^2 + x + 4$ and $f(2) = 2^2 + 2 + 4 = 10.$

39.

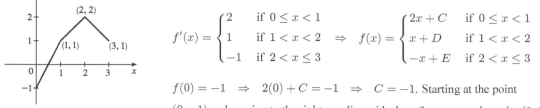

$$f'(x) = \begin{cases} 2 & \text{if } 0 \le x < 1 \\ 1 & \text{if } 1 < x < 2 \\ -1 & \text{if } 2 < x \le 3 \end{cases} \Rightarrow f(x) = \begin{cases} 2x + C & \text{if } 0 \le x < 1 \\ x + D & \text{if } 1 < x < 2 \\ -x + E & \text{if } 2 < x \le 3 \end{cases}$$

$f(0) = -1 \Rightarrow 2(0) + C = -1 \Rightarrow C = -1$. Starting at the point

$(0, -1)$ and moving to the right on a line with slope 2 gets us to the point $(1, 1)$.

The slope for $1 < x < 2$ is 1, so we get to the point $(2, 2)$. Here we have used the fact that f is continuous. We can include the

point $x = 1$ on either the first or the second part of f. The line connecting $(1, 1)$ to $(2, 2)$ is $y = x$, so $D = 0$. The slope for

$2 < x \le 3$ is -1, so we get to $(3, 1)$. $f(3) = 1 \Rightarrow -3 + E = 1 \Rightarrow E = 4$. Thus

$$f(x) = \begin{cases} 2x - 1 & \text{if } 0 \le x \le 1 \\ x & \text{if } 1 < x < 2 \\ -x + 4 & \text{if } 2 \le x \le 3 \end{cases}$$

Note that $f'(x)$ does not exist at $x = 1$ or at $x = 2$.

41. $v(t) = s'(t) = \sin t - \cos t \Rightarrow s(t) = -\cos t - \sin t + C$. $s(0) = -1 + C$ and $s(0) = 0 \Rightarrow C = 1$, so

$s(t) = -\cos t - \sin t + 1$.

43. (a) We first observe that since the stone is dropped 450 m above the ground, $v(0) = 0$ and $s(0) = 450$.

$v'(t) = a(t) = -9.8 \Rightarrow v(t) = -9.8t + C$. Now $v(0) = 0 \Rightarrow C = 0$, so $v(t) = -9.8t \Rightarrow$

$s(t) = -4.9t^2 + D$. Last, $s(0) = 450 \Rightarrow D = 450^{\cdot} \Rightarrow s(t) = 450 - 4.9t^2$.

(b) The stone reaches the ground when $s(t) = 0$. $450 - 4.9t^2 = 0 \Rightarrow t^2 = 450/4.9 \Rightarrow t_1 = \sqrt{450/4.9} \approx 9.58$ s.

(c) The velocity with which the stone strikes the ground is $v(t_1) = -9.8\sqrt{450/4.9} \approx -93.9$ m/s.

(d) This is just reworking parts (a) and (b) with $v(0) = -5$. Using $v(t) = -9.8t + C$, $v(0) = -5 \Rightarrow 0 + C = -5 \Rightarrow$

$v(t) = -9.8t - 5$. So $s(t) = -4.9t^2 - 5t + D$ and $s(0) = 450 \Rightarrow D = 450 \Rightarrow s(t) = -4.9t^2 - 5t + 450$.

Solving $s(t) = 0$ by using the quadratic formula gives us $t = (5 \pm \sqrt{8845})/(-9.8) \Rightarrow t_1 \approx 9.09$ s.

45. By Exercise 44 with $a = -9.8$, $s(t) = -4.9t^2 + v_0 t + s_0$ and $v(t) = s'(t) = -9.8t + v_0$. So

$[v(t)]^2 = (-9.8t + v_0)^2 = (9.8)^2 t^2 - 19.6v_0 t + v_0^2 = v_0^2 + 96.04t^2 - 19.6v_0 t = v_0^2 - 19.6(-4.9t^2 + v_0 t)$.

But $-4.9t^2 + v_0 t$ is just $s(t)$ without the s_0 term; that is, $s(t) - s_0$. Thus, $[v(t)]^2 = v_0^2 - 19.6[s(t) - s_0]$.

47. Marginal cost $= 1.92 - 0.002x = C'(x) \Rightarrow C(x) = 1.92x - 0.001x^2 + K$. But $C(1) = 1.92 - 0.001 + K = 562 \Rightarrow$

$K = 560.081$. Therefore, $C(x) = 1.92x - 0.001x^2 + 560.081 \Rightarrow C(100) = 742.081$, so the cost of producing

100 items is \$742.08.

49. Using Exercise 44 with $a = -32$, $v_0 = 0$, and $s_0 = h$ (the height of the cliff), we know that the height at time t is

$s(t) = -16t^2 + h$. $v(t) = s'(t) = -32t$ and $v(t) = -120 \Rightarrow -32t = -120 \Rightarrow t = 3.75$, so

$0 = s(3.75) = -16(3.75)^2 + h \Rightarrow h = 16(3.75)^2 = 225$ ft.

51. $a(t) = k$, the initial velocity is 30 mi/h $= 30 \cdot \frac{5280}{3600} = 44$ ft/s, and the final velocity (after 5 seconds) is

50 mi/h $= 50 \cdot \frac{5280}{3600} = \frac{220}{3}$ ft/s. So $v(t) = kt + C$ and $v(0) = 44 \;\Rightarrow\; C = 44$. Thus, $v(t) = kt + 44 \;\Rightarrow\;$

$v(5) = 5k + 44$. But $v(5) = \frac{220}{3}$, so $5k + 44 = \frac{220}{3} \;\Rightarrow\; 5k = \frac{88}{3} \;\Rightarrow\; k = \frac{88}{15} \approx 5.87$ ft/s^2.

53. Let the acceleration be $a(t) = k$ km/h^2. We have $v(0) = 100$ km/h and we can take the initial position $s(0)$ to be 0.

We want the time t_f for which $v(t) = 0$ to satisfy $s(t) < 0.08$ km. In general, $v'(t) = a(t) = k$, so $v(t) = kt + C$,

where $C = v(0) = 100$. Now $s'(t) = v(t) = kt + 100$, so $s(t) = \frac{1}{2}kt^2 + 100t + D$, where $D = s(0) = 0$.

Thus, $s(t) = \frac{1}{2}kt^2 + 100t$. Since $v(t_f) = 0$, we have $kt_f + 100 = 0$ or $t_f = -100/k$, so

$$s(t_f) = \frac{1}{2}k\left(-\frac{100}{k}\right)^2 + 100\left(-\frac{100}{k}\right) = 10{,}000\left(\frac{1}{2k} - \frac{1}{k}\right) = -\frac{5{,}000}{k}. \text{ The condition } s(t_f) \text{ must satisfy is}$$

$-\dfrac{5{,}000}{k} < 0.08 \;\Rightarrow\; -\dfrac{5{,}000}{0.08} > k \quad [k \text{ is negative}] \;\Rightarrow\; k < -62{,}500$ km/h^2, or equivalently,

$k < -\frac{3125}{648} \approx -4.82$ m/s^2.

55. (a) The Mean Value Theorem says that there exists a number c in the interval (x_1, x_2) such that $H'(c) = \dfrac{H(x_2) - H(x_1)}{x_2 - x_1}$.

Since $H = G - F$ and G and F are antiderivatives of f, $H'(c) = G'(c) - F'(c) = f(c) - f(c) = 0$. So now

$\dfrac{H(x_2) - H(x_1)}{x_2 - x_1} = 0 \;\Rightarrow\; H(x_2) - H(x_1) = 0 \, (x_2 \neq x_1) \;\Rightarrow\; H(x_2) = H(x_1)$. Since this is true for any

$x_1 < x_2$ in I, H must be a constant function.

(b) We have $H = G - F$ and $H(x) = C$, so $C = G - F \;\Rightarrow\; G(x) = F(x) + C$. Thus, any antiderivative G can be

expressed as $F(x) + C$.

57. (a) First note that 90 mi/h $= 90 \times \frac{5280}{3600}$ ft/s $= 132$ ft/s. Then $a(t) = 4$ ft/s$^2 \;\Rightarrow\; v(t) = 4t + C$, but $v(0) = 0 \;\Rightarrow\;$

$C = 0$. Now $4t = 132$ when $t = \frac{132}{4} = 33$ s, so it takes 33 s to reach 132 ft/s. Therefore, taking $s(0) = 0$, we have

$s(t) = 2t^2$, $0 \le t \le 33$. So $s(33) = 2178$ ft. 15 minutes $= 15(60) = 900$ s, so for $33 < t \le 933$ we have

$v(t) = 132$ ft/s $\;\Rightarrow\; s(933) = 132(900) + 2178 = 120{,}978$ ft $= 22.9125$ mi.

(b) As in part (a), the train accelerates for 33 s and travels 2178 ft while doing so. Similarly, it decelerates for 33 s and travels

2178 ft at the end of its trip. During the remaining $900 - 66 = 834$ s it travels at 132 ft/s, so the distance traveled is

$132 \cdot 834 = 110{,}088$ ft. Thus, the total distance is $2178 + 110{,}088 + 2178 = 114{,}444$ ft $= 21.675$ mi.

(c) 45 mi $= 45(5280) = 237{,}600$ ft. Subtract $2(2178)$ to take care of the speeding up and slowing down, and we have

$233{,}244$ ft at 132 ft/s for a trip of $233{,}244/132 = 1767$ s at 90 mi/h. The total time is

$1767 + 2(33) = 1833$ s $= 30$ min 33 s $= 30.55$ min.

(d) $37.5(60) = 2250$ s. $2250 - 2(33) = 2184$ s at maximum speed. $2184(132) + 2(2178) = 292{,}644$ total feet or

$292{,}644/5280 = 55.425$ mi.

4   Review

CONCEPT CHECK

1. A function f has an **absolute maximum** at $x = c$ if $f(c)$ is the largest function value on the entire domain of f, whereas f has a **local maximum** at c if $f(c)$ is the largest function value when x is near c. See Figure 6 in Section 4.2.

2. (a) See Theorem 4.2.3.

   (b) See the Closed Interval Method before Example 6 in Section 4.2.

3. (a) See Theorem 4.2.4.

   (b) See Definition 4.2.5.

4. See the Mean Value Theorem in Section 4.3. Geometric interpretation—there is some point P on the graph of a function f [on the interval (a, b)] where the tangent line is parallel to the secant line that connects $(a, f(a))$ and $(b, f(b))$.

5. (a) See the I/D Test before Example 2 in Section 4.3.

   (b) A function f is concave upward on an interval I if f' is an increasing function on I (or, equivalently, the graph of f lies above all of its tangent lines on I).

   (c) See the Concavity Test before Example 4 in Section 4.3.

   (d) An inflection point is a point where a curve changes its direction of concavity. They can be found by determining the points at which the second derivative changes sign.

6. (a) See the First Derivative Test after Example 2 in Section 4.3.

   (b) See the Second Derivative Test before Example 4 in Section 4.3.

   (c) See the note before Example 5 in Section 4.3.

7. (a) See l'Hospital's Rule and the three notes that follow it in Section 4.5.

   (b) Write fg as $\dfrac{f}{1/g}$ or $\dfrac{g}{1/f}$.

   (c) Convert the difference into a quotient using a common denominator, rationalizing, factoring, or some other method.

   (d) Convert the power to a product by taking the natural logarithm of both sides of $y = f^g$ or by writing f^g as $e^{g \ln f}$.

8. Without calculus you could get misleading graphs that fail to show the most interesting features of a function. See Example 1 in Section 4.4.

9. (a) See Figure 3 in Section 4.7.

   (b) $x_2 = x_1 - \dfrac{f(x_1)}{f'(x_1)}$

   (c) $x_{n+1} = x_n - \dfrac{f(x_n)}{f'(x_n)}$

   (d) Newton's method is likely to fail or to work very slowly when $f'(x_1)$ is close to 0. It also fails when $f'(x_i)$ is undefined, such as with $f(x) = 1/x - 2$ and $x_1 = 1$.

10. (a) See the definition at the beginning of Section 4.8.

    (b) If F_1 and F_2 are both antiderivatives of f on an interval I, then they differ by a constant.

TRUE-FALSE QUIZ

1. False. For example, take $f(x) = x^3$, then $f'(x) = 3x^2$ and $f'(0) = 0$, but $f(0) = 0$ is not a maximum or minimum; $(0, 0)$ is an inflection point.

3. False. For example, $f(x) = x$ is continuous on $(0, 1)$ but attains neither a maximum nor a minimum value on $(0, 1)$. Don't confuse this with f being continuous on the *closed* interval $[a, b]$, which would make the statement true.

5. True. This is an example of part (b) of the I/D Test.

7. False. $f'(x) = g'(x) \Rightarrow f(x) = g(x) + C$. For example, if $f(x) = x + 2$ and $g(x) = x + 1$, then $f'(x) = g'(x) = 1$, but $f(x) \neq g(x)$.

9. True. The graph of one such function is sketched.

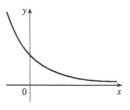

11. True. Let $x_1 < x_2$ where $x_1, x_2 \in I$. Then $f(x_1) < f(x_2)$ and $g(x_1) < g(x_2)$ [since f and g are increasing on I], so $(f + g)(x_1) = f(x_1) + g(x_1) < f(x_2) + g(x_2) = (f + g)(x_2)$.

13. False. Take $f(x) = x$ and $g(x) = x - 1$. Then both f and g are increasing on $(0, 1)$. But $f(x)\, g(x) = x(x - 1)$ is not increasing on $(0, 1)$.

15. True. Let $x_1, x_2 \in I$ and $x_1 < x_2$. Then $f(x_1) < f(x_2)$ [f is increasing] $\Rightarrow$ $\dfrac{1}{f(x_1)} > \dfrac{1}{f(x_2)}$ [f is positive] $\Rightarrow$

$g(x_1) > g(x_2) \Rightarrow g(x) = 1/f(x)$ is decreasing on I.

17. True. If f is periodic, then there is a number p such that $f(x + p) = f(p)$ for all x. Differentiating gives $f'(x) = f'(x + p) \cdot (x + p)' = f'(x + p) \cdot 1 = f'(x + p)$, so f' is periodic.

19. True. By the Mean Value Theorem, there exists a number c in $(0, 1)$ such that $f(1) - f(0) = f'(c)(1 - 0) = f'(c)$. Since $f'(c)$ is nonzero, $f(1) - f(0) \neq 0$, so $f(1) \neq f(0)$.

EXERCISES

1. $f(x) = x^3 - 6x^2 + 9x + 1$, $[2, 4]$. $f'(x) = 3x^2 - 12x + 9 = 3(x^2 - 4x + 3) = 3(x - 1)(x - 3)$. $f'(x) = 0 \Rightarrow$ $x = 1$ or $x = 3$, but 1 is not in the interval. $f'(x) > 0$ for $3 < x < 4$ and $f'(x) < 0$ for $2 < x < 3$, so $f(3) = 1$ is a local minimum value. Checking the endpoints, we find $f(2) = 3$ and $f(4) = 5$. Thus, $f(3) = 1$ is the absolute minimum value and $f(4) = 5$ is the absolute maximum value.

3. $f(x) = \dfrac{3x-4}{x^2+1}$, $[-2,2]$. $f'(x) = \dfrac{(x^2+1)(3) - (3x-4)(2x)}{(x^2+1)^2} = \dfrac{-(3x^2 - 8x - 3)}{(x^2+1)^2} = \dfrac{-(3x+1)(x-3)}{(x^2+1)^2}$.

$f'(x) = 0 \Rightarrow x = -\frac{1}{3}$ or $x = 3$, but 3 is not in the interval. $f'(x) > 0$ for $-\frac{1}{3} < x < 2$ and $f'(x) < 0$ for

$-2 < x < -\frac{1}{3}$, so $f\left(-\frac{1}{3}\right) = \frac{-5}{10/9} = -\frac{9}{2}$ is a local minimum value. Checking the endpoints, we find $f(-2) = -2$ and

$f(2) = \frac{2}{5}$. Thus, $f\left(-\frac{1}{3}\right) = -\frac{9}{2}$ is the absolute minimum value and $f(2) = \frac{2}{5}$ is the absolute maximum value.

5. $f(x) = x + \sin 2x$, $[0, \pi]$. $f'(x) = 1 + 2\cos 2x = 0 \Leftrightarrow \cos 2x = -\frac{1}{2} \Leftrightarrow 2x = \frac{2\pi}{3}$ or $\frac{4\pi}{3} \Leftrightarrow x = \frac{\pi}{3}$ or $\frac{2\pi}{3}$.

$f''(x) = -4\sin 2x$, so $f''\left(\frac{\pi}{3}\right) = -4\sin\frac{2\pi}{3} = -2\sqrt{3} < 0$ and $f''\left(\frac{2\pi}{3}\right) = -4\sin\frac{4\pi}{3} = 2\sqrt{3} > 0$, so

$f\left(\frac{\pi}{3}\right) = \frac{\pi}{3} + \frac{\sqrt{3}}{2} \approx 1.91$ is a local maximum value and $f\left(\frac{2\pi}{3}\right) = \frac{2\pi}{3} - \frac{\sqrt{3}}{2} \approx 1.23$ is a local minimum value. Also $f(0) = 0$

and $f(\pi) = \pi$, so $f(0) = 0$ is the absolute minimum value and $f(\pi) = \pi$ is the absolute maximum value.

7. (a) $f(x) = 2 - 2x - x^3$ is a polynomial, so there is no asymptote.

(b) $f'(x) = -2 - 3x^2 = -1(3x^2 + 2) < 0$, so f is decreasing on $\mathbb{R}$.

(c) No local extrema

(d) $f''(x) = -6x < 0$ on $(0, \infty)$ and $f''(x) > 0$ on $(-\infty, 0)$, so f is

CD on $(0, \infty)$ and CU on $(-\infty, 0)$. IP at $(0, 2)$

(e)

9. (a) $f(x) = x + \sqrt{1-x}$ has no asymptote.

(b) $f'(x) = 1 - 1/\left(2\sqrt{1-x}\right) = 0 \Leftrightarrow 2\sqrt{1-x} = 1 \Leftrightarrow$

$1 - x = \frac{1}{4} \Leftrightarrow x = \frac{3}{4}$ and $f'(x) > 0 \Leftrightarrow x < \frac{3}{4}$, so f is increasing

on $\left(-\infty, \frac{3}{4}\right)$ and decreasing on $\left(\frac{3}{4}, 1\right)$.

(c) $f\left(\frac{3}{4}\right) = \frac{3}{4} + \sqrt{1 - \frac{3}{4}} = \frac{3}{4} + \sqrt{\frac{1}{4}} = \frac{3}{4} + \frac{1}{2} = \frac{5}{4}$ is a local maximum.

(d) $f''(x) = -\dfrac{1}{4(1-x)^{3/2}} < 0$ on the domain of f, so f is CD on $(-\infty, 1)$. No IP

(e)

11. (a) $y = f(x) = \sin^2 x - 2\cos x$ has no asymptote.

(b) $y' = 2\sin x \cos x + 2\sin x = 2\sin x (\cos x + 1)$. $y' = 0 \Leftrightarrow \sin x = 0$ or $\cos x = -1 \Leftrightarrow x = n\pi$ or

$x = (2n+1)\pi$. $y' > 0$ when $\sin x > 0$, since $\cos x + 1 \geq 0$ for all x. Therefore, $y' > 0$ (and so f is increasing) on

$(2n\pi, (2n+1)\pi)$; $y' < 0$ (and so f is decreasing) on $((2n-1)\pi, 2n\pi)$ or equivalently, $((2n+1)\pi, (2n+2)\pi)$.

(c) Local maxima are $f((2n+1)\pi) = 2$; local minima are $f(2n\pi) = -2$.

(d) $y' = \sin 2x + 2\sin x \Rightarrow$

$y'' = 2\cos 2x + 2\cos x = 2(2\cos^2 x - 1) + 2\cos x$

$\quad = 4\cos^2 x + 2\cos x - 2 = 2(2\cos^2 x + \cos x - 1)$

$\quad = 2(2\cos x - 1)(\cos x + 1)$

$y'' = 0 \Leftrightarrow \cos x = \frac{1}{2}$ or $-1 \Leftrightarrow x = 2n\pi \pm \frac{\pi}{3}$ or $x = (2n+1)\pi$.

$y'' > 0$ (and so f is CU) on $\left(2n\pi - \frac{\pi}{3}, 2n\pi + \frac{\pi}{3}\right)$; $y'' \leq 0$ (and so f is

CD) on $\left(2n\pi + \frac{\pi}{3}, 2n\pi + \frac{5\pi}{3}\right)$. IPs at $\left(2n\pi \pm \frac{\pi}{3}, -\frac{1}{4}\right)$

(e)

13. (a) $\lim\limits_{x \to \pm\infty} \left(e^x + e^{-3x}\right) = \infty$, no asymptote.

(e)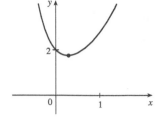

(b) $y = f(x) = e^x + e^{-3x}$ $\Rightarrow$ $f'(x) = e^x - 3e^{-3x} = e^{-3x}(e^{4x} - 3) > 0$ $\Leftrightarrow$

$e^{4x} > 3$ $\Leftrightarrow$ $4x > \ln 3$ $\Leftrightarrow$ $x > \frac{1}{4}\ln 3$, so f is increasing on $\left(\frac{1}{4}\ln 3, \infty\right)$

and decreasing on $\left(-\infty, \frac{1}{4}\ln 3\right)$.

(c) $f\left(\frac{1}{4}\ln 3\right) = 3^{1/4} + 3^{-3/4} \approx 1.75$ is a local and absolute minimum.

(d) $f''(x) = e^x + 9e^{-3x} > 0$, so f is CU on $(-\infty, \infty)$.   No IP

15. $f(x) = \dfrac{x^2 - 1}{x^3}$ $\Rightarrow$ $f'(x) = \dfrac{x^3(2x) - (x^2-1)3x^2}{x^6} = \dfrac{3 - x^2}{x^4}$ $\Rightarrow$

$f''(x) = \dfrac{x^4(-2x) - (3 - x^2)4x^3}{x^8} = \dfrac{2x^2 - 12}{x^5}$

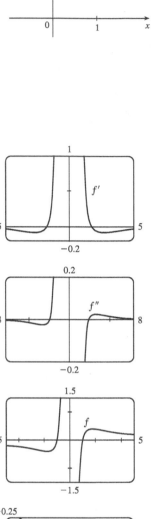

Estimates: From the graphs of f' and f'', it appears that f is increasing on

$(-1.73, 0)$ and $(0, 1.73)$ and decreasing on $(-\infty, -1.73)$ and $(1.73, \infty)$;

f has a local maximum of about $f(1.73) = 0.38$ and a local minimum of about

$f(-1.7) = -0.38$; f is CU on $(-2.45, 0)$ and $(2.45, \infty)$, and CD on

$(-\infty, -2.45)$ and $(0, 2.45)$; and f has inflection points at about

$(-2.45, -0.34)$ and $(2.45, 0.34)$.

Exact: Now $f'(x) = \dfrac{3 - x^2}{x^4}$ is positive for $0 < x^2 < 3$, that is, f is increasing

on $\left(-\sqrt{3}, 0\right)$ and $\left(0, \sqrt{3}\right)$; and $f'(x)$ is negative (and so f is decreasing) on

$\left(-\infty, -\sqrt{3}\right)$ and $\left(\sqrt{3}, \infty\right)$. $f'(x) = 0$ when $x = \pm\sqrt{3}$.

f' goes from positive to negative at $x = \sqrt{3}$, so f has a local maximum of

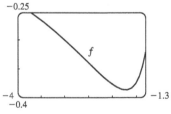

$f\left(\sqrt{3}\right) = \dfrac{\left(\sqrt{3}\right)^2 - 1}{\left(\sqrt{3}\right)^3} = \dfrac{2\sqrt{3}}{9}$; and since f is odd, we know that maxima on the

interval $(0, \infty)$ correspond to minima on $(-\infty, 0)$, so f has a local minimum of

$f\left(-\sqrt{3}\right) = -\dfrac{2\sqrt{3}}{9}$. Also, $f''(x) = \dfrac{2x^2 - 12}{x^5}$ is positive (so f is CU) on

$\left(-\sqrt{6}, 0\right)$ and $\left(\sqrt{6}, \infty\right)$, and negative (so f is CD) on $\left(-\infty, -\sqrt{6}\right)$ and

$\left(0, \sqrt{6}\right)$. There are IP at $\left(\sqrt{6}, \dfrac{5\sqrt{6}}{36}\right)$ and $\left(-\sqrt{6}, -\dfrac{5\sqrt{6}}{36}\right)$.

17. $f(x) = 3x^6 - 5x^5 + x^4 - 5x^3 - 2x^2 + 2 \Rightarrow f'(x) = 18x^5 - 25x^4 + 4x^3 - 15x^2 - 4x \Rightarrow$

$f''(x) = 90x^4 - 100x^3 + 12x^2 - 30x - 4$

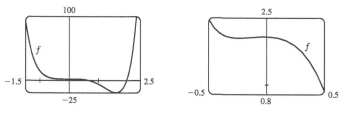

From the graphs of f' and f'', it appears that f is increasing on $(-0.23, 0)$ and $(1.62, \infty)$ and decreasing on $(-\infty, -0.23)$

and $(0, 1.62)$; f has a local maximum of $f(0) = 2$ and local minima of about $f(-0.23) = 1.96$ and $f(1.62) = -19.2$;

f is CU on $(-\infty, -0.12)$ and $(1.24, \infty)$ and CD on $(-0.12, 1.24)$; and f has inflection points at about $(-0.12, 1.98)$ and

$(1.24, -12.1)$.

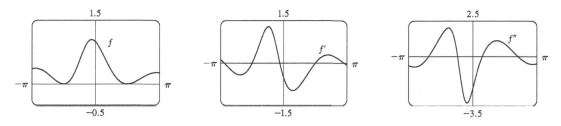

19.

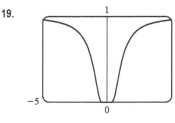

From the graph, we estimate the points of inflection to be about $(\pm 0.82, 0.22)$.

$f(x) = e^{-1/x^2} \Rightarrow f'(x) = 2x^{-3}e^{-1/x^2} \Rightarrow$

$f''(x) = 2[x^{-3}(2x^{-3})e^{-1/x^2} + e^{-1/x^2}(-3x^{-4})] = 2x^{-6}e^{-1/x^2}(2 - 3x^2)$.

This is 0 when $2 - 3x^2 = 0 \Leftrightarrow x = \pm\sqrt{\frac{2}{3}}$, so the inflection points

are $\left(\pm\sqrt{\frac{2}{3}}, e^{-3/2}\right)$.

21. $f(x) = \dfrac{\cos^2 x}{\sqrt{x^2 + x + 1}}, \ -\pi \le x \le \pi \Rightarrow f'(x) = -\dfrac{\cos x\,[(2x+1)\cos x + 4(x^2 + x + 1)\sin x]}{2(x^2 + x + 1)^{3/2}} \Rightarrow$

$f''(x) = -\dfrac{(8x^4 + 16x^3 + 16x^2 + 8x + 9)\cos^2 x - 8(x^2 + x + 1)(2x + 1)\sin x \, \cos x - 8(x^2 + x + 1)^2 \sin^2 x}{4(x^2 + x + 1)^{5/2}}$

$f(x) = 0 \Leftrightarrow x = \pm\frac{\pi}{2}; \quad f'(x) = 0 \Leftrightarrow x \approx -2.96, -1.57, -0.18, 1.57, 3.01;$

$f''(x) = 0 \Leftrightarrow x \approx -2.16, -0.75, 0.46, \text{ and } 2.21.$

The x-coordinates of the maximum points are the values at which f' changes from positive to negative, that is, -2.96,

-0.18, and 3.01. The x-coordinates of the minimum points are the values at which f' changes from negative to positive, that is, -1.57 and 1.57. The x-coordinates of the inflection points are the values at which f'' changes sign, that is, -2.16, -0.75, 0.46, and 2.21.

23. The family of functions $f(x) = \ln(\sin x + C)$ all have the same period and all have maximum values at $x = \frac{\pi}{2} + 2\pi n$. Since the domain of ln is $(0, \infty)$, f has a graph only if $\sin x + C > 0$ somewhere. Since $-1 \le \sin x \le 1$, this happens if $C > -1$, that is, f has no graph if $C \le -1$. Similarly, if $C > 1$, then $\sin x + C > 0$ and f is continuous on $(-\infty, \infty)$. As C increases, the graph of

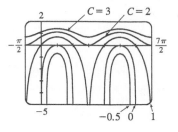

f is shifted vertically upward and flattens out. If $-1 < C \le 1$, f is defined where $\sin x + C > 0$ $\Leftrightarrow$ $\sin x > -C$ $\Leftrightarrow$ $\sin^{-1}(-C) < x < \pi - \sin^{-1}(-C)$. Since the period is 2π, the domain of f is $\big(2n\pi + \sin^{-1}(-C), (2n+1)\pi - \sin^{-1}(-C)\big)$, n an integer.

25. For $(1, 6)$ to be on the curve $y = x^3 + ax^2 + bx + 1$, we have that $6 = 1 + a + b + 1$ $\Rightarrow$ $b = 4 - a$. Now $y' = 3x^2 + 2ax + b$ and $y'' = 6x + 2a$. Also, for $(1, 6)$ to be an inflection point it must be true that $y''(1) = 6(1) + 2a = 0$ $\Rightarrow$ $a = -3$ $\Rightarrow$ $b = 4 - (-3) = 7$. Note that with $a = -3$, we have $y'' = 6x - 6 = 6(x - 1)$, so y'' changes sign at $x = 1$, proving that $(1, 6)$ is a point of inflection. [This does not follow from the fact that $y''(1) = 0$.]

27. This limit has the form $\frac{0}{0}$. $\displaystyle\lim_{x \to 0} \frac{\tan \pi x}{\ln(1 + x)} \overset{\text{H}}{=} \lim_{x \to 0} \frac{\pi \sec^2 \pi x}{1/(1 + x)} = \frac{\pi \cdot 1^2}{1/1} = \pi$

29. This limit has the form $\frac{0}{0}$. $\displaystyle\lim_{x \to 0} \frac{e^{4x} - 1 - 4x}{x^2} \overset{\text{H}}{=} \lim_{x \to 0} \frac{4e^{4x} - 4}{2x} \overset{\text{H}}{=} \lim_{x \to 0} \frac{16e^{4x}}{2} = \lim_{x \to 0} 8e^{4x} = 8 \cdot 1 = 8$

31. This limit has the form $\infty \cdot 0$. $\displaystyle\lim_{x \to \infty} x^3 e^{-x} = \lim_{x \to \infty} \frac{x^3}{e^x} \overset{\text{H}}{=} \lim_{x \to \infty} \frac{3x^2}{e^x} \overset{\text{H}}{=} \lim_{x \to \infty} \frac{6x}{e^x} \overset{\text{H}}{=} \lim_{x \to \infty} \frac{6}{e^x} = 0$

33. This limit has the form $\infty - \infty$.

$$\lim_{x \to 1^+} \left(\frac{x}{x - 1} - \frac{1}{\ln x} \right) = \lim_{x \to 1^+} \left(\frac{x \ln x - x + 1}{(x - 1) \ln x} \right) \overset{\text{H}}{=} \lim_{x \to 1^+} \frac{x \cdot (1/x) + \ln x - 1}{(x - 1) \cdot (1/x) + \ln x} = \lim_{x \to 1^+} \frac{\ln x}{1 - 1/x + \ln x}$$

$$\overset{\text{H}}{=} \lim_{x \to 1^+} \frac{1/x}{1/x^2 + 1/x} = \frac{1}{1 + 1} = \frac{1}{2}$$

35. We are given $d\theta/dt = -0.25$ rad/h. $\tan \theta = 400/x$ $\Rightarrow$ $x = 400 \cot \theta$ $\Rightarrow$ $\dfrac{dx}{dt} = -400 \csc^2 \theta \dfrac{d\theta}{dt}$. When $\theta = \frac{\pi}{6}$,

$\dfrac{dx}{dt} = -400(2)^2(-0.25) = 400$ ft/h.

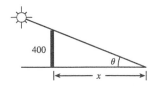

37. Given $dh/dt = 5$ and $dx/dt = 15$, find dz/dt. $z^2 = x^2 + h^2$ $\Rightarrow$

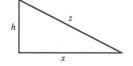

$$2z\frac{dz}{dt} = 2x\frac{dx}{dt} + 2h\frac{dh}{dt} \quad \Rightarrow \quad \frac{dz}{dt} = \frac{1}{z}(15x + 5h). \text{ When } t = 3,$$

$$h = 45 + 3(5) = 60 \text{ and } x = 15(3) = 45 \quad \Rightarrow \quad z = \sqrt{45^2 + 60^2} = 75,$$

$$\text{so } \frac{dz}{dt} = \frac{1}{75}[15(45) + 5(60)] = 13 \text{ ft/s}.$$

39. Call the two integers x and y. Then $x + 4y = 1000$, so $x = 1000 - 4y$. Their product is $P = xy = (1000 - 4y)y$, so our

problem is to maximize the function $P(y) = 1000y - 4y^2$, where $0 < y < 250$ and y is an integer. $P'(y) = 1000 - 8y$, so

$P'(y) = 0 \Leftrightarrow y = 125$. $P''(y) = -8 < 0$, so $P(125) = 62{,}500$ is an absolute maximum. Since the optimal y turned

out to be an integer, we have found the desired pair of numbers, namely $x = 1000 - 4(125) = 500$ and $y = 125$.

41.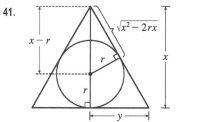

By similar triangles, $\dfrac{y}{x} = \dfrac{r}{\sqrt{x^2 - 2rx}}$, so the area of the triangle is

$$A(x) = \tfrac{1}{2}(2y)x = xy = \frac{rx^2}{\sqrt{x^2 - 2rx}} \quad \Rightarrow$$

$$A'(x) = \frac{2rx\sqrt{x^2 - 2rx} - rx^2(x - r)/\sqrt{x^2 - 2rx}}{x^2 - 2rx} = \frac{rx^2(x - 3r)}{(x^2 - 2rx)^{3/2}} = 0$$

when $x = 3r$.

$A'(x) < 0$ when $2r < x < 3r$, $A'(x) > 0$ when $x > 3r$. So $x = 3r$ gives a minimum and $A(3r) = \dfrac{r(9r^2)}{\sqrt{3}\,r} = 3\sqrt{3}\,r^2$.

43.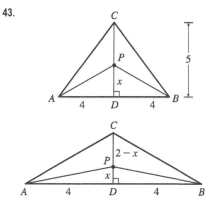

We minimize $L(x) = |PA| + |PB| + |PC| = 2\sqrt{x^2 + 16} + (5 - x)$,

$0 \le x \le 5$. $L'(x) = 2x/\sqrt{x^2 + 16} - 1 = 0 \Leftrightarrow 2x = \sqrt{x^2 + 16} \Leftrightarrow$

$4x^2 = x^2 + 16 \Leftrightarrow x = \frac{4}{\sqrt{3}}$. $L(0) = 13$, $L\left(\frac{4}{\sqrt{3}}\right) \approx 11.9$, $L(5) \approx 12.8$, so the

minimum occurs when $x = \frac{4}{\sqrt{3}} \approx 2.3$.

If $|CD| = 2$, $L(x)$ changes from $(5 - x)$ to $(2 - x)$ with $0 \le x \le 2$. But we still

get $L'(x) = 0 \Leftrightarrow x = \frac{4}{\sqrt{3}}$, which isn't in the interval $[0, 2]$. Now $L(0) = 10$

and $L(2) = 2\sqrt{20} = 4\sqrt{5} \approx 8.9$. The minimum occurs when $P = C$.

45. $v = K\sqrt{\dfrac{L}{C} + \dfrac{C}{L}} \Rightarrow \dfrac{dv}{dL} = \dfrac{K}{2\sqrt{(L/C) + (C/L)}}\left(\dfrac{1}{C} - \dfrac{C}{L^2}\right) = 0 \Leftrightarrow \dfrac{1}{C} = \dfrac{C}{L^2} \Leftrightarrow L^2 = C^2 \Leftrightarrow L = C.$

This gives the minimum velocity since $v' < 0$ for $0 < L < C$ and $v' > 0$ for $L > C$.

47. Let x denote the number of \$1 decreases in ticket price. Then the ticket price is $\$12 - \$1(x)$, and the average attendance is

$11{,}000 + 1000(x)$. Now the revenue per game is

$$R(x) = (\text{price per person}) \times (\text{number of people per game})$$

$$= (12 - x)(11{,}000 + 1000x) = -1000x^2 + 1000x + 132{,}000$$

for $0 \le x \le 4$ [since the seating capacity is 15,000] $\Rightarrow R'(x) = -2000x + 1000 = 0 \Leftrightarrow x = 0.5$. This is a maximum since $R''(x) = -2000 < 0$ for all x. Now we must check the value of $R(x) = (12 - x)(11{,}000 + 1000x)$ at $x = 0.5$ and at the endpoints of the domain to see which value of x gives the maximum value of R.

$R(0) = (12)(11{,}000) = 132{,}000$, $R(0.5) = (11.5)(11{,}500) = 132{,}250$, and $R(4) = (8)(15{,}000) = 120{,}000$. Thus, the maximum revenue of $132{,}250$ per game occurs when the average attendance is $11{,}500$ and the ticket price is 11.50.

49. $f(t) = \cos t + t - t^2 \;\Rightarrow\; f'(t) = -\sin t + 1 - 2t$. $f'(t)$ exists for all

t, so to find the maximum of f, we can examine the zeros of f'.

From the graph of f', we see that a good choice for t_1 is $t_1 = 0.3$.

Use $g(t) = -\sin t + 1 - 2t$ and $g'(t) = -\cos t - 2$ to obtain

$t_2 \approx 0.33535293$, $t_3 \approx 0.33541803 \approx t_4$. Since $f''(t) = -\cos t - 2 < 0$

for all t, $f(0.33541803) \approx 1.16718557$ is the absolute maximum.

51. $f(x) = e^x - (2/\sqrt{x}) = e^x - 2x^{-1/2} \;\Rightarrow\; F(x) = e^x - 2\dfrac{x^{-1/2+1}}{-1/2+1} + C = e^x - 2\dfrac{x^{1/2}}{1/2} + C = e^x - 4\sqrt{x} + C$

53. $f'(t) = 2t - 3\sin t \;\Rightarrow\; f(t) = t^2 + 3\cos t + C$.

$f(0) = 3 + C$ and $f(0) = 5 \;\Rightarrow\; C = 2$, so $f(t) = t^2 + 3\cos t + 2$.

55. $f''(x) = 1 - 6x + 48x^2 \;\Rightarrow\; f'(x) = x - 3x^2 + 16x^3 + C$. $f'(0) = C$ and $f'(0) = 2 \;\Rightarrow\; C = 2$, so

$f'(x) = x - 3x^2 + 16x^3 + 2$ and hence, $f(x) = \frac{1}{2}x^2 - x^3 + 4x^4 + 2x + D$.

$f(0) = D$ and $f(0) = 1 \;\Rightarrow\; D = 1$, so $f(x) = \frac{1}{2}x^2 - x^3 + 4x^4 + 2x + 1$.

57. $v(t) = s'(t) = 2t - \dfrac{1}{1+t^2} \;\Rightarrow\; s(t) = t^2 - \tan^{-1} t + C$.

$s(0) = 0 - 0 + C = C$ and $s(0) = 1 \;\Rightarrow\; C = 1$, so $s(t) = t^2 - \tan^{-1} t + 1$.

59. (a) Since f is 0 just to the left of the y-axis, we must have a minimum of F at the same place since we are increasing through

$(0,0)$ on F. There must be a local maximum to the left of $x = -3$, since f changes from positive to negative there.

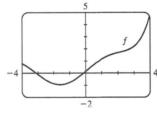

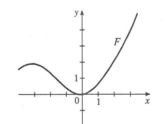

(b) $f(x) = 0.1e^x + \sin x \;\Rightarrow\;$

$F(x) = 0.1e^x - \cos x + C$. $F(0) = 0 \;\Rightarrow\;$

$0.1 - 1 + C = 0 \;\Rightarrow\; C = 0.9$, so

$F(x) = 0.1e^x - \cos x + 0.9$.

(c)

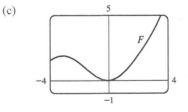

61. Choosing the positive direction to be upward, we have $a(t) = -9.8 \Rightarrow v(t) = -9.8t + v_0$, but $v(0) = 0 = v_0 \Rightarrow$

$v(t) = -9.8t = s'(t) \Rightarrow s(t) = -4.9t^2 + s_0$, but $s(0) = s_0 = 500 \Rightarrow s(t) = -4.9t^2 + 500$. When $s = 0$,

$-4.9t^2 + 500 = 0 \Rightarrow t_1 = \sqrt{\frac{500}{4.9}} \approx 10.1 \Rightarrow v(t_1) = -9.8\sqrt{\frac{500}{4.9}} \approx -98.995$ m/s. Since the canister has been

designed to withstand an impact velocity of 100 m/s, the canister will *not burst*.

63. (a)

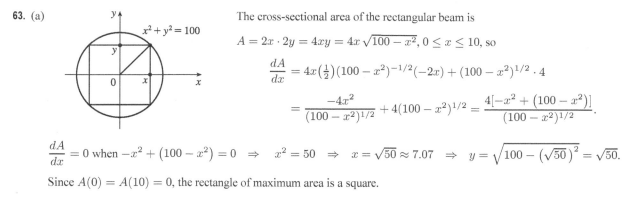

The cross-sectional area of the rectangular beam is

$A = 2x \cdot 2y = 4xy = 4x\sqrt{100 - x^2}, 0 \le x \le 10$, so

$\dfrac{dA}{dx} = 4x\left(\frac{1}{2}\right)(100 - x^2)^{-1/2}(-2x) + (100 - x^2)^{1/2} \cdot 4$

$= \dfrac{-4x^2}{(100 - x^2)^{1/2}} + 4(100 - x^2)^{1/2} = \dfrac{4[-x^2 + (100 - x^2)]}{(100 - x^2)^{1/2}}$.

$\dfrac{dA}{dx} = 0$ when $-x^2 + (100 - x^2) = 0 \Rightarrow x^2 = 50 \Rightarrow x = \sqrt{50} \approx 7.07 \Rightarrow y = \sqrt{100 - (\sqrt{50})^2} = \sqrt{50}$.

Since $A(0) = A(10) = 0$, the rectangle of maximum area is a square.

(b)

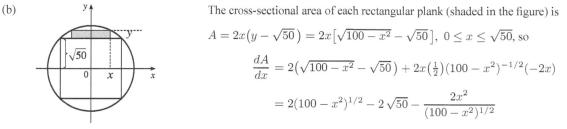

The cross-sectional area of each rectangular plank (shaded in the figure) is

$A = 2x(y - \sqrt{50}) = 2x[\sqrt{100 - x^2} - \sqrt{50}], 0 \le x \le \sqrt{50}$, so

$\dfrac{dA}{dx} = 2(\sqrt{100 - x^2} - \sqrt{50}) + 2x\left(\frac{1}{2}\right)(100 - x^2)^{-1/2}(-2x)$

$= 2(100 - x^2)^{1/2} - 2\sqrt{50} - \dfrac{2x^2}{(100 - x^2)^{1/2}}$

Set $\dfrac{dA}{dx} = 0$: $(100 - x^2) - \sqrt{50}(100 - x^2)^{1/2} - x^2 = 0 \Rightarrow 100 - 2x^2 = \sqrt{50}(100 - x^2)^{1/2} \Rightarrow$

$10{,}000 - 400x^2 + 4x^4 = 50(100 - x^2) \Rightarrow 4x^4 - 350x^2 + 5000 = 0 \Rightarrow 2x^4 - 175x^2 + 2500 = 0 \Rightarrow$

$x^2 = \dfrac{175 \pm \sqrt{10{,}625}}{4} \approx 69.52$ or $17.98 \Rightarrow x \approx 8.34$ or 4.24. But $8.34 > \sqrt{50}$, so $x_1 \approx 4.24 \Rightarrow$

$y - \sqrt{50} = \sqrt{100 - x_1^2} - \sqrt{50} \approx 1.99$. Each plank should have dimensions about $8\frac{1}{2}$ inches by 2 inches.

(c) From the figure in part (a), the width is $2x$ and the depth is $2y$, so the strength is

$S = k(2x)(2y)^2 = 8kxy^2 = 8kx(100 - x^2) = 800kx - 8kx^3, 0 \le x \le 10$. $dS/dx = 800k - 24kx^2 = 0$ when

$24kx^2 = 800k \Rightarrow x^2 = \frac{100}{3} \Rightarrow x = \frac{10}{\sqrt{3}} \Rightarrow y = \sqrt{\frac{200}{3}} = \frac{10\sqrt{2}}{\sqrt{3}} = \sqrt{2}\,x$. Since $S(0) = S(10) = 0$, the

maximum strength occurs when $x = \frac{10}{\sqrt{3}}$. The dimensions should be $\frac{20}{\sqrt{3}} \approx 11.55$ inches by $\frac{20\sqrt{2}}{\sqrt{3}} \approx 16.33$ inches.

65. (a) $I = \dfrac{k \cos \theta}{d^2} = \dfrac{k(h/d)}{d^2} = k \dfrac{h}{d^3} = k \dfrac{h}{\left(\sqrt{40^2 + h^2}\right)^3} = k \dfrac{h}{(1600 + h^2)^{3/2}} \quad \Rightarrow$

$$\frac{dI}{dh} = k \frac{(1600 + h^2)^{3/2} - h\frac{3}{2}(1600 + h^2)^{1/2} \cdot 2h}{[(1600 + h^2)^{3/2}]^2} = \frac{k(1600 + h^2)^{1/2}(1600 + h^2 - 3h^2)}{(1600 + h^2)^{3/2}}$$

$$= \frac{k(1600 - 2h^2)}{(1600 + h^2)^{5/2}} \qquad [k \text{ is the constant of proportionality}]$$

Set $dI/dh = 0$: $1600 - 2h^2 = 0 \quad \Rightarrow \quad h^2 = 800 \quad \Rightarrow \quad h = \sqrt{800} = 20\sqrt{2}$. By the First Derivative Test, I has a local

maximum at $h = 20\sqrt{2} \approx 28$ ft.

(b)

$\dfrac{dx}{dt} = 4$ ft/s

$I = \dfrac{k \cos \theta}{d^2} = \dfrac{k[(h-4)/d]}{d^2} = \dfrac{k(h-4)}{d^3}$

$\qquad = \dfrac{k(h-4)}{[(h-4)^2 + x^2]^{3/2}} = k(h-4)\left[(h-4)^2 + x^2\right]^{-3/2}$

$$\frac{dI}{dt} = \frac{dI}{dx} \cdot \frac{dx}{dt} = k(h-4)\left(-\tfrac{3}{2}\right)\left[(h-4)^2 + x^2\right]^{-5/2} \cdot 2x \cdot \frac{dx}{dt}$$

$$= k(h-4)(-3x)\left[(h-4)^2 + x^2\right]^{-5/2} \cdot 4 = \frac{-12xk(h-4)}{[(h-4)^2 + x^2]^{5/2}}$$

$$\frac{dI}{dt}\bigg|_{x=40} = -\frac{480k(h-4)}{[(h-4)^2 + 1600]^{5/2}}$$

1. Let $y = f(x) = e^{-x^2}$. The area of the rectangle under the curve from $-x$ to x is $A(x) = 2xe^{-x^2}$ where $x \geq 0$. We maximize

$A(x)$: $A'(x) = 2e^{-x^2} - 4x^2 e^{-x^2} = 2e^{-x^2}(1 - 2x^2) = 0 \Rightarrow x = \frac{1}{\sqrt{2}}$. This gives a maximum since $A'(x) > 0$

for $0 \leq x < \frac{1}{\sqrt{2}}$ and $A'(x) < 0$ for $x > \frac{1}{\sqrt{2}}$. We next determine the points of inflection of $f(x)$. Notice that

$f'(x) = -2xe^{-x^2} = -A(x)$. So $f''(x) = -A'(x)$ and hence, $f''(x) < 0$ for $-\frac{1}{\sqrt{2}} < x < \frac{1}{\sqrt{2}}$ and $f''(x) > 0$ for $x < -\frac{1}{\sqrt{2}}$

and $x > \frac{1}{\sqrt{2}}$. So $f(x)$ changes concavity at $x = \pm\frac{1}{\sqrt{2}}$, and the two vertices of the rectangle of largest area are at the inflection

points.

3. First, we recognize some symmetry in the inequality: $\dfrac{e^{x+y}}{xy} \geq e^2 \Leftrightarrow \dfrac{e^x}{x} \cdot \dfrac{e^y}{y} \geq e \cdot e$. This suggests that we need to show

that $\dfrac{e^x}{x} \geq e$ for $x > 0$. If we can do this, then the inequality $\dfrac{e^y}{y} \geq e$ is true, and the given inequality follows. $f(x) = \dfrac{e^x}{x} \Rightarrow$

$f'(x) = \dfrac{xe^x - e^x}{x^2} = \dfrac{e^x(x-1)}{x^2} = 0 \Rightarrow x = 1$. By the First Derivative Test, we have a minimum of $f(1) = e$, so

$e^x/x \geq e$ for all x.

5. $f(x)$ has the form $e^{g(x)}$, so it will have an absolute maximum (minimum) where g has an absolute maximum (minimum).

$g(x) = 10|x-2| - x^2 = \begin{cases} 10(x-2) - x^2 & \text{if } x - 2 > 0 \\ 10[-(x-2)] - x^2 & \text{if } x - 2 < 0 \end{cases} = \begin{cases} -x^2 + 10x - 20 & \text{if } x > 2 \\ -x^2 - 10x + 20 & \text{if } x < 2 \end{cases} \Rightarrow$

$g'(x) = \begin{cases} -2x + 10 & \text{if } x > 2 \\ -2x - 10 & \text{if } x < 2 \end{cases}$

$g'(x) = 0$ if $x = -5$ or $x = 5$, and $g'(2)$ does not exist, so the critical numbers of g are -5, 2, and 5. Since $g''(x) = -2$ for

all $x \neq 2$, g is concave downward on $(-\infty, 2)$ and $(2, \infty)$, and g will attain its absolute maximum at one of the critical

numbers. Since $g(-5) = 45$, $g(2) = -4$, and $g(5) = 5$, we see that $f(-5) = e^{45}$ is the absolute maximum value of f. Also,

$\lim\limits_{x \to \infty} g(x) = -\infty$, so $\lim\limits_{x \to \infty} f(x) = \lim\limits_{x \to \infty} e^{g(x)} = 0$. But $f(x) > 0$ for all x, so there is no absolute minimum value of f.

7. Differentiating $x^2 + xy + y^2 = 12$ implicitly with respect to x gives $2x + y + x\dfrac{dy}{dx} + 2y\dfrac{dy}{dx} = 0$, so $\dfrac{dy}{dx} = -\dfrac{2x+y}{x+2y}$.

At a highest or lowest point, $\dfrac{dy}{dx} = 0 \Leftrightarrow y = -2x$. Substituting $-2x$ for y in the original equation gives

$x^2 + x(-2x) + (-2x)^2 = 12$, so $3x^2 = 12$ and $x = \pm 2$. If $x = 2$, then $y = -2x = -4$, and if $x = -2$ then $y = 4$. Thus,

the highest and lowest points are $(-2, 4)$ and $(2, -4)$.

9. Let $L = \lim\limits_{x \to 0} \dfrac{ax^2 + \sin bx + \sin cx + \sin dx}{3x^2 + 5x^4 + 7x^6}$. Now L has the indeterminate form of type $\frac{0}{0}$, so we can apply l'Hospital's

Rule. $L = \lim\limits_{x \to 0} \dfrac{2ax + b \cos bx + c \cos cx + d \cos dx}{6x + 20x^3 + 42x^5}$. The denominator approaches 0 as $x \to 0$, so the numerator must also

approach 0 (because the limit exists). But the numerator approaches $0 + b + c + d$, so $b + c + d = 0$. Apply l'Hospital's Rule

again. $L = \lim\limits_{x \to 0} \dfrac{2a - b^2 \sin bx - c^2 \sin cx - d^2 \sin dx}{6 + 60x^2 + 210x^4} = \dfrac{2a - 0}{6 + 0} = \dfrac{2a}{6}$, which must equal 8.

$\dfrac{2a}{6} = 8 \;\Rightarrow\; a = 24$. Thus, $a + b + c + d = a + (b + c + d) = 24 + 0 = 24$.

11. $f(x) = \left(a^2 + a - 6\right) \cos 2x + (a - 2)x + \cos 1 \;\Rightarrow\; f'(x) = -\left(a^2 + a - 6\right) \sin 2x\,(2) + (a - 2)$. The derivative exists

for all x, so the only possible critical points will occur where $f'(x) = 0 \;\Leftrightarrow\; 2(a - 2)(a + 3) \sin 2x = a - 2 \;\Leftrightarrow\;$

either $a = 2$ or $2(a + 3) \sin 2x = 1$, with the latter implying that $\sin 2x = \dfrac{1}{2(a + 3)}$. Since the range of $\sin 2x$ is $[-1, 1]$,

this equation has no solution whenever either $\dfrac{1}{2(a + 3)} < -1$ or $\dfrac{1}{2(a + 3)} > 1$. Solving these inequalities, we get

$-\frac{7}{2} < a < -\frac{5}{2}$.

13.

$y = cx^3 + e^x \;\Rightarrow\; y' = 3cx^2 + e^x \;\Rightarrow\; y'' = 6cx + e^x$. The curve will have

inflection points when y'' changes sign. $y'' = 0 \;\Rightarrow\; -6cx = e^x$, so y'' will change

sign when the line $y = -6cx$ intersects the curve $y = e^x$ (but is not tangent to it).

Note that if $c = 0$, the curve is just $y = e^x$, which has no inflection point.

The first figure shows that for $c > 0$, $y = -6cx$ will intersect $y = e^x$ once, so

$y = cx^3 + e^x$ will have one inflection point.

The second figure shows that for $c < 0$, the line $y = -6cx$ can intersect the curve

$y = e^x$ in two points (two inflection points), be tangent to it (no inflection point), or not

intersect it (no inflection point). The tangent line at (a, e^a) has slope e^a, but from the

diagram we see that the slope is $\dfrac{e^a}{a}$. So $\dfrac{e^a}{a} = e^a \;\Rightarrow\; a = 1$. Thus, the slope is e.

The line $y = -6cx$ must have slope greater than e, so $-6c > e \;\Rightarrow\; c < -e/6$.

Therefore, the curve $y = cx^3 + e^x$ will have one inflection point if $c > 0$ and two inflection points if $c < -e/6$.

15. $y = x^2 \;\Rightarrow\; y' = 2x$, so the slope of the tangent line at $P(a, a^2)$ is $2a$ and the slope of the normal line is $-\dfrac{1}{2a}$ for $a \neq 0$.

An equation of the normal line is $y - a^2 = -\dfrac{1}{2a}(x - a)$. Substitute x^2 for y to find the x-coordinates of the two points of intersection of the parabola and the normal line. $x^2 - a^2 = -\dfrac{x}{2a} + \dfrac{1}{2} \Rightarrow 2ax^2 + x - 2a^3 - a = 0 \Rightarrow$

$$x = \frac{-1 \pm \sqrt{1 - 4(2a)(-2a^3 - a)}}{2(2a)} = \frac{-1 \pm \sqrt{1 + 16a^4 + 8a^2}}{4a} = \frac{-1 \pm \sqrt{(4a^2 + 1)^2}}{4a} = \frac{-1 \pm (4a^2 + 1)}{4a}$$

$$= \frac{4a^2}{4a} \quad \text{or} \quad \frac{-4a^2 - 2}{4a}, \text{ or equivalently, } a \text{ or } -a - \frac{1}{2a}.$$

So the point Q has coordinates $\left(-a - \dfrac{1}{2a}, \left(-a - \dfrac{1}{2a}\right)^2\right)$. The square S of the distance from P to Q is given by

$$S = \left(-a - \frac{1}{2a} - a\right)^2 + \left[\left(-a - \frac{1}{2a}\right)^2 - a^2\right]^2 = \left(-2a - \frac{1}{2a}\right)^2 + \left[\left(a^2 + 1 + \frac{1}{4a^2}\right) - a^2\right]^2$$

$$= \left(4a^2 + 2 + \frac{1}{4a^2}\right) + \left(1 + \frac{1}{4a^2}\right)^2 = \left(4a^2 + 2 + \frac{1}{4a^2}\right) + 1 + \frac{2}{4a^2} + \frac{1}{16a^4} = 4a^2 + 3 + \frac{3}{4a^2} + \frac{1}{16a^4}$$

$S' = 8a - \dfrac{6}{4a^3} - \dfrac{4}{16a^5} = 8a - \dfrac{3}{2a^3} - \dfrac{1}{4a^5} = \dfrac{32a^6 - 6a^2 - 1}{4a^5}$. The only real positive zero of the equation $S' = 0$ is

$a = \dfrac{1}{\sqrt{2}}$. Since $S'' = 8 + \dfrac{9}{2a^4} + \dfrac{5}{4a^6} > 0$, $a = \dfrac{1}{\sqrt{2}}$ corresponds to the shortest possible length of the line segment PQ.

17. $A = \left(x_1, x_1^2\right)$ and $B = \left(x_2, x_2^2\right)$, where x_1 and x_2 are the solutions of the quadratic equation $x^2 = mx + b$. Let $P = \left(x, x^2\right)$ and set $A_1 = (x_1, 0)$, $B_1 = (x_2, 0)$, and $P_1 = (x, 0)$. Let $f(x)$ denote the area of triangle PAB. Then $f(x)$ can be expressed in terms of the areas of three trapezoids as follows:

$$f(x) = \text{area}\,(A_1 ABB_1) - \text{area}\,(A_1 APP_1) - \text{area}\,(B_1 BPP_1)$$

$$= \tfrac{1}{2}\left(x_1^2 + x_2^2\right)(x_2 - x_1) - \tfrac{1}{2}\left(x_1^2 + x^2\right)(x - x_1) - \tfrac{1}{2}\left(x^2 + x_2^2\right)(x_2 - x)$$

After expanding and canceling terms, we get

$f(x) = \tfrac{1}{2}\left(x_2 x_1^2 - x_1 x_2^2 - xx_1^2 + x_1 x^2 - x_2 x^2 + xx_2^2\right) = \tfrac{1}{2}\left[x_1^2(x_2 - x) + x_2^2(x - x_1) + x^2(x_1 - x_2)\right]$

$f'(x) = \tfrac{1}{2}\left[-x_1^2 + x_2^2 + 2x(x_1 - x_2)\right].\quad f''(x) = \tfrac{1}{2}[2(x_1 - x_2)] = x_1 - x_2 < 0$ since $x_2 > x_1$.

$f'(x) = 0 \Rightarrow 2x(x_1 - x_2) = x_1^2 - x_2^2 \Rightarrow x_P = \tfrac{1}{2}(x_1 + x_2)$.

$$f(x_P) = \tfrac{1}{2}\left(x_1^2\left[\tfrac{1}{2}(x_2 - x_1)\right] + x_2^2\left[\tfrac{1}{2}(x_2 - x_1)\right] + \tfrac{1}{4}(x_1 + x_2)^2(x_1 - x_2)\right)$$

$$= \tfrac{1}{2}\left[\tfrac{1}{2}(x_2 - x_1)\left(x_1^2 + x_2^2\right) - \tfrac{1}{4}(x_2 - x_1)(x_1 + x_2)^2\right] = \tfrac{1}{8}(x_2 - x_1)\left[2\left(x_1^2 + x_2^2\right) - \left(x_1^2 + 2x_1 x_2 + x_2^2\right)\right]$$

$$= \tfrac{1}{8}(x_2 - x_1)\left(x_1^2 - 2x_1 x_2 + x_2^2\right) = \tfrac{1}{8}(x_2 - x_1)(x_1 - x_2)^2 = \tfrac{1}{8}(x_2 - x_1)(x_2 - x_1)^2 = \tfrac{1}{8}(x_2 - x_1)^3$$

To put this in terms of m and b, we solve the system $y = x_1^2$ and $y = mx_1 + b$, giving us $x_1^2 - mx_1 - b = 0 \Rightarrow$

$x_1 = \tfrac{1}{2}\left(m - \sqrt{m^2 + 4b}\right)$. Similarly, $x_2 = \tfrac{1}{2}\left(m + \sqrt{m^2 + 4b}\right)$. The area is then $\tfrac{1}{8}(x_2 - x_1)^3 = \tfrac{1}{8}\left(\sqrt{m^2 + 4b}\right)^3$,

and is attained at the point $P\left(x_P, x_P^2\right) = P\left(\tfrac{1}{2}m, \tfrac{1}{4}m^2\right)$.

Note. Another way to get an expression for $f(x)$ is to use the formula for an area of a triangle in terms of the coordinates of the vertices: $f(x) = \tfrac{1}{2}\left[\left(x_2 x_1^2 - x_1 x_2^2\right) + \left(x_1 x^2 - xx_1^2\right) + \left(xx_2^2 - x_2 x^2\right)\right]$.

19. Let $s_A(t)$ and $s_B(t)$ be the position functions for cars A and B and let $f(t) = s_A(t) - s_B(t)$. Since A passed B twice (B passed A once), there must be three values of t such that $f(t) = 0$. Let these times be denoted t_1, t_2, and t_3. By the Mean Value Theorem, we know that for some number c_1 in (t_1, t_2), $f'(c_1) = \dfrac{f(t_2) - f(t_1)}{t_2 - t_1}$, but $f(t_2) - f(t_1) = 0$,

so $f'(c_1) = 0 \iff s'_A(c_1) - s'_B(c_1) = 0 \iff v_A(c_1) - v_B(c_1) = 0 \implies v_A(c_1) = v_B(c_1)$.

By a similar argument, there exists some number c_2 in (t_2, t_3) such that $v_A(c_2) = v_B(c_2)$. Now let $g(t) = v_A(t) - v_B(t)$ and apply the Mean Value Theorem on $[c_1, c_2]$ with $c_1 < c < c_2$. $g'(c) = \dfrac{g(c_2) - g(c_1)}{c_2 - c_1}$,

but $g(c_2) = g(c_1) = 0$, so $g'(c) = 0 \implies v'_A(c) - v'_B(c) = 0 \implies a_A(c) - a_B(c) = 0 \implies a_A(c) = a_B(c)$; that is, A and B had equal accelerations at $t = c$.

21.

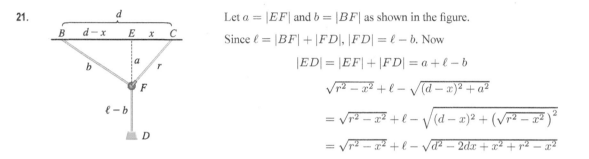

Let $a = |EF|$ and $b = |BF|$ as shown in the figure. Since $\ell = |BF| + |FD|$, $|FD| = \ell - b$. Now

$$|ED| = |EF| + |FD| = a + \ell - b$$

$$\sqrt{r^2 - x^2} + \ell - \sqrt{(d-x)^2 + a^2}$$

$$= \sqrt{r^2 - x^2} + \ell - \sqrt{(d-x)^2 + \left(\sqrt{r^2 - x^2}\right)^2}$$

$$= \sqrt{r^2 - x^2} + \ell - \sqrt{d^2 - 2dx + x^2 + r^2 - x^2}$$

Let $f(x) = \sqrt{r^2 - x^2} + \ell - \sqrt{d^2 + r^2 - 2dx}$.

$$f'(x) = \tfrac{1}{2}\left(r^2 - x^2\right)^{-1/2}(-2x) - \tfrac{1}{2}\left(d^2 + r^2 - 2dx\right)^{-1/2}(-2d) = \frac{-x}{\sqrt{r^2 - x^2}} + \frac{d}{\sqrt{d^2 + r^2 - 2dx}}.$$

$$f'(x) = 0 \implies \frac{x}{\sqrt{r^2 - x^2}} = \frac{d}{\sqrt{d^2 + r^2 - 2dx}} \implies \frac{x^2}{r^2 - x^2} = \frac{d^2}{d^2 + r^2 - 2dx} \implies$$

$$d^2 x^2 + r^2 x^2 - 2dx^3 = d^2 r^2 - d^2 x^2 \implies 0 = 2dx^3 - 2d^2 x^2 - r^2 x^2 + d^2 r^2 \implies$$

$$0 = 2dx^2(x - d) - r^2\left(x^2 - d^2\right) \implies 0 = 2dx^2(x - d) - r^2(x + d)(x - d) \implies 0 = (x - d)\left[2dx^2 - r^2(x + d)\right]$$

But $d > r > x$, so $x \neq d$. Thus, we solve $2dx^2 - r^2 x - dr^2 = 0$ for x:

$$x = \frac{-(-r^2) \pm \sqrt{(-r^2)^2 - 4(2d)(-dr^2)}}{2(2d)} = \frac{r^2 \pm \sqrt{r^4 + 8d^2 r^2}}{4d}.$$ Because $\sqrt{r^4 + 8d^2 r^2} > r^2$, the "negative" can be

discarded. Thus, $x = \dfrac{r^2 + \sqrt{r^2}\sqrt{r^2 + 8d^2}}{4d} = \dfrac{r^2 + r\sqrt{r^2 + 8d^2}}{4d} \quad [r > 0] \quad = \dfrac{r}{4d}\left(r + \sqrt{r^2 + 8d^2}\right)$. The maximum

value of $|ED|$ occurs at this value of x.

23.

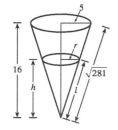

By similar triangles, $\dfrac{r}{5} = \dfrac{h}{16} \;\Rightarrow\; r = \dfrac{5h}{16}$. The volume of the cone is

$$V = \tfrac{1}{3}\pi r^2 h = \tfrac{1}{3}\pi \left(\dfrac{5h}{16}\right)^2 h = \dfrac{25\pi}{768}h^3, \text{ so } \dfrac{dV}{dt} = \dfrac{25\pi}{256}h^2\dfrac{dh}{dt}. \text{ Now the rate of}$$

change of the volume is also equal to the difference of what is being added

($2 \text{ cm}^3/\text{min}$) and what is oozing out ($k\pi r l$, where $\pi r l$ is the area of the cone and k

is a proportionality constant). Thus, $\dfrac{dV}{dt} = 2 - k\pi r l$.

Equating the two expressions for $\dfrac{dV}{dt}$ and substituting $h = 10$, $\dfrac{dh}{dt} = -0.3$, $r = \dfrac{5(10)}{16} = \dfrac{25}{8}$, and $\dfrac{l}{\sqrt{281}} = \dfrac{10}{16} \;\Leftrightarrow$

$l = \dfrac{5}{8}\sqrt{281}$, we get $\dfrac{25\pi}{256}(10)^2(-0.3) = 2 - k\pi\dfrac{25}{8}\cdot\dfrac{5}{8}\sqrt{281} \;\Leftrightarrow\; \dfrac{125k\pi\sqrt{281}}{64} = 2 + \dfrac{750\pi}{256}.$ Solving for k gives us

$k = \dfrac{256 + 375\pi}{250\pi\sqrt{281}}$. To maintain a certain height, the rate of oozing, $k\pi r l$, must equal the rate of the liquid being poured in;

that is, $\dfrac{dV}{dt} = 0$. Thus, the rate at which we should pour the liquid into the container is

$$k\pi r l = \dfrac{256 + 375\pi}{250\pi\sqrt{281}} \cdot \pi \cdot \dfrac{25}{8} \cdot \dfrac{5\sqrt{281}}{8} = \dfrac{256 + 375\pi}{128} \approx 11.204 \text{ cm}^3/\text{min}$$

5 ☐ INTEGRALS

5.1 Areas and Distances

1. (a) Since f is *increasing*, we can obtain a *lower* estimate by using *left* endpoints. We are instructed to use four rectangles, so $n = 4$.

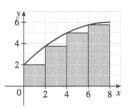

$$L_4 = \sum_{i=1}^{4} f(x_{i-1})\,\Delta x \quad \left[\Delta x = \frac{b-a}{n} = \frac{8-0}{4} = 2\right]$$

$$= f(x_0) \cdot 2 + f(x_1) \cdot 2 + f(x_2) \cdot 2 + f(x_3) \cdot 2$$

$$= 2[f(0) + f(2) + f(4) + f(6)]$$

$$= 2(2 + 3.75 + 5 + 5.75) = 2(16.5) = 33$$

Since f is *increasing*, we can obtain a *upper* estimate by using *right* endpoints.

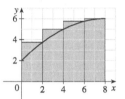

$$R_4 = \sum_{i=1}^{4} f(x_i)\,\Delta x$$

$$= f(x_1) \cdot 2 + f(x_2) \cdot 2 + f(x_3) \cdot 2 + f(x_4) \cdot 2$$

$$= 2[f(2) + f(4) + f(6) + f(8)]$$

$$= 2(3.75 + 5 + 5.75 + 6) = 2(20.5) = 41$$

Comparing R_4 to L_4, we see that we have added the area of the rightmost upper rectangle, $f(8) \cdot 2$, to the sum and subtracted the area of the leftmost lower rectangle, $f(0) \cdot 2$, from the sum.

(b) $$L_8 = \sum_{i=1}^{8} f(x_{i-1})\Delta x \quad \left[\Delta x = \frac{8-0}{8} = 1\right]$$

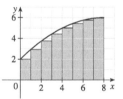

$$= 1[f(x_0) + f(x_1) + \cdots + f(x_7)]$$

$$= f(0) + f(1) + \cdots + f(7)$$

$$\approx 2 + 2.9 + 3.75 + 4.4 + 5 + 5.4 + 5.75 + 5.9$$

$$= 35.1$$

$$R_8 = \sum_{i=1}^{8} f(x_i)\Delta x = f(1) + f(2) + \cdots + f(8)$$

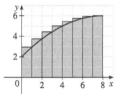

$$= L_8 + 1 \cdot f(8) - 1 \cdot f(0) \quad \begin{bmatrix} \text{add rightmost upper rectangle,} \\ \text{subtract leftmost lower rectangle} \end{bmatrix}$$

$$= 35.1 + 6 - 2 = 39.1$$

3. (a) $$R_4 = \sum_{i=1}^{4} f(x_i)\,\Delta x \quad \left[\Delta x = \frac{\pi/2 - 0}{4} = \frac{\pi}{8}\right] = \left[\sum_{i=1}^{4} f(x_i)\right]\Delta x$$

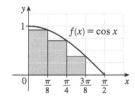

$$= [f(x_1) + f(x_2) + f(x_3) + f(x_4)]\,\Delta x$$

$$= \left[\cos\frac{\pi}{8} + \cos\frac{2\pi}{8} + \cos\frac{3\pi}{8} + \cos\frac{4\pi}{8}\right]\frac{\pi}{8}$$

$$\approx (0.9239 + 0.7071 + 0.3827 + 0)\frac{\pi}{8} \approx 0.7908$$

Since f is *decreasing* on $[0, \pi/2]$, an *underestimate* is obtained by using the *right* endpoint approximation, R_4.

205

(b) $L_4 = \sum_{i=1}^{4} f(x_{i-1})\,\Delta x = \left[\sum_{i=1}^{4} f(x_{i-1})\right]\Delta x$

$\qquad = [f(x_0) + f(x_1) + f(x_2) + f(x_3)]\,\Delta x$

$\qquad = \left[\cos 0 + \cos\frac{\pi}{8} + \cos\frac{2\pi}{8} + \cos\frac{3\pi}{8}\right]\frac{\pi}{8}$

$\qquad \approx (1 + 0.9239 + 0.7071 + 0.3827)\frac{\pi}{8} \approx 1.1835$

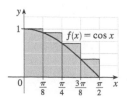

L_4 is an overestimate. Alternatively, we could just add the area of the leftmost upper rectangle and subtract the area of the rightmost lower rectangle; that is, $L_4 = R_4 + f(0)\cdot\frac{\pi}{8} - f\left(\frac{\pi}{2}\right)\cdot\frac{\pi}{8}$.

5. (a) $f(x) = 1 + x^2$ and $\Delta x = \dfrac{2-(-1)}{3} = 1 \quad\Rightarrow$

$\qquad R_3 = 1\cdot f(0) + 1\cdot f(1) + 1\cdot f(2) = 1\cdot 1 + 1\cdot 2 + 1\cdot 5 = 8.$

$\qquad \Delta x = \dfrac{2-(-1)}{6} = 0.5 \quad\Rightarrow$

$\qquad R_6 = 0.5[f(-0.5) + f(0) + f(0.5) + f(1) + f(1.5) + f(2)]$

$\qquad\quad = 0.5(1.25 + 1 + 1.25 + 2 + 3.25 + 5)$

$\qquad\quad = 0.5(13.75) = 6.875$

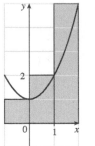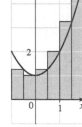

(b) $L_3 = 1\cdot f(-1) + 1\cdot f(0) + 1\cdot f(1) = 1\cdot 2 + 1\cdot 1 + 1\cdot 2 = 5$

$\qquad L_6 = 0.5[f(-1) + f(-0.5) + f(0) + f(0.5) + f(1) + f(1.5)]$

$\qquad\quad = 0.5(2 + 1.25 + 1 + 1.25 + 2 + 3.25)$

$\qquad\quad = 0.5(10.75) = 5.375$

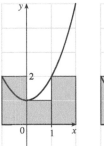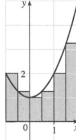

(c) $M_3 = 1\cdot f(-0.5) + 1\cdot f(0.5) + 1\cdot f(1.5)$

$\qquad\quad = 1\cdot 1.25 + 1\cdot 1.25 + 1\cdot 3.25 = 5.75$

$\qquad M_6 = 0.5[f(-0.75) + f(-0.25) + f(0.25)$

$\qquad\qquad\quad + f(0.75) + f(1.25) + f(1.75)]$

$\qquad\quad = 0.5(1.5625 + 1.0625 + 1.0625 + 1.5625 + 2.5625 + 4.0625)$

$\qquad\quad = 0.5(11.875) = 5.9375$

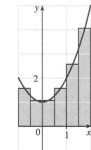

(d) M_6 appears to be the best estimate.

7. Here is one possible algorithm (ordered sequence of operations) for calculating the sums:

1 Let SUM = 0, X_MIN = 0, X_MAX = 1, N = 10 (depending on which sum we are calculating),

DELTA_X = (X_MAX - X_MIN)/N, and RIGHT_ENDPOINT = X_MIN + DELTA_X.

2 Repeat steps 2a, 2b in sequence until RIGHT_ENDPOINT > X_MAX.

2a Add (RIGHT_ENDPOINT)^4 to SUM.

Add DELTA_X to RIGHT_ENDPOINT.

At the end of this procedure, (DELTA_X)·(SUM) is equal to the answer we are looking for. We find that

$$R_{10} = \frac{1}{10} \sum_{i=1}^{10} \left(\frac{i}{10} \right)^4 \approx 0.2533, \ R_{30} = \frac{1}{30} \sum_{i=1}^{30} \left(\frac{i}{30} \right)^4 \approx 0.2170, \ R_{50} = \frac{1}{50} \sum_{i=1}^{50} \left(\frac{i}{50} \right)^4 \approx 0.2101, \text{ and}$$

$$R_{100} = \frac{1}{100} \sum_{i=1}^{100} \left(\frac{i}{100} \right)^4 \approx 0.2050.$$ It appears that the exact area is 0.2.   The following display shows the program

SUMRIGHT and its output from a TI-83 Plus calculator. To generalize the program, we have input (rather than assign)

values for Xmin, Xmax, and N. Also, the function, x^4, is assigned to Y_1, enabling us to evaluate any right sum merely

by changing Y_1 and running the program.

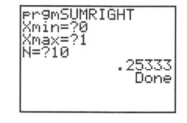

9. In Maple, we have to perform a number of steps before getting a numerical answer. After loading the student package

[command: `with(student);`] we use the command

`left_sum:=leftsum(1/(x^2+1),x=0..1,10 [or 30, or 50]);` which gives us the expression in summation

notation. To get a numerical approximation to the sum, we use `evalf(left_sum);`. Mathematica does not have a special

command for these sums, so we must type them in manually. For example, the first left sum is given by

`(1/10)*Sum[1/(((i-1)/10)^2+1)],{i,1,10}]`, and we use the N command on the resulting output to get a

numerical approximation.

In Derive, we use the `LEFT_RIEMANN` command to get the left sums, but must define the right sums ourselves.

(We can define a new function using `LEFT_RIEMANN` with k ranging from 1 to n instead of from 0 to $n - 1$.)

(a) With $f(x) = \dfrac{1}{x^2 + 1}$, $0 \le x \le 1$, the left sums are of the form $L_n = \dfrac{1}{n} \sum_{i=1}^{n} \dfrac{1}{\left(\frac{i-1}{n} \right)^2 + 1}$. Specifically, $L_{10} \approx 0.8100$,

$L_{30} \approx 0.7937$, and $L_{50} \approx 0.7904$. The right sums are of the form $R_n = \dfrac{1}{n} \sum_{i=1}^{n} \dfrac{1}{\left(\frac{i}{n} \right)^2 + 1}$. Specifically, $R_{10} \approx 0.7600$,

$R_{30} \approx 0.7770$, and $R_{50} \approx 0.7804$.

(b) In Maple, we use the `leftbox` (with the same arguments as `left_sum`) and `rightbox` commands to generate the graphs.

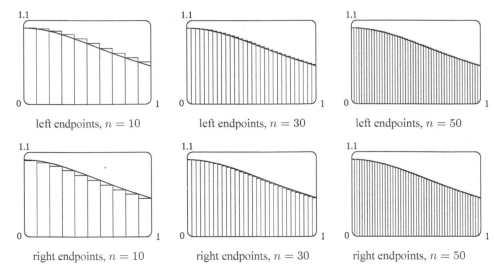

left endpoints, $n = 10$ left endpoints, $n = 30$ left endpoints, $n = 50$

right endpoints, $n = 10$ right endpoints, $n = 30$ right endpoints, $n = 50$

(c) We know that since $y = 1/(x^2 + 1)$ is a decreasing function on $(0, 1)$, all of the left sums are larger than the actual area, and all of the right sums are smaller than the actual area. Since the left sum with $n = 50$ is about $0.7904 < 0.791$ and the right sum with $n = 50$ is about $0.7804 > 0.780$, we conclude that $0.780 < R_{50} < $ exact area $< L_{50} < 0.791$, so the exact area is between 0.780 and 0.791.

11. Since v is an increasing function, L_6 will give us a lower estimate and R_6 will give us an upper estimate.

$$L_6 = (0 \text{ ft/s})(0.5 \text{ s}) + (6.2)(0.5) + (10.8)(0.5) + (14.9)(0.5) + (18.1)(0.5) + (19.4)(0.5) = 0.5(69.4) = 34.7 \text{ ft}$$

$$R_6 = 0.5(6.2 + 10.8 + 14.9 + 18.1 + 19.4 + 20.2) = 0.5(89.6) = 44.8 \text{ ft}$$

13. Lower estimate for oil leakage: $R_5 = (7.6 + 6.8 + 6.2 + 5.7 + 5.3)(2) = (31.6)(2) = 63.2 \text{ L}.$

Upper estimate for oil leakage: $L_5 = (8.7 + 7.6 + 6.8 + 6.2 + 5.7)(2) = (35)(2) = 70 \text{ L}.$

15. For a decreasing function, using left endpoints gives us an overestimate and using right endpoints results in an underestimate. We will use M_6 to get an estimate. $\Delta t = 1$, so

$$M_6 = 1[v(0.5) + v(1.5) + v(2.5) + v(3.5) + v(4.5) + v(5.5)] \approx 55 + 40 + 28 + 18 + 10 + 4 = 155 \text{ ft}$$

For a very rough check on the above calculation, we can draw a line from $(0, 70)$ to $(6, 0)$ and calculate the area of the triangle: $\frac{1}{2}(70)(6) = 210$. This is clearly an overestimate, so our midpoint estimate of 155 is reasonable.

17. $f(x) = \dfrac{2x}{x^2 + 1}$, $1 \le x \le 3$. $\Delta x = (3 - 1)/n = 2/n$ and $x_i = 1 + i\Delta x = 1 + 2i/n$.

$$A = \lim_{n \to \infty} R_n = \lim_{n \to \infty} \sum_{i=1}^{n} f(x_i)\Delta x = \lim_{n \to \infty} \sum_{i=1}^{n} \frac{2(1 + 2i/n)}{(1 + 2i/n)^2 + 1} \cdot \frac{2}{n}.$$

19. $f(x) = x \cos x$, $0 \le x \le \frac{\pi}{2}$. $\Delta x = (\frac{\pi}{2} - 0)/n = \frac{\pi}{2}/n$ and $x_i = 0 + i\,\Delta x = \frac{\pi}{2}i/n$.

$$A = \lim_{n \to \infty} R_n = \lim_{n \to \infty} \sum_{i=1}^{n} f(x_i)\,\Delta x = \lim_{n \to \infty} \sum_{i=1}^{n} \frac{i\pi}{2n} \cos\left(\frac{i\pi}{2n}\right) \cdot \frac{\pi}{2n}.$$

21. $\displaystyle\lim_{n \to \infty} \sum_{i=1}^{n} \frac{\pi}{4n} \tan \frac{i\pi}{4n}$ can be interpreted as the area of the region lying under the graph of $y = \tan x$ on the interval $\left[0, \frac{\pi}{4}\right]$,

since for $y = \tan x$ on $\left[0, \frac{\pi}{4}\right]$ with $\Delta x = \dfrac{\pi/4 - 0}{n} = \dfrac{\pi}{4n}$, $x_i = 0 + i\,\Delta x = \dfrac{i\pi}{4n}$, and $x_i^* = x_i$, the expression for the area is

$A = \displaystyle\lim_{n \to \infty} \sum_{i=1}^{n} f(x_i^*)\,\Delta x = \lim_{n \to \infty} \sum_{i=1}^{n} \tan\left(\frac{i\pi}{4n}\right) \frac{\pi}{4n}$. Note that this answer is not unique, since the expression for the area is

the same for the function $y = \tan(x - k\pi)$ on the interval $\left[k\pi, k\pi + \frac{\pi}{4}\right]$, where k is any integer.

23. (a) Since f is an increasing function, L_n is an underestimate of A and R_n is an overestimate of A. Thus, A, L_n, and R_n are

related by the inequality $L_n < A < R_n$.

(b) $R_n = f(x_1)\Delta x + f(x_2)\Delta x + \cdots + f(x_n)\Delta x$

$\qquad L_n = f(x_0)\Delta x + f(x_1)\Delta x + \cdots + f(x_{n-1})\Delta x$

$\qquad R_n - L_n = f(x_n)\Delta x - f(x_0)\Delta x = \Delta x[f(x_n) - f(x_0)] = \dfrac{b-a}{n}[f(b) - f(a)]$

(c) $A > L_n$, so $R_n - A < R_n - L_n$; that is,

$$R_n - A < \frac{b-a}{n}[f(b) - f(a)]$$

25. (a) $y = f(x) = x^5$. $\Delta x = \dfrac{2-0}{n} = \dfrac{2}{n}$ and $x_i = 0 + i\,\Delta x = \dfrac{2i}{n}$.

$$A = \lim_{n \to \infty} R_n = \lim_{n \to \infty} \sum_{i=1}^{n} f(x_i)\,\Delta x = \lim_{n \to \infty} \sum_{i=1}^{n} \left(\frac{2i}{n}\right)^5 \cdot \frac{2}{n} = \lim_{n \to \infty} \sum_{i=1}^{n} \frac{32i^5}{n^5} \cdot \frac{2}{n} = \lim_{n \to \infty} \frac{64}{n^6} \sum_{i=1}^{n} i^5.$$

(b) $\displaystyle\sum_{i=1}^{n} i^5 \overset{\text{CAS}}{=} \frac{n^2(n+1)^2(2n^2 + 2n - 1)}{12}$

(c) $\displaystyle\lim_{n \to \infty} \frac{64}{n^6} \cdot \frac{n^2(n+1)^2(2n^2 + 2n - 1)}{12} = \frac{64}{12} \lim_{n \to \infty} \frac{(n^2 + 2n + 1)(2n^2 + 2n - 1)}{n^2 \cdot n^2}$

$$= \frac{16}{3} \lim_{n \to \infty} \left(1 + \frac{2}{n} + \frac{1}{n^2}\right)\left(2 + \frac{2}{n} - \frac{1}{n^2}\right) = \frac{16}{3} \cdot 1 \cdot 2 = \frac{32}{3}$$

27. $y = f(x) = \cos x$. $\Delta x = \dfrac{b-0}{n} = \dfrac{b}{n}$ and $x_i = 0 + i\,\Delta x = \dfrac{bi}{n}$.

$$A = \lim_{n \to \infty} R_n = \lim_{n \to \infty} \sum_{i=1}^{n} f(x_i)\,\Delta x = \lim_{n \to \infty} \sum_{i=1}^{n} \cos\left(\frac{bi}{n}\right) \cdot \frac{b}{n} \overset{\text{CAS}}{=} \lim_{n \to \infty} \left[\frac{b\sin\left(b\left(\frac{1}{2n} + 1\right)\right)}{2n\sin\left(\frac{b}{2n}\right)} - \frac{b}{2n}\right] \overset{\text{CAS}}{=} \sin b$$

If $b = \frac{\pi}{2}$, then $A = \sin\frac{\pi}{2} = 1$.

5.2   The Definite Integral

1. $f(x) = 3 - \frac{1}{2}x$, $2 \le x \le 14$. $\Delta x = \dfrac{b-a}{n} = \dfrac{14-2}{6} = 2$.

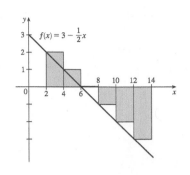

Since we are using left endpoints, $x_i^* = x_{i-1}$.

$L_6 = \displaystyle\sum_{i=1}^{6} f(x_{i-1})\,\Delta x$

$ = (\Delta x)\,[f(x_0) + f(x_1) + f(x_2) + f(x_3) + f(x_4) + f(x_5)]$

$ = 2[f(2) + f(4) + f(6) + f(8) + f(10) + f(12)]$

$ = 2[2 + 1 + 0 + (-1) + (-2) + (-3)] = 2(-3) = -6$

The Riemann sum represents the sum of the areas of the two rectangles above the x-axis minus the sum of the areas of the three rectangles below the x-axis; that is, the *net area* of the rectangles with respect to the x-axis.

3. $f(x) = e^x - 2$, $0 \le x \le 2$. $\Delta x = \dfrac{b-a}{n} = \dfrac{2-0}{4} = \dfrac{1}{2}$.

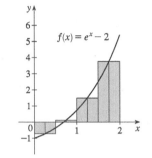

Since we are using midpoints, $x_i^* = \overline{x}_i = \frac{1}{2}(x_{i-1} + x_i)$.

$M_4 = \displaystyle\sum_{i=1}^{4} f(\overline{x}_i)\,\Delta x = (\Delta x)\,[f(\overline{x}_1) + f(\overline{x}_2) + f(\overline{x}_3) + f(\overline{x}_4)]$

$ = \frac{1}{2}\left[f\left(\frac{1}{4}\right) + f\left(\frac{3}{4}\right) + f\left(\frac{5}{4}\right) + f\left(\frac{7}{4}\right)\right]$

$ = \frac{1}{2}\left[(e^{1/4} - 2) + (e^{3/4} - 2) + (e^{5/4} - 2) + (e^{7/4} - 2)\right]$

$ \approx 2.322986$

The Riemann sum represents the sum of the areas of the three rectangles above the x-axis minus the area of the rectangle below the x-axis; that is, the *net area* of the rectangles with respect to the x-axis.

5. $\Delta x = (b-a)/n = (8-0)/4 = 8/4 = 2$.

(a) Using the right endpoints to approximate $\int_0^8 f(x)\,dx$, we have

$\displaystyle\sum_{i=1}^{4} f(x_i)\,\Delta x = 2[f(2) + f(4) + f(6) + f(8)] \approx 2[1 + 2 + (-2) + 1] = 4$.

(b) Using the left endpoints to approximate $\int_0^8 f(x)\,dx$, we have

$\displaystyle\sum_{i=1}^{4} f(x_{i-1})\,\Delta x = 2[f(0) + f(2) + f(4) + f(6)] \approx 2[2 + 1 + 2 + (-2)] = 6$.

(c) Using the midpoint of each subinterval to approximate $\int_0^8 f(x)\,dx$, we have

$\displaystyle\sum_{i=1}^{4} f(\overline{x}_i)\,\Delta x = 2[f(1) + f(3) + f(5) + f(7)] \approx 2[3 + 2 + 1 + (-1)] = 10$.

7. Since f is increasing, $L_5 \le \int_{10}^{30} f(x)\,dx \le R_5$.

Lower estimate $= L_5 = \sum\limits_{i=1}^{5} f(x_{i-1})\Delta x = 4[f(10) + f(14) + f(18) + f(22) + f(26)]$

$$= 4[-12 + (-6) + (-2) + 1 + 3] = 4(-16) = -64$$

Upper estimate $= R_5 = \sum\limits_{i=1}^{5} f(x)\Delta x = 4[f(14) + f(18) + f(22) + f(26) + f(30)]$

$$= 4[-6 + (-2) + 1 + 3 + 8] = 4(4) = 16$$

9. $\Delta x = (10 - 2)/4 = 2$, so the endpoints are 2, 4, 6, 8, and 10, and the midpoints are 3, 5, 7, and 9. The Midpoint Rule

gives $\int_2^{10} \sqrt{x^3 + 1}\,dx \approx \sum\limits_{i=1}^{4} f(\overline{x}_i)\,\Delta x = 2\left(\sqrt{3^3 + 1} + \sqrt{5^3 + 1} + \sqrt{7^3 + 1} + \sqrt{9^3 + 1}\right) \approx 124.1644$.

11. $\Delta x = (1 - 0)/5 = 0.2$, so the endpoints are 0, 0.2, 0.4, 0.6, 0.8, and 1, and the midpoints are 0.1, 0.3, 0.5, 0.7, and 0.9.
The Midpoint Rule gives

$$\int_0^1 \sin(x^2)\,dx \approx \sum\limits_{i=1}^{5} f(\overline{x}_i)\,\Delta x = 0.2\left[\sin(0.1)^2 + \sin(0.3)^2 + \sin(0.5)^2 + \sin(0.7)^2 + \sin(0.9)^2\right] \approx 0.3084.$$

13. In Maple, we use the command `with(student);` to load the sum and box commands, then

`m:=middlesum(sin(x^2),x=0..1,5);` which gives us the sum in summation notation, then `M:=evalf(m);` which

gives $M_5 \approx 0.30843908$, confirming the result of Exercise 11. The command `middlebox(sin(x^2),x=0..1,5)`

generates the graph. Repeating for $n = 10$ and $n = 20$ gives $M_{10} \approx 0.30981629$ and $M_{20} \approx 0.31015563$.

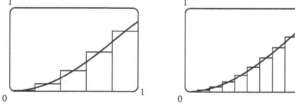 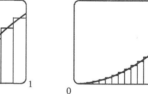 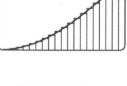

15. We'll create the table of values to approximate $\int_0^\pi \sin x\,dx$ by using the
program in the solution to Exercise 5.1.7 with $Y_1 = \sin x$, Xmin $= 0$,
Xmax $= \pi$, and $n = 5, 10, 50$, and 100.

The values of R_n appear to be approaching 2.

n	R_n
5	1.933766
10	1.983524
50	1.999342
100	1.999836

17. On $[2, 6]$, $\lim\limits_{n \to \infty} \sum\limits_{i=1}^{n} x_i \ln(1 + x_i^2)\,\Delta x = \int_2^6 x \ln(1 + x^2)\,dx$.

19. On $[1, 8]$, $\lim\limits_{n \to \infty} \sum\limits_{i=1}^{n} \sqrt{2x_i^* + (x_i^*)^2}\,\Delta x = \int_1^8 \sqrt{2x + x^2}\,dx$.

21. Note that $\Delta x = \dfrac{5 - (-1)}{n} = \dfrac{6}{n}$ and $x_i = -1 + i\,\Delta x = -1 + \dfrac{6i}{n}$.

$$\int_{-1}^{5}(1+3x)\,dx = \lim_{n\to\infty}\sum_{i=1}^{n}f(x_i)\,\Delta x = \lim_{n\to\infty}\sum_{i=1}^{n}\left[1+3\left(-1+\frac{6i}{n}\right)\right]\frac{6}{n} = \lim_{n\to\infty}\frac{6}{n}\sum_{i=1}^{n}\left[-2+\frac{18i}{n}\right]$$

$$= \lim_{n\to\infty}\frac{6}{n}\left[\sum_{i=1}^{n}(-2)+\sum_{i=1}^{n}\frac{18i}{n}\right] = \lim_{n\to\infty}\frac{6}{n}\left[-2n+\frac{18}{n}\sum_{i=1}^{n}i\right]$$

$$= \lim_{n\to\infty}\frac{6}{n}\left[-2n+\frac{18}{n}\cdot\frac{n(n+1)}{2}\right] = \lim_{n\to\infty}\left[-12+\frac{108}{n^2}\cdot\frac{n(n+1)}{2}\right]$$

$$= \lim_{n\to\infty}\left[-12+54\frac{n+1}{n}\right] = \lim_{n\to\infty}\left[-12+54\left(1+\frac{1}{n}\right)\right] = -12+54\cdot 1 = 42$$

23. Note that $\Delta x = \dfrac{2-0}{n} = \dfrac{2}{n}$ and $x_i = 0 + i\,\Delta x = \dfrac{2i}{n}$.

$$\int_{0}^{2}(2-x^2)\,dx = \lim_{n\to\infty}\sum_{i=1}^{n}f(x_i)\,\Delta x = \lim_{n\to\infty}\sum_{i=1}^{n}\left(2-\frac{4i^2}{n^2}\right)\left(\frac{2}{n}\right) = \lim_{n\to\infty}\frac{2}{n}\left[\sum_{i=1}^{n}2-\frac{4}{n^2}\sum_{i=1}^{n}i^2\right]$$

$$= \lim_{n\to\infty}\frac{2}{n}\left(2n-\frac{4}{n^2}\sum_{i=1}^{n}i^2\right) = \lim_{n\to\infty}\left[4-\frac{8}{n^3}\cdot\frac{n(n+1)(2n+1)}{6}\right]$$

$$= \lim_{n\to\infty}\left(4-\frac{4}{3}\cdot\frac{n+1}{n}\cdot\frac{2n+1}{n}\right) = \lim_{n\to\infty}\left[4-\frac{4}{3}\left(1+\frac{1}{n}\right)\left(2+\frac{1}{n}\right)\right] = 4 - \tfrac{4}{3}\cdot 1\cdot 2 = \tfrac{4}{3}$$

25. Note that $\Delta x = \dfrac{2-1}{n} = \dfrac{1}{n}$ and $x_i = 1 + i\,\Delta x = 1 + i(1/n) = 1 + i/n$.

$$\int_{1}^{2}x^3\,dx = \lim_{n\to\infty}\sum_{i=1}^{n}f(x_i)\,\Delta x = \lim_{n\to\infty}\sum_{i=1}^{n}\left(1+\frac{i}{n}\right)^3\left(\frac{1}{n}\right) = \lim_{n\to\infty}\frac{1}{n}\sum_{i=1}^{n}\left(\frac{n+i}{n}\right)^3$$

$$= \lim_{n\to\infty}\frac{1}{n^4}\sum_{i=1}^{n}\left(n^3+3n^2 i+3ni^2+i^3\right) = \lim_{n\to\infty}\frac{1}{n^4}\left[\sum_{i=1}^{n}n^3+\sum_{i=1}^{n}3n^2 i+\sum_{i=1}^{n}3ni^2+\sum_{i=1}^{n}i^3\right]$$

$$= \lim_{n\to\infty}\frac{1}{n^4}\left[n\cdot n^3+3n^2\sum_{i=1}^{n}i+3n\sum_{i=1}^{n}i^2+\sum_{i=1}^{n}i^3\right]$$

$$= \lim_{n\to\infty}\left[1+\frac{3}{n^2}\cdot\frac{n(n+1)}{2}+\frac{3}{n^3}\cdot\frac{n(n+1)(2n+1)}{6}+\frac{1}{n^4}\cdot\frac{n^2(n+1)^2}{4}\right]$$

$$= \lim_{n\to\infty}\left[1+\frac{3}{2}\cdot\frac{n+1}{n}+\frac{1}{2}\cdot\frac{n+1}{n}\cdot\frac{2n+1}{n}+\frac{1}{4}\cdot\frac{(n+1)^2}{n^2}\right]$$

$$= \lim_{n\to\infty}\left[1+\frac{3}{2}\left(1+\frac{1}{n}\right)+\frac{1}{2}\left(1+\frac{1}{n}\right)\left(2+\frac{1}{n}\right)+\frac{1}{4}\left(1+\frac{1}{n}\right)^2\right] = 1+\frac{3}{2}+\tfrac{1}{2}\cdot 2+\tfrac{1}{4} = 3.75$$

27. $f(x) = \dfrac{x}{1+x^5}$, $a = 2$, $b = 6$, and $\Delta x = \dfrac{6-2}{n} = \dfrac{4}{n}$. Using Theorem 4, we get $x_i^* = x_i = 2 + i\,\Delta x = 2 + \dfrac{4i}{n}$,

so $\displaystyle\int_{2}^{6}\frac{x}{1+x^5}\,dx = \lim_{n\to\infty}R_n = \lim_{n\to\infty}\sum_{i=1}^{n}\frac{2+\dfrac{4i}{n}}{1+\left(2+\dfrac{4i}{n}\right)^5}\cdot\frac{4}{n}.$

29. $\Delta x = (\pi - 0)/n = \pi/n$ and $x_i^* = x_i = \pi i/n$.

$$\int_0^\pi \sin 5x \, dx = \lim_{n \to \infty} \sum_{i=1}^n (\sin 5x_i)\left(\frac{\pi}{n}\right) = \lim_{n \to \infty} \sum_{i=1}^n \left(\sin \frac{5\pi i}{n}\right)\frac{\pi}{n} \overset{\text{CAS}}{=} \pi \lim_{n \to \infty} \frac{1}{n} \cot\left(\frac{5\pi}{2n}\right) \overset{\text{CAS}}{=} \pi\left(\frac{2}{5\pi}\right) = \frac{2}{5}$$

31. (a) Think of $\int_0^2 f(x)\, dx$ as the area of a trapezoid with bases 1 and 3 and height 2. The area of a trapezoid is $A = \frac{1}{2}(b + B)h$,

so $\int_0^2 f(x)\, dx = \frac{1}{2}(1 + 3)2 = 4$.

(b) $\int_0^5 f(x)\, dx = \int_0^2 f(x)\, dx + \int_2^3 f(x)\, dx + \int_3^5 f(x)\, dx$

          trapezoid   rectangle   triangle

$$= \tfrac{1}{2}(1 + 3)2 + \quad 3 \cdot 1 \quad + \quad \tfrac{1}{2} \cdot 2 \cdot 3 \quad = 4 + 3 + 3 = 10$$

(c) $\int_5^7 f(x)\, dx$ is the negative of the area of the triangle with base 2 and height 3. $\int_5^7 f(x)\, dx = -\frac{1}{2} \cdot 2 \cdot 3 = -3$.

(d) $\int_7^9 f(x)\, dx$ is the negative of the area of a trapezoid with bases 3 and 2 and height 2, so it equals

$-\frac{1}{2}(B + b)h = -\frac{1}{2}(3 + 2)2 = -5$. Thus,

$$\int_0^9 f(x)\, dx = \int_0^5 f(x)\, dx + \int_5^7 f(x)\, dx + \int_7^9 f(x)\, dx = 10 + (-3) + (-5) = 2.$$

33. $\int_0^3 \left(\frac{1}{2}x - 1\right) dx$ can be interpreted as the area of the triangle above the x-axis

minus the area of the triangle below the x-axis; that is,

$$\frac{1}{2}(1)\left(\frac{1}{2}\right) - \frac{1}{2}(2)(1) = \frac{1}{4} - 1 = -\frac{3}{4}.$$

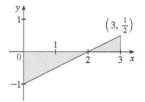

35. $\int_{-3}^0 \left(1 + \sqrt{9 - x^2}\right) dx$ can be interpreted as the area under the graph of

$f(x) = 1 + \sqrt{9 - x^2}$ between $x = -3$ and $x = 0$. This is equal to one-quarter

the area of the circle with radius 3, plus the area of the rectangle, so

$$\int_{-3}^0 \left(1 + \sqrt{9 - x^2}\right) dx = \frac{1}{4}\pi \cdot 3^2 + 1 \cdot 3 = 3 + \frac{9}{4}\pi.$$

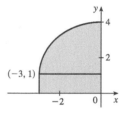

37. $\int_{-1}^2 |x|\, dx$ can be interpreted as the sum of the areas of the two shaded

triangles; that is, $\frac{1}{2}(1)(1) + \frac{1}{2}(2)(2) = \frac{1}{2} + \frac{4}{2} = \frac{5}{2}$.

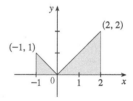

39. $\int_\pi^\pi \sin^2 x \cos^4 x \, dx = 0$ since the limits of intergration are equal.

41. $\int_{-2}^2 f(x)\, dx + \int_2^5 f(x)\, dx - \int_{-2}^{-1} f(x)\, dx = \int_{-2}^5 f(x)\, dx + \int_{-1}^{-2} f(x)\, dx$ [by Property 5 and reversing limits]

$$= \int_{-1}^5 f(x)\, dx \qquad\qquad\qquad \text{[Property 5]}$$

43. $\int_0^9 [2f(x) + 3g(x)]\, dx = 2\int_0^9 f(x)\, dx + 3\int_0^9 g(x)\, dx = 2(37) + 3(16) = 122$

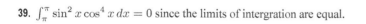

45. $\int_1^3 e^{x+2}\, dx = \int_1^3 e^x \cdot e^2\, dx = e^2 \int_1^3 e^x\, dx = e^2(e^3 - e) = e^5 - e^3$

47. $\int_0^3 f(x)\, dx$ is clearly less than -1 and has the smallest value. The slope of the tangent line of f at $x = 1$, $f'(1)$, has a value

between -1 and 0, so it has the next smallest value. The largest value is $\int_3^8 f(x)\, dx$, followed by $\int_4^8 f(x)\, dx$, which has a

value about 1 unit less than $\int_3^8 f(x)\, dx$. Still positive, but with a smaller value than $\int_4^8 f(x)\, dx$, is $\int_0^8 f(x)\, dx$. Ordering these

quantities from smallest to largest gives us

$$\int_0^3 f(x)\, dx < f'(1) < \int_0^8 f(x)\, dx < \int_4^8 f(x)\, dx < \int_3^8 f(x)\, dx \quad \text{or} \quad B < E < A < D < C$$

49. $I = \int_{-4}^2 [f(x) + 2x + 5]\, dx = \int_{-4}^2 f(x)\, dx + 2\int_{-4}^2 x\, dx + \int_{-4}^2 5\, dx$

$= I_1 + 2I_2 + I_3$

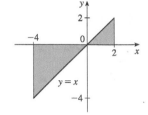

$I_1 = -3$ [area below x-axis] $\quad +3 - 3 = -3$

$I_2 = -\frac{1}{2}(4)(4)$ [area of triangle, see figure] $\quad + \frac{1}{2}(2)(2)$

$= -8 + 2 = -6$

$I_3 = 5[2 - (-4)] = 5(6) = 30$

Thus, $I = -3 + 2(-6) + 30 = 15$.

51. If $-1 \leq x \leq 1$, then $0 \leq x^2 \leq 1$ and $1 \leq 1 + x^2 \leq 2$, so $1 \leq \sqrt{1+x^2} \leq \sqrt{2}$ and

$1[1 - (-1)] \leq \int_{-1}^1 \sqrt{1+x^2}\, dx \leq \sqrt{2}[1 - (-1)]$ [Property 8]; that is, $2 \leq \int_{-1}^1 \sqrt{1+x^2}\, dx \leq 2\sqrt{2}$.

53. $\displaystyle\lim_{n\to\infty} \sum_{i=1}^n \frac{i^4}{n^5} = \lim_{n\to\infty} \sum_{i=1}^n \frac{i^4}{n^4} \cdot \frac{1}{n} = \lim_{n\to\infty} \sum_{i=1}^n \left(\frac{i}{n}\right)^4 \frac{1}{n}$. At this point, we need to recognize the limit as being of the form

$\displaystyle\lim_{n\to\infty} \sum_{i=1}^n f(x_i)\, \Delta x$, where $\Delta x = (1-0)/n = 1/n$, $x_i = 0 + i\,\Delta x = i/n$, and $f(x) = x^4$. Thus, the definite integral

is $\int_0^1 x^4\, dx$.

55. Suppose that f is integrable on $[0, 1]$, that is, $\displaystyle\lim_{n\to\infty} \sum_{i=1}^n f(x_i^*)\, \Delta x$ exists for any choice of x_i^* in $[x_{i-1}, x_i]$. Let n denote a

positive integer and divide the interval $[0, 1]$ into n equal subintervals $\left[0, \dfrac{1}{n}\right], \left[\dfrac{1}{n}, \dfrac{2}{n}\right], ..., \left[\dfrac{n-1}{n}, 1\right]$. If we choose x_i^* to be

a rational number in the ith subinterval, then we obtain the Riemann sum $\displaystyle\sum_{i=1}^n f(x_i^*) \cdot \dfrac{1}{n} = 0$, so

$\displaystyle\lim_{n\to\infty} \sum_{i=1}^n f(x_i^*) \cdot \dfrac{1}{n} = \lim_{n\to\infty} 0 = 0$. Now suppose we choose x_i^* to be an irrational number. Then we get

$\displaystyle\sum_{i=1}^n f(x_i^*) \cdot \dfrac{1}{n} = \sum_{i=1}^n 1 \cdot \dfrac{1}{n} = n \cdot \dfrac{1}{n} = 1$ for each n, so $\displaystyle\lim_{n\to\infty} \sum_{i=1}^n f(x_i^*) \cdot \dfrac{1}{n} = \lim_{n\to\infty} 1 = 1$. Since the value of

$\displaystyle\lim_{n\to\infty} \sum_{i=1}^n f(x_i^*)\, \Delta x$ depends on the choice of the sample points x_i^*, the limit does not exist, and f is not integrable on $[0, 1]$.

5.3   Evaluating Definite Integrals

1. $\int_{-2}^{3}(x^2-3)\,dx = \left[\frac{1}{3}x^3 - 3x\right]_{-2}^{3} = (9-9) - \left(-\frac{8}{3}+6\right) = \frac{8}{3} - \frac{18}{3} = -\frac{10}{3}$

3. $\int_{0}^{2}\left(x^4 - \frac{3}{4}x^2 + \frac{2}{3}x - 1\right)dx = \left[\frac{1}{5}x^5 - \frac{1}{4}x^3 + \frac{1}{3}x^2 - x\right]_{0}^{2} = \left(\frac{32}{5} - 2 + \frac{4}{3} - 2\right) - 0 = \frac{96-30+20-30}{15} = \frac{56}{15}$

5. $\int_{0}^{1}x^{4/5}\,dx = \left[\frac{5}{9}x^{9/5}\right]_{0}^{1} = \frac{5}{9} - 0 = \frac{5}{9}$

7. $\int_{-1}^{0}(2x - e^x)\,dx = \left[x^2 - e^x\right]_{-1}^{0} = (0-1) - \left(1 - e^{-1}\right) = -2 + 1/e$

9. $\int_{1}^{2}(1+2y)^2\,dy = \int_{1}^{2}(1 + 4y + 4y^2)\,dy = \left[y + 2y^2 + \frac{4}{3}y^3\right]_{1}^{2} = \left(2 + 8 + \frac{32}{3}\right) - \left(1 + 2 + \frac{4}{3}\right) = \frac{62}{3} - \frac{13}{3} = \frac{49}{3}$

11. $\int_{1}^{9}\frac{x-1}{\sqrt{x}}\,dx = \int_{1}^{9}\left(\frac{x}{\sqrt{x}} - \frac{1}{\sqrt{x}}\right)dx = \int_{1}^{9}(x^{1/2} - x^{-1/2})\,dx = \left[\frac{2}{3}x^{3/2} - 2x^{1/2}\right]_{1}^{9}$

$= \left(\frac{2}{3}\cdot 27 - 2\cdot 3\right) - \left(\frac{2}{3} - 2\right) = 12 - \left(-\frac{4}{3}\right) = \frac{40}{3}$

13. $\int_{0}^{1}x\left(\sqrt[3]{x} + \sqrt[4]{x}\right)dx = \int_{0}^{1}(x^{4/3} + x^{5/4})\,dx = \left[\frac{3}{7}x^{7/3} + \frac{4}{9}x^{9/4}\right]_{0}^{1} = \left(\frac{3}{7} + \frac{4}{9}\right) - 0 = \frac{55}{63}$

15. $\int_{0}^{\pi/4}\sec^2 t\,dt = \left[\tan t\right]_{0}^{\pi/4} = \tan\frac{\pi}{4} - \tan 0 = 1 - 0 = 1$

17. $\int_{1}^{9}\frac{1}{2x}\,dx = \frac{1}{2}\int_{1}^{9}\frac{1}{x}\,dx = \frac{1}{2}\left[\ln|x|\right]_{1}^{9} = \frac{1}{2}(\ln 9 - \ln 1) = \frac{1}{2}\ln 9 - 0 = \ln 9^{1/2} = \ln 3$

19. $\int_{1/2}^{\sqrt{3}/2}\frac{6}{\sqrt{1-t^2}}\,dt = 6\int_{1/2}^{\sqrt{3}/2}\frac{1}{\sqrt{1-t^2}}\,dt = 6\left[\sin^{-1}t\right]_{1/2}^{\sqrt{3}/2} = 6\left[\sin^{-1}\left(\frac{\sqrt{3}}{2}\right) - \sin^{-1}\left(\frac{1}{2}\right)\right] = 6\left(\frac{\pi}{3} - \frac{\pi}{6}\right) = 6\left(\frac{\pi}{6}\right) = \pi$

21. $\int_{-1}^{1}e^{u+1}\,du = \left[e^{u+1}\right]_{-1}^{1} = e^2 - e^0 = e^2 - 1$ [or start with $e^{u+1} = e^u e^1$]

23. $\int_{1}^{2}\frac{v^3 + 3v^6}{v^4} = \int_{1}^{2}\left(\frac{1}{v} + 3v^2\right)dv = \left[\ln|v| + v^3\right]_{1}^{2} = (\ln 2 + 8) - (\ln 1 + 1) = \ln 2 + 7$

25. $\int_{0}^{\pi/4}\frac{1 + \cos^2\theta}{\cos^2\theta}\,d\theta = \int_{0}^{\pi/4}\left(\frac{1}{\cos^2\theta} + \frac{\cos^2\theta}{\cos^2\theta}\right)d\theta = \int_{0}^{\pi/4}(\sec^2\theta + 1)\,d\theta$

$= \left[\tan\theta + \theta\right]_{0}^{\pi/4} = \left(\tan\frac{\pi}{4} + \frac{\pi}{4}\right) - (0+0) = 1 + \frac{\pi}{4}$

27. $\int_{0}^{1/\sqrt{3}}\frac{t^2-1}{t^4-1}\,dt = \int_{0}^{1/\sqrt{3}}\frac{t^2-1}{(t^2+1)(t^2-1)}\,dt = \int_{0}^{1/\sqrt{3}}\frac{1}{t^2+1}\,dt = \left[\arctan t\right]_{0}^{1/\sqrt{3}} = \arctan\left(1/\sqrt{3}\right) - \arctan 0$

$= \frac{\pi}{6} - 0 = \frac{\pi}{6}$

29. $\int_{-1}^{2}(x - 2\,|x|)\,dx = \int_{-1}^{0}[x - 2(-x)]\,dx + \int_{0}^{2}[x - 2(x)]\,dx = \int_{-1}^{0}3x\,dx + \int_{0}^{2}(-x)\,dx = 3\left[\frac{1}{2}x^2\right]_{-1}^{0} - \left[\frac{1}{2}x^2\right]_{0}^{2}$

$= 3\left(0 - \frac{1}{2}\right) - (2 - 0) = -\frac{7}{2} = -3.5$

31. $f(x) = 1/x^2$ is not continuous on the interval $[-1, 3]$, so the Evaluation Theorem does not apply. In fact, f has an infinite

discontinuity at $x = 0$, so $\int_{-1}^{3}(1/x^2)\,dx$ does not exist.

33. It appears that the area under the graph is about $\frac{2}{3}$ of the area of the viewing

rectangle, or about $\frac{2}{3}\pi \approx 2.1$. The actual area is

$\int_0^\pi \sin x \, dx = [-\cos x]_0^\pi = (-\cos \pi) - (-\cos 0) = -(-1) + 1 = 2.$

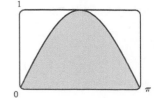

35. The graph shows that $y = 1 - 2x - 5x^4$ has x-intercepts at

$x = a \approx -0.86$ and at $x = b \approx 0.42$. So the area of the region that

lies under the curve and above the x-axis is

$\int_a^b (1 - 2x - 5x^4) \, dx = [x - x^2 - x^5]_a^b$

$\qquad = (b - b^2 - b^5) - (a - a^2 - a^5)$

$\qquad \approx 1.36$

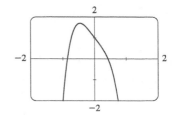

37. $\int_{-1}^2 x^3 \, dx = \left[\frac{1}{4}x^4\right]_{-1}^2 = 4 - \frac{1}{4} = \frac{15}{4} = 3.75$

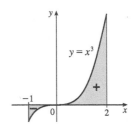

39. $\dfrac{d}{dx}\left[\sin x - \frac{1}{3}\sin^3 x + C\right] = \dfrac{d}{dx}\left[\sin x - \frac{1}{3}(\sin x)^3 + C\right] = \cos x - \frac{1}{3} \cdot 3(\sin x)^2 (\cos x) + 0$

$\qquad\qquad = \cos x(1 - \sin^2 x) = \cos x(\cos^2 x) = \cos^3 x$

41. $\int \left(\cos x + \frac{1}{2}x\right) dx = \sin x + \frac{1}{4}x^2 + C.$ The members of the family

in the figure correspond to $C = -5, 0, 5,$ and 10.

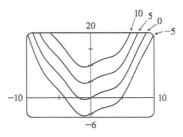

43. $\displaystyle\int (1 - t)(2 + t^2) \, dt = \int (2 - 2t + t^2 - t^3) \, dt = 2t - 2\dfrac{t^2}{2} + \dfrac{t^3}{3} - \dfrac{t^4}{4} + C = 2t - t^2 + \frac{1}{3}t^3 - \frac{1}{4}t^4 + C$

45. $\int (1 + \tan^2 \alpha) \, d\alpha = \int \sec^2 \alpha \, d\alpha = \tan \alpha + C$

47. $\displaystyle\int \dfrac{\sin x}{1 - \sin^2 x} \, dx = \int \dfrac{\sin x}{\cos^2 x} \, dx = \int \dfrac{1}{\cos x} \cdot \dfrac{\sin x}{\cos x} \, dx = \int \sec x \tan x \, dx = \sec x + C$

49. $A = \int_0^2 (2y - y^2) \, dy = \left[y^2 - \frac{1}{3}y^3\right]_0^2 = \left(4 - \frac{8}{3}\right) - 0 = \frac{4}{3}$

51. If $w'(t)$ is the rate of change of weight in pounds per year, then $w(t)$ represents the weight in pounds of the child at age t. We

know from the Net Change Theorem that $\int_5^{10} w'(t) \, dt = w(10) - w(5)$, so the integral represents the increase in the child's

weight (in pounds) between the ages of 5 and 10.

53. Since $r(t)$ is the rate at which oil leaks, we can write $r(t) = -V'(t)$, where $V(t)$ is the volume of oil at time t. [Note that the minus sign is needed because V is decreasing, so $V'(t)$ is negative, but $r(t)$ is positive.] Thus, by the Net Change Theorem, $\int_0^{120} r(t)\,dt = -\int_0^{120} V'(t)\,dt = -[V(120) - V(0)] = V(0) - V(120)$, which is the number of gallons of oil that leaked from the tank in the first two hours (120 minutes).

55. By the Net Change Theorem, $\int_{1000}^{5000} R'(x)\,dx = R(5000) - R(1000)$, so it represents the increase in revenue when production is increased from 1000 units to 5000 units.

57. In general, the unit of measurement for $\int_a^b f(x)\,dx$ is the product of the unit for $f(x)$ and the unit for x. Since $f(x)$ is measured in newtons and x is measured in meters, the units for $\int_0^{100} f(x)\,dx$ are newton-meters. (A newton-meter is abbreviated N·m.)

59. (a) Displacement $= \int_0^3 (3t - 5)\,dt = \left[\frac{3}{2}t^2 - 5t\right]_0^3 = \frac{27}{2} - 15 = -\frac{3}{2}$ m

  (b) Distance traveled $= \int_0^3 |3t - 5|\,dt = \int_0^{5/3} (5 - 3t)\,dt + \int_{5/3}^3 (3t - 5)\,dt$

  $= \left[5t - \frac{3}{2}t^2\right]_0^{5/3} + \left[\frac{3}{2}t^2 - 5t\right]_{5/3}^3 = \frac{25}{3} - \frac{3}{2} \cdot \frac{25}{9} + \frac{27}{2} - 15 - \left(\frac{3}{2} \cdot \frac{25}{9} - \frac{25}{3}\right) = \frac{41}{6}$ m

61. (a) $v'(t) = a(t) = t + 4 \;\Rightarrow\; v(t) = \frac{1}{2}t^2 + 4t + C \;\Rightarrow\; v(0) = C = 5 \;\Rightarrow\; v(t) = \frac{1}{2}t^2 + 4t + 5$ m/s

  (b) Distance traveled $= \int_0^{10} |v(t)|\,dt = \int_0^{10} \left|\frac{1}{2}t^2 + 4t + 5\right|\,dt = \int_0^{10} \left(\frac{1}{2}t^2 + 4t + 5\right)\,dt = \left[\frac{1}{6}t^3 + 2t^2 + 5t\right]_0^{10}$

  $= \frac{500}{3} + 200 + 50 = 416\frac{2}{3}$ m

63. Since $m'(x) = \rho(x)$, $m = \int_0^4 \rho(x)\,dx = \int_0^4 \left(9 + 2\sqrt{x}\right)\,dx = \left[9x + \frac{4}{3}x^{3/2}\right]_0^4 = 36 + \frac{32}{3} - 0 = \frac{140}{3} = 46\frac{2}{3}$ kg.

65. Let s be the position of the car. We know from Equation 2 that $s(100) - s(0) = \int_0^{100} v(t)\,dt$. We use the Midpoint Rule for $0 \le t \le 100$ with $n = 5$. Note that the length of each of the five time intervals is 20 seconds $= \frac{20}{3600}$ hour $= \frac{1}{180}$ hour. So the distance traveled is

$\int_0^{100} v(t)\,dt \approx \frac{1}{180}[v(10) + v(30) + v(50) + v(70) + v(90)] = \frac{1}{180}(38 + 58 + 51 + 53 + 47) = \frac{247}{180} \approx 1.4$ miles.

67. From the Net Change Theorem, the increase in cost if the production level is raised from 2000 yards to 4000 yards is $C(4000) - C(2000) = \int_{2000}^{4000} C'(x)\,dx$.

$\int_{2000}^{4000} C'(x)\,dx = \int_{2000}^{4000} \left(3 - 0.01x + 0.000006x^2\right)\,dx = \left[3x - 0.005x^2 + 0.000002x^3\right]_{2000}^{4000} = 60{,}000 - 2{,}000 = \$58{,}000$

69. (a) We can find the area between the Lorenz curve and the line $y = x$ by subtracting the area under $y = L(x)$ from the area under $y = x$. Thus,

$$\text{coefficient of inequality} = \frac{\text{area between Lorenz curve and line } y = x}{\text{area under line } y = x} = \frac{\int_0^1 [x - L(x)]\,dx}{\int_0^1 x\,dx}$$

$$= \frac{\int_0^1 [x - L(x)]\,dx}{[x^2/2]_0^1} = \frac{\int_0^1 [x - L(x)]\,dx}{1/2} = 2\int_0^1 [x - L(x)]\,dx$$

  (b) $L(x) = \frac{5}{12}x^2 + \frac{7}{12}x \;\Rightarrow\; L(50\%) = L\left(\frac{1}{2}\right) = \frac{5}{48} + \frac{7}{24} = \frac{19}{48} = 0.3958\overline{3}$, so the bottom 50% of the households receive at most about 40% of the income. Using the result in part (a),

$$\text{coefficient of inequality} = 2\int_0^1 [x - L(x)]\,dx = 2\int_0^1 \left(x - \tfrac{5}{12}x^2 - \tfrac{7}{12}x\right) dx = 2\int_0^1 \left(\tfrac{5}{12}x - \tfrac{5}{12}x^2\right) dx$$

$$= 2\int_0^1 \tfrac{5}{12}(x - x^2)\,dx = \tfrac{5}{6}\left[\tfrac{1}{2}x^2 - \tfrac{1}{3}x^3\right]_0^1 = \tfrac{5}{6}\left(\tfrac{1}{2} - \tfrac{1}{3}\right) = \tfrac{5}{6}\left(\tfrac{1}{6}\right) = \tfrac{5}{36}$$

71. (a) Let $f(x) = \sqrt{x}$ $\Rightarrow$ $f'(x) = 1/(2\sqrt{x}) > 0$ for $x > 0$ $\Rightarrow$ f is increasing on $(0, \infty)$. If $x \geq 0$, then $x^3 \geq 0$, so

$1 + x^3 \geq 1$ and since f is increasing, this means that $f(1 + x^3) \geq f(1)$ $\Rightarrow$ $\sqrt{1 + x^3} \geq 1$ for $x \geq 0$. Next let

$g(t) = t^2 - t$ $\Rightarrow$ $g'(t) = 2t - 1$ $\Rightarrow$ $g'(t) > 0$ when $t \geq 1$. Thus, g is increasing on $(1, \infty)$. And since $g(1) = 0$,

$g(t) \geq 0$ when $t \geq 1$. Now let $t = \sqrt{1 + x^3}$, where $x \geq 0$. $\sqrt{1 + x^3} \geq 1$ (from above) $\Rightarrow$ $t \geq 1$ $\Rightarrow$ $g(t) \geq 0$ $\Rightarrow$

$(1 + x^3) - \sqrt{1 + x^3} \geq 0$ for $x \geq 0$. Therefore, $1 \leq \sqrt{1 + x^3} \leq 1 + x^3$ for $x \geq 0$.

(b) From part (a) and Property 7: $\int_0^1 1\,dx \leq \int_0^1 \sqrt{1 + x^3}\,dx \leq \int_0^1 (1 + x^3)\,dx$ $\Leftrightarrow$

$[x]_0^1 \leq \int_0^1 \sqrt{1 + x^3}\,dx \leq [x + \tfrac{1}{4}x^4]_0^1$ $\Leftrightarrow$ $1 \leq \int_0^1 \sqrt{1 + x^3}\,dx \leq 1 + \tfrac{1}{4} = 1.25$.

73. The second derivative is the derivative of the first derivative, so we'll apply the Net Change Theorem with $F = h'$.

$\int_1^2 h''(u)\,du = \int_1^2 (h')'(u)\,du = h'(2) - h'(1) = 5 - 2 = 3$. The other information is unnecessary.

75. $\displaystyle\lim_{n\to\infty} \sum_{i=1}^{n} \frac{i^3}{n^4} = \lim_{n\to\infty} \frac{1 - 0}{n} \sum_{i=1}^{n} \left(\frac{i}{n}\right)^3 = \int_0^1 x^3\,dx = \left[\frac{x^4}{4}\right]_0^1 = \frac{1}{4}$

5.4 The Fundamental Theorem of Calculus

1. One process undoes what the other one does. The precise version of this statement is given by the Fundamental Theorem of Calculus. See the statement of this theorem and the paragraph that follows it on page 371.

3. (a) $g(x) = \int_0^x f(t)\,dt$.

(d)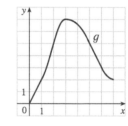

$g(0) = \int_0^0 f(t)\,dt = 0$

$g(1) = \int_0^1 f(t)\,dt = 1 \cdot 2 = 2$ [rectangle],

$g(2) = \int_0^2 f(t)\,dt = \int_0^1 f(t)\,dt + \int_1^2 f(t)\,dt = g(1) + \int_1^2 f(t)\,dt$

$\quad = 2 + 1 \cdot 2 + \tfrac{1}{2} \cdot 1 \cdot 2 = 5$ [rectangle plus triangle],

$g(3) = \int_0^3 f(t)\,dt = g(2) + \int_2^3 f(t)\,dt = 5 + \tfrac{1}{2} \cdot 1 \cdot 4 = 7$,

$g(6) = g(3) + \int_3^6 f(t)\,dt$ [the integral is negative since f lies under the x-axis]

$\quad = 7 + \left[-\left(\tfrac{1}{2} \cdot 2 \cdot 2 + 1 \cdot 2\right)\right] = 7 - 4 = 3$

(b) g is increasing on $(0, 3)$ because as x increases from 0 to 3, we keep adding more area.

(c) g has a maximum value when we start subtracting area; that is, at $x = 3$.

5.

$y = 1 + t^2$

$g(x) \longrightarrow$

(a) By FTC1, $g(x) = \int_0^x (1 + t^2)\, dt \implies g'(x) = f(x) = 1 + x^2$.

(b) By FTC2, $g(x) = \int_0^x (1 + t^2)\, dt = \left[t + \tfrac{1}{3}t^3\right]_0^x = \left(x + \tfrac{1}{3}x^3\right) - 0 \implies g'(x) = 1 + x^2$.

7. $f(t) = \dfrac{1}{t^3 + 1}$ and $g(x) = \displaystyle\int_1^x \dfrac{1}{t^3 + 1}\, dt$, so by FTC1, $g'(x) = f(x) = \dfrac{1}{x^3 + 1}$. Note that the lower limit, 1, could be any

real number greater than -1 and not affect this answer.

9. $f(t) = t^2 \sin t$ and $g(y) = \int_2^y t^2 \sin t\, dt$, so by FTC1, $g'(y) = f(y) = y^2 \sin y$.

11. $F(x) = \displaystyle\int_x^\pi \sqrt{1 + \sec t}\, dt = -\int_\pi^x \sqrt{1 + \sec t}\, dt \implies F'(x) = -\dfrac{d}{dx}\int_\pi^x \sqrt{1 + \sec t}\, dt = -\sqrt{1 + \sec x}$

13. Let $u = \dfrac{1}{x}$. Then $\dfrac{du}{dx} = -\dfrac{1}{x^2}$. Also, $\dfrac{dh}{dx} = \dfrac{dh}{du}\dfrac{du}{dx}$, so

$$h'(x) = \dfrac{d}{dx}\int_2^{1/x} \arctan t\, dt = \dfrac{d}{du}\int_2^u \arctan t\, dt \cdot \dfrac{du}{dx} = \arctan u \dfrac{du}{dx} = -\dfrac{\arctan(1/x)}{x^2}.$$

15. Let $u = \tan x$. Then $\dfrac{du}{dx} = \sec^2 x$. Also, $\dfrac{dy}{dx} = \dfrac{dy}{du}\dfrac{du}{dx}$, so

$$y' = \dfrac{d}{dx}\int_0^{\tan x} \sqrt{t + \sqrt{t}}\, dt = \dfrac{d}{du}\int_0^u \sqrt{t + \sqrt{t}}\, dt \cdot \dfrac{du}{dx} = \sqrt{u + \sqrt{u}}\,\dfrac{du}{dx} = \sqrt{\tan x + \sqrt{\tan x}}\,\sec^2 x.$$

17. $g(x) = \displaystyle\int_{2x}^{3x} \dfrac{u^2 - 1}{u^2 + 1}\, du = \int_{2x}^0 \dfrac{u^2 - 1}{u^2 + 1}\, du + \int_0^{3x} \dfrac{u^2 - 1}{u^2 + 1}\, du = -\int_0^{2x} \dfrac{u^2 - 1}{u^2 + 1}\, du + \int_0^{3x} \dfrac{u^2 - 1}{u^2 + 1}\, du \implies$

$$g'(x) = -\dfrac{(2x)^2 - 1}{(2x)^2 + 1} \cdot \dfrac{d}{dx}(2x) + \dfrac{(3x)^2 - 1}{(3x)^2 + 1} \cdot \dfrac{d}{dx}(3x) = -2 \cdot \dfrac{4x^2 - 1}{4x^2 + 1} + 3 \cdot \dfrac{9x^2 - 1}{9x^2 + 1}$$

19. (a) By FTC1, $g'(x) = f(x)$. So $g'(x) = f(x) = 0$ at $x = 1, 3, 5, 7,$ and 9. g has local maxima at $x = 1$ and 5 (since $f = g'$

changes from positive to negative there) and local minima at $x = 3$ and 7. There is no local maximum or minimum at

$x = 9$, since f is not defined for $x > 9$.

(b) We can see from the graph that $\left|\int_0^1 f\, dt\right| < \left|\int_1^3 f\, dt\right| < \left|\int_3^5 f\, dt\right| < \left|\int_5^7 f\, dt\right| < \left|\int_7^9 f\, dt\right|$. So $g(1) = \left|\int_0^1 f\, dt\right|$,

$g(5) = \int_0^5 f\, dt = g(1) - \left|\int_1^3 f\, dt\right| + \left|\int_3^5 f\, dt\right|$, and $g(9) = \int_0^9 f\, dt = g(5) - \left|\int_5^7 f\, dt\right| + \left|\int_7^9 f\, dt\right|$. Thus,

$g(1) < g(5) < g(9)$, and so the absolute maximum of $g(x)$ occurs at $x = 9$.

(c) g is concave downward on those intervals where $g'' < 0$. But $g'(x) = f(x)$,

so $g''(x) = f'(x)$, which is negative on (approximately) $\left(\tfrac{1}{2}, 2\right)$, $(4, 6)$ and

$(8, 9)$. So g is concave downward on these intervals.

(d)

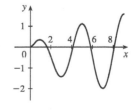

21. $f(x) = \displaystyle\int_0^x (1-t^2)e^{t^2}\, dt$ is increasing when $f'(x) = (1-x^2)e^{x^2}$ is positive.

Since $e^{x^2} > 0$, $f'(x) > 0 \ \Leftrightarrow\ 1 - x^2 > 0 \ \Leftrightarrow\ |x| < 1$, so f is increasing on $(-1, 1)$.

23. $y = \displaystyle\int_0^x \dfrac{t^2}{t^2 + t + 2}\, dt \ \Rightarrow\ y' = \dfrac{x^2}{x^2 + x + 2} \ \Rightarrow$

$y'' = \dfrac{(x^2 + x + 2)(2x) - x^2(2x + 1)}{(x^2 + x + 2)^2} = \dfrac{2x^3 + 2x^2 + 4x - 2x^3 - x^2}{(x^2 + x + 2)^2} = \dfrac{x^2 + 4x}{(x^2 + x + 2)^2} = \dfrac{x(x + 4)}{(x^2 + x + 2)^2}$.

The curve y is concave downward when $y'' < 0$; that is, on the interval $(-4, 0)$.

25. By FTC2, $\int_1^4 f'(x)\, dx = f(4) - f(1)$, so $17 = f(4) - 12 \ \Rightarrow\ f(4) = 17 + 12 = 29$.

27. (a) The Fresnel function $S(x) = \int_0^x \sin\!\left(\frac{\pi}{2}t^2\right) dt$ has local maximum values where $0 = S'(x) = \sin\!\left(\frac{\pi}{2}t^2\right)$ and

S' changes from positive to negative. For $x > 0$, this happens when $\frac{\pi}{2}x^2 = (2n - 1)\pi$ [odd multiples of π] $\Leftrightarrow$

$x^2 = 2(2n - 1) \ \Leftrightarrow\ x = \sqrt{4n - 2}$, n any positive integer. For $x < 0$, S' changes from positive to negative where

$\frac{\pi}{2}x^2 = 2n\pi$ [even multiples of π] $\Leftrightarrow\ x^2 = 4n \ \Leftrightarrow\ x = -2\sqrt{n}$. S' does not change sign at $x = 0$.

(b) S is concave upward on those intervals where $S''(x) > 0$. Differentiating our expression for $S'(x)$, we get

$S''(x) = \cos\!\left(\frac{\pi}{2}x^2\right)\!\left(2\frac{\pi}{2}x\right) = \pi x \cos\!\left(\frac{\pi}{2}x^2\right)$. For $x > 0$, $S''(x) > 0$ where $\cos\!\left(\frac{\pi}{2}x^2\right) > 0 \ \Leftrightarrow\ 0 < \frac{\pi}{2}x^2 < \frac{\pi}{2}$ or

$\left(2n - \frac{1}{2}\right)\pi < \frac{\pi}{2}x^2 < \left(2n + \frac{1}{2}\right)\pi$, n any integer $\Leftrightarrow\ 0 < x < 1$ or $\sqrt{4n - 1} < x < \sqrt{4n + 1}$, n any positive integer.

For $x < 0$, $S''(x) > 0$ where $\cos\!\left(\frac{\pi}{2}x^2\right) < 0 \ \Leftrightarrow\ \left(2n - \frac{3}{2}\right)\pi < \frac{\pi}{2}x^2 < \left(2n - \frac{1}{2}\right)\pi$, n any integer $\Leftrightarrow$

$4n - 3 < x^2 < 4n - 1 \ \Leftrightarrow\ \sqrt{4n - 3} < |x| < \sqrt{4n - 1} \ \Rightarrow\ \sqrt{4n - 3} < -x < \sqrt{4n - 1} \ \Rightarrow$

$-\sqrt{4n - 3} > x > -\sqrt{4n - 1}$, so the intervals of upward concavity for $x < 0$ are $\left(-\sqrt{4n - 1}, -\sqrt{4n - 3}\right)$, n any

positive integer. To summarize: S is concave upward on the intervals $(0, 1)$, $\left(-\sqrt{3}, -1\right)$, $\left(\sqrt{3}, \sqrt{5}\right)$, $\left(-\sqrt{7}, -\sqrt{5}\right)$,

$\left(\sqrt{7}, 3\right)$, ...

(c) In Maple, we use `plot({int(sin(Pi*t^2/2),t=0..x),0.2},x=0..2);`. Note that

Maple recognizes the Fresnel function, calling it `FresnelS(x)`. In Mathematica, we use

`Plot[{Integrate[Sin[Pi*t^2/2],{t,0,x}],0.2},{x,0,2}]`. In Derive, we load the utility file

FRESNEL and plot `FRESNEL_SIN(x)`. From the graphs, we see that $\int_0^x \sin\!\left(\frac{\pi}{2}t^2\right) dt = 0.2$ at $x \approx 0.74$.

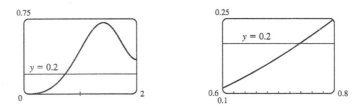

29. By FTC2, $\int_1^x f'(t)\, dt = f(x) - f(1) \ \Rightarrow\ f(x) = f(1) + \int_1^x f'(t)\, dt = f(1) + \int_1^x \left(2^t / t\right) dt$. This integral cannot be

expressed in a simpler form. Since we want $f(1) = 0$, we have $f(x) = \int_1^x \left(2^t / t\right) dt$.

31. Using FTC1, we differentiate both sides of $6 + \int_a^x \dfrac{f(t)}{t^2}\,dt = 2\sqrt{x}$ to get $\dfrac{f(x)}{x^2} = 2\dfrac{1}{2\sqrt{x}}$ $\Rightarrow$ $f(x) = x^{3/2}$.

To find a, we substitute $x = a$ in the original equation to obtain $6 + \int_a^a \dfrac{f(t)}{t^2}\,dt = 2\sqrt{a}$ $\Rightarrow$ $6 + 0 = 2\sqrt{a}$ $\Rightarrow$

$3 = \sqrt{a}$ $\Rightarrow$ $a = 9$.

33. (a) Let $F(t) = \int_0^t f(s)\,ds$. Then, by FTC1, $F'(t) = f(t) = $ rate of depreciation, so $F(t)$ represents the loss in value over the interval $[0, t]$.

(b) $C(t) = \dfrac{1}{t}\left[A + \int_0^t f(s)\,ds\right] = \dfrac{A + F(t)}{t}$ represents the average expenditure per unit of t during the interval $[0, t]$, assuming that there has been only one overhaul during that time period. The company wants to minimize average expenditure.

(c) $C(t) = \dfrac{1}{t}\left[A + \int_0^t f(s)\,ds\right]$. Using FTC1, we have $C'(t) = -\dfrac{1}{t^2}\left[A + \int_0^t f(s)\,ds\right] + \dfrac{1}{t}f(t)$.

$C'(t) = 0$ $\Rightarrow$ $t\,f(t) = A + \int_0^t f(s)\,ds$ $\Rightarrow$ $f(t) = \dfrac{1}{t}\left[A + \int_0^t f(s)\,ds\right] = C(t)$.

5.5   The Substitution Rule

1. Let $u = -x$. Then $du = -\,dx$, so $dx = -\,du$. Thus, $\int e^{-x}\,dx = \int e^u(-du) = -e^u + C = -e^{-x} + C$. Don't forget that it is often very easy to check an indefinite integration by differentiating your answer. In this case,

$\dfrac{d}{dx}(-e^{-x} + C) = -[e^{-x}(-1)] = e^{-x}$, the desired result.

3. Let $u = x^3 + 1$. Then $du = 3x^2\,dx$ and $x^2\,dx = \frac{1}{3}\,du$, so

$\displaystyle\int x^2\sqrt{x^3 + 1}\,dx = \int \sqrt{u}\left(\tfrac{1}{3}\,du\right) = \dfrac{1}{3}\dfrac{u^{3/2}}{3/2} + C = \dfrac{1}{3}\cdot\dfrac{2}{3}u^{3/2} + C = \tfrac{2}{9}(x^3 + 1)^{3/2} + C$.

5. Let $u = \cos\theta$. Then $du = -\sin\theta\,d\theta$ and $\sin\theta\,d\theta = -du$, so

$\displaystyle\int \cos^3\theta \sin\theta\,d\theta = \int u^3\,(-du) = -\dfrac{u^4}{4} + C = -\tfrac{1}{4}\cos^4\theta + C$.

7. Let $u = x^2$. Then $du = 2x\,dx$ and $x\,dx = \frac{1}{2}\,du$, so $\int x\sin(x^2)\,dx = \int \sin u\left(\tfrac{1}{2}\,du\right) = -\tfrac{1}{2}\cos u + C = -\tfrac{1}{2}\cos(x^2) + C$.

9. Let $u = 3x - 2$. Then $du = 3\,dx$ and $dx = \frac{1}{3}\,du$, so $\int (3x - 2)^{20}\,dx = \int u^{20}\left(\tfrac{1}{3}\,du\right) = \tfrac{1}{3}\cdot\tfrac{1}{21}u^{21} + C = \tfrac{1}{63}(3x - 2)^{21} + C$.

11. Let $u = \pi t$. Then $du = \pi\,dt$ and $dt = \frac{1}{\pi}\,du$, so $\int \sin\pi t\,dt = \int \sin u\left(\tfrac{1}{\pi}\,du\right) = \tfrac{1}{\pi}(-\cos u) + C = -\tfrac{1}{\pi}\cos\pi t + C$.

13. Let $u = \ln x$. Then $du = \dfrac{dx}{x}$, so $\displaystyle\int \dfrac{(\ln x)^2}{x}\,dx = \int u^2\,du = \tfrac{1}{3}u^3 + C = \tfrac{1}{3}(\ln x)^3 + C$.

15. Let $u = 5 - 3x$. Then $du = -3\,dx$ and $dx = -\frac{1}{3}\,du$, so

$\displaystyle\int \dfrac{dx}{5 - 3x} = \int \dfrac{1}{u}\left(-\tfrac{1}{3}\,du\right) = -\tfrac{1}{3}\ln|u| + C = -\tfrac{1}{3}\ln|5 - 3x| + C$.

17. Let $u = 3ax + bx^3$. Then $du = (3a + 3bx^2)\,dx = 3(a + bx^2)\,dx$, so

$$\int \frac{a + bx^2}{\sqrt{3ax + bx^3}}\,dx = \int \frac{\frac{1}{3}\,du}{u^{1/2}} = \frac{1}{3}\int u^{-1/2}\,du = \frac{1}{3}\cdot 2u^2 + C = \frac{2}{3}\sqrt{3ax + bx^3} + C.$$

19. Let $u = 1 + e^x$. Then $du = e^x\,dx$, so $\int e^x\sqrt{1 + e^x}\,dx = \int \sqrt{u}\,du = \frac{2}{3}u^{3/2} + C = \frac{2}{3}(1 + e^x)^{3/2} + C.$

Or: Let $u = \sqrt{1 + e^x}$. Then $u^2 = 1 + e^x$ and $2u\,du = e^x\,dx$, so

$\int e^x\sqrt{1 + e^x}\,dx = \int u \cdot 2u\,du = \frac{2}{3}u^3 + C = \frac{2}{3}(1 + e^x)^{3/2} + C.$

21. Let $u = \sin x$. Then $du = \cos x\,dx$, so $\displaystyle\int \frac{\cos x}{\sin^2 x}\,dx = \int \frac{1}{u^2}\,du = \int u^{-2}\,du = \frac{u^{-1}}{-1} + C = -\frac{1}{u} + C = -\frac{1}{\sin x} + C$

$[\text{or } -\csc x + C]$.

23. Let $u = x^3 + 3x$. Then $du = (3x^2 + 3)\,dx$ and $\frac{1}{3}\,du = (x^2 + 1)\,dx$, so

$\int (x^2 + 1)(x^3 + 3x)^4\,dx = \int u^4\left(\frac{1}{3}\,du\right) = \frac{1}{3}\cdot\frac{1}{5}u^5 + C = \frac{1}{15}(x^3 + 3x)^5 + C.$

25. Let $u = \cot x$. Then $du = -\csc^2 x\,dx$ and $\csc^2 x\,dx = -du$, so

$$\int \sqrt{\cot x}\,\csc^2 x\,dx = \int \sqrt{u}\,(-du) = -\frac{u^{3/2}}{3/2} + C = -\frac{2}{3}(\cot x)^{3/2} + C.$$

27. Let $u = \sin^{-1} x$. Then $du = \dfrac{1}{\sqrt{1 - x^2}}\,dx$, so $\displaystyle\int \frac{dx}{\sqrt{1 - x^2}\,\sin^{-1} x} = \int \frac{1}{u}\,du = \ln|u| + C = \ln\left|\sin^{-1} x\right| + C.$

29. Let $u = \sec x$. Then $du = \sec x\tan x\,dx$, so

$\int \sec^3 x\tan x\,dx = \int \sec^2 x\,(\sec x\tan x)\,dx = \int u^2\,du = \frac{1}{3}u^3 + C = \frac{1}{3}\sec^3 x + C.$

31. Let $u = 2x + 5$. Then $du = 2\,dx$ and $x = \frac{1}{2}(u - 5)$, so

$\int x(2x + 5)^8\,dx = \int \frac{1}{2}(u - 5)u^8\left(\frac{1}{2}\,du\right) = \frac{1}{4}\int (u^9 - 5u^8)\,du$

$\qquad = \frac{1}{4}\left(\frac{1}{10}u^{10} - \frac{5}{9}u^9\right) + C = \frac{1}{40}(2x + 5)^{10} - \frac{5}{36}(2x + 5)^9 + C$

33. $\displaystyle\int \frac{\sin 2x}{1 + \cos^2 x}\,dx = 2\int \frac{\sin x\cos x}{1 + \cos^2 x}\,dx = 2I.$ Let $u = \cos x$. Then $du = -\sin x\,dx$, so

$2I = -2\displaystyle\int \frac{u\,du}{1 + u^2} = -2\cdot\frac{1}{2}\ln(1 + u^2) + C = -\ln(1 + u^2) + C = -\ln(1 + \cos^2 x) + C.$

Or: Let $u = 1 + \cos^2 x$.

35. Let $u = 1 + x^2$. Then $du = 2x\,dx$, so

$$\int \frac{1 + x}{1 + x^2}\,dx = \int \frac{1}{1 + x^2}\,dx + \int \frac{x}{1 + x^2}\,dx = \tan^{-1} x + \int \frac{\frac{1}{2}\,du}{u} = \tan^{-1} x + \frac{1}{2}\ln|u| + C$$

$$= \tan^{-1} x + \frac{1}{2}\ln\left|1 + x^2\right| + C = \tan^{-1} x + \frac{1}{2}\ln\left(1 + x^2\right) + C \quad [\text{since } 1 + x^2 > 0].$$

37. $f(x) = x(x^2 - 1)^3$. $u = x^2 - 1$ $\Rightarrow$ $du = 2x\,dx$, so

$$\int x(x^2 - 1)^3\,dx = \int u^3\left(\tfrac{1}{2}\,du\right) = \tfrac{1}{8}u^4 + C = \tfrac{1}{8}(x^2 - 1)^4 + C$$

Where f is positive (negative), F is increasing (decreasing). Where f changes from negative to positive (positive to negative), F has a local minimum (maximum).

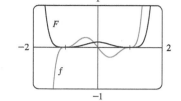

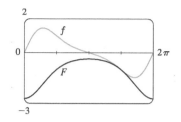

39. $f(x) = e^{\cos x} \sin x$. $u = \cos x$ $\Rightarrow$ $du = -\sin x\,dx$, so

$$\int e^u\,(-du) = -e^u + C = -e^{\cos x} + C$$

Note that at $x = \pi$, f changes from positive to negative and F has a local maximum. Also, both f and F are periodic with period 2π, so at $x = 0$ and at $x = 2\pi$, f changes from negative to positive and F has a local minimum.

41. Let $u = \tfrac{\pi}{2}t$, so $du = \tfrac{\pi}{2}\,dt$. When $t = 0$, $u = 0$; when $t = 1$, $u = \tfrac{\pi}{2}$. Thus,

$$\int_0^1 \cos(\pi t/2)\,dt = \int_0^{\pi/2} \cos u\left(\tfrac{2}{\pi}\,du\right) = \tfrac{2}{\pi}\left[\sin u\right]_0^{\pi/2} = \tfrac{2}{\pi}\left(\sin\tfrac{\pi}{2} - \sin 0\right) = \tfrac{2}{\pi}(1 - 0) = \tfrac{2}{\pi}$$

43. Let $u = 1 + 7x$, so $du = 7\,dx$. When $x = 0$, $u = 1$; when $x = 1$, $u = 8$. Thus,

$$\int_0^1 \sqrt[3]{1 + 7x}\,dx = \int_1^8 u^{1/3}\left(\tfrac{1}{7}\,du\right) = \tfrac{1}{7}\left[\tfrac{3}{4}u^{4/3}\right]_1^8 = \tfrac{3}{28}(8^{4/3} - 1^{4/3}) = \tfrac{3}{28}(16 - 1) = \tfrac{45}{28}$$

45. Let $u = 1 + 2x^3$, so $du = 6x^2\,dx$. When $x = 0$, $u = 1$; when $x = 1$, $u = 3$. Thus,

$$\int_0^1 x^2\left(1 + 2x^3\right)^5\,dx = \int_1^3 u^5\left(\tfrac{1}{6}\,du\right) = \tfrac{1}{6}\left[\tfrac{1}{6}u^6\right]_1^3 = \tfrac{1}{36}(3^6 - 1^6) = \tfrac{1}{36}(729 - 1) = \tfrac{728}{36} = \tfrac{182}{9}.$$

47. Let $u = \sqrt{x}$, so $du = \dfrac{1}{2\sqrt{x}}\,dx$. When $x = 1$, $u = 1$; when $x = 4$, $u = 2$.

Thus, $\displaystyle\int_1^4 \dfrac{e^{\sqrt{x}}}{\sqrt{x}}\,dx = \int_1^2 e^u\,(2\,du) = 2\left[e^u\right]_1^2 = 2(e^2 - e)$.

49. $\int_{-\pi/4}^{\pi/4}(x^3 + x^4 \tan x)\,dx = 0$ by Theorem 6(b), since $f(x) = x^3 + x^4 \tan x$ is an odd function.

51. Let $u = x - 1$, so $u + 1 = x$ and $du = dx$. When $x = 1$, $u = 0$; when $x = 2$, $u = 1$. Thus,

$$\int_1^2 x\sqrt{x - 1}\,dx = \int_0^1 (u + 1)\sqrt{u}\,du = \int_0^1 (u^{3/2} + u^{1/2})\,du = \left[\tfrac{2}{5}u^{5/2} + \tfrac{2}{3}u^{3/2}\right]_0^1 = \tfrac{2}{5} + \tfrac{2}{3} = \tfrac{16}{15}.$$

53. Let $u = e^z + z$, so $du = (e^z + 1)\,dz$. When $z = 0$, $u = 1$; when $z = 1$, $u = e + 1$. Thus,

$$\int_0^1 \dfrac{e^z + 1}{e^z + z}\,dz = \int_1^{e+1} \dfrac{1}{u}\,du = \left[\ln|u|\right]_1^{e+1} = \ln|e + 1| - \ln|1| = \ln(e + 1).$$

55. Let $u = \ln x$, so $du = \dfrac{dx}{x}$. When $x = e$, $u = 1$; when $x = e^4$; $u = 4$. Thus,

$$\int_e^{e^4} \dfrac{dx}{x\sqrt{\ln x}} = \int_1^4 u^{-1/2}\,du = 2\left[u^{1/2}\right]_1^4 = 2(2 - 1) = 2.$$

57. Let $u = 1 + \sqrt{x}$, so $du = \dfrac{1}{2\sqrt{x}}\,dx \;\Rightarrow\; 2\sqrt{x}\,du = dx \;\Rightarrow\; 2(u-1)\,du = dx$. When $x = 0$, $u = 1$; when $x = 1$,

$u = 2$. Thus,

$$\int_0^1 \frac{dx}{(1+\sqrt{x})^4} = \int_1^2 \frac{1}{u^4}\cdot[2(u-1)\,du] = 2\int_1^2\left(\frac{1}{u^3} - \frac{1}{u^4}\right)du = 2\left[-\frac{1}{2u^2} + \frac{1}{3u^3}\right]_1^2$$

$$= 2\left[\left(-\tfrac{1}{8} + \tfrac{1}{24}\right) - \left(-\tfrac{1}{2} + \tfrac{1}{3}\right)\right] = 2\left(\tfrac{1}{12}\right) = \tfrac{1}{6}$$

59. First write the integral as a sum of two integrals:

$I = \int_{-2}^2 (x+3)\sqrt{4-x^2}\,dx = I_1 + I_2 = \int_{-2}^2 x\sqrt{4-x^2}\,dx + \int_{-2}^2 3\sqrt{4-x^2}\,dx$. $I_1 = 0$ by Theorem 6(b), since

$f(x) = x\sqrt{4-x^2}$ is an odd function and we are integrating from $x = -2$ to $x = 2$. We interpret I_2 as three times the area of

a semicircle with radius 2, so $I = 0 + 3\cdot\frac{1}{2}\left(\pi\cdot 2^2\right) = 6\pi$.

61. First Figure Let $u = \sqrt{x}$, so $x = u^2$ and $dx = 2u\,du$. When $x = 0$, $u = 0$; when $x = 1$, $u = 1$. Thus,

$A_1 = \int_0^1 e^{\sqrt{x}}\,dx = \int_0^1 e^u(2u\,du) = 2\int_0^1 ue^u\,du$.

Second Figure $A_2 = \int_0^1 2xe^x\,dx = 2\int_0^1 ue^u\,du$.

Third Figure Let $u = \sin x$, so $du = \cos x\,dx$. When $x = 0$, $u = 0$; when $x = \frac{\pi}{2}$, $u = 1$. Thus,

$A_3 = \int_0^{\pi/2} e^{\sin x}\sin 2x\,dx = \int_0^{\pi/2} e^{\sin x}(2\sin x\cos x)\,dx = \int_0^1 e^u(2u\,du) = 2\int_0^1 ue^u\,du$.

Since $A_1 = A_2 = A_3$, all three areas are equal.

63. The rate is measured in liters per minute. Integrating from $t = 0$ minutes to $t = 60$ minutes will give us the total amount of oil

that leaks out (in liters) during the first hour.

$\int_0^{60} r(t)\,dt = \int_0^{60} 100e^{-0.01t}\,dt \qquad [u = -0.01t, du = -0.01dt]$

$\qquad = 100\int_0^{-0.6} e^u(-100\,du) = -10{,}000\left[e^u\right]_0^{-0.6} = -10{,}000(e^{-0.6} - 1) \approx 4511.9 \approx 4512$ liters

65. The volume of inhaled air in the lungs at time t is

$$V(t) = \int_0^t f(u)\,du = \int_0^t \frac{1}{2}\sin\left(\frac{2\pi}{5}u\right)du = \int_0^{2\pi t/5} \frac{1}{2}\sin v\left(\frac{5}{2\pi}\,dv\right) \qquad \left[\text{substitute } v = \tfrac{2\pi}{5}u,\ dv = \tfrac{2\pi}{5}\,du\right]$$

$$= \frac{5}{4\pi}\left[-\cos v\right]_0^{2\pi t/5} = \frac{5}{4\pi}\left[-\cos\left(\frac{2\pi}{5}t\right) + 1\right] = \frac{5}{4\pi}\left[1 - \cos\left(\frac{2\pi}{5}t\right)\right] \text{ liters}$$

67. Let $u = 2x$. Then $du = 2\,dx$, so $\int_0^2 f(2x)\,dx = \int_0^4 f(u)\left(\frac{1}{2}\,du\right) = \frac{1}{2}\int_0^4 f(u)\,du = \frac{1}{2}(10) = 5$.

69. Let $u = -x$. Then $du = -dx$, so

$\int_a^b f(-x)\,dx = \int_{-a}^{-b} f(u)(-du) = \int_{-b}^{-a} f(u)\,du = \int_{-b}^{-a} f(x)\,dx$

From the diagram, we see that the equality follows from the fact that we are

reflecting the graph of f, and the limits of integration, about the y-axis.

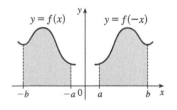

71. Let $u = 1 - x$. Then $x = 1 - u$ and $dx = -du$, so

$\int_0^1 x^a(1-x)^b\,dx = \int_1^0 (1-u)^a u^b(-du) = \int_0^1 u^b(1-u)^a\,du = \int_0^1 x^b(1-x)^a\,dx$.

5.6   Integration by Parts

1. Let $u = \ln x$, $dv = x^2\, dx$ $\Rightarrow$ $du = \frac{1}{x}\, dx$, $v = \frac{1}{3}x^3$. Then by Equation 2,

$$\int x^2 \ln x\, dx = (\ln x)\left(\tfrac{1}{3}x^3\right) - \int \left(\tfrac{1}{3}x^3\right)\left(\tfrac{1}{x}\right)\, dx = \tfrac{1}{3}x^3 \ln x - \tfrac{1}{3}\int x^2\, dx = \tfrac{1}{3}x^3 \ln x - \tfrac{1}{3}\left(\tfrac{1}{3}x^3\right) + C$$

$$= \tfrac{1}{3}x^3 \ln x - \tfrac{1}{9}x^3 + C \quad \left[\text{or } \tfrac{1}{3}x^3\left(\ln x - \tfrac{1}{3}\right) + C\right]$$

Note: A mnemonic device which is helpful for selecting u when using integration by parts is the LIATE principle of precedence for u:

Logarithmic

Inverse trigonometric

Algebraic

Trigonometric

Exponential

If the integrand has several factors, then we try to choose among them a u which appears as high as possible on the list. For example, in $\int xe^{2x}\, dx$ the integrand is xe^{2x}, which is the product of an algebraic function (x) and an exponential function (e^{2x}). Since Algebraic appears before Exponential, we choose $u = x$. Sometimes the integration turns out to be similar regardless of the selection of u and dv, but it is advisable to refer to LIATE when in doubt.

3. Let $u = x$, $dv = \cos 5x\, dx$ $\Rightarrow$ $du = dx$, $v = \frac{1}{5}\sin 5x$. Then by Equation 2,

$$\int x \cos 5x\, dx = \tfrac{1}{5}x \sin 5x - \int \tfrac{1}{5}\sin 5x\, dx = \tfrac{1}{5}x \sin 5x + \tfrac{1}{25}\cos 5x + C.$$

5. Let $u = r$, $dv = e^{r/2}\, dr$ $\Rightarrow$ $du = dr$, $v = 2e^{r/2}$.

Then $\int re^{r/2}\, dr = 2re^{r/2} - \int 2e^{r/2}\, dr = 2re^{r/2} - 4e^{r/2} + C = 2(r-2)e^{r/2} + C.$

7. Let $u = x^2$, $dv = \sin \pi x\, dx$ $\Rightarrow$ $du = 2x\, dx$ and $v = -\frac{1}{\pi}\cos \pi x$. Then

$$I = \int x^2 \sin \pi x\, dx = -\tfrac{1}{\pi}x^2 \cos \pi x + \tfrac{2}{\pi}\int x \cos \pi x\, dx \quad (\star). \text{ Next let } U = x, \ dV = \cos \pi x\, dx \ \Rightarrow \ dU = dx,$$

$V = \frac{1}{\pi}\sin \pi x$, so $\int x \cos \pi x\, dx = \frac{1}{\pi}x \sin \pi x - \frac{1}{\pi}\int \sin \pi x\, dx = \frac{1}{\pi}x \sin \pi x + \frac{1}{\pi^2}\cos \pi x + C_1$.

Substituting for $\int x \cos \pi x\, dx$ in $(\star)$, we get

$$I = -\tfrac{1}{\pi}x^2 \cos \pi x + \tfrac{2}{\pi}\left(\tfrac{1}{\pi}x \sin \pi x + \tfrac{1}{\pi^2}\cos \pi x + C_1\right) = -\tfrac{1}{\pi}x^2 \cos \pi x + \tfrac{2}{\pi^2}x \sin \pi x + \tfrac{2}{\pi^3}\cos \pi x + C, \text{ where } C = \tfrac{2}{\pi}C_1.$$

9. Let $u = \ln \sqrt[3]{x}$, $dv = dx$ $\Rightarrow$ $du = \frac{1}{\sqrt[3]{x}}\left(\frac{1}{3}x^{-2/3}\right)dx = \frac{1}{3x}\, dx$, $v = x$. Then

$$\int \ln \sqrt[3]{x}\, dx = x \ln \sqrt[3]{x} - \int x \cdot \frac{1}{3x}\, dx = x \ln \sqrt[3]{x} - \frac{1}{3}x + C.$$

Second solution: Rewrite $\int \ln \sqrt[3]{x}\, dx = \frac{1}{3}\int \ln x\, dx$, and apply Example 2.

Third solution: Substitute $y = \sqrt[3]{x}$, to obtain $\int \ln \sqrt[3]{x}\, dx = 3\int y^2 \ln y\, dy$, and apply Exercise 1.

11. Let $u = \arctan 4t$, $dv = dt$ $\Rightarrow$ $du = \frac{4}{1 + (4t)^2}\, dt = \frac{4}{1 + 16t^2}\, dt$, $v = t$. Then

$$\int \arctan 4t\, dt = t \arctan 4t - \int \frac{4t}{1 + 16t^2}\, dt = t \arctan 4t - \frac{1}{8}\int \frac{32t}{1 + 16t^2}\, dt = t \arctan 4t - \tfrac{1}{8}\ln(1 + 16t^2) + C.$$

13. First let $u = \sin 3\theta$, $dv = e^{2\theta}\, d\theta$ $\Rightarrow$ $du = 3\cos 3\theta\, d\theta$, $v = \frac{1}{2}e^{2\theta}$. Then

$$I = \int e^{2\theta} \sin 3\theta\, d\theta = \tfrac{1}{2}e^{2\theta} \sin 3\theta - \tfrac{3}{2}\int e^{2\theta} \cos 3\theta\, d\theta. \text{ Next let } U = \cos 3\theta, \ dV = e^{2\theta}\, d\theta \ \Rightarrow \ dU = -3\sin 3\theta\, d\theta,$$

$V = \frac{1}{2}e^{2\theta}$ to get $\int e^{2\theta} \cos 3\theta\, d\theta = \frac{1}{2}e^{2\theta} \cos 3\theta + \frac{3}{2}\int e^{2\theta} \sin 3\theta\, d\theta$. Substituting in the previous formula gives

$I = \frac{1}{2}e^{2\theta}\sin 3\theta - \frac{3}{4}e^{2\theta}\cos 3\theta - \frac{9}{4}\int e^{2\theta}\sin 3\theta\,d\theta = \frac{1}{2}e^{2\theta}\sin 3\theta - \frac{3}{4}e^{2\theta}\cos 3\theta - \frac{9}{4}I \Rightarrow$

$\frac{13}{4}I = \frac{1}{2}e^{2\theta}\sin 3\theta - \frac{3}{4}e^{2\theta}\cos 3\theta + C_1$. Hence, $I = \frac{1}{13}e^{2\theta}(2\sin 3\theta - 3\cos 3\theta) + C$, where $C = \frac{4}{13}C_1$.

15. Let $u = t$, $dv = \sin 3t\,dt \Rightarrow du = dt$, $v = -\frac{1}{3}\cos 3t$. Then

$\int_0^\pi t\sin 3t\,dt = \left[-\frac{1}{3}t\cos 3t\right]_0^\pi + \frac{1}{3}\int_0^\pi \cos 3t\,dt = \left(\frac{1}{3}\pi - 0\right) + \frac{1}{9}\left[\sin 3t\right]_0^\pi = \frac{\pi}{3}$.

17. Let $u = \ln x$, $dv = x^{-2}\,dx \Rightarrow du = \dfrac{1}{x}\,dx$, $v = -x^{-1}$. By (6),

$\displaystyle\int_1^2 \frac{\ln x}{x^2}\,dx = \left[-\frac{\ln x}{x}\right]_1^2 + \int_1^2 x^{-2}\,dx = -\frac{1}{2}\ln 2 + \ln 1 + \left[-\frac{1}{x}\right]_1^2 = -\frac{1}{2}\ln 2 + 0 - \frac{1}{2} + 1 = \frac{1}{2} - \frac{1}{2}\ln 2.$

19. Let $u = y$, $dv = \dfrac{dy}{e^{2y}} = e^{-2y}\,dy \Rightarrow du = dy$, $v = -\frac{1}{2}e^{-2y}$. Then

$\displaystyle\int_0^1 \frac{y}{e^{2y}}\,dy = \left[-\frac{1}{2}ye^{-2y}\right]_0^1 + \frac{1}{2}\int_0^1 e^{-2y}\,dy = \left(-\frac{1}{2}e^{-2} + 0\right) - \frac{1}{4}\left[e^{-2y}\right]_0^1 = -\frac{1}{2}e^{-2} - \frac{1}{4}e^{-2} + \frac{1}{4} = \frac{1}{4} - \frac{3}{4}e^{-2}.$

21. Let $u = \cos^{-1}x$, $dv = dx \Rightarrow du = -\dfrac{dx}{\sqrt{1-x^2}}$, $v = x$. Then

$I = \displaystyle\int_0^{1/2}\cos^{-1}x\,dx = \left[x\cos^{-1}x\right]_0^{1/2} + \int_0^{1/2}\frac{x\,dx}{\sqrt{1-x^2}} = \frac{1}{2}\cdot\frac{\pi}{3} + \int_1^{3/4}t^{-1/2}\left[-\frac{1}{2}dt\right]$, where $t = 1 - x^2 \Rightarrow$

$dt = -2x\,dx$. Thus, $I = \frac{\pi}{6} + \frac{1}{2}\int_{3/4}^1 t^{-1/2}\,dt = \frac{\pi}{6} + \left[\sqrt{t}\right]_{3/4}^1 = \frac{\pi}{6} + 1 - \frac{\sqrt{3}}{2} = \frac{1}{6}\left(\pi + 6 - 3\sqrt{3}\right)$.

23. Let $u = (\ln x)^2$, $dv = dx \Rightarrow du = \dfrac{2}{x}\ln x\,dx$, $v = x$. By (6), $I = \int_1^2 (\ln x)^2\,dx = \left[x(\ln x)^2\right]_1^2 - 2\int_1^2 \ln x\,dx$.

To evaluate the last integral, let $U = \ln x$, $dV = dx \Rightarrow dU = \dfrac{1}{x}\,dx$, $V = x$. Thus,

$$I = \left[x(\ln x)^2\right]_1^2 - 2\left(\left[x\ln x\right]_1^2 - \int_1^2 dx\right) = \left[x(\ln x)^2 - 2x\ln x + 2x\right]_1^2$$

$$= \left(2(\ln 2)^2 - 4\ln 2 + 4\right) - (0 - 0 + 2) = 2(\ln 2)^2 - 4\ln 2 + 2$$

25. Let $y = \sqrt{x}$, so that $dy = \frac{1}{2}x^{-1/2}\,dx = \dfrac{1}{2\sqrt{x}}\,dx = \dfrac{1}{2y}\,dx$. Thus, $\int\cos\sqrt{x}\,dx = \int\cos y\,(2y\,dy) = 2\int y\cos y\,dy$. Now

use parts with $u = y$, $dv = \cos y\,dy$, $du = dy$, $v = \sin y$ to get $\int y\cos y\,dy = y\sin y - \int\sin y\,dy = y\sin y + \cos y + C_1$,

so $\int\cos\sqrt{x}\,dx = 2y\sin y + 2\cos y + C = 2\sqrt{x}\sin\sqrt{x} + 2\cos\sqrt{x} + C$.

27. Let $x = \theta^2$, so that $dx = 2\theta\,d\theta$. Thus, $\displaystyle\int_{\sqrt{\pi/2}}^{\sqrt{\pi}}\theta^3\cos(\theta^2)\,d\theta = \int_{\sqrt{\pi/2}}^{\sqrt{\pi}}\theta^2\cos(\theta^2)\cdot\frac{1}{2}(2\theta\,d\theta) = \frac{1}{2}\int_{\pi/2}^\pi x\cos x\,dx$. Now use

parts with $u = x$, $dv = \cos x\,dx$, $du = dx$, $v = \sin x$ to get

$$\frac{1}{2}\int_{\pi/2}^\pi x\cos x\,dx = \frac{1}{2}\left(\left[x\sin x\right]_{\pi/2}^\pi - \int_{\pi/2}^\pi \sin x\,dx\right) = \frac{1}{2}\left[x\sin x + \cos x\right]_{\pi/2}^\pi$$

$$= \frac{1}{2}(\pi\sin\pi + \cos\pi) - \frac{1}{2}\left(\frac{\pi}{2}\sin\frac{\pi}{2} + \cos\frac{\pi}{2}\right) = \frac{1}{2}(\pi\cdot 0 - 1) - \frac{1}{2}\left(\frac{\pi}{2}\cdot 1 + 0\right) = -\frac{1}{2} - \frac{\pi}{4}$$

29. Let $y = 1 + x$, so that $dy = dx$. Thus, $\int x\ln(1+x)\,dx = \int(y-1)\ln y\,dy$. Now use parts with $u = \ln y$, $dv = (y-1)\,dy$,

$du = \frac{1}{y}\,dy$, $v = \frac{1}{2}y^2 - y$ to get

$$\int(y-1)\ln y\,dy = \left(\tfrac{1}{2}y^2 - y\right)\ln y - \int\left(\tfrac{1}{2}y - 1\right)dy = \tfrac{1}{2}y(y-2)\ln y - \tfrac{1}{4}y^2 + y + C$$

$$= \tfrac{1}{2}(1+x)(x-1)\ln(1+x) - \tfrac{1}{4}(1+x)^2 + 1 + x + C,$$

which can be written as $\frac{1}{2}(x^2 - 1)\ln(1+x) - \frac{1}{4}x^2 + \frac{1}{2}x + \frac{3}{4} + C$.

31. Let $u = x$, $dv = e^{-2x}\,dx$ $\Rightarrow$ $du = dx$, $v = -\frac{1}{2}e^{-2x}$. Then

$\int xe^{-2x}\,dx = -\frac{1}{2}xe^{-2x} + \int \frac{1}{2}e^{-2x}\,dx = -\frac{1}{2}xe^{-2x} - \frac{1}{4}e^{-2x} + C$. We

see from the graph that this is reasonable, since F has a minimum where f

changes from negative to positive. Also, F increases where f is positive and

F decreases where f is negative.

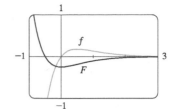

33. Let $u = \frac{1}{2}x^2$, $dv = 2x\sqrt{1+x^2}\,dx$ $\Rightarrow$ $du = x\,dx$, $v = \frac{2}{3}(1+x^2)^{3/2}$.

Then

$\int x^3\sqrt{1+x^2}\,dx = \frac{1}{2}x^2\left[\frac{2}{3}(1+x^2)^{3/2}\right] - \frac{2}{3}\int x(1+x^2)^{3/2}dx$

$\quad\quad = \frac{1}{3}x^2(1+x^2)^{3/2} - \frac{2}{3}\cdot\frac{2}{5}\cdot\frac{1}{2}(1+x^2)^{5/2} + C$

$\quad\quad = \frac{1}{3}x^2(1+x^2)^{3/2} - \frac{2}{15}(1+x^2)^{5/2} + C$

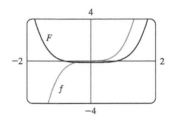

We see from the graph that this is reasonable, since F increases where f is positive and F decreases where f is negative.

Note also that f is an odd function and F is an even function.

Another method: Use substitution with $u = 1 + x^2$ to get $\frac{1}{5}(1+x^2)^{5/2} - \frac{1}{3}(1+x^2)^{3/2} + C$.

35. (a) Take $n = 2$ in Example 6 to get $\displaystyle\int \sin^2 x\,dx = -\frac{1}{2}\cos x\sin x + \frac{1}{2}\int 1\,dx = \frac{x}{2} - \frac{\sin 2x}{4} + C$.

(b) $\int \sin^4 x\,dx = -\frac{1}{4}\cos x\sin^3 x + \frac{3}{4}\int \sin^2 x\,dx = -\frac{1}{4}\cos x\sin^3 x + \frac{3}{8}x - \frac{3}{16}\sin 2x + C$.

37. (a) From Example 6, $\displaystyle\int \sin^n x\,dx = -\frac{1}{n}\cos x\sin^{n-1}x + \frac{n-1}{n}\int \sin^{n-2}x\,dx$. Using (6),

$$\int_0^{\pi/2}\sin^n x\,dx = \left[-\frac{\cos x\sin^{n-1}x}{n}\right]_0^{\pi/2} + \frac{n-1}{n}\int_0^{\pi/2}\sin^{n-2}x\,dx$$

$$= (0 - 0) + \frac{n-1}{n}\int_0^{\pi/2}\sin^{n-2}x\,dx = \frac{n-1}{n}\int_0^{\pi/2}\sin^{n-2}x\,dx$$

(b) Using $n = 3$ in part (a), we have $\int_0^{\pi/2}\sin^3 x\,dx = \frac{2}{3}\int_0^{\pi/2}\sin x\,dx = \left[-\frac{2}{3}\cos x\right]_0^{\pi/2} = \frac{2}{3}$.

Using $n = 5$ in part (a), we have $\int_0^{\pi/2}\sin^5 x\,dx = \frac{4}{5}\int_0^{\pi/2}\sin^3 x\,dx = \frac{4}{5}\cdot\frac{2}{3} = \frac{8}{15}$.

(c) The formula holds for $n = 1$ (that is, $2n + 1 = 3$) by (b). Assume it holds for some $k \geq 1$. Then

$$\int_0^{\pi/2}\sin^{2k+1}x\,dx = \frac{2\cdot 4\cdot 6\cdot\,\cdots\,\cdot(2k)}{3\cdot 5\cdot 7\cdot\,\cdots\,\cdot(2k+1)}.\ \text{By Example 6,}$$

$$\int_0^{\pi/2}\sin^{2k+3}x\,dx = \frac{2k+2}{2k+3}\int_0^{\pi/2}\sin^{2k+1}x\,dx = \frac{2k+2}{2k+3}\cdot\frac{2\cdot 4\cdot 6\cdot\,\cdots\,\cdot(2k)}{3\cdot 5\cdot 7\cdot\,\cdots\,\cdot(2k+1)}$$

$$= \frac{2\cdot 4\cdot 6\cdot\,\cdots\,\cdot(2k)[2(k+1)]}{3\cdot 5\cdot 7\cdot\,\cdots\,\cdot(2k+1)[2(k+1)+1]},$$

so the formula holds for $n = k + 1$. By induction, the formula holds for all $n \geq 1$.

39. Let $u = (\ln x)^n$, $dv = dx$ $\Rightarrow$ $du = n(\ln x)^{n-1}(dx/x)$, $v = x$. By Equation 2,

$\int(\ln x)^n\,dx = x(\ln x)^n - \int nx(\ln x)^{n-1}(dx/x) = x(\ln x)^n - n\int(\ln x)^{n-1}\,dx$.

41. By repeated applications of the reduction formula in Exercise 39,

$$\int (\ln x)^3 \, dx = x \, (\ln x)^3 - 3 \int (\ln x)^2 \, dx = x(\ln x)^3 - 3\big[x(\ln x)^2 - 2 \int (\ln x)^1 \, dx\big]$$

$$= x \, (\ln x)^3 - 3x(\ln x)^2 + 6\big[x(\ln x)^1 - 1 \int (\ln x)^0 \, dx\big]$$

$$= x \, (\ln x)^3 - 3x(\ln x)^2 + 6x \ln x - 6 \int 1 \, dx = x \, (\ln x)^3 - 3x(\ln x)^2 + 6x \ln x - 6x + C$$

43. Since $v(t) > 0$ for all t, the desired distance is $s(t) = \int_0^t v(w) \, dw = \int_0^t w^2 e^{-w} \, dw$.

First let $u = w^2$, $dv = e^{-w} \, dw$ $\Rightarrow$ $du = 2w \, dw$, $v = -e^{-w}$. Then $s(t) = \big[-w^2 e^{-w}\big]_0^t + 2 \int_0^t w e^{-w} \, dw$.

Next let $U = w$, $dV = e^{-w} \, dw$ $\Rightarrow$ $dU = dw$, $V = -e^{-w}$. Then

$$s(t) = -t^2 e^{-t} + 2\Big(\big[-w e^{-w}\big]_0^t + \int_0^t e^{-w} \, dw\Big) = -t^2 e^{-t} + 2\Big(-te^{-t} + 0 + \big[-e^{-w}\big]_0^t\Big)$$

$$= -t^2 e^{-t} + 2(-te^{-t} - e^{-t} + 1) = -t^2 e^{-t} - 2te^{-t} - 2e^{-t} + 2 = 2 - e^{-t}(t^2 + 2t + 2) \text{ meters}$$

45. For $I = \int_1^4 x f''(x) \, dx$, let $u = x$, $dv = f''(x) \, dx$ $\Rightarrow$ $du = dx$, $v = f'(x)$. Then

$$I = \big[x f'(x)\big]_1^4 - \int_1^4 f'(x) \, dx = 4 f'(4) - 1 \cdot f'(1) - [f(4) - f(1)] = 4 \cdot 3 - 1 \cdot 5 - (7 - 2) = 12 - 5 - 5 = 2.$$

We used the fact that f'' is continuous to guarantee that I exists.

47. Suppose $f(0) = g(0) = 0$ and let $u = f(x)$, $dv = g''(x) \, dx$ $\Rightarrow$ $du = f'(x) \, dx$, $v = g'(x)$.

Then $\int_0^a f(x) g''(x) \, dx = \Big[f(x) g'(x)\Big]_0^a - \int_0^a f'(x) g'(x) \, dx = f(a) g'(a) - \int_0^a f'(x) g'(x) \, dx$.

Now let $U = f'(x)$, $dV = g'(x) \, dx$ $\Rightarrow$ $dU = f''(x) \, dx$ and $V = g(x)$, so

$$\int_0^a f'(x) g'(x) \, dx = \Big[f'(x) g(x)\Big]_0^a - \int_0^a f''(x) g(x) \, dx = f'(a) g(a) - \int_0^a f''(x) g(x) \, dx.$$

Combining the two results, we get $\int_0^a f(x) g''(x) \, dx = f(a) g'(a) - f'(a) g(a) + \int_0^a f''(x) g(x) \, dx$.

5.7 Additional Techniques of Integration

1. $\int \sin^3 x \cos^2 x \, dx = \int \sin^2 x \cos^2 x \sin x \, dx = \int (1 - \cos^2 x) \cos^2 x \sin x \, dx$

$$= \int (1 - u^2) u^2 (-du) \qquad [u = \cos x, \; du = -\sin x \, dx]$$

$$= \int (u^2 - 1) u^2 \, du = \int (u^4 - u^2) \, du = \tfrac{1}{5} u^5 - \tfrac{1}{3} u^3 + C = \tfrac{1}{5} \cos^5 x - \tfrac{1}{3} \cos^3 x + C$$

3. $\int_{\pi/2}^{3\pi/4} \sin^5 x \cos^3 x \, dx = \int_{\pi/2}^{3\pi/4} \sin^5 x \cos^2 x \cos x \, dx = \int_{\pi/2}^{3\pi/4} \sin^5 x \, (1 - \sin^2 x) \cos x \, dx$

$$= \int_1^{\sqrt{2}/2} u^5 (1 - u^2) \, du \qquad [u = \sin x, \; du = \cos x \, dx]$$

$$= \int_1^{\sqrt{2}/2} (u^5 - u^7) \, du = \big[\tfrac{1}{6} u^6 - \tfrac{1}{8} u^8\big]_1^{\sqrt{2}/2} = \Big(\tfrac{1/8}{6} - \tfrac{1/16}{8}\Big) - \big(\tfrac{1}{6} - \tfrac{1}{8}\big) = -\tfrac{11}{384}$$

5. $\int_0^{2\pi} \cos^2 (6\theta) \, d\theta = \tfrac{1}{2} \int_0^{2\pi} [1 + \cos(12\theta)] \, d\theta = \tfrac{1}{2} \big[\theta + \tfrac{1}{12} \sin(12\theta)\big]_0^{2\pi} = \tfrac{1}{2} [(2\pi + 0) - (0 + 0)] = \pi$

7. Let $u = \sec x$. Then $du = \sec x \tan x \, dx$, so

$$\int \tan^3 x \sec x \, dx = \int (\tan^2 x)(\tan x \sec x) \, dx = \int (\sec^2 x - 1)(\sec x \tan x \, dx)$$

$$= \int (u^2 - 1) \, du = \tfrac{1}{3} u^3 - u + C = \tfrac{1}{3} \sec^3 x - \sec x + C$$

9. Let $u = \tan x$. Then $du = \sec^2 x\, dx$, so

$$\int_0^{\pi/4} \tan^2 x \sec^4 x\, dx = \int_0^{\pi/4} \tan^2 x \sec^2 x\, (\sec^2 x\, dx) = \int_0^{\pi/4} \tan^2 x\, (1 + \tan^2 x)(\sec^2 x\, dx)$$

$$= \int_0^1 u^2 (1 + u^2)\, du = \int_0^1 (u^2 + u^4)\, du = \left[\tfrac{1}{3} u^3 + \tfrac{1}{5} u^5\right]_0^1 = \tfrac{1}{3} + \tfrac{1}{5} = \tfrac{8}{15}$$

11. $x = 3 \sin \theta$, where $-\pi/2 \le \theta \le \pi/2$. Then $dx = 3 \cos \theta\, d\theta$ and

$$\sqrt{9 - x^2} = \sqrt{9 - 9 \sin^2 \theta} = \sqrt{9 \cos^2 \theta} = 3\, |\cos \theta| = 3 \cos \theta. \text{ (Note that } \cos \theta \ge 0 \text{ because } -\pi/2 \le \theta \le \pi/2.)$$

Thus, substitution gives

$$\int \frac{\sqrt{9 - x^2}}{x^2}\, dx = \int \frac{3 \cos \theta}{9 \sin^2 \theta}\, 3 \cos \theta\, d\theta = \int \frac{\cos^2 \theta}{\sin^2 \theta}\, d\theta = \int \cot^2 \theta\, d\theta$$

$$= \int (\csc^2 \theta - 1)\, d\theta = -\cot \theta - \theta + C$$

Since this is an indefinite integral, we must return to the original

variable x. This can be done either by using trigonometric identities to

express $\cot \theta$ in terms of $\sin \theta = x/3$ or by drawing a diagram, as

shown, where θ is interpreted as an angle of a right triangle.

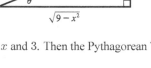

Since $\sin \theta = x/3$, we label the opposite side and the hypotenuse as having lengths x and 3. Then the Pythagorean Theorem

gives the length of the adjacent side as $\sqrt{9 - x^2}$, so we can simply read the value of $\cot \theta$ from the figure: $\cot \theta = \dfrac{\sqrt{9 - x^2}}{x}$.

(Although $\theta > 0$ in the diagram, this expression for $\cot \theta$ is valid even when $\theta < 0$.) Since $\sin \theta = x/3$, we have

$\theta = \sin^{-1}(x/3)$ and so $\displaystyle\int \frac{\sqrt{9 - x^2}}{x^2}\, dx = -\frac{\sqrt{9 - x^2}}{x} - \sin^{-1}\left(\frac{x}{3}\right) + C.$

13. $x = 2 \tan \theta$, where $-\pi/2 < \theta < \pi/2$. Then $dx = 2 \sec^2 \theta\, d\theta$ and

$$\sqrt{x^2 + 4} = \sqrt{(2 \tan \theta)^2 + 4} = \sqrt{4 \tan^2 \theta + 4}$$

$$= \sqrt{4(\tan^2 \theta + 1)} = 2 \sqrt{\sec^2 \theta} = 2\, |\sec \theta|$$

$$= 2 \sec \theta \quad [\text{since } \sec \theta \ge 0 \text{ for } -\pi/2 < \theta < \pi/2].$$

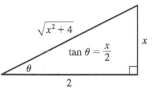

Thus, substitution gives

$$\int \frac{1}{x^2 \sqrt{x^2 + 4}}\, dx = \int \frac{1}{4 \tan^2 \theta\, (2 \sec \theta)}\, (2 \sec^2 \theta\, d\theta) = \frac{1}{4} \int \frac{\sec \theta}{\tan^2 \theta}\, d\theta = \frac{1}{4} \int \frac{1}{\cos \theta} \cdot \frac{\cos^2 \theta}{\sin^2 \theta}\, d\theta$$

$$= \frac{1}{4} \int \frac{\cos \theta}{\sin^2 \theta}\, d\theta = \frac{1}{4} \int \frac{1}{u^2}\, du \quad [u = \sin \theta,\, du = \cos \theta\, d\theta]$$

$$= \frac{1}{4}\left(-\frac{1}{u}\right) + C = -\frac{1}{4} \frac{1}{\sin \theta} + C = -\frac{1}{4} \cdot \frac{\sqrt{x^2 + 4}}{x} + C = -\frac{\sqrt{x^2 + 4}}{4x} + C$$

15. Let $t = \sec \theta$, so $dt = \sec \theta \tan \theta\, d\theta$, $t = \sqrt{2} \;\Rightarrow\; \theta = \frac{\pi}{4}$, and $t = 2 \;\Rightarrow\; \theta = \frac{\pi}{3}$. Then

$$\int_{\sqrt{2}}^2 \frac{1}{t^3 \sqrt{t^2 - 1}}\, dt = \int_{\pi/4}^{\pi/3} \frac{1}{\sec^3 \theta \tan \theta}\, \sec \theta \tan \theta\, d\theta = \int_{\pi/4}^{\pi/3} \frac{1}{\sec^2 \theta}\, d\theta = \int_{\pi/4}^{\pi/3} \cos^2 \theta\, d\theta$$

$$= \int_{\pi/4}^{\pi/3} \tfrac{1}{2}(1 + \cos 2\theta)\, d\theta = \tfrac{1}{2}\left[\theta + \tfrac{1}{2} \sin 2\theta\right]_{\pi/4}^{\pi/3}$$

$$= \tfrac{1}{2}\left[\left(\tfrac{\pi}{3} + \tfrac{1}{2} \tfrac{\sqrt{3}}{2}\right) - \left(\tfrac{\pi}{4} + \tfrac{1}{2} \cdot 1\right)\right] = \tfrac{1}{2}\left(\tfrac{\pi}{12} + \tfrac{\sqrt{3}}{4} - \tfrac{1}{2}\right) = \tfrac{\pi}{24} + \tfrac{\sqrt{3}}{8} - \tfrac{1}{4}$$

17. Let $x = 2\sin\theta$, where $-\pi/2 \le \theta \le \pi/2$. Then $dx = 2\cos\theta\,d\theta$ and

$$\sqrt{4 - x^2} = \sqrt{4 - 4\sin^2\theta} = \sqrt{4\cos^2\theta} = 2\left|\cos\theta\right| = 2\cos\theta.$$

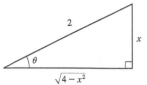

Thus, $\displaystyle\int \frac{dx}{x^2\sqrt{4 - x^2}} = \int \frac{2\cos\theta}{4\sin^2\theta(2\cos\theta)}\,d\theta = \frac{1}{4}\int \csc^2\theta\,d\theta$

$$= -\frac{1}{4}\cot\theta + C = -\frac{\sqrt{4 - x^2}}{4x} + C \quad \text{[see figure]}$$

19. (a) $\displaystyle\frac{2x}{(x + 3)(3x + 1)} = \frac{A}{x + 3} + \frac{B}{3x + 1}$

(b) $\displaystyle\frac{1}{x^3 + 2x^2 + x} = \frac{1}{x(x^2 + 2x + 1)} = \frac{1}{x(x + 1)^2} = \frac{A}{x} + \frac{B}{x + 1} + \frac{C}{(x + 1)^2}$

21. $\displaystyle\frac{5x + 1}{(2x + 1)(x - 1)} = \frac{A}{2x + 1} + \frac{B}{x - 1}$. Multiply both sides by $(2x + 1)(x - 1)$ to get $5x + 1 = A(x - 1) + B(2x + 1)\quad \Rightarrow$

$5x + 1 = Ax - A + 2Bx + B\quad \Rightarrow\quad 5x + 1 = (A + 2B)x + (-A + B)$.

The coefficients of x must be equal and the constant terms are also equal, so $A + 2B = 5$ and

$-A + B = 1$. Adding these equations gives us $3B = 6\quad\Leftrightarrow\quad B = 2$, and hence, $A = 1$. Thus,

$$\int \frac{5x + 1}{(2x + 1)(x - 1)}\,dx = \int \left(\frac{1}{2x + 1} + \frac{2}{x - 1}\right) dx = \tfrac{1}{2}\ln|2x + 1| + 2\ln|x - 1| + C.$$

Another method: Substituting 1 for x in the equation $5x + 1 = A(x - 1) + B(2x + 1)$ gives $6 = 3B\quad\Leftrightarrow\quad B = 2$.

Substituting $-\frac{1}{2}$ for x gives $-\frac{3}{2} = -\frac{3}{2}A\quad\Leftrightarrow\quad A = 1$.

23. $\displaystyle\frac{1}{x^2 - 1} = \frac{1}{(x + 1)(x - 1)} = \frac{A}{x + 1} + \frac{B}{x - 1}$. Multiply both sides by $(x + 1)(x - 1)$ to get $1 = A(x - 1) + B(x + 1)\quad\Rightarrow$

$1 = Ax - A + Bx + B\quad\Rightarrow\quad 1 = (A + B)x + (-A + B)$. The coefficients of x must be equal and the constant terms are

also equal, so $A + B = 0$ and $-A + B = 1$. Adding these equations gives us $2B = 1\quad\Leftrightarrow\quad B = \frac{1}{2}$, and hence, $A = -\frac{1}{2}$.

Thus

$$\int_2^3 \frac{1}{x^2 - 1}\,dx = \int_2^3 \left(\frac{-1/2}{x + 1} + \frac{1/2}{x - 1}\right) dx = \left[-\tfrac{1}{2}\ln|x + 1| + \tfrac{1}{2}\ln|x - 1|\right]_2^3$$

$$= \left(-\tfrac{1}{2}\ln 4 + \tfrac{1}{2}\ln 2\right) - \left(-\tfrac{1}{2}\ln 3 + \tfrac{1}{2}\ln 1\right) = \tfrac{1}{2}(\ln 2 + \ln 3 - \ln 4) \quad \left[\text{or } \tfrac{1}{2}\ln\tfrac{3}{2}\right]$$

Another method: Substituting 1 for x in the equation $1 = A(x - 1) + B(x + 1)$ gives $1 = 2B\quad\Leftrightarrow\quad B = \frac{1}{2}$.

Substituting -1 for x gives $1 = -2A\quad\Leftrightarrow\quad A = -\frac{1}{2}$.

25. $\displaystyle\frac{10}{(x - 1)(x^2 + 9)} = \frac{A}{x - 1} + \frac{Bx + C}{x^2 + 9}$. Multiply both sides by $(x - 1)(x^2 + 9)$ to get

$10 = A(x^2 + 9) + (Bx + C)(x - 1)\ (\star)$. Substituting 1 for x gives $10 = 10A\quad\Leftrightarrow\quad A = 1$. Substituting 0 for x gives

$10 = 9A - C\quad\Rightarrow\quad C = 9(1) - 10 = -1$. The coefficients of the x^2-terms in $(\star)$ must be equal, so $0 = A + B\quad\Rightarrow$

$B = -1$. Thus,

$$\int \frac{10}{(x - 1)(x^2 + 9)}\,dx = \int \left(\frac{1}{x - 1} + \frac{-x - 1}{x^2 + 9}\right) dx = \int \left(\frac{1}{x - 1} - \frac{x}{x^2 + 9} - \frac{1}{x^2 + 9}\right) dx$$

$$= \ln|x - 1| - \tfrac{1}{2}\ln(x^2 + 9) - \tfrac{1}{3}\tan^{-1}\left(\tfrac{x}{3}\right) + C$$

In the second term we used the substitution $u = x^2 + 9$ and in the last term we used Formula 10.

27. $\dfrac{x^3 + x^2 + 2x + 1}{(x^2 + 1)(x^2 + 2)} = \dfrac{Ax + B}{x^2 + 1} + \dfrac{Cx + D}{x^2 + 2}$. Multiply both sides by $(x^2 + 1)(x^2 + 2)$ to get

$x^3 + x^2 + 2x + 1 = (Ax + B)(x^2 + 2) + (Cx + D)(x^2 + 1) \quad \Leftrightarrow$

$x^3 + x^2 + 2x + 1 = (Ax^3 + Bx^2 + 2Ax + 2B) + (Cx^3 + Dx^2 + Cx + D) \quad \Leftrightarrow$

$x^3 + x^2 + 2x + 1 = (A + C)x^3 + (B + D)x^2 + (2A + C)x + (2B + D)$. Comparing coefficients gives us the following

system of equations:

$$A + C = 1 \quad \textbf{(1)} \qquad\qquad B + D = 1 \quad \textbf{(2)}$$
$$2A + C = 2 \quad \textbf{(3)} \qquad\qquad 2B + D = 1 \quad \textbf{(4)}$$

Subtracting equation **(1)** from equation **(3)** gives us $A = 1$, so $C = 0$. Subtracting equation **(2)** from equation **(4)** gives us

$B = 0$, so $D = 1$. Thus, $I = \displaystyle\int \dfrac{x^3 + x^2 + 2x + 1}{(x^2 + 1)(x^2 + 2)}\,dx = \int \left(\dfrac{x}{x^2 + 1} + \dfrac{1}{x^2 + 2} \right) dx$. For $\displaystyle\int \dfrac{x}{x^2 + 1}\,dx$, let $u = x^2 + 1$

so $du = 2x\,dx$ and then $\displaystyle\int \dfrac{x}{x^2 + 1}\,dx = \dfrac{1}{2} \int \dfrac{1}{u}\,du = \dfrac{1}{2}\ln|u| + C = \dfrac{1}{2}\ln(x^2 + 1) + C$. For $\displaystyle\int \dfrac{1}{x^2 + 2}\,dx$, use

Formula 10 with $a = \sqrt{2}$. So $\displaystyle\int \dfrac{1}{x^2 + 2}\,dx = \int \dfrac{1}{x^2 + \left(\sqrt{2}\right)^2}\,dx = \dfrac{1}{\sqrt{2}}\tan^{-1}\dfrac{x}{\sqrt{2}} + C$.

Thus, $I = \dfrac{1}{2}\ln(x^2 + 1) + \dfrac{1}{\sqrt{2}}\tan^{-1}\dfrac{x}{\sqrt{2}} + C$.

29. $\displaystyle\int \dfrac{x}{x - 6}\,dx = \int \dfrac{(x - 6) + 6}{x - 6}\,dx = \int \left(1 + \dfrac{6}{x - 6} \right) dx = x + 6\ln|x - 6| + C$

31.

$$x^2 + 4 \,)\overline{\begin{array}{l} x \\ x^3 + 0x^2 + 0x + 4 \\ \underline{ x^3 + 4x} \\ -4x + 4 \end{array}}$$

By long division, $\dfrac{x^3 + 4}{x^2 + 4} = x + \dfrac{-4x + 4}{x^2 + 4}$. Thus,

$\displaystyle\int \dfrac{x^3 + 4}{x^2 + 4}\,dx = \int \left(x + \dfrac{-4x + 4}{x^2 + 4} \right) dx = \int \left(x - \dfrac{4x}{x^2 + 4} + \dfrac{4}{x^2 + 2^2} \right) dx$

$\qquad = \dfrac{1}{2}x^2 - 4 \cdot \dfrac{1}{2}\ln|x^2 + 4| + 4 \cdot \dfrac{1}{2}\tan^{-1}\left(\dfrac{x}{2}\right) + C = \dfrac{1}{2}x^2 - 2\ln(x^2 + 4) + 2\tan^{-1}\left(\dfrac{x}{2}\right) + C$

33. Let $u = \sqrt{x}$, so $u^2 = x$ and $dx = 2u\,du$. Thus,

$$\int_9^{16} \dfrac{\sqrt{x}}{x - 4}\,dx = \int_3^4 \dfrac{u}{u^2 - 4}\,2u\,du = 2\int_3^4 \dfrac{u^2}{u^2 - 4}\,du = 2\int_3^4 \left(1 + \dfrac{4}{u^2 - 4} \right) du \qquad \text{[by long division]}$$

$$= 2 + 8\int_3^4 \dfrac{du}{(u + 2)(u - 2)} \quad (\star)$$

Multiply $\dfrac{1}{(u + 2)(u - 2)} = \dfrac{A}{u + 2} + \dfrac{B}{u - 2}$ by $(u + 2)(u - 2)$ to get $1 = A(u - 2) + B(u + 2)$. Equating coefficients we

get $A + B = 0$ and $-2A + 2B = 1$. Solving gives us $B = \frac{1}{4}$ and $A = -\frac{1}{4}$, so $\dfrac{1}{(u + 2)(u - 2)} = \dfrac{-1/4}{u + 2} + \dfrac{1/4}{u - 2}$ and $(\star)$ is

$$2 + 8\int_3^4 \left(\dfrac{-1/4}{u + 2} + \dfrac{1/4}{u - 2} \right) du = 2 + 8\left[-\tfrac{1}{4}\ln|u + 2| + \tfrac{1}{4}\ln|u - 2| \right]_3^4 = 2 + \left[2\ln|u - 2| - 2\ln|u + 2| \right]_3^4$$

$$= 2 + 2\left[\ln\left| \dfrac{u - 2}{u + 2} \right| \right]_3^4 = 2 + 2\left(\ln\tfrac{2}{6} - \ln\tfrac{1}{5} \right) = 2 + 2\ln\dfrac{2/6}{1/5}$$

$$= 2 + 2\ln\tfrac{5}{3} \text{ or } 2 + \ln\left(\tfrac{5}{3}\right)^2 = 2 + \ln\tfrac{25}{9}$$

35. $x^2 + x + 1 = x^2 + x + \frac{1}{4} + 1 - \frac{1}{4}$ [add and subtract the square of one-half the coefficient of x to complete the square]

$$= x^2 + x + \frac{1}{4} + \frac{3}{4} = \left(x + \frac{1}{2}\right)^2 + \left(\frac{\sqrt{3}}{2}\right)^2$$

So $I = \int \dfrac{dx}{x^2 + x + 1} = \int \dfrac{1}{\left(x + \frac{1}{2}\right)^2 + \left(\frac{\sqrt{3}}{2}\right)^2}\, dx$. Now let $u = x + \frac{1}{2}$ $\Rightarrow$ $du = dx$ and

$$I = \int \dfrac{1}{u^2 + \left(\frac{\sqrt{3}}{2}\right)^2}\, du = \dfrac{1}{\frac{\sqrt{3}}{2}} \tan^{-1} \dfrac{u}{\frac{\sqrt{3}}{2}} + C = \dfrac{2}{\sqrt{3}} \tan^{-1} \dfrac{2\left(x + \frac{1}{2}\right)}{\sqrt{3}} + C = \dfrac{2}{\sqrt{3}} \tan^{-1} \dfrac{2x + 1}{\sqrt{3}} + C.$$

5.8 Integration Using Tables and Computer Algebra Systems

Keep in mind that there are several ways to approach many of these exercises, and different methods can lead to different forms of the answer.

1. Let $u = \pi x$, so that $du = \pi\, dx$. Then

$$\int \tan^3(\pi x)\, dx = \int \tan^3 u \left(\tfrac{1}{\pi}\, du\right) = \tfrac{1}{\pi} \int \tan^3 u\, du \overset{69}{=} \tfrac{1}{\pi} \left[\tfrac{1}{2} \tan^2 u + \ln|\cos u|\right] + C$$

$$= \tfrac{1}{2\pi} \tan^2(\pi x) + \tfrac{1}{\pi} \ln|\cos(\pi x)| + C$$

3. Let $u = 2x$ and $a = 3$. Then $du = 2\, dx$ and

$$\int \dfrac{dx}{x^2 \sqrt{4x^2 + 9}} = \int \dfrac{\frac{1}{2}\, du}{\frac{u^2}{4} \sqrt{u^2 + a^2}} = 2 \int \dfrac{du}{u^2 \sqrt{a^2 + u^2}} \overset{28}{=} -2\, \dfrac{\sqrt{a^2 + u^2}}{a^2 u} + C$$

$$= -2\, \dfrac{\sqrt{4x^2 + 9}}{9 \cdot 2x} + C = -\dfrac{\sqrt{4x^2 + 9}}{9x} + C$$

5. Let $u = e^x$, so that $du = e^x\, dx$ and $e^{2x} = u^2$. Then

$$\int e^{2x} \arctan(e^x)\, dx = \int u^2 \arctan u \left(\dfrac{du}{u}\right) = \int u \arctan u\, du$$

$$\overset{92}{=} \dfrac{u^2 + 1}{2} \arctan u - \dfrac{u}{2} + C = \dfrac{1}{2}(e^{2x} + 1) \arctan(e^x) - \dfrac{1}{2} e^x + C$$

7. $\int x^3 \sin x\, dx \overset{84}{=} -x^3 \cos x + 3\int x^2 \cos x\, dx$, $\int x^2 \cos x\, dx \overset{85}{=} x^2 \sin x - 2\int x \sin x\, dx$, and

$\int x \sin x\, dx \overset{82}{=} \sin x - x \cos x + C$. Substituting, we get

$\int x^3 \sin x\, dx = -x^3 \cos x + 3\left[x^2 \sin x - 2(\sin x - x \cos x)\right] + C = -x^3 \cos x + 3x^2 \sin x - 6 \sin x + 6x \cos x + C$.

So $\int_0^\pi x^3 \sin x\, dx = \left[-x^3 \cos x + 3x^2 \sin x - 6 \sin x + 6x \cos x\right]_0^\pi = (-\pi^3 \cdot -1 + 6\pi \cdot -1) - (0) = \pi^3 - 6\pi$.

9. $\displaystyle\int \dfrac{\tan^3(1/z)}{z^2}\, dz \quad \begin{bmatrix} u = 1/z, \\ du = -dz/z^2 \end{bmatrix} = -\int \tan^3 u\, du \overset{69}{=} -\tfrac{1}{2} \tan^2 u - \ln|\cos u| + C = -\tfrac{1}{2} \tan^2\left(\tfrac{1}{z}\right) - \ln\left|\cos\left(\tfrac{1}{z}\right)\right| + C$

11. Let $z = 6 + 4y - 4y^2 = 6 - (4y^2 - 4y + 1) + 1 = 7 - (2y - 1)^2$, $u = 2y - 1$, and $a = \sqrt{7}$. Then $z = a^2 - u^2$, $du = 2\, dy$, and

$$\int y \sqrt{6 + 4y - 4y^2}\, dy = \int y \sqrt{z}\, dy = \int \tfrac{1}{2}(u + 1) \sqrt{a^2 - u^2}\, \tfrac{1}{2}\, du = \tfrac{1}{4}\int u \sqrt{a^2 - u^2}\, du + \tfrac{1}{4}\int \sqrt{a^2 - u^2}\, du$$

$$= \tfrac{1}{4}\int \sqrt{a^2 - u^2}\, du - \tfrac{1}{8}\int (-2u) \sqrt{a^2 - u^2}\, du$$

$$\overset{30}{=} \dfrac{u}{8} \sqrt{a^2 - u^2} + \dfrac{a^2}{8} \sin^{-1}\left(\dfrac{u}{a}\right) - \dfrac{1}{8}\int \sqrt{w}\, dw \quad \begin{bmatrix} w = a^2 - u^2, \\ dw = -2u\, du \end{bmatrix}$$

$$= \dfrac{2y - 1}{8} \sqrt{6 + 4y - 4y^2} + \dfrac{7}{8} \sin^{-1} \dfrac{2y - 1}{\sqrt{7}} - \dfrac{1}{8} \cdot \dfrac{2}{3} w^{3/2} + C$$

$$= \dfrac{2y - 1}{8} \sqrt{6 + 4y - 4y^2} + \dfrac{7}{8} \sin^{-1} \dfrac{2y - 1}{\sqrt{7}} - \dfrac{1}{12}(6 + 4y - 4y^2)^{3/2} + C$$

This can be rewritten as

$$\sqrt{6+4y-4y^2}\left[\frac{1}{8}(2y-1)-\frac{1}{12}(6+4y-4y^2)\right]+\frac{7}{8}\sin^{-1}\frac{2y-1}{\sqrt{7}}+C$$

$$=\left(\frac{1}{3}y^2-\frac{1}{12}y-\frac{5}{8}\right)\sqrt{6+4y-4y^2}+\frac{7}{8}\sin^{-1}\left(\frac{2y-1}{\sqrt{7}}\right)+C$$

$$=\frac{1}{24}(8y^2-2y-15)\sqrt{6+4y-4y^2}+\frac{7}{8}\sin^{-1}\left(\frac{2y-1}{\sqrt{7}}\right)+C$$

13. Let $u=\sin x$. Then $du=\cos x\,dx$, so

$$\int \sin^2 x\cos x\ln(\sin x)\,dx=\int u^2\ln u\,du\overset{101}{=}\frac{u^{2+1}}{(2+1)^2}[(2+1)\ln u-1]+C=\frac{1}{9}u^3(3\ln u-1)+C$$

$$=\frac{1}{9}\sin^3 x\,[3\ln(\sin x)-1]+C$$

15. Let $u=e^x$ and $a=\sqrt{3}$. Then $du=e^x\,dx$ and

$$\int\frac{e^x}{3-e^{2x}}\,dx=\int\frac{du}{a^2-u^2}\overset{19}{=}\frac{1}{2a}\ln\left|\frac{u+a}{u-a}\right|+C=\frac{1}{2\sqrt{3}}\ln\left|\frac{e^x+\sqrt{3}}{e^x-\sqrt{3}}\right|+C.$$

17. $\displaystyle\int\frac{x^4\,dx}{\sqrt{x^{10}-2}}=\int\frac{x^4\,dx}{\sqrt{(x^5)^2-2}}=\frac{1}{5}\int\frac{du}{\sqrt{u^2-2}}$ $\begin{bmatrix}u=x^5,\\ du=5x^4\,dx\end{bmatrix}$

$$\overset{43}{=}\frac{1}{5}\ln\left|u+\sqrt{u^2-2}\right|+C=\frac{1}{5}\ln\left|x^5+\sqrt{x^{10}-2}\right|+C$$

19. Let $u=\ln x$ and $a=2$. Then $du=dx/x$ and

$$\int\frac{\sqrt{4+(\ln x)^2}}{x}\,dx=\int\sqrt{a^2+u^2}\,du\overset{21}{=}\frac{u}{2}\sqrt{a^2+u^2}+\frac{a^2}{2}\ln\left(u+\sqrt{a^2+u^2}\right)+C$$

$$=\frac{1}{2}(\ln x)\sqrt{4+(\ln x)^2}+2\ln\left[\ln x+\sqrt{4+(\ln x)^2}\right]+C$$

21. Let $u=e^x$. Then $x=\ln u$, $dx=du/u$, so

$$\int\sqrt{e^{2x}-1}\,dx=\int\frac{\sqrt{u^2-1}}{u}\,du\overset{41}{=}\sqrt{u^2-1}-\cos^{-1}(1/u)+C=\sqrt{e^{2x}-1}-\cos^{-1}(e^{-x})+C.$$

23. (a) $\displaystyle\frac{d}{du}\left[\frac{1}{b^3}\left(a+bu-\frac{a^2}{a+bu}-2a\ln|a+bu|\right)+C\right]=\frac{1}{b^3}\left[b+\frac{ba^2}{(a+bu)^2}-\frac{2ab}{(a+bu)}\right]$

$$=\frac{1}{b^3}\left[\frac{b(a+bu)^2+ba^2-(a+bu)2ab}{(a+bu)^2}\right]=\frac{1}{b^3}\left[\frac{b^3u^2}{(a+bu)^2}\right]=\frac{u^2}{(a+bu)^2}$$

(b) Let $t=a+bu$ ⟹ $dt=b\,du$. Note that $u=\dfrac{t-a}{b}$ and $du=\dfrac{1}{b}\,dt$.

$$\int\frac{u^2\,du}{(a+bu)^2}=\frac{1}{b^3}\int\frac{(t-a)^2}{t^2}\,dt=\frac{1}{b^3}\int\frac{t^2-2at+a^2}{t^2}\,dt=\frac{1}{b^3}\int\left(1-\frac{2a}{t}+\frac{a^2}{t^2}\right)dt$$

$$=\frac{1}{b^3}\left(t-2a\ln|t|-\frac{a^2}{t}\right)+C=\frac{1}{b^3}\left(a+bu-\frac{a^2}{a+bu}-2a\ln|a+bu|\right)+C$$

25. Maple and Mathematica both give $\int\sec^4 x\,dx=\frac{2}{3}\tan x+\frac{1}{3}\tan x\sec^2 x$, while Derive gives the second

term as $\dfrac{\sin x}{3\cos^3 x}=\dfrac{1}{3}\dfrac{\sin x}{\cos x}\dfrac{1}{\cos^2 x}=\dfrac{1}{3}\tan x\sec^2 x$. Using Formula 77, we get

$\int\sec^4 x\,dx=\frac{1}{3}\tan x\sec^2 x+\frac{2}{3}\int\sec^2 x\,dx=\frac{1}{3}\tan x\sec^2 x+\frac{2}{3}\tan x+C.$

27. Derive gives $\int x^2 \sqrt{x^2 + 4}\, dx = \frac{1}{4}x(x^2 + 2)\sqrt{x^2 + 4} - 2\ln(\sqrt{x^2 + 4} + x)$. Maple gives

$\frac{1}{4}x(x^2 + 4)^{3/2} - \frac{1}{2}x\sqrt{x^2 + 4} - 2\operatorname{arcsinh}\left(\frac{1}{2}x\right)$. Applying the command `convert(%,ln);` yields

$$\frac{1}{4}x(x^2 + 4)^{3/2} - \frac{1}{2}x\sqrt{x^2 + 4} - 2\ln\left(\frac{1}{2}x + \frac{1}{2}\sqrt{x^2 + 4}\right) = \frac{1}{4}x(x^2 + 4)^{1/2}\left[(x^2 + 4) - 2\right] - 2\ln\left[(x + \sqrt{x^2 + 4})/2\right]$$

$$= \frac{1}{4}x(x^2 + 2)\sqrt{x^2 + 4} - 2\ln(\sqrt{x^2 + 4} + x) + 2\ln 2$$

Mathematica gives $\frac{1}{4}x(2 + x^2)\sqrt{3 + x^2} - 2\operatorname{arcsinh}(x/2)$. Applying the `TrigToExp` and `Simplify` commands gives

$\frac{1}{4}\left[x(2 + x^2)\sqrt{4 + x^2} - 8\log\left(\frac{1}{2}(x + \sqrt{4 + x^2})\right)\right] = \frac{1}{4}x(x^2 + 2)\sqrt{x^2 + 4} - 2\ln(x + \sqrt{4 + x^2}) + 2\ln 2$, so all are

equivalent (without constant).

Now use Formula 22 to get

$$\int x^2 \sqrt{2^2 + x^2}\, dx = \frac{x}{8}(2^2 + 2x^2)\sqrt{2^2 + x^2} - \frac{2^4}{8}\ln(x + \sqrt{2^2 + x^2}) + C$$

$$= \frac{x}{8}(2)(2 + x^2)\sqrt{4 + x^2} - 2\ln(x + \sqrt{4 + x^2}) + C$$

$$= \frac{1}{4}x(x^2 + 2)\sqrt{x^2 + 4} - 2\ln(\sqrt{x^2 + 4} + x) + C$$

29. Maple gives $\int x\sqrt{1 + 2x}\, dx = \frac{1}{10}(1 + 2x)^{5/2} - \frac{1}{6}(1 + 2x)^{3/2}$, Mathematica gives $\sqrt{1 + 2x}\left(\frac{2}{5}x^2 + \frac{1}{15}x - \frac{1}{15}\right)$, and Derive

gives $\frac{1}{15}(1 + 2x)^{3/2}(3x - 1)$. The first two expressions can be simplified to Derive's result. If we use Formula 54, we get

$$\int x\sqrt{1 + 2x}\, dx = \frac{2}{15(2)^2}(3 \cdot 2x - 2 \cdot 1)(1 + 2x)^{3/2} + C = \frac{1}{30}(6x - 2)(1 + 2x)^{3/2} + C = \frac{1}{15}(3x - 1)(1 + 2x)^{3/2}.$$

31. Maple gives $\int \tan^5 x\, dx = \frac{1}{4}\tan^4 x - \frac{1}{2}\tan^2 x + \frac{1}{2}\ln(1 + \tan^2 x)$, Mathematica gives

$\int \tan^5 x\, dx = \frac{1}{4}[-1 - 2\cos(2x)]\sec^4 x - \ln(\cos x)$, and Derive gives $\int \tan^5 x\, dx = \frac{1}{4}\tan^4 x - \frac{1}{2}\tan^2 x - \ln(\cos x)$.

These expressions are equivalent, and none includes absolute value bars or a constant of integration. Note that Mathematica's

and Derive's expressions suggest that the integral is undefined where $\cos x < 0$, which is not the case. Using Formula 75,

$\int \tan^5 x\, dx = \frac{1}{5 - 1}\tan^{5 - 1} x - \int \tan^{5 - 2} x\, dx = \frac{1}{4}\tan^4 x - \int \tan^3 x\, dx$. Using Formula 69,

$\int \tan^3 x\, dx = \frac{1}{2}\tan^2 x + \ln|\cos x| + C$, so $\int \tan^5 x\, dx = \frac{1}{4}\tan^4 x - \frac{1}{2}\tan^2 x - \ln|\cos x| + C$.

33. (a) $F(x) = \int f(x)\, dx = \int \frac{1}{x\sqrt{1 - x^2}}\, dx \overset{35}{\underset{1}{=}} -\frac{1}{1}\ln\left|\frac{1 + \sqrt{1 - x^2}}{x}\right| + C = -\ln\left|\frac{1 + \sqrt{1 - x^2}}{x}\right| + C.$

f has domain $\{x \mid x \neq 0,\, 1 - x^2 > 0\} = \{x \mid x \neq 0,\, |x| < 1\} = (-1, 0) \cup (0, 1)$. F has the same domain.

(b) Derive gives $F(x) = \ln(\sqrt{1 - x^2} - 1) - \ln x$ and Mathematica gives $F(x) = \ln x - \ln(1 + \sqrt{1 - x^2})$.

Both are correct if you take absolute values of the logarithm arguments, and both would then have the

same domain. Maple gives $F(x) = -\operatorname{arctanh}(1/\sqrt{1 - x^2})$. This function has domain

$\{x \mid |x| < 1,\, -1 < 1/\sqrt{1 - x^2} < 1\} = \{x \mid |x| < 1,\, 1/\sqrt{1 - x^2} < 1\} = \{x \mid |x| < 1,\, \sqrt{1 - x^2} > 1\} = \emptyset,$

the empty set! If we apply the command `convert(%,ln);` to Maple's answer, we get

$-\frac{1}{2}\ln\left(\frac{1}{\sqrt{1 - x^2}} + 1\right) + \frac{1}{2}\ln\left(1 - \frac{1}{\sqrt{1 - x^2}}\right)$, which has the same domain, $\emptyset$.

5.9   Approximate Integration

1. (a) $\Delta x = (b - a)/n = (4 - 0)/2 = 2$

$$L_2 = \sum_{i=1}^{2} f(x_{i-1})\,\Delta x = f(x_0)\cdot 2 + f(x_1)\cdot 2 = 2\left[f(0) + f(2)\right] = 2(0.5 + 2.5) = 6$$

$$R_2 = \sum_{i=1}^{2} f(x_i)\,\Delta x = f(x_1)\cdot 2 + f(x_2)\cdot 2 = 2\left[f(2) + f(4)\right] = 2(2.5 + 3.5) = 12$$

$$M_2 = \sum_{i=1}^{2} f(\overline{x}_i)\Delta x = f(\overline{x}_1)\cdot 2 + f(\overline{x}_2)\cdot 2 = 2\left[f(1) + f(3)\right] \approx 2(1.6 + 3.2) = 9.6$$

(b)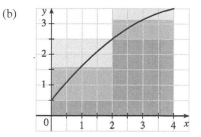

L_2 is an underestimate, since the area under the small rectangles is less than the area under the curve, and R_2 is an overestimate, since the area under the large rectangles is greater than the area under the curve. It appears that M_2 is an overestimate, though it is fairly close to I. See the solution to Exercise 39 for a proof of the fact that if f is concave down on $[a, b]$, then the Midpoint Rule is an overestimate of $\int_a^b f(x)\,dx$.

(c) $T_2 = \left(\frac{1}{2}\Delta x\right)\left[f(x_0) + 2f(x_1) + f(x_2)\right] = \frac{2}{2}[f(0) + 2f(2) + f(4)] = 0.5 + 2(2.5) + 3.5 = 9.$

This approximation is an underestimate, since the graph is concave down. Thus, $T_2 = 9 < I$. See the solution to Exercise 39 for a general proof of this conclusion.

(d) For any n, we will have $L_n < T_n < I < M_n < R_n$.

3. $f(x) = \cos\left(x^2\right),\ \Delta x = \frac{1 - 0}{4} = \frac{1}{4}$

(a) $T_4 = \frac{1}{4\cdot 2}\left[f(0) + 2f\left(\frac{1}{4}\right) + 2f\left(\frac{2}{4}\right) + 2f\left(\frac{3}{4}\right) + f(1)\right] \approx 0.895759$

(b) $M_4 = \frac{1}{4}\left[f\left(\frac{1}{8}\right) + f\left(\frac{3}{8}\right) + f\left(\frac{5}{8}\right) + f\left(\frac{7}{8}\right)\right] \approx 0.908907$

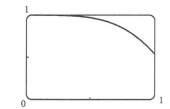

The graph shows that f is concave down on $[0, 1]$. So T_4 is an underestimate and M_4 is an overestimate. We can conclude that

$0.895759 < \int_0^1 \cos\left(x^2\right)dx < 0.908907.$

5. (a) $f(x) = \dfrac{x}{1 + x^2}, \quad \Delta x = \dfrac{b - a}{n} = \dfrac{2 - 0}{10} = \dfrac{1}{5}$

$$M_{10} = \frac{1}{5}\left[f\left(\frac{1}{10}\right) + f\left(\frac{3}{10}\right) + f\left(\frac{5}{10}\right) + \cdots + f\left(\frac{19}{10}\right)\right] \approx 0.806598$$

(b) $S_{10} = \dfrac{1}{5\cdot 3}\left[f(0) + 4f\left(\frac{1}{5}\right) + 2f\left(\frac{2}{5}\right) + 4f\left(\frac{3}{5}\right) + 2f\left(\frac{4}{5}\right) + \cdots + 4f\left(\frac{9}{5}\right) + f(2)\right] \approx 0.804779$

$$Actual:\ I = \int_0^2 \frac{x}{1 + x^2}\,dx = \left[\tfrac{1}{2}\ln\left|1 + x^2\right|\right]_0^2 \qquad [u = 1 + x^2,\, du = 2x\,dx]$$

$$= \tfrac{1}{2}\ln 5 - \tfrac{1}{2}\ln 1 = \tfrac{1}{2}\ln 5 \approx 0.804719$$

$Errors:\ E_M = $ actual $- M_{10} = I - M_{10} \approx -0.001879$

$\qquad E_S = $ actual $- S_{10} = I - S_{10} \approx -0.000060$

7. $f(x) = \sqrt[4]{1+x^2}$, $\quad \Delta x = \dfrac{2-0}{8} = \dfrac{1}{4}$

(a) $T_8 = \frac{1}{4 \cdot 2}\left[f(0) + 2f\left(\frac{1}{4}\right) + 2f\left(\frac{1}{2}\right) + \cdots + 2f\left(\frac{3}{2}\right) + 2f\left(\frac{7}{4}\right) + f(2)\right] \approx 2.413790$

(b) $M_8 = \frac{1}{4}\left[f\left(\frac{1}{8}\right) + f\left(\frac{3}{8}\right) + \cdots + f\left(\frac{13}{8}\right) + f\left(\frac{15}{8}\right)\right] \approx 2.411453$

(c) $S_8 = \frac{1}{4 \cdot 3}\left[f(0) + 4f\left(\frac{1}{4}\right) + 2f\left(\frac{1}{2}\right) + 4f\left(\frac{3}{4}\right) + 2f(1) + 4f\left(\frac{5}{4}\right) + 2f\left(\frac{3}{2}\right) + 4f\left(\frac{7}{4}\right) + f(2)\right] \approx 2.412232$

9. $f(x) = \dfrac{\ln x}{1+x}$, $\Delta x = \dfrac{2-1}{10} = \dfrac{1}{10}$

(a) $T_{10} = \frac{1}{10 \cdot 2}\left[f(1) + 2f(1.1) + 2f(1.2) + \cdots + 2f(1.8) + 2f(1.9) + f(2)\right] \approx 0.146879$

(b) $M_{10} = \frac{1}{10}\left[f(1.05) + f(1.15) + \cdots + f(1.85) + f(1.95)\right] \approx 0.147391$

(c) $S_{10} = \frac{1}{10 \cdot 3}[f(1) + 4f(1.1) + 2f(1.2) + 4f(1.3) + 2f(1.4) + 4f(1.5) + 2f(1.6) + 4f(1.7)$
$\qquad\qquad + 2f(1.8) + 4f(1.9) + f(2)]$

$\qquad \approx 0.147219$

11. $f(t) = \sin(e^{t/2})$, $\Delta t = \dfrac{\frac{1}{2}-0}{8} = \dfrac{1}{16}$

(a) $T_8 = \frac{1}{16 \cdot 2}\left[f(0) + 2f\left(\frac{1}{16}\right) + 2f\left(\frac{2}{16}\right) + \cdots + 2f\left(\frac{7}{16}\right) + f\left(\frac{1}{2}\right)\right] \approx 0.451948$

(b) $M_8 = \frac{1}{16}\left[f\left(\frac{1}{32}\right) + f\left(\frac{3}{32}\right) + f\left(\frac{5}{32}\right) + \cdots + f\left(\frac{13}{32}\right) + f\left(\frac{15}{32}\right)\right] \approx 0.451991$

(c) $S_8 = \frac{1}{16 \cdot 3}\left[f(0) + 4f\left(\frac{1}{16}\right) + 2f\left(\frac{2}{16}\right) + \cdots + 4f\left(\frac{7}{16}\right) + f\left(\frac{1}{2}\right)\right] \approx 0.451976$

13. $f(t) = e^{\sqrt{t}}\sin t$, $\Delta t = \dfrac{4-0}{8} = \dfrac{1}{2}$

(a) $T_8 = \frac{1}{2 \cdot 2}\left[f(0) + 2f\left(\frac{1}{2}\right) + 2f(1) + 2f\left(\frac{3}{2}\right) + 2f(2) + 2f\left(\frac{5}{2}\right) + 2f(3) + 2f\left(\frac{7}{2}\right) + f(4)\right] \approx 4.513618$

(b) $M_8 = \frac{1}{2}\left[f\left(\frac{1}{4}\right) + f\left(\frac{3}{4}\right) + f\left(\frac{5}{4}\right) + f\left(\frac{7}{4}\right) + f\left(\frac{9}{4}\right) + f\left(\frac{11}{4}\right) + f\left(\frac{13}{4}\right) + f\left(\frac{15}{4}\right)\right] \approx 4.748256$

(c) $S_8 = \frac{1}{2 \cdot 3}\left[f(0) + 4f\left(\frac{1}{2}\right) + 2f(1) + 4f\left(\frac{3}{2}\right) + 2f(2) + 4f\left(\frac{5}{2}\right) + 2f(3) + 4f\left(\frac{7}{2}\right) + f(4)\right] \approx 4.675111$

15. $f(x) = \dfrac{\cos x}{x}$, $\Delta x = \dfrac{5-1}{8} = \dfrac{1}{2}$

(a) $T_8 = \frac{1}{2 \cdot 2}\left[f(1) + 2f\left(\frac{3}{2}\right) + 2f(2) + \cdots + 2f(4) + 2f\left(\frac{9}{2}\right) + f(5)\right] \approx -0.495333$

(b) $M_8 = \frac{1}{2}\left[f\left(\frac{5}{4}\right) + f\left(\frac{7}{4}\right) + f\left(\frac{9}{4}\right) + f\left(\frac{11}{4}\right) + f\left(\frac{13}{4}\right) + f\left(\frac{15}{4}\right) + f\left(\frac{17}{4}\right) + f\left(\frac{19}{4}\right)\right] \approx -0.543321$

(c) $S_8 = \frac{1}{2 \cdot 3}\left[f(1) + 4f\left(\frac{3}{2}\right) + 2f(2) + 4f\left(\frac{5}{2}\right) + 2f(3) + 4f\left(\frac{7}{2}\right) + 2f(4) + 4f\left(\frac{9}{2}\right) + f(5)\right] \approx -0.526123$

17. $f(x) = \cos(x^2)$, $\Delta x = \frac{1-0}{8} = \frac{1}{8}$

(a) $T_8 = \frac{1}{8 \cdot 2}\left\{f(0) + 2\left[f\left(\frac{1}{8}\right) + f\left(\frac{2}{8}\right) + \cdots + f\left(\frac{7}{8}\right)\right] + f(1)\right\} \approx 0.902333$

$\qquad M_8 = \frac{1}{8}\left[f\left(\frac{1}{16}\right) + f\left(\frac{3}{16}\right) + f\left(\frac{5}{16}\right) + \cdots + f\left(\frac{15}{16}\right)\right] = 0.905620$

(b) $f(x) = \cos(x^2)$, $f'(x) = -2x\sin(x^2)$, $f''(x) = -2\sin(x^2) - 4x^2\cos(x^2)$. For $0 \le x \le 1$, sin and cos are positive,

so $|f''(x)| = 2\sin(x^2) + 4x^2\cos(x^2) \le 2 \cdot 1 + 4 \cdot 1 \cdot 1 = 6$ since $\sin(x^2) \le 1$ and $\cos(x^2) \le 1$ for all x,

and $x^2 \le 1$ for $0 \le x \le 1$. So for $n = 8$, we take $K = 6$, $a = 0$, and $b = 1$ in Theorem 3, to get

$|E_T| \le 6 \cdot 1^3 / (12 \cdot 8^2) = \frac{1}{128} = 0.0078125$ and $|E_M| \le \frac{1}{256} = 0.00390625$. [A better estimate is obtained by noting

from a graph of f'' that $|f''(x)| \le 4$ for $0 \le x \le 1$.]

(c) Take $K = 6$ [as in part (b)] in Theorem 3. $|E_T| \le \dfrac{K(b-a)^3}{12n^2} \le 0.0001 \quad \Leftrightarrow \quad \dfrac{6(1-0)^3}{12n^2} \le 10^{-4} \quad \Leftrightarrow$

$\dfrac{1}{2n^2} \le \dfrac{1}{10^4} \quad \Leftrightarrow \quad 2n^2 \ge 10^4 \quad \Leftrightarrow \quad n^2 \ge 5000 \quad \Leftrightarrow \quad n \ge 71$. Take $n = 71$ for T_n. For E_M, again take $K = 6$ in

Theorem 3 to get $|E_M| \le 10^{-4} \quad \Leftrightarrow \quad 4n^2 \ge 10^4 \quad \Leftrightarrow \quad n^2 \ge 2500 \quad \Leftrightarrow \quad n \ge 50$. Take $n = 50$ for M_n.

19. $f(x) = \sin x$, $\Delta x = \frac{\pi - 0}{10} = \frac{\pi}{10}$

(a) $T_{10} = \frac{\pi}{10 \cdot 2} \left[f(0) + 2f\left(\frac{\pi}{10}\right) + 2f\left(\frac{2\pi}{10}\right) + \cdots + 2f\left(\frac{9\pi}{10}\right) + f(\pi) \right] \approx 1.983524$

$M_{10} = \frac{\pi}{10} \left[f\left(\frac{\pi}{20}\right) + f\left(\frac{3\pi}{20}\right) + f\left(\frac{5\pi}{20}\right) + \cdots + f\left(\frac{19\pi}{20}\right) \right] \approx 2.008248$

$S_{10} = \frac{\pi}{10 \cdot 3} \left[f(0) + 4f\left(\frac{\pi}{10}\right) + 2f\left(\frac{2\pi}{10}\right) + 4f\left(\frac{3\pi}{10}\right) + \cdots + 4f\left(\frac{9\pi}{10}\right) + f(\pi) \right] \approx 2.000110$

Since $I = \int_0^\pi \sin x\, dx = \left[-\cos x \right]_0^\pi = 1 - (-1) = 2$, $E_T = I - T_{10} \approx 0.016476$, $E_M = I - M_{10} \approx -0.008248$,

and $E_S = I - S_{10} \approx -0.000110$.

(b) $f(x) = \sin x \quad \Rightarrow \quad \left| f^{(n)}(x) \right| \le 1$, so take $K = 1$ for all error estimates.

$|E_T| \le \dfrac{K(b-a)^3}{12n^2} = \dfrac{1(\pi - 0)^3}{12(10)^2} = \dfrac{\pi^3}{1200} \approx 0.025839.$ $|E_M| \le \dfrac{|E_T|}{2} = \dfrac{\pi^3}{2400} \approx 0.012919.$

$|E_S| \le \dfrac{K(b-a)^5}{180n^4} = \dfrac{1(\pi - 0)^5}{180(10)^4} = \dfrac{\pi^5}{1,800,000} \approx 0.000170.$

The actual error is about 64% of the error estimate in all three cases.

(c) $|E_T| \le 0.00001 \quad \Leftrightarrow \quad \dfrac{\pi^3}{12n^2} \le \dfrac{1}{10^5} \quad \Leftrightarrow \quad n^2 \ge \dfrac{10^5 \pi^3}{12} \quad \Rightarrow \quad n \ge 508.3$. Take $n = 509$ for T_n.

$|E_M| \le 0.00001 \quad \Leftrightarrow \quad \dfrac{\pi^3}{24n^2} \le \dfrac{1}{10^5} \quad \Leftrightarrow \quad n^2 \ge \dfrac{10^5 \pi^3}{24} \quad \Rightarrow \quad n \ge 359.4$. Take $n = 360$ for M_n.

$|E_S| \le 0.00001 \quad \Leftrightarrow \quad \dfrac{\pi^5}{180n^4} \le \dfrac{1}{10^5} \quad \Leftrightarrow \quad n^4 \ge \dfrac{10^5 \pi^5}{180} \quad \Rightarrow \quad n \ge 20.3.$

Take $n = 22$ for S_n (since n must be even).

21. (a) Using a CAS, we differentiate $f(x) = e^{\cos x}$ twice, and find that

$f''(x) = e^{\cos x}(\sin^2 x - \cos x)$. From the graph, we see that the maximum

value of $|f''(x)|$ occurs at the endpoints of the interval $[0, 2\pi]$.

Since $f''(0) = -e$, we can use $K = e$ or $K = 2.8$.

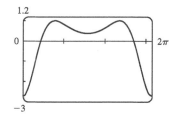

(b) A CAS gives $M_{10} \approx 7.954926518$. (In Maple, use `student[middlesum]`.)

(c) Using Theorem 3 for the Midpoint Rule, with $K = e$, we get $|E_M| \le \dfrac{e(2\pi - 0)^3}{24 \cdot 10^2} \approx 0.280945995.$

With $K = 2.8$, we get $|E_M| \le \dfrac{2.8(2\pi - 0)^3}{24 \cdot 10^2} = 0.289391916.$

(d) A CAS gives $I \approx 7.954926521$.

(e) The actual error is only about 3×10^{-9}, much less than the estimate in part (c).

(f) We use the CAS to differentiate twice more, and then graph

$$f^{(4)}(x) = e^{\cos x}(\sin^4 x - 6 \sin^2 x \cos x + 3 - 7 \sin^2 x + \cos x).$$

From the graph, we see that the maximum value of $\left|f^{(4)}(x)\right|$ occurs at the

endpoints of the interval $[0, 2\pi]$. Since $f^{(4)}(0) = 4e$, we can use $K = 4e$

or $K = 10.9$.

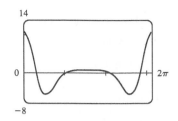

(g) A CAS gives $S_{10} \approx 7.953789422$. (In Maple, use student[simpson].)

(h) Using Theorem 4 with $K = 4e$, we get $|E_S| \leq \dfrac{4e(2\pi - 0)^5}{180 \cdot 10^4} \approx 0.059153618$.

With $K = 10.9$, we get $|E_S| \leq \dfrac{10.9(2\pi - 0)^5}{180 \cdot 10^4} \approx 0.059299814$.

(i) The actual error is about $7.954926521 - 7.953789422 \approx 0.00114$. This is quite a bit smaller than the estimate in part (h), though the difference is not nearly as great as it was in the case of the Midpoint Rule.

(j) To ensure that $|E_S| \leq 0.0001$, we use Theorem 4: $|E_S| \leq \dfrac{4e(2\pi)^5}{180 \cdot n^4} \leq 0.0001 \quad \Rightarrow \quad \dfrac{4e(2\pi)^5}{180 \cdot 0.0001} \leq n^4 \quad \Rightarrow$

$n^4 \geq 5{,}915{,}362 \quad \Leftrightarrow \quad n \geq 49.3$. So we must take $n \geq 50$ to ensure that $|I - S_n| \leq 0.0001$.

($K = 10.9$ leads to the same value of n.)

23. $I = \int_0^1 xe^x \, dx = \left[(x - 1)e^x\right]_0^1$ [parts or Formula 96] $= 0 - (-1) = 1$, $f(x) = xe^x$, $\Delta x = 1/n$

$n = 5$: $L_5 = \frac{1}{5}[f(0) + f(0.2) + f(0.4) + f(0.6) + f(0.8)] \approx 0.742943$

$R_5 = \frac{1}{5}[f(0.2) + f(0.4) + f(0.6) + f(0.8) + f(1)] \approx 1.286599$

$T_5 = \frac{1}{5 \cdot 2}[f(0) + 2f(0.2) + 2f(0.4) + 2f(0.6) + 2f(0.8) + f(1)] \approx 1.014771$

$M_5 = \frac{1}{5}[f(0.1) + f(0.3) + f(0.5) + f(0.7) + f(0.9)] \approx 0.992621$

$E_L = I - L_5 \approx 1 - 0.742943 = 0.257057$

$E_R \approx 1 - 1.286599 = -0.286599$

$E_T \approx 1 - 1.014771 = -0.014771$

$E_M \approx 1 - 0.992621 = 0.007379$

$n = 10$: $L_{10} - \frac{1}{10}[f(0) + f(0.1) + f(0.2) + \cdots + f(0.9)] \approx 0.867782$

$R_{10} = \frac{1}{10}[f(0.1) + f(0.2) + \cdots + f(0.9) + f(1)] \approx 1.139610$

$T_{10} = \frac{1}{10 \cdot 2}\{f(0) + 2[f(0.1) + f(0.2) + \cdots + f(0.9)] + f(1)\} \approx 1.003696$

$M_{10} = \frac{1}{10}[f(0.05) + f(0.15) + \cdots + f(0.85) + f(0.95)] \approx 0.998152$

$E_L = I - L_{10} \approx 1 - 0.867782 = 0.132218$

$E_R \approx 1 - 1.139610 = -0.139610$

$E_T \approx 1 - 1.003696 = -0.003696$

$E_M \approx 1 - 0.998152 = 0.001848$

$n = 20$: $L_{20} = \frac{1}{20}[f(0) + f(0.05) + f(0.10) + \cdots + f(0.95)] \approx 0.932967$

$R_{20} = \frac{1}{20}[f(0.05) + f(0.10) + \cdots + f(0.95) + f(1)] \approx 1.068881$

$T_{20} = \frac{1}{20 \cdot 2}\{f(0) + 2[f(0.05) + f(0.10) + \cdots + f(0.95)] + f(1)\} \approx 1.000924$

$M_{20} = \frac{1}{20}[f(0.025) + f(0.075) + f(0.125) + \cdots + f(0.975)] \approx 0.999538$

$E_L = I - L_{20} \approx 1 - 0.932967 = 0.067033$

$E_R \approx 1 - 1.068881 = -0.068881$

$E_T \approx 1 - 1.000924 = -0.000924$

$E_M \approx 1 - 0.999538 = 0.000462$

n	L_n	R_n	T_n	M_n
5	0.742943	1.286599	1.014771	0.992621
10	0.867782	1.139610	1.003696	0.998152
20	0.932967	1.068881	1.000924	0.999538

n	E_L	E_R	E_T	E_M
5	0.257057	−0.286599	−0.014771	0.007379
10	0.132218	−0.139610	−0.003696	0.001848
20	0.067033	−0.068881	−0.000924	0.000462

Observations:

1. E_L and E_R are always opposite in sign, as are E_T and E_M.

2. As n is doubled, E_L and E_R are decreased by about a factor of 2, and E_T and E_M are decreased by a factor of about 4.

3. The Midpoint approximation is about twice as accurate as the Trapezoidal approximation.

4. All the approximations become more accurate as the value of n increases.

5. The Midpoint and Trapezoidal approximations are much more accurate than the endpoint approximations.

25. $I = \int_0^2 x^4\,dx = \left[\frac{1}{5}x^5\right]_0^2 = \frac{32}{5} - 0 = 6.4$, $f(x) = x^4$, $\Delta x = \frac{2-0}{n} = \frac{2}{n}$

$n = 6$: $T_6 = \frac{2}{6 \cdot 2}\{f(0) + 2[f(\frac{1}{3}) + f(\frac{2}{3}) + f(\frac{3}{3}) + f(\frac{4}{3}) + f(\frac{5}{3})] + f(2)\} \approx 6.695473$

$M_6 = \frac{2}{6}[f(\frac{1}{6}) + f(\frac{3}{6}) + f(\frac{5}{6}) + f(\frac{7}{6}) + f(\frac{9}{6}) + f(\frac{11}{6})] \approx 6.252572$

$S_6 = \frac{2}{6 \cdot 3}[f(0) + 4f(\frac{1}{3}) + 2f(\frac{2}{3}) + 4f(\frac{3}{3}) + 2f(\frac{4}{3}) + 4f(\frac{5}{3}) + f(2)] \approx 6.403292$

$E_T = I - T_6 \approx 6.4 - 6.695473 = -0.295473$

$E_M \approx 6.4 - 6.252572 = 0.147428$

$E_S \approx 6.4 - 6.403292 = -0.003292$

$n = 12$: $T_{12} = \frac{2}{12 \cdot 2}\{f(0) + 2[f(\frac{1}{6}) + f(\frac{2}{6}) + f(\frac{3}{6}) + \cdots + f(\frac{11}{6})] + f(2)\} \approx 6.474023$

$M_6 = \frac{2}{12}[f(\frac{1}{12}) + f(\frac{3}{12}) + f(\frac{5}{12}) + \cdots + f(\frac{23}{12})] \approx 6.363008$

$S_6 = \frac{2}{12 \cdot 3}[f(0) + 4f(\frac{1}{6}) + 2f(\frac{2}{6}) + 4f(\frac{3}{6}) + 2f(\frac{4}{6}) + \cdots + 4f(\frac{11}{6}) + f(2)] \approx 6.400206$

$E_T = I - T_{12} \approx 6.4 - 6.474023 = -0.074023$

$E_M \approx 6.4 - 6.363008 = 0.036992$

$E_S \approx 6.4 - 6.400206 = -0.000206$

n	T_n	M_n	S_n
6	6.695473	6.252572	6.403292
12	6.474023	6.363008	6.400206

n	E_T	E_M	E_S
6	−0.295473	0.147428	−0.003292
12	−0.074023	0.036992	−0.000206

[continued]

Observations:

1. E_T and E_M are opposite in sign and decrease by a factor of about 4 as n is doubled.

2. The Simpson's approximation is much more accurate than the Midpoint and Trapezoidal approximations, and E_S seems to decrease by a factor of about 16 as n is doubled.

27. $\Delta x = (b - a)/n = (6 - 0)/6 = 1$

(a) $T_6 = \frac{\Delta x}{2}[f(0) + 2f(1) + 2f(2) + 2f(3) + 2f(4) + 2f(5) + f(6)]$

$\approx \frac{1}{2}[3 + 2(5) + 2(4) + 2(2) + 2(2.8) + 2(4) + 1]$

$= \frac{1}{2}(39.6) = 19.8$

(b) $M_6 = \Delta x[f(0.5) + f(1.5) + f(2.5) + f(3.5) + f(4.5) + f(5.5)]$

$\approx 1[4.5 + 4.7 + 2.6 + 2.2 + 3.4 + 3.2]$

$= 20.6$

(c) $S_6 = \frac{\Delta x}{3}[f(0) + 4f(1) + 2f(2) + 4f(3) + 2f(4) + 4f(5) + f(6)]$

$\approx \frac{1}{3}[3 + 4(5) + 2(4) + 4(2) + 2(2.8) + 4(4) + 1]$

$= \frac{1}{3}(61.6) = 20.5\overline{3}$

29. By the Net Change Theorem, the increase in velocity is equal to $\int_0^6 a(t)\,dt$. We use Simpson's Rule with $n = 6$ and $\Delta t = (6 - 0)/6 = 1$ to estimate this integral:

$\int_0^6 a(t)\,dt \approx S_6 = \frac{1}{3}[a(0) + 4a(1) + 2a(2) + 4a(3) + 2a(4) + 4a(5) + a(6)]$

$\approx \frac{1}{3}[0 + 4(0.5) + 2(4.1) + 4(9.8) + 2(12.9) + 4(9.5) + 0] = \frac{1}{3}(113.2) = 37.7\overline{3}$ ft/s

31. By the Net Change Theorem, the energy used is equal to $\int_0^6 P(t)\,dt$. We use Simpson's Rule with $n = 12$ and $\Delta t = \frac{6-0}{12} = \frac{1}{2}$ to estimate this integral:

$\int_0^6 P(t)\,dt \approx S_{12} = \frac{1/2}{3}[P(0) + 4P(0.5) + 2P(1) + 4P(1.5) + 2P(2) + 4P(2.5) + 2P(3)$

$\qquad + 4P(3.5) + 2P(4) + 4P(4.5) + 2P(5) + 4P(5.5) + P(6)]$

$= \frac{1}{6}[1814 + 4(1735) + 2(1686) + 4(1646) + 2(1637) + 4(1609) + 2(1604)$

$\qquad + 4(1611) + 2(1621) + 4(1666) + 2(1745) + 4(1886) + 2052]$

$= \frac{1}{6}(61{,}064) = 10{,}177.\overline{3}$ megawatt-hours

33. (a) We are given the function values at the endpoints of 8 intervals of length 0.4, so we'll use the Midpoint Rule with $n = 8/2 = 4$ and $\Delta x = (3.2 - 0)/4 = 0.8$.

$\int_0^{3.2} f(x)\,dx \approx M_4 = 0.8[f(0.4) + f(1.2) + f(2.0) + f(2.8)] = 0.8[6.5 + 6.4 + 7.6 + 8.8]$

$= 0.8(29.3) = 23.44$

(b) $-4 \le f''(x) \le 1 \;\Rightarrow\; |f''(x)| \le 4$, so use $K = 4$, $a = 0$, $b = 3.2$, and $n = 4$ in Theorem 3.

So $|E_M| \le \dfrac{4(3.2 - 0)^3}{24(4)^2} = \dfrac{128}{375} = 0.341\overline{3}$.

35. $I(\theta) = \dfrac{N^2 \sin^2 k}{k^2}$, where $k = \dfrac{\pi N d \sin \theta}{\lambda}$, $N = 10{,}000$, $d = 10^{-4}$, and $\lambda = 632.8 \times 10^{-9}$. So $I(\theta) = \dfrac{(10^4)^2 \sin^2 k}{k^2}$,

where $k = \dfrac{\pi(10^4)(10^{-4}) \sin \theta}{632.8 \times 10^{-9}}$. Now $n = 10$ and $\Delta\theta = \dfrac{10^{-6} - (-10^{-6})}{10} = 2 \times 10^{-7}$, so

$M_{10} = 2 \times 10^{-7}[I(-0.0000009) + I(-0.0000007) + \cdots + I(0.0000009)] \approx 59.4$.

37. Consider the function f whose graph is shown. The area $\int_0^2 f(x)\, dx$

is close to 2. The Trapezoidal Rule gives

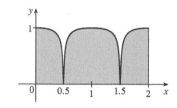

$T_2 = \frac{2-0}{2 \cdot 2}\,[f(0) + 2f(1) + f(2)] = \frac{1}{2}\,[1 + 2 \cdot 1 + 1] = 2.$

The Midpoint Rule gives $M_2 = \frac{2-0}{2}\,[f(0.5) + f(1.5)] = 1[0 + 0] = 0$,

so the Trapezoidal Rule is more accurate.

39. Since the Trapezoidal and Midpoint approximations on the interval $[a, b]$ are the sums of the Trapezoidal and Midpoint

approximations on the subintervals $[x_{i-1}, x_i]$, $i = 1, 2, \ldots, n$, we can focus our attention on one such interval. The condition

$f''(x) < 0$ for $a \le x \le b$ means that the graph of f is concave down as in Figure 5. In that figure, T_n is the area of the

trapezoid $AQRD$, $\int_a^b f(x)\, dx$ is the area of the region $AQPRD$, and M_n is the area of the trapezoid $ABCD$, so

$T_n < \int_a^b f(x)\, dx < M_n$. In general, the condition $f'' < 0$ implies that the graph of f on $[a, b]$ lies above the chord joining the

points $(a, f(a))$ and $(b, f(b))$. Thus, $\int_a^b f(x)\, dx > T_n$. Since M_n is the area under a tangent to the graph, and since $f'' < 0$

implies that the tangent lies above the graph, we also have $M_n > \int_a^b f(x)\, dx$. Thus, $T_n < \int_a^b f(x)\, dx < M_n$.

41. $T_n = \frac{1}{2}\,\Delta x\,[f(x_0) + 2f(x_1) + \cdots + 2f(x_{n-1}) + f(x_n)]$ and

$M_n = \Delta x\,[f(\overline{x}_1) + f(\overline{x}_2) + \cdots + f(\overline{x}_{n-1}) + f(\overline{x}_n)]$, where $\overline{x}_i = \frac{1}{2}(x_{i-1} + x_i)$. Now

$T_{2n} = \frac{1}{2}\left(\frac{1}{2}\Delta x\right)[f(x_0) + 2f(\overline{x}_1) + 2f(x_1) + 2f(\overline{x}_2) + 2f(x_2) + \cdots + 2f(\overline{x}_{n-1}) + 2f(x_{n-1}) + 2f(\overline{x}_n) + f(x_n)]$ so

$\frac{1}{2}(T_n + M_n) = \frac{1}{2}T_n + \frac{1}{2}M_n$

$\qquad = \frac{1}{4}\Delta x[f(x_0) + 2f(x_1) + \cdots + 2f(x_{n-1}) + f(x_n)] + \frac{1}{4}\Delta x[2f(\overline{x}_1) + 2f(\overline{x}_2) + \cdots + 2f(\overline{x}_{n-1}) + 2f(\overline{x}_n)]$

$\qquad = T_{2n}$

5.10 Improper Integrals

1. **(a)** Since $\int_1^\infty x^4 e^{-x^4}\, dx$ has an infinite interval of integration, it is an improper integral of Type I.

(b) Since $y = \sec x$ has an infinite discontinuity at $x = \frac{\pi}{2}$, $\int_0^{\pi/2} \sec x\, dx$ is a Type II improper integral.

(c) Since $y = \dfrac{x}{(x-2)(x-3)}$ has an infinite discontinuity at $x = 2$, $\displaystyle\int_0^2 \dfrac{x}{x^2 - 5x + 6}\, dx$ is a Type II improper integral.

(d) Since $\displaystyle\int_{-\infty}^0 \dfrac{1}{x^2 + 5}\, dx$ has an infinite interval of integration, it is an improper integral of Type I.

3. The area under the graph of $y = 1/x^3 = x^{-3}$ between $x = 1$ and $x = t$ is

$A(t) = \int_1^t x^{-3}\, dx = \left[-\frac{1}{2}x^{-2}\right]_1^t = -\frac{1}{2}t^{-2} - \left(-\frac{1}{2}\right) = \frac{1}{2} - 1/(2t^2)$. So the area for $1 \le x \le 10$ is

$A(10) = 0.5 - 0.005 = 0.495$, the area for $1 \le x \le 100$ is $A(100) = 0.5 - 0.00005 = 0.49995$, and the area for

$1 \le x \le 1000$ is $A(1000) = 0.5 - 0.0000005 = 0.4999995$. The total area under the curve for $x \ge 1$ is $\lim_{t \to \infty} A(t) = \lim_{t \to \infty} \left[\frac{1}{2} - 1/(2t^2)\right] = \frac{1}{2}$.

5. $\int_3^\infty \frac{1}{(x-2)^{3/2}}\, dx = \lim_{t \to \infty} \int_3^t (x-2)^{-3/2}\, dx = \lim_{t \to \infty} \left[-2(x-2)^{-1/2}\right]_3^t \qquad [u = x - 2,\, du = dx]$

$$= \lim_{t \to \infty} \left(\frac{-2}{\sqrt{t-2}} + \frac{2}{\sqrt{1}}\right) = 0 + 2 = 2. \qquad \text{Convergent}$$

7. $\int_{-\infty}^{-1} \frac{1}{\sqrt{2-w}}\, dw = \lim_{t \to -\infty} \int_t^{-1} \frac{1}{\sqrt{2-w}}\, dw = \lim_{t \to -\infty} \left[-2\sqrt{2-w}\right]_t^{-1} \qquad [u = 2 - w,\, du = -dw]$

$$= \lim_{t \to -\infty} \left[-2\sqrt{3} + 2\sqrt{2-t}\right] = \infty. \qquad \text{Divergent}$$

9. $\int_4^\infty e^{-y/2}\, dy = \lim_{t \to \infty} \int_4^t e^{-y/2}\, dy = \lim_{t \to \infty} \left[-2e^{-y/2}\right]_4^t = \lim_{t \to \infty} (-2e^{-t/2} + 2e^{-2}) = 0 + 2e^{-2} = 2e^{-2}$.

Convergent

11. $\int_{2\pi}^\infty \sin\theta\, d\theta = \lim_{t \to \infty} \int_{2\pi}^t \sin\theta\, d\theta = \lim_{t \to \infty} \left[-\cos\theta\right]_{2\pi}^t = \lim_{t \to \infty} (-\cos t + 1)$. This limit does not exist, so the integral is divergent. Divergent

13. $\int_{-\infty}^\infty xe^{-x^2}\, dx = \int_{-\infty}^0 xe^{-x^2}\, dx + \int_0^\infty xe^{-x^2}\, dx$.

$\int_{-\infty}^0 xe^{-x^2}\, dx = \lim_{t \to -\infty} \left(-\frac{1}{2}\right)\left[e^{-x^2}\right]_t^0 = \lim_{t \to -\infty} \left(-\frac{1}{2}\right)\left(1 - e^{-t^2}\right) = -\frac{1}{2} \cdot 1 = -\frac{1}{2}$, and

$\int_0^\infty xe^{-x^2}\, dx = \lim_{t \to \infty} \left(-\frac{1}{2}\right)\left[e^{-x^2}\right]_0^t = \lim_{t \to \infty} \left(-\frac{1}{2}\right)\left(e^{-t^2} - 1\right) = -\frac{1}{2} \cdot (-1) = \frac{1}{2}$.

Therefore, $\int_{-\infty}^\infty xe^{-x^2}\, dx = -\frac{1}{2} + \frac{1}{2} = 0$. Convergent

15. $\int_1^\infty \frac{x+1}{x^2+2x}\, dx = \lim_{t \to \infty} \int_1^t \frac{\frac{1}{2}(2x+2)}{x^2+2x}\, dx = \frac{1}{2} \lim_{t \to \infty} \left[\ln(x^2+2x)\right]_1^t = \frac{1}{2} \lim_{t \to \infty} \left[\ln(t^2+2t) - \ln 3\right] = \infty$.

Divergent

17. $\int_0^\infty se^{-5s}\, ds = \lim_{t \to \infty} \int_0^t se^{-5s}\, ds = \lim_{t \to \infty} \left[-\frac{1}{5}se^{-5s} - \frac{1}{25}e^{-5s}\right]$ $\left[\begin{array}{l}\text{by integration by}\\ \text{parts with } u = s\end{array}\right]$

$$= \lim_{t \to \infty} \left(-\frac{1}{5}te^{-5t} - \frac{1}{25}e^{-5t} + \frac{1}{25}\right) = 0 - 0 + \frac{1}{25} \qquad [\text{by l'Hospital's Rule}]$$

$$= \frac{1}{25}. \qquad \text{Convergent}$$

19. $\int_1^\infty \frac{\ln x}{x}\, dx = \lim_{t \to \infty} \left[\frac{(\ln x)^2}{2}\right]_1^t$ $\left[\begin{array}{l}\text{by substitution with}\\ u = \ln x,\, du = dx/x\end{array}\right]$ $= \lim_{t \to \infty} \frac{(\ln t)^2}{2} = \infty$. Divergent

21. $\int_{-\infty}^\infty \frac{x^2}{9+x^6}\, dx = \int_{-\infty}^0 \frac{x^2}{9+x^6}\, dx + \int_0^\infty \frac{x^2}{9+x^6}\, dx = 2\int_0^\infty \frac{x^2}{9+x^6}\, dx$ [since the integrand is even].

Now $\displaystyle\int \frac{x^2\, dx}{9+x^6}$ $\left[\begin{array}{l}u = x^3\\ du = 3x^2 dx\end{array}\right]$ $= \int \frac{\frac{1}{3}du}{9+u^2}$ $\left[\begin{array}{l}u = 3v\\ du = 3\, dv\end{array}\right]$ $= \int \frac{\frac{1}{3}(3\, dv)}{9+9v^2} = \frac{1}{9}\int \frac{dv}{1+v^2}$

$$= \frac{1}{9}\tan^{-1} v + C = \frac{1}{9}\tan^{-1}\left(\frac{u}{3}\right) + C = \frac{1}{9}\tan^{-1}\left(\frac{x^3}{3}\right) + C,$$

so $2 \int_0^\infty \frac{x^2}{9+x^6}\,dx = 2 \lim_{t\to\infty} \int_0^t \frac{x^2}{9+x^6}\,dx = 2 \lim_{t\to\infty}\left[\frac{1}{9}\tan^{-1}\left(\frac{x^3}{3}\right)\right]_0^t = 2 \lim_{t\to\infty}\frac{1}{9}\tan^{-1}\left(\frac{t^3}{3}\right) = \frac{2}{9}\cdot\frac{\pi}{2} = \frac{\pi}{9}.$

Convergent

23. $\int_e^\infty \frac{1}{x(\ln x)^3}\,dx = \lim_{t\to\infty}\int_e^t \frac{1}{x(\ln x)^3}\,dx = \lim_{t\to\infty}\int_1^{\ln t} u^{-3}\,du \quad \begin{bmatrix} u = \ln x, \\ du = dx/x \end{bmatrix} = \lim_{t\to\infty}\left[-\frac{1}{2u^2}\right]_1^{\ln t}$

$= \lim_{t\to\infty}\left[-\frac{1}{2(\ln t)^2} + \frac{1}{2}\right] = 0 + \frac{1}{2} = \frac{1}{2}.$ Convergent

25. $\int_0^1 \frac{3}{x^5}\,dx = \lim_{t\to 0^+}\int_t^1 3x^{-5}\,dx = \lim_{t\to 0^+}\left[-\frac{3}{4x^4}\right]_t^1 = -\frac{3}{4}\lim_{t\to 0^+}\left(1 - \frac{1}{t^4}\right) = \infty.$ Divergent

27. $\int_{-2}^{14} \frac{dx}{\sqrt[4]{x+2}} = \lim_{t\to -2^+}\int_t^{14}(x+2)^{-1/4}\,dx = \lim_{t\to -2^+}\left[\frac{4}{3}(x+2)^{3/4}\right]_t^{14} = \frac{4}{3}\lim_{t\to -2^+}\left[16^{3/4} - (t+2)^{3/4}\right]$

$= \frac{4}{3}(8 - 0) = \frac{32}{3}.$ Convergent

29. There is an infinite discontinuity at $x = 1$. $\int_0^{33}(x-1)^{-1/5}\,dx = \int_0^1 (x-1)^{-1/5}\,dx + \int_1^{33}(x-1)^{-1/5}\,dx.$ Here

$\int_0^1 (x-1)^{-1/5}\,dx = \lim_{t\to 1^-}\int_0^t (x-1)^{-1/5}\,dx = \lim_{t\to 1^-}\left[\frac{5}{4}(x-1)^{4/5}\right]_0^t = \lim_{t\to 1^-}\left[\frac{5}{4}(t-1)^{4/5} - \frac{5}{4}\right] = -\frac{5}{4}$ and

$\int_1^{33}(x-1)^{-1/5}\,dx = \lim_{t\to 1^+}\int_t^{33}(x-1)^{-1/5}\,dx = \lim_{t\to 1^+}\left[\frac{5}{4}(x-1)^{4/5}\right]_t^{33} = \lim_{t\to 1^+}\left[\frac{5}{4}\cdot 16 - \frac{5}{4}(t-1)^{4/5}\right] = 20.$

Thus, $\int_0^{33}(x-1)^{-1/5}\,dx = -\frac{5}{4} + 20 = \frac{75}{4}.$ Convergent

31. There is an infinite discontinuity at $x = 0$. $\int_{-1}^1 \frac{e^x}{e^x - 1}\,dx = \int_{-1}^0 \frac{e^x}{e^x - 1}\,dx + \int_0^1 \frac{e^x}{e^x - 1}\,dx.$

$\int_{-1}^0 \frac{e^x}{e^x - 1}\,dx = \lim_{t\to 0^-}\int_{-1}^t \frac{e^x}{e^x - 1}\,dx = \lim_{t\to 0^-}\left[\ln|e^x - 1|\right]_{-1}^t = \lim_{t\to 0^-}\left[\ln|e^t - 1| - \ln|e^{-1} - 1|\right] = -\infty,$

so $\int_{-1}^1 \frac{e^x}{e^x - 1}\,dx$ is divergent. The integral $\int_0^1 \frac{e^x}{e^x - 1}\,dx$ also diverges since

$\int_0^1 \frac{e^x}{e^x - 1}\,dx = \lim_{t\to 0^+}\int_t^1 \frac{e^x}{e^x - 1}\,dx = \lim_{t\to 0^+}\left[\ln|e^x - 1|\right]_t^1 = \lim_{t\to 0^+}\left[\ln|e - 1| - \ln|e^t - 1|\right] = \infty.$ Divergent

33. $I = \int_0^2 z^2 \ln z\,dz = \lim_{t\to 0^+}\int_t^2 z^2 \ln z\,dz = \lim_{t\to 0^+}\left[\frac{z^3}{3^2}(3\ln z - 1)\right]_t^2$ $\begin{bmatrix}\text{integrate by parts} \\ \text{or use Formula 101}\end{bmatrix}$

$= \lim_{t\to 0^+}\left[\frac{8}{9}(3\ln 2 - 1) - \frac{1}{9}t^3(3\ln t - 1)\right] = \frac{8}{3}\ln 2 - \frac{8}{9} - \frac{1}{9}\lim_{t\to 0^+}\left[t^3(3\ln t - 1)\right] = \frac{8}{3}\ln 2 - \frac{8}{9} - \frac{1}{9}L.$

Now $L = \lim_{t\to 0^+}\left[t^3(3\ln t - 1)\right] = \lim_{t\to 0^+}\frac{3\ln t - 1}{t^{-3}} \overset{\text{H}}{=} \lim_{t\to 0^+}\frac{3/t}{-3/t^4} = \lim_{t\to 0^+}(-t^3) = 0.$

Thus, $L = 0$ and $I = \frac{8}{3}\ln 2 - \frac{8}{9}.$ Convergent

35.

$\text{Area} = \int_{-\infty}^1 e^x\,dx = \lim_{t\to -\infty}\left[e^x\right]_t^1 = e - \lim_{t\to -\infty}e^t = e$

37.

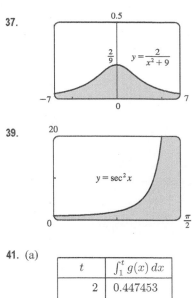

$$\text{Area} = \int_{-\infty}^{\infty} \frac{2}{x^2+9}\, dx = 2 \cdot 2 \int_0^{\infty} \frac{1}{x^2+9}\, dx = 4 \lim_{t \to \infty} \int_0^t \frac{1}{x^2+9}\, dx$$

$$= 4 \lim_{t \to \infty} \left[\frac{1}{3} \tan^{-1} \frac{x}{3} \right]_0^t = \frac{4}{3} \lim_{t \to \infty} \left[\tan^{-1} \frac{t}{3} - 0 \right] = \frac{4}{3} \cdot \frac{\pi}{2} = \frac{2\pi}{3}$$

39.

$$\text{Area} = \int_0^{\pi/2} \sec^2 x\, dx = \lim_{t \to (\pi/2)^-} \int_0^t \sec^2 x\, dx = \lim_{t \to (\pi/2)^-} [\tan x]_0^t$$

$$= \lim_{t \to (\pi/2)^-} (\tan t - 0) = \infty$$

Infinite area

41. (a)

t	$\int_1^t g(x)\, dx$
2	0.447453
5	0.577101
10	0.621306
100	0.668479
1000	0.672957
10,000	0.673407

$$g(x) = \frac{\sin^2 x}{x^2}.$$

It appears that the integral is convergent.

(b) $-1 \le \sin x \le 1 \;\Rightarrow\; 0 \le \sin^2 x \le 1 \;\Rightarrow\; 0 \le \dfrac{\sin^2 x}{x^2} \le \dfrac{1}{x^2}$. Since $\displaystyle\int_1^{\infty} \frac{1}{x^2}\, dx$ is convergent

[Equation 2 with $p = 2 > 1$], $\displaystyle\int_1^{\infty} \frac{\sin^2 x}{x^2}\, dx$ is convergent by the Comparison Theorem.

(c) Since $\int_1^{\infty} f(x)\, dx$ is finite and the area under $g(x)$ is less than the area under $f(x)$ on any interval $[1, t]$, $\int_1^{\infty} g(x)\, dx$ must be finite; that is, the integral is convergent.

43. For $x > 0$, $\dfrac{x}{x^3+1} < \dfrac{x}{x^3} = \dfrac{1}{x^2}$. $\displaystyle\int_1^{\infty} \frac{1}{x^2}\, dx$ is convergent by Equation 2 with $p = 2 > 1$, so $\displaystyle\int_1^{\infty} \frac{x}{x^3+1}\, dx$ is convergent

by the Comparison Theorem. $\displaystyle\int_0^1 \frac{x}{x^3+1}\, dx$ is a constant, so $\displaystyle\int_0^{\infty} \frac{x}{x^3+1}\, dx = \int_0^1 \frac{x}{x^3+1}\, dx + \int_1^{\infty} \frac{x}{x^3+1}\, dx$ is also

convergent.

45. For $x > 1$, $f(x) = \dfrac{x+1}{\sqrt{x^4-x}} > \dfrac{x+1}{\sqrt{x^4}} > \dfrac{x}{x^2} = \dfrac{1}{x}$, so $\displaystyle\int_2^{\infty} f(x)\, dx$ diverges by comparison with $\displaystyle\int_2^{\infty} \frac{1}{x}\, dx$, which diverges

by Equation 2 with $p = 1 \le 1$. Thus, $\int_1^{\infty} f(x)\, dx = \int_1^2 f(x)\, dx + \int_2^{\infty} f(x)\, dx$ also diverges.

47. For $0 < x \le 1$, $\dfrac{\sec^2 x}{x\sqrt{x}} > \dfrac{1}{x^{3/2}}$. Now

$$I = \int_0^1 x^{-3/2}\,dx = \lim_{t\to 0^+}\int_t^1 x^{-3/2}\,dx = \lim_{t\to 0^+}\Big[-2x^{-1/2}\Big]_t^1 = \lim_{t\to 0^+}\left(-2 + \frac{2}{\sqrt{t}}\right) = \infty,\ \text{so } I \text{ is divergent, and by}$$

comparison, $\displaystyle\int_0^1 \frac{\sec^2 x}{x\sqrt{x}}$ is divergent.

49. $\displaystyle\int_0^\infty \frac{dx}{\sqrt{x}\,(1+x)} = \int_0^1 \frac{dx}{\sqrt{x}\,(1+x)} + \int_1^\infty \frac{dx}{\sqrt{x}\,(1+x)} = \lim_{t\to 0^+}\int_t^1 \frac{dx}{\sqrt{x}\,(1+x)} + \lim_{t\to\infty}\int_1^t \frac{dx}{\sqrt{x}\,(1+x)}$. Now

$$\int \frac{dx}{\sqrt{x}\,(1+x)} = \int \frac{2u\,du}{u(1+u^2)}\ \begin{bmatrix} u = \sqrt{x},\, x = u^2, \\ dx = 2u\,du \end{bmatrix} = 2\int \frac{du}{1+u^2} = 2\tan^{-1}u + C = 2\tan^{-1}\sqrt{x} + C,\ \text{so}$$

$$\int_0^\infty \frac{dx}{\sqrt{x}\,(1+x)} = \lim_{t\to 0^+}\Big[2\tan^{-1}\sqrt{x}\,\Big]_t^1 + \lim_{t\to\infty}\Big[2\tan^{-1}\sqrt{x}\,\Big]_1^t$$

$$= \lim_{t\to 0^+}\Big[2\big(\tfrac{\pi}{4}\big) - 2\tan^{-1}\sqrt{t}\,\Big] + \lim_{t\to\infty}\Big[2\tan^{-1}\sqrt{t} - 2\big(\tfrac{\pi}{4}\big)\Big] = \tfrac{\pi}{2} - 0 + 2\big(\tfrac{\pi}{2}\big) - \tfrac{\pi}{2} = \pi.$$

51. If $p = 1$, then $\displaystyle\int_0^1 \frac{dx}{x^p} = \lim_{t\to 0^+}\int_t^1 \frac{dx}{x} = \lim_{t\to 0^+}\,[\ln x]_t^1 = \infty.$ Divergent.

If $p \ne 1$, then $\displaystyle\int_0^1 \frac{dx}{x^p} = \lim_{t\to 0^+}\int_t^1 \frac{dx}{x^p}$ [note that the integral is not improper if $p < 0$]

$$= \lim_{t\to 0^+}\left[\frac{x^{-p+1}}{-p+1}\right]_t^1 = \lim_{t\to 0^+}\frac{1}{1-p}\left[1 - \frac{1}{t^{p-1}}\right]$$

If $p > 1$, then $p - 1 > 0$, so $\dfrac{1}{t^{p-1}} \to \infty$ as $t \to 0^+$, and the integral diverges.

If $p < 1$, then $p - 1 < 0$, so $\dfrac{1}{t^{p-1}} \to 0$ as $t \to 0^+$ and $\displaystyle\int_0^1 \frac{dx}{x^p} = \frac{1}{1-p}\left[\lim_{t\to 0^+}\left(1 - t^{1-p}\right)\right] = \frac{1}{1-p}.$

Thus, the integral converges if and only if $p < 1$, and in that case its value is $\dfrac{1}{1-p}$.

53. (a) $I = \int_{-\infty}^\infty x\,dx = \int_{-\infty}^0 x\,dx + \int_0^\infty x\,dx$, and $\int_0^\infty x\,dx = \lim_{t\to\infty}\int_0^t x\,dx = \lim_{t\to\infty}\big[\tfrac{1}{2}x^2\big]_0^t = \lim_{t\to\infty}\big[\tfrac{1}{2}t^2 - 0\big] = \infty,$

   so I is divergent.

(b) $\int_{-t}^t x\,dx = \big[\tfrac{1}{2}x^2\big]_{-t}^t = \tfrac{1}{2}t^2 - \tfrac{1}{2}t^2 = 0$, so $\lim_{t\to\infty}\int_{-t}^t x\,dx = 0$. Therefore, $\int_{-\infty}^\infty x\,dx \ne \lim_{t\to\infty}\int_{-t}^t x\,dx.$

55. We would expect a small percentage of bulbs to burn out in the first few hundred hours, most of the bulbs to burn out after
close to 700 hours, and a few overachievers to burn on and on.

(a)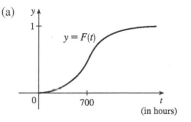

(b) $r(t) = F'(t)$ is the rate at which the fraction $F(t)$ of burnt-out bulbs increases as t increases. This could be interpreted as a fractional burnout rate.

(c) $\int_0^\infty r(t)\,dt = \lim_{x\to\infty} F(x) = 1$, since all of the bulbs will eventually burn out.

57. $I = \int_0^\infty te^{kt}\,dt = \lim_{s\to\infty}\left[\frac{1}{k^2}(kt-1)e^{kt}\right]_0^s$ [Formula 96, or parts] $= \lim_{s\to\infty}\left[\left(\frac{1}{k}se^{ks} - \frac{1}{k^2}e^{ks}\right) - \left(-\frac{1}{k^2}\right)\right].$

Since $k < 0$ the first two terms approach 0 (you can verify that the first term does so with l'Hospital's Rule), so the limit is equal to $1/k^2$. Thus, $M = -kI = -k\left(1/k^2\right) = -1/k = -1/(-0.000121) \approx 8264.5$ years.

59. $I = \int_a^\infty \frac{1}{x^2+1}\,dx = \lim_{t\to\infty}\int_a^t \frac{1}{x^2+1}\,dx = \lim_{t\to\infty}\left[\tan^{-1}x\right]_a^t = \lim_{t\to\infty}\left(\tan^{-1}t - \tan^{-1}a\right) = \frac{\pi}{2} - \tan^{-1}a.$

$I < 0.001 \quad\Rightarrow\quad \frac{\pi}{2} - \tan^{-1}a < 0.001 \quad\Rightarrow\quad \tan^{-1}a > \frac{\pi}{2} - 0.001 \quad\Rightarrow\quad a > \tan\left(\frac{\pi}{2} - 0.001\right) \approx 1000.$

61. We use integration by parts: let $u = x$, $dv = xe^{-x^2}\,dx \quad\Rightarrow\quad du = dx$, $v = -\frac{1}{2}e^{-x^2}$. So

$$\int_0^\infty x^2 e^{-x^2}\,dx = \lim_{t\to\infty}\left[-\frac{1}{2}xe^{-x^2}\right]_0^t + \frac{1}{2}\int_0^\infty e^{-x^2}\,dx = \lim_{t\to\infty}\left[-\frac{t}{2e^{t^2}}\right] + \frac{1}{2}\int_0^\infty e^{-x^2}\,dx = \frac{1}{2}\int_0^\infty e^{-x^2}\,dx$$

(The limit is 0 by l'Hospital's Rule.)

63. For the first part of the integral, let $x = 2\tan\theta \quad\Rightarrow\quad dx = 2\sec^2\theta\,d\theta.$

$$\int \frac{1}{\sqrt{x^2+4}}\,dx = \int \frac{2\sec^2\theta}{2\sec\theta}\,d\theta = \int \sec\theta\,d\theta = \ln|\sec\theta + \tan\theta|.$$

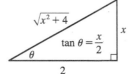

From the figure, $\tan\theta = \frac{x}{2}$, and $\sec\theta = \frac{\sqrt{x^2+4}}{2}$. So

$$I = \int_0^\infty \left(\frac{1}{\sqrt{x^2+4}} - \frac{C}{x+2}\right)dx = \lim_{t\to\infty}\left[\ln\left|\frac{\sqrt{x^2+4}}{2} + \frac{x}{2}\right| - C\ln|x+2|\right]_0^t$$

$$= \lim_{t\to\infty}\left[\ln\frac{\sqrt{t^2+4}+t}{2} - C\ln(t+2) - (\ln 1 - C\ln 2)\right]$$

$$= \lim_{t\to\infty}\left[\ln\left(\frac{\sqrt{t^2+4}+t}{2(t+2)^C}\right) + \ln 2^C\right] = \ln\left(\lim_{t\to\infty}\frac{t+\sqrt{t^2+4}}{(t+2)^C}\right) + \ln 2^{C-1}$$

Now $L = \lim_{t\to\infty}\frac{t+\sqrt{t^2+4}}{(t+2)^C} \overset{\text{H}}{=} \lim_{t\to\infty}\frac{1+t/\sqrt{t^2+4}}{C(t+2)^{C-1}} = \frac{2}{C\lim_{t\to\infty}(t+2)^{C-1}}.$

If $C < 1$, $L = \infty$ and I diverges.

If $C = 1$, $L = 2$ and I converges to $\ln 2 + \ln 2^0 = \ln 2.$

If $C > 1$, $L = 0$ and I diverges to $-\infty.$

65. No, $I = \int_0^\infty f(x)\,dx$ must be *divergent*. Since $\lim_{x\to\infty} f(x) = 1$, there must exist an N such that if $x \geq N$, then $f(x) \geq \frac{1}{2}$.

Thus, $I = I_1 + I_2 = \int_0^N f(x)\,dx + \int_N^\infty f(x)\,dx$, where I_1 is an ordinary definite integral that has a finite value, and I_2 is improper and diverges by comparison with the divergent integral $\int_N^\infty \frac{1}{2}\,dx.$

5   Review

1. (a) $\sum_{i=1}^{n} f(x_i^*)\,\Delta x$ is an expression for a Riemann sum of a function f.

 x_i^* is a point in the ith subinterval $[x_{i-1}, x_i]$ and Δx is the length of the subintervals.

 (b) See Figure 1 in Section 5.2.

 (c) In Section 5.2, see Figure 3 and the paragraph beside it.

2. (a) See Definition 5.2.2.

 (b) See Figure 2 in Section 5.2.

 (c) In Section 5.2, see Figure 4 and the paragraph by it (contains "**net area**").

3. (a) See the Evaluation Theorem at the beginning of Section 5.3.

 (b) See the Net Change Theorem after Example 6 in Section 5.3.

4. $\int_{t_1}^{t_2} r(t)\,dt$ represents the change in the amount of water in the reservoir between time t_1 and time t_2.

5. (a) $\int_{60}^{120} v(t)\,dt$ represents the change in position of the particle from $t = 60$ to $t = 120$ seconds.

 (b) $\int_{60}^{120} |v(t)|\,dt$ represents the total distance traveled by the particle from $t = 60$ to 120 seconds.

 (c) $\int_{60}^{120} a(t)\,dt$ represents the change in the velocity of the particle from $t = 60$ to $t = 120$ seconds.

6. (a) $\int f(x)\,dx$ is the family of functions $\{F \mid F' = f\}$. Any two such functions differ by a constant.

 (b) The connection is given by the Evaluation Theorem: $\int_a^b f(x)\,dx = \left[\int f(x)\,dx\right]_a^b$ if f is continuous.

7. See the Fundamental Theorem of Calculus after Example 5 in Section 5.4.

8. (a) See the Substitution Rule (5.5.4). This says that it is permissible to operate with the dx after an integral sign as if it were a differential.

 (b) See Formula 5.6.1 or 5.6.2. We try to choose $u = f(x)$ to be a function that becomes simpler when differentiated (or at least not more complicated) as long as $dv = g'(x)\,dx$ can be readily integrated to give v.

9. See the Midpoint Rule, the Trapezoidal Rule, and Simpson's Rule, as well as their associated error bounds, all in Section 5.9. We would expect the best estimate to be given by Simpson's Rule.

10. See Definitions 1(a), (b), and (c) in Section 5.10.

11. See Definitions 3(b), (a), and (c) in Section 5.10.

12. See the Comparison Theorem after Example 8 in Section 5.10.

13. The precise version of this statement is given by the Fundamental Theorem of Calculus. See the statement of this theorem and the paragraph that follows it in Section 5.4.

TRUE-FALSE QUIZ

1. True by Property 2 of the Integral in Section 5.2.

3. True by Property 3 of the Integral in Section 5.2.

5. False.   For example, let $f(x) = x^2$. Then $\int_0^1 \sqrt{x^2}\,dx = \int_0^1 x\,dx = \frac{1}{2}$, but $\sqrt{\int_0^1 x^2\,dx} = \sqrt{\frac{1}{3}} = \frac{1}{\sqrt{3}}$.

7. True by Comparison Property 7 of the Integral in Section 5.2.

9. True.   The integrand is an odd function that is continuous on $[-1, 1]$, so the result follows from Theorem 5.5.6(b).

11. False.   This is an improper integral, since the denominator vanishes at $x = 1$.

$$\int_0^4 \frac{x}{x^2 - 1}\,dx = \int_0^1 \frac{x}{x^2 - 1}\,dx + \int_1^4 \frac{x}{x^2 - 1}\,dx \text{ and}$$

$$\int_0^1 \frac{x}{x^2 - 1}\,dx = \lim_{t \to 1^-} \int_0^t \frac{x}{x^2 - 1}\,dx = \lim_{t \to 1^-}\left[\tfrac{1}{2}\ln\left|x^2 - 1\right|\right]_0^t = \lim_{t \to 1^-}\tfrac{1}{2}\ln\left|t^2 - 1\right| = \infty$$

So the integral diverges.

13. False.   See the paragraph before Note 4 and Figure 4 in Section 5.2, and notice that $y = x - x^3 < 0$ for $1 < x \le 2$.

15. False.   For example, the function $y = |x|$ is continuous on $\mathbb{R}$, but has no derivative at $x = 0$.

17. False.   See Exercise 53 in Section 5.10.

19. False.   If $f(x) = 1/x$, then f is continuous and decreasing on $[1, \infty)$ with $\lim_{x \to \infty} f(x) = 0$, but $\int_1^\infty f(x)\,dx$ is divergent.

21. False.   Take $f(x) = 1$ for all x and $g(x) = -1$ for all x. Then $\int_a^\infty f(x)\,dx = \infty$ [divergent]

and $\int_a^\infty g(x)\,dx = -\infty$ [divergent],   but $\int_a^\infty [f(x) + g(x)]\,dx = 0$ [convergent].

23. False. $\int_a^b f(x)\,dx$ is a constant, so $\dfrac{d}{dx}\left(\int_a^b f(x)\,dx\right) = 0$, not $f(x)$ [unless $f(x) = 0$]. Compare the given statement carefully with FTC1, in which the upper limit in the integral is x.

EXERCISES

1. (a)

$$L_6 = \sum_{i=1}^{6} f(x_{i-1})\,\Delta x \quad [\Delta x = \tfrac{6-0}{6} = 1]$$

$$= f(x_0) \cdot 1 + f(x_1) \cdot 1 + f(x_2) \cdot 1 + f(x_3) \cdot 1 + f(x_4) \cdot 1 + f(x_5) \cdot 1$$

$$\approx 2 + 3.5 + 4 + 2 + (-1) + (-2.5) = 8$$

The Riemann sum represents the sum of the areas of the four rectangles above the x-axis minus the sum of the areas of the two rectangles below the x-axis.

(b)

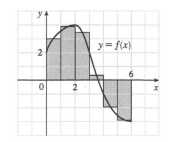

$$M_6 = \sum_{i=1}^{6} f(\overline{x}_i)\,\Delta x \quad [\Delta x = \tfrac{6-0}{6} = 1]$$

$$= f(\overline{x}_1)\cdot 1 + f(\overline{x}_2)\cdot 1 + f(\overline{x}_3)\cdot 1 + f(\overline{x}_4)\cdot 1 + f(\overline{x}_5)\cdot 1 + f(\overline{x}_6)\cdot 1$$

$$= f(0.5) + f(1.5) + f(2.5) + f(3.5) + f(4.5) + f(5.5)$$

$$\approx 3 + 3.9 + 3.4 + 0.3 + (-2) + (-2.9) = 5.7$$

3. $\int_0^1 \left(x + \sqrt{1-x^2}\right)dx = \int_0^1 x\,dx + \int_0^1 \sqrt{1-x^2}\,dx = I_1 + I_2.$

I_1 can be interpreted as the area of the triangle shown in the figure

and I_2 can be interpreted as the area of the quarter-circle.

Area $= \frac{1}{2}(1)(1) + \frac{1}{4}(\pi)(1)^2 = \frac{1}{2} + \frac{\pi}{4}.$

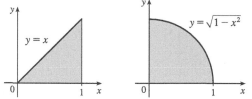

5. $\int_0^6 f(x)\,dx = \int_0^4 f(x)\,dx + \int_4^6 f(x)\,dx \;\Rightarrow\; 10 = 7 + \int_4^6 f(x)\,dx \;\Rightarrow\; \int_4^6 f(x)\,dx = 10 - 7 = 3$

7. First note that either a or b must be the graph of $\int_0^x f(t)\,dt$, since $\int_0^0 f(t)\,dt = 0$, and $c(0) \neq 0$. Now notice that $b > 0$ when c

is increasing, and that $c > 0$ when a is increasing. It follows that c is the graph of $f(x)$, b is the graph of $f'(x)$, and a is the

graph of $\int_0^x f(t)\,dt.$

9. $\int_1^2 \left(8x^3 + 3x^2\right)dx = \left[8\cdot\frac{1}{4}x^4 + 3\cdot\frac{1}{3}x^3\right]_1^2 = \left[2x^4 + x^3\right]_1^2 = \left(2\cdot 2^4 + 2^3\right) - (2+1) = 40 - 3 = 37$

11. $\int_0^1 \left(1 - x^9\right)dx = \left[x - \frac{1}{10}x^{10}\right]_0^1 = \left(1 - \frac{1}{10}\right) - 0 = \frac{9}{10}$

13. $\displaystyle\int \left(\frac{1-x}{x}\right)^2 dx = \int \left(\frac{1}{x} - 1\right)^2 dx = \int \left(\frac{1}{x^2} - \frac{2}{x} + 1\right)dx = -\frac{1}{x} - 2\ln|x| + x + C$

15. $u = x^2 + 1$, $du = 2x\,dx$, so $\displaystyle\int_0^1 \frac{x}{x^2+1}\,dx = \int_1^2 \frac{1}{u}\left(\frac{1}{2}\,du\right) = \frac{1}{2}\left[\ln u\right]_1^2 = \frac{1}{2}\ln 2.$

17. Let $u = v^3$, so $du = 3v^2\,dv$. When $v = 0$, $u = 0$; when $v = 1$, $u = 1$. Thus,

$\int_0^1 v^2 \cos(v^3)\,dv = \int_0^1 \cos u\left(\frac{1}{3}\,du\right) = \frac{1}{3}\left[\sin u\right]_0^1 = \frac{1}{3}(\sin 1 - 0) = \frac{1}{3}\sin 1.$

19. $\int_0^1 e^{\pi t}\,dt = \left[\frac{1}{\pi}e^{\pi t}\right]_0^1 = \frac{1}{\pi}(e^{\pi} - 1)$

21. Let $u = x^2 + 4x$. Then $du = (2x + 4)\,dx = 2(x+2)\,dx$, so

$\displaystyle\int \frac{x+2}{\sqrt{x^2+4x}}\,dx = \int u^{-1/2}\left(\frac{1}{2}\,du\right) = \frac{1}{2}\cdot 2u^{1/2} + C = \sqrt{u} + C = \sqrt{x^2+4x} + C.$

23. $\displaystyle\int_0^5 \frac{x}{x+10}\,dx = \int_0^5 \left(1 - \frac{10}{x+10}\right)dx = \left[x - 10\ln(x+10)\right]_0^5 = 5 - 10\ln 15 + 10\ln 10$

$= 5 + 10\ln\frac{10}{15} = 5 + 10\ln\frac{2}{3}$

25. $\displaystyle\int_{-\pi/4}^{\pi/4} \frac{t^4 \tan t}{2 + \cos t}\, dt = 0$ by Theorem 5.5.6(b), since $f(t) = \dfrac{t^4 \tan t}{2 + \cos t}$ is an odd function.

27. $\displaystyle\int_1^4 x^{3/2} \ln x\, dx$ $\left[\begin{array}{ll} u = \ln x, & dv = x^{3/2}\, dx, \\ du = dx/x & v = \frac{2}{5} x^{5/2} \end{array}\right] = \frac{2}{5}\Big[x^{5/2}\ln x\Big]_1^4 - \frac{2}{5}\int_1^4 x^{3/2}\, dx = \frac{2}{5}(32 \ln 4 - \ln 1) - \frac{2}{5}\Big[\frac{2}{5}x^{5/2}\Big]_1^4$

$$= \frac{2}{5}(64 \ln 2) - \frac{4}{25}(32 - 1) = \frac{128}{5}\ln 2 - \frac{124}{25} \quad \Big[\text{or } \frac{64}{5}\ln 4 - \frac{124}{25}\Big]$$

29. $\dfrac{1}{t^2 + 6t + 8} = \dfrac{1}{(t+2)(t+4)} = \dfrac{A}{t+2} + \dfrac{B}{t+4}$. Multiply both sides by $(t+2)(t+4)$ to get $1 = A(t+4) + B(t+2)$.

Substituting -4 for t gives $1 = -2B$ $\Leftrightarrow$ $B = -\frac{1}{2}$. Substituting -2 for t gives $1 = 2A$ $\Leftrightarrow$ $A = \frac{1}{2}$. Thus,

$$\int \frac{dt}{t^2 + 6t + 8} = \int \left(\frac{1/2}{t+2} - \frac{1/2}{t+4}\right) dt = \tfrac{1}{2}\ln|t+2| - \tfrac{1}{2}\ln|t+4| + C = \tfrac{1}{2}\ln\left|\frac{t+2}{t+4}\right| + C.$$

31. Let $w = \sqrt[3]{x}$. Then $w^3 = x$ and $3w^2\, dw = dx$, so $\int e^{\sqrt[3]{x}}\, dx = \int e^w \cdot 3w^2\, dw = 3I$. To evaluate I, let $u = w^2$,

$dv = e^w\, dw$ $\Rightarrow$ $du = 2w\, dw$, $v = e^w$, so $I = \int w^2 e^w\, dw = w^2 e^w - \int 2we^w\, dw$. Now let $U = w$, $dV = e^w\, dw$ $\Rightarrow$

$dU = dw$, $V = e^w$. Thus, $I = w^2 e^w - 2\big[we^w - \int e^w\, dw\big] = w^2 e^w - 2we^w + 2e^w + C_1$, and hence

$$3I = 3e^w(w^2 - 2w + 2) + C = 3e^{\sqrt[3]{x}}(x^{2/3} - 2x^{1/3} + 2) + C.$$

33. Let $u = 1 + \sec\theta$. Then $du = \sec\theta\tan\theta\, d\theta$, so

$$\int \frac{\sec\theta\tan\theta}{1 + \sec\theta}\, d\theta = \int \frac{1}{1+\sec\theta}(\sec\theta\tan\theta\, d\theta) = \int \frac{1}{u}\, du = \ln|u| + C = \ln|1 + \sec\theta| + C.$$

35. Let $u = 1 + \sin x$. Then $du = \cos x\, dx$, so

$$\int \frac{\cos x\, dx}{\sqrt{1 + \sin x}} = \int u^{-1/2}\, du = 2u^{1/2} + C = 2\sqrt{1 + \sin x} + C.$$

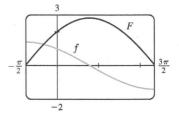

37. From the graph, it appears that the area under the curve $y = x\sqrt{x}$ between $x = 0$

and $x = 4$ is somewhat less than half the area of an 8×4 rectangle, so perhaps

about 13 or 14. To find the exact value, we evaluate

$$\int_0^4 x\sqrt{x}\, dx = \int_0^4 x^{3/2}\, dx = \Big[\tfrac{2}{5}x^{5/2}\Big]_0^4 = \tfrac{2}{5}(4)^{5/2} = \tfrac{64}{5} = 12.8.$$

39. $\displaystyle F(x) = \int_0^x \frac{t^2}{1 + t^3}\, dt$ $\Rightarrow$ $\displaystyle F'(x) = \frac{d}{dx}\int_0^x \frac{t^2}{1 + t^3}\, dt = \frac{x^2}{1 + x^3}$

41. $y = \int_{\sqrt{x}}^{x} \frac{e^t}{t}\,dt = \int_{\sqrt{x}}^{1} \frac{e^t}{t}\,dt + \int_{1}^{x} \frac{e^t}{t}\,dt = -\int_{1}^{\sqrt{x}} \frac{e^t}{t}\,dt + \int_{1}^{x} \frac{e^t}{t}\,dt \;\Rightarrow$

$\dfrac{dy}{dx} = -\dfrac{d}{dx}\left(\int_{1}^{\sqrt{x}} \frac{e^t}{t}\,dt\right) + \dfrac{d}{dx}\left(\int_{1}^{x} \frac{e^t}{t}\,dt\right)$. Let $u = \sqrt{x}$. Then

$$\frac{d}{dx}\int_{1}^{\sqrt{x}} \frac{e^t}{t}\,dt = \frac{d}{dx}\int_{1}^{u} \frac{e^t}{t}\,dt = \frac{d}{du}\left(\int_{1}^{u} \frac{e^t}{t}\,dt\right)\frac{du}{dx} = \frac{e^u}{u}\cdot\frac{1}{2\sqrt{x}} = \frac{e^{\sqrt{x}}}{\sqrt{x}}\cdot\frac{1}{2\sqrt{x}} = \frac{e^{\sqrt{x}}}{2x},$$

so $\dfrac{dy}{dx} = -\dfrac{e^{\sqrt{x}}}{2x} + \dfrac{e^x}{x}$.

43. $u = e^x \;\Rightarrow\; du = e^x\,dx$, so

$\int e^x\sqrt{1-e^{2x}}\,dx = \int \sqrt{1-u^2}\,du \overset{30}{=} \tfrac{1}{2}u\sqrt{1-u^2} + \tfrac{1}{2}\sin^{-1}u + C = \tfrac{1}{2}\left[e^x\sqrt{1-e^{2x}} + \sin^{-1}(e^x)\right] + C.$

45. $\displaystyle\int \sqrt{x^2+x+1}\,dx = \int \sqrt{x^2 + x + \tfrac{1}{4} + \tfrac{3}{4}}\,dx = \int \sqrt{\left(x+\tfrac{1}{2}\right)^2 + \tfrac{3}{4}}\,dx$

$$= \int \sqrt{u^2 + \left(\tfrac{\sqrt{3}}{2}\right)^2}\,du \qquad [u = x+\tfrac{1}{2},\, du = dx]$$

$$\overset{21}{=} \tfrac{1}{2}u\sqrt{u^2+\tfrac{3}{4}} + \tfrac{3}{8}\ln\left(u + \sqrt{u^2+\tfrac{3}{4}}\right) + C$$

$$= \frac{2x+1}{4}\sqrt{x^2+x+1} + \tfrac{3}{8}\ln\left(x+\tfrac{1}{2} + \sqrt{x^2+x+1}\right) + C$$

47. $f(x) = \sqrt{1+x^4}$, $\;\Delta x = \dfrac{b-a}{n} = \dfrac{1-0}{10} = \dfrac{1}{10}$.

(a) $T_{10} = \frac{1}{10\cdot 2}\{f(0) + 2\,[f(0.1) + f(0.2) + \cdots + f(0.9)] + f(1)\} \approx 1.090608$

(b) $M_{10} = \frac{1}{10}\left[f\left(\tfrac{1}{20}\right) + f\left(\tfrac{3}{20}\right) + f\left(\tfrac{5}{20}\right) + \cdots + f\left(\tfrac{19}{20}\right)\right] \approx 1.088840$

(c) $S_{10} = \frac{1}{10\cdot 3}[f(0) + 4f(0.1) + 2f(0.2) + \cdots + 4f(0.9) + f(1)] \approx 1.089429$

f is concave upward, so the Trapezoidal Rule gives us an overestimate, the Midpoint Rule gives an underestimate, and we cannot tell whether Simpson's Rule gives us an overestimate or an underestimate.

49. $f(x) = (1+x^4)^{1/2}$, $f'(x) = \tfrac{1}{2}(1+x^4)^{-1/2}(4x^3) = 2x^3(1+x^4)^{-1/2}$, $f''(x) = (2x^6 + 6x^2)(1+x^4)^{-3/2}$.

A graph of f'' on $[0,1]$ shows that it has its maximum at $x = 1$, so $|f''(x)| \le f''(1) = \sqrt{8}$ on $[0,1]$. By taking $K = \sqrt{8}$, we find that the error in Exercise 47(a) is bounded by $\dfrac{K(b-a)^3}{12n^2} = \dfrac{\sqrt{8}}{1200} \approx 0.0024$, and in (b) by about $\tfrac{1}{2}(0.0024) = 0.0012$.

Note: Another way to estimate K is to let $x = 1$ in the factor $2x^6 + 6x^2$ (maximizing the numerator) and let $x = 0$ in the factor $(1+x^4)^{-3/2}$ (minimizing the denominator). Doing so gives us $K = 8$ and errors of $0.00\overline{6}$ and $0.00\overline{3}$. Using $K = 8$ for the Trapezoidal Rule, we have $|E_T| \le \dfrac{K(b-a)^3}{12n^2} \le 0.00001 \;\Leftrightarrow\; \dfrac{8(1-0)^3}{12n^2} \le \dfrac{1}{100{,}000} \;\Leftrightarrow\; n^2 \ge \dfrac{800{,}000}{12} \;\Leftrightarrow$

$n \gtrsim 258.2$, so we should take $n = 259$. For the Midpoint Rule, $|E_M| \le \dfrac{K(b-a)^3}{24n^2} \le 0.00001 \;\Leftrightarrow\; n^2 \ge \dfrac{800{,}000}{24} \;\Leftrightarrow$

$n \gtrsim 182.6$, so we should take $n = 183$.

51. (a) $f(x) = \sin(\sin x)$. A CAS gives

$$f^{(4)}(x) = \sin(\sin x)[\cos^4 x + 7\cos^2 x - 3]$$
$$+ \cos(\sin x)[6\cos^2 x \sin x + \sin x]$$

From the graph, we see that $\left|f^{(4)}(x)\right| < 3.8$ for $x \in [0, \pi]$.

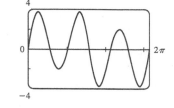

(b) We use Simpson's Rule with $f(x) = \sin(\sin x)$ and $\Delta x = \frac{\pi}{10}$:

$$\int_0^\pi f(x)\, dx \approx \frac{\pi}{10 \cdot 3}\left[f(0) + 4f\left(\frac{\pi}{10}\right) + 2f\left(\frac{2\pi}{10}\right) + \cdots + 4f\left(\frac{9\pi}{10}\right) + f(\pi)\right] \approx 1.786721$$

From part (a), we know that $\left|f^{(4)}(x)\right| < 3.8$ on $[0, \pi]$, so we use Theorem 8.7.4 with $K = 3.8$, and estimate the error

as $|E_S| \le \dfrac{3.8(\pi - 0)^5}{180(10)^4} \approx 0.000646.$

(c) If we want the error to be less than 0.00001, we must have $|E_S| \le \dfrac{3.8\pi^5}{180n^4} \le 0.00001,$

so $n^4 \ge \dfrac{3.8\pi^5}{180(0.00001)} \approx 646{,}041.6 \;\Rightarrow\; n \ge 28.35.$ Since n must be even for Simpson's Rule, we must have $n \ge 30$

to ensure the desired accuracy.

53. If $1 \le x \le 3$, then $\sqrt{1^2 + 3} \le \sqrt{x^2 + 3} \le \sqrt{3^2 + 3} \;\Rightarrow\; 2 \le \sqrt{x^2 + 3} \le 2\sqrt{3}$, so

$2(3 - 1) \le \int_1^3 \sqrt{x^2 + 3}\, dx \le 2\sqrt{3}(3 - 1);$ that is, $4 \le \int_1^3 \sqrt{x^2 + 3}\, dx \le 4\sqrt{3}.$

55. $\displaystyle\int_1^\infty \frac{1}{(2x+1)^3}\, dx = \lim_{t \to \infty} \int_1^t \frac{1}{(2x+1)^3}\, dx = \lim_{t \to \infty} \int_1^t \tfrac{1}{2}(2x+1)^{-3}\, 2\, dx = \lim_{t \to \infty}\left[-\frac{1}{4(2x+1)^2}\right]_1^t$

$$= -\frac{1}{4}\lim_{t \to \infty}\left[\frac{1}{(2t+1)^2} - \frac{1}{9}\right] = -\frac{1}{4}\left(0 - \frac{1}{9}\right) = \frac{1}{36}$$

57. $\displaystyle\int_{-\infty}^0 e^{-2x}\, dx = \lim_{t \to -\infty} \int_t^0 e^{-2x}\, dx = \lim_{t \to -\infty}\left[-\tfrac{1}{2}e^{-2x}\right]_t^0 = \lim_{t \to -\infty}\left(-\tfrac{1}{2} + \tfrac{1}{2}e^{-2t}\right) = \infty.$ Divergent

59. Let $u = \ln x$. Then $du = dx/x$, so $\displaystyle\int \frac{dx}{x\sqrt{\ln x}} = \int \frac{du}{\sqrt{u}} = 2\sqrt{u} + C = 2\sqrt{\ln x} + C.$

Thus, $\displaystyle\int_1^e \frac{dx}{x\sqrt{\ln x}} = \lim_{t \to 1^+} \int_t^e \frac{dx}{x\sqrt{\ln x}} = \lim_{t \to 1^+}\left[2\sqrt{\ln x}\right]_t^e = \lim_{t \to 1^+}\left(2\sqrt{\ln e} - 2\sqrt{\ln t}\right) = 2 \cdot 1 - 2 \cdot 0 = 2.$

61. $\dfrac{x^3}{x^5 + 2} \le \dfrac{x^3}{x^5} = \dfrac{1}{x^2}$ for x in $[1, \infty)$. $\displaystyle\int_1^\infty \frac{1}{x^2}\, dx$ is convergent by (5.10.2) with $p = 2 > 1$. Therefore, $\displaystyle\int_1^\infty \frac{x^3}{x^5 + 2}\, dx$ is

convergent by the Comparison Theorem.

63. (a) Displacement $= \displaystyle\int_0^5 (t^2 - t)\, dt = \left[\tfrac{1}{3}t^3 - \tfrac{1}{2}t^2\right]_0^5 = \frac{125}{3} - \frac{25}{2} = \frac{175}{6} = 29.1\overline{6}$ meters

(b) Distance traveled $= \displaystyle\int_0^5 |t^2 - t|\, dt = \int_0^5 |t(t - 1)|\, dt = \int_0^1 (t - t^2)\, dt + \int_1^5 (t^2 - t)\, dt$

$$= \left[\tfrac{1}{2}t^2 - \tfrac{1}{3}t^3\right]_0^1 + \left[\tfrac{1}{3}t^3 - \tfrac{1}{2}t^2\right]_1^5 = \tfrac{1}{2} - \tfrac{1}{3} - 0 + \left(\tfrac{125}{3} - \tfrac{25}{2}\right) - \left(\tfrac{1}{3} - \tfrac{1}{2}\right) = \frac{177}{6} = 29.5 \text{ meters}$$

65. Note that $r(t) = b'(t)$, where $b(t) =$ the number of barrels of oil consumed up to time t. So, by the Net Change Theorem, $\int_0^8 r(t)\,dt = b(8) - b(0)$ represents the number of barrels of oil consumed from Jan. 1, 2000, through Jan. 1, 2008.

67. Both numerator and denominator approach 0 as $a \to 0$, so we use l'Hospital's Rule. (Note that we are differentiating *with respect to a*, since that is the quantity which is changing.) We also use FTC1:

$$\lim_{a \to 0} T(x,t) = \lim_{a \to 0} \frac{C \int_0^a e^{-(x-u)^2/(4kt)}\,du}{a\sqrt{4\pi kt}} \overset{H}{=} \lim_{a \to 0} \frac{Ce^{-(x-a)^2/(4kt)}}{\sqrt{4\pi kt}} = \frac{Ce^{-x^2/(4kt)}}{\sqrt{4\pi kt}}$$

69. Using FTC1, we differentiate both sides of the given equation, $\int_0^x f(t)\,dt = xe^{2x} + \int_0^x e^{-t} f(t)\,dt$, and get

$$f(x) = e^{2x} + 2xe^{2x} + e^{-x}f(x) \quad \Rightarrow \quad f(x)\left(1 - e^{-x}\right) = e^{2x} + 2xe^{2x} \quad \Rightarrow \quad f(x) = \frac{e^{2x}(1+2x)}{1 - e^{-x}}.$$

71. Let $u = f(x)$ and $du = f'(x)\,dx$. So $2\int_a^b f(x)f'(x)\,dx = 2\int_{f(a)}^{f(b)} u\,du = \left[u^2\right]_{f(a)}^{f(b)} = [f(b)]^2 - [f(a)]^2$.

73. By the Fundamental Theorem of Calculus,

$$\int_0^\infty f'(x)\,dx = \lim_{t \to \infty} \int_0^t f'(x)\,dx = \lim_{t \to \infty}[f(t) - f(0)] = \lim_{t \to \infty} f(t) - f(0) = 0 - f(0) = -f(0).$$

☐ FOCUS ON PROBLEM SOLVING

1.

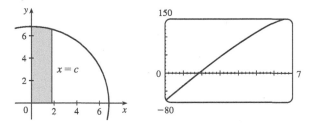

By symmetry, the problem can be reduced to finding the line $x = c$ such that the shaded area is one-third of the area of the quarter-circle. An equation of the semicircle is $y = \sqrt{49 - x^2}$, so we require that $\int_0^c \sqrt{49 - x^2}\, dx = \frac{1}{3} \cdot \frac{1}{4}\pi(7)^2$ ⇔

$\left[\frac{1}{2}x\sqrt{49 - x^2} + \frac{49}{2}\sin^{-1}(x/7)\right]_0^c = \frac{49}{12}\pi$ [by Formula 30]   ⇔ $\frac{1}{2}c\sqrt{49 - c^2} + \frac{49}{2}\sin^{-1}(c/7) = \frac{49}{12}\pi$.

This equation would be difficult to solve exactly, so we plot the left-hand side as a function of c, and find that the equation holds for $c \approx 1.85$. So the cuts should be made at distances of about 1.85 inches from the center of the pizza.

3. Differentiating both sides of the equation $x \sin \pi x = \int_0^{x^2} f(t)\, dt$ (using FTC1 and the Chain Rule for the right side) gives

$\sin \pi x + \pi x \cos \pi x = 2x f(x^2)$. Letting $x = 2$ so that $f(x^2) = f(4)$, we obtain $\sin 2\pi + 2\pi \cos 2\pi = 4f(4)$, so

$f(4) = \frac{1}{4}(0 + 2\pi \cdot 1) = \frac{\pi}{2}$.

5. Differentiating the given equation, $\int_0^x f(t)\, dt = [f(x)]^2$, using FTC1 gives $f(x) = 2f(x)\,f'(x)$ ⇒

$f(x)[2f'(x) - 1] = 0$, so $f(x) = 0$ or $f'(x) = \frac{1}{2}$. Since $f(x)$ is never 0, we must have $f'(x) = \frac{1}{2}$ and $f'(x) = \frac{1}{2}$ ⇒

$f(x) = \frac{1}{2}x + C$. To find C, we substitute into the given equation to get $\int_0^x \left(\frac{1}{2}t + C\right)dt = \left(\frac{1}{2}x + C\right)^2$ ⇔

$\frac{1}{4}x^2 + Cx = \frac{1}{4}x^2 + Cx + C^2$. It follows that $C^2 = 0$, so $C = 0$, and $f(x) = \frac{1}{2}x$.

7. By l'Hospital's Rule and the Fundamental Theorem, using the notation $\exp(y) = e^y$,

$$\lim_{x \to 0} \frac{\int_0^x (1 - \tan 2t)^{1/t}\, dt}{x} \overset{\mathrm{H}}{=} \lim_{x \to 0} \frac{(1 - \tan 2x)^{1/x}}{1} = \exp\left(\lim_{x \to 0} \frac{\ln(1 - \tan 2x)}{x}\right)$$

$$\overset{\mathrm{H}}{=} \exp\left(\lim_{x \to 0} \frac{-2\sec^2 2x}{1 - \tan 2x}\right) = \exp\left(\frac{-2 \cdot 1^2}{1 - 0}\right) = e^{-2}$$

9. For $I = \int_0^4 xe^{(x-2)^4}\, dx$, let $u = x - 2$ so that $x = u + 2$ and $dx = du$. Then

$I = \int_{-2}^2 (u + 2)e^{u^4}\, du = \int_{-2}^2 ue^{u^4}\, du + \int_{-2}^2 2e^{u^4}\, du$

$= 0$ [by 5.5.6(b)] $+ 2\int_0^4 e^{(x-2)^4}\, dx = 2k$.

11. Such a function cannot exist. $f'(x) > 3$ for all x means that f is differentiable (and hence continuous) for all x. So by FTC2,

$\int_1^4 f'(x)\, dx = f(4) - f(1) = 7 - (-1) = 8$. However, if $f'(x) > 3$ for all x, then $\int_1^4 f'(x)\, dx \geq 3 \cdot (4 - 1) = 9$ by

Comparison Property 8 in Section 5.2.

[continued]

Another solution: By the Mean Value Theorem, there exists a number $c \in (1, 4)$ such that

$$f'(c) = \frac{f(4) - f(1)}{4 - 1} = \frac{7 - (-1)}{3} = \frac{8}{3} \quad \Rightarrow \quad 8 = 3f'(c). \text{ But } f'(x) > 3 \quad \Rightarrow \quad 3f'(c) > 9, \text{ so such a function cannot}$$

exist.

13. $f(x) = 2 + x - x^2 = (-x + 2)(x + 1) = 0 \iff x = 2 \text{ or } x = -1.$ $f(x) \geq 0$ for $x \in [-1, 2]$ and $f(x) < 0$ everywhere

else. The integral $\int_a^b (2 + x - x^2)\, dx$ has a maximum on the interval where the integrand is positive, which is $[-1, 2]$. So

$a = -1, b = 2.$ (Any larger interval gives a smaller integral since $f(x) < 0$ outside $[-1, 2]$. Any smaller interval also gives a

smaller integral since $f(x) \geq 0$ in $[-1, 2]$.)

15. By FTC1, $\dfrac{d}{dx} \int_0^x \left(\int_1^{\sin t} \sqrt{1 + u^4}\, du \right) dt = \int_1^{\sin x} \sqrt{1 + u^4}\, du.$ Again using FTC1,

$$\frac{d^2}{dx^2} \int_0^x \left(\int_1^{\sin t} \sqrt{1 + u^4}\, du \right) dt = \frac{d}{dx} \int_1^{\sin x} \sqrt{1 + u^4}\, du = \sqrt{1 + \sin^4 x}\, \cos x.$$

17. Write $I = \displaystyle\int \frac{x^8}{(1 + x^6)^2}\, dx = \int x^3 \cdot \frac{x^5}{(1 + x^6)^2}\, dx.$ Integrate by parts with $u = x^3$, $dv = \dfrac{x^5}{(1 + x^6)^2}\, dx$. Then

$du = 3x^2\, dx, v = -\dfrac{1}{6(1 + x^6)} \quad \Rightarrow \quad I = -\dfrac{x^3}{6(1 + x^6)} + \dfrac{1}{2}\displaystyle\int \frac{x^2}{1 + x^6}\, dx.$ Substitute $t = x^3$ in this latter integral.

$\displaystyle\int \frac{x^2}{1 + x^6}\, dx = \frac{1}{3}\int \frac{dt}{1 + t^2} = \frac{1}{3}\tan^{-1} t + C = \frac{1}{3}\tan^{-1}(x^3) + C.$ Therefore $I = -\dfrac{x^3}{6(1 + x^6)} + \dfrac{1}{6}\tan^{-1}(x^3) + C.$

Returning to the improper integral,

$$\int_{-1}^{\infty} \left(\frac{x^4}{1 + x^6} \right)^2 dx = \lim_{t \to \infty} \int_{-1}^{t} \frac{x^8}{(1 + x^6)^2}\, dx = \lim_{t \to \infty} \left[-\frac{x^3}{6(1 + x^6)} + \frac{1}{6}\tan^{-1}(x^3) \right]_{-1}^{t}$$

$$= \lim_{t \to \infty} \left(-\frac{t^3}{6(1 + t^6)} + \frac{1}{6}\tan^{-1}(t^3) + \frac{-1}{6(1 + 1)} - \frac{1}{6}\tan^{-1}(-1) \right)$$

$$= 0 + \frac{1}{6}\left(\frac{\pi}{2} \right) - \frac{1}{12} - \frac{1}{6}\left(-\frac{\pi}{4} \right) = \frac{\pi}{12} - \frac{1}{12} + \frac{\pi}{24} = \frac{\pi}{8} - \frac{1}{12}$$

19. The given integral represents the difference of the shaded areas, which appears to

be 0. It can be calculated by integrating with respect to either x or y, so we find x

in terms of y for each curve: $y = \sqrt[3]{1 - x^7} \Rightarrow x = \sqrt[7]{1 - y^3}$ and

$y = \sqrt[7]{1 - x^3} \Rightarrow x = \sqrt[3]{1 - y^7}$, so

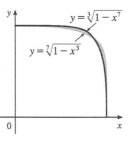

$\int_0^1 \left(\sqrt[3]{1 - y^7} - \sqrt[7]{1 - y^3} \right) dy = \int_0^1 \left(\sqrt[7]{1 - x^3} - \sqrt[3]{1 - x^7} \right) dx.$ But this

equation is of the form $z = -z$. So $\int_0^1 \left(\sqrt[3]{1 - x^7} - \sqrt[7]{1 - x^3} \right) dx = 0.$

21. In accordance with the hint, we let $I_k = \int_0^1 (1 - x^2)^k\, dx$, and we find an expression for I_{k+1} in terms of I_k. We integrate

I_{k+1} by parts with $u = (1 - x^2)^{k+1}$, $dv = dx \Rightarrow du = (k + 1)(1 - x^2)^k(-2x), v = x$, and then split the remaining integral into identifiable quantities:

$$I_{k+1} = \left[x(1-x^2)^{k+1}\right]_0^1 + 2(k+1)\int_0^1 x^2(1-x^2)^k \, dx = (2k+2)\int_0^1 (1-x^2)^k \left[1-(1-x^2)\right] dx$$

$$= (2k+2)(I_k - I_{k+1})$$

So $I_{k+1}\left[1+(2k+2)\right] = (2k+2)I_k \Rightarrow I_{k+1} = \dfrac{2k+2}{2k+3}I_k.$

Now to complete the proof, we use induction: $I_0 = 1 = \dfrac{2^0\,(0!)^2}{1!}$, so the formula holds for $n = 0$. Now suppose it holds

for $n = k$. Then

$$I_{k+1} = \frac{2k+2}{2k+3}I_k = \frac{2k+2}{2k+3}\left[\frac{2^{2k}\,(k!)^2}{(2k+1)!}\right] = \frac{2(k+1)2^{2k}(k!)^2}{(2k+3)(2k+1)!} = \frac{2(k+1)2^{2k}(k!)^2}{(2k+3)(2k+1)!} \cdot \frac{2(k+1)}{2k+2}$$

$$= \frac{[2(k+1)]^2\,2^{2k}(k!)^2}{(2k+3)(2k+2)(2k+1)!} = \frac{2^{2(k+1)}\,[(k+1)!]^2}{[2(k+1)+1]!}$$

So by induction, the formula holds for all integers $n \geq 0$.

23. (a) The tangent to the curve $y = f(x)$ at $x = x_0$ has the equation $y - f(x_0) = f'(x_0)(x - x_0)$. The y-intercept

of this tangent line is $f(x_0) - f'(x_0)x_0$. Thus, L is the distance from the point $(0, f(x_0) - f'(x_0)x_0)$ to

the point $(x_0, f(x_0))$; that is, $L^2 = x_0^2 + [f'(x_0)]^2\,x_0^2$, so $[f'(x_0)]^2 = \dfrac{L^2 - x_0^2}{x_0^2}$ and $f'(x_0) = -\dfrac{\sqrt{L^2 - x_0^2}}{x_0}$

for $0 < x_0 < L$.

(b) $\dfrac{dy}{dx} = -\dfrac{\sqrt{L^2-x^2}}{x} \Rightarrow y = \int\left(-\dfrac{\sqrt{L^2-x^2}}{x}\right)dx.$

Let $x = L\sin\theta$. Then $dx = L\cos\theta\,d\theta$ and

$$y = \int\frac{-L\cos\theta\,L\cos\theta\,d\theta}{L\sin\theta} = L\int\frac{\sin^2\theta-1}{\sin\theta}\,d\theta = L\int(\sin\theta-\csc\theta)\,d\theta$$

$$= -L\cos\theta - L\ln|\csc\theta - \cot\theta| + C = -\sqrt{L^2-x^2} - L\ln\left(\frac{L}{x} - \frac{\sqrt{L^2-x^2}}{x}\right) + C$$

When $x = L$, $y = 0$, and $0 = -0 - L\ln(1-0) + C$, so $C = 0$. Therefore, $y = -\sqrt{L^2-x^2} - L\ln\left(\dfrac{L-\sqrt{L^2-x^2}}{x}\right).$

6 ☐ APPLICATIONS OF INTEGRATION

6.1 More about Areas

1. $A = \int_{x=0}^{x=4} (y_T - y_B)\, dx = \int_0^4 \left[(5x - x^2) - x\right] dx = \int_0^4 (4x - x^2)\, dx = \left[2x^2 - \frac{1}{3}x^3\right]_0^4 = \left(32 - \frac{64}{3}\right) - (0) = \frac{32}{3}$

3. $A = \int_{y=-1}^{y=1} (x_R - x_L)\, dy = \int_{-1}^1 \left[e^y - (y^2 - 2)\right] dy = \int_{-1}^1 \left(e^y - y^2 + 2\right) dy$

$\qquad = \left[e^y - \frac{1}{3}y^3 + 2y\right]_{-1}^1 = \left(e^1 - \frac{1}{3} + 2\right) - \left(e^{-1} + \frac{1}{3} - 2\right) = e - \frac{1}{e} + \frac{10}{3}$

5. $A = \int_{-1}^1 \left[e^x - (x^2 - 1)\right]\, dx = \left[e^x - \frac{1}{3}x^3 + x\right]_{-1}^1$

$\qquad = \left(e - \frac{1}{3} + 1\right) - \left(e^{-1} + \frac{1}{3} - 1\right) = e - \frac{1}{e} + \frac{4}{3}$

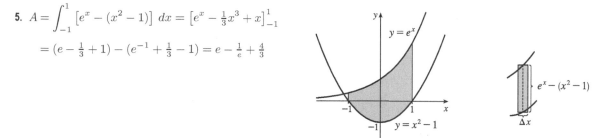

7. $A = \int_0^1 \left(\sqrt{x} - x^2\right) dx$

$\qquad = \left[\frac{2}{3}x^{3/2} - \frac{1}{3}x^3\right]_0^1 \quad,$

$\qquad = \frac{2}{3} - \frac{1}{3} = \frac{1}{3}$

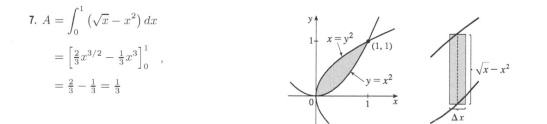

9. The curves intersect when $1 - y^2 = y^2 - 1 \;\Leftrightarrow\; 2 = 2y^2 \;\Leftrightarrow\; y^2 = 1 \;\Leftrightarrow\; y = \pm 1$.

$A = \int_{-1}^1 \left[(1 - y^2) - (y^2 - 1)\right] dy$

$\quad = \int_{-1}^1 2(1 - y^2)\, dy$

$\quad = 2 \cdot 2 \int_0^1 (1 - y^2)\, dy$

$\quad = 4\left[y - \frac{1}{3}y^3\right]_0^1 = 4\left(1 - \frac{1}{3}\right) = \frac{8}{3}$

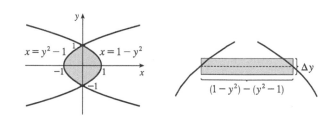

11. $2y^2 = 4 + y^2 \iff y^2 = 4 \iff y = \pm 2$, so

$$A = \int_{-2}^{2} \left[(4 + y^2) - 2y^2 \right] dy$$

$$= 2 \int_{0}^{2} (4 - y^2)\, dy \qquad \text{[by symmetry]}$$

$$= 2 \left[4y - \tfrac{1}{3}y^3 \right]_0^2 = 2 \left(8 - \tfrac{8}{3} \right) = \tfrac{32}{3}$$

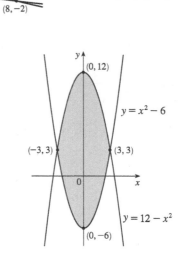

13. $12 - x^2 = x^2 - 6 \iff 2x^2 = 18 \iff$

$x^2 = 9 \iff x = \pm 3$, so

$$A = \int_{-3}^{3} \left[(12 - x^2) - (x^2 - 6) \right] dx$$

$$= 2 \int_{0}^{3} (18 - 2x^2)\, dx \qquad \text{[by symmetry]}$$

$$= 2 \left[18x - \tfrac{2}{3}x^3 \right]_0^3 = 2 \left[(54 - 18) - 0 \right]$$

$$= 2(36) = 72$$

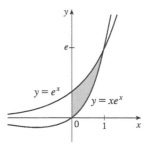

15. $e^x = xe^x \iff e^x - xe^x = 0 \iff e^x(1 - x) = 0 \iff x = 1.$

$$A = \int_{0}^{1} (e^x - xe^x)\, dx$$

$$= \left[e^x - (xe^x - e^x) \right]_0^1 \quad \text{[use parts with } u = x \text{ and } dv = e^x\, dx]$$

$$= \left[2e^x - xe^x \right]_0^1 = (2e - e) - (2 - 0) = e - 2$$

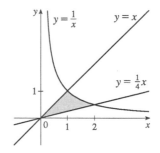

17. $1/x = x \iff 1 = x^2 \iff x = \pm 1$ and $1/x = \tfrac{1}{4}x \iff$

$4 = x^2 \iff x = \pm 2$, so for $x > 0$,

$$A = \int_{0}^{1} \left(x - \tfrac{1}{4}x \right) dx + \int_{1}^{2} \left(\tfrac{1}{x} - \tfrac{1}{4}x \right) dx$$

$$= \int_{0}^{1} \left(\tfrac{3}{4}x \right) dx + \int_{1}^{2} \left(\tfrac{1}{x} - \tfrac{1}{4}x \right) dx$$

$$= \left[\tfrac{3}{8}x^2 \right]_0^1 + \left[\ln |x| - \tfrac{1}{8}x^2 \right]_1^2$$

$$= \tfrac{3}{8} + \left(\ln 2 - \tfrac{1}{2} \right) - \left(0 - \tfrac{1}{8} \right) = \ln 2$$

19.

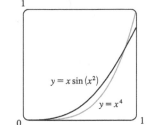

From the graph, we see that the curves intersect at $x = 0$ and $x = a \approx 0.896$, with $x \sin(x^2) > x^4$ on $(0, a)$. So the area A of the region bounded by the curves is

$$A = \int_0^a \left[x \sin(x^2) - x^4 \right] dx = \left[-\tfrac{1}{2} \cos(x^2) - \tfrac{1}{5} x^5 \right]_0^a$$

$$= -\tfrac{1}{2} \cos(a^2) - \tfrac{1}{5} a^5 + \tfrac{1}{2} \approx 0.037$$

21. From the graph, we see that the curves intersect at $x = 1$ and $x = a \approx 1.382$, with $\sqrt{x-1} > x^2 \ln x$ on $(1, a)$. The area A of the region bounded by the curves is

$$A = \int_1^a \left[\sqrt{x-1} - x^2 \ln x \right] dx$$

$$= \left[\tfrac{2}{3}(x-1)^{3/2} - \left(\tfrac{1}{3} x^3 \ln x - \tfrac{1}{9} x^3 \right) \right]_1^a \quad \text{[by Exercise 5.6.1]}$$

$$\approx 0.05$$

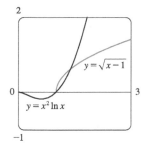

23. $\cos x = \sin 2x = 2 \sin x \cos x \quad \Leftrightarrow \quad 2 \sin x \cos x - \cos x = 0 \quad \Leftrightarrow \quad \cos x (2 \sin x - 1) = 0 \quad \Leftrightarrow$

$2 \sin x = 1$ or $\cos x = 0 \quad \Leftrightarrow \quad x = \tfrac{\pi}{6}$ or $\tfrac{\pi}{2}$.

$$A = \int_0^{\pi/6} (\cos x - \sin 2x)\, dx + \int_{\pi/6}^{\pi/2} (\sin 2x - \cos x)\, dx$$

$$= \left[\sin x + \tfrac{1}{2} \cos 2x \right]_0^{\pi/6} + \left[-\tfrac{1}{2} \cos 2x - \sin x \right]_{\pi/6}^{\pi/2}$$

$$= \left(\tfrac{1}{2} + \tfrac{1}{2} \cdot \tfrac{1}{2} \right) - \left(0 + \tfrac{1}{2} \cdot 1 \right) + \left[-\tfrac{1}{2} \cdot (-1) - 1 \right] - \left(-\tfrac{1}{2} \cdot \tfrac{1}{2} - \tfrac{1}{2} \right)$$

$$= \tfrac{3}{4} - \tfrac{1}{2} - \tfrac{1}{2} + \tfrac{3}{4} = \tfrac{1}{2}$$

25. As in Example 4, we approximate the distance between the two cars after ten seconds using Simpson's Rule with $\Delta t = 1 \text{ s} = \tfrac{1}{3600} \text{ h}$.

$$\text{distance}_{\text{Kelly}} - \text{distance}_{\text{Chris}} = \int_0^{10} v_K\, dt - \int_0^{10} v_C\, dt = \int_0^{10} (v_K - v_C)\, dt \approx S_{10}$$

$$= \tfrac{1}{3 \cdot 3600} \left[(0 - 0) + 4(22 - 20) + 2(37 - 32) + 4(52 - 46) + 2(61 - 54) + 4(71 - 62) \right.$$

$$\left. + 2(80 - 69) + 4(86 - 75) + 2(93 - 81) + 4(98 - 86) + (102 - 90) \right]$$

$$= \tfrac{1}{10,800} (242) = \tfrac{121}{5400} \text{ mi}$$

So after 10 seconds, Kelly's car is about $\dfrac{121}{5400} \text{ mi} \left(5280 \dfrac{\text{ft}}{\text{mi}} \right) \approx 118$ ft ahead of Chris's.

27. If $x =$ distance from left end of pool and $w = w(x) =$ width at x, then Simpson's Rule with $n = 8$ and $\Delta x = 2$ gives

$$\text{Area} = \int_0^{16} w\, dx \approx \tfrac{2}{3} [0 + 4(6.2) + 2(7.2) + 4(6.8) + 2(5.6) + 4(5.0) + 2(4.8) + 4(4.8) + 0] = \tfrac{2}{3}(126.4) \approx 84 \text{ m}^2.$$

29. For $0 \le t \le 10$, $b(t) > d(t)$, so the area between the curves is given by

$$\int_0^{10} [b(t) - d(t)]\, dt = \int_0^{10} (2200e^{0.024t} - 1460e^{0.018t})\, dt = \left[\frac{2200}{0.024} e^{0.024t} - \frac{1460}{0.018} e^{0.018t} \right]_0^{10}$$

$$= \left(\frac{275{,}000}{3} e^{0.24} - \frac{730{,}000}{9} e^{0.18} \right) - \left(\frac{275{,}000}{3} - \frac{730{,}000}{9} \right) \approx 8868 \text{ people}$$

This area A represents the increase in population over a 10-year period.

31. Let the equation of the large circle be $x^2 + y^2 = R^2$. Then the equation of

the small circle is $x^2 + (y - b)^2 = r^2$, where $b = \sqrt{R^2 - r^2}$ is the distance

between the centers of the circles. The desired area is

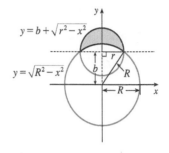

$$A = \int_{-r}^{r} \left[(b + \sqrt{r^2 - x^2}) - \sqrt{R^2 - x^2} \right] dx$$

$$= 2 \int_0^r (b + \sqrt{r^2 - x^2} - \sqrt{R^2 - x^2})\, dx$$

$$= 2 \int_0^r b\, dx + 2 \int_0^r \sqrt{r^2 - x^2}\, dx - 2 \int_0^r \sqrt{R^2 - x^2}\, dx$$

The first integral is just $2br = 2r\sqrt{R^2 - r^2}$. The second integral represents the area of a quarter-circle of radius r, so its value

is $\frac{1}{4}\pi r^2$. To evaluate the other integral, note that

$$\int \sqrt{a^2 - x^2}\, dx = \int a^2 \cos^2\theta\, d\theta \quad [x = a\sin\theta,\, dx = a\cos\theta\, d\theta] \ = (\tfrac{1}{2}a^2)\int (1 + \cos 2\theta)\, d\theta$$

$$= \tfrac{1}{2}a^2 \left(\theta + \tfrac{1}{2}\sin 2\theta\right) + C = \tfrac{1}{2}a^2 (\theta + \sin\theta\,\cos\theta) + C$$

$$= \frac{a^2}{2}\arcsin\!\left(\frac{x}{a}\right) + \frac{a^2}{2}\left(\frac{x}{a}\right)\frac{\sqrt{a^2 - x^2}}{a} + C = \frac{a^2}{2}\arcsin\!\left(\frac{x}{a}\right) + \frac{x}{2}\sqrt{a^2 - x^2} + C$$

Thus, the desired area is

$$A = 2r\sqrt{R^2 - r^2} + 2\left(\tfrac{1}{4}\pi r^2\right) - \left[R^2 \arcsin(x/R) + x\sqrt{R^2 - x^2} \right]_0^r$$

$$= 2r\sqrt{R^2 - r^2} + \tfrac{1}{2}\pi r^2 - \left[R^2 \arcsin(r/R) + r\sqrt{R^2 - r^2} \right] = r\sqrt{R^2 - r^2} + \tfrac{\pi}{2}r^2 - R^2 \arcsin(r/R)$$

33. By symmetry of the ellipse about the x- and y-axes,

$$A = 4 \int_0^a y\, dx = 4 \int_{\pi/2}^0 b\sin\theta\,(-a\sin\theta)\, d\theta \qquad \begin{bmatrix} x = a\cos\theta = 0 & \Rightarrow & \theta = \frac{\pi}{2}, \\ x = a\cos\theta = a & \Rightarrow & \theta = 0, \end{bmatrix}$$

$$= 4ab \int_0^{\pi/2} \sin^2\theta\, d\theta = 4ab \int_0^{\pi/2} \tfrac{1}{2}(1 - \cos 2\theta)\, d\theta$$

$$= 2ab \left[\theta - \tfrac{1}{2}\sin 2\theta\right]_0^{\pi/2} = 2ab\left(\tfrac{\pi}{2}\right) = \pi ab$$

Note that the formula for the area of a circle, $A = \pi r^2$, is just a special case of this formula with $a = b = r$.

35. The curve $x = 1 + e^t$, $y = t - t^2 = t(1 - t)$ intersects the x-axis when $y = 0$,

that is, when $t = 0$ and $t = 1$. The corresponding values of x are 2 and $1 + e$.

The shaded area is given by

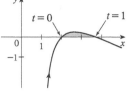

$$\int_{x=2}^{x=1+e} (y_T - y_B) \, dx = \int_{t=0}^{t=1} [y(t) - 0] \, x'(t) \, dt = \int_0^1 (t - t^2) e^t \, dt$$

$$= \int_0^1 t e^t \, dt - \int_0^1 t^2 e^t \, dt = \int_0^1 t e^t \, dt - [t^2 e^t]_0^1 + 2 \int_0^1 t e^t \, dt \qquad \text{[Formula 97 or parts]}$$

$$= 3 \int_0^1 t e^t \, dt - (e - 0) = 3 [(t - 1)e^t]_0^1 - e \qquad \text{[Formula 96 or parts]}$$

$$= 3[0 - (-1)] - e = 3 - e$$

37. By symmetry, the area of the region enclosed by the loop is twice the area above

the x-axis inside the loop. $y = 0 \iff t^3 - 3t = 0 \iff t(t^2 - 3) = 0 \iff$

$t = 0, \pm\sqrt{3}$. The top half of the loop is described by $x = t^2$, $y = t^3 - 3t$,

$-\sqrt{3} \leq t \leq 0$, so, using the Substitution Rule with $y = t^3 - 3t$ and $dx = 2t \, dt$,

we find that

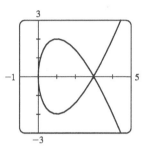

$$\text{Area} = 2 \int_0^3 y \, dx = 2 \int_0^{-\sqrt{3}} (t^3 - 3t) 2t \, dt = 4 \int_0^{-\sqrt{3}} (t^4 - 3t^2) \, dt$$

$$= 4 \left[\frac{1}{5} t^5 - t^3\right]_0^{-\sqrt{3}} = 4 \left[\frac{1}{5}(-3^{1/2})^5 - (-3^{1/2})^3\right]$$

$$= 4 \left[\frac{1}{5}(-9\sqrt{3}) - (-3\sqrt{3})\right] = \frac{24}{5}\sqrt{3} \approx 8.31.$$

39. We first assume that $c > 0$, since c can be replaced by $-c$ in both equations without changing the graphs, and if $c = 0$ the

curves do not enclose a region. We see from the graph that the enclosed area A lies between $x = -c$ and $x = c$, and by

symmetry, it is equal to four times the area in the first quadrant. The enclosed area is

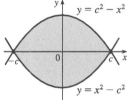

$$A = 4 \int_0^c (c^2 - x^2) \, dx = 4 \left[c^2 x - \frac{1}{3} x^3\right]_0^c = 4 \left(c^3 - \frac{1}{3} c^3\right) = 4 \left(\frac{2}{3} c^3\right) = \frac{8}{3} c^3$$

So $A = 576 \iff \frac{8}{3} c^3 = 576 \iff c^3 = 216 \iff c = \sqrt[3]{216} = 6.$

Note that $c = -6$ is another solution, since the graphs are the same.

41.

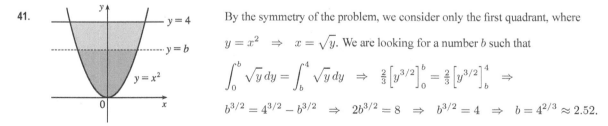

By the symmetry of the problem, we consider only the first quadrant, where

$y = x^2 \implies x = \sqrt{y}$. We are looking for a number b such that

$$\int_0^b \sqrt{y} \, dy = \int_b^4 \sqrt{y} \, dy \implies \frac{2}{3} \left[y^{3/2}\right]_0^b = \frac{2}{3} \left[y^{3/2}\right]_b^4 \implies$$

$$b^{3/2} = 4^{3/2} - b^{3/2} \implies 2b^{3/2} = 8 \implies b^{3/2} = 4 \implies b = 4^{2/3} \approx 2.52.$$

43. The area under the graph of f from 0 to t is equal to $\int_0^t f(x) \, dx$, so the requirement is that $\int_0^t f(x) \, dx = t^3$ for all t. We

differentiate both sides of this equation with respect to t (with the help of FTC1) to get $f(t) = 3t^2$. This function is positive

and continuous, as required.

45. The curve and the line will determine a region when they intersect at two or

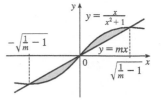

more points. So we solve the equation $x/(x^2+1) = mx$ $\Rightarrow$

$x = x(mx^2 + m)$ $\Rightarrow$ $x(mx^2 + m) - x = 0$ $\Rightarrow$

$x(mx^2 + m - 1) = 0$ $\Rightarrow$ $x = 0$ or $mx^2 + m - 1 = 0$ $\Rightarrow$

$x = 0$ or $x^2 = \dfrac{1-m}{m}$ $\Rightarrow$ $x = 0$ or $x = \pm\sqrt{\dfrac{1}{m} - 1}$. Note that if $m = 1$, this has only the solution $x = 0$, and no region

is determined. But if $1/m - 1 > 0$ $\Leftrightarrow$ $1/m > 1$ $\Leftrightarrow$ $0 < m < 1$, then there are two solutions. [Another way of seeing

this is to observe that the slope of the tangent to $y = x/(x^2+1)$ at the origin is $y'(0) = 1$ and therefore we must have

$0 < m < 1$.] Note that we cannot just integrate between the positive and negative roots, since the curve and the line cross at

the origin. Since mx and $x/(x^2+1)$ are both odd functions, the total area is twice the area between the curves on the interval

$\left[0, \sqrt{1/m - 1}\right]$. So the total area enclosed is

$$2\int_0^{\sqrt{1/m-1}} \left[\frac{x}{x^2+1} - mx\right] dx = 2\left[\tfrac{1}{2}\ln(x^2+1) - \tfrac{1}{2}mx^2\right]_0^{\sqrt{1/m-1}} = [\ln(1/m - 1 + 1) - m(1/m - 1)] - (\ln 1 - 0)$$

$$= \ln(1/m) - 1 + m = m - \ln m - 1$$

6.2 Volumes

1. A cross-section is a disk with radius $2 - \tfrac{1}{2}x$, so its area is $A(x) = \pi\left(2 - \tfrac{1}{2}x\right)^2$.

$$V = \int_1^2 A(x)\,dx = \int_1^2 \pi\left(2 - \tfrac{1}{2}x\right)^2 dx$$

$$= \pi \int_1^2 \left(4 - 2x + \tfrac{1}{4}x^2\right) dx$$

$$= \pi\left[4x - x^2 + \tfrac{1}{12}x^3\right]_1^2$$

$$= \pi\left[\left(8 - 4 + \tfrac{8}{12}\right) - \left(4 - 1 + \tfrac{1}{12}\right)\right]$$

$$= \pi\left(1 + \tfrac{7}{12}\right) = \tfrac{19}{12}\pi$$

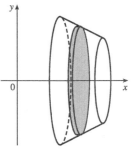

3. A cross-section is a disk with radius $2\sqrt{y}$, so its area is

$$A(y) = \pi\left(2\sqrt{y}\right)^2.$$

$$V = \int_0^9 A(y)\,dy = \int_0^9 \pi\left(2\sqrt{y}\right)^2 dy = 4\pi\int_0^9 y\,dy$$

$$= 4\pi\left[\tfrac{1}{2}y^2\right]_0^9 = 2\pi(81) = 162\pi$$

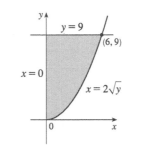

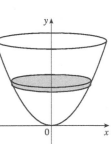

5. A cross-section is a washer (annulus) with inner
radius x^3 and outer radius x, so its area is
$$A(x) = \pi(x)^2 - \pi(x^3)^2 = \pi(x^2 - x^6).$$

$$V = \int_0^1 A(x)\,dx = \int_0^1 \pi(x^2 - x^6)\,dx$$

$$= \pi\left[\tfrac{1}{3}x^3 - \tfrac{1}{7}x^7\right]_0^1 = \pi\left(\tfrac{1}{3} - \tfrac{1}{7}\right) = \tfrac{4}{21}\pi$$

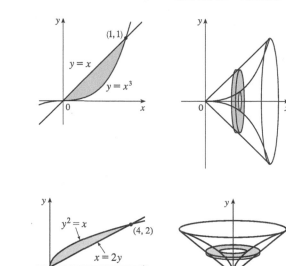

7. A cross-section is a washer with inner radius y^2
and outer radius $2y$, so its area is
$$A(y) = \pi(2y)^2 - \pi(y^2)^2 = \pi(4y^2 - y^4).$$

$$V = \int_0^2 A(y)\,dy = \pi\int_0^2 (4y^2 - y^4)\,dy$$

$$= \pi\left[\tfrac{4}{3}y^3 - \tfrac{1}{5}y^5\right]_0^2 = \pi\left(\tfrac{32}{3} - \tfrac{32}{5}\right) = \tfrac{64}{15}\pi$$

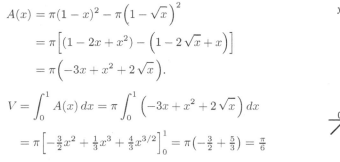

9. A cross-section is a washer with inner radius $1 - \sqrt{x}$ and outer radius $1 - x$, so its area is

$$A(x) = \pi(1 - x)^2 - \pi\left(1 - \sqrt{x}\right)^2$$

$$= \pi\left[(1 - 2x + x^2) - \left(1 - 2\sqrt{x} + x\right)\right]$$

$$= \pi\left(-3x + x^2 + 2\sqrt{x}\right).$$

$$V = \int_0^1 A(x)\,dx = \pi\int_0^1 \left(-3x + x^2 + 2\sqrt{x}\right)dx$$

$$= \pi\left[-\tfrac{3}{2}x^2 + \tfrac{1}{3}x^3 + \tfrac{4}{3}x^{3/2}\right]_0^1 = \pi\left(-\tfrac{3}{2} + \tfrac{5}{3}\right) = \tfrac{\pi}{6}$$

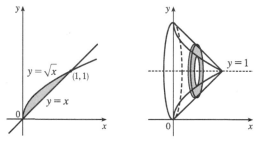

11. A cross-section is a washer with inner radius $(1 + \sec x) - 1 = \sec x$ and outer radius $3 - 1 = 2$, so its area is

$$A(x) = \pi\left[2^2 - (\sec x)^2\right] = \pi(4 - \sec^2 x).$$

$$V = \int_{-\pi/3}^{\pi/3} A(x)\,dx = \int_{-\pi/3}^{\pi/3} \pi(4 - \sec^2 x)\,dx$$

$$= 2\pi\int_0^{\pi/3} (4 - \sec^2 x)\,dx \qquad \text{[by symmetry]}$$

$$= 2\pi\left[4x - \tan x\right]_0^{\pi/3} = 2\pi\left[\left(\tfrac{4\pi}{3} - \sqrt{3}\right) - 0\right]$$

$$= 2\pi\left(\tfrac{4\pi}{3} - \sqrt{3}\right)$$

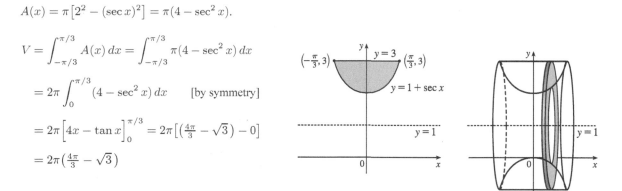

13. A cross-section is a disk with radius $1/x$, so its area is $A(x) = \pi(1/x)^2$.

$$V = \int_1^2 A(x)\,dx = \int_1^2 \pi\left(\frac{1}{x}\right)^2 dx$$

$$= \pi \int_1^2 \frac{1}{x^2}\,dx = \pi\left[-\frac{1}{x}\right]_1^2$$

$$= \pi\left[-\frac{1}{2} - (-1)\right] = \frac{\pi}{2}$$

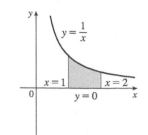

15. The curves $x - y = 1$ and $y = x^2 - 4x + 3$ intersect when

$x - 1 = x^2 - 4x + 3 \iff 0 = x^2 - 5x + 4 \iff$

$0 = (x-1)(x-4) \iff x = 1$ or 4. A cross-section is a washer with

inner radius $3 - (x - 1)$ and outer radius $3 - (x^2 - 4x + 3)$, so its area is

$A(x) = \pi[3 - (x^2 - 4x + 3)]^2 - \pi[3 - (x - 1)]^2.$

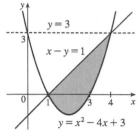

$$V = \int_1^4 A(x)\,dx = \pi \int_1^4 \left\{[3 - (x^2 - 4x + 3)]^2 - [3 - (x - 1)]^2\right\} dx$$

$$= \pi \int_1^4 \left[(4x - x^2)^2 - (4 - x)^2\right] dx = \pi \int_1^4 (16x^2 - 8x^3 + x^4 - 16 + 8x - x^2)\,dx$$

$$= \pi \int_1^4 (x^4 - 8x^3 + 15x^2 + 8x - 16)\,dx = \pi\left[\tfrac{1}{5}x^5 - 2x^4 + 5x^3 + 4x^2 - 16x\right]_1^4$$

$$= \pi\left[\left(\tfrac{1024}{5} - 512 + 320 + 64 - 64\right) - \left(\tfrac{1}{5} - 2 + 5 + 4 - 16\right)\right] = \pi\left(\tfrac{1023}{5} - 183\right) = \tfrac{108}{5}\pi$$

17. $y = \sqrt{x} \Rightarrow x = y^2$ and $y = x^3 \Rightarrow x = \sqrt[3]{y}$. A cross-section is a

washer with inner radius $1 - \sqrt[3]{y}$ and outer radius $1 - y^2$, so its area is

$A(y) = \pi(1 - y^2)^2 - \pi\left(1 - \sqrt[3]{y}\right)^2.$

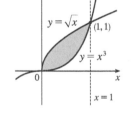

$$V = \int_0^1 A(y)\,dy = \int_0^1 \left[\pi(1 - y^2)^2 - \pi\left(1 - \sqrt[3]{y}\right)^2\right] dy$$

$$= \pi \int_0^1 \left[(1 - 2y^2 + y^4) - (1 - 2y^{1/3} + y^{2/3})\right] dy$$

$$= \pi \int_0^1 (-2y^2 + y^4 + 2y^{1/3} - y^{2/3})\,dy = \pi\left[-\tfrac{2}{3}y^3 + \tfrac{1}{5}y^5 + \tfrac{3}{2}y^{4/3} - \tfrac{3}{5}y^{5/3}\right]_0^1 = \pi\left(-\tfrac{2}{3} + \tfrac{1}{5} + \tfrac{3}{2} - \tfrac{3}{5}\right) = \tfrac{13\pi}{30}$$

19. $\displaystyle V = \pi \int_{-\sqrt{8}}^{\sqrt{8}} \left\{[3 - (-2)]^2 - \left[\sqrt{y^2 + 1} - (-2)\right]^2\right\} dy$

$$= \pi \int_{-2\sqrt{2}}^{2\sqrt{2}} \left[5^2 - \left(\sqrt{1 + y^2} + 2\right)^2\right] dy$$

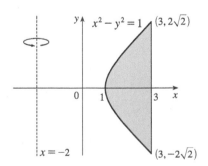

21.

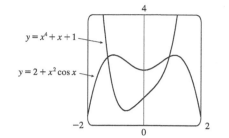

$y = 2 + x^2 \cos x$ and $y = x^4 + x + 1$ intersect at

$x = a \approx -1.288$ and $x = b \approx 0.884$.

$$V = \pi \int_a^b \left[(2 + x^2 \cos x)^2 - (x^4 + x + 1)^2 \right] dx \approx 23.780$$

23. $V = \pi \int_0^\pi \left\{ \left[\sin^2 x - (-1) \right]^2 - [0 - (-1)]^2 \right\} dx$

$\overset{\text{CAS}}{=} \frac{11}{8} \pi^2$

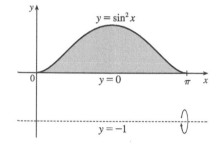

25. (a) $\pi \int_0^{\pi/2} \cos^2 x \, dx$ describes the volume of the solid obtained by rotating the region

$\mathcal{R} = \left\{ (x, y) \mid 0 \le x \le \frac{\pi}{2}, 0 \le y \le \cos x \right\}$ of the xy-plane about the x-axis.

(b) $\pi \int_0^1 (y^4 - y^8) \, dy = \pi \int_0^1 \left[(y^2)^2 - (y^4)^2 \right] dy$ describes the volume of the solid obtained by rotating the region

$\mathcal{R} = \left\{ (x, y) \mid 0 \le y \le 1, y^4 \le x \le y^2 \right\}$ of the xy-plane about the y-axis.

27. There are 10 subintervals over the 15-cm length, so we'll use $n = 10/2 = 5$ for the Midpoint Rule.

$$V = \int_0^{15} A(x) \, dx \approx M_5 = \frac{15 - 0}{5} [A(1.5) + A(4.5) + A(7.5) + A(10.5) + A(13.5)]$$

$$= 3(18 + 79 + 106 + 128 + 39) = 3 \cdot 370 = 1110 \text{ cm}^3$$

29. (a) Using disks, $V = \int_2^{10} \pi [f(x)]^2 \, dx = \pi \int_2^{10} [f(x)]^2 \, dx = \pi I_2$. Now use Simpson's Rule to approximate I_2:

$$I_2 \approx S_8 = \frac{10 - 2}{3(8)} \left\{ [f(2)]^2 + 4[f(3)]^2 + 2[f(4)]^2 + 4[f(5)]^2 + 2[f(6)]^2 \right.$$

$$\left. + 4[f(7)]^2 + 2[f(8)]^2 + 4[f(9)]^2 + [f(10)]^2 \right\}$$

$$\approx \frac{1}{3} \left[(0)^2 + 4(1.5)^2 + 2(1.9)^2 + 4(2.2)^2 + 2(3.0)^2 + 4(3.8)^2 + 2(4.0)^2 + 4(3.1)^2 + (0)^2 \right]$$

$$= \frac{1}{3}(181.78)$$

Thus, $V \approx \pi \cdot \frac{1}{3}(181.78) \approx 190.4$ or 190 cubic units.

(b) $V = \int_0^4 \pi \left[(\text{outer radius})^2 - (\text{inner radius})^2 \right] dy$

$$\approx \pi \frac{4 - 0}{4 \cdot 3} \left\{ [10^2 - 2^2] + 4 [(9.8)^2 - (2.5)^2] + 2 [(9.5)^2 - (4.3)^2] + 4 [(9.1)^2 - (6.0)^2] + [8^2 - 8^2] \right\}$$

$$= \frac{\pi}{3}(785.92) \approx 823 \text{ units}^3$$

31. We'll form a right circular cone with height h and base radius r by revolving the line $y = \frac{r}{h}x$ about the x-axis.

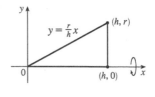

$$V = \pi \int_0^h \left(\frac{r}{h}x\right)^2 dx = \pi \int_0^h \frac{r^2}{h^2}x^2 dx = \pi \frac{r^2}{h^2}\left[\frac{1}{3}x^3\right]_0^h$$

$$= \pi \frac{r^2}{h^2}\left(\frac{1}{3}h^3\right) = \frac{1}{3}\pi r^2 h$$

Another solution: Revolve $x = -\dfrac{r}{h}y + r$ about the y-axis.

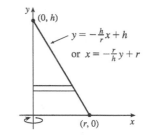

$$V = \pi \int_0^h \left(-\frac{r}{h}y + r\right)^2 dy \overset{*}{=} \pi \int_0^h \left[\frac{r^2}{h^2}y^2 - \frac{2r^2}{h}y + r^2\right] dy$$

$$= \pi \left[\frac{r^2}{3h^2}y^3 - \frac{r^2}{h}y^2 + r^2 y\right]_0^h = \pi\left(\tfrac{1}{3}r^2 h - r^2 h + r^2 h\right) = \tfrac{1}{3}\pi r^2 h$$

* Or use substitution with $u = r - \dfrac{r}{h}y$ and $du = -\dfrac{r}{h}\,dy$ to get

$$\pi \int_r^0 u^2 \left(-\frac{h}{r}\,du\right) = -\pi \frac{h}{r}\left[\frac{1}{3}u^3\right]_r^0 = -\pi \frac{h}{r}\left(-\frac{1}{3}r^3\right) = \frac{1}{3}\pi r^2 h.$$

33. $x^2 + y^2 = r^2 \Leftrightarrow x^2 = r^2 - y^2$

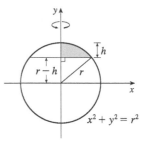

$$V = \pi \int_{r-h}^r (r^2 - y^2)\,dy = \pi\left[r^2 y - \frac{y^3}{3}\right]_{r-h}^r$$

$$= \pi\left\{\left[r^3 - \frac{r^3}{3}\right] - \left[r^2(r-h) - \frac{(r-h)^3}{3}\right]\right\}$$

$$= \pi\left\{\tfrac{2}{3}r^3 - \tfrac{1}{3}(r-h)\left[3r^2 - (r-h)^2\right]\right\}$$

$$= \tfrac{1}{3}\pi\left\{2r^3 - (r-h)\left[3r^2 - (r^2 - 2rh + h^2)\right]\right\}$$

$$= \tfrac{1}{3}\pi\left\{2r^3 - (r-h)\left[2r^2 + 2rh - h^2\right]\right\}$$

$$= \tfrac{1}{3}\pi\left(2r^3 - 2r^3 - 2r^2 h + rh^2 + 2r^2 h + 2rh^2 - h^3\right)$$

$$= \tfrac{1}{3}\pi\left(3rh^2 - h^3\right) = \tfrac{1}{3}\pi h^2(3r - h), \text{ or, equivalently, } \pi h^2\left(r - \frac{h}{3}\right)$$

35. For a cross-section at height y, we see from similar triangles that $\dfrac{\alpha/2}{b/2} = \dfrac{h-y}{h}$, so $\alpha = b\left(1 - \dfrac{y}{h}\right)$.

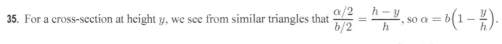

Similarly, for cross-sections having $2b$ as their base and β replacing α, $\beta = 2b\left(1 - \dfrac{y}{h}\right)$. So

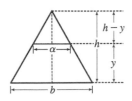

$$V = \int_0^h A(y)\,dy = \int_0^h \left[b\left(1 - \frac{y}{h}\right)\right]\left[2b\left(1 - \frac{y}{h}\right)\right] dy$$

$$= \int_0^h 2b^2\left(1 - \frac{y}{h}\right)^2 dy = 2b^2 \int_0^h \left(1 - \frac{2y}{h} + \frac{y^2}{h^2}\right) dy$$

$$= 2b^2\left[y - \frac{y^2}{h} + \frac{y^3}{3h^2}\right]_0^h = 2b^2\left[h - h + \tfrac{1}{3}h\right]$$

$$= \tfrac{2}{3}b^2 h \quad \left[= \tfrac{1}{3}Bh \text{ where } B \text{ is the area of the base, as with any pyramid.}\right]$$

37. A cross-section at height z is a triangle similar to the base, so we'll multiply the legs of the base triangle, 3 and 4, by a proportionality factor of $(5 - z)/5$. Thus, the triangle at height z has area

$$A(z) = \frac{1}{2} \cdot 3\left(\frac{5-z}{5}\right) \cdot 4\left(\frac{5-z}{5}\right) = 6\left(1 - \frac{z}{5}\right)^2, \text{ so}$$

$$V = \int_0^5 A(z)\, dz = 6 \int_0^5 \left(1 - \frac{z}{5}\right)^2 dz = 6 \int_1^0 u^2 (-5\, du) \qquad \begin{bmatrix} u = 1 - z/5, \\ du = -\frac{1}{5}\, dz \end{bmatrix}$$

$$= -30\left[\tfrac{1}{3} u^3\right]_1^0 = -30\left(-\tfrac{1}{3}\right) = 10 \text{ cm}^3$$

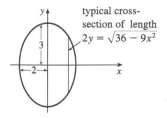

39. If l is a leg of the isosceles right triangle and $2y$ is the hypotenuse,

then $l^2 + l^2 = (2y)^2 \quad \Rightarrow \quad 2l^2 = 4y^2 \quad \Rightarrow \quad l^2 = 2y^2$.

$$V = \int_{-2}^2 A(x)\, dx = 2 \int_0^2 A(x)\, dx = 2 \int_0^2 \tfrac{1}{2}(l)(l)\, dx = 2 \int_0^2 y^2\, dx$$

$$= 2 \int_0^2 \tfrac{1}{4}(36 - 9x^2)\, dx = \tfrac{9}{2} \int_0^2 (4 - x^2)\, dx$$

$$= \tfrac{9}{2}\left[4x - \tfrac{1}{3}x^3\right]_0^2 = \tfrac{9}{2}\left(8 - \tfrac{8}{3}\right) = 24$$

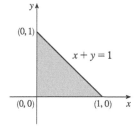

typical cross-section of length $2y = \sqrt{36 - 9x^2}$

41. The cross-section of the base corresponding to the coordinate x has length $y = 1 - x$. The corresponding square with side s has area $A(x) = s^2 = (1 - x)^2 = 1 - 2x + x^2$. Therefore,

$$V = \int_0^1 A(x)\, dx = \int_0^1 (1 - 2x + x^2)\, dx$$

$$= \left[x - x^2 + \tfrac{1}{3}x^3\right]_0^1 = \left(1 - 1 + \tfrac{1}{3}\right) - 0 = \tfrac{1}{3}$$

Or: $\displaystyle\int_0^1 (1 - x)^2\, dx = \int_1^0 u^2(-du) \quad [u = 1 - x] = \left[\tfrac{1}{3}u^3\right]_0^1 = \tfrac{1}{3}$

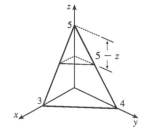

$x + y = 1$

43. The cross-section of the base b corresponding to the coordinate x has length $1 - x^2$. The height h also has length $1 - x^2$, so the corresponding isosceles triangle has area $A(x) = \tfrac{1}{2}bh = \tfrac{1}{2}(1 - x^2)^2$. Therefore,

$$V = \int_{-1}^1 \tfrac{1}{2}(1 - x^2)^2\, dx$$

$$= 2 \cdot \tfrac{1}{2} \int_0^1 (1 - 2x^2 + x^4)\, dx \qquad \text{[by symmetry]}$$

$$= \left[x - \tfrac{2}{3}x^3 + \tfrac{1}{5}x^5\right]_0^1 = \left(1 - \tfrac{2}{3} + \tfrac{1}{5}\right) - 0 = \tfrac{8}{15}$$

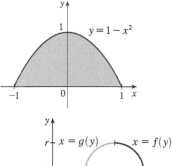

$y = 1 - x^2$

45. (a) The torus is obtained by rotating the circle $(x - R)^2 + y^2 = r^2$ about the y-axis. Solving for x, we see that the right half of the circle is given by $x = R + \sqrt{r^2 - y^2} = f(y)$ and the left half by $x = R - \sqrt{r^2 - y^2} = g(y)$. So

$x = g(y)$ ⟍ $x = f(y)$ ⟍ $(R, 0)$

$$V = \pi \int_{-r}^{r} \left\{ [f(y)]^2 - [g(y)]^2 \right\} dy$$

$$= 2\pi \int_0^r \left[\left(R^2 + 2R\sqrt{r^2 - y^2} + r^2 - y^2 \right) - \left(R^2 - 2R\sqrt{r^2 - y^2} + r^2 - y^2 \right) \right] dy$$

$$= 2\pi \int_0^r 4R\sqrt{r^2 - y^2}\, dy = 8\pi R \int_0^r \sqrt{r^2 - y^2}\, dy$$

(b) Observe that the integral represents a quarter of the area of a circle with radius r, so

$$8\pi R \int_0^r \sqrt{r^2 - y^2}\, dy = 8\pi R \cdot \tfrac{1}{4}\pi r^2 = 2\pi^2 r^2 R.$$

47. (a) Volume$(S_1) = \int_0^h A(z)\, dz = $ Volume(S_2) since the cross-sectional area $A(z)$ at height z is the same for both solids.

(b) By Cavalieri's Principle, the volume of the cylinder in the figure is the same as that of a right circular cylinder with radius r and height h, that is, $\pi r^2 h$.

49. The volume is obtained by rotating the area common to two circles of radius r, as shown. The volume of the right half is

$$V_{\text{right}} = \pi \int_0^{r/2} y^2\, dx = \pi \int_0^{r/2} \left[r^2 - \left(\tfrac{1}{2}r + x \right)^2 \right] dx$$

$$= \pi \left[r^2 x - \tfrac{1}{3} \left(\tfrac{1}{2}r + x \right)^3 \right]_0^{r/2} = \pi \left[\left(\tfrac{1}{2}r^3 - \tfrac{1}{3}r^3 \right) - \left(0 - \tfrac{1}{24}r^3 \right) \right] = \tfrac{5}{24}\pi r^3$$

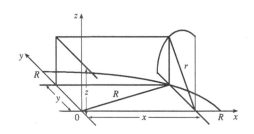

So by symmetry, the total volume is twice this, or $\tfrac{5}{12}\pi r^3$.

Another solution: We observe that the volume is the twice the volume of a cap of a sphere, so we can use the formula from Exercise 33 with $h = \tfrac{1}{2}r$: $V = 2 \cdot \tfrac{1}{3}\pi h^2 (3r - h) = \tfrac{2}{3}\pi \left(\tfrac{1}{2}r \right)^2 \left(3r - \tfrac{1}{2}r \right) = \tfrac{5}{12}\pi r^3$.

51. Take the x-axis to be the axis of the cylindrical hole of radius r. A quarter of the cross-section through y, perpendicular to the y-axis, is the rectangle shown. Using the Pythagorean Theorem twice, we see that the dimensions of this rectangle are

$x = \sqrt{R^2 - y^2}$ and $z = \sqrt{r^2 - y^2}$, so

$\tfrac{1}{4}A(y) = xz = \sqrt{r^2 - y^2}\sqrt{R^2 - y^2}$, and

$$V = \int_{-r}^{r} A(y)\, dy = \int_{-r}^{r} 4\sqrt{r^2 - y^2}\sqrt{R^2 - y^2}\, dy$$

$$= 8 \int_0^r \sqrt{r^2 - y^2}\sqrt{R^2 - y^2}\, dy$$

53. (a) The radius of the barrel is the same at each end by symmetry, since the function $y = R - cx^2$ is even. Since the barrel is obtained by rotating the graph of the function y about the x-axis, this radius is equal to the value of y at $x = \tfrac{1}{2}h$, which is $R - c\left(\tfrac{1}{2}h \right)^2 = R - d = r$.

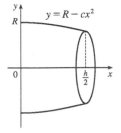

(b) The barrel is symmetric about the y-axis, so its volume is twice the volume of that part of the barrel for $x > 0$. Also, the barrel is a volume of rotation, so

$$V = 2\int_0^{h/2} \pi y^2\, dx = 2\pi \int_0^{h/2} \left(R - cx^2\right)^2 dx = 2\pi\left[R^2 x - \tfrac{2}{3}Rcx^3 + \tfrac{1}{5}c^2 x^5\right]_0^{h/2}$$

$$= 2\pi\left(\tfrac{1}{2}R^2 h - \tfrac{1}{12}Rch^3 + \tfrac{1}{160}c^2 h^5\right)$$

Trying to make this look more like the expression we want, we rewrite it as $V = \tfrac{1}{3}\pi h\left[2R^2 + \left(R^2 - \tfrac{1}{2}Rch^2 + \tfrac{3}{80}c^2 h^4\right)\right]$.

But $R^2 - \tfrac{1}{2}Rch^2 + \tfrac{3}{80}c^2 h^4 = \left(R - \tfrac{1}{4}ch^2\right)^2 - \tfrac{1}{40}c^2 h^4 = (R - d)^2 - \tfrac{2}{5}\left(\tfrac{1}{4}ch^2\right)^2 = r^2 - \tfrac{2}{5}d^2$.

Substituting this back into V, we see that $V = \tfrac{1}{3}\pi h\left(2R^2 + r^2 - \tfrac{2}{5}d^2\right)$, as required.

6.3   Volumes by Cylindrical Shells

1.

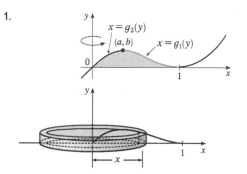

If we were to use the "washer" method, we would first have to locate the local maximum point (a, b) of $y = x(x - 1)^2$ using the methods of Chapter 4. Then we would have to solve the equation $y = x(x - 1)^2$ for x in terms of y to obtain the functions $x = g_1(y)$ and $x = g_2(y)$ shown in the first figure. This step would be difficult because it involves the cubic formula. Finally we would find the volume using

$$V = \pi \int_0^b \left\{[g_1(y)]^2 - [g_2(y)]^2\right\} dy.$$

Using shells, we find that a typical approximating shell has radius x, so its circumference is $2\pi x$. Its height is y, that is, $x(x-1)^2$. So the total volume is

$$V = \int_0^1 2\pi x\left[x(x-1)^2\right] dx = 2\pi \int_0^1 \left(x^4 - 2x^3 + x^2\right) dx = 2\pi\left[\frac{x^5}{5} - 2\frac{x^4}{4} + \frac{x^3}{3}\right]_0^1 = \frac{\pi}{15}$$

3. $V = \displaystyle\int_1^2 2\pi x \cdot \frac{1}{x}\, dx = 2\pi \int_1^2 1\, dx$

$= 2\pi\big[\,x\,\big]_1^2 = 2\pi(2 - 1) = 2\pi$

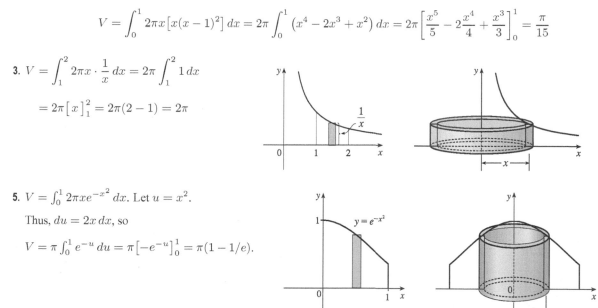

5. $V = \int_0^1 2\pi x e^{-x^2}\, dx$. Let $u = x^2$.

Thus, $du = 2x\, dx$, so

$V = \pi \int_0^1 e^{-u}\, du = \pi\big[-e^{-u}\big]_0^1 = \pi(1 - 1/e)$.

7. The curves intersect when $4(x-2)^2 = x^2 - 4x + 7$ $\Leftrightarrow$ $4x^2 - 16x + 16 = x^2 - 4x + 7$ $\Leftrightarrow$

$3x^2 - 12x + 9 = 0$ $\Leftrightarrow$ $3(x^2 - 4x + 3) = 0$ $\Leftrightarrow$ $3(x-1)(x-3) = 0$, so $x = 1$ or 3.

$V = 2\pi \int_1^3 \left\{ x\left[(x^2 - 4x + 7) - 4(x-2)^2\right] \right\} dx = 2\pi \int_1^3 \left[x(x^2 - 4x + 7 - 4x^2 + 16x - 16) \right] dx$

$= 2\pi \int_1^3 \left[x(-3x^2 + 12x - 9) \right] dx = 2\pi(-3) \int_1^3 (x^3 - 4x^2 + 3x) dx = -6\pi \left[\frac{1}{4}x^4 - \frac{4}{3}x^3 + \frac{3}{2}x^2 \right]_1^3$

$= -6\pi \left[\left(\frac{81}{4} - 36 + \frac{27}{2} \right) - \left(\frac{1}{4} - \frac{4}{3} + \frac{3}{2} \right) \right] = -6\pi \left(20 - 36 + 12 + \frac{4}{3} \right) = -6\pi \left(-\frac{8}{3} \right) = 16\pi$

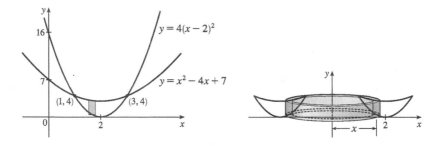

9. $V = \int_1^2 2\pi y(1 + y^2) \, dy = 2\pi \int_1^2 (y + y^3) \, dy = 2\pi \left[\frac{1}{2}y^2 + \frac{1}{4}y^4 \right]_1^2$

$= 2\pi \left[(2 + 4) - \left(\frac{1}{2} + \frac{1}{4} \right) \right] = 2\pi \left(\frac{21}{4} \right) = \frac{21}{2}\pi$

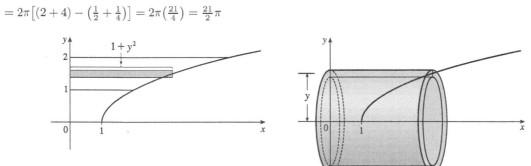

11. The height of the shell is $2 - \left[1 + (y-2)^2 \right] = 1 - (y-2)^2 = 1 - \left(y^2 - 4y + 4 \right) = -y^2 + 4y - 3$.

$V = 2\pi \int_1^3 y(-y^2 + 4y - 3) \, dy$

$= 2\pi \int_1^3 (-y^3 + 4y^2 - 3y) \, dy$

$= 2\pi \left[-\frac{1}{4}y^4 + \frac{4}{3}y^3 - \frac{3}{2}y^2 \right]_1^3$

$= 2\pi \left[\left(-\frac{81}{4} + 36 - \frac{27}{2} \right) - \left(-\frac{1}{4} + \frac{4}{3} - \frac{3}{2} \right) \right]$

$= 2\pi \left(\frac{8}{3} \right) = \frac{16}{3}\pi$

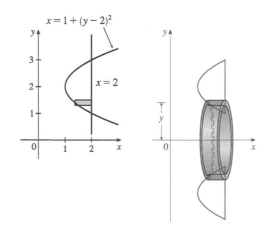

13. The shell has radius $2 - x$, circumference $2\pi(2 - x)$, and height x^4.

$$V = \int_0^1 2\pi(2 - x)x^4\,dx$$

$$= 2\pi \int_0^1 (2x^4 - x^5)\,dx$$

$$= 2\pi\left[\tfrac{2}{5}x^5 - \tfrac{1}{6}x^6\right]_0^1$$

$$= 2\pi\left[\left(\tfrac{2}{5} - \tfrac{1}{6}\right) - 0\right] = 2\pi\left(\tfrac{7}{30}\right) = \tfrac{7}{15}\pi$$

15. The shell has radius $x - 1$, circumference $2\pi(x - 1)$, and height $(4x - x^2) - 3 = -x^2 + 4x - 3$.

$$V = \int_1^3 2\pi(x - 1)(-x^2 + 4x - 3)\,dx$$

$$= 2\pi \int_1^3 (-x^3 + 5x^2 - 7x + 3)\,dx$$

$$= 2\pi\left[-\tfrac{1}{4}x^4 + \tfrac{5}{3}x^3 - \tfrac{7}{2}x^2 + 3x\right]_1^3$$

$$= 2\pi\left[\left(-\tfrac{81}{4} + 45 - \tfrac{63}{2} + 9\right) - \left(-\tfrac{1}{4} + \tfrac{5}{3} - \tfrac{7}{2} + 3\right)\right]$$

$$= 2\pi\left(\tfrac{4}{3}\right) = \tfrac{8}{3}\pi$$

17. The shell has radius $1 - y$, circumference $2\pi(1 - y)$, and height $1 - \sqrt[3]{y}$ $\left[y = x^3 \;\Leftrightarrow\; x = \sqrt[3]{y}\right]$.

$$V = \int_0^1 2\pi(1 - y)(1 - y^{1/3})\,dy$$

$$= 2\pi \int_0^1 (1 - y - y^{1/3} + y^{4/3})\,dy$$

$$= 2\pi\left[y - \tfrac{1}{2}y^2 - \tfrac{3}{4}y^{4/3} + \tfrac{3}{7}y^{7/3}\right]_0^1$$

$$= 2\pi\left[\left(1 - \tfrac{1}{2} - \tfrac{3}{4} + \tfrac{3}{7}\right) - 0\right]$$

$$= 2\pi\left(\tfrac{5}{28}\right) = \tfrac{5}{14}\pi$$

19. $V = \int_0^\pi 2\pi(4 - y)\sqrt{\sin y}\,dy$

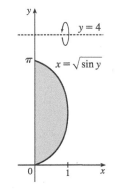

21. $V = \int_0^1 2\pi x \sqrt{1 + x^3} \, dx$. Let $f(x) = x\sqrt{1+x^3}$. Then Simpson's Rule with $n = 10$ gives

$$\int_0^1 f(x) \, dx \approx \tfrac{1-0}{10\cdot3}[f(0) + 4f(0.1) + 2f(0.2) + \cdots + 4f(0.9) + f(1)]$$

$$\approx \tfrac{1}{30}(17.65)$$

Multiplying by 2π gives $V \approx 3.70$.

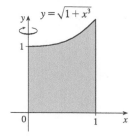

23. (a) $\int_0^3 2\pi x^5 \, dx = 2\pi \int_0^3 x(x^4) \, dx$. The solid is obtained by rotating the region $0 \le y \le x^4$, $0 \le x \le 3$ about the y-axis using cylindrical shells.

(b) $\int_0^1 2\pi(3-y)(1-y^2) \, dy$. The solid is obtained by rotating the region bounded by (i) $x = 1 - y^2$, $x = 0$, and $y = 0$ or

(ii) $x = y^2$, $x = 1$, and $y = 0$ about the line $y = 3$ using cylindrical shells.

25.
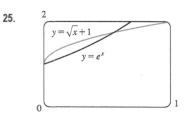

From the graph, the curves intersect at $x = 0$ and $x = a \approx 0.56$, with $\sqrt{x} + 1 > e^x$ on the interval $(0, a)$. So the volume of the solid obtained by rotating the region about the y-axis is

$$V = 2\pi \int_0^a x\left[\left(\sqrt{x} + 1\right) - e^x\right] \, dx \approx 0.13.$$

27. $V = 2\pi \displaystyle\int_0^{\pi/2} \left[\left(\tfrac{\pi}{2} - x\right)\left(\sin^2 x - \sin^4 x\right)\right] dx$

$\overset{\text{CAS}}{=} \tfrac{1}{32}\pi^3$

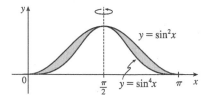

29. Use shells:

$V = \int_2^4 2\pi x(-x^2 + 6x - 8) \, dx = 2\pi \int_2^4 (-x^3 + 6x^2 - 8x) \, dx$

$= 2\pi \left[-\tfrac{1}{4}x^4 + 2x^3 - 4x^2\right]_2^4$

$= 2\pi[(-64 + 128 - 64) - (-4 + 16 - 16)]$

$= 2\pi(4) = 8\pi$

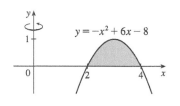

31. Use disks: $x^2 + (y-1)^2 = 1 \iff x = \pm\sqrt{1 - (y-1)^2}$

$V = \pi \displaystyle\int_0^2 \left[\sqrt{1 - (y-1)^2}\right]^2 dy = \pi \displaystyle\int_0^2 (2y - y^2) \, dy$

$= \pi\left[y^2 - \tfrac{1}{3}y^3\right]_0^2 = \pi\left(4 - \tfrac{8}{3}\right) = \tfrac{4}{3}\pi$

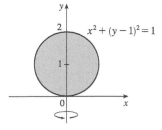

33. Use shells:

$$V = \int_1^4 2\pi[x - (-1)][5 - (x + 4/x)]\,dx$$

$$= 2\pi \int_1^4 (x + 1)(5 - x - 4/x)\,dx$$

$$= 2\pi \int_1^4 (5x - x^2 - 4 + 5 - x - 4/x)\,dx$$

$$= 2\pi \int_1^4 (-x^2 + 4x + 1 - 4/x)\,dx = 2\pi\left[-\tfrac{1}{3}x^3 + 2x^2 + x - 4\ln x\right]_1^4$$

$$= 2\pi\left[\left(-\tfrac{64}{3} + 32 + 4 - 4\ln 4\right) - \left(-\tfrac{1}{3} + 2 + 1 - 0\right)\right]$$

$$= 2\pi(12 - 4\ln 4) = 8\pi(3 - \ln 4)$$

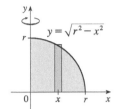

35. Use shells:

$$V = 2\int_0^r 2\pi x\sqrt{r^2 - x^2}\,dx = -2\pi \int_0^r (r^2 - x^2)^{1/2}(-2x)\,dx$$

$$= \left[-2\pi \cdot \tfrac{2}{3}(r^2 - x^2)^{3/2}\right]_0^r = -\tfrac{4}{3}\pi(0 - r^3) = \tfrac{4}{3}\pi r^3$$

37. $V = 2\pi \int_0^r x\left(-\dfrac{h}{r}x + h\right)dx = 2\pi h \int_0^r \left(-\dfrac{x^2}{r} + x\right)dx$

$$= 2\pi h\left[-\dfrac{x^3}{3r} + \dfrac{x^2}{2}\right]_0^r = 2\pi h\dfrac{r^2}{6} = \dfrac{\pi r^2 h}{3}$$

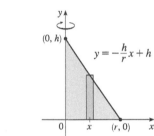

6.4   Arc Length

1. $y = 2x - 5 \;\Rightarrow\; L = \int_{-1}^3 \sqrt{1 + (dy/dx)^2}\,dx = \int_{-1}^3 \sqrt{1 + (2)^2}\,dx = \sqrt{5}\,[3 - (-1)] = 4\sqrt{5}.$

The arc length can be calculated using the distance formula, since the curve is a line segment, so

$$L = [\text{distance from } (-1, -7) \text{ to } (3, 1)] = \sqrt{[3 - (-1)]^2 + [1 - (-7)]^2} = \sqrt{80} = 4\sqrt{5}$$

3. $y = \sin x \;\Rightarrow\; dy/dx = \cos x \;\Rightarrow\; 1 + (dy/dx)^2 = 1 + \cos^2 x.$ So $L = \int_0^\pi \sqrt{1 + \cos^2 x}\,dx \approx 3.8202.$

5. $x = t + \cos t, \;\; y = t - \sin t, \;\; 0 \le t \le 2\pi.$ $dx/dt = 1 - \sin t$ and $dy/dt = 1 - \cos t,$ so

$$\left(\dfrac{dx}{dt}\right)^2 + \left(\dfrac{dy}{dt}\right)^2 = (1 - \sin t)^2 + (1 - \cos t)^2 = (1 - 2\sin t + \sin^2 t) + (1 - 2\cos t + \cos^2 t) = 3 - 2\sin t - 2\cos t.$$

Thus, $L = \int_a^b \sqrt{(dx/dt)^2 + (dy/dt)^2}\,dt = \int_0^{2\pi} \sqrt{3 - 2\sin t - 2\cos t}\,dt \approx 10.0367.$

7. $x = 1 + 3t^2$, $y = 4 + 2t^3$, $0 \le t \le 1$. $dx/dt = 6t$ and $dy/dt = 6t^2$, so $(dx/dt)^2 + (dy/dt)^2 = 36t^2 + 36t^4$

Thus, $L = \int_0^1 \sqrt{36t^2 + 36t^4}\, dt = \int_0^1 6t\sqrt{1+t^2}\, dt = 6\int_1^2 \sqrt{u}\left(\tfrac{1}{2}du\right)$ $[u = 1+t^2, du = 2t\, dt]$

$= 3\left[\tfrac{2}{3}u^{3/2}\right]_1^2 = 2(2^{3/2} - 1) = 2(2\sqrt{2} - 1)$

9. $x = y^{3/2}$ $\Rightarrow$ $1 + (dx/dy)^2 = 1 + \left(\tfrac{3}{2}y^{1/2}\right)^2 = 1 + \tfrac{9}{4}y$.

$L = \int_0^1 \sqrt{1 + \tfrac{9}{4}y}\, dy = \int_1^{13/4} \sqrt{u}\left(\tfrac{4}{9}\, du\right)$ $[u = 1 + \tfrac{9}{4}y, du = \tfrac{9}{4}\, dy]$

$= \tfrac{4}{9} \cdot \tfrac{2}{3}\left[u^{3/2}\right]_1^{13/4} = \tfrac{8}{27}\left(\tfrac{13\sqrt{13}}{8} - 1\right) = \tfrac{13\sqrt{13} - 8}{27}$.

11. $y = \dfrac{1}{4}x^2 - \dfrac{1}{2}\ln x$ $\Rightarrow$ $y' = \dfrac{1}{2}x - \dfrac{1}{2x}$ $\Rightarrow$ $1 + (y')^2 = 1 + \left(\dfrac{1}{4}x^2 - \dfrac{1}{2} + \dfrac{1}{4x^2}\right) = \dfrac{1}{4}x^2 + \dfrac{1}{2} + \dfrac{1}{4x^2} = \left(\dfrac{1}{2}x + \dfrac{1}{2x}\right)^2$.

So

$$L = \int_1^2 \sqrt{1 + (y')^2}\, dx = \int_1^2 \left|\dfrac{1}{2}x + \dfrac{1}{2x}\right| dx = \int_1^2 \left(\dfrac{1}{2}x + \dfrac{1}{2x}\right) dx$$

$$= \left[\dfrac{1}{4}x^2 + \dfrac{1}{2}\ln|x|\right]_1^2 = \left(1 + \dfrac{1}{2}\ln 2\right) - \left(\dfrac{1}{4} + 0\right) = \dfrac{3}{4} + \dfrac{1}{2}\ln 2$$

13.

$x = e^t - t$, $y = 4e^{t/2}$, $-8 \le t \le 3$

$\left(\dfrac{dx}{dt}\right)^2 + \left(\dfrac{dy}{dt}\right)^2 = (e^t - 1)^2 + (2e^{t/2})^2 = e^{2t} - 2e^t + 1 + 4e^t$

$= e^{2t} + 2e^t + 1 = (e^t + 1)^2$

$L = \int_{-8}^3 \sqrt{(e^t + 1)^2}\, dt = \int_{-8}^3 (e^t + 1)\, dt = \left[e^t + t\right]_{-8}^{3t}$

$= (e^3 + 3) - (e^{-8} - 8) = e^3 - e^{-8} + 11$

15.

$x = e^t \cos t$, $y = e^t \sin t$, $0 \le t \le \pi$.

$\left(\dfrac{dx}{dt}\right)^2 + \left(\dfrac{dy}{dt}\right)^2 = [e^t(\cos t - \sin t)]^2 + [e^t(\sin t + \cos t)]^2$

$= (e^t)^2(\cos^2 t - 2\cos t \sin t + \sin^2 t)$

$+ (e^t)^2(\sin^2 t + 2\sin t \cos t + \cos^2 t$

$= e^{2t}(2\cos^2 t + 2\sin^2 t) = 2e^{2t}$

Thus, $L = \int_0^\pi \sqrt{2e^{2t}}\, dt = \int_0^\pi \sqrt{2}\, e^t\, dt = \sqrt{2}\left[e^t\right]_0^\pi = \sqrt{2}\,(e^\pi - 1)$.

17. $y = xe^{-x}$ $\Rightarrow$ $dy/dx = e^{-x} - xe^{-x} = e^{-x}(1 - x)$ $\Rightarrow$ $1 + (dy/dx)^2 = 1 + e^{-2x}(1 - x)^2$. Let

$f(x) = \sqrt{1 + (dy/dx)^2} = \sqrt{1 + e^{-2x}(1 - x)^2}$. Then $L = \int_0^5 f(x)\, dx$. Since $n = 10$, $\Delta x = \dfrac{5 - 0}{10} = \dfrac{1}{2}$. Now

$L \approx S_{10} = \dfrac{1/2}{3}\left[f(0) + 4f\left(\tfrac{1}{2}\right) + 2f(1) + 4f\left(\tfrac{3}{2}\right) + 2f(2) + 4f\left(\tfrac{5}{2}\right) + 2f(3) + 4f\left(\tfrac{7}{2}\right) + 2f(4) + 4f\left(\tfrac{9}{2}\right) + f(5)\right]$

≈ 5.115840

The value of the integral produced by a calculator is 5.113568 (to six decimal places).

19. $x = \sin t$, $y = t^2$ $\Rightarrow$ $(dx/dt)^2 + (dy/dt)^2 = (\cos t)^2 + (2t)^2 = \cos^2 t + 4t^2$ $\Rightarrow$ $L = \int_0^{2\pi} \sqrt{\cos^2 t + 4t^2}\, dt$.

Using Simpson's Rule with $n = 10$, $\Delta t = \dfrac{2\pi - 0}{10} = \dfrac{\pi}{5}$, and $f(t) = \sqrt{\cos^2 t + 4t^2}\, dt$, we get

$$L \approx S_{10} = \tfrac{2\pi-0}{3(10)} \left[f(0) + 4f(\tfrac{\pi}{5}) + 2f(\tfrac{2\pi}{5}) + 4f(\tfrac{3\pi}{5}) + 2f(\tfrac{4\pi}{5}) + 4f(\pi) + 2f(\tfrac{6\pi}{5}) \right.$$
$$\left. + 4f(\tfrac{7\pi}{5}) + 2f(\tfrac{8\pi}{5}) + 4f(\tfrac{9\pi}{5}) + f(2\pi) \right]$$
$$\approx 40.056222$$

The value of the integral produced by a calculator is 40.051156 (to six decimal places).

21. (a)

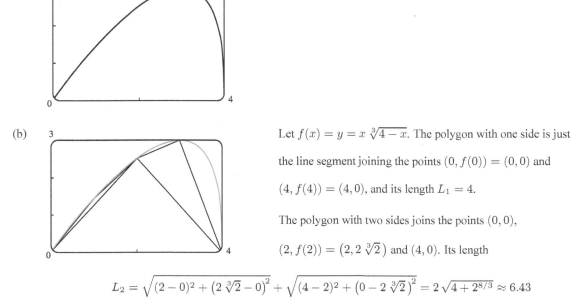

(b) Let $f(x) = y = x\sqrt[3]{4 - x}$. The polygon with one side is just the line segment joining the points $(0, f(0)) = (0, 0)$ and $(4, f(4)) = (4, 0)$, and its length $L_1 = 4$.

The polygon with two sides joins the points $(0, 0)$, $(2, f(2)) = (2, 2\sqrt[3]{2})$ and $(4, 0)$. Its length

$$L_2 = \sqrt{(2-0)^2 + (2\sqrt[3]{2} - 0)^2} + \sqrt{(4-2)^2 + (0 - 2\sqrt[3]{2})^2} = 2\sqrt{4 + 2^{8/3}} \approx 6.43$$

Similarly, the inscribed polygon with four sides joins the points $(0, 0)$, $(1, \sqrt[3]{3})$, $(2, 2\sqrt[3]{2})$, $(3, 3)$, and $(4, 0)$, so its length

$$L_3 = \sqrt{1 + (\sqrt[3]{3})^2} + \sqrt{1 + (2\sqrt[3]{2} - \sqrt[3]{3})^2} + \sqrt{1 + (3 - 2\sqrt[3]{2})^2} + \sqrt{1 + 9} \approx 7.50$$

(c) Using the arc length formula with $\dfrac{dy}{dx} = x\left[\tfrac{1}{3}(4 - x)^{-2/3}(-1)\right] + \sqrt[3]{4 - x} = \dfrac{12 - 4x}{3(4 - x)^{2/3}}$, the length of the curve is

$$L = \int_0^4 \sqrt{1 + \left(\dfrac{dy}{dx}\right)^2}\, dx = \int_0^4 \sqrt{1 + \left[\dfrac{12 - 4x}{3(4 - x)^{2/3}}\right]^2}\, dx.$$

(d) According to a calculator, the length of the curve is $L \approx 7.7988$. The actual value is larger than any of the approximations in part (b). This is always true, since any approximating straight line between two points on the curve is shorter than the length of the curve between the two points.

23. $x = t^3 \quad \Rightarrow \quad dx/dt = 3t^2$ and $y = t^4 \quad \Rightarrow \quad dy/dt = 4t^3$. So

$$L = \int_0^1 \sqrt{9t^4 + 16t^6}\, dt = \int_0^1 \sqrt{t^4(9 + 16t^2)}\, dt = \int_0^1 t^2\sqrt{9 + 16t^2}\, dt.$$

Now use Formula 22 from the table of integrals to evaluate L.

$$L = \int_0^4 \left(\tfrac{1}{4}u\right)^2 \sqrt{a^2 + u^2}\,\left(\tfrac{1}{4}du\right) \qquad [a = 3,\, u = 4t,\, du = 4\,dt]$$

$$= \tfrac{1}{64}\int_0^4 u^2 \sqrt{a^2 + u^2}\, du = \tfrac{1}{64}\left[\tfrac{u}{8}\left(9 + 2u^2\right)\sqrt{9 + u^2} - \tfrac{81}{8}\ln\left(u + \sqrt{9 + u^2}\right)\right]_0^4$$

$$= \tfrac{1}{64}\left\{\left[\tfrac{1}{2}\cdot 41 \cdot 5 - \tfrac{81}{8}\ln(4 + 5)\right] - \left[0 - \tfrac{81}{8}\ln 3\right]\right\}$$

$$= \tfrac{1}{64}\left[\tfrac{205}{2} - \tfrac{81}{8}(2\ln 3) + \tfrac{81}{8}\ln 3\right] \qquad [\ln 9 = \ln 3^2 = 2\ln 3]$$

$$= \tfrac{1}{64}\left(\tfrac{205}{2} - \tfrac{81}{8}\ln 3\right) = \tfrac{205}{128} - \tfrac{81}{512}\ln 3 \approx 1.428.$$

25. $y = \ln(\cos x) \quad \Rightarrow \quad y' = \dfrac{1}{\cos x}(-\sin x) = -\tan x \quad \Rightarrow \quad 1 + (y')^2 = 1 + \tan^2 x = \sec^2 x.$

So $L = \int_0^{\pi/4} \sec x\, dx \overset{14}{=} \left[\ln|\sec x + \tan x|\right]_0^{\pi/4} = \ln\left(\sqrt{2} + 1\right) - \ln(1 + 0) = \ln\left(\sqrt{2} + 1\right) \approx 0.881.$

27. The prey hits the ground when $y = 0 \quad \Leftrightarrow \quad 180 - \tfrac{1}{45}x^2 = 0 \quad \Leftrightarrow \quad x^2 = 45\cdot 180 \quad \Rightarrow \quad x = \sqrt{8100} = 90,$

since x must be positive. $y' = -\tfrac{2}{45}x \quad \Rightarrow \quad 1 + (y')^2 = 1 + \tfrac{4}{45^2}x^2$, so the distance traveled by the prey is

$$L = \int_0^{90} \sqrt{1 + \frac{4}{45^2}x^2}\, dx = \int_0^4 \sqrt{1 + u^2}\left(\tfrac{45}{2}\, du\right) \qquad \left[\begin{array}{l} u = \tfrac{2}{45}x, \\ du = \tfrac{2}{45}\, dx \end{array}\right]$$

$$\overset{21}{=} \tfrac{45}{2}\left[\tfrac{1}{2}u\sqrt{1 + u^2} + \tfrac{1}{2}\ln\left(u + \sqrt{1 + u^2}\right)\right]_0^4 = \tfrac{45}{2}\left[2\sqrt{17} + \tfrac{1}{2}\ln\left(4 + \sqrt{17}\right)\right] = 45\sqrt{17} + \tfrac{45}{4}\ln\left(4 + \sqrt{17}\right) \approx 209.1 \text{ m}$$

29. The sine wave has amplitude 1 and period 14, since it goes through two periods in a distance of 28 in., so its equation is

$y = 1\sin\left(\tfrac{2\pi}{14}x\right) = \sin\left(\tfrac{\pi}{7}x\right)$. The width w of the flat metal sheet needed to make the panel is the arc length of the sine curve

from $x = 0$ to $x = 28$. We set up the integral to evaluate w using the arc length formula with $\dfrac{dy}{dx} = \tfrac{\pi}{7}\cos\left(\tfrac{\pi}{7}x\right)$:

$L = \int_0^{28} \sqrt{1 + \left[\tfrac{\pi}{7}\cos\left(\tfrac{\pi}{7}x\right)\right]^2}\, dx = 2\int_0^{14}\sqrt{1 + \left[\tfrac{\pi}{7}\cos\left(\tfrac{\pi}{7}x\right)\right]^2}\, dx$. This integral would be very difficult to evaluate exactly,

so we use a CAS, and find that $L \approx 29.36$ inches.

31. $x = a\sin\theta,\ y = b\cos\theta,\ 0 \le \theta \le 2\pi.$

$$\left(\tfrac{dx}{dt}\right)^2 + \left(\tfrac{dy}{dt}\right)^2 = (a\cos\theta)^2 + (-b\sin\theta)^2 = a^2\cos^2\theta + b^2\sin^2\theta = a^2(1 - \sin^2\theta) + b^2\sin^2\theta$$

$$= a^2 - (a^2 - b^2)\sin^2\theta = a^2 - c^2\sin^2\theta = a^2\left(1 - \frac{c^2}{a^2}\sin^2\theta\right) = a^2(1 - e^2\sin^2\theta)$$

So $L = 4\int_0^{\pi/2}\sqrt{a^2\left(1 - e^2\sin^2\theta\right)}\, d\theta$ [by symmetry] $= 4a\int_0^{\pi/2}\sqrt{1 - e^2\sin^2\theta}\, d\theta.$

33. (a) $x = 11\cos t - 4\cos(11t/2)$, $y = 11\sin t - 4\sin(11t/2)$.

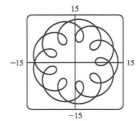

Notice that $0 \le t \le 2\pi$ does not give the complete curve because

$x(0) \ne x(2\pi)$. In fact, we must take $t \in [0, 4\pi]$ in order to obtain the

complete curve, since the first term in each of the parametric equations has

period 2π and the second has period $\frac{2\pi}{11/2} = \frac{4\pi}{11}$, and the least common

integer multiple of these two numbers is 4π.

(b) We use the CAS to find the derivatives dx/dt and dy/dt, and then use Formula 1 to find the arc length. Recent versions

of Maple express the integral $\int_0^{4\pi} \sqrt{(dx/dt)^2 + (dy/dt)^2}\, dt$ as $88E(2\sqrt{2}\,i)$, where $E(x)$ is the elliptic integral

$\displaystyle\int_0^1 \frac{\sqrt{1 - x^2 t^2}}{\sqrt{1 - t^2}}\, dt$ and i is the imaginary number $\sqrt{-1}$.

Some earlier versions of Maple (as well as Mathematica) cannot do the integral exactly, so we use the command

`evalf(Int(sqrt(diff(x,t)^2+diff(y,t)^2),t=0..4*Pi));` to estimate the length, and find that the arc

length is approximately 294.03. Derive's `Para_arc_length` function in the utility file `Int_apps` simplifies the

integral to $11 \int_0^{4\pi} \sqrt{-4\cos t\,\cos\left(\frac{11t}{2}\right) - 4\sin t\,\sin\left(\frac{11t}{2}\right) + 5}\, dt$.

6.5   Average Value of a Function

1. $f_{\text{ave}} = \frac{1}{b-a}\int_a^b f(x)\,dx = \frac{1}{4-0}\int_0^4 (4x - x^2)\,dx = \frac{1}{4}\left[2x^2 - \frac{1}{3}x^3\right]_0^4 = \frac{1}{4}\left[\left(32 - \frac{64}{3}\right) - 0\right] = \frac{1}{4}\left(\frac{32}{3}\right) = \frac{8}{3}$

3. $g_{\text{ave}} = \frac{1}{b-a}\int_a^b g(x)\,dx = \frac{1}{8-1}\int_1^8 \sqrt[3]{x}\,dx = \frac{1}{7}\left[\frac{3}{4}x^{4/3}\right]_1^8 = \frac{3}{28}(16 - 1) = \frac{45}{28}$

5. $h_{\text{ave}} = \frac{1}{\pi - 0}\int_0^\pi \cos^4 x\,\sin x\,dx = \frac{1}{\pi}\int_1^{-1} u^4(-du)$ $[u = \cos x,\ du = -\sin x\,dx]$

$= \frac{1}{\pi}\int_{-1}^1 u^4\,du = \frac{1}{\pi}\cdot 2\int_0^1 u^4\,du$ [by Theorem 5.5.6(a)] $= \frac{2}{\pi}\left[\frac{1}{5}u^5\right]_0^1 = \frac{2}{5\pi}$

7. (a) $f_{\text{ave}} = \dfrac{1}{5-2}\int_2^5 (x-3)^2\,dx = \dfrac{1}{3}\left[\dfrac{1}{3}(x-3)^3\right]_2^5$

$= \frac{1}{9}\left[2^3 - (-1)^3\right] = \frac{1}{9}(8 + 1) = 1$

(b) $f(c) = f_{\text{ave}}$ $\Leftrightarrow$ $(c-3)^2 = 1$ $\Leftrightarrow$

$c - 3 = \pm 1$ $\Leftrightarrow$ $c = 2$ or 4

(c)

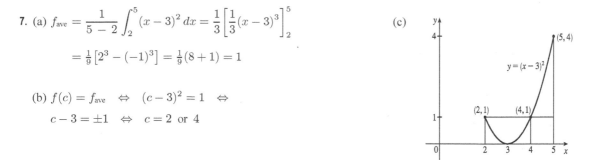

9. (a) $f_{\text{ave}} = \dfrac{1}{\pi - 0} \displaystyle\int_0^\pi (2\sin x - \sin 2x)\,dx$

$\qquad = \frac{1}{\pi}\left[-2\cos x + \frac{1}{2}\cos 2x\right]_0^\pi$

$\qquad = \frac{1}{\pi}\left[\left(2 + \frac{1}{2}\right) - \left(-2 + \frac{1}{2}\right)\right] = \frac{4}{\pi}$

(b) $f(c) = f_{\text{ave}} \;\Leftrightarrow\; 2\sin c - \sin 2c = \frac{4}{\pi} \;\Leftrightarrow$

$\quad c_1 \approx 1.238 \;\text{ or }\; c_2 \approx 2.808$

(c)

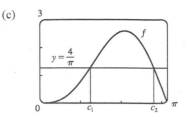

11. f is continuous on $[1,3]$, so by the Mean Value Theorem for Integrals there exists a number c in $[1,3]$ such that

$\displaystyle\int_1^3 f(x)\,dx = f(c)(3-1) \;\Rightarrow\; 8 = 2f(c)$; that is, there is a number c such that $f(c) = \frac{8}{2} = 4$.

13. $f_{\text{ave}} = \dfrac{1}{b-a}\displaystyle\int_a^b f(x)\,dx \approx \dfrac{1}{50-20}S_6$

$\qquad = \frac{1}{30}\cdot\frac{50-20}{6\cdot 3}[f(20) + 4f(25) + 2f(30) + 4f(35) + 2f(40) + 4f(45) + f(50)]$

$\qquad = \frac{1}{18}[42 + 4(38) + 2(31) + 4(29) + 2(35) + 4(48) + 60] = \frac{1}{18}(694) = \frac{347}{9} \approx 38.6$

15. Let $t = 0$ and $t = 12$ correspond to 9 AM and 9 PM, respectively.

$$T_{\text{ave}} = \tfrac{1}{12-0}\int_0^{12}\left[50 + 14\sin\tfrac{1}{12}\pi t\right]dt = \tfrac{1}{12}\left[50t - 14\cdot\tfrac{12}{\pi}\cos\tfrac{1}{12}\pi t\right]_0^{12}$$

$$= \tfrac{1}{12}\left[50\cdot 12 + 14\cdot\tfrac{12}{\pi} + 14\cdot\tfrac{12}{\pi}\right] = \left(50 + \tfrac{28}{\pi}\right)\,^\circ\text{F} \approx 59^\circ\text{F}$$

17. $\rho_{\text{ave}} = \dfrac{1}{8}\displaystyle\int_0^8 \dfrac{12}{\sqrt{x+1}}\,dx = \dfrac{3}{2}\displaystyle\int_0^8 (x+1)^{-1/2}\,dx = \left[3\sqrt{x+1}\right]_0^8 = 9 - 3 = 6\;\text{kg/m}$

19. $V_{\text{ave}} = \frac{1}{5}\int_0^5 V(t)\,dt = \frac{1}{5}\int_0^5 \frac{5}{4\pi}\left[1 - \cos\left(\frac{2}{5}\pi t\right)\right]dt = \frac{1}{4\pi}\int_0^5\left[1 - \cos\left(\frac{2}{5}\pi t\right)\right]dt$

$\qquad = \frac{1}{4\pi}\left[t - \frac{5}{2\pi}\sin\left(\frac{2}{5}\pi t\right)\right]_0^5 = \frac{1}{4\pi}\left[(5-0) - 0\right] = \frac{5}{4\pi} \approx 0.4\;\text{L}$

21. Let $F(x) = \int_a^x f(t)\,dt$ for x in $[a,b]$. Then F is continuous on $[a,b]$ and differentiable on (a,b), so by the Mean Value

Theorem there is a number c in (a,b) such that $F(b) - F(a) = F'(c)(b-a)$. But $F'(x) = f(x)$ by the Fundamental

Theorem of Calculus. Therefore, $\int_a^b f(t)\,dt - 0 = f(c)(b-a)$.

6.6 Applications to Physics and Engineering

1. $W = \displaystyle\int_a^b f(x)\,dx = \displaystyle\int_0^9 \dfrac{10}{(1+x)^2}\,dx = 10\displaystyle\int_1^{10}\dfrac{1}{u^2}\,du \quad [u = 1 + x,\; du = dx] \;= 10\left[-\dfrac{1}{u}\right]_1^{10} = 10\left(-\tfrac{1}{10} + 1\right) = 9\;\text{ft-lb}$

3. The force function is given by $F(x)$ (in newtons) and the work (in joules) is the area under the curve, given by

$\displaystyle\int_0^8 F(x)\,dx = \int_0^4 F(x)\,dx + \int_4^8 F(x)\,dx = \frac{1}{2}(4)(30) + (4)(30) = 180\;\text{J}$.

5. According to Hooke's Law, the force required to maintain a spring stretched x units beyond its natural length is proportional to x, that is, $f(x) = kx$. Here, the amount stretched is $4 \text{ in.} = \frac{1}{3}$ ft and the force is 10 lb. Thus, $10 = k\left(\frac{1}{3}\right) \quad \Rightarrow$

$k = 30$ lb/ft, and $f(x) = 30x$. The work done in stretching the spring from its natural length to $6 \text{ in.} = \frac{1}{2}$ ft beyond its natural

length is $W = \int_0^{1/2} 30x \, dx = \left[15x^2\right]_0^{1/2} = \frac{15}{4}$ ft-lb.

7. (a) If $\int_0^{0.12} kx \, dx = 2$ J, then $2 = \left[\frac{1}{2}kx^2\right]_0^{0.12} = \frac{1}{2}k(0.0144) = 0.0072k$ and $k = \frac{2}{0.0072} = \frac{2500}{9} \approx 277.78$ N/m.

Thus, the work needed to stretch the spring from 35 cm to 40 cm is

$\int_{0.05}^{0.10} \frac{2500}{9} x \, dx = \left[\frac{1250}{9}x^2\right]_{1/20}^{1/10} = \frac{1250}{9}\left(\frac{1}{100} - \frac{1}{400}\right) = \frac{25}{24} \approx 1.04$ J.

(b) $f(x) = kx$, so $30 = \frac{2500}{9}x$ and $x = \frac{270}{2500}$ m $= 10.8$ cm

9. The distance from 20 cm to 30 cm is 0.1 m, so with $f(x) = kx$, we get $W_1 = \int_0^{0.1} kx \, dx = k\left[\frac{1}{2}x^2\right]_0^{0.1} = \frac{1}{200}k$.

Now $W_2 = \int_{0.1}^{0.2} kx \, dx = k\left[\frac{1}{2}x^2\right]_{0.1}^{0.2} = k\left(\frac{4}{200} - \frac{1}{200}\right) = \frac{3}{200}k$. Thus, $W_2 = 3W_1$.

In Exercises 11–18, n is the number of subintervals of length Δx, and x_i^* is a sample point in the ith subinterval $[x_{i-1}, x_i]$.

11. (a) The portion of the rope from x ft to $(x + \Delta x)$ ft below the top of the building weighs $\frac{1}{2}\Delta x$ lb and must be lifted x_i^* ft,

so its contribution to the total work is $\frac{1}{2}x_i^* \Delta x$ ft-lb. The total work is

$$W = \lim_{n \to \infty} \sum_{i=1}^{n} \frac{1}{2}x_i^* \Delta x = \int_0^{50} \frac{1}{2}x \, dx = \left[\frac{1}{4}x^2\right]_0^{50} = \frac{2500}{4} = 625 \text{ ft-lb}$$

Notice that the exact height of the building does not matter (as long as it is more than 50 ft).

(b) When half the rope is pulled to the top of the building, the work to lift the top half of the rope is

$W_1 = \int_0^{25} \frac{1}{2}x \, dx = \left[\frac{1}{4}x^2\right]_0^{25} = \frac{625}{4}$ ft-lb. The bottom half of the rope is lifted 25 ft and the work needed to accomplish

that is $W_2 = \int_{25}^{50} \frac{1}{2} \cdot 25 \, dx = \frac{25}{2}\left[x\right]_{25}^{50} = \frac{625}{2}$ ft-lb. The total work done in pulling half the rope to the top of the building

is $W = W_1 + W_2 = \frac{625}{2} + \frac{625}{4} = \frac{3}{4} \cdot 625 = \frac{1875}{4}$ ft-lb.

13. The work needed to lift the cable is $\lim_{n \to \infty} \sum_{i=1}^{n} 2x_i^* \Delta x = \int_0^{500} 2x \, dx = \left[x^2\right]_0^{500} = 250,000$ ft-lb. The work needed to lift

the coal is $800 \text{ lb} \cdot 500 \text{ ft} = 400,000$ ft-lb. Thus, the total work required is $250,000 + 400,000 = 650,000$ ft-lb.

15. At a height of x meters ($0 \le x \le 12$), the mass of the rope is $(0.8 \text{ kg/m})(12 - x \text{ m}) = (9.6 - 0.8x)$ kg and the mass of the

water is $\left(\frac{36}{12} \text{ kg/m}\right)(12 - x \text{ m}) = (36 - 3x)$ kg. The mass of the bucket is 10 kg, so the total mass is

$(9.6 - 0.8x) + (36 - 3x) + 10 = (55.6 - 3.8x)$ kg, and hence, the total force is $9.8(55.6 - 3.8x)$ N. The work needed to lift

the bucket Δx m through the ith subinterval of $[0, 12]$ is $9.8(55.6 - 3.8x_i^*)\Delta x$, so the total work is

$$W = \lim_{n \to \infty} \sum_{i=1}^{n} 9.8(55.6 - 3.8x_i^*) \Delta x = \int_0^{12} (9.8)(55.6 - 3.8x) \, dx = 9.8\left[55.6x - 1.9x^2\right]_0^{12} = 9.8(393.6) \approx 3857 \text{ J}$$

17. A "slice" of water Δx m thick and lying at a depth of x_i^* m (where $0 \le x_i^* \le \frac{1}{2}$) has volume $(2 \times 1 \times \Delta x)$ m^3, a mass of

$2000 \, \Delta x$ kg, weighs about $(9.8)(2000 \, \Delta x) = 19{,}600 \, \Delta x$ N, and thus requires about $19{,}600 x_i^* \, \Delta x$ J of work for its removal.

So $W = \lim\limits_{n \to \infty} \sum\limits_{i=1}^{n} 19{,}600 x_i^* \, \Delta x = \int_0^{1/2} 19{,}600x \, dx = \left[9800x^2\right]_0^{1/2} = 2450$ J.

19. A rectangular "slice" of water Δx m thick and lying x m above the bottom has width x m and volume $8x \, \Delta x$ m^3. It weighs

about $(9.8 \times 1000)(8x \, \Delta x)$ N, and must be lifted $(5 - x)$ m by the pump, so the work needed is about

$(9.8 \times 10^3)(5 - x)(8x \, \Delta x)$ J. The total work required is

$$W \approx \int_0^3 (9.8 \times 10^3)(5 - x)8x \, dx = (9.8 \times 10^3) \int_0^3 (40x - 8x^2) \, dx = (9.8 \times 10^3)\left[20x^2 - \tfrac{8}{3}x^3\right]_0^3$$

$$= (9.8 \times 10^3)(180 - 72) = (9.8 \times 10^3)(108) = 1058.4 \times 10^3 \approx 1.06 \times 10^6 \text{ J}$$

21. Let x measure depth (in feet) below the spout at the top of the tank. A horizontal

disk-shaped "slice" of water Δx ft thick and lying at coordinate x has radius

$\frac{3}{8}(16 - x)$ ft $(\star)$ and volume $\pi r^2 \Delta x = \pi \cdot \frac{9}{64}(16 - x)^2 \, \Delta x$ ft^3. It weighs

about $(62.5)\frac{9\pi}{64}(16 - x)^2 \, \Delta x$ lb and must be lifted x ft by the pump, so the

work needed to pump it out is about $(62.5)x\frac{9\pi}{64}(16 - x)^2 \, \Delta x$ ft-lb. The total

work required is

$$W \approx \int_0^8 (62.5)x \frac{9\pi}{64}(16 - x)^2 \, dx = (62.5)\frac{9\pi}{64} \int_0^8 x(256 - 32x + x^2) \, dx$$

$$= (62.5)\frac{9\pi}{64} \int_0^8 (256x - 32x^2 + x^3) \, dx = (62.5)\frac{9\pi}{64}\left[128x^2 - \tfrac{32}{3}x^3 + \tfrac{1}{4}x^4\right]_0^8$$

$$= (62.5)\frac{9\pi}{64}\left(\frac{11{,}264}{3}\right) = 33{,}000\pi \approx 1.04 \times 10^5 \text{ ft-lb}$$

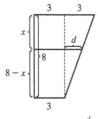

$(\star)$ From similar triangles, $\dfrac{d}{8 - x} = \dfrac{3}{8}$.

So $r = 3 + d = 3 + \tfrac{3}{8}(8 - x)$

$= \dfrac{3(8)}{8} + \dfrac{3}{8}(8 - x)$

$= \tfrac{3}{8}(16 - x)$

23. If only 4.7×10^5 J of work is done, then only the water above a certain level (call

it h) will be pumped out. So we use the same formula as in Exercise 19, except that

the work is fixed, and we are trying to find the lower limit of integration:

$4.7 \times 10^5 \approx \int_h^3 (9.8 \times 10^3)(5 - x)8x \, dx = (9.8 \times 10^3)\left[20x^2 - \tfrac{8}{3}x^3\right]_h^3 \quad \Leftrightarrow$

$\frac{4.7}{9.8} \times 10^2 \approx 48 = \left(20 \cdot 3^2 - \tfrac{8}{3} \cdot 3^3\right) - \left(20h^2 - \tfrac{8}{3}h^3\right) \quad \Leftrightarrow$

$2h^3 - 15h^2 + 45 = 0$. To find the solution of this equation, we plot $2h^3 - 15h^2 + 45$ between $h = 0$ and $h = 3$.

We see that the equation is satisfied for $h \approx 2.0$. So the depth of water remaining in the tank is about 2.0 m.

25. $V = \pi r^2 x$, so V is a function of x and P can also be regarded as a function of x. If $V_1 = \pi r^2 x_1$ and $V_2 = \pi r^2 x_2$, then

$$W = \int_{x_1}^{x_2} F(x) \, dx = \int_{x_1}^{x_2} \pi r^2 P(V(x)) \, dx = \int_{x_1}^{x_2} P(V(x)) \, dV(x) \qquad [\text{Let } V(x) = \pi r^2 x, \text{ so } dV(x) = \pi r^2 \, dx.]$$

$$= \int_{V_1}^{V_2} P(V) \, dV \quad \text{by the Substitution Rule.}$$

27. (a) $W = \int_a^b F(r)\,dr = \int_a^b G\frac{m_1 m_2}{r^2}\,dr = Gm_1m_2\left[\frac{-1}{r}\right]_a^b = Gm_1m_2\left(\frac{1}{a} - \frac{1}{b}\right)$

(b) By part (a), $W = GMm\left(\frac{1}{R} - \frac{1}{R+1{,}000{,}000}\right)$ where M = mass of the earth in kg, R = radius of the earth in m,

and m = mass of satellite in kg. (Note that 1000 km = 1,000,000 m.) Thus,

$$W = (6.67 \times 10^{-11})(5.98 \times 10^{24})(1000) \times \left(\frac{1}{6.37 \times 10^6} - \frac{1}{7.37 \times 10^6}\right) \approx 8.50 \times 10^9 \text{ J}$$

29. The weight density of water is $\delta = 62.5 \text{ lb/ft}^3$.

(a) $P = \delta d \approx (62.5 \text{ lb/ft}^3)(3 \text{ ft}) = 187.5 \text{ lb/ft}^2$

(b) $F = PA \approx (187.5 \text{ lb/ft}^2)(5 \text{ ft})(2 \text{ ft}) = 1875 \text{ lb}$.   ($A$ is the area of the bottom of the tank.)

(c) As in Example 1, the area of the ith strip is $2\,(\Delta x)$ and the pressure is $\delta d = \delta x_i$. Thus,

$F = \int_0^3 \delta x \cdot 2\,dx \approx (62.5)(2) \int_0^3 x\,dx = 125\left[\frac{1}{2}x^2\right]_0^3 = 125\left(\frac{9}{2}\right) = 562.5 \text{ lb}$.

31. Set up a vertical x-axis as shown. The base of the triangle shown in the figure

has length $\sqrt{3^2 - (x_i^*)^2}$, so $w_i = 2\sqrt{9 - (x_i^*)^2}$, and the area of the ith

rectangular strip is $2\sqrt{9 - (x_i^*)^2}\,\Delta x$. The ith rectangular strip is $(x_i^* - 1)$ m

below the surface level of the water, so the pressure on the strip is $\rho g(x_i^* - 1)$.

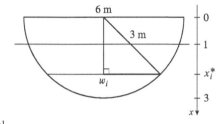

The hydrostatic force on the strip is $\rho g(x_i^* - 1) \cdot 2\sqrt{9 - (x_i^*)^2}\,\Delta x$ and the total

force on the plate $\approx \sum\limits_{i=1}^n \rho g(x_i^* - 1) \cdot 2\sqrt{9 - (x_i^*)^2}\,\Delta x$. The total force

$$F = \lim \sum_{i=1}^n \rho g(x_i^* - 1) \cdot 2\sqrt{9 - (x_i^*)^2}\,\Delta x = 2\rho g \int_1^3 (x-1)\sqrt{9 - x^2}\,dx$$

$$= 2\rho g \int_1^3 x\sqrt{9-x^2}\,dx - 2\rho g \int_1^3 \sqrt{9-x^2}\,dx \overset{30}{=} 2\rho g\left[-\frac{1}{3}(9-x^2)^{3/2}\right]_1^3 - 2\rho g\left[\frac{x}{2}\sqrt{9-x^2} + \frac{9}{2}\sin^{-1}\left(\frac{x}{3}\right)\right]_1^3$$

$$= 2\rho g\left[0 + \frac{1}{3}(8\sqrt{8})\right] - 2\rho g\left[(0 + \frac{9}{2}\cdot\frac{\pi}{2}) - (\frac{1}{2}\sqrt{8} + \frac{9}{2}\sin^{-1}(\frac{1}{3}))\right]$$

$$= \frac{32}{3}\sqrt{2}\,\rho g - \frac{9\pi}{2}\rho g + 2\sqrt{2}\,\rho g + 9\left[\sin^{-1}(\frac{1}{3})\right]\rho g = \left(\frac{38}{3}\sqrt{2} - \frac{9\pi}{2} + 9\sin^{-1}(\frac{1}{3})\right)\rho g$$

$$\approx 6.835 \cdot 1000 \cdot 9.8 \approx 6.7 \times 10^4 \text{ N}$$

Note: If you set up a typical coordinate system with the water level at $y = -1$, then $F = \int_{-3}^{-1} \rho g(-1 - y) 2\sqrt{9 - y^2}\,dy$.

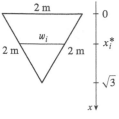

33. Set up a vertical x-axis as shown. Then the area of the ith rectangular strip is

$$\left(2 - \frac{2}{\sqrt{3}}\, x_i^*\right)\Delta x. \quad \left[\text{By similar triangles, } \frac{w_i}{2} = \frac{\sqrt{3} - x_i^*}{\sqrt{3}}, \text{ so } w_i = 2 - \frac{2}{\sqrt{3}}\, x_i^*.\right]$$

The pressure on the strip is $\rho g x_i^*$, so the hydrostatic force on the strip is

$$\rho g x_i^*\left(2 - \frac{2}{\sqrt{3}}\, x_i^*\right)\Delta x \text{ and the hydrostatic force on the plate} \approx \sum_{i=1}^{n} \rho g x_i^*\left(2 - \frac{2}{\sqrt{3}}\, x_i^*\right)\Delta x.$$

The total force

$$F = \lim_{n \to \infty} \sum_{i=1}^{n} \rho g x_i^*\left(2 - \frac{2}{\sqrt{3}}\, x_i^*\right)\Delta x = \int_0^{\sqrt{3}} \rho g x\left(2 - \frac{2}{\sqrt{3}}\, x\right) dx = \rho g \int_0^{\sqrt{3}}\left(2x - \frac{2}{\sqrt{3}}\, x^2\right) dx$$

$$= \rho g\left[x^2 - \frac{2}{3\sqrt{3}}\, x^3\right]_0^{\sqrt{3}} = \rho g\left[(3 - 2) - 0\right] = \rho g \approx 1000 \cdot 9.8 = 9.8 \times 10^3 \text{ N}$$

35. Set up coordinate axes as shown in the figure. The length of the ith strip is

$2\sqrt{25 - (y_i^*)^2}$ and its area is $2\sqrt{25 - (y_i^*)^2}\,\Delta y$. The pressure on this strip is

approximately $\delta d_i = 62.5(7 - y_i^*)$ and so the force on the strip is approximately

$62.5(7 - y_i^*)2\sqrt{25 - (y_i^*)^2}\,\Delta y$. The total force

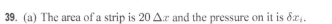

$$F = \lim_{n \to \infty} \sum_{i=1}^{n} 62.5(7 - y_i^*)2\sqrt{25 - (y_i^*)^2}\,\Delta y = 125 \int_0^5 (7 - y)\sqrt{25 - y^2}\, dy$$

$$= 125\left\{\int_0^5 7\sqrt{25 - y^2}\, dy - \int_0^5 y\sqrt{25 - y^2}\, dy\right\} = 125\left\{7\int_0^5 \sqrt{25 - y^2}\, dy - \left[-\tfrac{1}{3}(25 - y^2)^{3/2}\right]_0^5\right\}$$

$$= 125\left\{7\left(\tfrac{1}{4}\pi \cdot 5^2\right) + \tfrac{1}{3}(0 - 125)\right\} = 125\left(\tfrac{175\pi}{4} - \tfrac{125}{3}\right) \approx 11{,}972 \approx 1.2 \times 10^4 \text{ lb}$$

37. By similar triangles, $\dfrac{8}{4\sqrt{3}} = \dfrac{w_i}{x_i^*} \;\Rightarrow\; w_i = \dfrac{2x_i^*}{\sqrt{3}}$. The area of the ith

rectangular strip is $\dfrac{2x_i^*}{\sqrt{3}}\,\Delta x$ and the pressure on it is $\rho g(4\sqrt{3} - x_i^*)$.

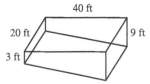

$$F = \int_0^{4\sqrt{3}} \rho g\left(4\sqrt{3} - x\right)\frac{2x}{\sqrt{3}}\, dx = 8\rho g \int_0^{4\sqrt{3}} x\, dx - \frac{2\rho g}{\sqrt{3}}\int_0^{4\sqrt{3}} x^2\, dx$$

$$= 4\rho g\left[x^2\right]_0^{4\sqrt{3}} - \frac{2\rho g}{3\sqrt{3}}\left[x^3\right]_0^{4\sqrt{3}} = 192\rho g - \frac{2\rho g}{3\sqrt{3}}\, 64 \cdot 3\sqrt{3} = 192\rho g - 128\rho g = 64\rho g$$

$$\approx 64(840)(9.8) \approx 5.27 \times 10^5 \text{ N}$$

39. (a) The area of a strip is $20\,\Delta x$ and the pressure on it is δx_i.

$$F = \int_0^3 \delta x 20\, dx = 20\delta\left[\tfrac{1}{2}x^2\right]_0^3 = 20\delta \cdot \tfrac{9}{2} = 90\delta$$

$$= 90(62.5) = 5625 \text{ lb} \approx 5.63 \times 10^3 \text{ lb}$$

(b) $F = \int_0^9 \delta x 20\, dx = 20\delta\left[\tfrac{1}{2}x^2\right]_0^9 = 20\delta \cdot \tfrac{81}{2} = 810\delta = 810(62.5) = 50{,}625 \text{ lb} \approx 5.06 \times 10^4 \text{ lb}$.

(c) For the first 3 ft, the length of the side is constant at 40 ft. For $3 < x \le 9$, we can use similar triangles to find the length a:

$$\frac{a}{40} = \frac{9-x}{6} \quad \Rightarrow \quad a = 40 \cdot \frac{9-x}{6}.$$

$$F = \int_0^3 \delta x 40 \, dx + \int_3^9 \delta x (40) \frac{9-x}{6} \, dx = 40\delta\left[\tfrac{1}{2}x^2\right]_0^3 + \tfrac{20}{3}\delta \int_3^9 (9x - x^2) \, dx = 180\delta + \tfrac{20}{3}\delta\left[\tfrac{9}{2}x^2 - \tfrac{1}{3}x^3\right]_3^9$$

$$= 180\delta + \tfrac{20}{3}\delta\left[\left(\tfrac{729}{2} - 243\right) - \left(\tfrac{81}{2} - 9\right)\right] = 180\delta + 600\delta = 780\delta = 780(62.5) = 48{,}750 \text{ lb} \approx 4.88 \times 10^4 \text{ lb}$$

(d) For any right triangle with hypotenuse on the bottom,

$$\sin\theta = \frac{\Delta x}{\text{hypotenuse}} \quad \Rightarrow$$

$$\text{hypotenuse} = \Delta x \csc\theta = \Delta x \frac{\sqrt{40^2 + 6^2}}{6} = \frac{\sqrt{409}}{3}\Delta x.$$

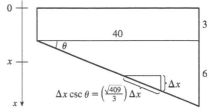

$$F = \int_3^9 \delta x 20 \frac{\sqrt{409}}{3} \, dx = \tfrac{1}{3}\left(20\sqrt{409}\right)\delta\left[\tfrac{1}{2}x^2\right]_3^9$$

$$= \tfrac{1}{3} \cdot 10\sqrt{409}\,\delta(81 - 9) \approx 303{,}356 \text{ lb} \approx 3.03 \times 10^5 \text{ lb}$$

41. $F = \int_2^5 \rho g x \cdot w(x) \, dx$, where $w(x)$ is the width of the plate at depth x. Since $n = 6$, $\Delta x = \frac{5-2}{6} = \frac{1}{2}$, and

$$F \approx S_6$$

$$= \rho g \cdot \frac{1/2}{3}[2 \cdot w(2) + 4 \cdot 2.5 \cdot w(2.5) + 2 \cdot 3 \cdot w(3) + 4 \cdot 3.5 \cdot w(3.5) + 2 \cdot 4 \cdot w(4) + 4 \cdot 4.5 \cdot w(4.5) + 5 \cdot w(5)]$$

$$= \tfrac{1}{6}\rho g(2 \cdot 0 + 10 \cdot 0.8 + 6 \cdot 1.7 + 14 \cdot 2.4 + 8 \cdot 2.9 + 18 \cdot 3.3 + 5 \cdot 3.6)$$

$$= \tfrac{1}{6}(1000)(9.8)(152.4) \approx 2.5 \times 10^5 \text{ N}$$

43. $m = \sum\limits_{i=1}^{3} m_i = 6 + 5 + 10 = 21.$

$$M_x = \sum_{i=1}^{3} m_i y_i = 6(5) + 5(-2) + 10(-1) = 10; \quad M_y = \sum_{i=1}^{3} m_i x_i = 6(1) + 5(3) + 10(-2) = 1.$$

$$\overline{x} = \frac{M_y}{m} = \frac{1}{21} \text{ and } \overline{y} = \frac{M_x}{m} = \frac{10}{21}, \text{ so the center of mass of the system is } \left(\tfrac{1}{21}, \tfrac{10}{21}\right).$$

45. Since the region in the figure is symmetric about the y-axis, we know that $\overline{x} = 0$. The region is "bottom-heavy," so we know that $\overline{y} < 2$, and we might guess that $\overline{y} = 1.5$.

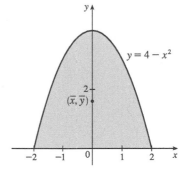

$$A = \int_{-2}^{2}(4 - x^2) \, dx = 2\int_0^2 (4 - x^2) \, dx = 2\left[4x - \tfrac{1}{3}x^3\right]_0^2$$

$$= 2\left(8 - \tfrac{8}{3}\right) = \tfrac{32}{3}.$$

$$\overline{x} = \tfrac{1}{A}\int_{-2}^{2} x(4 - x^2) \, dx = 0 \text{ since } f(x) = x(4 - x^2) \text{ is an odd}$$

function (or since the region is symmetric about the y-axis).

$$\overline{y} = \tfrac{1}{A}\int_{-2}^{2}\tfrac{1}{2}(4 - x^2)^2 \, dx = \tfrac{3}{32} \cdot \tfrac{1}{2} \cdot 2\int_0^2 (16 - 8x^2 + x^4) \, dx = \tfrac{3}{32}\left[16x - \tfrac{8}{3}x^3 + \tfrac{1}{5}x^5\right]_0^2$$

$$= \tfrac{3}{32}\left(32 - \tfrac{64}{3} + \tfrac{32}{5}\right) = 3\left(1 - \tfrac{2}{3} + \tfrac{1}{5}\right) = 3\left(\tfrac{8}{15}\right) = \tfrac{8}{5}$$

Thus, the centroid is $(\overline{x}, \overline{y}) = \left(0, \tfrac{8}{5}\right)$.

47. The region in the figure is "right-heavy" and "bottom-heavy," so we know

$\overline{x} > 0.5$ and $\overline{y} < 1$, and we might guess that $\overline{x} = 0.6$ and $\overline{y} = 0.9$.

$A = \int_0^1 e^x\, dx = [e^x]_0^1 = e - 1.$

$\overline{x} = \frac{1}{A} \int_0^1 x e^x\, dx = \frac{1}{e-1}[x e^x - e^x]_0^1$　　[by parts]

$\quad = \frac{1}{e-1}[0 - (-1)] = \frac{1}{e-1}.$

$\overline{y} = \frac{1}{A} \int_0^1 \frac{1}{2}(e^x)^2\, dx = \frac{1}{e-1} \cdot \frac{1}{4}[e^{2x}]_0^1 = \frac{1}{4(e-1)}(e^2 - 1) = \frac{e+1}{4}.$

Thus, the centroid is $(\overline{x}, \overline{y}) = \left(\frac{1}{e-1}, \frac{e+1}{4}\right) \approx (0.58, 0.93).$

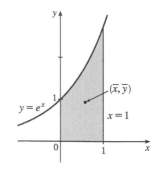

49. The line has equation $y = \frac{3}{4}x.$　$A = \frac{1}{2}(4)(3) = 6$, so $m = \rho A = 10(6) = 60.$

$$M_x = \rho \int_0^4 \frac{1}{2}\left(\frac{3}{4}x\right)^2 dx = 10 \int_0^4 \frac{9}{32} x^2\, dx = \frac{45}{16}\left[\frac{1}{3}x^3\right]_0^4 = \frac{45}{16}\left(\frac{64}{3}\right) = 60$$

$$M_y = \rho \int_0^4 x\left(\frac{3}{4}x\right) dx = \frac{15}{2}\int_0^4 x^2\, dx = \frac{15}{2}\left[\frac{1}{3}x^3\right]_0^4 = \frac{15}{2}\left(\frac{64}{3}\right) = 160$$

$\overline{x} = \dfrac{M_y}{m} = \dfrac{160}{60} = \dfrac{8}{3}$ and $\overline{y} = \dfrac{M_x}{m} = \dfrac{60}{60} = 1.$ Thus, the centroid is $(\overline{x}, \overline{y}) = \left(\frac{8}{3}, 1\right).$

51. (a)

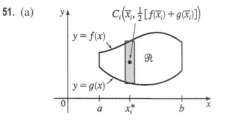

Suppose the region lies between two curves $y = f(x)$ and $y = g(x)$ where $f(x) \geq g(x)$, as illustrated in the figure. Use n subintervals determined by points x_i with $a = x_0 < x_1 < \cdots < x_n = b$ and choose $x_i^* = \overline{x}_i$ to be the midpoint of the ith subinterval; that is, $\overline{x}_i = \frac{1}{2}(x_{i-1} + x_i)$. Then the centroid of the ith approximating rectangle R_i is its center $C_i = \left(\overline{x}_i, \frac{1}{2}[f(\overline{x}_i) + g(\overline{x}_i)]\right).$

Its area is $[f(\overline{x}_i) - g(\overline{x}_i)]\, \Delta x$, so its mass is $\rho[f(\overline{x}_i) - g(\overline{x}_i)]\, \Delta x.$

Thus, $M_y(R_i) = \rho[f(\overline{x}_i) - g(\overline{x}_i)]\, \Delta x \cdot \overline{x}_i = \rho \overline{x}_i[f(\overline{x}_i) - g(\overline{x}_i)]\, \Delta x$ and

$M_x(R_i) = \rho[f(\overline{x}_i) - g(\overline{x}_i)]\, \Delta x \cdot \frac{1}{2}[f(\overline{x}_i) + g(\overline{x}_i)] = \rho \cdot \frac{1}{2}\left\{[f(\overline{x}_i)]^2 - [g(\overline{x}_i)]^2\right\} \Delta x.$ Summing over i and taking

the limit as $n \to \infty$, we get $M_y = \displaystyle\lim_{n \to \infty} \sum_{i=1}^{n} \rho \overline{x}_i[f(\overline{x}_i) - g(\overline{x}_i)]\, \Delta x = \rho \int_a^b x[f(x) - g(x)]\, dx$ and

$M_x = \displaystyle\lim_{n \to \infty} \sum_{i=1}^{n} \rho \cdot \frac{1}{2}\left[f(\overline{x}_i)^2 - g(\overline{x}_i)^2\right] \Delta x = \rho \int_a^b \frac{1}{2}\left\{[f(x)]^2 - [g(x)]^2\right\} dx.$ Thus,

$\overline{x} = \dfrac{M_y}{m} = \dfrac{M_y}{\rho A} = \dfrac{1}{A}\displaystyle\int_a^b x[f(x) - g(x)]\, dx$ and $\overline{y} = \dfrac{M_x}{m} = \dfrac{M_x}{\rho A} = \dfrac{1}{A}\displaystyle\int_a^b \frac{1}{2}\left\{[f(x)]^2 - [g(x)]^2\right\} dx.$

(b)

The region is sketched in the figure. We take $f(x) = x, g(x) = x^2, a = 0,$ and $b = 1$ in the formulas in part (a). First we note that the area of the region is $A = \int_0^1 (x - x^2)\, dx = \left[\frac{1}{2}x^2 - \frac{1}{3}x^3\right]_0^1 = \frac{1}{6}.$

Therefore, $\bar{x} = \frac{1}{A}\int_0^1 x[f(x) - g(x)]\,dx = \frac{1}{1/6}\int_0^1 x(x - x^2)\,dx = 6\int_0^1 (x^2 - x^3)\,dx = 6\left[\frac{1}{3}x^3 - \frac{1}{4}x^4\right]_0^1 = \frac{1}{2}$

and $\bar{y} = \frac{1}{A}\int_0^1 \frac{1}{2}\left\{[f(x)]^2 - [g(x)]^2\right\}dx = \frac{1}{1/6}\int_0^1 \frac{1}{2}(x^2 - x^4)\,dx = 3\left[\frac{1}{3}x^3 - \frac{1}{5}x^5\right]_0^1 = \frac{2}{5}.$

The centroid is $\left(\frac{1}{2}, \frac{2}{5}\right)$.

6.7   Applications to Economics and Biology

1. By the Net Change Theorem, $C(2000) - C(0) = \int_0^{2000} C'(x)\,dx$ $\Rightarrow$

$$C(2000) = 20{,}000 + \int_0^{2000}(5 - 0.008x + 0.000009x^2)\,dx = 20{,}000 + \left[5x - 0.004x^2 + 0.000003x^3\right]_0^{2000}$$

$$= 20{,}000 + 10{,}000 - 0.004(4{,}000{,}000) + 0.000003(8{,}000{,}000{,}000) = 30{,}000 - 16{,}000 + 24{,}000$$

$$= \$38{,}000$$

3. If the production level is raised from 1200 units to 1600 units, then the increase in cost is

$$C(1600) - C(1200) = \int_{1200}^{1600} C'(x)\,dx = \int_{1200}^{1600}(74 + 1.1x - 0.002x^2 + 0.00004x^3)\,dx$$

$$= \left[74x + 0.55x^2 - \frac{0.002}{3}x^3 + 0.00001x^4\right]_{1200}^{1600} = 64{,}331{,}733.33 - 20{,}464{,}800 = \$43{,}866{,}933.33$$

5. $p(x) = 10$ $\Rightarrow$ $\dfrac{450}{x + 8} = 10$ $\Rightarrow$ $x + 8 = 45$ $\Rightarrow$ $x = 37.$

Consumer surplus $= \displaystyle\int_0^{37}[p(x) - 10]\,dx = \int_0^{37}\left(\frac{450}{x + 8} - 10\right)dx$

$$= \left[450\ln(x + 8) - 10x\right]_0^{37} = (450\ln 45 - 370) - 450\ln 8$$

$$= 450\ln\left(\frac{45}{8}\right) - 370 \approx \$407.25$$

7. $P = p_S(x)$ $\Rightarrow$ $400 = 200 + 0.2x^{3/2}$ $\Rightarrow$ $200 = 0.2x^{3/2}$ $\Rightarrow$ $1000 = x^{3/2}$ $\Rightarrow$ $x = 1000^{2/3} = 100.$

Producer surplus $= \displaystyle\int_0^{100}[P - p_S(x)]\,dx = \int_0^{100}[400 - (200 + 0.2x^{3/2})]\,dx = \int_0^{100}\left(200 - \frac{1}{5}x^{3/2}\right)dx$

$$= \left[200x - \frac{2}{25}x^{5/2}\right]_0^{100} = 20{,}000 - 8{,}000 = \$12{,}000$$

9. $p(x) = \dfrac{800{,}000e^{-x/5000}}{x + 20{,}000} = 16$ $\Rightarrow$ $x = x_1 \approx 3727.04.$

Consumer surplus $= \int_0^{x_1}[p(x) - 16]\,dx \approx \$37{,}753$

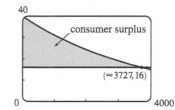

11. $f(8) - f(4) = \int_4^8 f'(t)\,dt = \int_4^8 \sqrt{t}\,dt = \left[\frac{2}{3}t^{3/2}\right]_4^8 = \frac{2}{3}\left(16\sqrt{2} - 8\right) \approx \$9.75$ million

13. $N = \int_a^b Ax^{-k}\, dx = A\left[\dfrac{x^{-k+1}}{-k+1}\right]_a^b = \dfrac{A}{1-k}\left(b^{1-k} - a^{1-k}\right).$

Similarly, $\int_a^b Ax^{1-k}\, dx = A\left[\dfrac{x^{2-k}}{2-k}\right]_a^b = \dfrac{A}{2-k}\left(b^{2-k} - a^{2-k}\right).$

Thus, $\bar{x} = \dfrac{1}{N}\int_a^b Ax^{1-k}\, dx = \dfrac{[A/(2-k)](b^{2-k} - a^{2-k})}{[A/(1-k)](b^{1-k} - a^{1-k})} = \dfrac{(1-k)(b^{2-k} - a^{2-k})}{(2-k)(b^{1-k} - a^{1-k})}.$

15. $F = \dfrac{\pi P R^4}{8\eta l} = \dfrac{\pi (4000)(0.008)^4}{8(0.027)(2)} \approx 1.19 \times 10^{-4} \text{ cm}^3/\text{s}$

17. From (3), $F = \dfrac{A}{\int_0^T c(t)\, dt} = \dfrac{6}{20I}$, where

$$I = \int_0^{10} te^{-0.6t}\, dt = \left[\dfrac{1}{(-0.6)^2}(-0.6t - 1)\, e^{-0.6t}\right]_0^{10} \begin{bmatrix} \text{integrating} \\ \text{by parts} \end{bmatrix} = \tfrac{1}{0.36}(-7e^{-6} + 1)$$

Thus, $F = \dfrac{6(0.36)}{20(1 - 7e^{-6})} = \dfrac{0.108}{1 - 7e^{-6}} \approx 0.1099 \text{ L/s or } 6.594 \text{ L/min}.$

19. As in Example 2, we will estimate the cardiac output using Simpson's Rule with $\Delta t = (16 - 0)/8 = 2$.

$$\int_0^{16} c(t)\, dt \approx \tfrac{2}{3}[c(0) + 4c(2) + 2c(4) + 4c(6) + 2c(8) + 4c(10) + 2c(12) + 4c(14) + c(16)]$$

$$\approx \tfrac{2}{3}[0 + 4(6.1) + 2(7.4) + 4(6.7) + 2(5.4) + 4(4.1) + 2(3.0) + 4(2.1) + 1.5]$$

$$= \tfrac{2}{3}(109.1) = 72.7\overline{3} \text{ mg} \cdot \text{s/L}$$

Therefore, $F \approx \dfrac{A}{72.7\overline{3}} = \dfrac{7}{72.7\overline{3}} \approx 0.0962 \text{ L/s or } 5.77 \text{ L/min}.$

6.8 Probability

1. (a) $\int_{30,000}^{40,000} f(x)\, dx$ is the probability that a randomly chosen tire will have a lifetime between 30,000 and 40,000 miles.

(b) $\int_{25,000}^{\infty} f(x)\, dx$ is the probability that a randomly chosen tire will have a lifetime of at least 25,000 miles.

3. (a) In general, we must satisfy the two conditions that are mentioned before Example 1—namely, (1) $f(x) \geq 0$ for all x, and (2) $\int_{-\infty}^{\infty} f(x)\, dx = 1$. For $0 \leq x \leq 4$, we have $f(x) = \tfrac{3}{64}x\sqrt{16 - x^2} \geq 0$, so $f(x) \geq 0$ for all x. Also,

$$\int_{-\infty}^{\infty} f(x)\, dx = \int_0^4 \tfrac{3}{64}x\sqrt{16 - x^2}\, dx = -\tfrac{3}{128}\int_0^4 (16 - x^2)^{1/2}(-2x)\, dx = -\tfrac{3}{128}\left[\tfrac{2}{3}(16 - x^2)^{3/2}\right]_0^4$$

$$= -\tfrac{1}{64}\left[(16 - x^2)^{3/2}\right]_0^4 = -\tfrac{1}{64}(0 - 64) = 1.$$

Therefore, f is a probability density function.

(b) $P(X < 2) = \int_{-\infty}^2 f(x)\, dx = \int_0^2 \tfrac{3}{64}x\sqrt{16 - x^2}\, dx = -\tfrac{3}{128}\int_0^2 (16 - x^2)^{1/2}(-2x)\, dx$

$= -\tfrac{3}{128}\left[\tfrac{2}{3}(16 - x^2)^{3/2}\right]_0^2 = -\tfrac{1}{64}\left[(16 - x^2)^{3/2}\right]_0^2 = -\tfrac{1}{64}(12^{3/2} - 16^{3/2})$

$= \tfrac{1}{64}(64 - 12\sqrt{12}) = \tfrac{1}{64}(64 - 24\sqrt{3}) = 1 - \tfrac{3}{8}\sqrt{3} \approx 0.350481$

5. (a) In general, we must satisfy the two conditions that are mentioned before Example 1—namely, (1) $f(x) \geq 0$ for all x,

and (2) $\int_{-\infty}^{\infty} f(x)\,dx = 1$. If $c \geq 0$, then $f(x) \geq 0$, so condition (1) is satisfied. For condition (2), we see that

$$\int_{-\infty}^{\infty} f(x)\,dx = \int_{-\infty}^{\infty} \frac{c}{1+x^2}\,dx \text{ and}$$

$$\int_{0}^{\infty} \frac{c}{1+x^2}\,dx = \lim_{t\to\infty} \int_{0}^{t} \frac{c}{1+x^2}\,dx = c\lim_{t\to\infty} \left[\tan^{-1} x\right]_{0}^{t} = c\lim_{t\to\infty} \tan^{-1} t = c\left(\frac{\pi}{2}\right)$$

Similarly, $\quad \int_{-\infty}^{0} \frac{c}{1+x^2}\,dx = c\left(\frac{\pi}{2}\right)$, so $\int_{-\infty}^{\infty} \frac{c}{1+x^2}\,dx = 2c\left(\frac{\pi}{2}\right) = c\pi$.

Since $c\pi$ must equal 1, we must have $c = 1/\pi$ so that f is a probability density function.

(b) $P(-1 < X < 1) = \int_{-1}^{1} \frac{1/\pi}{1+x^2}\,dx = \frac{2}{\pi} \int_{0}^{1} \frac{1}{1+x^2}\,dx = \frac{2}{\pi}\left[\tan^{-1} x\right]_{0}^{1} = \frac{2}{\pi}\left(\frac{\pi}{4} - 0\right) = \frac{1}{2}$

7. (a) In general, we must satisfy the two conditions that are mentioned before Example 1—namely, (1) $f(x) \geq 0$ for all x,

and (2) $\int_{-\infty}^{\infty} f(x)\,dx = 1$. Since $f(x) = 0$ or $f(x) = 0.1$, condition (1) is satisfied. For condition (2), we see that

$\int_{-\infty}^{\infty} f(x)\,dx = \int_{0}^{10} 0.1\,dx = \left[\frac{1}{10}x\right]_{0}^{10} = 1$. Thus, $f(x)$ is a probability density function for the spinner's values.

(b) Since all the numbers between 0 and 10 are equally likely to be selected, we expect the mean to be halfway between the

endpoints of the interval; that is, $x = 5$.

$$\mu = \int_{-\infty}^{\infty} xf(x)\,dx = \int_{0}^{10} x(0.1)\,dx = \left[\frac{1}{20}x^2\right]_{0}^{10} = \frac{100}{20} = 5, \quad \text{as expected.}$$

9. We need to find m so that $\int_{m}^{\infty} f(t)\,dt = \frac{1}{2} \Rightarrow \lim_{x\to\infty} \int_{m}^{x} \frac{1}{5}e^{-t/5}\,dt = \frac{1}{2} \Rightarrow \lim_{x\to\infty} \left[\frac{1}{5}(-5)e^{-t/5}\right]_{m}^{x} = \frac{1}{2} \Rightarrow$

$(-1)(0 - e^{-m/5}) = \frac{1}{2} \Rightarrow e^{-m/5} = \frac{1}{2} \Rightarrow -m/5 = \ln\frac{1}{2} \Rightarrow m = -5\ln\frac{1}{2} = 5\ln 2 \approx 3.47$ min.

11. We use an exponential density function with $\mu = 2.5$ min.

(a) $P(X > 4) = \int_{4}^{\infty} f(t)\,dt = \lim_{x\to\infty} \int_{4}^{x} \frac{1}{2.5}e^{-t/2.5}\,dt = \lim_{x\to\infty} \left[-e^{-t/2.5}\right]_{4}^{x} = 0 + e^{-4/2.5} \approx 0.202$

(b) $P(0 \leq X \leq 2) = \int_{0}^{2} f(t)\,dt = \left[-e^{-t/2.5}\right]_{0}^{2} = -e^{-2/2.5} + 1 \approx 0.551$

(c) We need to find a value a so that $P(X \geq a) = 0.02$, or, equivalently, $P(0 \leq X \leq a) = 0.98 \Leftrightarrow$

$\int_{0}^{a} f(t)\,dt = 0.98 \Leftrightarrow \left[-e^{-t/2.5}\right]_{0}^{a} = 0.98 \Leftrightarrow -e^{-a/2.5} + 1 = 0.98 \Leftrightarrow e^{-a/2.5} = 0.02 \Leftrightarrow$

$-a/2.5 = \ln 0.02 \Leftrightarrow a = -2.5\ln\frac{1}{50} = 2.5\ln 50 \approx 9.78$ min ≈ 10 min. The ad should say that if you aren't served

within 10 minutes, you get a free hamburger.

13. $P(X \geq 10) = \int_{10}^{\infty} \frac{1}{4.2\sqrt{2\pi}} \exp\left(-\frac{(x-9.4)^2}{2\cdot 4.2^2}\right)\,dx$. To avoid the improper integral we approximate it by the integral from

10 to 100. Thus, $P(X \geq 10) \approx \int_{10}^{100} \frac{1}{4.2\sqrt{2\pi}} \exp\left(-\frac{(x-9.4)^2}{2\cdot 4.2^2}\right)\,dx \approx 0.443$ (using a calculator or computer to estimate

the integral), so about 44 percent of the households throw out at least 10 lb of paper a week.

Note: We can't evaluate $1 - P(0 \leq X \leq 10)$ for this problem since a significant amount of area lies to the left of $X = 0$.

15. (a) $P(0 \le X \le 100) = \displaystyle\int_0^{100} \frac{1}{8\sqrt{2\pi}} \exp\left(-\frac{(x-112)^2}{2\cdot 8^2}\right) dx \approx 0.0668$ (using a calculator or computer to estimate the

integral), so there is about a 6.68% chance that a randomly chosen vehicle is traveling at a legal speed.

(b) $P(X \ge 125) = \displaystyle\int_{125}^\infty \frac{1}{8\sqrt{2\pi}} \exp\left(-\frac{(x-112)^2}{2\cdot 8^2}\right) dx = \int_{125}^\infty f(x)\, dx$. In this case, we could use a calculator or computer

to estimate either $\int_{125}^{300} f(x)\, dx$ or $1 - \int_0^{125} f(x)\, dx$. Both are approximately 0.0521, so about 5.21% of the motorists are

targeted.

17. $P(\mu - 2\sigma \le X \le \mu + 2\sigma) = \displaystyle\int_{\mu-2\sigma}^{\mu+2\sigma} \frac{1}{\sigma\sqrt{2\pi}} \exp\left(-\frac{(x-\mu)^2}{2\sigma^2}\right) dx$. Substituting $t = \dfrac{x-\mu}{\sigma}$ and $dt = \dfrac{1}{\sigma}\, dx$ gives us

$\displaystyle\int_{-2}^{2} \frac{1}{\sigma\sqrt{2\pi}} e^{-t^2/2}(\sigma\, dt) = \frac{1}{\sqrt{2\pi}} \int_{-2}^{2} e^{-t^2/2}\, dt \approx 0.9545.$

6 Review

CONCEPT CHECK

1. (a) See Section 6.1, Figure 2 and Equations 6.1.1 and 6.1.2.

(b) Instead of using "top minus bottom" and integrating from left to right, we use "right minus left" and integrate from bottom to top. See Figures 9 and 10 in Section 6.1.

2. The numerical value of the area represents the number of meters by which Sue is ahead of Kathy after 1 minute.

3. (a) See the discussion in Section 6.2, near Figures 2 and 3, ending in the Definition of Volume.

(b) See the discussion between Examples 5 and 6 in Section 6.2. If the cross-section is a disk, find the radius in terms of x or y and use $A = \pi(\text{radius})^2$. If the cross-section is a washer, find the inner radius r_{in} and outer radius r_{out} and use $A = \pi(r_{\text{out}}^2) - \pi(r_{\text{in}}^2)$.

4. (a) $V = 2\pi rh\, \Delta r = (\text{circumference})(\text{height})(\text{thickness})$

(b) For a typical shell, find the circumference and height in terms of x or y and calculate $V = \int_a^b (\text{circumference})(\text{height})(dx \text{ or } dy)$, where a and b are the limits on x or y.

(c) Sometimes slicing produces washers or disks whose radii are difficult (or impossible) to find explicitly. On other occasions, the cylindrical shell method leads to an easier integral than slicing does.

5. (a) The length of a curve is defined to be the limit of the lengths of the inscribed polygons, as described near Figure 3 in Section 6.4.

(b) See Equation 6.4.1.

(c) See Equations 6.4.2 and 6.4.3.

6. (a) The average value of a function f on an interval $[a, b]$ is $f_{ave} = \dfrac{1}{b-a} \displaystyle\int_a^b f(x)\,dx$.

 (b) The Mean Value Theorem for Integrals says that there is a number c at which the value of f is exactly equal to the average value of the function, that is, $f(c) = f_{ave}$. For a geometric interpretation of the Mean Value Theorem for Integrals, see Figure 2 in Section 6.4 and the discussion that accompanies it.

7. $\int_0^6 f(x)\,dx$ represents the amount of work done. Its units are newton-meters, or joules.

8. Let $c(x)$ be the cross-sectional length of the wall (measured parallel to the surface of the fluid) at depth x. Then the hydrostatic force against the wall is given by $F = \int_a^b \delta x c(x)\,dx$, where a and b are the lower and upper limits for x at points of the wall and δ is the weight density of the fluid.

9. (a) The center of mass is the point at which the plate balances horizontally.

 (b) See Equations 6.6.12.

10. See Figure 3 in Section 6.6, and the discussion which precedes it.

11. (a) See the definition in the first paragraph of the subsection *Cardiac Output* in Section 6.7.

 (b) See the discussion in the second paragraph of the subsection *Cardiac Output* in Section 6.7.

12. A probability density function f is a function on the domain of a continuous random variable X such that $\int_a^b f(x)\,dx$ measures the probability that X lies between a and b. Such a function f has nonnegative values and satisfies the relation $\int_D f(x)\,dx = 1$, where D is the domain of the corresponding random variable X. If $D = \mathbb{R}$, or if we define $f(x) = 0$ for real numbers $x \notin D$, then $\int_{-\infty}^{\infty} f(x)\,dx = 1$. (Of course, to work with f in this way, we must assume that the integrals of f exist.)

13. (a) $\int_0^{130} f(x)\,dx$ represents the probability that the weight of a randomly chosen female college student is less than 130 pounds.

 (b) $\mu = \int_{-\infty}^{\infty} xf(x)\,dx = \int_0^{\infty} xf(x)\,dx$

 (c) The median of f is the number m such that $\int_m^{\infty} f(x)\,dx = \frac{1}{2}$.

14. See the discussion near Equation 3 in Section 6.8.

EXERCISES

1. The curves intersect when $x^2 = 4x - x^2 \iff 2x^2 - 4x = 0 \iff$
$2x(x-2) = 0 \iff x = 0$ or 2.

$A = \int_0^2 \left[(4x - x^2) - x^2\right] dx = \int_0^2 (4x - 2x^2)\,dx$

$\quad = \left[2x^2 - \frac{2}{3}x^3\right]_0^2 = \left[\left(8 - \frac{16}{3}\right) - 0\right] = \frac{8}{3}$

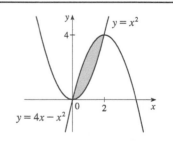

3. If $x \geq 0$, then $|x| = x$, and the graphs intersect when $x = 1 - 2x^2 \iff 2x^2 + x - 1 = 0 \iff (2x - 1)(x + 1) = 0 \iff$

$x = \frac{1}{2}$ or -1, but $-1 < 0$. By symmetry, we can double the area from $x = 0$ to $x = \frac{1}{2}$.

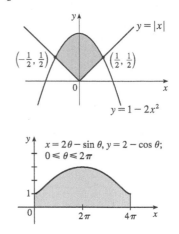

$$A = 2 \int_0^{1/2} \left[(1 - 2x^2) - x\right] dx = 2 \int_0^{1/2} (-2x^2 - x + 1) \, dx$$

$$= 2\left[-\tfrac{2}{3}x^3 - \tfrac{1}{2}x^2 + x\right]_0^{1/2} = 2\left[\left(-\tfrac{1}{12} - \tfrac{1}{8} + \tfrac{1}{2}\right) - 0\right]$$

$$= 2\left(\tfrac{7}{24}\right) = \tfrac{7}{12}$$

5. $x = 2\theta - \sin\theta \implies dx = (2 - \cos\theta) \, d\theta$

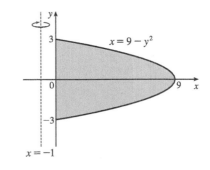

$$A = \int_0^{2\pi} y \, dx = \int_0^{2\pi} \left[(2 - \cos\theta)(2 - \cos\theta)\right] d\theta$$

$$= \int_0^{2\pi} \left(4 - 4\cos\theta + \cos^2\theta\right) d\theta = \int_0^{2\pi} \left(4 - 4\cos\theta + \tfrac{1}{2} + \tfrac{1}{2}\cos 2\theta\right) d\theta$$

$$= \left[4\theta - 4\sin\theta + \tfrac{1}{2}\theta + \tfrac{1}{4}\sin 2\theta\right]_0^{2\pi} = (8\pi - 0 + \pi + 0) - (0) = 9\pi$$

7. (a) Using the Midpoint Rule on $[0, 1]$ with $f(x) = \tan(x^2)$ and $n = 4$, we estimate

$$A = \int_0^1 \tan(x^2) \, dx \approx \tfrac{1}{4}\left[\tan\left(\left(\tfrac{1}{8}\right)^2\right) + \tan\left(\left(\tfrac{3}{8}\right)^2\right) + \tan\left(\left(\tfrac{5}{8}\right)^2\right) + \tan\left(\left(\tfrac{7}{8}\right)^2\right)\right] \approx \tfrac{1}{4}(1.53) \approx 0.38$$

(b) Using the Midpoint Rule on $[0, 1]$ with $f(x) = \pi \tan^2(x^2)$ (for disks) and $n = 4$, we estimate

$$V = \int_0^1 f(x) \, dx \approx \tfrac{1}{4}\pi\left[\tan^2\left(\left(\tfrac{1}{8}\right)^2\right) + \tan^2\left(\left(\tfrac{3}{8}\right)^2\right) + \tan^2\left(\left(\tfrac{5}{8}\right)^2\right) + \tan^2\left(\left(\tfrac{7}{8}\right)^2\right)\right] \approx \tfrac{\pi}{4}(1.114) \approx 0.87$$

9. (a) A cross-section is a washer with inner radius x^2 and outer radius x.

$$V = \int_0^1 \pi\left[(x)^2 - (x^2)^2\right] dx = \int_0^1 \pi(x^2 - x^4) \, dx = \pi\left[\tfrac{1}{3}x^3 - \tfrac{1}{5}x^5\right]_0^1 = \pi\left[\tfrac{1}{3} - \tfrac{1}{5}\right] = \tfrac{2}{15}\pi$$

(b) A cross-section is a washer with inner radius y and outer radius $\sqrt{y}$.

$$V = \int_0^1 \pi\left[\left(\sqrt{y}\right)^2 - y^2\right] dy = \int_0^1 \pi(y - y^2) \, dy = \pi\left[\tfrac{1}{2}y^2 - \tfrac{1}{3}y^3\right]_0^1 = \pi\left[\tfrac{1}{2} - \tfrac{1}{3}\right] = \tfrac{\pi}{6}$$

(c) A cross-section is a washer with inner radius $2 - x$ and outer radius $2 - x^2$.

$$V = \int_0^1 \pi\left[(2 - x^2)^2 - (2 - x)^2\right] dx = \int_0^1 \pi(x^4 - 5x^2 + 4x) \, dx = \pi\left[\tfrac{1}{5}x^5 - \tfrac{5}{3}x^3 + 2x^2\right]_0^1 = \pi\left[\tfrac{1}{5} - \tfrac{5}{3} + 2\right] = \tfrac{8}{15}\pi$$

11. $V = \pi \int_{-3}^{3} \left\{\left[(9 - y^2) - (-1)\right]^2 - [0 - (-1)]^2\right\} dy$

$$= 2\pi \int_0^3 \left[(10 - y^2)^2 - 1\right] dy = 2\pi \int_0^3 (100 - 20y^2 + y^4 - 1) \, dy$$

$$= 2\pi \int_0^3 (99 - 20y^2 + y^4) \, dy = 2\pi\left[99y - \tfrac{20}{3}y^3 + \tfrac{1}{5}y^5\right]_0^3$$

$$= 2\pi\left(297 - 180 + \tfrac{243}{5}\right) = \tfrac{1656}{5}\pi$$

13. The graph of $x^2 - y^2 = a^2$ is a hyperbola with right and left branches.

Solving for y gives us $y^2 = x^2 - a^2 \;\Rightarrow\; y = \pm\sqrt{x^2 - a^2}$.

We'll use shells and the height of each shell is

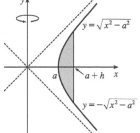

$$\sqrt{x^2 - a^2} - \left(-\sqrt{x^2 - a^2}\right) = 2\sqrt{x^2 - a^2}.$$

The volume is $V = \int_a^{a+h} 2\pi x \cdot 2\sqrt{x^2 - a^2}\,dx$. To evaluate, let $u = x^2 - a^2$,

so $du = 2x\,dx$ and $x\,dx = \tfrac{1}{2}\,du$. When $x = a$, $u = 0$, and when $x = a + h$,

$u = (a+h)^2 - a^2 = a^2 + 2ah + h^2 - a^2 = 2ah + h^2$.

Thus, $V = 4\pi \displaystyle\int_0^{2ah+h^2} \sqrt{u}\left(\tfrac{1}{2}\,du\right) = 2\pi\left[\tfrac{2}{3}u^{3/2}\right]_0^{2ah+h^2} = \tfrac{4}{3}\pi\left(2ah + h^2\right)^{3/2}.$

15. A shell has radius $\tfrac{\pi}{2} - x$, circumference $2\pi\left(\tfrac{\pi}{2} - x\right)$, and height $\cos^2 x - \tfrac{1}{4}$.

$y = \cos^2 x$ intersects $y = \tfrac{1}{4}$ when $\cos^2 x = \tfrac{1}{4} \;\Leftrightarrow$

$\cos x = \pm\tfrac{1}{2} \quad [\,|x| \le \pi/2\,] \;\Leftrightarrow\; x = \pm\tfrac{\pi}{3}.$

$$V = \int_{-\pi/3}^{\pi/3} 2\pi\left(\tfrac{\pi}{2} - x\right)\left(\cos^2 x - \tfrac{1}{4}\right) dx$$

17. (a) $\int_0^{\pi/2} 2\pi \cos^2 x\,dx = \int_0^{\pi/2} \pi\left(\sqrt{2}\cos x\right)^2 dx$

The solid is obtained by rotating the region $\mathcal{R} = \left\{(x,y) \mid 0 \le x \le \tfrac{\pi}{2}, 0 \le y \le \sqrt{2}\cos x\right\}$ about the x-axis.

(b) The solid is obtained by rotating the region $\mathcal{R} = \left\{(x,y) \mid 0 \le x \le 1, 2 - \sqrt{x} \le y \le 2 - x^2\right\}$ about the x-axis.

Or: The solid is obtained by rotating the region $\mathcal{R} = \left\{(x,y) \mid 0 \le x \le 1, x^2 \le y \le \sqrt{x}\,\right\}$ about the line $y = 2$.

19. Take the base to be the disk $x^2 + y^2 \le 9$. Then $V = \int_{-3}^3 A(x)\,dx$, where $A(x_0)$ is the area of the isosceles right triangle

whose hypotenuse lies along the line $x = x_0$ in the xy-plane. The length of the hypotenuse is $2\sqrt{9 - x^2}$ and the length of

each leg is $\sqrt{2}\sqrt{9 - x^2}$. $A(x) = \tfrac{1}{2}\left(\sqrt{2}\sqrt{9 - x^2}\right)^2 = 9 - x^2$, so

$$V = 2\int_0^3 A(x)\,dx = 2\int_0^3 (9 - x^2)\,dx = 2\left[9x - \tfrac{1}{3}x^3\right]_0^3 = 2(27 - 9) = 36$$

21. Equilateral triangles with sides measuring $\tfrac{1}{4}x$ meters have height $\tfrac{1}{4}x\sin 60^\circ = \tfrac{\sqrt{3}}{8}x$. Therefore,

$$A(x) = \tfrac{1}{2}\cdot\tfrac{1}{4}x\cdot\tfrac{\sqrt{3}}{8}x = \tfrac{\sqrt{3}}{64}x^2. \quad V = \int_0^{20} A(x)\,dx = \tfrac{\sqrt{3}}{64}\int_0^{20} x^2\,dx = \tfrac{\sqrt{3}}{64}\left[\tfrac{1}{3}x^3\right]_0^{20} = \tfrac{8000\sqrt{3}}{64\cdot 3} = \tfrac{125\sqrt{3}}{3}\ \mathrm{m}^3.$$

23. $x = 3t^2$, $y = 2t^3$, $0 \le t \le 2$.

$L = \int_0^2 \sqrt{(dx/dt)^2 + (dy/dt)^2}\,dt = \int_0^2 \sqrt{(6t)^2 + (6t^2)^2}\,dt = \int_0^2 \sqrt{36t^2 + 36t^4}\,dt = 6\int_0^2 t\sqrt{1 + t^2}\,dt$

$= 6\int_1^5 \sqrt{u}\left(\tfrac{1}{2}du\right)\ \left[u = 1 + t^2, du = 2t\,dt\right] = 3\left[\tfrac{2}{3}u^{3/2}\right]_1^5 = 2\left(5\sqrt{5} - 1\right)$

25. $y = \frac{1}{6}(x^2 + 4)^{3/2}$ $\Rightarrow$ $dy/dx = \frac{1}{4}(x^2 + 4)^{1/2}(2x)$ $\Rightarrow$

$1 + (dy/dx)^2 = 1 + \left[\frac{1}{2}x(x^2 + 4)^{1/2}\right]^2 = 1 + \frac{1}{4}x^2(x^2 + 4) = \frac{1}{4}x^4 + x^2 + 1 = \left(\frac{1}{2}x^2 + 1\right)^2$.

Thus, $L = \int_0^3 \sqrt{\left(\frac{1}{2}x^2 + 1\right)^2}\, dx = \int_0^3 \left(\frac{1}{2}x^2 + 1\right) dx = \left[\frac{1}{6}x^3 + x\right]_0^3 = \frac{15}{2}$.

27. $f(x) = kx$ $\Rightarrow$ $30\text{ N} = k(15 - 12)\text{ cm}$ $\Rightarrow$ $k = 10\text{ N/cm} = 1000\text{ N/m}$. $20\text{ cm} - 12\text{ cm} = 0.08\text{ m}$ $\Rightarrow$

$W = \int_0^{0.08} kx\, dx = 1000 \int_0^{0.08} x\, dx = 500\left[x^2\right]_0^{0.08} = 500(0.08)^2 = 3.2\text{ N·m} = 3.2\text{ J}$.

29. (a) The parabola has equation $y = ax^2$ with vertex at the origin and passing through

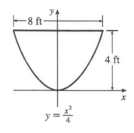

$(4,4)$. $4 = a \cdot 4^2$ $\Rightarrow$ $a = \frac{1}{4}$ $\Rightarrow$ $y = \frac{1}{4}x^2$ $\Rightarrow$ $x^2 = 4y$ $\Rightarrow$

$x = 2\sqrt{y}$. Each circular disk has radius $2\sqrt{y}$ and is moved $4 - y$ ft.

$W = \int_0^4 \pi \left(2\sqrt{y}\right)^2 62.5(4 - y)\, dy = 250\pi \int_0^4 y(4 - y)\, dy$

$= 250\pi \left[2y^2 - \frac{1}{3}y^3\right]_0^4 = 250\pi \left(32 - \frac{64}{3}\right) = \frac{8000\pi}{3} \approx 8378$ ft-lb

(b) In part (a) we knew the final water level (0) but not the amount of work done. Here

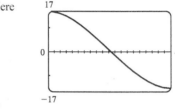

we use the same equation, except with the work fixed, and the lower limit of

integration (that is, the final water level — call it h) unknown: $W = 4000$ $\Leftrightarrow$

$250\pi \left[2y^2 - \frac{1}{3}y^3\right]_h^4 = 4000$ $\Leftrightarrow$ $\frac{16}{\pi} = \left[\left(32 - \frac{64}{3}\right) - \left(2h^2 - \frac{1}{3}h^3\right)\right]$ $\Leftrightarrow$

$h^3 - 6h^2 + 32 - \frac{48}{\pi} = 0$. We graph the function $f(h) = h^3 - 6h^2 + 32 - \frac{48}{\pi}$

on the interval $[0, 4]$ to see where it is 0. From the graph, $f(h) = 0$ for $h \approx 2.1$.

So the depth of water remaining is about 2.1 ft.

31. As in Example 4 of Section 6.6, $\dfrac{a}{2 - x} = \dfrac{1}{2}$ $\Rightarrow$ $2a = 2 - x$ and $w = 2(1.5 + a) = 3 + 2a = 3 + 2 - x = 5 - x$.

Thus, $F = \int_0^2 \rho gx(5 - x)\, dx = \rho g\left[\frac{5}{2}x^2 - \frac{1}{3}x^3\right]_0^2 = \rho g\left(10 - \frac{8}{3}\right) = \frac{22}{3}\delta$ $[\rho g = \delta]$ $\approx \frac{22}{3} \cdot 62.5 \approx 458$ lb.

33. $x = 100$ $\Rightarrow$ $P = 2000 - 0.1(100) - 0.01(100)^2 = 1890$

Consumer surplus $= \int_0^{100}[p(x) - P]\, dx = \int_0^{100}\left(2000 - 0.1x - 0.01x^2 - 1890\right) dx$

$= \left[110x - 0.05x^2 - \frac{0.01}{3}x^3\right]_0^{100} = 11{,}000 - 500 - \frac{10{,}000}{3} \approx \$7166.67$

35. $\displaystyle\lim_{h \to 0} f_{\text{ave}} = \lim_{h \to 0} \frac{1}{(x + h) - x} \int_x^{x+h} f(t)\, dt = \lim_{h \to 0} \frac{F(x + h) - F(x)}{h}$, where $F(x) = \int_a^x f(t)\, dt$. But we recognize this

limit as being $F'(x)$ by the definition of a derivative. Therefore, $\displaystyle\lim_{h \to 0} f_{\text{ave}} = F'(x) = f(x)$ by FTC1.

37. $f(x) = \begin{cases} \frac{\pi}{20}\sin\left(\frac{\pi}{10}x\right) & \text{if } 0 \le x \le 10 \\ 0 & \text{if } x < 0 \text{ or } x > 10 \end{cases}$

(a) $f(x) \ge 0$ for all real numbers x and

$$\int_{-\infty}^{\infty} f(x)\,dx = \int_0^{10} \frac{\pi}{20}\sin\left(\frac{\pi}{10}x\right) dx = \frac{\pi}{20} \cdot \frac{10}{\pi}\left[-\cos\left(\frac{\pi}{10}x\right)\right]_0^{10} = \frac{1}{2}(-\cos\pi + \cos 0) = \frac{1}{2}(1+1) = 1$$

Therefore, f is a probability density function.

(b) $P(X < 4) = \int_{-\infty}^{4} f(x)\,dx = \int_0^4 \frac{\pi}{20}\sin\left(\frac{\pi}{10}x\right) dx = \frac{1}{2}\left[-\cos\left(\frac{\pi}{10}x\right)\right]_0^4 = \frac{1}{2}\left(-\cos\frac{2\pi}{5} + \cos 0\right)$

$\approx \frac{1}{2}(-0.309017 + 1) \approx 0.3455$

(c) $\mu = \int_{-\infty}^{\infty} x f(x)\,dx = \int_0^{10} \frac{\pi}{20} x \sin\left(\frac{\pi}{10}x\right) dx$

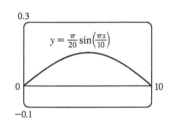

$= \int_0^{\pi} \frac{\pi}{20} \cdot \frac{10}{\pi} u(\sin u)\left(\frac{10}{\pi}\right) du \qquad [u = \frac{\pi}{10}x,\ du = \frac{\pi}{10}\,dx]$

$= \frac{5}{\pi} \int_0^{\pi} u \sin u\,du \overset{82}{=} \frac{5}{\pi}\left[\sin u - u\cos u\right]_0^{\pi} = \frac{5}{\pi}[0 - \pi(-1)] = 5$

This answer is expected because the graph of f is symmetric about the

line $x = 5$.

39. (a) The probability density function is $f(t) = \begin{cases} 0 & \text{if } t < 0 \\ \frac{1}{8}e^{-t/8} & \text{if } t \ge 0 \end{cases}$

$P(0 \le X \le 3) = \int_0^3 \frac{1}{8}e^{-t/8}\,dt = \left[-e^{-t/8}\right]_0^3 = -e^{-3/8} + 1 \approx 0.3127$

(b) $P(X > 10) = \int_{10}^{\infty} \frac{1}{8}e^{-t/8}\,dt = \lim_{x\to\infty}\left[-e^{-t/8}\right]_{10}^{x} = \lim_{x\to\infty}\left(-e^{-x/8} + e^{-10/8}\right) = 0 + e^{-5/4} \approx 0.2865$

(c) We need to find m such that $P(X \ge m) = \frac{1}{2}$ $\Rightarrow$ $\int_m^{\infty} \frac{1}{8}e^{-t/8}\,dt = \frac{1}{2}$ $\Rightarrow$ $\lim_{x\to\infty}\left[-e^{-t/8}\right]_m^{x} = \frac{1}{2}$ $\Rightarrow$

$\lim_{x\to\infty}\left(-e^{-x/8} + e^{-m/8}\right) = \frac{1}{2}$ $\Rightarrow$ $e^{-m/8} = \frac{1}{2}$ $\Rightarrow$ $-m/8 = \ln\frac{1}{2}$ $\Rightarrow$ $m = -8\ln\frac{1}{2} = 8\ln 2 \approx 5.55$ minutes.

☐ FOCUS ON PROBLEM SOLVING

1. The volume generated from $x = 0$ to $x = b$ is $\int_0^b \pi [f(x)]^2 \, dx$. Hence, we are given that $b^2 = \int_0^b \pi [f(x)]^2 \, dx$ for all $b > 0$.

   Differentiating both sides of this equation with respect to b using the Fundamental Theorem of Calculus gives

   $2b = \pi [f(b)]^2 \quad \Rightarrow \quad f(b) = \sqrt{2b/\pi}$, since f is positive. Therefore, $f(x) = \sqrt{2x/\pi}$.

3. (a) $V = \pi h^2 (r - h/3) = \frac{1}{3} \pi h^2 (3r - h)$. See the solution to Exercise 6.2.33.

   (b) The smaller segment has height $h = 1 - x$ and so by part (a) its volume is

   $V = \frac{1}{3} \pi (1 - x)^2 [3(1) - (1 - x)] = \frac{1}{3} \pi (x - 1)^2 (x + 2)$. This volume must be $\frac{1}{3}$ of the total volume of the sphere,

   which is $\frac{4}{3} \pi (1)^3$. So $\frac{1}{3} \pi (x - 1)^2 (x + 2) = \frac{1}{3} \left(\frac{4}{3} \pi \right) \quad \Rightarrow \quad (x^2 - 2x + 1)(x + 2) = \frac{4}{3} \quad \Rightarrow \quad x^3 - 3x + 2 = \frac{4}{3} \quad \Rightarrow$

   $3x^3 - 9x + 2 = 0$. Using Newton's method with $f(x) = 3x^3 - 9x + 2$, $f'(x) = 9x^2 - 9$, we get

   $x_{n+1} = x_n - \dfrac{3x_n^3 - 9x_n + 2}{9x_n^2 - 9}$. Taking $x_1 = 0$, we get $x_2 \approx 0.2222$, and $x_3 \approx 0.2261 \approx x_4$, so, correct to four decimal

   places, $x \approx 0.2261$.

   (c) With $r = 0.5$ and $s = 0.75$, the equation $x^3 - 3rx^2 + 4r^3 s = 0$ becomes $x^3 - 3(0.5)x^2 + 4(0.5)^3(0.75) = 0 \quad \Rightarrow$

   $x^3 - \frac{3}{2} x^2 + 4 \left(\frac{1}{8} \right) \frac{3}{4} = 0 \quad \Rightarrow \quad 8x^3 - 12x^2 + 3 = 0$. We use Newton's method with $f(x) = 8x^3 - 12x^2 + 3$,

   $f'(x) = 24x^2 - 24x$, so $x_{n+1} = x_n - \dfrac{8x_n^3 - 12x_n^2 + 3}{24x_n^2 - 24x_n}$. Take $x_1 = 0.5$. Then $x_2 \approx 0.6667$, and $x_3 \approx 0.6736 \approx x_4$.

   So to four decimal places the depth is 0.6736 m.

   (d) (i) From part (a) with $r = 5$ in., the volume of water in the bowl is

   $V = \frac{1}{3} \pi h^2 (3r - h) = \frac{1}{3} \pi h^2 (15 - h) = 5\pi h^2 - \frac{1}{3} \pi h^3$. We are given that $\dfrac{dV}{dt} = 0.2$ in^3/s and we want to find $\dfrac{dh}{dt}$

   when $h = 3$. Now $\dfrac{dV}{dt} = 10\pi h \dfrac{dh}{dt} - \pi h^2 \dfrac{dh}{dt}$, so $\dfrac{dh}{dt} = \dfrac{0.2}{\pi (10h - h^2)}$. When $h = 3$, we have

   $\dfrac{dh}{dt} = \dfrac{0.2}{\pi (10 \cdot 3 - 3^2)} = \dfrac{1}{105\pi} \approx 0.003$ in/s.

   (ii) From part (a), the volume of water required to fill the bowl from the instant that the water is 4 in. deep is

   $V = \frac{1}{2} \cdot \frac{4}{3} \pi (5)^3 - \frac{1}{3} \pi (4)^2 (15 - 4) = \frac{2}{3} \cdot 125\pi - \frac{16}{3} \cdot 11\pi = \frac{74}{3} \pi$. To find the time required to fill the bowl we divide

   this volume by the rate: Time $= \frac{74\pi/3}{0.2} = \frac{370\pi}{3} \approx 387$ s ≈ 6.5 min.

5. We are given that the rate of change of the volume of water is $\dfrac{dV}{dt} = -kA(x)$, where k is some positive constant and $A(x)$ is

   the area of the surface when the water has depth x. Now we are concerned with the rate of change of the depth of the water

   with respect to time, that is, $\dfrac{dx}{dt}$. But by the Chain Rule, $\dfrac{dV}{dt} = \dfrac{dV}{dx} \dfrac{dx}{dt}$, so the first equation can be written

$\dfrac{dV}{dx}\dfrac{dx}{dt} = -kA(x)$ $(\star)$. Also, we know that the total volume of water up to a depth x is $V(x) = \int_0^x A(s)\, ds$, where $A(s)$ is the area of a cross-section of the water at a depth s. Differentiating this equation with respect to x, we get $dV/dx = A(x)$. Substituting this into equation $\star$, we get $A(x)(dx/dt) = -kA(x)$ $\Rightarrow$ $dx/dt = -k$, a constant.

7. To find the height of the pyramid, we use similar triangles. The first figure shows a cross-section of the pyramid passing through the top and through two opposite corners of the square base. Now $|BD| = b$, since it is a radius of the sphere, which has diameter $2b$ since it is tangent to the opposite sides of the square base. Also, $|AD| = b$ since $\triangle ADB$ is isosceles. So the height is $|AB| = \sqrt{b^2 + b^2} = \sqrt{2}\,b$.

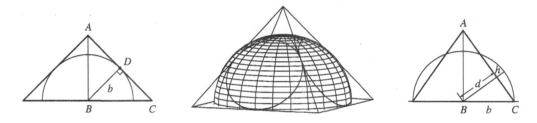

We first observe that the shared volume is equal to half the volume of the sphere, minus the sum of the four equal volumes (caps of the sphere) cut off by the triangular faces of the pyramid. See Exercise 6.2.33 for a derivation of the formula for the volume of a cap of a sphere. To use the formula, we need to find the perpendicular distance h of each triangular face from the surface of the sphere. We first find the distance d from the center of the sphere to one of the triangular faces. The third figure shows a cross-section of the pyramid through the top and through the midpoints of opposite sides of the square base. From similar triangles we find that

$$\frac{d}{b} = \frac{|AB|}{|AC|} = \frac{\sqrt{2}\,b}{\sqrt{b^2 + (\sqrt{2}\,b)^2}} \quad\Rightarrow\quad d = \frac{\sqrt{2}\,b^2}{\sqrt{3b^2}} = \frac{\sqrt{6}}{3}\,b$$

So $h = b - d = b - \frac{\sqrt{6}}{3}b = \frac{3 - \sqrt{6}}{3}b$. So, using the formula $V = \pi h^2(r - h/3)$ from Exercise 6.2.33 with $r = b$, we find that the volume of each of the caps is $\pi\left(\frac{3-\sqrt{6}}{3}b\right)^2\left(b - \frac{3-\sqrt{6}}{3\cdot 3}b\right) = \frac{15 - 6\sqrt{6}}{9}\cdot\frac{6+\sqrt{6}}{9}\pi b^3 = \left(\frac{2}{3} - \frac{7}{27}\sqrt{6}\right)\pi b^3$. So, using our first observation, the shared volume is $V = \frac{1}{2}\left(\frac{4}{3}\pi b^3\right) - 4\left(\frac{2}{3} - \frac{7}{27}\sqrt{6}\right)\pi b^3 = \left(\frac{28}{27}\sqrt{6} - 2\right)\pi b^3$.

9. $x = \displaystyle\int_1^t \frac{\cos u}{u}\,du$, $y = \displaystyle\int_1^t \frac{\sin u}{u}\,du$, so by FTC1, we have $\dfrac{dx}{dt} = \dfrac{\cos t}{t}$ and $\dfrac{dy}{dt} = \dfrac{\sin t}{t}$. Vertical tangent lines occur when $dx/dt = 0$ $\Leftrightarrow$ $\cos t = 0$ $\Leftrightarrow$ $t = \frac{\pi}{2} + n\pi$. The parameter value corresponding to the origin, $(x, y) = (0, 0)$, is $t = 1$, so the nearest vertical tangent occurs when $t = \frac{\pi}{2}$. Therefore, the arc length between these points is

$$L = \int_1^{\pi/2} \sqrt{\left(\frac{dx}{dt}\right)^2 + \left(\frac{dy}{dt}\right)^2}\, dt = \int_1^{\pi/2} \sqrt{\frac{\cos^2 t}{t^2} + \frac{\sin^2 t}{t^2}}\, dt = \int_1^{\pi/2} \frac{dt}{t} = \left[\ln t\right]_1^{\pi/2} = \ln\frac{\pi}{2}$$

11.

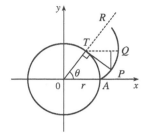

The coordinates of T are $(x_1, y_1) = (r \cos \theta, r \sin \theta)$. Since TP was unwound from arc TA, TP has length $r\theta$. Also $\angle PTQ = \angle PTR - \angle QTR = \frac{1}{2}\pi - \theta$, so P has coordinates

$$x = x_1 + |TP| \cos \angle PTQ = r \cos \theta + r\theta \cos\left(\tfrac{1}{2}\pi - \theta\right) = r(\cos \theta + \theta \sin \theta),$$

$$y = y_1 + |TP| \sin \angle PTQ = r \sin \theta - r\theta \sin\left(\tfrac{1}{2}\pi - \theta\right) = r(\sin \theta - \theta \cos \theta).$$

13. We can assume that the cut is made along a vertical line $x = b > 0$, that the disk's boundary is the circle $x^2 + y^2 = 1$, and that the center of mass of the smaller piece (to the right of $x = b$) is $\left(\frac{1}{2}, 0\right)$. We wish to find b to two decimal places. We have $\dfrac{1}{2} = \overline{x} = \dfrac{\int_b^1 x \cdot 2\sqrt{1 - x^2}\, dx}{\int_b^1 2\sqrt{1 - x^2}\, dx}$. Evaluating the

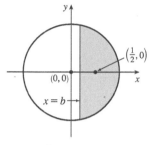

numerator gives us $-\int_b^1 (1 - x^2)^{1/2}(-2x)\, dx = -\frac{2}{3}\left[(1 - x^2)^{3/2}\right]_b^1 = -\frac{2}{3}\left[0 - (1 - b^2)^{3/2}\right] = \frac{2}{3}(1 - b^2)^{3/2}$.

Using Formula 30 in the table of integrals, we find that the denominator is

$\left[x\sqrt{1 - x^2} + \sin^{-1} x\right]_b^1 = \left(0 + \frac{\pi}{2}\right) - \left(b\sqrt{1 - b^2} + \sin^{-1} b\right)$. Thus, we have $\dfrac{1}{2} = \overline{x} = \dfrac{\frac{2}{3}(1 - b^2)^{3/2}}{\frac{\pi}{2} - b\sqrt{1 - b^2} - \sin^{-1} b}$, or,

equivalently, $\frac{2}{3}(1 - b^2)^{3/2} = \frac{\pi}{4} - \frac{1}{2}b\sqrt{1 - b^2} - \frac{1}{2}\sin^{-1} b$. Solving this equation numerically with a calculator or CAS, we

obtain $b \approx 0.138173$, or $b = 0.14$ m to two decimal places.

15. The cubic polynomial passes through the origin, so let its equation be

$y = px^3 + qx^2 + rx$. The curves intersect when $px^3 + qx^2 + rx = x^2 \iff$

$px^3 + (q - 1)x^2 + rx = 0$. Call the left side $f(x)$. Since $f(a) = f(b) = 0$,

another form of f is

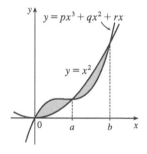

$$f(x) = px(x - a)(x - b) = px[x^2 - (a + b)x + ab]$$
$$= p[x^3 - (a + b)x^2 + abx]$$

Since the two areas are equal, we must have $\int_0^a f(x)\, dx = -\int_a^b f(x)\, dx \;\Rightarrow$

$[F(x)]_0^a = [F(x)]_b^a \;\Rightarrow\; F(a) - F(0) = F(a) - F(b) \;\Rightarrow\; F(0) = F(b)$, where F is an antiderivative of f.

Now $F(x) = \int f(x)\, dx = \int p[x^3 - (a + b)x^2 + abx]\, dx = p\left[\frac{1}{4}x^4 - \frac{1}{3}(a + b)x^3 + \frac{1}{2}abx^2\right] + C$, so

$F(0) = F(b) \;\Rightarrow\; C = p\left[\frac{1}{4}b^4 - \frac{1}{3}(a + b)b^3 + \frac{1}{2}ab^3\right] + C \;\Rightarrow\; 0 = p\left[\frac{1}{4}b^4 - \frac{1}{3}(a + b)b^3 + \frac{1}{2}ab^3\right] \;\Rightarrow$

$0 = 3b - 4(a + b) + 6a$ [multiply by $12/(pb^3)$, $b \neq 0$] $\;\Rightarrow\; 0 = 3b - 4a - 4b + 6a \;\Rightarrow\; b = 2a$.

Hence, b is twice the value of a.